Scott Foresman - Addison Wesley
MIDDLE SCHOOL MATH
Course 2

Randall I. Charles John A. Dossey Steven J. Leinwand
Cathy L. Seeley Charles B. Vonder Embse

L. Carey Bolster • Janet H. Caldwell • Dwight A. Cooley • Warren D. Crown
Linda Proudfit • Alma B. Ramírez • Jeanne F. Ramos • Freddie Lee Renfro
David F. Robitaille • Jane Swafford

Teacher's Edition

Volume 1

Chapters 1–6

Scott Foresman
Addison Wesley

Editorial Offices: Menlo Park, California • Glenview, Illinois
Sales Offices: Reading, Massachusetts • Atlanta, Georgia • Glenview, Illinois
Carrollton, Texas • Menlo Park, California

http://www.sf.aw.com

Math

that Makes Sense...

"I learn best when math is interesting to me."

The Student's Perspective

"If we are to reach all students, we must strive for meaningful, challenging, and relevant learning in the classroom."

The Research Perspective

Printed in the United States of America

ISBN 0-201-36428-X

2 3 4 5 6 7 8 9 10–DOW–02 01 00 99 98

Teacher

The Teacher's Perspective

*"My primary concern in teaching is to help **all** my students succeed."*

from **EVERY** *Perspective*

What kind of a math program are you looking for? What about your students? And how about mathematics education research? Can one program really satisfy *all* points of view? Through its content, features, and format, *Scott Foresman - Addison Wesley Middle School MATH* recognizes the real-life needs and concerns specific to middle school—supported by research but grounded in real classroom experience.

Welcome to a math program that excels from every perspective—especially yours!

search

Math that Connects to the Student's World

Middle school students have a perspective all their own. We've tapped into their world with experiences and information that grab their attention and don't let go.

"I want to know when I'll use this."

Real, age-appropriate data
Data based on what middle school students buy, eat, study in school, and enjoy permeate every lesson.

Cool themes like *Spiders, Disasters, Food,* and *Whales*
Student-friendly topics blend learning with what kids love.

MathSURF Internet Site
MathSURF's up and so is student interest! Kids can go online to explore text content of every chapter in safe and exciting destinations around the world.

Interactive CD-ROM
Interactive lessons for every chapter provide an exciting environment for learning.

Math that Promotes High School Success

Teachers in today's middle schools need a program that prepares their students for high school math. That means rigorous content, including preparation for algebra and geometry, NTCM content and process standards—PLUS practical strategies for taking tests and problem solving.

*"My students need to be prepared for high school math. And let's face it, how they perform is a reflection of how **I** perform!"*

Performance

The building blocks of algebra

Prepare students for success in high school math with instruction in mathematical reasoning.

Course 1—focuses on *numerical reasoning.*

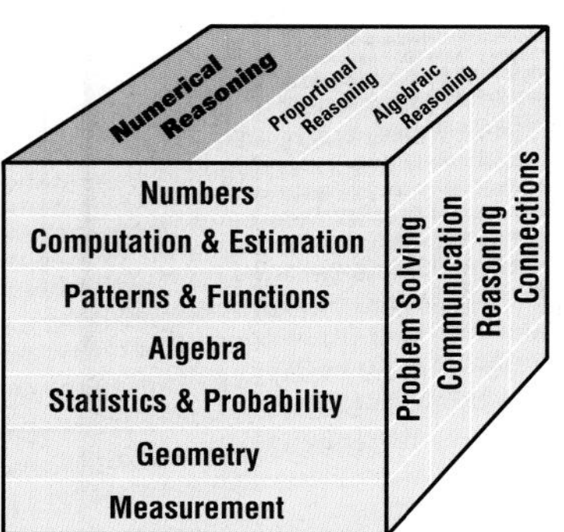

Course 2—focuses on *proportional reasoning.*

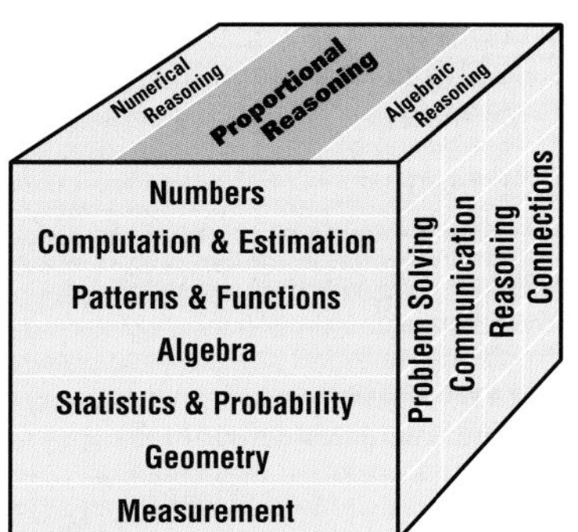

Course 3—focuses on *algebraic reasoning.*

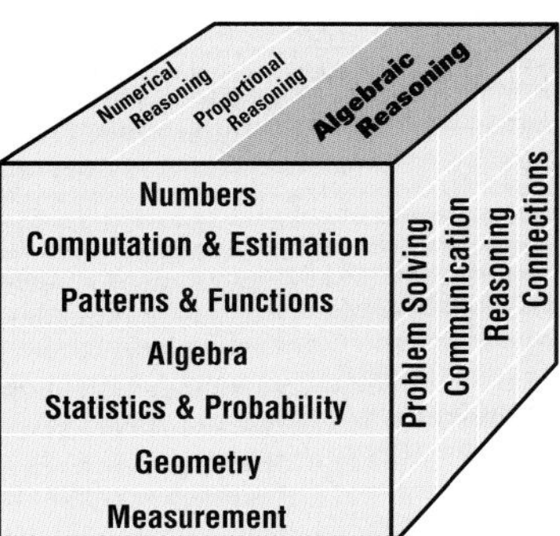

Test prep strategies

The next step in strategies! Helping students be smart about how they take standardized tests builds confidence and leads to success.

Problem solving that's no problem

Sharpen students' problem-solving skills with numerous opportunities to analyze and use the problem-solving process.

A Program that Supports Teaching Success

Teachers in today's middle schools face unique challenges—from improving student performance to adapting to each student's unique learning needs. This program is designed to help you meet those challenges. You'll find help for every teaching need—including *block scheduling* and *interdisciplinary team teaching,* PLUS *outstanding technology,* and more!

Student Edition

Colorful lessons, filled with student-oriented data, have a unique "middle school" look.

Teacher's Edition

(with Teacher's Resource Planner CD-ROM)

Two hardbound volumes, packaged with a CD-ROM Planner, provide complete lesson plans plus practical help to meet your every challenge—block scheduling, team teaching, and more.

Teacher's Resource Package

Practice Masters

Exercises reinforce content of every lesson. Also available as a workbook.

Alternative Lessons (Reteaching Masters)

Masters for every lesson offer another look at skills and concepts.

Extend Your Thinking (Enrichment Masters)

Masters enhance thinking skills and creativity in every lesson.

Problem-Solving Masters (for Guided Problem Solving)

Masters guide students step-by-step through one problem from every Student Edition exercise set. Also available as a workbook.

Assessment Sourcebook

Options to help profile students as learners. Includes multiple-choice, short-response, performance, and mixed-format chapter tests, as well as section quizzes and record forms.

Home and Community Connections

Make math a family affair! Booklet with letters in English and Spanish, also provides classroom tips, community projects, and more.

Teacher's Toolkit

Saves time with a variety of Management Resources, plus Teaching Tool Transparencies.

Technology Masters

Computer and calculator activities energize lessons with the power of technology.

Chapter Project Masters

Masters support the on-going project in each Student Edition chapter.

Interdisciplinary Team Teaching

Math across the curriculum! Masters provide an engaging 2-page interdisciplinary lesson for each section.

Resources to Customize Instruction

Print Resources

Block Scheduling Handbook
Practical suggestions let you tailor the program to various block scheduling formats.

Overhead Transparency Package
Daily Transparencies (for Problem of the Day, Review, and Quick Quiz) and Lesson Enhancement Transparencies help enliven class presentations.

Multilingual Handbook
Enhanced math glossary with examples in multiple languages provides a valuable resource for teaching. Especially useful with ESL students.

Mathematics Dictionary
Handy reference tool of middle school math terms.

Solutions Manual
Manual includes convenient solutions to Student Edition exercises.

Technology

Teacher's Resource Planner CD-ROM
The entire Teacher's Resource Package on CD-ROM! Includes an electronic planning guide which allows you to set criteria when planning lessons, customize worksheets, correlate your curriculum to specific objectives, and more!

Interactive CD-ROM
Interactive, multimedia lessons with built-in math tools help students explore concepts in enjoyable and involving ways.

MathSURF Internet Site (for Students)
Math on the Web! Provides links to other sites, project ideas, interactive surveys and more.

MathSURF Internet Site (for Teachers)
Offers exciting opportunities for in-service ideas and sharing.

MathSURF Internet Site (for Parents)
This Web site offers a variety of practical tips to parents.

TestWorks: Test and Practice CD-ROM
CD-ROM saves hours of test-prep time by generating and customizing tests and worksheets.

Manipulative Kits

Student Manipulative Kit
Quantities of angle rulers, Power Polygons, and other items help students grasp mathematics concepts on a concrete level.

Teacher's Overhead Manipulative Kit
Kit makes demonstrating concepts from an overhead projector easy and convenient.

Authors with Middle School Expertise!

Math that makes sense from every perspective—it's a commitment we've kept in all aspects of this program, including our outstanding team of authors. Their expertise in mathematics education brings to the program extensive knowledge of how middle school students learn math and how best to teach them.

Expertise

"Students learn and perform better when they are taught in ways that match their own strengths."

Charles B. Vonder Embse

Professor of Mathematics Education and Mathematics

Central Michigan University
Mt. Pleasant, Michigan

Member of NCTM Instructional Issues Advisory Committee

Member of the Advisory Board of Teachers Teaching with Technology (T^3)

Jane Swafford

Professor of Mathematics

Illinois State University
Normal, Illinois

Randall I. Charles

Professor, Department of Mathematics and Computer Science

San Jose State University
San Jose, California

Past Vice-President, National Council of Supervisors of Mathematics

Co-author of two NCTM publications on teaching and evaluating progress in problem solving

Dwight A. Cooley

Assistant Principal

Mary Louise Phillips
Elementary School
Fort Worth, Texas

Member, NCTM Board of Directors

John A. Dossey

Distinguished University
Professor of Mathematics

Illinois State University
Normal, Illinois

Past President, NCTM

Guided development of NCTM Standards

Recipient, NCTM Lifetime Achievement Award

Chairman, Conference Board of the Mathematical Sciences

"A program that asks real-life questions provides rich possibilities for students."

Steven J. Leinwand

Mathematics Consultant

Connecticut Department
of Education
Hartford, Connecticut

Member, NCTM Board of Directors

Past President, National Council of Supervisors of Mathematics

Cathy L. Seeley

Director of Policy and Professional
Development for Texas SSI

University of Texas
Austin, Texas

Texas State Mathematics Supervisor

Writer, Curriculum and Evaluation Standards for School Mathematics

Member, NCTM Board of Directors

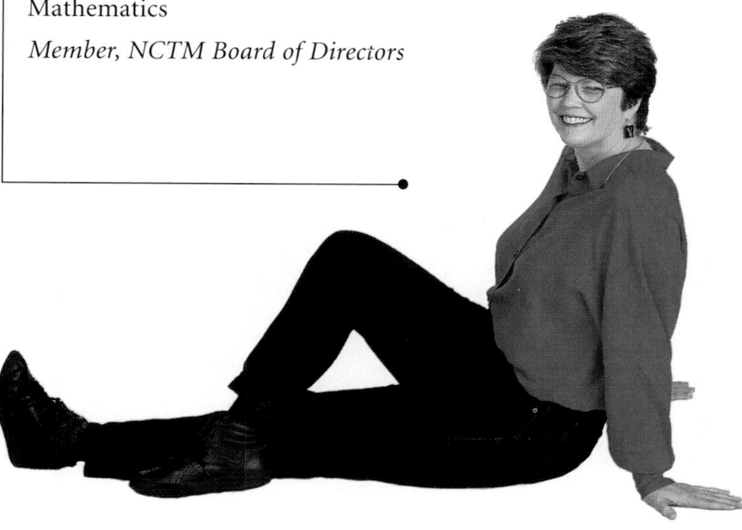

Turn the page, for more authors!

More Authors with Middle School Expertise!

Freddie Lee Renfro
Coordinator of Mathematics
Fort Bend Independent
School District
Sugarland, Texas

L. Carey Bolster
Director, K–12 Math Projects
Public Broadcasting Service
MATHLINE
Alexandria, Virginia

More

"Students construct new learning from a basis of prior knowledge and experience."

Linda Proudfit
University Professor of
Mathematics and Computer
Education
Governors State University
University Park, Illinois

Janet H. Caldwell
Professor of Mathematics
Rowan University
Glassboro, New Jersey

David F. Robitaille

Professor of Mathematics Education

University of British Columbia
Vancouver, British Columbia, Canada

Alma Ramírez

Bilingual Mathematics and Science Teacher

Oakland Charter Academy
Oakland, California

"To be successful in high school, students need a solid foundation in mathematical reasoning."

Jeanne F. Ramos

Assistant Principal

Nobel Middle School
Los Angeles, California

Warren D. Crown

Professor of Mathematics Education

Rutgers, The State University of New Jersey
New Brunswick, New Jersey

Expertise

Contributors from Across the Country!

A Nationwide Perspective

Educators from across the country helped shape this program with valuable input about local needs and concerns.

Contributing Writers

Phillip E. Duren
California State University
Hayward, CA

Kathy A. Ross
Loyola University (LaSIP)
New Orleans, LA

Sheryl M. Yamada
Beverly Hills High School
Beverly Hills, CA

Content Reviewers

Ann Boltz
Coldwater, MI

John David Bridges
Greenville, SC

Glenn Bruckhart
Fort Collins, CO

Sharon Bourgeois Butler
Spring, TX

Carol Cameron
Seattle, WA

Steven T. Cottrell
Farmington, UT

Patricia Creel
Lawrenceville, GA

Wendi M. Cyford
New Market, MD

Scott Firkins
Owensboro, KY

Madelaine Gallin
New York, NY

Roy E. Griggs
Boise, ID

Lucy Hahn
Boise, ID

Allison Harris
Seattle, WA

Clay Hutson
Kingsport, TN

Beryl W. Jackson
Alexandria, VA

Janet Jomp
Wilson, NC

Ann P. Lawrence
Marietta, GA

Cheryl McCormack
Indianapolis, IN

Gary McCracken
Tuscaloosa, AL

Allison McNaughton
Marstons Mills, MA

Sandra A. Nagy
Mesa, AZ

Kent Novak
Greene, RI

Jeff C. Nusbaum
Rock Island, IL

Vince O'Connor
Milwaukee, WI

Mary Lynn Raith
Pittsburgh, PA

Kathleen Rieke
Zionsville, IN

Ellen G. Robertson
Norwich, NY

Nancy Rolsen
Worthington, OH

Edith Roos
Helena, MT

Lynn A. Sandro
Cedar Springs, MI

Carol Sims
Arcadia, CA

Paul E. Smith
Newburgh, IN

Donald M. Smyton
Kenmore, NY

Stella M. Turner
Indianapolis, IN

Tommie Walsh
Lubbock, TX

Terri Weaver
Houston, TX

Jacqueline Weilmuenster
Colleyville, TX

Multicultural Reviewers

Mary Margaret Capraro
Hialeah, FL

Robert Capraro
Miami, FL

Bettye Forte
Fort Worth, TX

Hector Hirigoyen
Miami, FL

James E. Hopkins
Auburn, WA

Patricia Locke
Mobridge, SD

Jimmie Rios
Fort Worth, TX

Linda Skinner
Edmond, OK

ESL Reviewers

Anna Uhl Chamot
Washington, DC

Jimmie Rios
Fort Worth, TX

Inclusion Reviewers

Lucy Blood
Amesbury, MA

Janett Borg
Monroe, UT

John David Bridges
Greenville, SC

Edith Roos
Helena, MT

Cross-Curricular Reviewers

Janett Borg
Monroe, UT

Kurt Brorson
Bethesda, MD

Geoffrey Chester
Washington, DC

Trudi Hammel Garland
Orinda, CA

M. Frank Watt Ireton
Washington, DC

Donna Krasnow
Carmel, CA

Chelcie Liu
San Francisco, CA

Edith Roos
Helena, MT

Technology Reviewers

Kurt Brorson
Bethesda, MD

Beverly W. Nichols
Overland Park, KS

Susan Rhodes
Springfield, IL

David L. Stout
Pensacola, FL

TABLE OF CONTENTS

Teacher's Edition

VOLUME 1: CHAPTERS 1–6

VOLUME 2: CHAPTERS 7–12

FROM THE AUTHORS

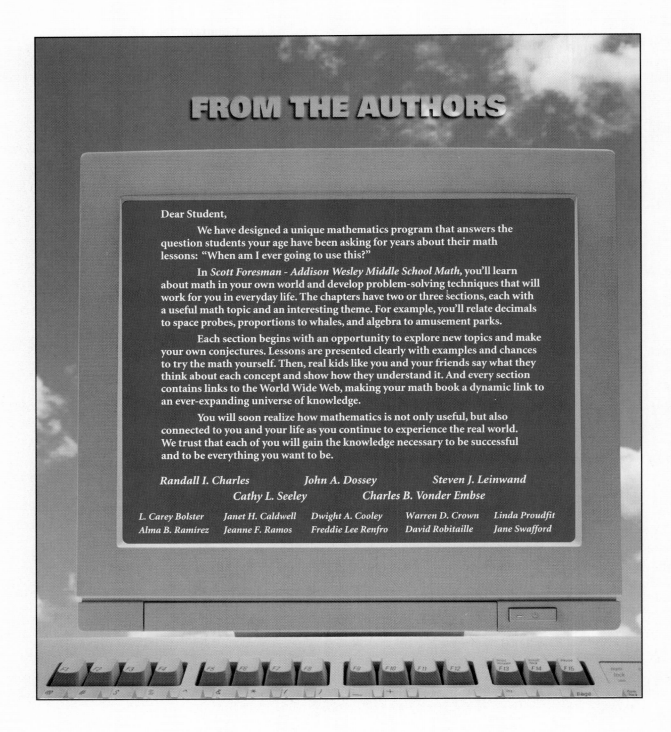

FROM THE AUTHORS

Dear Student,

We have designed a unique mathematics program that answers the question students your age have been asking for years about their math lessons: "When am I ever going to use this?"

In *Scott Foresman - Addison Wesley Middle School Math*, you'll learn about math in your own world and develop problem-solving techniques that will work for you in everyday life. The chapters have two or three sections, each with a useful math topic and an interesting theme. For example, you'll relate decimals to space probes, proportions to whales, and algebra to amusement parks.

Each section begins with an opportunity to explore new topics and make your own conjectures. Lessons are presented clearly with examples and chances to try the math yourself. Then, real kids like you and your friends say what they think about each concept and show how they understand it. And every section contains links to the World Wide Web, making your math book a dynamic link to an ever-expanding universe of knowledge.

You will soon realize how mathematics is not only useful, but also connected to you and your life as you continue to experience the real world. We trust that each of you will gain the knowledge necessary to be successful and to be everything you want to be.

Randall I. Charles *John A. Dossey* *Steven J. Leinwand*
Cathy L. Seeley *Charles B. Vonder Embse*

L. Carey Bolster *Janet H. Caldwell* *Dwight A. Cooley* *Warren D. Crown* *Linda Proudfit*
Alma B. Ramirez *Jeanne F. Ramos* *Freddie Lee Renfro* *David Robitaille* *Jane Swafford*

CHAPTER 1

Making Sense of the World of Data

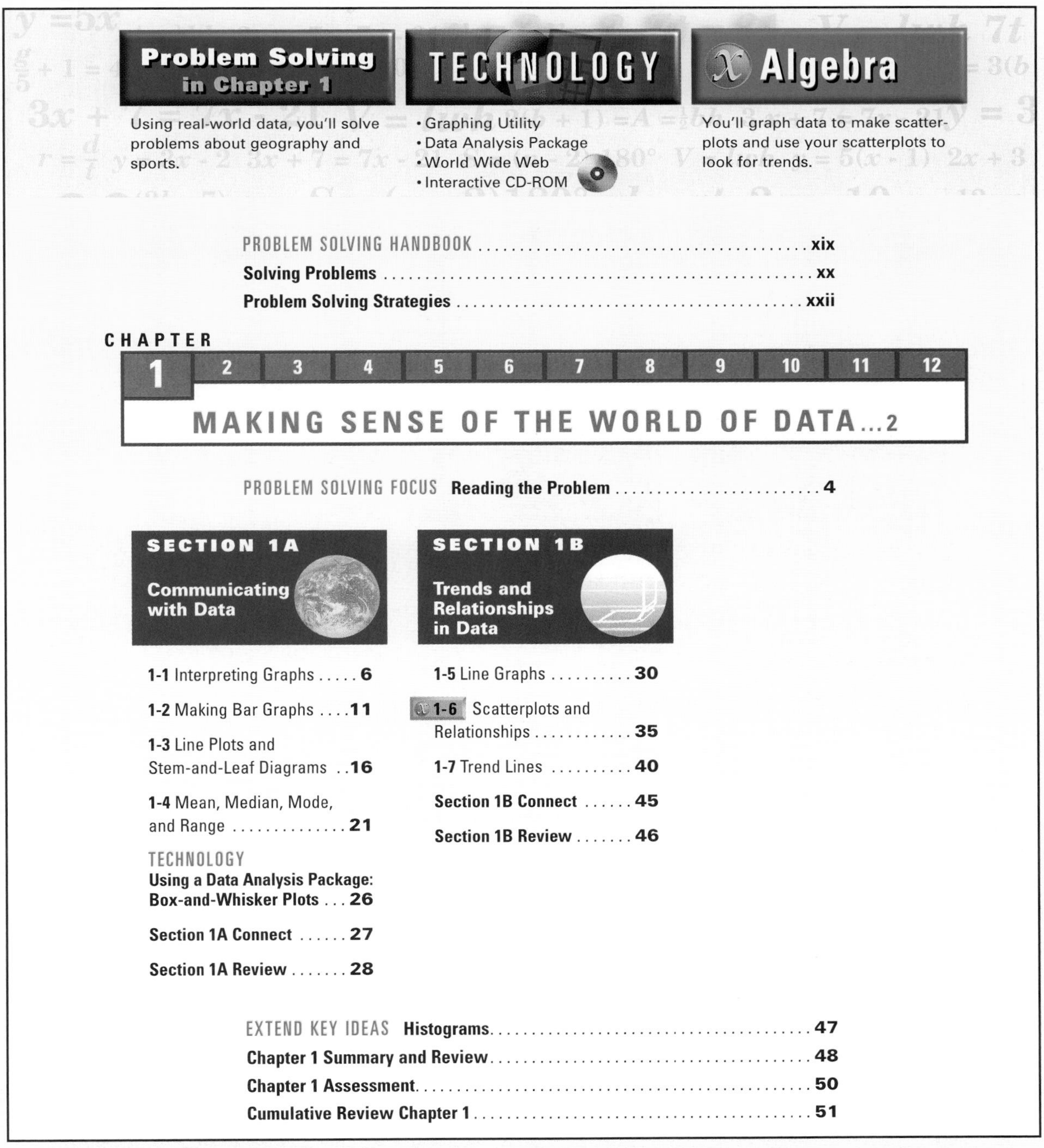

Problem Solving in Chapter 1

Using real-world data, you'll solve problems about geography and sports.

TECHNOLOGY

- Graphing Utility
- Data Analysis Package
- World Wide Web
- Interactive CD-ROM

Algebra

You'll graph data to make scatterplots and use your scatterplots to look for trends.

CHAPTER 2

The Language of Algebra: Formulas, Expressions, and Equations

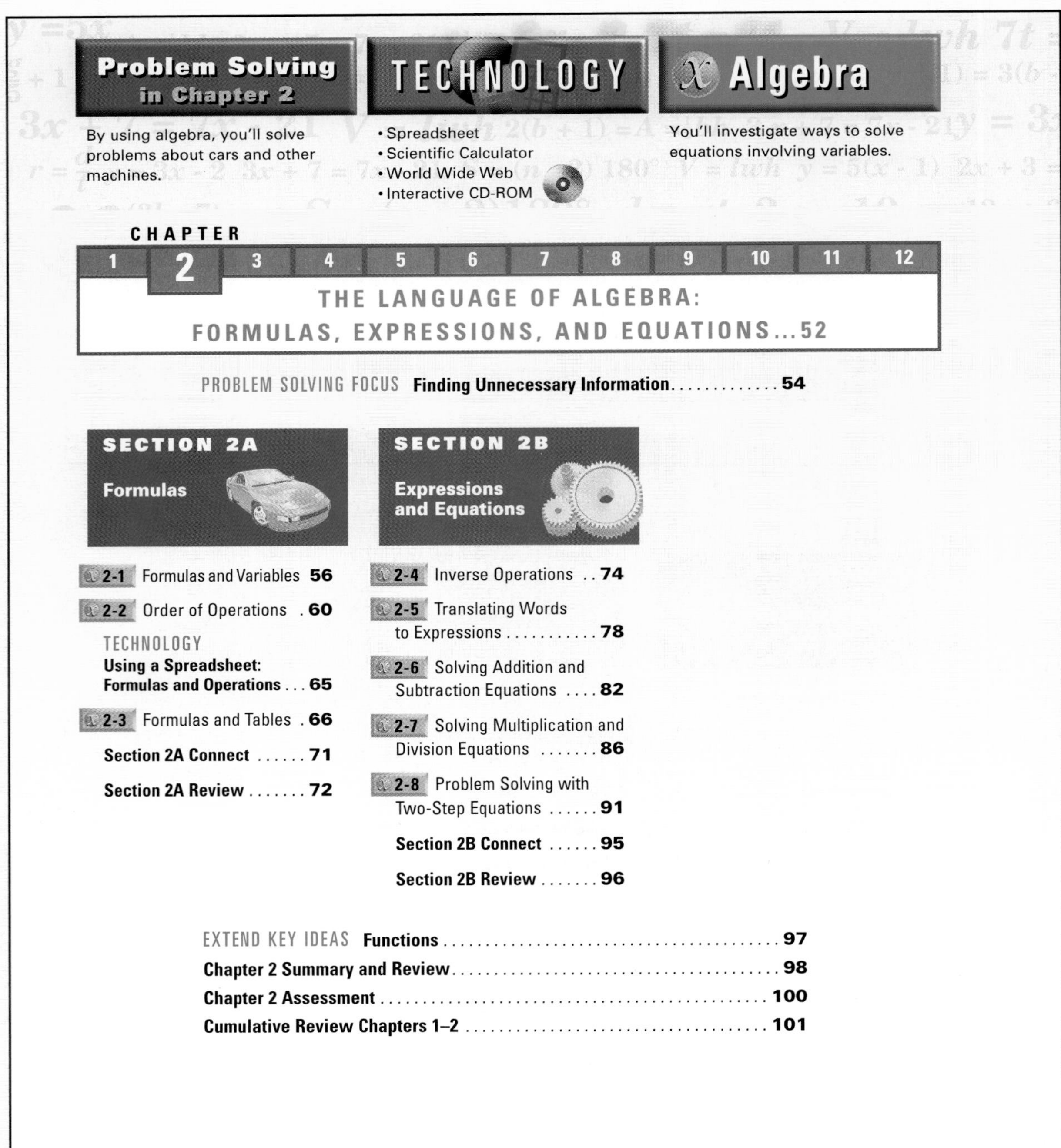

Problem Solving in Chapter 2
By using algebra, you'll solve problems about cars and other machines.
TECHNOLOGY
• Spreadsheet
• Scientific Calculator
• World Wide Web
• Interactive CD-ROM
Algebra
You'll investigate ways to solve equations involving variables.

CHAPTER 3

Number Sense: Decimals and Fractions

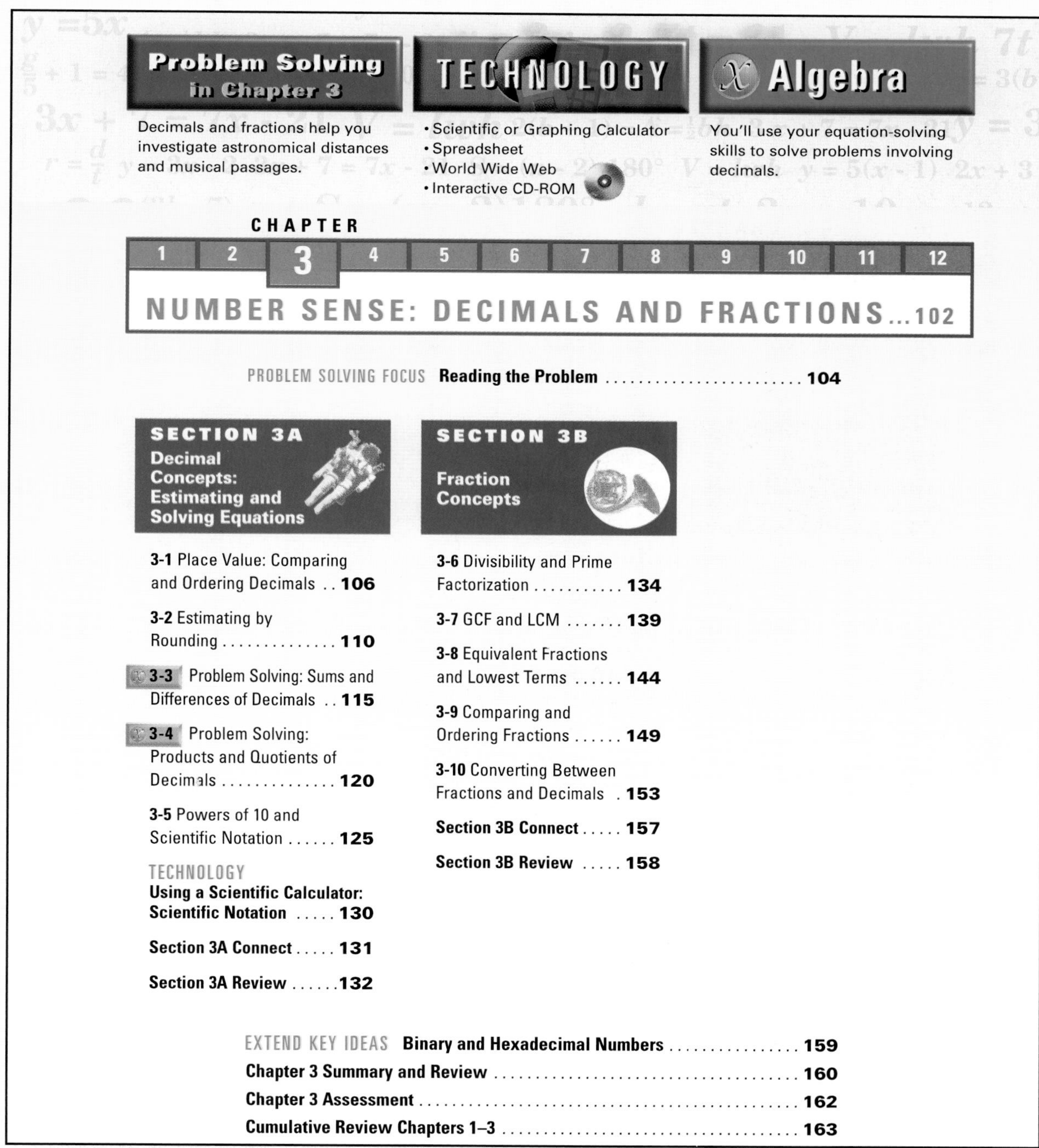

Problem Solving in Chapter 3

Decimals and fractions help you investigate astronomical distances and musical passages.

TECHNOLOGY

- Scientific or Graphing Calculator
- Spreadsheet
- World Wide Web
- Interactive CD-ROM

Algebra

You'll use your equation-solving skills to solve problems involving decimals.

CHAPTER 1 2 3 4 5 6 7 8 9 10 11 12

CHAPTER 4

Operations with Fractions

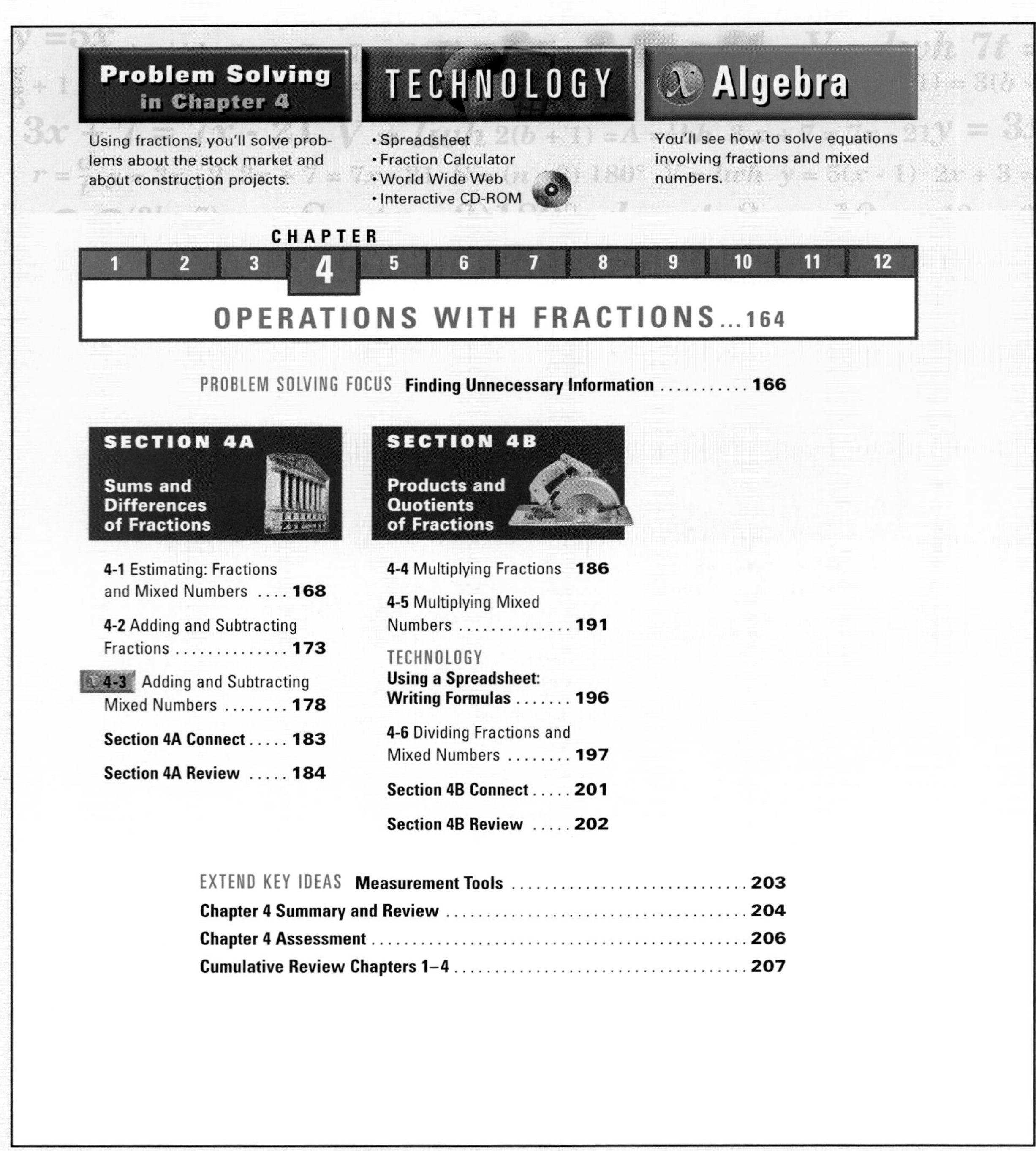

Problem Solving in Chapter 4

Using fractions, you'll solve problems about the stock market and about construction projects.

TECHNOLOGY

- Spreadsheet
- Fraction Calculator
- World Wide Web
- Interactive CD-ROM

Algebra

You'll see how to solve equations involving fractions and mixed numbers.

CHAPTER 1 2 3 **4** 5 6 7 8 9 10 11 12

CHAPTER 5

Geometry and Measurement

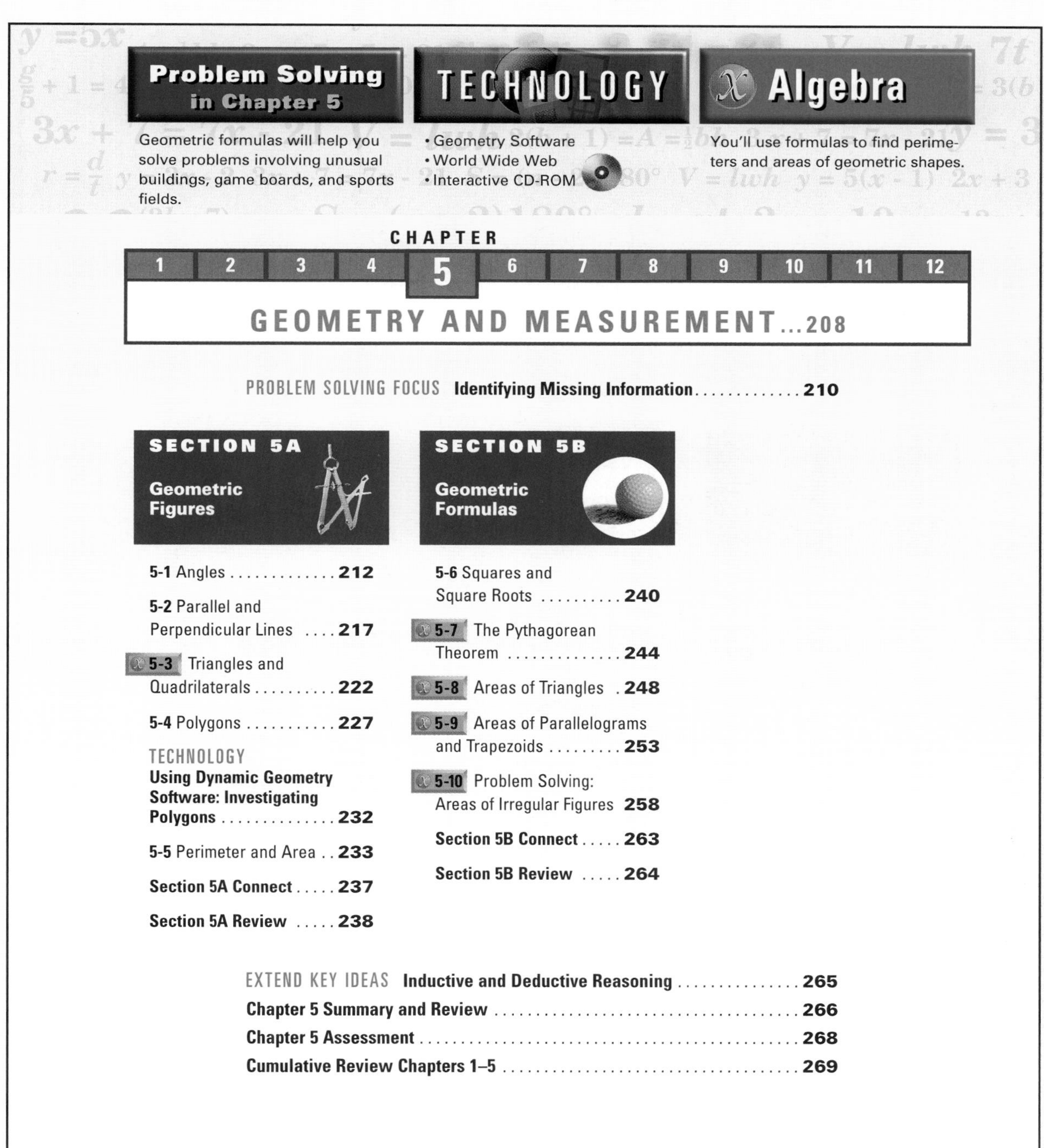

Problem Solving in Chapter 5

Geometric formulas will help you solve problems involving unusual buildings, game boards, and sports fields.

TECHNOLOGY

- Geometry Software
- World Wide Web
- Interactive CD-ROM

Algebra

You'll use formulas to find perimeters and areas of geometric shapes.

CHAPTER 1 2 3 4 **5** 6 7 8 9 10 11 12

CHAPTER 6

Ratios, Rates, and Proportions

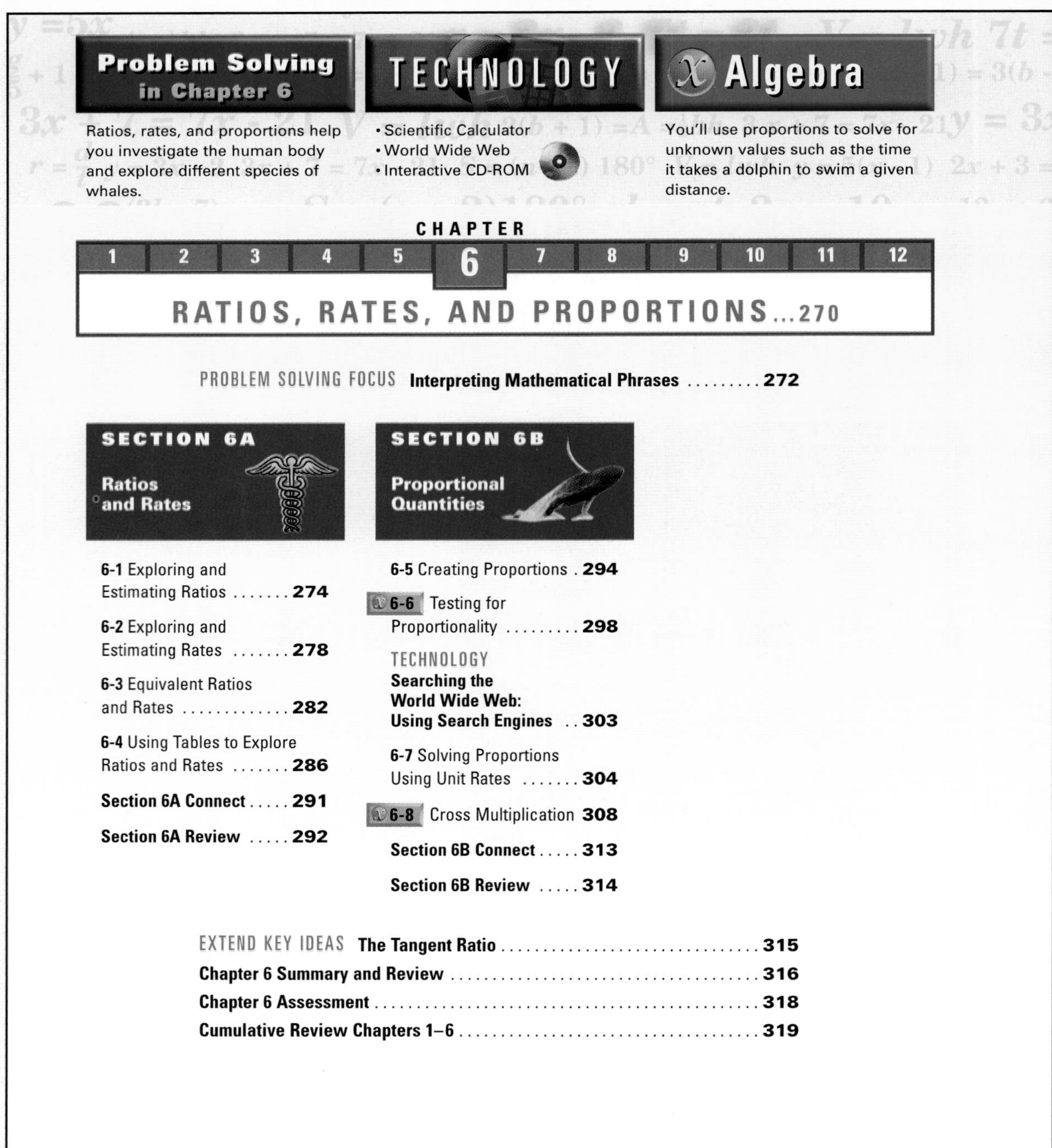

CHAPTER 7

Proportion, Scale, and Similarity

Problem Solving in Chapter 7

Maps and models of movie monsters show why scales are useful and important. Rates help you solve problems related to conservation.

TECHNOLOGY

- Geometry Software
- World Wide Web
- Interactive CD-ROM

Algebra

You'll use proportions to solve for unknown lengths in geometric figures, on maps, and on scale models.

CHAPTER

1 2 3 4 5 6 **7** 8 9 10 11 12

CHAPTER 8

Percents

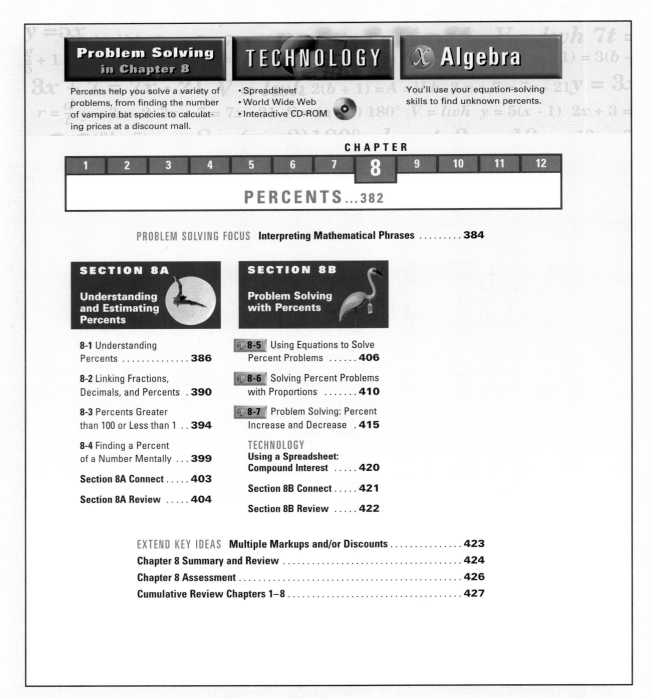

Problem Solving in Chapter 8

Percents help you solve a variety of problems, from finding the number of vampire bat species to calculating prices at a discount mall.

TECHNOLOGY

- Spreadsheet
- World Wide Web
- Interactive CD-ROM

Algebra

You'll use your equation-solving skills to find unknown percents.

CHAPTER

1 2 3 4 5 6 7 **8** 9 10 11 12

PERCENTS...382

CHAPTER 9

Integers

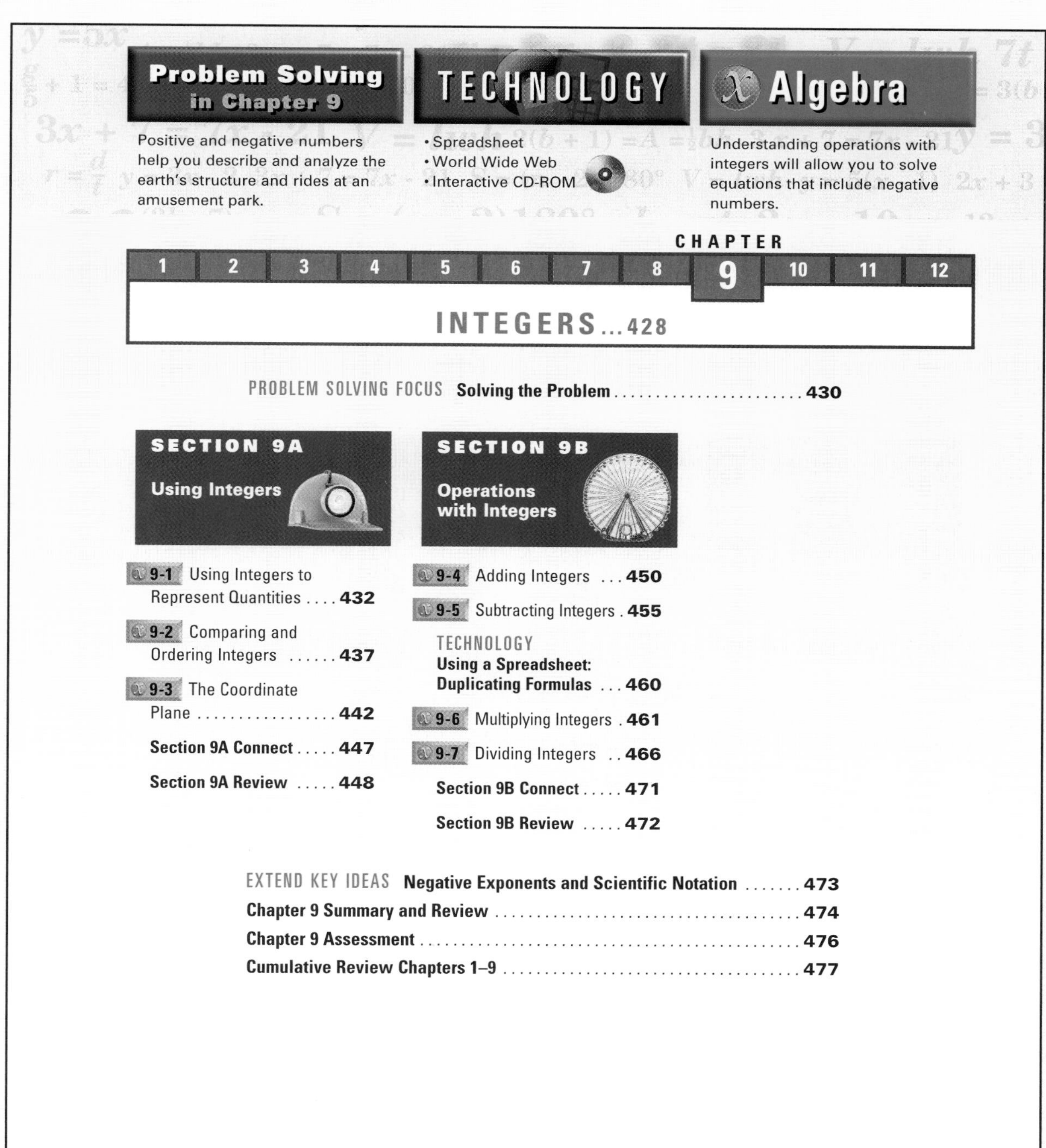
Problem Solving in Chapter 9
Positive and negative numbers help you describe and analyze the earth's structure and rides at an amusement park.
TECHNOLOGY
• Spreadsheet
• World Wide Web
• Interactive CD-ROM
Algebra
Understanding operations with integers will allow you to solve equations that include negative numbers.
CHAPTER
1 2 3 4 5 6 7 8 9 10 11 12
INTEGERS...428
SECTION 9A
Using Integers
SECTION 9B
Operations with Integers

CHAPTER 10

The Patterns of Algebra: Equations and Graphs

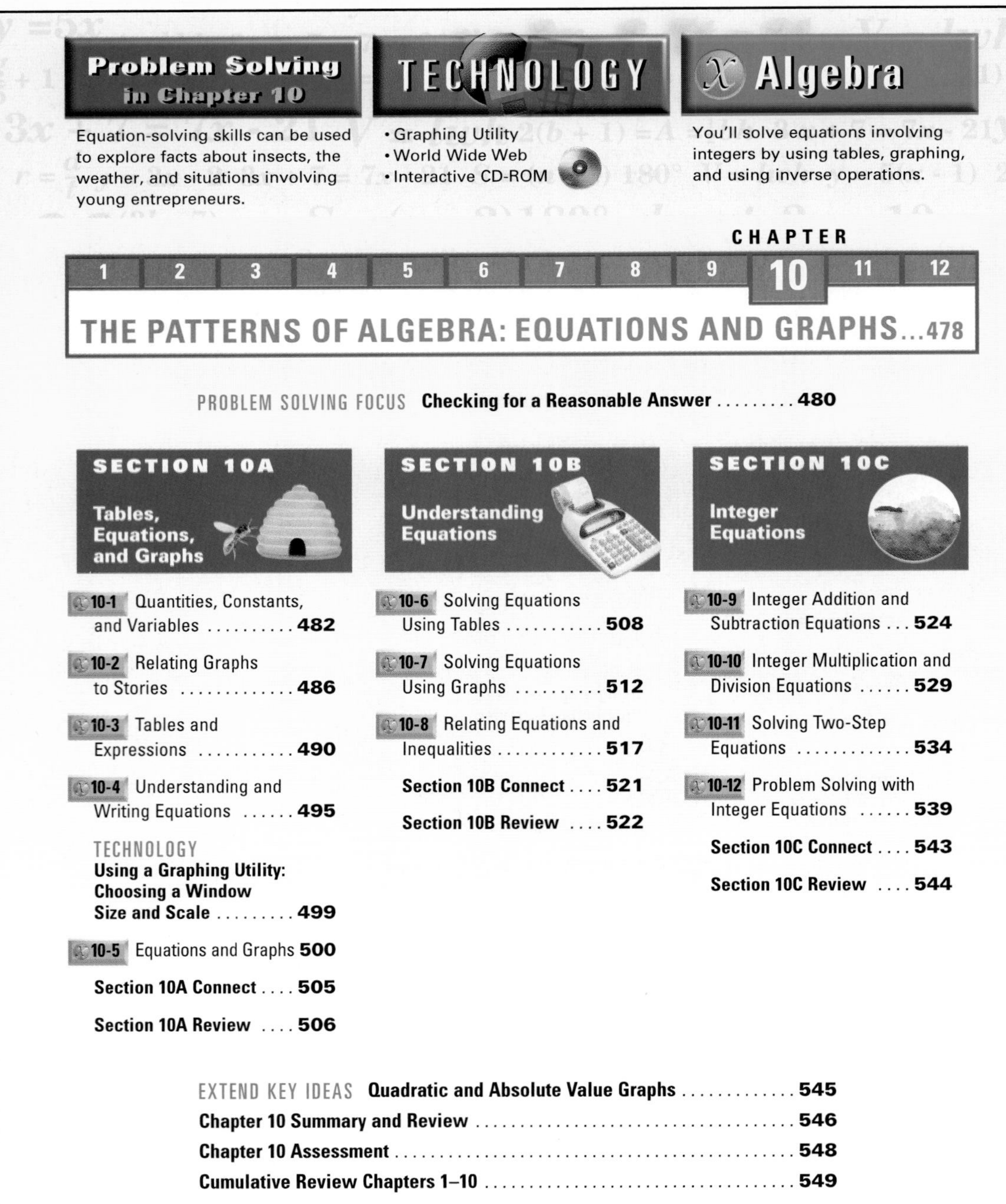

Problem Solving in Chapter 10

Equation-solving skills can be used to explore facts about insects, the weather, and situations involving young entrepreneurs.

TECHNOLOGY

- Graphing Utility
- World Wide Web
- Interactive CD-ROM

Algebra

You'll solve equations involving integers by using tables, graphing, and using inverse operations.

CHAPTER 1 2 3 4 5 6 7 8 9 **10** 11 12

CHAPTER 11

Geometry: Solids, Circles, and Transformations

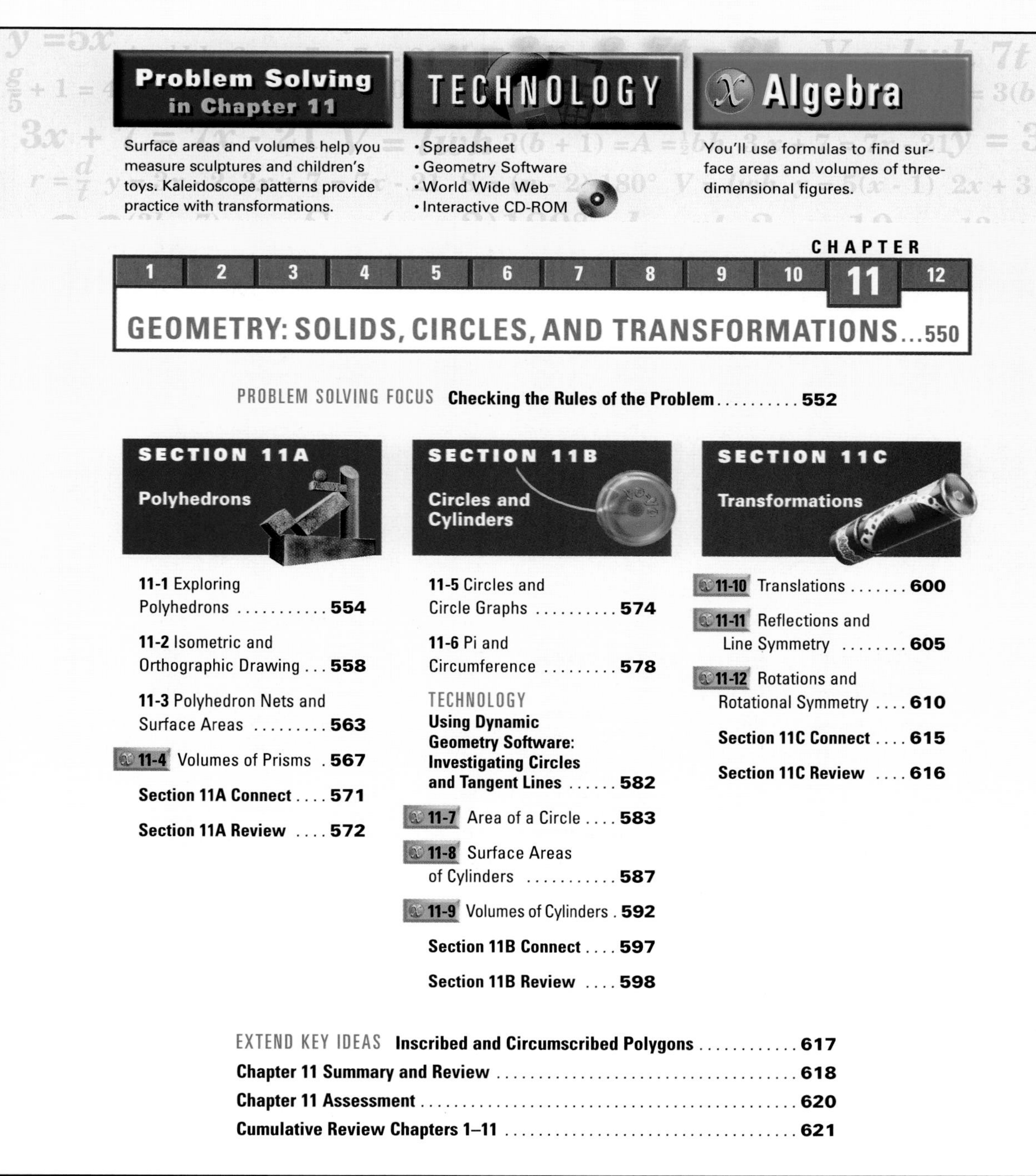

Problem Solving in Chapter 11

Surface areas and volumes help you measure sculptures and children's toys. Kaleidoscope patterns provide practice with transformations.

TECHNOLOGY

- Spreadsheet
- Geometry Software
- World Wide Web
- Interactive CD-ROM

Algebra

You'll use formulas to find surface areas and volumes of three-dimensional figures.

CHAPTER 1 2 3 4 5 6 7 8 9 10 **11** 12

CHAPTER 12

Counting and Probability

Problem Solving in Chapter 12

Examples from detective work and board games will illustrate how you can use probability to analyze a situation.

TECHNOLOGY

- Graphing Calculator
- World Wide Web
- Interactive CD-ROM

Algebra

You'll use formulas to help find geometric probabilities.

CHAPTER 1 2 3 4 5 6 7 8 9 10 11 **12**

Pacing Guide

The pacing suggested in the chart at the right assumes one day for most lessons, one day for end-of-section Connect and Review, and two days for end-of-chapter Summary, Review, and Assessment. The same number of days per chapter is used for the block scheduling options. For example, see page 2D.

You may need to adjust pacing to meet the needs of your students and your district curriculum.

	CHAPTER	PAGES	NUMBER OF DAYS
1	Making Sense of the World of Data	2–51	12
2	The Language of Algebra: Formulas, Expressions, and Equations	52–101	13
3	Number Sense: Decimals and Fractions	102–163	16
4	Operations with Fractions	164–207	11
5	Geometry and Measurement	208–269	15
6	Ratios, Rates, and Proportions	270–319	14
7	Proportion, Scale, and Similarity	320–381	16
8	Percents	382–427	12
9	Integers	428–477	13
10	The Patterns of Algebra: Equations and Graphs	478–549	18
11	Geometry: Solids, Circles, and Transformations	550–621	18
12	Counting and Probability	622–671	12
	Total Days		**170**

Materials List

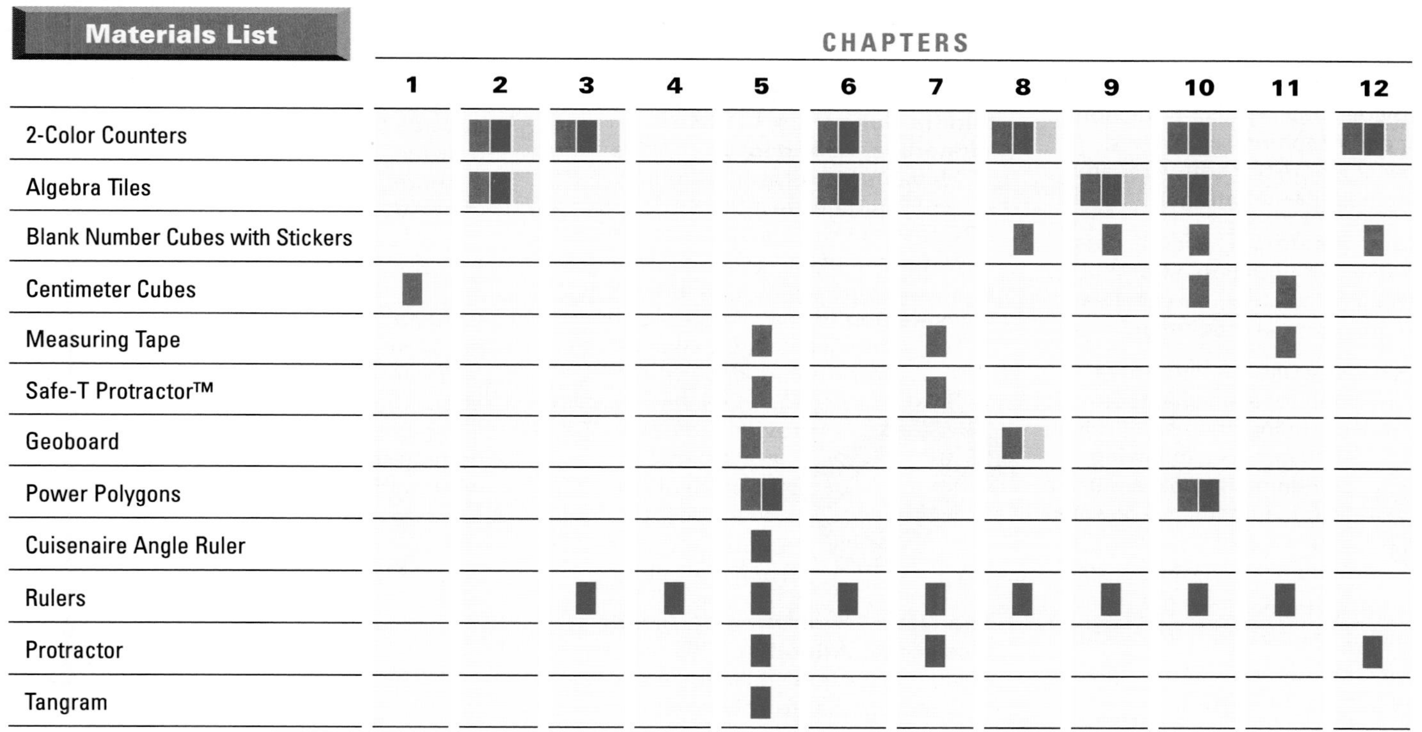

	CHAPTERS 1	2	3	4	5	6	7	8	9	10	11	12
2-Color Counters		■■□	■■□			■■□		■■□		■■□		■■□
Algebra Tiles		■■□				■■□			■■□	■■□		
Blank Number Cubes with Stickers								■	■	■		■
Centimeter Cubes	■									■	■	
Measuring Tape					■		■				■	
Safe-T Protractor™					■		■					
Geoboard					■□			■□				
Power Polygons					■■					■■		
Cuisenaire Angle Ruler					■							
Rulers			■	■	■	■	■	■	■	■	■	
Protractor					■		■					■
Tangram					■							

■ **Student Manipulative Kit** □ **Teacher's Overhead Manipulative Kit** ■ **Transparencies in Teacher's ToolKit**

Technology in Course 2

TECHNOLOGY FOR STUDENTS

Technology Used in Lessons Students should have access to scientific calculators for appropriate use as needed. In lessons, calculators are used to develop concepts involving repeating decimals, order of operations, and powers of 10. Calculators are also used to solve problems involving large numbers or real-world data requiring tedious computation. Emphasize that it is not appropriate to use calculators instead of mental computation or simple paper-pencil computation. Emphasize the importance of estimating to check if answers are reasonable. Options for using spreadsheets appear at times in the Explore part of lesson development.

Calculator Hint and Technology Link These features appear in lesson development to offer tips about calculator key sequences and displays.

Technology Pages The "Technology" pages provide activities using fraction, scientific, and graphing calculators; spreadsheets; geometry software; and search engines for the Internet.

Technology Masters These masters offer activities with fraction, scientific, and graphing calculators; spreadsheets; graphers; and geometry software.

Interactive CD-ROM An interactive lesson is provided for each chapter to enhance understanding and use of lesson concepts. The following built-in math tools are used with the interactive lessons and can also be used with other lessons when helpful.

- Spreadsheet/Grapher Tool for exploring mathematical relationships
- Equation Grapher Tool for graphing equations in 1 or 4 quadrants
- Line Plot Tool for making line plots
- Place Value Blocks Tool for concept development involving whole numbers, decimals, and integers.
- Fraction Tool for fraction models used to learn concepts and computation
- Geometry Tool for work with two-dimensional figures
- 3D Blocks Tool for work with solids
- Probability Tool for doing simulations
- Journal for student writing and for preparing written presentations that can include graphics

Mathsurf Internet Site Students go to the Scott Foresman - Addison Wesley website www.mathsurf.com using references given in the Student Book on chapter and section openers. Once at the site, students are given data and questions, or sent to other sites worldwide to gather and share data, or directed to use a search engine to research a specific term.

Wide World of Mathematics for Middle School on CD-ROM, Videodisc, or Videotape *Wide World of Mathematics* presents reports and video footage from ABC News and ABC Sports broadcasts to demonstrate how math is used in the real world. The videotape version includes an investigation for each video segment. The videodisc version also includes on-screen questions and data. The CD-ROM version also provides interactive math games. Segments on the video are referenced in the Teacher's Edition.

The New Adventures of Jasper Woodbury Videodisc This is a set of videodiscs that challenge students to work together to solve problems presented in engaging stories. Problem solutions encourage logical thinking and deductive reasoning. Episodes on the videodiscs are referenced in the Teacher's Edition.

TECHNOLOGY FOR TEACHERS

Teacher's Resource Planner CD-ROM The planner lets you preview and customize blackline masters in the program. It also offers an interactive planner that lets you map out a plan for the year or month as well as generate either default or customized daily lesson plans. Lesson plans include resources, correlations, assignment guides, space to write notes, and more.

TestWorks: Test and Practice Software This software lets you generate default as well as customized tests and worksheets in free response, multiple choice, or mixed formats. The software is packaged on a CD-ROM.

Internet Site for Teachers Go online at www.teacher.mathsurf.com to hear new ideas, get information about program components, and link to other Internet sites.

TECHNOLOGY FOR PARENTS

Internet Site for Parents Parents can go online at www.parent.mathsurf.com to get information about the program along with ideas for helping their children with math at home.

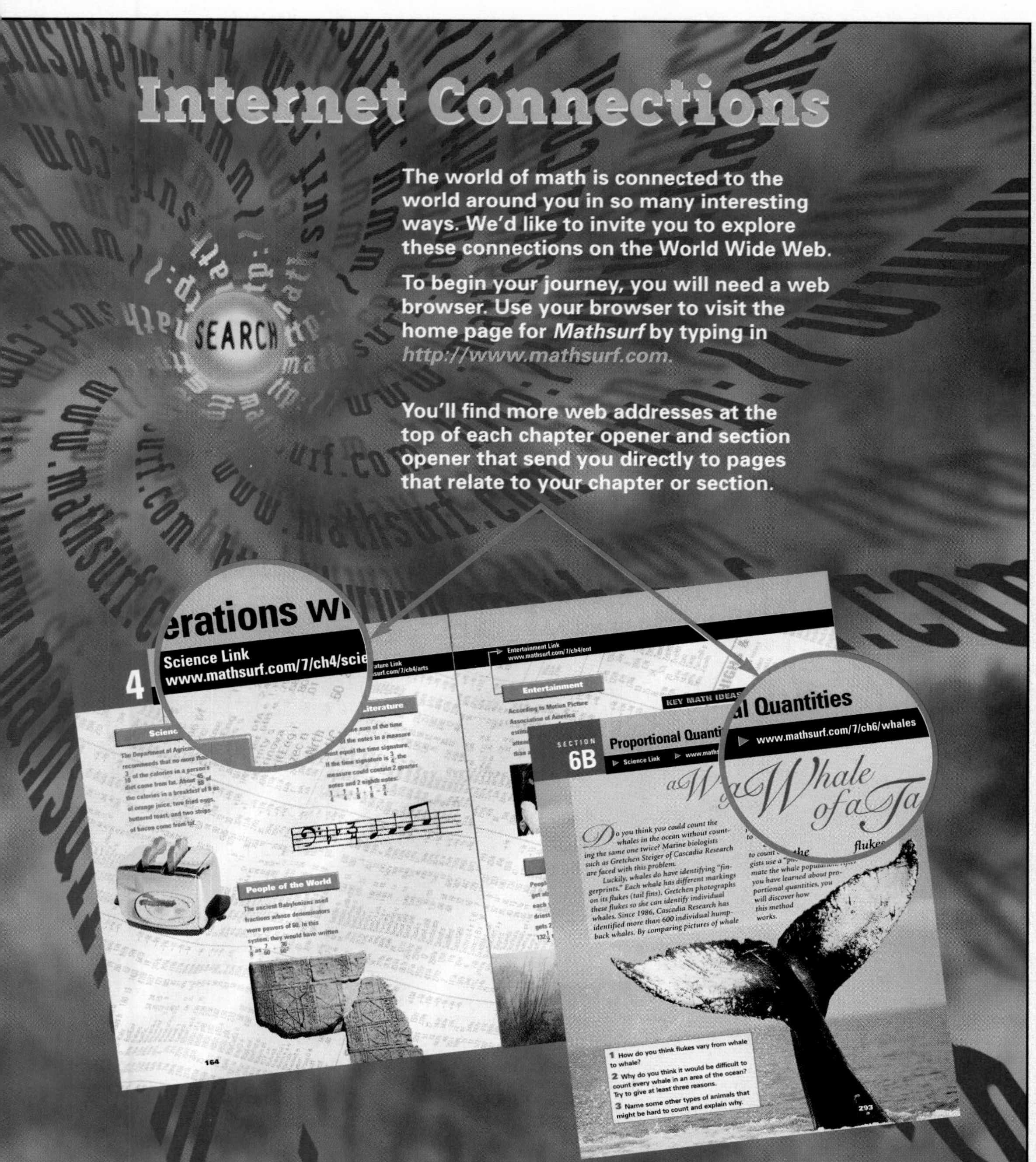

Internet Connections

The world of math is connected to the world around you in so many interesting ways. We'd like to invite you to explore these connections on the World Wide Web.

To begin your journey, you will need a web browser. Use your browser to visit the home page for *Mathsurf* by typing in http://www.mathsurf.com.

You'll find more web addresses at the top of each chapter opener and section opener that send you directly to pages that relate to your chapter or section.

INTERNET CONNECTIONS

If your school or students have access to the World Wide Web point out the Web site addresses across the top of the chapter and section openers. Then show students how they can use the Web site addresses given to find interdisciplinary links for the topics discussed in the chapter. Let students work in small groups to browse the Web; tell them to note interesting information that they find and share it with the class.

You might want to discuss with students some advantages of researching on the Internet.

- Information may provide more complete details on recently recorded facts than newspapers, magazines, or reference books.
- It is often possible to find information about obscure topics that might be difficult to find elsewhere.
- It is easy to interact with the person who created a Web site.

You might also note some of the disadvantages.

- Information might remain at a Web site for only a short period of time.
- There is little or no regulation of what information does or does not appear on the Internet.
- Fact-checking is not required for information on the Internet; facts may be incorrect.

You may want to use the Teacher's Edition notes found on the chapter and section openers. These notes provide an activity for each link which does not require access to the World Wide Web.

PROBLEM SOLVING AND APPLICATIONS

"Problem solving is the process by which students experience the power and usefulness of mathematics in the world around them."

from The NCTM Standards

Scott Foresman-Addison Wesley Middle School Mathematics is a problem solving based program that provides students with a wide range of problem-solving tools. When you teach mathematics from a problem-solving viewpoint, you provide students with the key skills and attitudes needed to be successful in mathematics.

Point out the logos at the top of this page. These logos are used throughout the book to help students analyze the problem-solving process.

- The Problem Solving Guidelines logo lists the four steps students should consider when solving a problem: understand, plan, solve, and look back.
- The Problem Solving Strategies logo reminds students of strategies they can use in problem solving.
- Problem Solving Tips provide helpful hints for specific problems students are asked to solve.
- In **What Do You Think?** students see two ways to solve a problem. Then they discuss how they might solve the problem.

Students will encounter a diverse selection of problem-solving applications in the program. Discuss the six examples given on this page. Ask students if they can think of other uses of mathematics.

Throughout the book students will see connections to different disciplines, as well as to business, industry, career, and consumer topics. You might have groups of students page through their books to find references to connections other than those named at the bottom of this page.

Problem Solving and Applications

Math is all around you. Having good math skills can help you solve problems every day. What kinds of problems can you solve using mathematics?

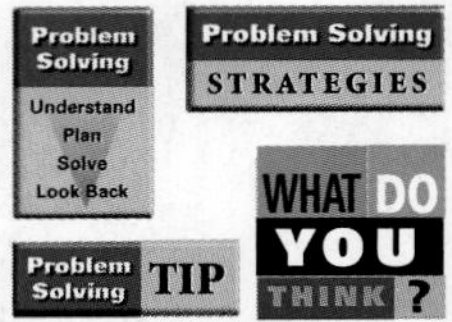

Math is also connected to the other subjects you are studying.
Look on these pages to find some examples of how math is connected to:

Science			
p. 9	p. 20	p. 58	p. 69
p. 114	p. 123	p. 177	p. 190
p. 216	p. 226	p. 277	p. 280
p. 347	p. 392	p. 397	p. 401
p. 435	p. 440	p. 493	p. 503

History			
p. 15	p. 89	p. 107	p. 181
p. 189	p. 195	p. 236	p. 251
p. 311	p. 335	p. 342	p. 351
p. 422	p. 456	p. 560	p. 576
p. 581	p. 591	p. 598	p. 657

Geography			
p. 9	p. 28	p. 76	p. 172
p. 220	p. 235	p. 257	p. 324
p. 327	p. 331	p. 332	p. 336
p. 339	p. 342	p. 398	p. 436
p. 458	p. 577	p. 604	p. 609

PROBLEM SOLVING HANDBOOK

We live in an Information Age. Today, by using the Internet and other tools, you can find more information more quickly than ever before. But knowing how to *find* information and knowing how to *use* it are two very different skills!

The key to success in almost any career is the ability to solve problems. If you don't have good problem-solving skills, you won't be able to use even the most accurate, up-to-date information.

Your teacher and textbook will help guide you, but to become a better problem solver, you must do the real exploring yourself. As you investigate challenging problems, you'll need to think logically, use technology appropriately, and work with others cooperatively.

Along the way, you'll find yourself asking and answering the question, "What do you think?" By asking this question, you'll learn about creative strategies used by your classmates. By answering it, you'll learn how to present your ideas to others with clarity and confidence.

The students shown here will be sharing their thinking with you throughout this book. But the key question will always be

"What do you think?"

1. Why is it important to hear about creative strategies used by your classmates?
2. How can sharing your ideas with other students help you become a better problem solver?

PROBLEM SOLVING HANDBOOK

This Problem Solving Handbook provides students with an opportunity to focus on the problem-solving process and to preview the problem-solving strategies used throughout this book. The following strategies are included in the Handbook

- Look for a Pattern
- Make an Organized List
- Make a Table
- Guess and Check
- Work Backward
- Use Logical Reasoning
- Draw a Diagram
- Solve a Simpler Problem

About What Do You Think?

It is important for students to understand that there is no single right way to solve a problem. In **What Do You Think?** your students have the opportunity to see how other students solve a problem. This feature is designed to help create an atmosphere that allows your students to discuss strategies with classmates, and to explain their thinking. It encourages them to be flexible.

Ask ...

- Why would working in groups be helpful when solving a problem?
- Have you ever known the answer to a problem but did not give it because you were afraid you might be wrong?
- Have you ever known the answer to a problem but could not explain how you arrived at the answer?
- Do you know that many problems have been solved only after people have pursued false leads—sometimes for many years?

Answers for What Do You Think?

1. So you can learn about many different approaches to problem solving. You may also find that some of their ideas help you solve problems.
2. Possible answer: To explain your thinking to others, you must be sure you understand it yourself.

PROBLEM SOLVING HANDBOOK

About Problem Solving

Throughout this book, students will use the following four steps to guide them through solving a problem:

- Understand
- Plan
- Solve
- Look Back

These Problem-Solving Guidelines appear on both Teaching Tool Transparencies 2 and 3: Guided Problem Solving and on Teaching Tool Transparency 16: Problem-Solving Guidelines.

- On Transparencies 2 and 3, each guideline is followed by questions and space to write the solution to the problem. You may want to use these transparencies when you discuss a strategy; they are referenced in the Teacher's Edition with *Choose a Strategy* problems.
- Transparency 16 is similar to Transparencies 2 and 3. It presents the Problem-Soving Guidelines in a one-page format that can be used at any time.

You may wish to use these transparencies as you discuss the strategies on the following pages.

Solving Problems

You've solved many problems in your previous math classes. Now you'll look more closely at some methods that can help you solve problems. ◄

Problem Solving Getting Started

You solve problems every day. Some, like the problem of how much change you should get back when you pay for something, are straightforward. You can usually apply your knowledge of mathematics to find a quick solution to a problem such as this.

Others, such as the problem of which school activities to join, are harder to solve. There are many choices, and the result of each choice is not clear. Still others, such as the problem of which occupation to choose, may not even have exact or permanent solutions. You solve them the best way you can. But you should be ready to take another look at your solution if the situation changes.

No matter what problem you're tackling, you need a plan or a strategy for solving it. A plan or strategy will help you to understand the problem, to work out a creative solution, and to check that the solution makes sense.

Problem Solving

Understand
Plan
Solve
Look Back

PROBLEM-SOLVING GUIDELINES

❶ UNDERSTAND the Problem

- What do you know?
- What do you need to find out?

❷ Develop a PLAN

- Have you ever solved a similar problem?
- What strategies can you use?
- Estimate an answer.

❸ SOLVE the Problem

- Do you need to try another strategy?
- What is the solution?

❹ LOOK BACK

- Did you answer the right question?
- Does your answer make sense?

Example

Mrs. Cutler wants to install pine paneling on one wall of her den. The wall is 8 ft tall and 12 ft wide. An 8 ft panel that is 9 in. wide costs $9.95. Find the cost of the panels.

❶ UNDERSTAND the Problem

You *know* the size of the wall and the size and cost of a panel. You *need to find* the cost of all the panels needed to cover the wall.

❷ Develop a PLAN

You've *solved similar problems* involving the cost of a number of items that have the same price. To find the total cost, multiply the number of items by the unit price.

You can *estimate the answer.* Each panel is about 1 ft wide, so about 12 panels are needed. The total cost should be about 12 • $10, or $120.

One possible *strategy* is to draw a diagram to find the number of panels.

❸ SOLVE the Problem

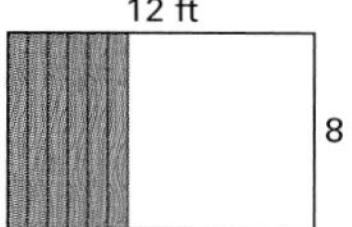

As you begin to sketch the wall, you might decide to use division to find out how many panels to draw.

But once you know the number of panels, you don't need a sketch! So *try another strategy.* Use division to find the number of panels.

Number of panels = 144 ÷ 9 = 16   12 ft = 144 in.

Total cost = 16 • $9.95, or $159.20

The *solution* is that the panels will cost $159.20.

❹ LOOK BACK

You *answered the right question.* Because your answer is close to your estimate of $120, *your answer makes sense.*

Check Your Understanding

1. What other strategies could you have used to solve the problem?

2. Why is it important to have a plan before you begin a solution?

About the Example

The example shows students how to use the Problem-Solving Guidelines.

Ask …

- In the Example, what does it mean to understand the problem? Possible answer: To decide what question the problem is asking and to determine what information is given to solve the problem.
- How do you develop a plan? Possible answer: Think about what is involved in solving the problem. You know the cost of one panel, so find the number of panels needed. since the height of both a panel and the room are the same, the number of panels is the number of 9 in. widths needed to make 12 ft.
- How does drawing a diagram help you solve the problem? Answers may vary.
- Why is *Look Back* important? Possible answer: It is a check to see if the question in the problem has been answered.

About Check Your Understanding

Following the examples in each lesson, you will find **Check Your Understanding** questions. These questions may be used for class discussion; they provide an opportunity to clarify the examples and to pinpoint areas that need more explanation.

Answers for Check Your Understanding

1. Possible answer: To find the number of panels needed to cover the wall, you could make a table comparing the number of panels to the total width.
2. Possible answer: If you don't have a plan, you can easily get off track and start doing work that doesn't really help you solve the problem.

PROBLEM SOLVING HANDBOOK

Problem-Solving Strategy: Look for a Pattern

Many problems that can be solved by looking for a pattern involve interpreting numerical or geometric relationships. Finding patterns allows students to find solutions to otherwise difficult or tedious problems.

- This strategy is often used in conjunction with Make a Table.
- Using concrete materials or drawing pictures can help students identify patterns.
- In real life, finding trends often involves looking for patterns in data.

About the Page

Students find a pattern that relates the number of people in one generation to the number in the next generation. They continue the pattern to solve the problem.

Ask ...

- Why did Debra list 4 grandparents for Generation 3? Each of her parents had 2 parents, so she has 4 grandparents.
- Assume that each generation represents 25 years. Estimate when Debra's great-great-great grandparents (Generation 6) would have lived. Between 125 and 150 years ago.
- How many more people are in Generation 10 than in Generation 6? $512 - 32 = 480$ more people.

Try It

You might ask students to state the rule they used to continue the patterns in these problems. Possible answers: Part a: Multiply by 3; Part b: Add 0.09 meters.

Answers for Try It

a. 243

b. 1.14 m

Problem Solving STRATEGIES

- Look for a Pattern
- Make an Organized List
- Make a Table
- Guess and Check
- Work Backward
- Use Logical Reasoning
- Draw a Diagram
- Solve a Simpler Problem

Look for a Pattern

Sometimes the numbers in a problem form a pattern. To solve the problem, you can find the rule that creates the pattern and use the rule to find the answer. ◂

Example

Debra made a list of her direct ancestors. She called herself Generation 1, her parents Generation 2, her grandparents Generation 3, and so on. How many people were there in Generation 6?

List the information you know:

Generation 1: 1 person

Generation 2: 2 parents

Generation 3: 4 grandparents

Each generation has twice as many people as the previous one. Use this rule to continue the pattern:

Generation 4: $4 \times 2 = 8$ great-grandparents

Generation 5: $8 \times 2 = 16$ great-great grandparents

Generation 6: $16 \times 2 = 32$ great-great-great grandparents

There were 32 people in Generation 6.

Try It

a. Lincoln School students use a phone tree to convey important information. The chairperson makes 3 calls to start the phone tree. On the second round, 9 calls are made. On the third round, 27 calls are made. How many calls are made on the fifth round?

b. In one week, a tomato plant grew from 0.78 meters tall to 0.87 meters tall. If the plant continues to grow at the same rate, how tall will it be three weeks later?

Make an Organized List

Problem Solving
STRATEGIES

- Look for a Pattern
- Make an Organized List
- Make a Table
- Guess and Check
- Work Backward
- Use Logical Reasoning
- Draw a Diagram
- Solve a Simpler Problem

Sometimes a problem asks you to find the number of ways in which something can be done. To solve the problem, you can list and count all the possibilities. The key to a correct solution is to organize your list carefully so you don't overlook any possibilities. ◄

Example

Fruit juice costs 40¢ in a vending machine. How many different combinations of quarters, dimes, and nickels must the machine be programmed to accept?

Since 2 quarters make 50¢, there can be no more than 1 quarter in any combination. Start by listing combinations with 1 quarter.

Then list combinations with 0 quarters. First list 4-dime combinations, then 3-dime combinations, and so on.

Finally, list combinations with 0 quarters and 0 dimes, only nickels.

The machine must be programmed to accept 7 different combinations of quarters, dimes, and nickels.

Quarters	Dimes	Nickels
1	1	1
1	0	3
0	4	0
0	3	2
0	2	4
0	1	6
0	0	8

Try It

a. All telephone area codes in one region of the country consist of the digits 2, 3, and 7. If no digit can be repeated, how many area codes containing only 2, 3, and 7 are possible?

b. Wise Owl book bags come in square or teardrop shapes. Each shape is available in red, blue, green, or yellow, and in small, medium, or large sizes. How many shape-color-size choices are available?

Problem-Solving Strategy
Make an Organized List

Many problems that require finding all possibilities or finding the number of combinations of things can be solved by making an organized list.

- This strategy is often used in conjunction with Make a Table or Find a Pattern.
- Often the same data can be organized in different ways.
- In real life, data or information must be organized before it can be interpreted.

About the Page

Students find combinations of quarters, dimes, and nickels that have a value of 40¢.

Ask ...

- What kind of organization do you see in the table? Possible answer: Beginning at the top the greatest number of quarters is considered first, then the greatest number of dimes, and so on.
- Suppose the vending machine company increased the cost of the fruit juice to 50¢. Now how many combinations of quarters, nickels and dimes are there? 10 different combinations.

Try It

For Part b, you might suggest that students use the first letter(s) of a name when making their list.

Answers for Try It

a. 6

b. 24

Problem-Solving Strategy: Make a Table

By making a table, students can organize information in a way that may help them recognize patterns that lead to generalizations.

- This strategy is often used in conjunction with Make an Organized List and Look for a Pattern.
- Students need to decide column and row headings before making a table.
- Students will encounter tables in many places, such as newspapers, magazines, textbooks, almanacs, and the Internet.

About the Page

Students make a table to help them compare the salaries of two people.

Ask ...

- If both people had started in January, how much more would Keithia have earned by June? $3000
- If Keithia's starting salary had been $2750 per month in February rather than $3000, in what month would the totals be the same? November

Try It

Students' tables may differ for these problems. You might discuss various approaches students used to find their answers.

Answers for Try It

a. 97¢

b. 90

Problem Solving STRATEGIES

- Look for a Pattern
- Make an Organized List
- Make a Table
- Guess and Check
- Work Backward
- Use Logical Reasoning
- Draw a Diagram
- Solve a Simpler Problem

Make a Table

A problem involving a relationship between two sets of numbers can often be solved by making a table. A table helps you organize data so you can spot the numerical relationship and find the answer. ◄

Example

In January, Hershel started a job that paid $2500 per month. In February, Keithia started a job that paid $3000 per month. In what month were the total amounts that the two had earned the same?

Make a table to organize data about each person's total earnings.

Month	January	February	March	April	May	June
Hershel's Total	2,500	5,000	7,500	10,000	12,500	15,000
Keithia's Total		3,000	6,000	9,000	12,000	15,000

The table shows that the amount by which Hershel's total exceeded Keithia's total decreased each month from February through June.

In June, both total amounts were the same.

Try It

a. In April, canned peaches sold for 79¢ and canned pears sold for 91¢. If the price of peaches increases 3¢ each month and the price of pears increases 1¢ each month, how much will both types of fruit sell for when their prices are the same?

b. At a traffic checkpoint, environmental safety officers checked every 18th car for excess carbon monoxide and every 15th car for a damaged exhaust system. If the first car at the checkpoint is car 1, what will be the number of the first car to be checked for both problems?

Guess and Check

Problem Solving

STRATEGIES

- Look for a Pattern
- Make an Organized List
- Make a Table
- Guess and Check
- Work Backward
- Use Logical Reasoning
- Draw a Diagram
- Solve a Simpler Problem

If you're not sure how to solve a problem, make an educated guess at the answer. Then check your guess. If it's wrong, revise your guess up or down. Repeat the pattern of *guess-check-revise* until you find the answer, or until you have an estimate that is close enough. ◄

Example

A rectangle has an area of 60 in^2. The length exceeds the width by 7 inches. Find the dimensions of the rectangle.

Guess: For a first guess, choose a length and width that multiply to 60.

Try $l = 10$ and $w = 6$. $10 \times 6 = 60$

Check: The length should be 7 greater than the width. $10 - 6 = 4$

Think: The difference isn't great enough. I need to increase the length.

Revise: Try $l = 15$ and $w = 4$. $15 \times 4 = 60$

Check: $15 - 4 = 11$

Think: Now the difference is *too* great. I need a length *between* my two guesses.

Revise: Try $l = 12$ and $w = 5$. $12 \times 5 = 60$

Check: $12 - 5 = 7$ ✔

The length of the rectangle is 12 in. and the width is 5 in.

Try It

a. Leon made long distance calls to two friends. One call lasted 8 minutes longer than the other. According to his phone bill, the two calls lasted a total of 42 minutes. How long was each call?

b. Two trains are 225 miles apart and traveling in opposite directions on parallel and adjacent tracks. If the eastbound train averages 50 miles per hour and the westbound train averages 40 miles per hour, how long will it take before they pass each other?

Problem-Solving Strategy Guess and Check

The Guess-and-Check Strategy is a systematic process of making reasonable guesses. It is an especially useful tool when the number of possible solutions is small and when it is relatively easy to determine if a guess is reasonable. Many of the problems that students solve now using Guess and Check will be solved later using algebra.

- This strategy is often used in conjunction with Look for a Pattern and Use Logical Reasoning.
- To be able to make good guesses, students must understand the problem.
- In real life, many important discoveries have been made using Guess and Check, which is also called Trial and Error.

About the Page

Students use information given about a rectangle and make educated guesses until they find its length and width.

Ask ...

- How do you find the area of a rectangle? Multiply the length and width.
- Would you have chosen 10 as a first guess for the length? If not, what would your guess have been? Answers may vary.

Try It

After students complete the problems, you might invite several students to share their series of guesses with the class.

Answers for Try It

a. 25 minutes and 17 minutes

b. $2\frac{1}{2}$ hours

Problem-Solving Strategy: Work Backward

The Work Backward Strategy involves beginning with a final result and examining, in reverse order, the steps leading to this result; thus discovering the initial conditions of the problem.

- Students may use this strategy in conjunction with other strategies such as Make an Organized List, Make a Table, and Look for a Pattern.
- Students can use inverse operations when they work backward.
- In real life, this strategy is used to solve puzzles and develop ways to win games.

About the Page

Students are given a current price and they work backward to find an original price.

Ask ...

- Why do you think the solution shown demonstrates working backward? The answer is found by starting with the end result and working back to the beginning.
- How might you check the answer? Possible answer: Begin at $42. Add $8 ($50), subtract $14 ($36), take one-half ($18). The answer checks.

Try It

If students are having trouble with a problem, suggest they follow the example. For each step, have them tell what happened and what they can conclude from this step.

Answers for Try It

a. $12

b. About 14,400 ft

Problem Solving STRATEGIES

- Look for a Pattern
- Make an Organized List
- Make a Table
- Guess and Check
- Work Backward
- Use Logical Reasoning
- Draw a Diagram
- Solve a Simpler Problem

Work Backward

A problem may give you the result of a series of steps and ask you to find the initial value. To solve the problem, you can work your way backward, step by step, to the beginning. ◄

Example

The Astro calculator was introduced in 1993. In 1994, the price was raised $8. In 1995, the price was lowered $14 because of lower demand. In 1996, the price was halved to $18 because of competition from a new calculator. Find the original price.

The problem describes three steps occurring in order (price raised, price lowered, price halved). It also tells you the end result (the final price was $18). To solve the problem, work backward to the beginning.

Step	What Happened	Conclusion
3	The price was halved to $18.	Before this step, the price was *twice* $18, or $36.
2	The price was lowered $14 to $36.	Before this step, the price was $14 *greater than* $36, or $50.
1	The price was raised $8 to $50.	Before this step, the price was $8 *less than* $50, or $42.

The original price of the calculator was $42.

Try It

a. At a sale, T-shirts were marked down $4. Pei bought 3 T-shirts. A sales tax of $2 was added to her bill, bringing the total cost to $26. Find the price of T-shirts before the sale.

b. Mount Whitney, Harney Peak, Mount Davis, and Woodall Mountain are the highest points in California, South Dakota, Pennsylvania, and Mississippi, respectively. Mount Whitney is about twice as tall as Harney Peak. Mount Davis is about 4020 feet less tall than Harney Peak and 4 times as tall as 806 ft Woodall Mountain. About how tall is Mount Whitney?

Use Logical Reasoning

Problem Solving STRATEGIES

- Look for a Pattern
- Make an Organized List
- Make a Table
- Guess and Check
- Work Backward
- Use Logical Reasoning
- Draw a Diagram
- Solve a Simpler Problem

To solve a problem using logical reasoning, decide how the facts of the problem are related to each other. Then work your way, step by step, from the given facts to a solution. As you work, be careful not to make false assumptions or to draw conclusions that are not based on facts. ◄

Example

Freda, Miguel, and Ann are a teacher, a miner, and a writer, though not necessarily in that order. Ann is the sister of the teacher. Miguel has never met the teacher or the miner. Match the people with their jobs.

Take clues one at a time. Use a grid to keep track of your conclusions.

1. Ann is the sister of the teacher, so she is not the teacher.

	Teacher	Miner	Writer
Freda			
Miguel			
Ann	no		

2. Miguel has never met the teacher or the miner.

   Miguel must be the writer.

   Freda must be the teacher.

   That means Ann is the miner.

	Teacher	Miner	Writer
Freda			
Miguel	no	no	yes
Ann	no		

	Teacher	Miner	Writer
Freda	yes	no	no
Miguel	no	no	yes
Ann	no	yes	no

Try It

a. Xiao, Gina, and Dena like math, history, and art best. Dena dislikes art. Gina knows the students who like art and math best. Match the students with their favorite subjects.

b. Antoine, Bill, and Carlos live in Dallas, Seattle, and Miami. Bill is the brother of the man who lives in Seattle. Either Antoine or Carlos lives in Dallas. Antoine is an only child. Match the people with their cities.

Problem-Solving Strategy: Use Logical Reasoning

Many problems that can be solved with logical reasoning involve more than simply using basic mathematical operations. They involve thinking clearly, organizing information, and drawing conclusions.

- This strategy is often used in conjunction with Make a Table or Draw a Diagram.
- In a logic table, students list all possibilities and eliminate those that do not fit the problem.
- In real life many puzzle problems involve logical thinking.

About the Page

Students work their way step-by-step through a logic puzzle.

Ask ...

- How do you know that Ann is not the teacher? She is the sister of the teacher.
- How do you know that Miguel is not the teacher or the miner? He has never met these people.
- How can you tell that Miguel is the writer? The chart shows that he is not the teacher or miner. The only choice left is the writer.
- How does knowing that Miguel is the writer help you fill in the chart? You can write "no" in the "writer" column for Freda and Ann.

Try It

You might want to help students set up their tables.

Answers for Try It

a. Gina: history; Dena: math; Xiao: art

b. Carlos: Seattle; Antoine: Dallas; Bill: Miami

Problem-Solving Strategy: Draw a Diagram

Representing the information in a problem in the form of a picture or diagram may help students see the conditions of the problem more clearly.

- Sometimes a diagram is more appropriate than a table when information overlaps.
- Sometimes diagrams can be sketches. Other times a more accurate drawing is necessary.
- In real life, instructions are often given with diagrams to clarify a procedure.

About the Page

Students draw a diagram to determine the order in which four people are standing.

Ask ...

- Could you solve this problem without drawing a diagram? Does the diagram make it easier? Answers may vary.
- Suppose that you were also told that Elise is between Alicia and Damont. Where would Elise be standing? You would be able to conclude that she is either between Alicia and Brenda or between Brenda and Damont.

Try It

Students may not draw the same diagrams to solve a problem. Invite students to share their work with classmates.

Answers for Try It

a. Dylan, Bonnie, Clint, Adam, Laleh

b. 42

Problem Solving STRATEGIES

- Look for a Pattern
- Make an Organized List
- Make a Table
- Guess and Check
- Work Backward
- Use Logical Reasoning
- Draw a Diagram
- Solve a Simpler Problem

Draw a Diagram

A problem may involve objects, places, or positions. To solve such a problem, it may help to draw a diagram and look for relationships among the given data. Then use the relationships to find the answer. ◄

Example

Alicia, Brenda, Cal, and Damont are in line in the cafeteria. Damont is somewhere behind Brenda. Alicia is somewhere behind Cal. Brenda is somewhere behind Alicia. Find the order of the four students.

Draw a diagram to straighten out the relationships among the students. Use letters to represent their positions.

Begin with the first item of information: Damont is behind Brenda. **Front B D**

The second item gives no information about Damont or Brenda, so skip to the third: Brenda is behind Alicia. Add Alicia to the diagram. **Front A B D**

Now use the second item: Alicia is behind Cal. **Front C A B D**

The order of the students is Cal, Alicia, Brenda, and Damont.

Try It

a. Clint is older than Laleh but younger than Bonnie. Adam is older than Laleh but younger than Clint. Bonnie is younger than Dylan. Order the 5 students from oldest to youngest.

b. A birthday cake measures 12 in. by 9 in. There are candles at the 4 corners and at 1-inch intervals around the border. How many candles are there on the cake?

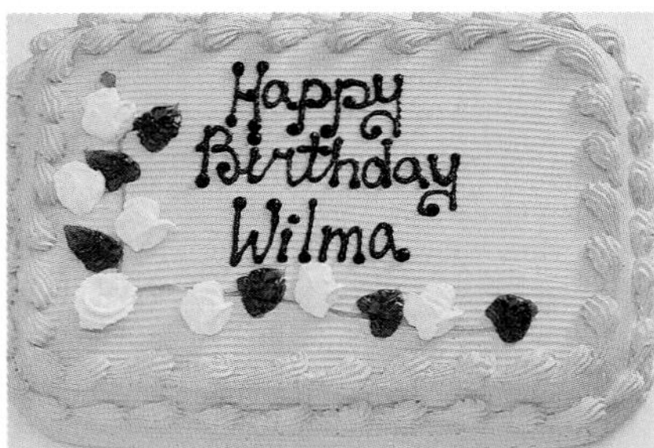

Solve a Simpler Problem

Problem Solving

STRATEGIES

- Look for a Pattern
- Make an Organized List
- Make a Table
- Guess and Check
- Work Backward
- Use Logical Reasoning
- Draw a Diagram
- Solve a Simpler Problem

A problem may contain large numbers or appear to require many steps. Instead of solving the given problem, solve a similar but simpler problem. Look for shortcuts, patterns, and relationships. Then use what you've learned to solve the original problem. ◄

Example

There are 64 teams in the state soccer tournament. A team is eliminated if it loses a game. How many games must be played to determine the state soccer champion?

You could draw a diagram listing 64 teams and count the number of games that must be played. But that would be very complicated. Instead, look at some simpler tournaments.

Number of Teams	Games Needed	
2	1	Team 1 plays Team 2 → Champion!
3	2	Team 2 plays Team 3 → Team 1 plays Team 2 or 3 → Champion!
4	3	Team 1 plays Team 2 → Team 1 or 2; Team 3 plays Team 4 → Team 3 or 4; Team 1 or 2 plays Team 3 or 4 → Champion!

The number of games needed is always 1 less than the number of teams. So a 64-team tournament requires 64 – 1 = 63 games.

Try It

a. How many cuts must you make in a long rope to create 47 jump ropes?

b. How many paths are there from *A* to *B*? You may move only in the directions of the arrows.

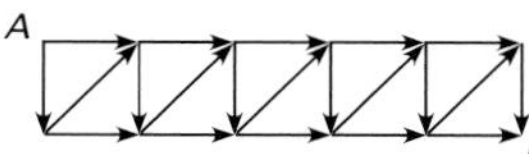

Problem-Solving Strategy: Solve a Simpler Problem

Using smaller numbers or temporarily ignoring some conditions often helps students develop a method they can use to solve a multiple-step problem. This strategy often proves useful with more complex problems.

- Solve a Simpler Problem can be used with one or more of the other strategies discussed in this Problem Solving Handbook.
- Initially, students may need help determining an appropriate simpler problem.
- Solve a Simpler Problem is especially helpful in finding geometric patterns.

About the Page

Students solve a simpler problem to help them set up a tournament schedule.

Ask ...

- How does solving the problem for 2, 3, and 4 teams help solve the problem for 64 teams? Possible answer: The relationship between the number of teams and the number of games needed for 2, 3, and 4 teams can be applied to 64 teams.
- How many games would be needed for 128 teams? 127 games

Try It

- You might ask students to describe the pattern they found for Part a. Possible answer: Number of ropes = Number of cuts + 1.

  Ask students what pattern they found in Part b. Possible answer: After 2, each number of routes is the sum of the preceding two numbers.

Answers for Try It

a. 46 if the rope is straight, 1 if the rope is twisted back and forth

b. 144 routes

Chapter 1

▶ OVERVIEW

Making Sense of the World of Data

Section 1A

Communicating with Data: Students learn to read and interpret bar and circle graphs, and to make bar graphs, line plots, and stem-and-leaf diagrams. Students find measures of central tendency and decide which measures best summarize the data.

1-1 Interpreting Graphs

1-2 Making Bar Graphs

1-3 Line Plots and Stem-and-Leaf Diagrams

1-4 Mean, Median, Mode, and Range

Section 1B

Trends and Relationships in Data: Students read, construct and interpret line graphs, scatterplots, and trend lines. Students identify relationships and trends in the data and use this information to make predictions.

1-5 Line Graphs

1-6 Scatterplots and Relationships

1-7 Trend Lines

Meeting NCTM Standards

Curriculum Standards

STANDARD			pages
1	**Problem Solving**	Skills and Strategies	4, 17, 18, 25, 31
		Applications	9–10, 14–15, 19–20, 24–25, 33–34, 38–39, 43–44
		Exploration	6, 11, 16, 21, 30, 35, 40
2	**Communication**	Oral	5, 8, 13, *16,* 18, 23, *25,* 29, 32, *34,* 37, 42
		Written	*4,* 10, 15, 20, 28, 39, 44, 46, 49
		Cooperative Learning	*6, 11, 16, 21, 30, 40*
3	**Reasoning**	Critical Thinking	10, 15, 20, 25, 34, 39, 44
4	**Connections**	Mathematical	See Standards 5, 7, 8, 10, 11 below.
		Interdisciplinary	Geography *5,* 9, 11, 12, 13, 14, 16, 27, 28; Language 7, 22; Science *2,* 3, *5,* 9, *10, 13,* 20, 36, *37,* 38; Social Studies *2,* 3, *8,* 10, 12, *15,* 18, *23,* 24, *25,* 33, 50; History 15, 31, *32,* 41; Sports 2, 19, 24, 29, 30, 33, 38, 39, *41,* 44, 45; Literature 2; Consumer 43; Nutrition 43; Career 6, *29;* Health, *29*
		Technology	11, 26, 29, 30, 33
		Cultural	2, 6, 7, 8, *15,* 17, *22,* 23, *42*
5	**Number and Number Relationships**		9, 24, 25
7	**Computation and Estimation**		9, *10, 31, 36*
8	**Patterns and Functions**		35–45
10	**Statistics**		5–51
11	**Probability**		10

Italic type indicates Teacher Edition reference.

Teaching Standards

Focus on Flexibility

No single classroom approach will work at all times. Teachers should use various approaches to enhance learning. At various times students should be allowed to

- work independently.
- work in pairs.
- engage in whole-class discussion.

Assessment Standards

Focus on Mathematics

Performance The Mathematics Standard stresses that assessment should reflect not only what students should know, but how they use that knowledge. Performance assessment provides students with a form to reason and communicate mathematically, and to make connections among ideas. The performance tasks in Chapter 1 have students

- organize and analyze data.
- make predictions.

TECHNOLOGY

For the Teacher

- **Teacher Resource Planner CD-ROM**
  Use the teacher planning CD-ROM to view resources available for Chapter 1. You can prepare custom lesson plans or use the default lesson plans provided.

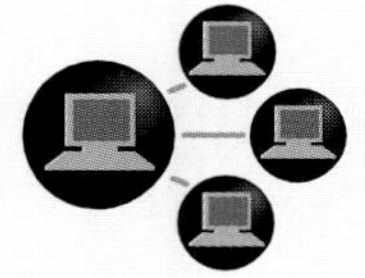

- **World Wide Web**
  Visit **www.teacher.mathsurf.com** for links to lesson plans from teachers and other professionals, NCTM information, and other sites.

- **TestWorks**
  TestWorks provides ready-made tests and can create custom tests and practice worksheets.

For the Parent

- **World Wide Web**
  Parents can use the Web site at **www.parent.mathsurf.com.**

For the Student

- **Interactive CD-ROM**
  Lesson 1-4 has an *Interactive CD-ROM Lesson*. The *Interactive CD-ROM Journal* and *Interactive CD-ROM Spreadsheet/Grapher Tool* are also used in Chapter 1.

- **Wide World of Mathematics™**
  Lesson 1-2 Middle School: Graphs in the News
  Lesson 1-5 Algebra: Saving Our Resources

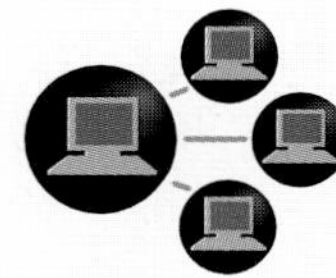

- **World Wide Web**
  Use with Chapter and Section Openers; Students can go online to the Scott Foresman-Addison Wesley Web site at **www.mathsurf.com/7/ch1** to collect information about chapter themes.

STANDARDIZED - TEST CORRELATION

SECTION 1A

LESSON	OBJECTIVE	ITBS Form M	CTBS 4th Ed.	CAT 5th Ed.	SAT 9th Ed.	MAT 7th Ed.	Your Form
1-1	• Read and interpret bar graphs.		✘	✘		✘	
	• Read and interpret circle graphs.	✘	✘	✘	✘		
1-2	• Create a bar graph from a table of data.						
	• Create a double-bar graph.						
1-3	• Make a line plot.						
	• Make a stem-and-leaf diagram.						
1-4	• Find the mean, median, and mode for a set of data.	✘	✘	✘	✘	✘	
	• Decide if the mean, median, or mode best summarizes a set of data.		✘	✘		✘	

SECTION 1B

LESSON	OBJECTIVE	ITBS Form M	CTBS 4th Ed.	CAT 5th Ed.	SAT 9th Ed.	MAT 7th Ed.	Your Form
1-5	• Read and interpret line graphs.	✘	✘		✘	✘	
	• Recognize trends.	✘			✘		
1-6	• Read and interpret scatterplots.						
	• Make scatterplots.						
	• Recognize relationships in data.	✘			✘		
1-7	• Construct trend lines.	✘					
	• Use trend lines to make predictions.	✘					

Key: ITBS - Iowa Test of Basic Skills; CTBS - Comprehensive Test of Basic Skills; CAT - California Achievement Test; SAT - Stanford Achievement Test; MAT - Metropolitan Achievement Test

ASSESSMENT PROGRAM

Traditional Assessment

QUICK QUIZZES	SECTION REVIEW	CHAPTER REVIEW	CHAPTER ASSESSMENT FREE RESPONSE	CHAPTER ASSESSMENT MULTIPLE CHOICE	CUMULATIVE REVIEW
TE: pp. 10, 15, 20, 25, 34, 39, 44	SE: pp. 28, 46 *Quiz 1A, 1B	SE: pp. 48–49	SE: p. 50 *Ch. 1 Tests Forms A, B, E	*Ch. 1 Tests Forms C, E	SE: p. 51 *Ch. 1 Test Form F

Alternate Assessment

INTERVIEW	JOURNAL	ONGOING	PERFORMANCE	PORTFOLIO	PROJECT	SELF
TE pp. 25, 34	SE: pp. 10, 15, 20, 28, 44, 46 TE: pp. 4, 10, 20	TE: pp. 6, 11, 16, 21, 30, 35, 40	SE: pp. 50, 51 *Ch. 1 Tests Forms D, E	TE: pp. 15, 39	SE: pp. 15, 39 TE: p. 3	TE: p. 44

*Tests and quizzes are in *Assessment Sourcebook.* Test Form E is a mixed response test. Forms for Alternate Assessment are also available in *Assessment Sourcebook.*

TestWorks: Test and Practice Software

REGULAR PACING

Day	5 classes per week
1	Chapter 1 Opener; Problem Solving Focus
2	Section **1A** Opener; Lesson **1-1**
3	Lesson **1-2**
4	Lesson **1-3**
5	Lesson **1-4**; Technology
6	**1A** Connect; **1A** Review
7	Section **1B** Opener; Lesson **1-5**
8	Lesson **1-6**
9	Lesson **1-7**
10	**1B** Connect; **1B** Review; Extend Key Ideas
11	Chapter 1 Summary and Review
12	Chapter 1 Assessment Cumulative Review, Chapter 1

BLOCK SCHEDULING OPTIONS

Block Scheduling for Complete Course

Chapter 1 may be presented in

- seven 90-minute blocks
- ten 75-minute blocks

Each block consists of a combination of

- Chapter and Section Openers
- Explores
- Lesson Development
- Problem Solving Focus
- Technology
- Extend Key Ideas
- Connect
- Review
- Assessment

For details, see *Block Scheduling Handbook.*

Block Scheduling for Interdisciplinary Course

Each block integrates math with another subject area.

In Chapter 1, interdisciplinary topics include

- Geography
- Sports Around the World

Themes for Interdisciplinary Team Teaching 1A and 1B are

- Climate in Hawaii
- Modern Olympics

For details, see *Block Scheduling Handbook.*

Block Scheduling for Lab-Based Course

In each block, 30–40 minutes is devoted to lab activities including

- Explores in the Student Edition
- Connect pages in the Student Edition
- Technology options in the Student Edition
- Reteaching Activities in the Teacher Edition

For details, see *Block Scheduling Handbook.*

Block Scheduling for Course with *Connected Mathematics*

In each block, investigations from **Connected Mathematics** replace or enhance the lessons in Chapter 1.

Connected Mathematics topics for Chapter 1 can be found in

- *Data Around Us*
- *Variables and Patterns*

For details, see *Block Scheduling Handbook.*

INTERDISCIPLINARY BULLETIN BOARD

Set Up

Prepare a bulletin board that includes an incomplete bar graph. The horizontal axis should list the names of some famous cities in the world. The vertical axis should indicate the population in millions from 0 to 9.

Procedure

For each city listed on the bar graph, have students:

- research information on its population, location, and famous landmarks.
- round off the population number to the nearest million and color a bar to the appropriate height on the graph.
- indicate the country and continent in which it is located and provide a picture of a famous landmark.

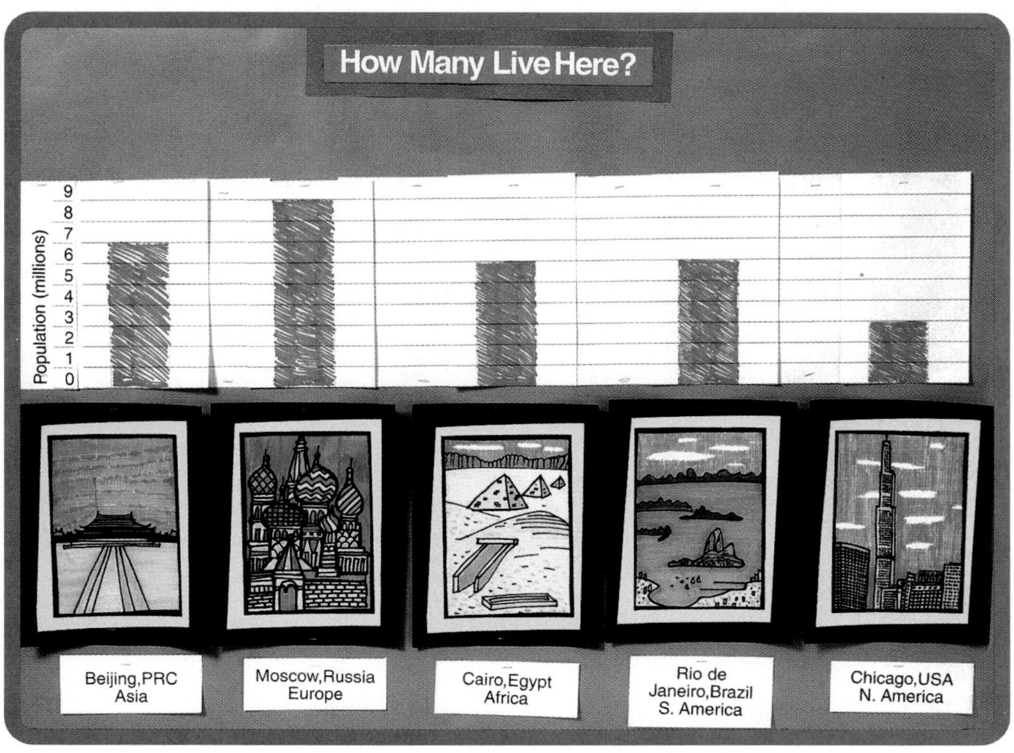

Chapter 1

The information on these pages shows how statistics are used in real-life situations.

World Wide Web

If your class has access to the World Wide Web, you might want to use the information found at the Web site addresses given.

Extensions

The following activities do not require access to the World Wide Web.

People of the World
Have groups of students find a line graph that displays information about another country. Ask them to summarize the information for the class.

Entertainment
The oldest trophy in professional athletics in North America is the Stanley Cup. The winner of the Stanley Cup is decided in post-season play-offs within the National Hockey League. Have students find which team possesses the Stanley Cup now.

Arts & Literature
Have students read at least a paragraph of their favorite book and keep a tally of the number of times each letter of the alphabet is used.

Science
Ask students if they think there is a strong relationship between age and height of students in their class. Answers will vary.

Social Studies
Explain that outside the continental U. S., Mt. Waialeale, Hawaii, is the wettest area in the U. S. (and also in the world) with 460 inches of rain annually. Have students find the driest area in the U. S. Death Valley, California, with 1.8 inches of rain annually.

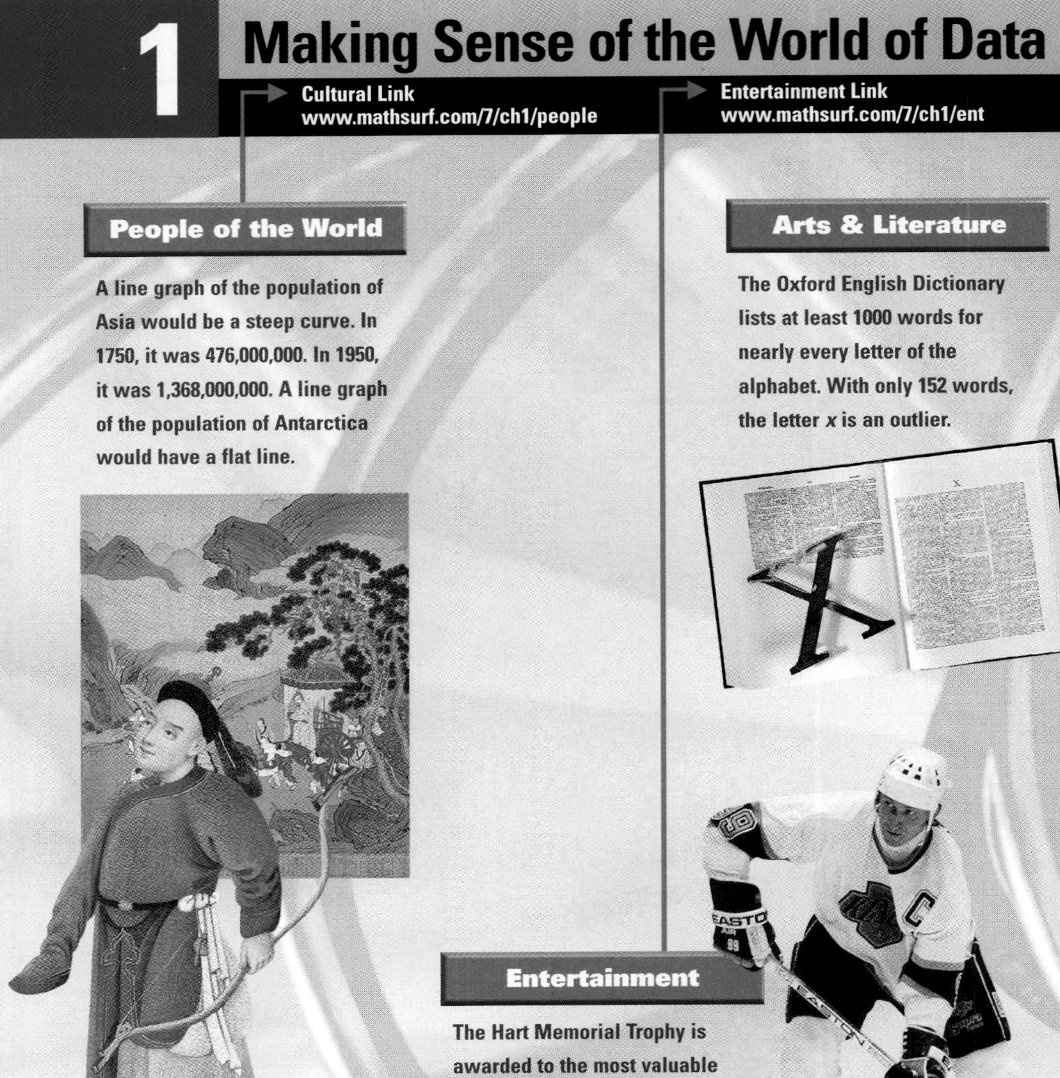

1 Making Sense of the World of Data

Cultural Link www.mathsurf.com/7/ch1/people

Entertainment Link www.mathsurf.com/7/ch1/ent

People of the World

A line graph of the population of Asia would be a steep curve. In 1750, it was 476,000,000. In 1950, it was 1,368,000,000. A line graph of the population of Antarctica would have a flat line.

Arts & Literature

The Oxford English Dictionary lists at least 1000 words for nearly every letter of the alphabet. With only 152 words, the letter *x* is an outlier.

Entertainment

The Hart Memorial Trophy is awarded to the most valuable hockey player in the National Hockey League. The hockey player who has received this award most often is Wayne Gretzky.

2

TEACHER TALK

Meet Edith Roos

Helena Middle School
Helena, Montana

My favorite activity to show mean, median, and mode is to have students make a "human" line plot. Students are given centimeter graph paper and are timed for exactly one minute as they put X's in the squares using their writing hand. The activity is repeated as students attempt to put X's in the squares using their non-writing hand. Then students divide their writing hand score by their non-writing hand score and round to the nearest whole number. Next they build the line plot by standing side by side in numerical order of their quotients, with students whose quotients are the same standing behind one another. This creates a 3-dimensional line plot from which the class modes can be easily determined and from which the class median can be found by counting from each end. I have students use calculators to find the class mean.

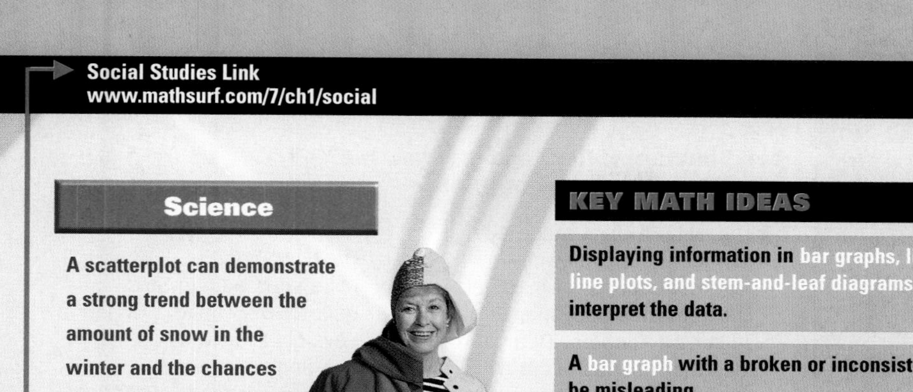

Social Studies Link
www.mathsurf.com/7/ch1/social

Science

A scatterplot can demonstrate a strong trend between the amount of snow in the winter and the chances of a flood the following spring.

Social Studies

Quillayute, Washington is considered the wettest area in the United States. It receives an average rainfall of 105 inches each year.

Annual Rainfall

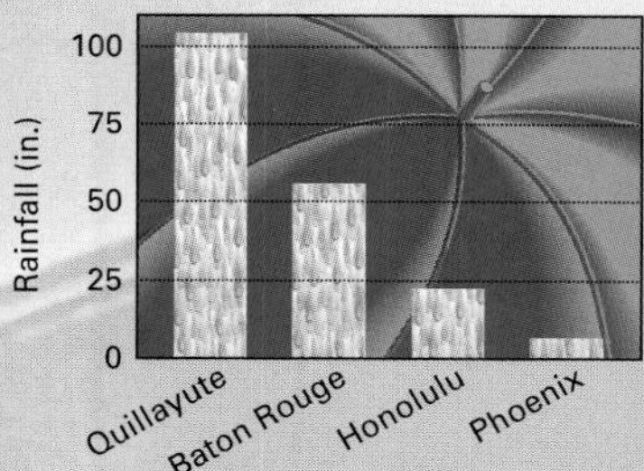

KEY MATH IDEAS

Displaying information in **bar graphs, line graphs, line plots, and stem-and-leaf diagrams** can help you interpret the data.

A **bar graph** with a broken or inconsistent scale can be misleading.

The average, middle, and most common values in a data set are its **mean, median, and mode**.

A **scatterplot** is a graph that shows relationships between two types of data.

Drawing a **trend line** for points on a scatterplot can help you make predictions about the data.

CHAPTER PROJECT

Problem Solving
Understand
Plan
Solve
Look Back

In this project, you will plan and conduct your own Olympics with many different games. Your events might include math, trivia, or other intellectual contests as well as athletic ones. Begin the project by listing the games you decide on. The competitions can be held and scored at different times.

3

Chapter Project

Students will make up, organize, and score interesting games for their own Olympics. Their games may be both sports oriented and intellectually oriented.

Resources
Chapter 1 Project Master

Introduce the Project

- Discuss types of games that students might use in their own Olympics. Help them compile a list of the types of games they plan to include.
- Talk about how students will be able to stage the games they have chosen and how the games might be scored.

Project Progress

Section A, page 15 Students design events and make rules for the athletic games, and formulate questions and scoring methods for intellectual games.

Section B, page 39 After students' Olympic events have taken place, students display the data they collected in appropriate graphs.

Community Project

A community project for Chapter 1 is available in *Home and Community Connections.*

Cooperative Learning

You may want to use Teaching Tool Transparency 1: Cooperative Learning Checklist with **Explore** and other group activities in this chapter.

PROJECT ASSESSMENT

You may choose to use this project as a performance assessment for the chapter.

Performance Assessment Key

Level 4 Full Accomplishment

Level 3 Substantial Accomplishment

Level 2 Partial Accomplishment

Level 1 Little Accomplishment

Suggested Scoring Rubric

Level	Criteria
4	•All necessary data is recorded and clearly organized •Appropriate graphs are drawn so that all winners can be identified.
3	•Most necessary data is recorded and organized. •Graphs may not be the most appropriate to identify the winners.
2	•Some data is recorded and an attempt is made to organize it. •Students draw graphs but winners may or may not be apparent.
1	•Little data is recorded and no attempt is made to organize it. •Inappropriate or no graphs are presented. Winners cannot be identified.

Problem Solving Focus

Reading the Problem

The Point
Students focus on reading and understanding the problem.

Resources
Teaching Tool Transparency 16: Problem-Solving Guidelines

 *Interactive CD-ROM Journal*

About the Page

Using the Problem-Solving Process
In order to solve a problem, students must be able to identify the information needed to solve it. Discuss these suggestions:

- Determine what the problem is about.
- Determine what the problem is asking.

Ask ...

- In Problem 1, who cut the fewest squares? How do you know? Tyra; We know that Tyra cut 4 fewer squares than Jo and that Tasha cut twice as many as Tyra.
- In Problem 2, what information did you need to find? The value of the Country Love quilt and the total value of each pair of quilts.

Answers for Problems

1. a. The number of squares cut for a quilt.
   b. The total number of squares the three sisters cut.
   c. 12
   d. 8
   e. Possible answer: Question: How many squares did Tasha cut? Answer: 16.
2. a. The values of different quilts.
   b. Should Mike trade his two quilts for two in the store?
   c. $900
   d. $1100
   e. Possible answer: Question: Which quilt is worth the most? Answer: Country Love.

Journal

Ask students to write about how the skills they learned in this lesson could be applied to solving a problem in another class, such as science, history, civics, or English. Suggest that they describe the problem and then write questions to help solve it.

Problem Solving
Understand
Plan
Solve
Look Back

Reading the Problem

As you read a problem, you may be overwhelmed by information. Breaking the information into small parts can help you understand what the problem is saying. Ask yourself questions to be sure you understand each part.

Problem Solving Focus

Read each problem, and answer the questions about the problem.

1 The Oben triplets made a memory quilt by sewing together squares of material cut from their baby blankets. Jo cut 12 squares. Tyra cut 4 less than Jo. Tasha cut twice as many as Tyra. How many squares did they cut all together?

a. What is the problem about?

b. What is the problem asking for?

c. How many squares did Jo cut?

d. How many squares did Tyra cut?

e. Write and answer a question of your own.

2 At the Amish Quilting Shop, Mike sees a Lone Star quilt for $550 and a Country Love quilt for twice as much. The dealer offers Mike both quilts in exchange for Mike's Wedding Wreath quilt, which is worth $800, and his Sampler quilt, which is worth $900. Should Mike make this trade?

a. What is the problem about?

b. What is the problem asking for?

c. How much is Mike's Sampler quilt worth?

d. How much is the Country Love quilt worth?

e. Write and answer a question of your own.

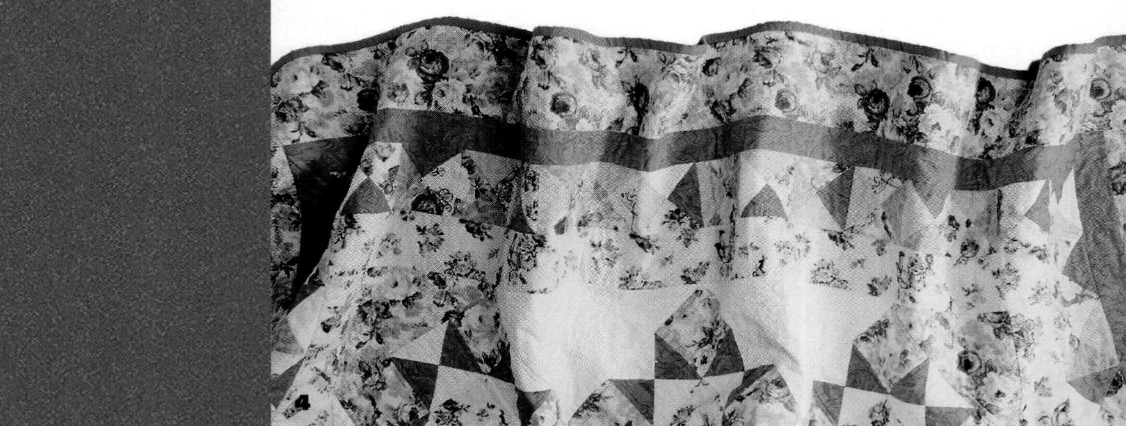

Additional Problem

The seventh grade class investigated the cost of hiring a DJ for 3 hours for a class party. They found that for 3 hours, Doc's DJ charges $50, Big Sound DJ charges $15 more than Doc's, and Rockin' Sound DJ charges $40. Two of the DJ's charge extra for weekends—Doc's charges $25 more and Rockin' Sound charges $40 more. Which DJ would cost the least for 3 hours on Saturday night?

1. What is the problem about? The cost of hiring a DJ for 3 hours on a Saturday night.
2. What is the problem asking you to find? Which DJ costs the least.
3. Which DJ should the class hire based on cost? Big Sound DJ.
4. Are there any other things the class might consider when hiring a DJ? Answers may vary.

Communicating with Data

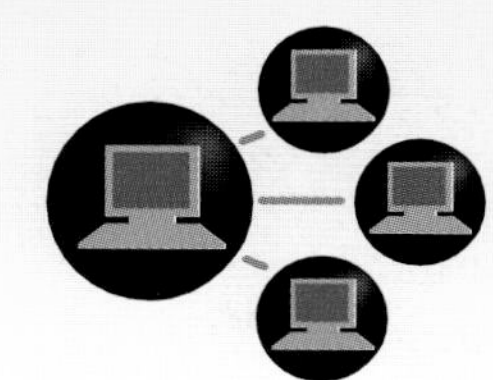

Visit **www.teacher.mathsurf.com** for links to lesson plans from teachers and other professionals, NCTM information, and other sites.

LESSON PLANNING GUIDE

Student Edition				Ancillaries*	
LESSON		MATERIALS	VOCABULARY	DAILY	OTHER
	Chapter 1 Opener				Ch. 1 Project Master Ch. 1 Community Project Teaching Tool Trans. 1
	Problem Solving Focus				Teaching Tool Trans. 16 *Interactive CD-ROM Journal*
	Section 1A Opener				
1-1	**Interpreting Graphs**		circle graph, sector, bar graph, vertical axis, horizontal axis	1-1	Lesson Enhance. Trans. 1, 2 Technology Master 1
1-2	**Making Bar Graphs**	graphing utility	scale, interval, double-bar graph	1-2	Lesson Enhance. Trans. 3, 4 Ch. 1 Project Master Technology Master 2 *WW Math*—Middle School *Interactive CD-ROM Spreadsheet/Grapher Tool*
1-3	**Line Plots and Stem-and-Leaf Diagrams**		line plot, outlier, stem-and-leaf diagram	1-3	Lesson Enhancement Transparencies 5, 6
1-4	**Mean, Median, Mode, and Range**	graph paper, scissors, tape	mean, median, mode, range	1-4	*Interactive CD-ROM Lesson*
	Technology	data analysis software or graphing calculator			*Interactive CD-ROM Spreadsheet/Grapher Tool*
	Connect	art supplies			Interdisc. Team Teaching 1A
	Review				Practice 1A; Quiz 1A; *TestWorks*

* Daily Ancillaries include Practice, Reteaching, Problem Solving, Enrichment, and Daily Transparency. Teaching Tool Transparencies are in *Teacher's Toolkits*. Lesson Enhancement Transparencies are in *Overhead Transparency Package*.

SKILLS TRACE

LESSON	SKILL	FIRST INTRODUCED GR. 5	GR. 6	GR. 7	DEVELOP	PRACTICE/ APPLY	REVIEW
1-1	**Reading and interpreting bar graphs.**	✘			pp. 6–8	pp. 9–10	pp. 48, 172, 236
1-2	**Creating bar graphs.**	✘			pp. 11–13	pp. 14–15	pp. 34, 48, 143, 190
1-3	**Making a line plot.**		✘		pp. 16–18	pp. 19–20	pp. 39, 48, 138, 195
	Making a stem-and-leaf plot.	✘					
1-4	**Finding the mean, median, mode, and range.**	✘			pp. 21–23	pp. 24–25	pp. 44, 48, 109, 156

CONNECTED MATHEMATICS

The unit *Data Around Us (Number Sense),* from the **Connected Mathematics** series, can be used with Section 1A.

INTERDISCIPLINARY TEAM TEACHING

Math and Science/Technology

(Worksheet pages 1–2: Teacher pages T1–T2)

In this lesson, students interpret graphs to understand climatic data.

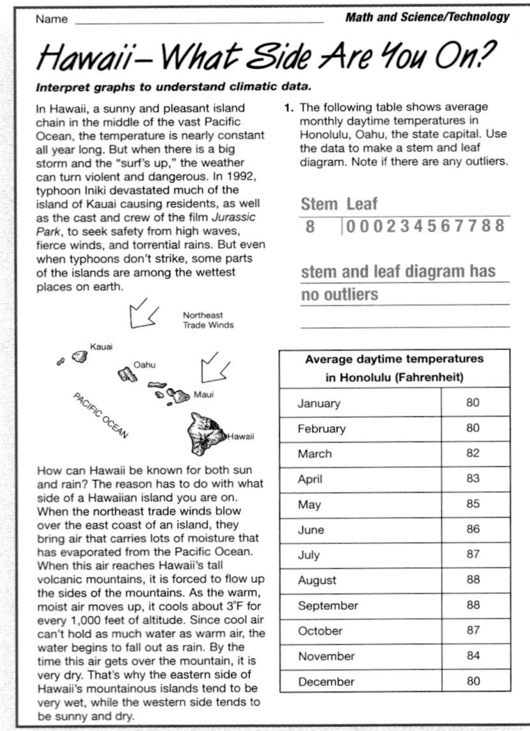

Name ______________________ *Math and Science/Technology*

Hawaii–What Side Are You On?

Interpret graphs to understand climatic data.

In Hawaii, a sunny and pleasant island chain in the middle of the vast Pacific Ocean, the temperature is nearly constant all year long. But when there is a big storm and the "surf's up," the weather can turn violent and dangerous. In 1992, typhoon Iniki devastated much of the island of Kauai causing residents, as well as the cast and crew of the film *Jurassic Park*, to seek safety from high waves, fierce winds, and torrential rains. But even when typhoons don't strike, some parts of the islands are among the wettest places on earth.

How can Hawaii be known for both sun and rain? The reason has to do with what side of a Hawaiian island you are on. When the northeast trade winds blow over the east coast of an island, they bring air that carries lots of moisture that has evaporated from the Pacific Ocean. When this air reaches Hawaii's tall volcanic mountains, it is forced to flow up the sides of the mountains. As the warm, moist air moves up, it cools about 3°F for every 1,000 feet of altitude. Since cool air can't hold as much water as warm air, the water begins to fall out as rain. By the time this air gets over the mountain, it is very dry. That's why the eastern side of Hawaii's mountainous islands tend to be very wet, while the western side tends to be sunny and dry.

1. The following table shows average monthly daytime temperatures in Honolulu, Oahu, the state capital. Use the data to make a stem and leaf diagram. Note if there are any outliers.

Stem	Leaf
8	0 0 0 2 3 4 5 6 7 7 8 8

stem and leaf diagram has no outliers

Average daytime temperatures in Honolulu (Fahrenheit)	
January	80
February	80
March	82
April	83
May	85
June	86
July	87
August	88
September	88
October	87
November	84
December	80

Name ______________________ *Math and Science/Technology*

2. From the table, you can derive the range, mean, median, and mode of the data.
   a. What is the temperature range? **80–88°**
   b. What is the mean temperature? **84.2°**
   c. Of the mean, median, and mode, which two are nearly identical? **median and mean**
3. The following table contrasts monthly rainfall in two Hawaiian locations. Make a double bar graph on the grid to show the data. A letter representing each month of the year should be placed on the horizontal axis *(x-axis)* and the number of inches of rain should be placed on the vertical axis *(y-axis)*. Draw the bars for each location side by side. Use a different colored pencil for each location.

Monthly Rainfall in Inches		
	Lahaina, Maui	Hilo, Hawaii
Jan	4	9.5
Feb	2.2	13
Mar	2.2	14
Apr	1	13
May	0.5	9.5
June	0.1	6
July	0.2	8.5
Aug	0.2	10
Sept	0.2	7
Oct	1	10
Nov	2	15
Dec	3	13

15
12
9
6
3
0
J F M A M J J A S O N D
Hilo, Hawaii
Lahaina, Maui

4. Do you think that the town of Lahaina is on the east or west coast of Maui? Explain. **See below.**
5. In Hilo, raindrops have been measured up to a whopping one-third of an inch in diameter—about the size of candy drops.
   a. In Hilo, which month gets the most rain? **See below.**
   b. On which side of the "Big Island" is Hilo likely to be? **See below.**
   c. Calculate Hilo's mean monthly rainfall. **See below.**
   d. The Big Island, Hawaii, is also the home of the only active volcanoes in Hawaii. Would you predict that rainfall on the east side of the volcanoes would be more like that of Hilo or Lahaina? Why? **See below.**
6. If you were developing a beach resort, which location would you be likely to choose, Hilo or Lahaina? Why? **See below.**

Answers

4. Lahaina is probably on the west coast because it is relatively dry.
5. a. November

   b. Hilo is probably on the east side, because it gets so much rain.

   c. 10.7 inches

   d. Hilo and the east side of the volcano probably have similar amounts of rain because the winds and rain are blown from the east coast toward the east side of the volcano, where they stop.
6. Lahaina is far less rainy and likely to be a good location for a beach resort. (It is!)

BIBLIOGRAPHY

FOR TEACHERS

Guinness Book of Sports Records. New York, NY: Facts on File, 1996.

Hunter, Brian, ed. *The Statesman's Year-Book.* New York, NY: St. Martin's Press, 1996–1997.

Jarrett, William S. *Timetables of Sports History*. New York, NY: Facts on File, 1993.

Spangler, David. *Math for Real Kids*. Glenview, IL: Good Year Books, 1997.

FOR STUDENTS

Gallant, Roy. *The Peopling of Planet Earth*. New York, NY: Macmillan, 1990.

Winckler, Suzanne. *Population Growth*. Minneapolis, MN: Lerner, 1991.

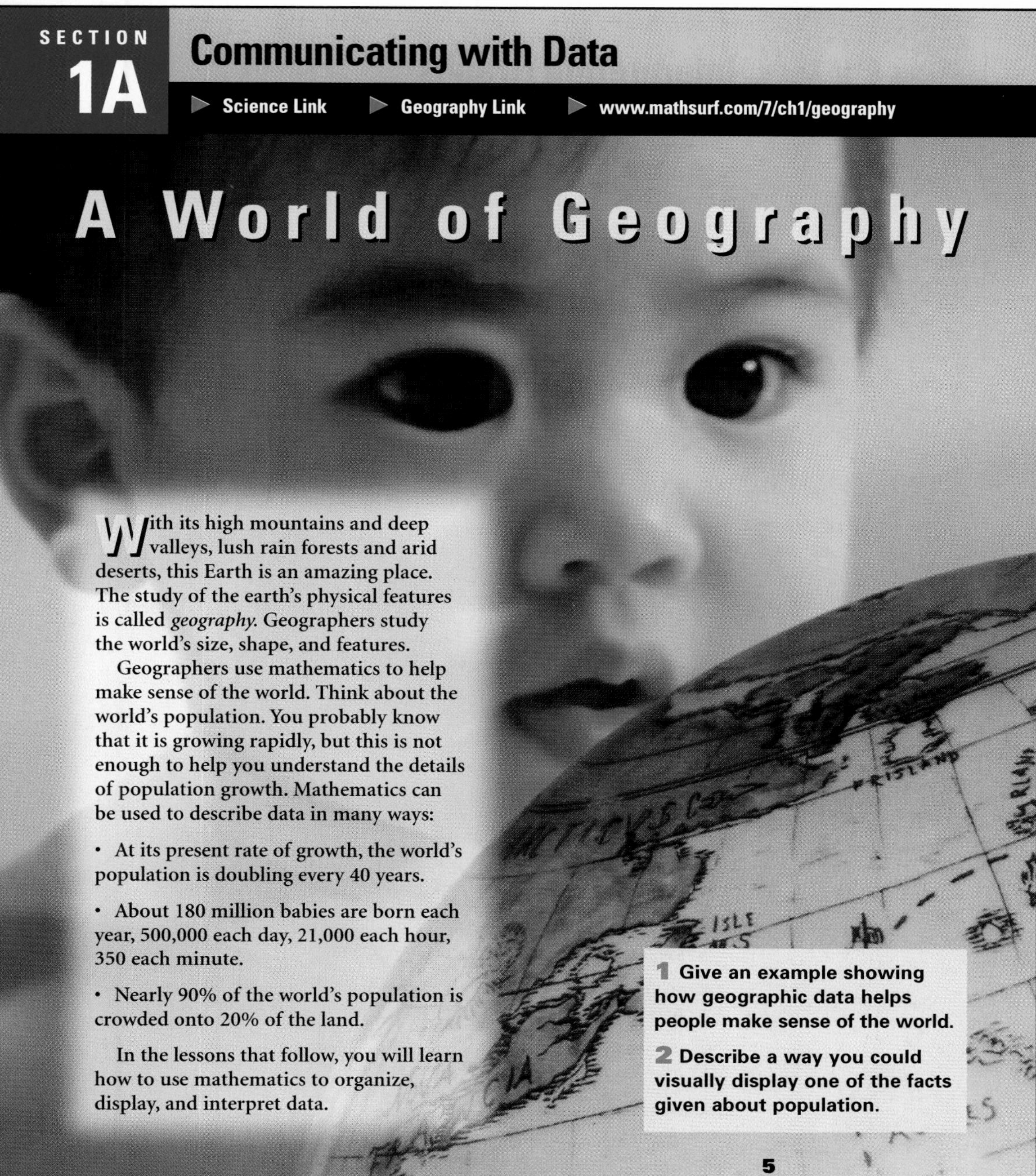

SECTION 1A
Communicating with Data
Science Link
Geography Link
www.mathsurf.com/7/ch1/geography
A World of Geography

With its high mountains and deep valleys, lush rain forests and arid deserts, this Earth is an amazing place. The study of the earth's physical features is called *geography.* Geographers study the world's size, shape, and features.

Geographers use mathematics to help make sense of the world. Think about the world's population. You probably know that it is growing rapidly, but this is not enough to help you understand the details of population growth. Mathematics can be used to describe data in many ways:

• At its present rate of growth, the world's population is doubling every 40 years.

• About 180 million babies are born each year, 500,000 each day, 21,000 each hour, 350 each minute.

• Nearly 90% of the world's population is crowded onto 20% of the land.

In the lessons that follow, you will learn how to use mathematics to organize, display, and interpret data.

1 Give an example showing how geographic data helps people make sense of the world.

2 Describe a way you could visually display one of the facts given about population.

5

Section 1A

Theme: Geography

World Wide Web

If your class has access to the World Wide Web, you might want to use the information found at the Web site address given. The interdisciplinary link relates to topics discussed in this section.

About the Page

This page introduces the theme of the section, geography, and describes how geographers use mathematics to compare and analyze information about our world.

Ask ...

- How would you tabulate population data for your school? city? country? the world?
- What are some ways you might collect and compare data?

Extensions

The following activities do not require access to the World Wide Web.

Science
As the world's population grows, scientists are seeking ways to increase the food supply. Have students estimate how much food is wasted each day in their school.

Geography
In 1994, the five most populous cities in the world were (1) Tokyo, (2) New York City, (3) São Paulo, (4) Mexico City, and (5) Shanghai. Have interested students locate these cities on a world map. They might also extend the list to the ten most populous cities.

Answers for Questions

1. Possible answer: It can help you compare sizes of countries and populations.
2. Possible answer: You could make a bar graph to show the population doubling.

Connect

On page 27, students will read a table containing statistical data about various countries and use graphs or plots to interpret and describe the data.

Where are we now?

In Grade 6, students read and compared data from different types of graphs.

They learned how to

- read numbers from graphs.
- organize data using tallies, frequency tables, bar graphs, line plots, and stem-and-leaf diagrams.
- calculate mean, median, and mode for sets of data.

Where are we going?

In Grade 7 Section 1A, students will

- read and interpret graphs.
- make bar and double bar graphs.
- use diagrams to show how frequently values occur and how they are distributed.
- decide if the mean, median, or mode best summarize a set of data.

1-1 Lesson Organizer

Objectives

- Read and interpret bar graphs.
- Read and interpret circle graphs.

Vocabulary

- Circle graph, sector, bar graph, vertical axis, horizontal axis

NCTM Standards

- 1–5, 7, 10, 11

Review

Write as a number.

1. 250 thousand 250,000
2. 3 million 3,000,000
3. 0.4 million 400,000
4. 1.5 million 1,500,000
5. 6.25 million 6,250,000

Available on Daily Transparency 1-1

▶ Lesson Link

Discuss with students which would be easier to understand, a paragraph describing the population of a country by ethnic groups or a graph displaying the same data.

1 Introduce

Lesson Enhancement Transparency 1 may be used with **Explore**.

The Point
Students determine which is the more appropriate type of graph to display data, a circle graph or a bar graph.

Ongoing Assessment
Watch for students who have difficulty estimating values on bar graphs when they fall between two labeled lines. Suggest that they imagine intermediate scale marks on the vertical axis.

1-1 Interpreting Graphs

You'll Learn ...

- to read and interpret bar graphs
- to read and interpret circle graphs

... How It's Used

Meteorologists use bar and circle graphs to show weather-related data. For instance, a bar graph can be used to compare this year's rainfall to the average.

Vocabulary

circle graph
sector
bar graph
vertical axis
horizontal axis

▶ Lesson Link In the past, you've seen many different types of graphs used to display information. In this lesson, you'll read and interpret two of the most common types of graphs. ◄

Explore Graphs

Population Pictures

Use these graphs of population in Southeast Asia to answer each question.

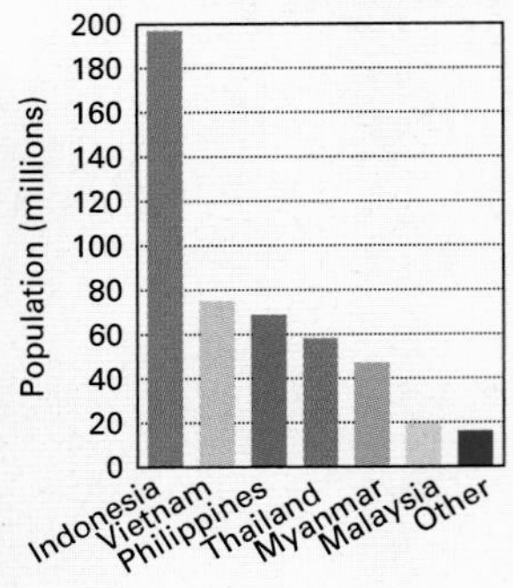

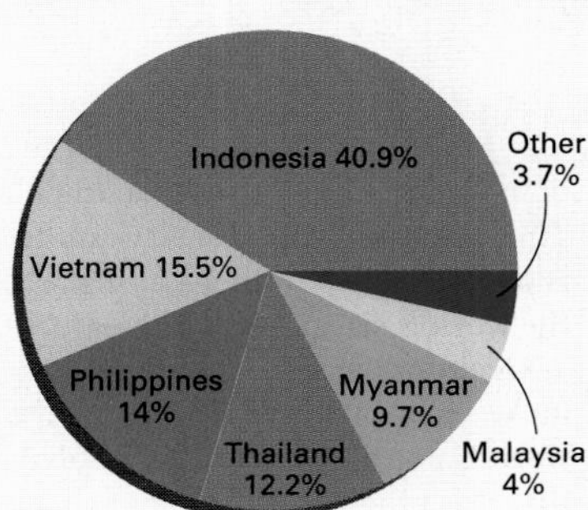

1. Which country has a population of about 60 million? Which graph did you use? Why?
2. Which country has nearly half the population of Southeast Asia? Which graph did you use? Why?
3. Which graph best shows the actual population of each country? Explain.
4. Which graph best shows the portion of the population of Southeast Asia that is in each country? Explain.
5. What can you learn from each type of graph that the other type doesn't tell you?

MEETING INDIVIDUAL NEEDS

Resources

1-1 Practice
1-1 Reteaching
1-1 Problem Solving
1-1 Enrichment
1-1 Daily Transparency
Problem of the Day
Review
Quick Quiz

Lesson Enhancement Transparencies 1, 2

Technology Master 1

Learning Modalities

Visual Draw circle and bar graphs on the board or overhead, and use colored markers or colored chalk to shade in the sectors or bars.

Social Provide students with magazines and newspapers with stories containing circle and bar graphs. Have them work together to read and interpret the graphs.

English Language Development

For students who have limited English ability, cut an orange in half to display the sections. Then compare the word *section* in an orange with the term *sector* in a circle graph.

The *Multilingual Handbook* with its glossary of math terms, illustrations, and worked-out examples, can help you with students who have limited English language skills. The glossary is provided in several langauges.

Learn Interpreting Graphs

A **circle graph** is divided into wedge-shaped **sectors**. The sectors show how portions of a set of data compare with the whole set.

The size of the sector can be compared to the entire circle. The data values can also be compared to each other by looking at the sizes of sectors.

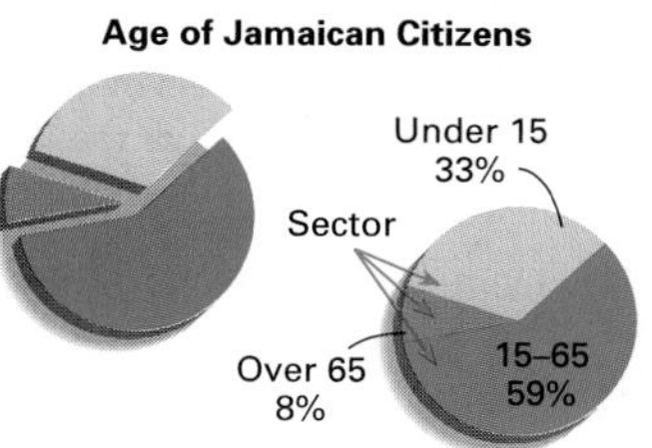
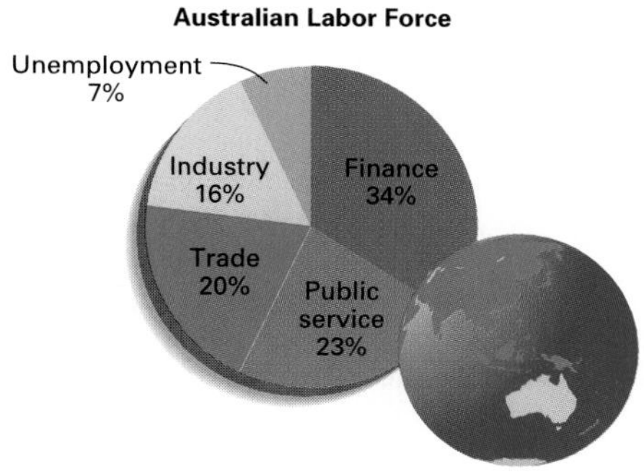

Remember

100% = the whole of any quantity. **[Previous course]**

Examples

The circle graph displays information about the labor force in Australia.

1 What type of job is most common?

Finance. It has the largest sector, 34%.

2 What two job types together make up half of the total labor force?

16% + 34% = 50%, so finance and industry make up half of the total labor force.

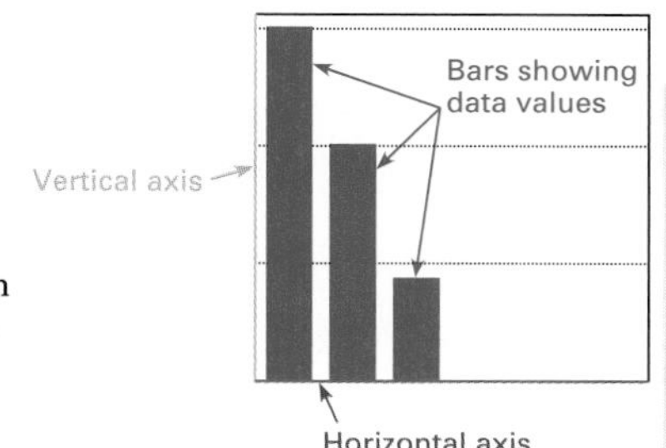

Try It

What two job types together make up 43% of the total labor force in Australia? Public service and trade.

A **bar graph** uses bars to display numerical data. The length of the bar tells you the value of the data. In the bar graph, the size of each data value can be found by looking at the **vertical axis**. The **horizontal axis** has a label for each bar. Bar graphs can be used to describe data values and to compare data values.

▶ Language Link

It is easy to remember which axis is horizontal—picture the sun going down over the horizon, where the land meets the sky!

For Groups That Finish Early
Distribute newspapers or magazines to groups and ask them to find circle and bar graphs. Have them write three questions that can be answered from the graphs.

Follow Up
Students' responses to Step 5 should reveal that a circle graph is more appropriate for comparing parts to a whole. A bar graph is more appropriate for showing comparisons and amounts.

Answers for Explore

1. Thailand; Bar graph; Shows the size of the population.
2. Indonesia; Circle graph because it is easy to compare the population of one country to the whole.
3. Bar graph; Length of bar shows size of the population.
4. Circle graph; Sector size shows fractions of the whole.
5. Bar graph—size of each population, Circle graph—percent that each population is of the whole.

2 Teach

Learn

Lesson Enhancement Transparency 2 may be used with **Learn**.

Show students examples of circle graphs that include percent labels. These percents can help them with comparisons. Also, you may wish to show them both vertical and horizontal bar graphs.

Alternate Examples

Refer to the circle graph for Examples 1 and 2 on page 7.

1. Which type of job makes up about $\frac{1}{4}$ the whole labor force in Australia?

   Public service, because its sector makes up about $\frac{1}{4}$ of the circle.

2. Which two job types have a difference equal to the sector for unemployment?

   23% − 16% = 7%, so the difference between public service and industry is equal to the sector for unemployment.

MATH EVERY DAY

▶ Problem of the Day

The *ranard*, a Thai musical instrument, is made up of 9 wooden bars. The shortest bar is 20 centimeters long. The length of each succeeding bar increases by 1 centimeter. To make a ranard, Van cuts each bar from a 32-centimeter strip of wood. How much wood does he waste? 72 centimeters of wood: 12 + 11 + 10 + 9 + 8 + 7 + 6 + 5 + 4

Available on Daily Transparency 1-1

An Extension is provided in the transparency package.

Fact of the Day

The Republic of Indonesia is made up of 13,500 islands.

Mental Math

Find each product mentally.

1. 60 × 10 600
2. 60 × 100 6000
3. 60 × 1000 60,000
4. 60 × 1,000,000 60,000,000

Alternate Examples

3. Would a bar graph or a circle graph better display what portion of your expenses are for food?

   A circle graph. The amount for each type of expense can be shown as a part of a whole.

4. Would a bar graph or a circle graph better display the number of students who graduated from your school each year for the last 5 years?

   A bar graph. The number of students graduating can be read from the axis.

3 Practice and Assess

Check

Be sure that students understand that graphs show differences and comparisons. Also check that students see how bar lengths correspond to values on the axis.

Answers for Check Your Understanding

1. It is best to use a bar graph when each item of the data is separate and the data do not add to a meaningful whole; A circle graph is best used when you are interested in comparing parts of a whole.
2. Because 100% represents the total of the data values being shown.
3. A broken axis can make differences in data values appear larger than they appear on a graph without a broken axis.

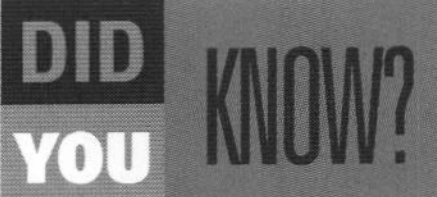

Saudi Arabia is about $\frac{1}{4}$ the size of the United States. It is a kingdom and its capital is Riyadh. Saudi Arabian money is called *Riyals;* 1 Riyal is worth about 27¢.

Examples

Decide whether a bar graph or a circle graph best displays the information.

3 The number of barrels of oil exported by Saudi Arabia in each of the last 4 years.

A bar graph. The number of barrels can be read from the vertical axis.

4 The comparison between the money spent on pumping a barrel of oil and the total cost of producing a barrel of oil.

A circle graph. The sector that represents the pumping costs can be compared to the entire circle.

Try It

Which type of graph would be the best to display the cost of a barrel of oil in each of the past 3 years? **A bar graph.**

An axis in a bar graph can be "broken" to make the graph easier to read. Breaking an axis, however, can mislead the reader. In a voter preference poll, Smith (32%) and Jones (30%) were almost tied.

But on the graph with the broken vertical axis, it looks as though Smith is far ahead of Jones. This is an example of a misleading graph.

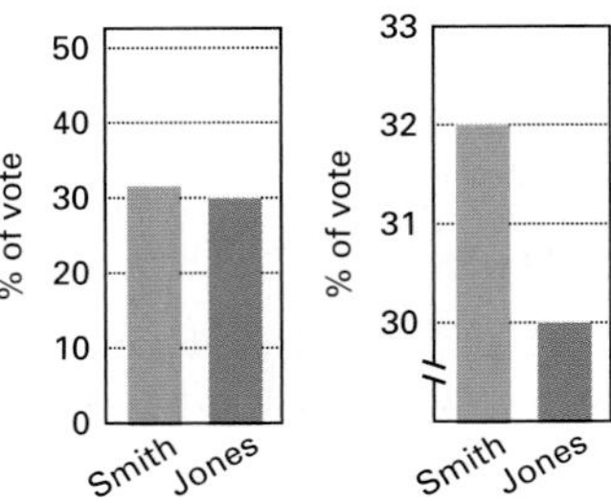

Test Prep

Sometimes you may see a vertical bar graph referred to as a column graph.

Check Your Understanding

1. When is it best to use a bar graph to display data? A circle graph?
2. Explain why the sum of the percents in a circle graph is always 100.
3. How can a bar graph with a broken vertical axis give a misleading impression?

MEETING MIDDLE SCHOOL CLASSROOM NEEDS

Tips from Middle School Teachers

I suggest that students follow this step-by-step process for analyzing a graph.

1. Read the title of the graph.
2. Read the labels along the sides.
3. Determine what units the graph uses.
4. Look for differences.

Social Studies Connection

Bangladesh has the 10th highest population of any country. Nearly half its 107 million people are under age 15. If the population continues to rise at the present rate, it will probably reach 140 million by the year 2000.

Team Teaching

Ask the social studies teachers to discuss with students different types of graphs used in social studies texts.

1-1 Exercises and Applications

Practice and Apply

Getting Started **Use the bar graph for Exercise 1, and the circle graph for Exercise 2.**

1. a. Which volcano is the highest? The lowest? **Ruiz; Hekla**

b. Which two volcanoes are closest in height? **Colima and Etna**

c. What does the vertical axis show? **Height in feet**

2. a. Number Sense List the oceans in order of size, from the largest to smallest. **Pacific, Atlantic, Indian, Arctic**

b. Estimation About what percent of the earth's surface that is covered by water is the Pacific Ocean? **About 45%**

Volcanoes of the World

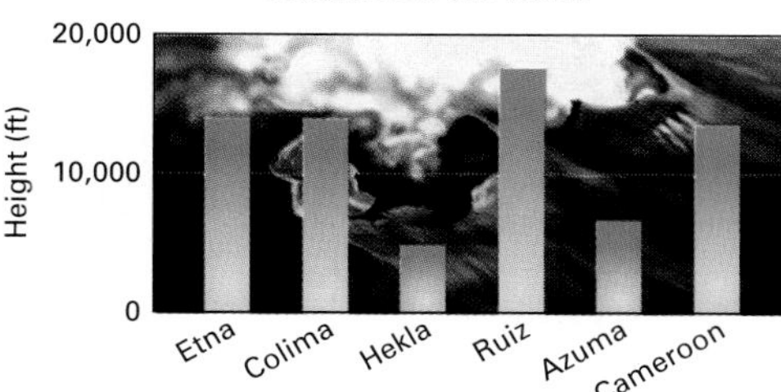

Ocean Sizes

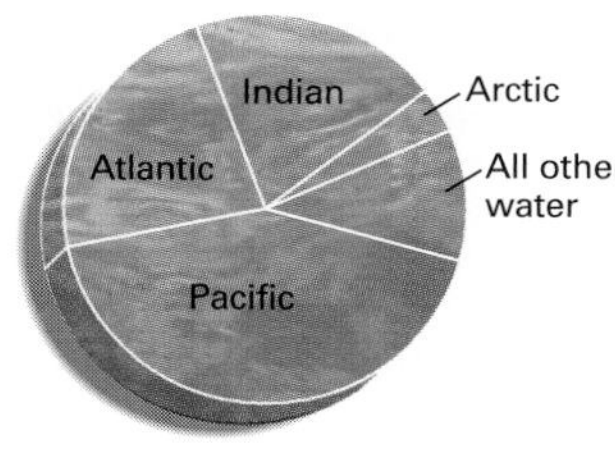

3. Geography Decide whether a bar graph or a circle graph would best display:

a. The heights of the six tallest mountains in the Andes. **Bar graph**

b. The percent of the world's annual coal supply produced by several nations. **Circle graph**

c. The amount of time you spend each day in different activities. **Circle graph**

Use the graph showing the amount of water stored behind the world's 10 largest dams for Exercises 4 and 5.

4. Science The Wadiharthar Dam stores enough water to take about 1 billion showers. Use the graph to estimate the number of showers you could take with Owens Falls water. **About 3 billion showers**

5. **Test Prep** Which dams store more water than the Aswan High Dam? **C**

Ⓐ Wadiharthar and Zeya

Ⓑ Kariba and Akosombo

Ⓒ Owens Falls and Bratsk

Ⓓ Bratsk and Kariba

Volume of Water Behind World's Greatest Dams

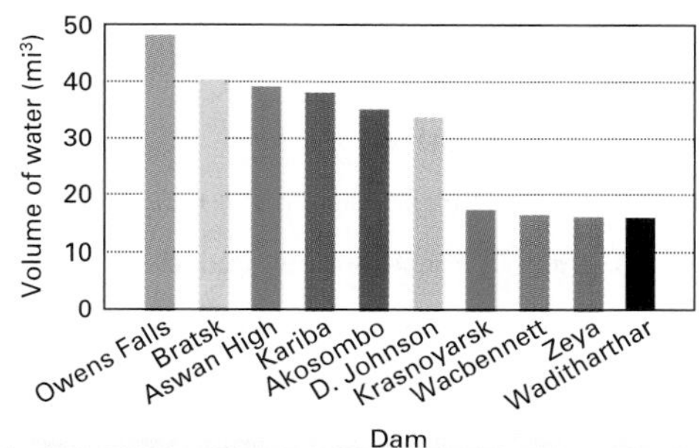

PRACTICE

Name ____________

Practice 1-1

Interpreting Graphs

Use the graph showing the three largest rice exporters for Exercises 1–3.

1991 Rice Exports (Value of export ($ millions): 0, 300, 600, 900, 1200, 1500; Country: Thailand, U.S., Italy)

1. Use the graph to estimate the value of U.S. rice exports in 1991. **$950,000,000**
2. List the countries in order from the most exported rice to the least exported rice. **Thailand, U.S., Italy**
3. Thailand exports about how many times as much rice as Italy? **About 3.3**

Career Use the graph showing reasons for unemployment in America for Exercises 4–6.

Reasons Americans were Unemployed in 1993 (Took a break from working; Left job; Lost job; First time to look for work)

4. Which reason describes about $\frac{1}{4}$ of unemployed Americans? **Took a break from working**
5. What was the most common reason for unemployment? **Lost job**
6. About what percent of unemployed Americans were looking for a job for the first time? **About 10%**

Use the graph showing U.S. recycling habits for Exercises 7–8.

U.S. Recycling (Percent recycled: 0, 50, 100; Material: Newspapers, Aluminum cans, Steel cans, Plastic containers, Glass containers)

7. About what percent of steel cans are recycled? **About 46%**
8. List the five recyclables shown in order from the most likely to be recycled to the least likely to be recycled. **Aluminum cans, steel cans, newspapers, glass containers, plastic containers**

RETEACHING

Name ____________

Alternative Lesson 1-1

Interpreting Graphs

A **circle graph** is divided into wedge-shaped sections that are called **sectors**. The sectors show how portions of a set of data compare with the whole set. The larger the sector, the more data of the whole set it represents. The smaller the sector, the less data it represents.

In a **bar graph**, the length of the bar tells you the value of the data. In a vertical bar graph, the size of the data value can be found by looking at the **vertical axis** (up and down). The **horizontal axis** (left to right) contains a label for each bar.

Example 1

The circle graph at the right displays information about the age of Jamaica's citizens. Which age group has the greatest number of people?

Age of Jamaica's Citizens (Sector; Under 15 (33%); Over 65 (8%); 15–65 (59%))

There are three sectors, each representing an age group. The greatest number of people are in the 15–65 age group.

Try It Tell which age group fits each description.

a. the least number of people **Over 65**

b. about $\frac{1}{3}$ of the people **Under 15**

c. a little over half of the total population **15–65**

Example 2

The bar graph at the right displays information about the labor force in Australia. About what percent of the labor force is employed in trade?

Labor Force in Australia (Percent of labor force: 0, 10, 20, 30, 40; Finance, Public service, Trade, Industry, Unemployment)

There are five bars, each representing the percent of workers employed in each type of position.

About 20% of the labor force is employed in trade.

Try It Estimate the percent for each type of job. **Possible answers:**

d. Finance **≈ 35%**

e. Public service **≈ 20%**

f. Industry **≈ 20%**

g. Unemployment **≈ 10%**

PRACTICE 1-1

1-1 Exercises and Applications

Assignment Guide

- **Basic** 1–3, 5–19 odds
- **Average** 1–5, 6–20 evens
- **Enriched** 3–5, 6–20 evens

Exercise Notes

Exercise 4

Science Discuss with students whether they think they use more than or fewer than 20 gallons of water to take a shower. Then ask if they can think of ways to decrease the amount of water they use.

Exercise 7

Extension Ask students which activities take about the same amount of time according to the circle graph. (Relaxing and housework; shopping and homework) Have students list their Saturday afternoon activities and tell which takes the most time and which takes the least time.

Reteaching

Activity

Each square on the graph below represents 10 vehicles. Think of it as a bar graph. Answer the following questions.

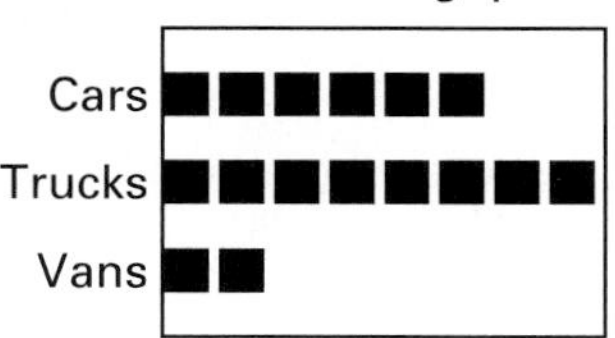

- How many cars are there? 60 cars
- How many trucks are there? 80 trucks
- How many vans are there? 20 vans
- How many vehicles are there all together? 160 vehicles
- How many times as many trucks as vans are there? 4 times

Exercise Notes

■ Exercise 9

Science Silicon does not appear as an isolated element, but in combination with other elements. These combinations, called *silicate* minerals, include sand, quartz, feldspar, granite, asbestos, clay, and mica.

■ Exercises 15–20

Estimation Have students estimate the sums before computing.

Exercise Answers

Possible answers for 8–11

8. Possible answer: There are many small amounts, and they would take up too much room to list.
9. Possible answer: Either graph could be used to show that the amount of aluminum is less.
10. a. Any set of data that involves comparing a part to the whole;

    b. Any set of data where individual data values are important.
11. A pie resembles a circle, and the slices are like sectors.

Alternate Assessment

You may want to use the *Interactive CD-ROM Journal* with this assessment.

Journal Have students give an example of a real-life situation in which they had to read and interpret a circle or bar graph to obtain information. Have them write the example in their journals.

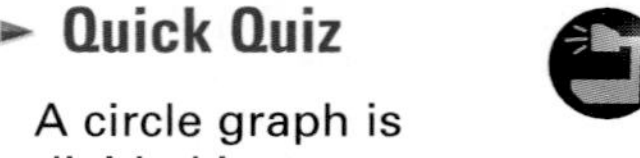

Quick Quiz

1. A circle graph is divided into ______. sectors
2. The sum of the percents on a circle graph is ______. 100%
3. Does a bar graph or a circle graph contain a vertical axis and a horizontal axis? Bar graph
4. Does a bar graph or a circle graph show fractions of a whole? Circle graph

Available on Daily Transparency 1-1

PROBLEM SOLVING 1-1

6. Social Studies The bar graph below is misleading. About how many times greater than the population of Seoul are the populations of Tokyo and Bombay? A little more than 2 times

Predicted 2015 Populations of Some Asian Cities

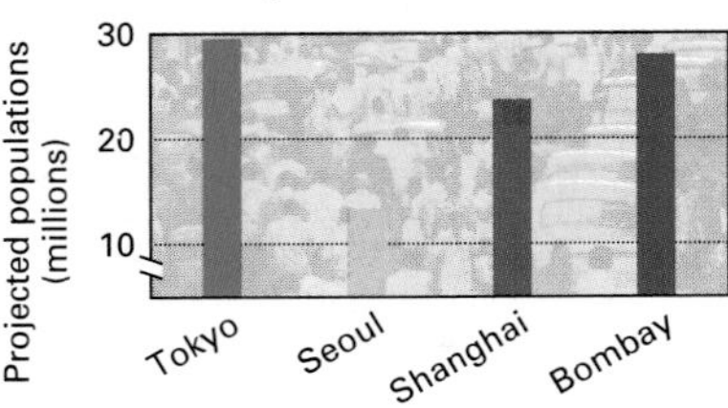

7. Chance The graph shows how your best friend spends her Saturday afternoons. What are you most likely to find her doing if you stop by unexpectedly? Gardening

Saturday Afternoon Activities

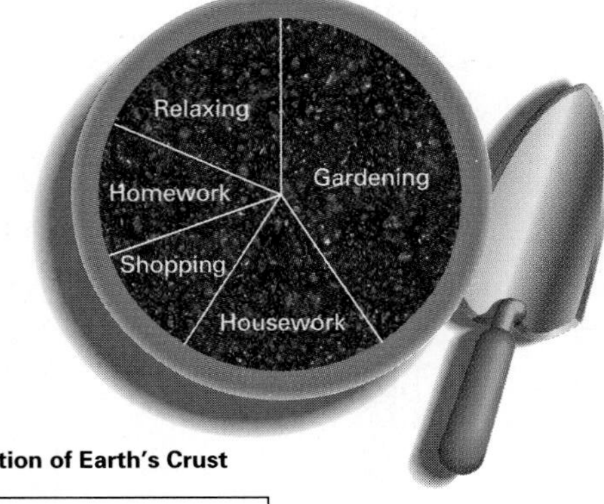

Problem Solving and Reasoning

These two graphs show the same information. Use them for Exercises 8 and 9.

Composition of Earth's Crust

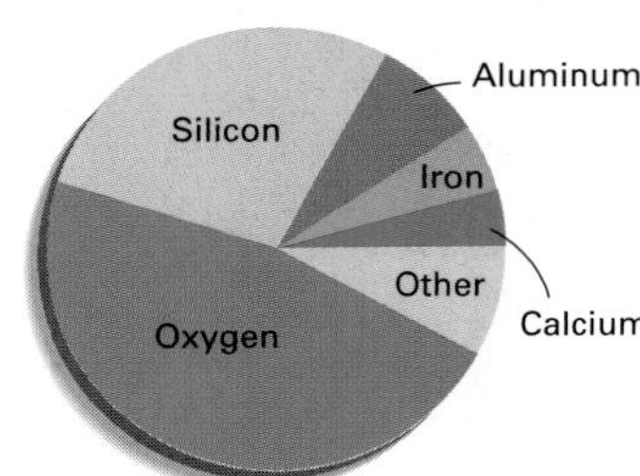

Composition of Earth's Crust

Percent: 0, 10, 20, 30, 40, 50

Oxygen, Silicon, Aluminum, Iron, Calcium, Other

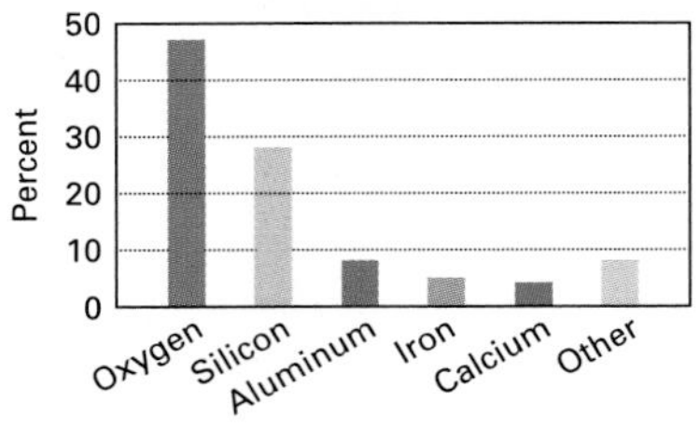

8. Critical Thinking Why do the graphs show "other"?

9. Communicate Use one of the graphs to compare the amounts of silicon and aluminum in the earth's crust. Which graph did you use? Explain.

10. Critical Thinking Give an example of two sets of data that would best be represented by: **a.** A circle graph and **b.** A bar graph.

11. Journal Circle graphs are often called "pie charts." Explain why you think this name is used.

Mixed Review

Write each as a number. *[Previous course]*

12. three thousand two hundred one 3,201

13. sixteen thousand two 16,002

14. 15 million 15,000,000

Add. *[Previous course]*

15. 34 + 99 133

16. 28 + 176 204

17. 543 + 395 938

18. 196 + 952 1148

19. 25 + 27 + 56 108

20. 379 + 32 + 8 419

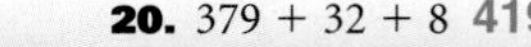

10 *Chapter 1 • Making Sense of the World of Data*

PROBLEM SOLVING

Name ______________________

Guided Problem Solving 1-1

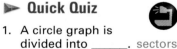

GPS PROBLEM 6, STUDENT PAGE 10

The bar graph at the right is misleading. About how many times greater than the population of Seoul are the populations of Tokyo and Bombay?

Predicted 2015 Populations of Some Asian Cities (Projected populations (millions): 10, 20, 30; Tokyo, Seoul, Shanghai, Bombay)

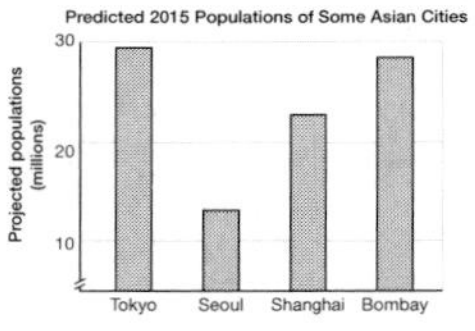

— Understand —

1. Underline the question.
2. About how much taller is the bar for Tokyo than the one for Seoul? About 3 times.
3. Why is this misleading? It is misleading because the vertical scale on the graph is broken.

— Plan —

4. Estimate the population of Tokyo. 30 million.
5. Estimate the population of Seoul. 14 million.
6. Estimate the population of Bombay. 30 million.

— Solve —

7. About how many times greater than the population of Seoul is the population of Tokyo? (Hint: Divide the estimated population of Tokyo by the estimated population of Seoul.) About 2 times.
8. About how many times greater than the population of Seoul is the population of Bombay? About 2 times.

— Look Back —

9. Look at your answers to Items 2 and 7. Explain how you would fix the graph so it is not misleading.
Possible answer: Do not use a broken vertical scale.

SOLVE ANOTHER PROBLEM

About how many times greater than the population of Seoul is the population of Shanghai? About $1\frac{1}{2}$ times.

ENRICHMENT

Name ______________________

Extend Your Thinking 1-1

Visual Thinking

Trace each shape below four times. Then cut them out.

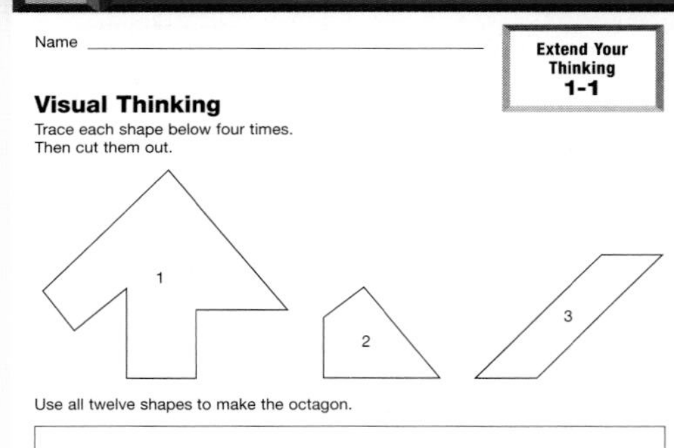

Use all twelve shapes to make the octagon.

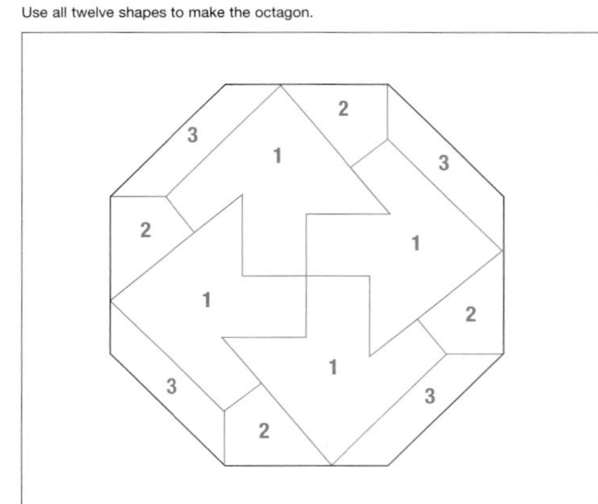

Making Bar Graphs

1-2

▶ Lesson Link You've read and interpreted data that is displayed in a bar graph. Now you will create bar graphs from tables of data. ◀

Explore Bar Graphs

Bars and Stripes

Materials: Graphing utility

The table shows the heights of the eight highest waterfalls.

Waterfall	Height (ft)
Angel Falls, Venezuela	3212
Tugela, South Africa	2014
Utigord, Norway	2625
Mongefossen, Norway	2540
Yosemite Falls, United States	2425
Ostre Mardola Foss, Norway	2154
Tyssestrengane, Norway	2120
Kukenaom, Venezuela	2000

1. Enter the data on a graphing utility. Make the minimum value on the vertical axis 0 and the maximum value on the vertical axis 4000. Then create a bar graph.
2. In what ways does the graph display the data effectively? In what ways is the display not effective?
3. Change either the maximum or the minimum on the vertical axis so that the data can be compared more easily. Describe the change and how you decided on it. Is the new display misleading?

You'll Learn ...

■ to create a bar graph from a table of data

■ to create a double-bar graph

... How It's Used

Newspapers and magazines need to show information in a format that is easily understood. Bar graphs do this.

Vocabulary

scale

interval

double-bar graph

Learn Making Bar Graphs

The **scale** of a bar graph is the "ruler" that measures the heights of the bars. The **interval** is the amount of space between the values on the scale. Before you create a bar graph, you need to choose the scale and the interval.

You also have to decide if you will use vertical or horizontal bars. Your decision may be based on what you want the graph to communicate.

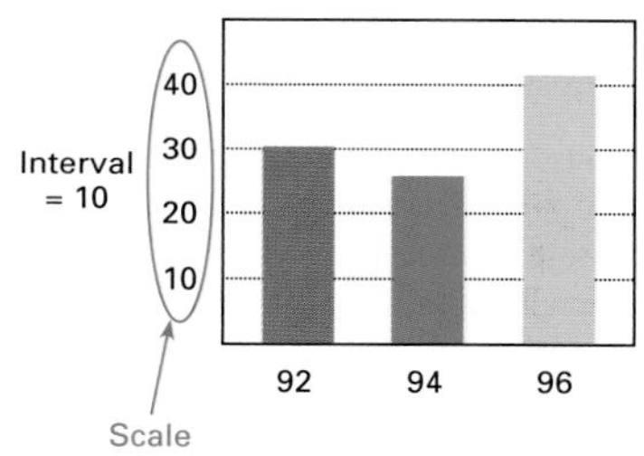

MEETING INDIVIDUAL NEEDS

Resources

1-2 Practice
1-2 Reteaching
1-2 Problem Solving
1-2 Enrichment
1-2 Daily Transparency
Problem of the Day
Review
Quick Quiz

Lesson Enhancement Transparencies 3, 4

Chapter 1 Project Master

Technology Master 2

Interactive CD-ROM Spreadsheet/ Grapher Tool

Wide World of Mathematics Middle School: Graphs in the News

Learning Modalities

Visual Grid paper with rather large squares can make for greater accuracy in handmade bar graphs, as students can make bars the width of the squares and the bars can be a square apart. The heights are also easy to determine by counting squares.

Social Have students work in pairs to generate their computer graphs.

Inclusion

Students could make a "math vocabulary reference notebook" for learning new words. Make sure students understand the terms *vertical* and *horizontal.* Use examples found in the classroom: door, blackboard.

1-2 Lesson Organizer

Objectives

■ Create a bar graph from a table of data.

■ Create a double-bar graph.

Vocabulary

■ Scale, interval, double-bar graph

Materials

■ Explore: Graphing utility

NCTM Standards

■ 1–4, 10

▶ Review

Order from least to greatest.

1. 379, 345, 335, 359
   335, 345, 359, 379
2. 2450, 2550, 2350, 2650
   2350, 2450, 2550, 2650
3. 9989, 9889, 9998, 9899
   9889, 9899, 9989, 9998

Available on Daily Transparency 1-2

▶ Lesson Link

Ask students if it is easier to remember data they saw in a table or in a bar graph.

1 Introduce

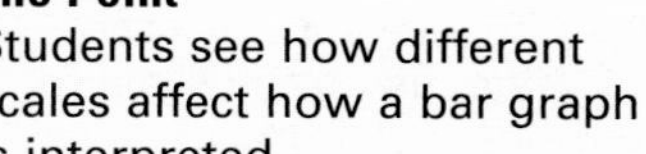
Explore

The Point
Students see how different scales affect how a bar graph is interpreted.

Ongoing Assessment
Watch for students who have difficulty setting up their table using a graphing utility.

For Groups That Finish Early
Use paper and pencil to make a horizontal bar graph using the data in **Explore**.

Answers for Explore on next page.

Answers for Explore

1.

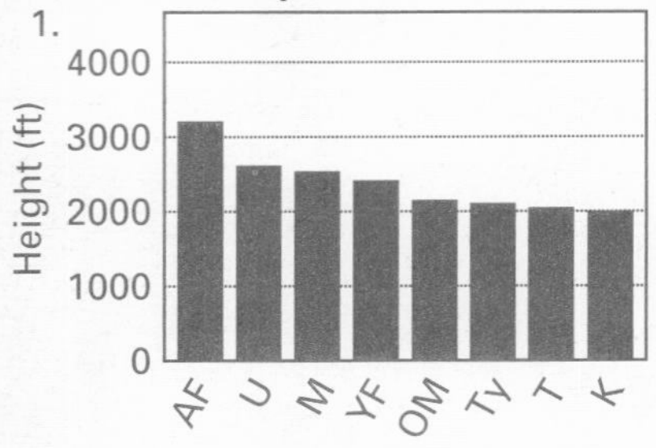

2. It shows the height of each waterfall; It is difficult to compare the heights.

3.

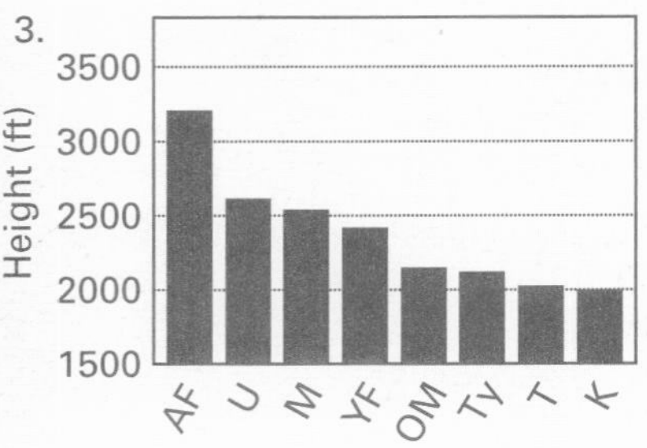

Changed the minimum value to 1500 to make comparisons easier to see; Could be misleading, since it looks as though Angel Falls is 3 times as high as Kukenaom.

2 Teach

Learn

You may wish to use Lesson Enhancement Transparencies 3 and 4 with **Learn**.

Alternate Examples

1. Use the data in Example 1 to create a vertical bar graph.

   Step 1 Graph is vertical.

   Step 2 Determine the scale and interval. The greatest value on the scale should be greater than 4500, so use 5000 with intervals of 1000.

   Step 3 Draw a bar for each data value, using the scale to determine its length.

   Step 4 Label and color the bars and give the graph a title.

World's Five Longest Mountain Ranges

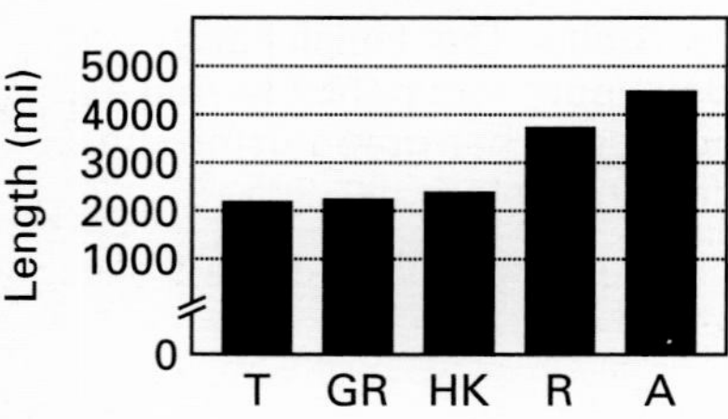

Example 1

Create a bar graph using data on the world's longest mountain ranges.

Step 1 Decide whether you will use vertical or horizontal bars. Since mountain ranges run horizontally, a horizontal graph seems better for displaying this data.

World's Five Longest Mountain Ranges

Mountain Range	Continent	Length (mi)
Andes	South America	4500
Rocky Mountains	North America	3750
Himalayas-Karakoram	Asia	2400
Great Dividing Range	Oceania	2250
Transantarctic	Antarctica	2200

Step 2 Determine the scale and interval. The greatest value on the scale should be slightly greater than the greatest data value. It should also be easy to divide into equal intervals.

A number ending in one or more zeros is often a good choice. Use 5000 for the greatest scale value, and an interval of 1000.

Step 3 Draw a bar for each data value, using the scale to determine its length.

Step 4 Label and color the bars and give the graph a title.

World's Five Longest Mountain Ranges

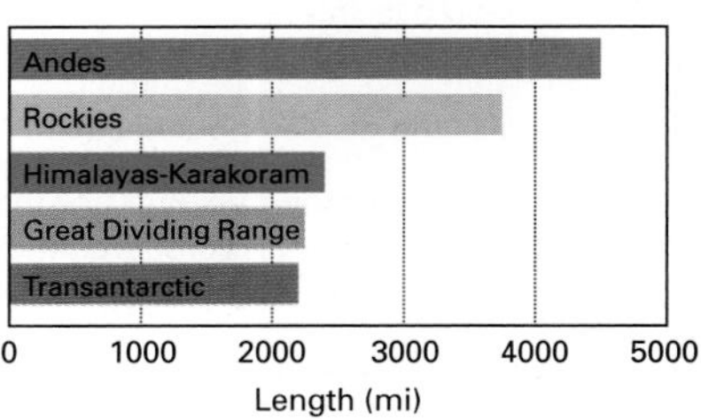

Because of the way data is arranged, you may decide to break a scale, or to start it at a number other than zero. In either case, be aware that readers may be misled.

Double-bar graphs allow you to compare two related data sets. Each double bar compares data for a given year. Changes from one year to the next are also easy to see.

Populations of North and South America

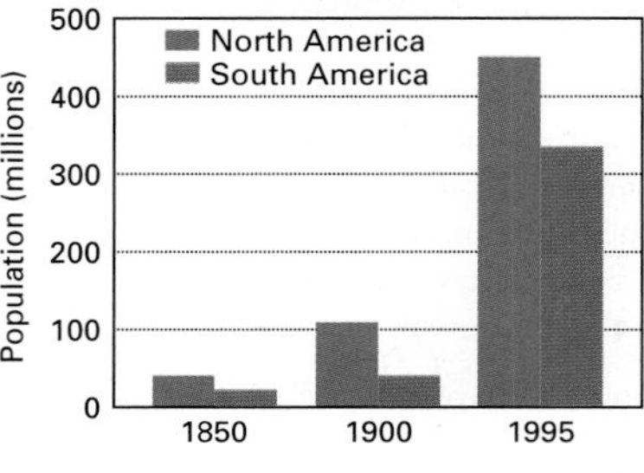

▶ Social Studies Link

Mount Everest, in the Himalayas, is the highest mountain in the world, at 29,028 ft. It was first climbed in 1953 by Edmund Hillary and Tenzing Norgay.

MATH EVERY DAY

▶ Problem of the Day

These two scales balance.

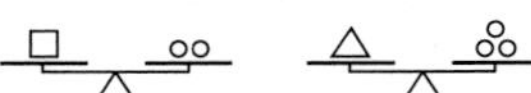

The symbols represent the same weights on the three scales below. Which ones balance?
Scales 2 and 3

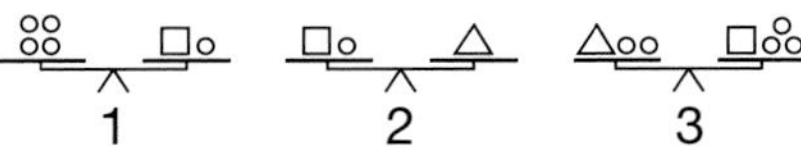

Available on Daily Transparency 1-2

An Extension is provided in the transparency package.

Fact of the Day

Niagara Falls, one of the best-known waterfalls in Canada and the U. S., is about 180 feet high and has a flow of about 212,200 cubic feet of water per second.

Mental Math

Give the first 8 multiples of each number.

1. 10 10, 20, 30, 40, 50, 60, 70, 80
2. 20 20, 40, 60, 80, 100, 120, 140, 160
3. 50 50, 100, 150, 200, 250, 300, 350, 400

Example 2

The table compares the populations of New York City and Mexico City metropolitan areas. Create a double-bar graph of the data.

Populations of New York City and Mexico City (millions)		
Year	Mexico City	New York City
1950	3.1	12.3
1970	9.4	16.2
1990	20.2	16.2

Mexico City

In creating a double-bar graph, you must consider both sets of data. Otherwise, the steps are the same as for a single-bar graph.

Step 1 Use a vertical bar graph.

Step 2 Determine the scale and the interval. The greatest value should be slightly greater than the greatest value in *both* columns of the table. Use 24 for the greatest scale value and an interval of 6.

Step 3 Draw pairs of bars to represent the data values for each year and assign a color to the data in each column. Indicate the color assigned to each bar.

Step 4 Label the axes and give the graph a title.

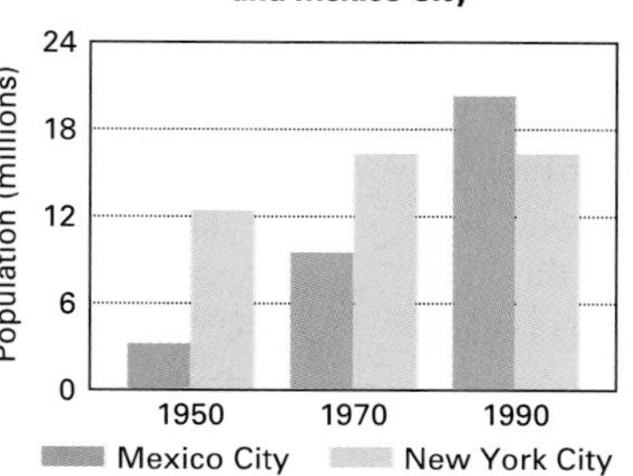

New York City

Try It

Make a double-bar graph of the irrigation data.

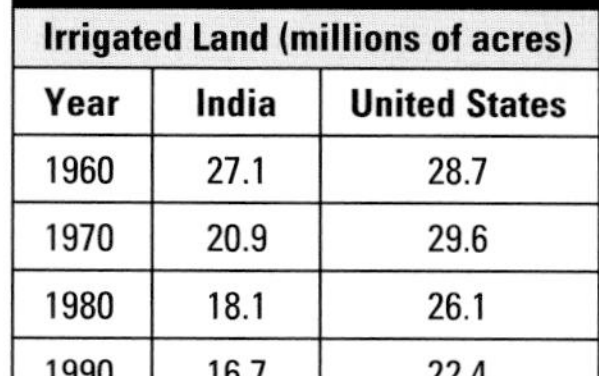

Irrigated Land (millions of acres)		
Year	India	United States
1960	27.1	28.7
1970	20.9	29.6
1980	18.1	26.1
1990	16.7	22.4

Study TIP
In a double-bar graph, you need to indicate which color bar belongs to which set of data.

Check Your Understanding

1. How can you decide what scale and interval to use on a bar graph?
2. Can any data be displayed in a bar graph? Explain.
3. How can a vertical bar graph be changed to a horizontal bar graph?

MEETING MIDDLE SCHOOL CLASSROOM NEEDS

Tips from Middle School Teachers

I have students keep a record of some relevant data, such as rainfall, temperature, or professional sports team or individual scoring for several weeks. Then I have them make bar graphs to be displayed on the class bulletin board.

Science Connection

There are three main types of mountains, depending on how they were formed—fault-block, folded, and domed. The Andes were formed when sedimentary rocks were folded by pressure inside the earth and bent into long ridges. Most of the highest peaks in the Andes were formed by volcanoes.

Team Teaching

Work with the social studies teacher to locate the highest mountains in the world. Make bar graphs comparing the heights of mountains.

Alternate Examples

2. Use the data in Example 2 to draw a horizontal double-bar graph.

   Step 1 The graph is horizontal.

   Step 2 Determine the scale and the interval. The greatest value on the scale should be greater than 20.2, so use 24 with intervals of 6.

   Step 3 Draw pairs of bars to represent the data values for each year, and assign a color to each set of data. Use a square to indicate the color assigned to each bar.

   Step 4 Label the axes and give the graph a title.

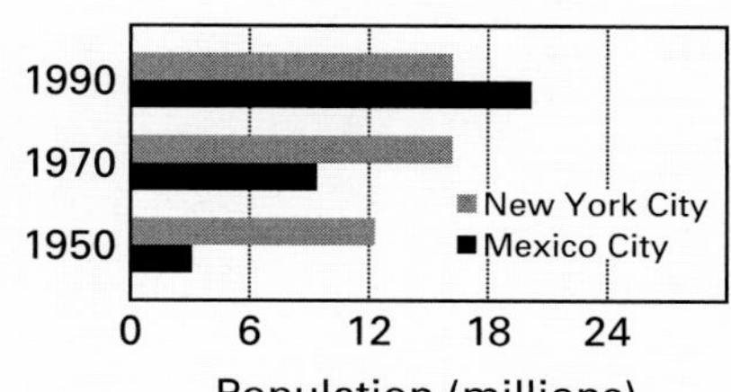

Answer for Try It

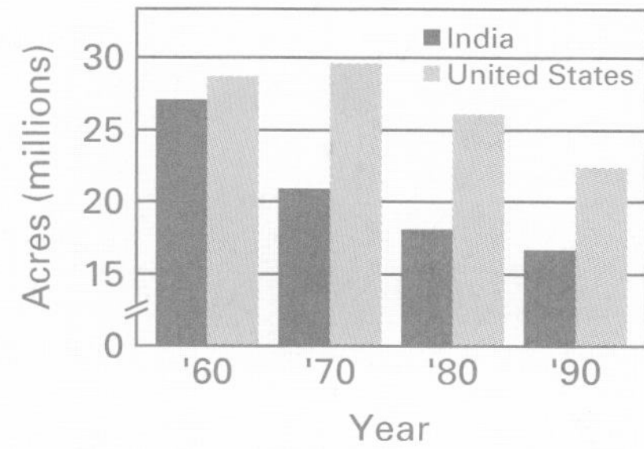

3 Practice and Assess

Check

Answers for Check Your Understanding

1. By checking the range of the data, making the greatest scale value slightly larger than the greatest data value, and dividing the axis into even intervals.
2. Yes, but it is not necessarily the best way to display it; when you are interested in the parts compared to the whole, a circle graph may be better.
3. By switching the vertical and horizontal scales.

Assignment Guide

- Basic
  1–10, 11–21 odds
- Average
  1–7 odds, 8–12, 14–22 evens
- Enriched
  1–7 odds, 8–12, 13–21 odds

Exercise Notes

Exercises 4–7

Error Prevention Encourage students to arrange the numbers from least to greatest to help in determining minimum and maximum values for the graph scales.

Exercise Answers

1. a. 250 million
   b. 50 million
2. a. Horizontal
   b. Ebro, Loire, Elbe, Rhine, Danube, Volga;
   c. Possible answers: 2500, 500
   d. **Lengths of European Rivers**

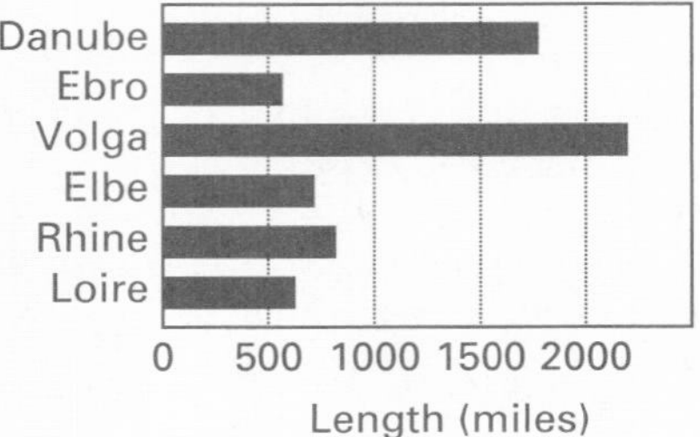

3. B

Possible answers for 4–7

4. Scale 0–100, interval 10.
5. Scale 1000–5000, interval 1000.
6. Scale 0–15, interval 1.
7. Scale 120–360, interval 40.

Reteaching

Activity

Materials: Graph paper

- Record the number of students absent from your math class each day for 5 days.
- Use graph paper to make a vertical bar graph, letting each square represent one student. Be sure to label the axes and to give your graph a title.

1-2 Exercises and Applications

PRACTICE 1-2

Practice and Apply

1. **Getting Started** Use the population graph to answer each question.

a. What is the greatest value shown on the vertical axis?

b. What is the interval?

Populations (1991)

Population (millions): 0, 50, 100, 150, 200, 250

France, Japan, Canada, United States, Mexico, Brazil

2. **Geography** Follow the steps below to make a bar graph of the lengths of some of Europe's rivers.

a. Which type of bar graph would best show this data—horizontal or vertical?

b. Rank the rivers in order, from shortest to longest.

c. What should you choose as the greatest value on your axis? As the interval?

d. Make a bar graph of the data.

River	Length (mi)
Danube	1780
Ebro	570
Volga	2200
Elbe	720
Rhine	820
Loire	630

3. **Test Prep** In which month was there the greatest difference in rainfall between Nashville and Seattle?

Ⓐ April Ⓑ July

Ⓒ November Ⓓ December

Monthly Rainfall

Rainfall (in.): 0, 2, 4, 6, 8

J F M A M J J A S O N D

Nashville Seattle

Choose a convenient scale and interval to use for graphing each set of data.

4. 70, 35, 55, 10, 43, 25, 80

5. 4700, 2000, 3400, 1650, 2800

6. 5, 8, 12, 11, 3, 6, 2, 9, 14

7. 190, 234, 179, 140, 322, 356

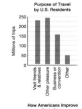

PRACTICE

Name ______________________

Practice 1-2

Making Bar Graphs

Choose a convenient scale and interval to use for graphing each set of data.

1. 85, 32, 91, 15, 24 scale 100 interval 10 or 20
2. 324, 430, 125, 63, 260 scale 500 interval 50 or 100

3. **Social Science** Make a bar graph to show the percentages of foreign-born people in the United States from 1960 to 1993.

Year	1960	1970	1980	1990	1993
Percentage	5.4%	4.7%	6.2%	7.9%	8.6%

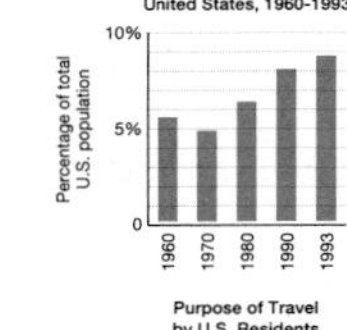

4. In 1991 U.S. residents traveled for many reasons– 226 million visited friends and relatives, 240 million had other pleasure reasons, 153 million traveled for business or convention, and 46 million traveled for other reasons. Make a bar graph to show the purpose of travel by U.S. residents.

Purpose of Travel by U.S. Residents

Millions of trips: 0, 50, 100, 150, 200, 250

Visit friends & relatives, Other pleasure, Business or convention, Other

5. **Health** Make a double-bar graph showing how Americans improved their diets in 1991 and 1993.

Percentage of surveyed adults who improved their diet by:	1991	1993
Adding vegetables	40%	52%
Adding fruits	27%	36%
Avoiding fats	21%	29%

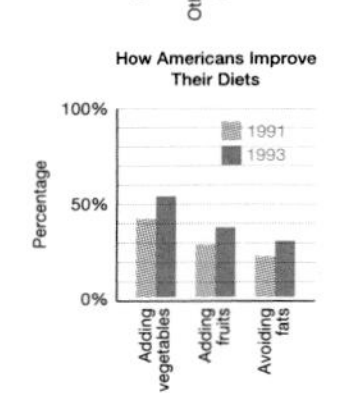

RETEACHING

Name ______________________

Alternative Lesson 1-2

Making Bar Graphs

The **scale** of a bar graph is the "ruler" that measures heights of the bars. The **interval** is the amount of space between each value on the scale.

Example

Make a bar graph using the data on population.

Karen followed these steps to make a bar graph using the data on population.

Year	Population (rounded to nearest million)
1950	3,000,000
1970	9,000,000
1990	20,000,000

Population of Mexico City

Step 1: Karen decided to use horizontal bars.

Step 2: She used intervals of 2 million so that all of the data would be easy to read.

Step 3: She drew the bars to represent the data.

Step 4: Karen wrote a title for the graph and labeled the bars.

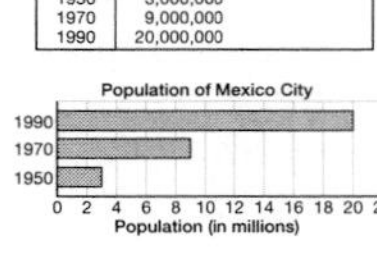

Try It Use the data on magazine subscriptions sold by students to complete the unfinished graph.

a. What interval was used on the horizontal scale? Interval of 3.

b. Why do you think this interval was chosen? The given data are multiples of 3.

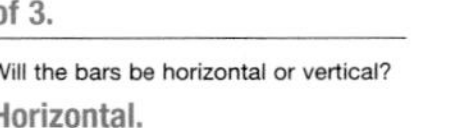

Types of Magazines Sold	
Hobbies	12
Movie	15
Sports	21
Science	9

c. Will the bars be horizontal or vertical? Horizontal.

d. Draw the bars that represent the data for sales of science, sports, and movie magazines.

e. Shade the bars. Label the horizontal axis. Give the graph a title.

Types of Magazines Sold

Science, Sports, Movie, Hobbies

0 3 6 9 12 15 18 21

Number of subscriptions

f. Write two problems that can be solved by using the graph.

Possible answer: How many more subscriptions to the movie magazine were sold than to the science magazine? Which magazine sold the most subscriptions?

8. History In the year 1910, many people immigrated to the United States—460,935 from northern and western Europe, 465,356 from eastern and southern Europe, 89,534 from the Americas, 23,533 from Asia, and 1,072 from Africa. Make a bar graph to show this data.

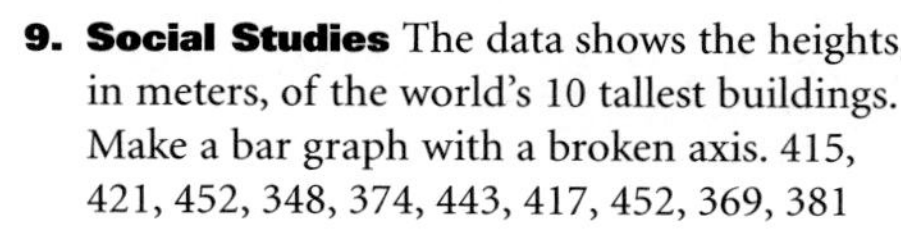

9. Social Studies The data shows the heights, in meters, of the world's 10 tallest buildings. Make a bar graph with a broken axis. 415, 421, 452, 348, 374, 443, 417, 452, 369, 381

10. Make a double-bar graph of the data from South America's three most populated cities.

Population—1994 and estimated 2015 (thousands)		
City	**1994**	**2015**
São Paolo, Brazil	16,110	20,800
Buenos Aires, Argentina	10,914	12,400
Rio de Janeiro, Brazil	9,817	11,600

PROBLEM SOLVING 1-2

Problem Solving and Reasoning

11. Critical Thinking Look at the table showing Armando's salary for the years 1996–2000.

GPS

a. Would this data best be shown on a bar graph or a circle graph?

b. Make a graph of the data.

c. What do you notice about Armando's salary in the years 1996–1999?

d. What do you think happened to Armando in the year 2000?

Year	Salary ($)
1996	20,000
1997	23,000
1998	26,000
1999	29,000
2000	35,000

12. Journal Sometimes a graph has a "broken" axis. Explain what this means and why you sometimes need to use one.

Mixed Review

Write each number in words. *[Previous course]*

13. 428 **14.** 2,489 **15.** 43,185 **16.** 130,396 **17.** 3,734,790

Subtract. *[Previous course]*

18. 94 − 23 71 **19.** 45 − 29 16 **20.** 147 − 32 115 **21.** 235 − 49 186 **22.** 527 − 76 451

Project Progress

Design the events for your games by making rules for the athletic events and deciding on questions and scoring methods for the thinking ones. Over the next few days, conduct your games. As each event takes place, record the results for each competitor on the chart.

Exercise Notes

■ Exercise 8

Multicultural In 1993, about 158,300 people immigrated to the United States from Europe; 358,000 from Asia; 355,300 from the Americas; and 27,800 from Africa.

■ Exercise 10

Social Studies The three most populated cities in North America are New York City, Los Angeles, and Chicago.

Project Progress

You may want to have students use Chapter 1 Project Master.

Exercise Answers

Answers for 8–12 on page C1.

13. Four hundred twenty-eight
14. Two thousand, four hundred eighty-nine
15. Forty three thousand, one hundred eighty-five
16. One hundred thirty thousand, three hundred ninety-six
17. Three million, seven hundred thirty-four thousand, seven hundred ninety

Alternate Assessment

Portfolio Have students describe the steps they would follow to create a bar graph that displays the number of students participating in various sports at school. Have them draw the bar graph and include it in their portfolio.

Quick Quiz

Tell what scale and interval you would use to graph each set of data.

1. 35, 24, 39, 42, 28, 16, 45 Scale 10–50, interval 5
2. 5600, 8800, 6300, 7100, 8200 Scale 5000–9000, interval 500
3. 3, 8, 2, 7, 9, 4, 5, 6 Scale 0–10, interval 1
4. 325, 125, 75, 25, 150, 250, 200 Scale 0–350, interval 50

Possible answers are given.

Available on Daily Transparency 1-2

PROBLEM SOLVING

Name ____________

Guided Problem Solving 1-2

GPS **PROBLEM 11, STUDENT PAGE 15**

Look at the table showing Armando's salary for the years 1996–2000.

Armando's Salary

Year	Salary in dollars
1996	20,000
1997	23,000
1998	26,000
1999	29,000
2000	35,000

a. Would this data best be shown on a bar graph or a circle graph?
b. Make a graph of the data.
c. What do you notice about Armando's salary in the years 1996 to 1999?
d. What do you think happened to Armando in the year 2000?

— Understand —

1. Will the graph show parts of a whole or different amounts? Different amounts.

— Plan —

2. Which of these scales would you choose for the vertical axis on the graph? a

a. Salary (in thousands of dollars) 0, 10, 20, 30, 40; Year 1996 1997 1998 1999 2000

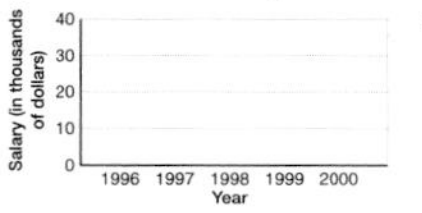

b. Salary (in thousands of dollars) 0, 5, 10, 15, 20; Year 1996 1997 1998 1999 2000

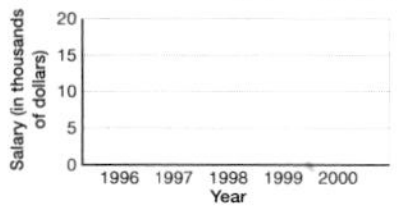

— Solve —

3. Draw your graph at the right.

Armando's Salary — Salary (in thousands of dollars) 0, 10, 20, 30, 40; Year 1996 1997 1998 1999 2000

4. Do the bars for 1996-1999 show a steady increase or decrease in Armando's salary? Steady increase.

5. What might have happened in the year 2000? Possible answer: The big jump in salary might indicate a promotion.

— Look Back —

6. Does your graph match the change in Armando's salary each year? Yes.

SOLVE ANOTHER PROBLEM

Suppose that Armando's salary in the year 2000 was $22,000. Describe how you would change the graph to reflect this information.
Possible answer: The vertical axis needs to go to $30,000.

ENRICHMENT

Name ____________

Extend Your Thinking 1-2

Critical Thinking

The planning committee for Summit County Board of Education is considering building an addition to the local high school. The bar graph on the right shows the enrollment in grades K–8 for the years 1991–1996.

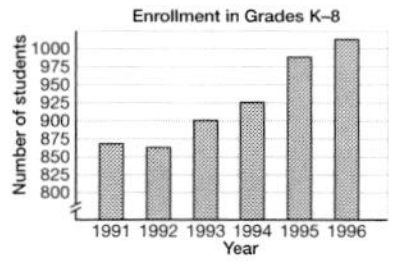

Enrollment in Grades K–8 — Number of students 800, 825, 850, 875, 900, 925, 950, 975, 1000; Year 1991 1992 1993 1994 1995 1996

Possible answers are given.

1. What does the bar graph tell you about the current trend in school enrollment in Summit County?
The number of students is increasing.

2. If a total enrollment of over 1050 students would require more classroom space than is currently available, in what year do you predict that the high school will need to have the addition completed? Explain.
About the year 1999, because the number of students has been increasing by about 25 students each year.

3. Suppose that one of the major county businesses recently announced that it would be relocating to another state. How might this affect the planning committee's decision? Explain.
Since the relocation will probably take many students out of local schools, the committee may decide to postpone building the addition.

4. Suppose that the state transportation board is considering building a new airport on the west side of Summit County. How might this affect the planning committee's decision? Explain.
It might bring new business to Summit County which may bring in more families with children so the addition may need to be built earlier than the year 1999.

5. What type of additional information should the planning committee look for before making its decision?
Any major changes in the community.

1-3 Lesson Organizer

Objectives

- Make a line plot.
- Make a stem-and-leaf diagram.

Vocabulary

- Line plot, outlier, stem-and-leaf diagram

NCTM Standards

- 1–4, 7, 10

▶ Review

In each number, identify the tens digit and the ones digit.

1. 36 Tens: 3; Ones: 6
2. 198 Tens: 9; Ones: 8
3. 347 Tens: 4; Ones: 7
4. 104 Tens: 0; Ones: 4

Available on Daily Transparency 1-3

1 Introduce

Explore

The Point
Students see similarities and differences between line plots and bar graphs.

Ongoing Assessment
Check that students have a total of 44 X's above the number line in their line plot.

For Groups That Finish Early
Repeat Step 1, making a bar graph instead of a line plot. Which graph do you think gives a clearer description of the data? Answers may vary.

Follow Up
Have students share their responses to Step 4. Discuss the fact that a graph can be used to find information beyond what is shown in the graph.

1-3 Line Plots and Stem-and-Leaf Diagrams

You'll Learn ...

- to make a line plot
- to make a stem-and-leaf diagram

... How It's Used

Basketball coaches need to keep track of each player's progress. A line plot gives a clear view of how well a player is performing.

Vocabulary

line plot
outlier
stem-and-leaf diagram

▶ Lesson Link You know how to use a bar graph to display information. In this lesson, you will learn two ways to show how frequently values occur and how they are distributed. ◀

Explore Line Plots

Double Time

Doubling time is the length of time it takes a population to double. The faster a population grows, the shorter its doubling time. The table shows the doubling times of the 44 African countries south of the Sahara Desert.

Population Doubling Times (yr)						
25	23	23	21	21	22	21
27	28	20	24	26	25	28
27	22	28	35	19	19	24
22	22	20	23	25	48	26
22	22	23	38	20	28	25
27	26	22	20	19	19	22
18	22					

1. Draw and label a number line to include every doubling time in the table. Put in an × for each doubling time. Stack ×'s one above the other. The ×'s for 23, 24, and 25 are shown.

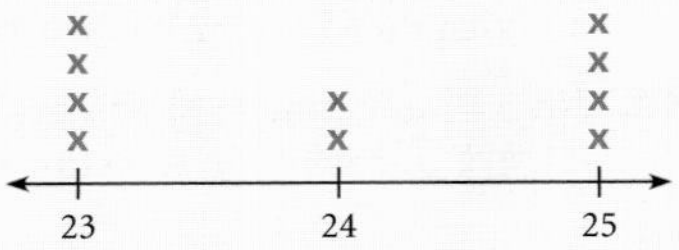

23	24	25
x x x x	x x	x x x x

2. What does your completed plot show you?
3. How is the plot like a bar graph? How is it different?
4. In 1994, the nation of Namibia had a population of 1.5 million and a doubling time of 22 years. If its doubling time does not change, in what year is Namibia's population expected to be 3 million? Explain.

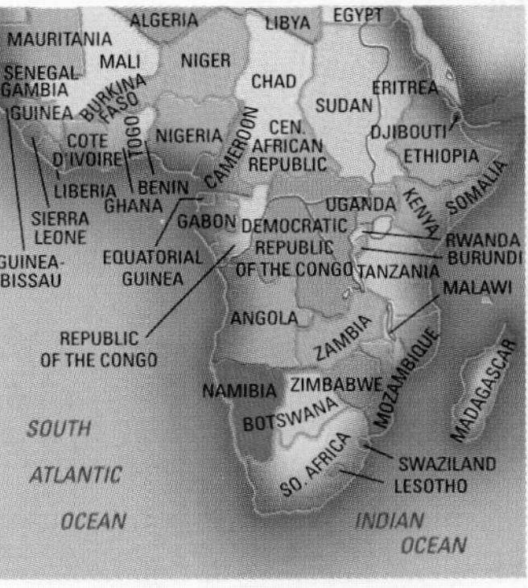

MEETING INDIVIDUAL NEEDS

Resources

- 1-3 Practice
- 1-3 Reteaching
- 1-3 Problem Solving
- 1-3 Enrichment
- 1-3 Daily Transparency
  - Problem of the Day
  - Review
  - Quick Quiz
- Lesson Enhancement Transparencies 5, 6

Learning Modalities

Kinesthetic Provide opportunities for students to construct line plots using concrete objects such as buttons or coins.

Visual Students might find it interesting and more descriptive to use symbols rather than x's to make their line plots.

English Language Development

To help limited-English-speaking students, write the numbers 20, 22, 23, 24, 24, 26, and 28 on the chalkboard. Then draw a diagram of a stem with 8 leaves on the right side of the stem. Label the stem 2, and write the 8 ones digits on the leaves, one to each leaf. Explain that just as a stem can have many leaves, the stem-and-leaf diagram can have one stem and many leaves.

For these same students, assess journal entries for conceptual understanding, rather than correct language usage.

Learn — Line Plots and Stem-and-Leaf Diagrams

A **line plot** shows how many times each data value occurs. A number line and ×'s are used to organize the data. Line plots make it easy to see data values that are separated from the rest. Such data values are called **outliers**.

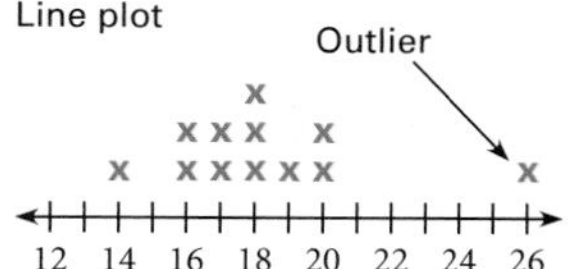

DID YOU KNOW?

Lacrosse is a very old game that was first played by Native Americans. A lacrosse stick has a net at the end, in which players catch the ball.

Example 1

Make a line plot of the data and describe the resulting plot.

Number of Players on a Team

Sport	Players	Sport	Players	Sport	Players
Baseball	9	Handball, team	7	Rugby, league	13
Basketball	5	Hockey	6	Rugby, union	15
Cricket	11	Lacrosse, men's	10	Soccer	11
Field hockey	11	Lacrosse, women's	12	Softball, fast-pitch	9
Football, American	11	Netball	7	Speedball	11
Football, Canadian	12	Polo	4	Volleyball	6
Football, Gaelic	15	Roller hockey	15	Water polo	7

Step 1 Decide on a scale. Because the smallest data value is 4 and the largest data value is 15, choose a scale from 4 to 16. Use an interval of 2.

Step 2 Mark an × for each data value.

The line plot shows that the most common team size is 11. More than half of the data values fall in the interval from 9 to 13. Teams of 7 and 15 are also common.

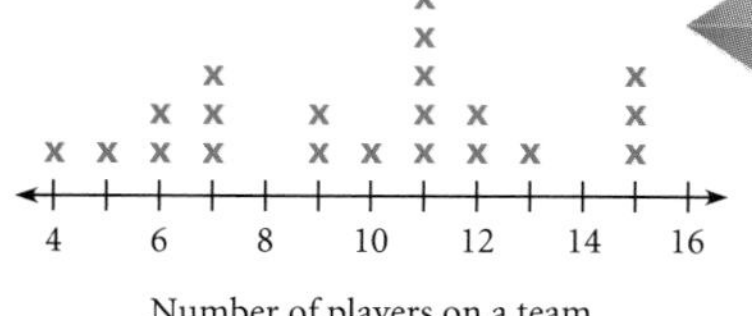

Problem Solving TIP

It is easy to miss a value, so be sure the number of ×'s you make matches the number of data values in the table.

Like a line plot, a **stem-and-leaf diagram** shows how often data values occur and how they are distributed. A stem-and-leaf diagram displays data horizontally.

Each data value is split into a *stem* and a *leaf*. For a two-digit value, the tens digit is the stem and the ones digit is the leaf. Single-digit values have stems of 0. For a three-digit value, the first two digits make up the stem.

123 is written as 12 | 3.

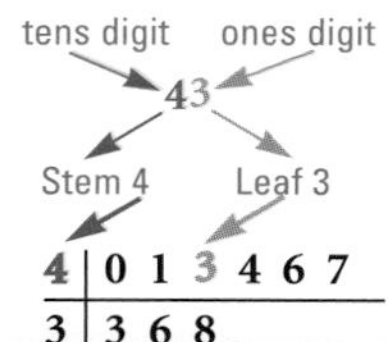

MATH EVERY DAY

Problem of the Day

The Teen Music Club has 12 country CDs, 23 jazz CDs, 10 gospel CDs, and 375 rock CDs. Why is this information difficult to show on a bar graph? Because the range is so great, it is difficult to choose a reasonable scale for the number of CDs.

Available on Daily Transparency 1-3

An Extension is provided in the transparency package.

Fact of the Day

With an area of about 17,400,000 mi², Asia has about 57% of the world's population. Africa, with an area of 11,700,000 mi², has about 15%.

Mental Math

Find each sum mentally.

1. 200 + 300 500
2. 600 + 500 1100
3. 2000 + 6000 + 1000 9000
4. 300 + 700 + 50 1050
5. 400 + 800 + 250 1450

Answers for Explore

1. See page C1.
2. Frequency with which each item appears.
3. Similar: Like bars in a bar graph, the heights of the stacked X's show how the data is distributed. Different: To find a frequency, you count Xs in a line plot and read the height of a bar on a bar graph.
4. 2016; Namibia's population will double in 22 years, and 2016 is 22 years after 1994.

2 Teach

Learn

Lesson Enhancement Transparencies 5 and 6 may be used with **Learn**.

Alternate Examples

1. Make a line plot of the data and describe the resulting plot.

Herbert Basketball Team

Game	Points	Game	Points
1	74	5	76
2	76	6	77
3	79	7	80
4	80	8	76

Step 1 Decide on a scale for the number line. Because the smallest data value is 74, and the largest is 80, choose a scale from 74 to 80. Use intervals of 2.

Step 2 Mark an X for each data value.

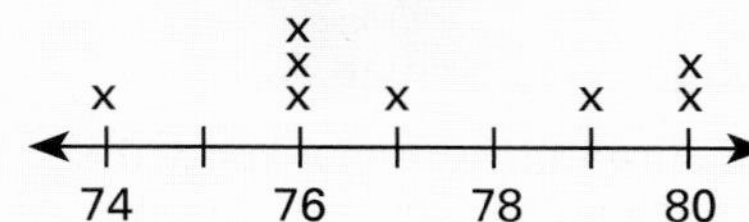

The line plot shows that the most frequent number of points is 76 and that more than half of the data falls below 78.

Alternate Examples

2. Make a stem-and-leaf diagram of the following data.

   Class Scores on a Social Studies Test

   88, 75, 80, 90, 94, 82, 65, 83, 80, 96, 91, 95, 54, 63, 65, 78, 75, 71, 92, 88, 92, 96, 95, 82, 88, 65, 75

   Step 1 Order the data values from smallest to largest.

   54. 63, 65, 65, 65, 71, 75, 75, 75, 78, 80, 80, 82, 82, 83, 88, 88, 88, 90, 91, 92, 92, 94, 95, 95, 96, 96

   Step 2 Separate each item into a stem and a leaf, Use the tens digit for the stem and the ones digit for the leaf.

   Step 3 List the stems in a column from largest to smallest. List the leaves in order beside their stems.

stem	leaf
9	0, 1, 2, 2, 4, 5, 5, 6, 6
8	0, 0, 2, 2, 3, 8, 8, 8
7	1, 5, 5, 5, 8
6	3, 5, 5, 5
5	4

   The diagram shows that most of the data values are in the 80s or 90s. The diagram also shows that the lowest score was 54 and the highest was 96.

Note: The stems in a stem-and-leaf diagram can be shown in ascending or descending order, whichever is more appropriate.

Answers for Try It on page C1.

3 Practice and Assess

Check

Be sure that students know that the stem can have any number of digits, but the leaf has only one.

Answers for Check Your Understanding

1. Stem: 58, leaf: 9; Stem: 0, leaf: 6.
2. Possible answer: Each tens digit is like a plant stem with individual leaves. Each ones digit represents a leaf.
3. A line plot clearly shows an outlier because the outlier is separated from the other values.

Example 2

Social Studies Link

Auckland is the largest city in New Zealand, but Wellington is the capital. New Zealand was the first nation to allow women to vote.

The table gives the high temperature in Auckland, New Zealand, on each day during the month of April. Make a stem-and-leaf diagram of the data.

Daily High Temperatures in Auckland, New Zealand (°F)					
75	67	83	90	79	74
70	71	72	78	76	67
66	80	77	77	84	74
64	76	79	82	76	85
71	81	69	83	75	84

Step 1 Order the data values from smallest to largest.

64, 66, 67, 67, 69, 70, 71, 71, 72, 74, 74, 75, 75, 76, 76, 76, 77, 77, 78, 79, 79, 80, 81, 82, 83, 83, 84, 84, 85, 90

Step 2 Separate each item into a stem and a leaf. Use the tens digit for the stem and the ones digit for the leaf.

Step 3 List the stems in a column from largest to smallest. List the leaves in order beside their stems.

Stem	Leaf
9	0
8	0 1 2 3 3 4 4 5
7	0 1 1 2 4 4 5 5 6 6 6 7 7 8 9 9
6	4 6 7 7 9

The diagram shows that most of the data values are in the 70s. The plot also clearly shows the highest temperature, 90°F, and the lowest temperature, 64°F.

Make an organized list.

Try It

a. Make a line plot of the data.

b. Make a stem-and-leaf diagram of the data.

c. Compare the two graphs.

Ages of Employees Surveyed					
21	27	30	33	17	20
15	23	21	30	42	24
30	17	21	16	22	23
16	21	30	17	23	28

Check Your Understanding

1. How would you put 589 on a stem-and-leaf diagram? What about 6?
2. How do you think the stem-and-leaf diagram got its name?
3. Explain how you could use a line plot to decide if there were any outliers in a data set.

MEETING MIDDLE SCHOOL CLASSROOM NEEDS

Tips from Middle School Teachers

My students sometimes have difficulty making a stem-and-leaf diagram with data values having three or more digits. I remind them that each leaf should be only a ones digit, while the stem is made up of the remaining digits.

Social Studies Connection

Namibia, formerly South-West Africa, is located on the southwestern coast of Africa. It was controlled by the government of South Africa from 1916 to 1990. In 1989, the South West Africa People's Organization received a majority in the assembly as a result of UN-supervised elections. They wrote a constitution, and Namibia became an independent republic on March 21, 1990.

Team Teaching

Work with an art teacher to help students design and make interesting stem-and-leaf diagrams.

1-3 Exercises and Applications

Practice and Apply

1. **Getting Started** Follow the steps below to make a line plot of the number of raisins in each of 24 boxes.

32	35	29	31	30	33	31	32	34	32	36	33
32	34	33	30	35	31	33	33	32	32	34	32

  a. Find the smallest number of raisins shown.
  b. Find the largest number of raisins shown.
  c. Draw a section of the number line to include these two values.
  d. Choose an interval.
  e. Mark an × for each value in the chart.
  f. Are there any outliers?

2. **Sports** Baseball Hall-of-Famer Rod Carew had 3053 hits in his major-league career. His home-run total for each of the 19 seasons he played from 1967 through 1985 is given in the table.

8	1	8	4	2	0	6	3	14	9
14	5	3	3	2	3	2	3	2	

  a. Make a line plot of the number of home runs hit by Rod Carew.
  b. What does the line plot tell you about Rod Carew's home runs?

3. The stem-and-leaf diagram shows the number of phone calls made by 20 of Joan's classmates over a two-week period. What was the greatest number of phone calls made? The least?

Phone Calls Made

Stem	Leaf
4	7
3	5 9
2	0 1 2 6
1	1 2 2 4 5 6 6 7
0	0 3 5 8 8

4. Show the data from Question 3 on a line plot. What does it show more clearly than the stem-and-leaf diagram?

5. **Test Prep** A data value with a stem of 52 and a leaf of 4 is displayed in a stem-and-leaf diagram. The number represented is:

Ⓐ 4 Ⓑ 52.4 Ⓒ 452 Ⓓ 524

Make a line plot for each set of data and name any outliers.

6. 2, 3, 1, 2, 1, 4, 2, 2, 4, 2
7. 11, 13, 14, 17, 11, 12, 12, 14, 17, 12

1-3 Exercises and Applications

Assignment Guide

- **Basic** 1–6, 8, 10, 11–31 odds
- **Average** 1–5, 7, 9, 10–30 evens
- **Enriched** 1–5, 7, 9, 10–12, 14–30 evens

Exercise Notes

Exercise 5

Test Prep Choice B assumes that the vertical segment separating the stem from the leaf is a decimal point, while choice C has interchanged the stem and the leaf.

Exercise Answers

Answers for Exercises 1–7 on page C2.

PRACTICE

Name ____________________

Practice 1-3

Line Plots and Stem-and-Leaf Diagrams

Make a line plot for each set of data and name any outliers.

1. 6, 9, 7, 9, 2, 8, 7, 9

Outliers: 2

2. 31, 29, 32, 30, 33, 32, 30, 32

Outliers: None

Make a stem-and-leaf diagram for each set of data.

3. Number of musicians in local orchestras:
63, 41, 49, 34, 47, 62, 60, 38

What is the smallest number of musicians? 34

What is the largest number of musicians? 63

stem	leaf
3	48
4	179
5	
6	023

4. Salaries (in thousands of dollars) at a local company:
36, 61, 42, 55, 39, 31, 47, 52, 33, 40, 39

stem	leaf
3	13699
4	027
5	25
6	1

5. The stem-and-leaf plot shows the number of customers during different hours of the day at a local fast-food restaurant. How many customers arrived during the busiest hour?

49

stem	leaf
1	1 7 9
2	1 1 4 7 7
3	1 6 7 8
4	2 3 5 8 9

6. **Social Studies** The number of state senators in each of the southern states is given below. Make a stem-and-leaf diagram for the data.

stem	leaf
2	1
3	1345589
4	00678
5	026

State	AL	AR	DE	FL	GA	KY	LA	MD	MS	NC	OK	SC	TN	TX	VA	WV
Senators	35	35	21	40	56	38	39	47	52	50	48	46	33	31	40	34

RETEACHING

Name ____________________

Alternative Lesson 1-3

Line Plots and Stem-and-Leaf Diagrams

There are many ways to display data. Two ways to display these geography test scores for eleven students are shown below.

78, 86, 96, 86, 92, 78, 96, 90, 86, 82, 80

Example 1

Make a line plot of the data above.

A **line plot** shows how many times each data value occurs and gives a visual representation of the way the data is distributed. The data values are shown on a number line and an "x" is placed above a value each time it occurs.

Geography Test Scores

78 80 82 84 86 88 90 92 94 96 98

Example 2

Make a stem-and-leaf diagram of the data.

In a **stem-and-leaf diagram** each data value has two parts, a **stem** and a **leaf.** For a two-digit value the tens digit is the stem and the ones digit is the leaf, so 7|8 represents a score of 78.

Time Spent on Chores

Stem	Leaf
7	8 8
8	0 2 6 6 6
9	0 2 6 6

Try It Make a line plot of these data about the time students spend on chores each day.

20	25	28	32	20	26
33	26	19	32	28	20

a. What will be the lowest number on your scale? 19

b. What will be the highest number on your scale? 33

c. Draw your line plot in the space below.

18 20 22 24 26 28 30 32 34

Make a stem-and-leaf diagram of the data about chores.

d. Write the data in order from least to greatest.
19, 20, 20, 20, 25, 26, 26, 28, 28, 32, 32, 33

e. List the leaves in order beside their stems.

Stem	Leaf
1	9
2	0 0 0 5 6 6 8 8
3	2 2 3

Reteaching

Activity

Materials: Index cards, scissors.

- Write each of these numbers on an index card: 12, 12, 15, 20, 22, 23, 30, 31.
- Shuffle the cards and arrange them in three piles according to their tens digits.
- Cut each card apart between the tens and ones digits, keeping the tens separate from the ones. In the tens pile, stack the 1s into one pile, the 2s into another pile, and the 3s into a third pile.
- For each tens pile, arrange the ones digits from least to greatest to the right of the 1, 2, or 3. You have made a stem-and-leaf diagram of the numbers on the cards.

Exercise Answers

8.

Stem	Leaf
1	6 9
2	5 7 8 9
3	1 2 5 9
4	0

9.

Stem	Leaf
0	5 8
1	2 4 6 7 9
2	0 3 3 5 5 8
3	8

10. Possible answer: The average April temperature is higher in Portland than in Boston.

11. a.

Stem	Leaf
4	6 8 9 9
5	0 1 2 4 4 6 7 7 7 7 8
6	1 1 4 5 8

b. Possible answer: Most were in their 50s.

c. Possible answer: No; The data set has so many different values it may be too strung out.

12. Possible answers: Alike: They both show the data values and their distribution. Different: Line plot makes it easier to see the frequency of each value and shows outliers.

Alternate Assessment

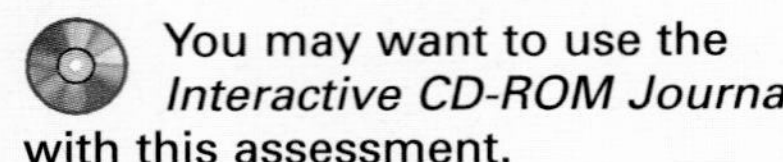

You may want to use the *Interactive CD-ROM Journal* with this assessment.

Journal Have students write paragraphs about the four different types of graphs. Have them tell what type of data is best represented by each kind of graph.

Quick Quiz

Data:
28, 19, 15, 23, 15, 16, 15

1. Make a line plot of the data given above.

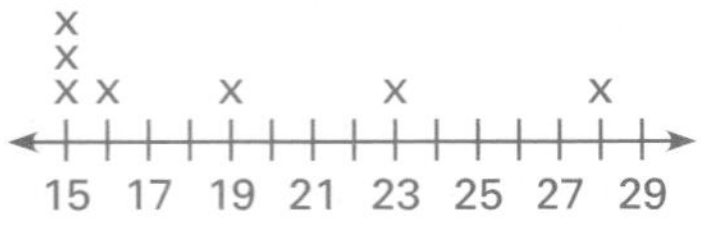

```
X
X
X X    X     X     X
<+-+-+-+-+-+-+-+-+-+-+-+-+-+-+->
15  17  19  21  23  25  27  29
```

2. Make a stem-and-leaf diagram of the above data.

stem	leaf
1	5, 5, 5, 6, 9
2	3, 8

Available on Daily Transparency 1-3

PROBLEM SOLVING 1-3

Make a stem-and-leaf diagram for each set of data.

8. Science Days of incubation for birds of various species: 27, 19, 35, 28, 25, 16, 40, 39, 32, 29, 31

9. Number of students in various school clubs: 12, 38, 5, 23, 8, 25, 14, 19, 25, 16, 23, 28, 17, 20

Problem Solving and Reasoning

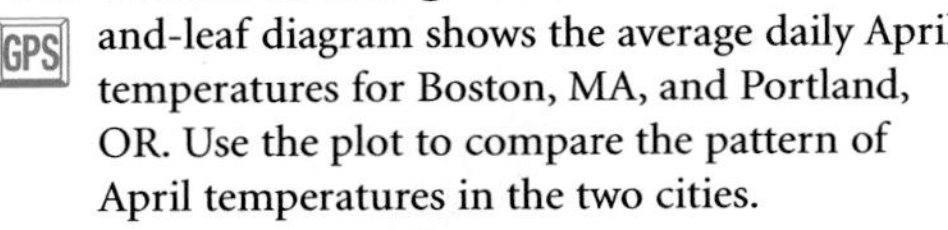

10. Critical Thinking GPS The back-to-back stem-and-leaf diagram shows the average daily April temperatures for Boston, MA, and Portland, OR. Use the plot to compare the pattern of April temperatures in the two cities.

Boston, MA		Portland, OR
	7	1
2 2	6	0 0 0 1 1 1 1 2 3 3 4 5
9 8 7 7 7 5 3 3 1 1 1 0	5	2 5 5 5 6 6 6 7 8 9 9
8 8 8 7 4 4 2 2 0 0	4	2 2 3 4 4 5
6 6 4 3 3 0	3	

11. Critical Thinking The table shows the ages of the first 20 American presidents when they took office.

a. Make a stem-and-leaf diagram to show this data.

b. What conclusions can you draw from your diagram?

c. Would a line plot be a sensible way to show this data? Explain.

President	Age	President	Age
George Washington	57	James Polk	49
John Adams	61	Zachary Taylor	64
Thomas Jefferson	57	Millard Fillmore	50
James Madison	57	Franklin Pierce	48
James Monroe	58	James Buchanan	65
John Quincy Adams	57	Abraham Lincoln	52
Andrew Jackson	61	Andrew Johnson	56
Martin Van Buren	54	Ulysses Grant	46
William Harrison	68	Rutherford Hayes	54
John Tyler	51	James Garfield	49

12. Journal How are line plots and stem-and-leaf diagrams alike? How are they different?

Mixed Review

Multiply. *[Previous course]*

13. 82 × 5 410 **14.** 6 × 68 408 **15.** 89 × 40 3560

16. 17 × 44 748 **17.** 130 × 62 8060 **18.** 42 × 556 23,352

19. 850 × 417 354,450 **20.** 526 × 421 221,446 **21.** 23 × 907 20,861

Round to the nearest thousand. *[Previous course]*

22. 9,489 9000 **23.** 100,687 101,000 **24.** 543 1000

25. 23,500 24,000 **26.** 187,555 188,000 **27.** 4,499 4000

28. 1,475,327 1,475,000 **29.** 499 0

30. 1,750 2000 **31.** 9,631 10,000

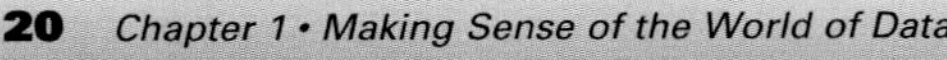

20 *Chapter 1 • Making Sense of the World of Data*

PROBLEM SOLVING

Name ______________________

Guided Problem Solving 1-3

GPS PROBLEM 10, STUDENT PAGE 20

The back-to-back stem-and-leaf diagram shows the average daily April temperatures for Boston, MA, and Portland, OR. Use the plot to compare the pattern of April temperatures in the two cities.

Boston, MA		Portland, OR
	7	1
2 2	6	0 0 0 1 1 1 1 2 3 3 4 5
9 8 7 7 7 5 3 3 1 1 1 0	5	2 5 5 5 6 6 6 7 8 9 9
8 8 8 7 4 4 2 2 0 0	4	2 2 3 4 4 5
6 6 4 4 3 3 0	3	

— Understand —

1. What do the digits in the stem represent? 7, 6, 5, 4, and 3 tens.

2. Which leaves, on the right or the left, show temperatures for each city?

a. Portland Right b. Boston Left

— Plan —

3. The lowest temperature for Boston was 30°. The highest temperature was 62°. For Portland, what was the

a. lowest temperature? 42° b. highest temperature? 71°

4. How many more days was the temperature in the 60s and 70s in Portland than in Boston? 11 days

— Solve —

5. Write a sentence comparing the temperature patterns for the two cities.
Portland's temperatures are higher in April than Boston's.

— Look Back —

6. How can you compare the pattern without comparing the actual temperatures?
Possible answer: There are more entries for the larger stems for Portland and more entries for the smaller stems for Boston indicating higher temperatures for Portland in April.

SOLVE ANOTHER PROBLEM

The back-to-back stem-and-leaf diagram shows the number of minutes two teams practice each day. What pattern do you notice?

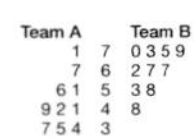

Team A		Team B
1	7	0 3 5 9
7	6	2 7 7
6 1	5	3 8
9 2 1	4	8
7 5 4	3	

Team B spent more time practicing than Team A.

ENRICHMENT

Name ______________________

Extend Your Thinking 1-3

Visual Thinking

Circle the letter of the figure in each row that is different from the others.

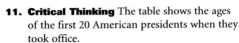

1.

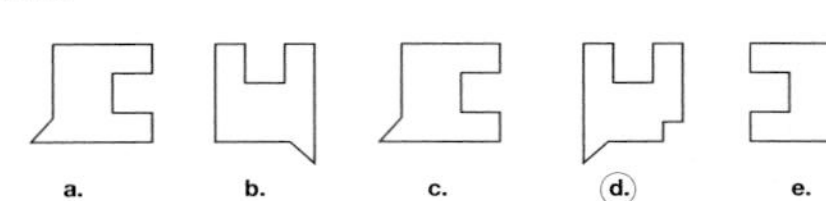

2.

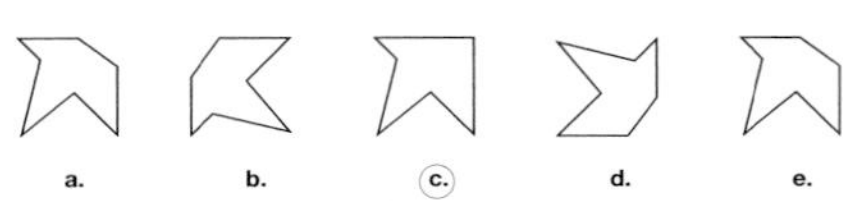

3.

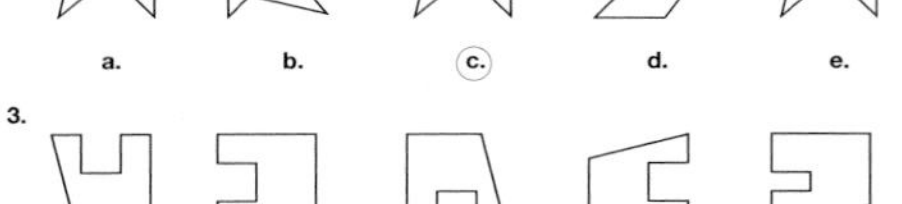

4.

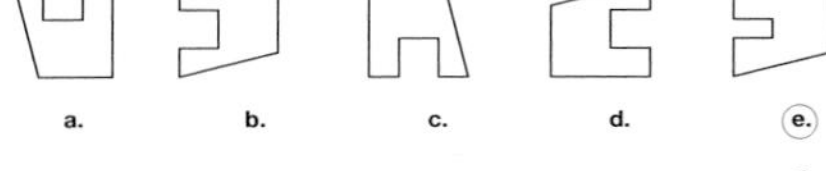

5.

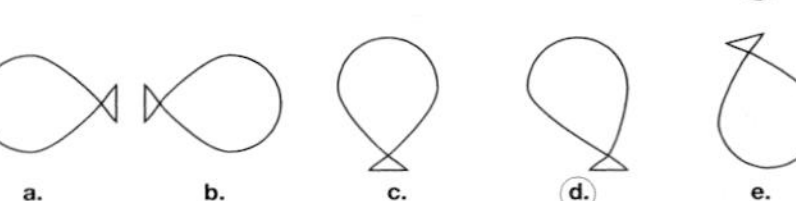

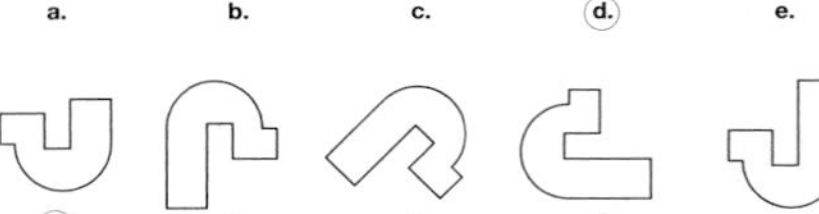

Mean, Median, Mode, and Range

1-4

▶ Lesson Link You have used different types of graphs to display all the values in a data set. Now you will learn to use a single number to describe a collection of data. ◀

You'll Learn ...

- to find the mean, median, mode, and range for a set of data
- to decide if the mean, median, or mode best summarizes a set of data

... How It's Used

When making decisions about planting crops, farmers need to consider the average temperature, rainfall, and yield.

Vocabulary

mean

median

mode

range

Explore Mean

Food for Thought

Materials: Graph paper, Scissors, Tape

As populations increase, more food is needed to feed the world's people. *Arable land* is land fit for raising crops.

Central American Arable Land (%)	
Country	**Amount**
Belize	2
Costa Rica	6
El Salvador	27
Guatemala	12
Honduras	14
Mexico	12
Nicaragua	9
Panama	6

1. Use graph paper to make a horizontal bar graph of the data. Make the graph big enough so that you can easily cut out the bars.
2. Cut out each bar and tape the narrow sides together to form one large bar. Be sure the bars do not overlap. Fold the large bar in half, then in half again, then in half one more time.
3. Unfold the large bar and count the number of sections. What does the number of sections represent? What does the length of the large bar represent?
4. Measure the length of a section. How is the length of a section related to the length of the large bar?
5. Explain how the length of a section summarizes the table.

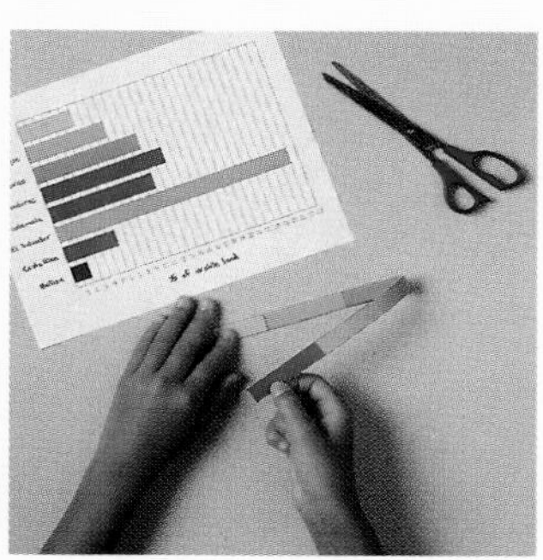

1-4 Lesson Organizer

Objectives

- Find the mean, median, mode, and range for a set of data.
- Decide if the mean, median, or mode best summarizes a set of data.

Vocabulary

- Mean, median, mode, range

Materials

- Explore: Graph paper, scissors, tape

NCTM Standards

- 1–5, 10

▶ Review

Order from least to greatest.

1. 15, 23, 4, 13, 19, 26, 22, 7
   4, 7, 13, 15, 19, 22, 23, 26
2. 189, 175, 198, 99, 125, 146
   99, 125, 146, 175, 189, 198
3. 3.45, 2.34, 4.78, 6.89, 4.36
   2.34, 3.45, 4.36, 4.78, 6.89

Available on Daily Transparency 1-4

MEETING INDIVIDUAL NEEDS

Resources

1-4 Practice

1-4 Reteaching

1-4 Problem Solving

1-4 Enrichment

1-4 Daily Transparency
- Problem of the Day
- Review
- Quick Quiz

Interactive CD-ROM Lesson

Learning Modalities

Visual Have an odd number of students arrange themselves in order of height from shortest to tallest. Identify students with heights that represent the median and the mode, if possible.

Kinesthetic Have students arrange an odd number of objects with different lengths from shortest to longest. Then have them identify the objects with lengths that represent the median and the mode.

Inclusion

Give students centimeter cubes and tell them to make groups of 5, 3, 10, 6, 4, 5, and 9 cubes. Have them arrange the groups from least to greatest and identify the middle number, or median, and the number that occurs most often, the mode. 5, 5 Ask how many groups there are. 7 Tell them to reorganize the groups into 7 groups of the same size, and ask how many are in each group. 6 Tell them that this is the mean, or average, number of cubes. Add new vocabulary to reference book.

1 Introduce

Explore

The Point
Students use a concrete model to gain an intuitive understanding of mean.

Ongoing Assessment
Be sure that students realize that the 8 sections are equal parts of the whole.

For Groups That Finish Early
Describe the result if the amount of arable land in every country had been 11%. The average would be 11%.

Answers for Explore on next page.

Answers for Explore

1.

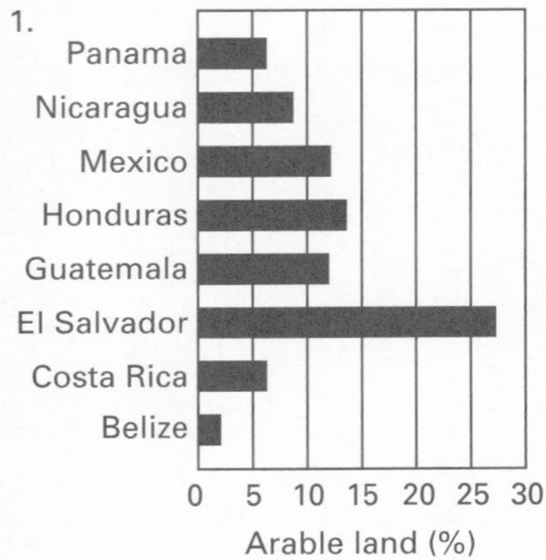

2–3. The number of data values; The sum of the data values.

4. It is $\frac{1}{8}$ the total length.

5. A section represents the average percent (the percent for each country if the percents were equally distributed among the countries).

2 Teach

Learn

Alternate Examples

1. Find the mean, median, and range of these data values: 62, 78, 55, 87, 68.

Mean

Divide the sum by the number of values.

$\frac{62 + 78 + 55 + 87 + 68}{5} = 70$

The mean is 70.

Median

Arrange the values in order.

55, 62, <u>68</u>, 78, 87

The middle data value is 68.

The median is 68.

Range

Subtract the lowest data value from the highest.

$87 - 55 = 32$

The range is 32.

Learn Mean, Median, Mode, and Range

Four numbers are commonly used to summarize a collection of data. Each has its own purpose.

DID YOU KNOW?

When people talk about the *average,* they are usually referring to the mean.

The **mean** is the *average* of a set of data. We find the mean by dividing the sum of the data values by the number of data values.

The **median** is the *middle* data value when the values are arranged in order. If there is no single middle value, the median is the mean of the two middle values.

The **mode** is the *most common* data value. If no value occurs more than once, there is no mode. If two or more values occur more than once and equally, there are two or more modes.

The **range** is the difference between the highest and lowest data values.

Example 1

Find the mean, median, and range of the data values.

36, 8, 3, 13, 75

Mean

$\frac{36 + 8 + 3 + 13 + 75}{5} = 27$ Divide the sum by the number of values.

The mean is 27.

Median

3, 8, $\boxed{13}$, 36, 75 Put the values in order.

↑

The middle data value is 13.

The median is 13.

Range

$75 - 3 = 72$ Subtract the lowest data value from the highest.

The range is 72.

Language Link

Sometimes, people talk about the range of a data set as "from (the lowest number) to (the highest number)." The range of this data set can be described as "from 3 to 75."

Try It

Find the mean, median, and range of the data values.

a. 28, 14, 59, 41, 50 **b.** 54, 45, 28, 36, 90, 23

a. Mean 38.4, median 41, range 45
b. Mean 46, median 40.5, range 67

MATH EVERY DAY

Problem of the Day

Jermaine has two coins that have a value of 6 cents. One coin is not a penny. What are the two coins? A penny and a nickel: although one coin is *not a* penny, the *other* is.

Available on Daily Transparency 1-4

An Extension is provided in the transparency package

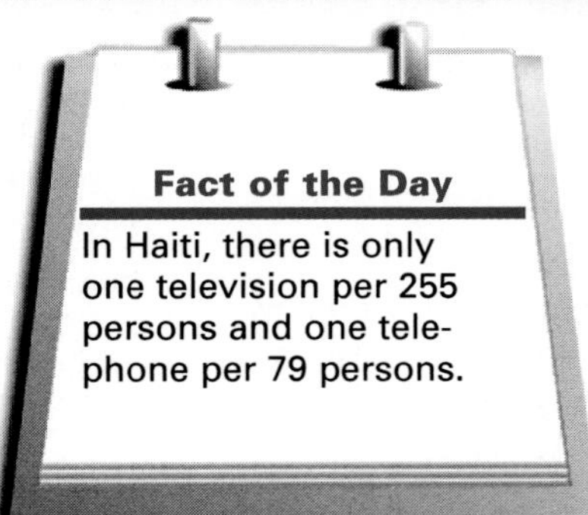

Fact of the Day
In Haiti, there is only one television per 255 persons and one telephone per 79 persons.

Mental Math

Find mentally the number that is the mean of the two numbers.

1. 10 and 12 11
2. 30 and 40 35
3. 200 and 400 300
4. 36 and 46 41

The mean is the number used most often to summarize data. But when there are outliers, the median often gives a better summary than the mean. The mode can be used to summarize a few data values when most are the same.

Example 2

Find the mean, median, and mode of the data on life expectancies in the six Caribbean countries and decide which gives the best summary of the data.

Life Expectancy in Caribbean Countries

Country	Cuba	Puerto Rico	Jamaica	Trinidad and Tobago	Dominican Republic	Haiti
Life Expectancy (yr)	77	75	75	70	69	45

Mean

$\frac{77 + 75 + 75 + 70 + 69 + 45}{6}$ Add the data values.

$= \frac{411}{6} = 68.5$ Divide by the number of data values.

The mean is 68.5 years.

Median The median is the mean of 70 and 75.

$\frac{70 + 75}{2}$ Add the two middle values.

45 69 **70** **75** 75 77

$= \frac{145}{2} = 72.5$ Divide by the number of middle values.

The median is 72.5 years.

Mode A life expectancy of 75 years appears twice. The mode is 75 years.

The *mean* (68.5) was influenced by Haiti (an outlier), so it is smaller than five of the six data values. The *mode* (75) is near the high end of the data. The best summary of the data is the *median* (72.5).

Iceland has the highest life expectancy, 79 years. The United States life expectancy is 76 years.

Test Prep

Sometimes a list of data that are all whole numbers has a mean and/or a median that are fractions or decimals.

Check Your Understanding

1. Why would you want to know the mean, median, or mode of a data set?
2. How does an outlier affect the mean, median, and mode?

MEETING MIDDLE SCHOOL CLASSROOM NEEDS

Tips from Middle School Teachers

Now that the students have studied mean, median, and mode, I have them decide which measure they would like me to use when looking at their test scores and figuring mid-term grades. We have some very spirited and interesting discussions.

Social Studies Connection

The Dominican Republic and Haiti are both on the island of Hispaniola in the Caribbean. On his second voyage across the Atlantic in 1493, Columbus brought Spanish explorers to the lands he reached. They founded a settlement on Hispaniola, thus beginning the conquest of America by Europeans, and laying the basis for the countries that we now know as Latin America. The area of the Caribbean Basin has 41 nations and dependent territories and has a population of more than 192 million people.

Team Teaching

With a social studies teacher, have a project comparing life expectancy for a certain age in the U.S. with that in Japan, in Kenya, or in other countries.

Alternate Examples

2. The heights in inches of six students in Mrs. Renfro's class are 58, 60, 62, 64, 65, and 66. Find the mean, median, and mode of the six heights. Which gives the best summary of the data?

Mean

$\frac{58 + 60 + 62 + 64 + 65 + 66}{6}$

$= \frac{375}{6}$

$= 62.5$

The mean is 62.5.

Median

58, 60, 62, 64, 65, 66

The median is the mean of 62 and 64.

$\frac{62 + 64}{2} = \frac{126}{2} = 63$

The median is 63.

Mode

No height appears more than once, so there is no mode.

The mean of the heights is 62.5 in., and the median is 63 in. Since the mean and median are very close and there are no outliers, either of these measures could give a good summary of the data.

3 Practice and Assess

Check

Have students describe how they would find the mean, median, and mode for a set of data. Then ask them to describe situations in which each measure is most appropriate.

Answers for Check Your Understanding

1. You might be more interested in a typical number to represent the group than in individual data values.
2. The presence of an outlier generally does not affect either the median or the mode. An outlier that is much greater than the other data values will cause the mean to be too high to accurately represent the data. An outlier that is much smaller than the other data will cause the mean to be too low.

Assignment Guide

- **Basic**
  1–3, 5, 9, 12, 13–23 odds
- **Average**
  1–12, 13–23 odds
- **Enriched**
  2–10 evens, 11–15, 16–22 evens

Exercise Answers

1. a. 5, 6, 17, 19, 23, 26, 34; Median: 19.
   b. 27, 38, 39, 45, 47, 48, 49, 52; Median: 46.
2. 1, 2, or 3 times; Mode: 4.
3. a. Mean: about 59.7; median: 59.5; range: 7; mode: 59;
   b. Since the mean, median, and mode are very close, any one would be an appropriate summary.
4. a. 9
   b. 747
   c. average: 83.
5. Mean: about 320.1; Median: 321.5; Modes: 320, 327; Range: 202.
6. The mode is 4, which is the least data value; because of the outlier 33, there are only 3 values greater than the mean which is about 10.7; the best choice is the median, 9.

Reteaching

Activity

Materials: Centimeter cubes

- Use cubes to represent this set of numbers as a bar graph: 5, 8, 7, 3, 5, 6, 1. Arrange the bars in order from least to greatest.
- What is the median? 5 How can you tell? It is in the middle. What is the range? 7 How did you find it? The greatest number is 8 and the least number is 1; $8 - 1 = 7$. What is the mode, or the number that occurs most often? 5
- Make 7 equal-length bars with these blocks. How many blocks are in each bar? 5 This number is the mean, or the average, number of blocks.

1-4 Exercises and Applications

PRACTICE 1-4

Practice and Apply

1. **Getting Started** Order each data set from the lowest to highest. Then find the median for each set.
   a. 5, 17, 6, 23, 34, 26, 19   **b.** 48, 39, 27, 52, 45, 47, 49, 38
2. Look at this set of data: 2, 5, 8, 4, 3, 7, 5, 4, 6, 4, 8. How often does each value appear? Find the mode(s) for the data set.
3. The table shows the heights of the students in Ms. McPherson's class.

Height (in.)	57	58	59	60	61	62	63	64
Number of Students	2	5	8	7	4	2	0	2

   a. Find the mean, median, range, and mode.
   b. Which of these measures best summarizes the class?
4. Mei Li scored 85, 78, 65, 77, 91, 88, 80, 93, and 90 points on her math tests.
   a. How many tests did she take?
   b. How many points did she score all together?
   c. What was her average (mean) score?
5. **Sports** In the 1994 season, American Football Conference football teams allowed 234, 204, 352, 327, 298, 306, 406, 356, 312, 327, 320, 320, 323, and 396 points to be scored against their teams. What was the mean number of points allowed? The median? The mode(s)? The range?
6. **Number Sense** Decide if the mean, median, or mode is the best summary of the data set 10, 4, 11, 33, 6, 12, 9, 4, 7. Explain.
7. **Social Studies** To answer the questions, use the table showing the 1993 populations of the 13 states that formed the original colonies.
   a. Find the mean population of these 13 states.
   b. Would the mean be a good number to summarize these populations? Explain.

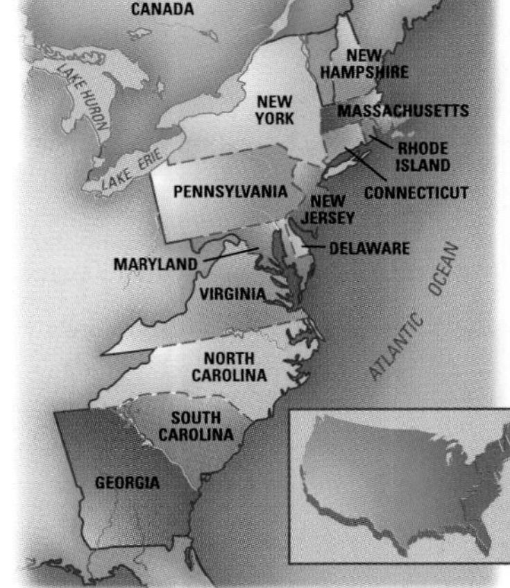

State	NH	MA	RI	CT	NY	NJ	PA	DE	MD	VA	NC	SC	GA
Population (100,000s)	11	60	10	33	181	78	120	7	49	63	67	36	66

PRACTICE

Name ____________

Practice 1-4

Mean, Median, Mode, and Range

Find the mean, median, mode(s), and range for each set of data.

1. 14, 16, 23, 18, 16, 16, 18, 21
   mean 17.75
   median 17
   mode(s) 16
   range 9
2. 3, 6, 12, 7, 9, 14, 8, 10
   mean 8.625
   median 8.5
   mode(s) None
   range 11
3. 13, 12, 11, 12, 13, 11, 12, 11, 13, 12
   mean 12
   median 12
   mode(s) 12
   range 2
4. 3, 0, 15, 11, 7, 6, 14, 7, 9
   mean 8
   median 7
   mode(s) 7
   range 15
5. **Social Science** The table shows the number of congressional representatives for each of the 50 states.

Number of reps.	1	2	3	4	5	6	7	8	9	10	11	12	13	16	19	20	21	23	30	31	52
Number of states	7	6	4	2	3	6	2	2	4	2	2	1	1	1	1	1	1	1	1	1	1

   a. Find the mean, median, and mode(s) for the number of representatives in a state.
   mean 8.7   median 6   mode(s) 1
   b. Which of these measures best summarizes the data set? Explain.
   Mean or median; Explanations will vary
   c. After the next census, the number of representatives in most states will change, but the total number will stay the same. Assuming that there are 50 states, do you expect the mean number of representatives per state to change? Explain.
   No, the mean will still be $\frac{435}{50} = 8.7$.

RETEACHING

Name ____________

Alternative Lesson 1-4

Mean, Median, Mode, and Range

The data at the right, showing the ages of students in a Tai Chi class, are listed in order and can be summarized in four ways.

23, 47, 47, 55, 57, 62

Example 1

Find the **mean**.

The mean is the *average* of a set of data. Find the mean by dividing the sum of the data values by the number of data values.

$23 + 47 + 47 + 55 + 57 + 62 = 291$
$291 \div 6 = 48.5$

The mean is 48.5.

Example 2

Find the **median**.

The median is the *middle* data value when the values are arranged in order. If there is no single middle value, the median is the mean of the two middle values.

23 47 47 55 57 62
51 ← Median

The median is 51 because $47 + 55 = 102$ and $102 \div 2 = 51$.

Example 3

Find the **mode**.

The mode is the *most common* data value. If no value occurs more than once, there is no mode.

23 (47) (47) 55 57 62
Mode

Since 47 occurs twice, the mode is 47.

Example 4

Find the **range**.

The range is the difference between the highest and lowest data values: $62 - 23 = 39$.

23 47 47 55 57 62
Lowest value   Highest value

The range is 39.

Try It Use the data at the right showing the number of yards a team gained by passing the football.

61, 68, 70, 70, 73, 76, 79, 87

Find the

a. mean. 73   **b.** median. 71.5
c. mode. 70   **d.** range. 26

8. **Number Sense** Use the line plot. Estimate the mean.

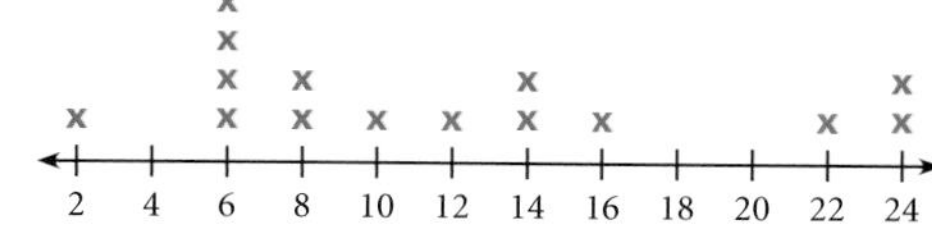

9. Find the mean, median, and mode of the data.

10. What is the median score represented by the stem-and-leaf diagram?

Stem	Leaf
4	4 5 7 8 9 9
3	0 2 5 5 8
2	3 7 7 7

11. **Test Prep** Look at this set of data: 16, 24, 17, 18, 16, 22, 23, 18, 18. The number 18 is:

Ⓐ the mean only.
Ⓑ the mean and median only.
Ⓒ the median and mode only.
Ⓓ the mean, median, and mode.

Problem Solving and Reasoning

12. **Choose a Strategy** Six piglets in a litter had an average or mean weight of 8 lb. Find two possibilities for the weight of each pig.

13. **Communicate** You can always find the mean and median for a set of data, but sometimes you may not be able to find the mode. Why?

14. **Critical Thinking** Carlotta was being interviewed for a job. She was told that the median salary at the company was $43,000. Should Carlotta expect to receive that salary? Explain.

15. **Critical Thinking** The average population density of Alaska is 0.99 people per square mile. Explain this statement.

Problem Solving STRATEGIES

- Look for a Pattern
- Make an Organized List
- Make a Table
- Guess and Check
- Work Backward
- Use Logical Reasoning
- Draw a Diagram
- Solve a Simpler Problem

PROBLEM SOLVING 1-4

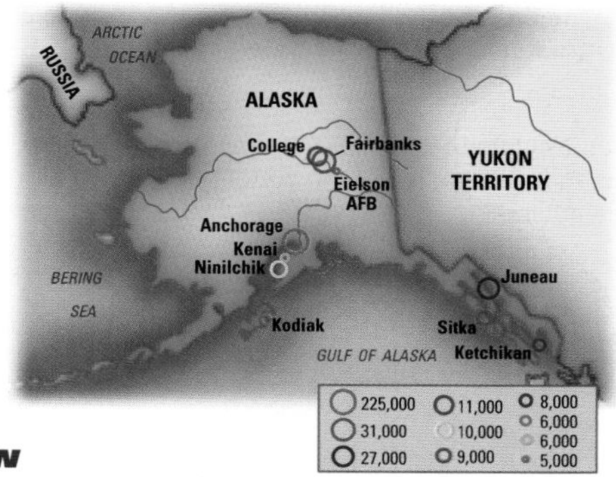

Mixed Review

Divide. *[Previous course]*

16. 56 ÷ 8 **7**
17. 47 ÷ 5 **9 R2**
18. 567 ÷ 9 **63**
19. 682 ÷ 7 **97 R3**
20. 588 ÷ 34 **17 R10**

Order from least to greatest. *[Previous course]*

21. 7,286 6,999 8,003
22. 13,145 13,201 12,895
23. 288 8,822 8,282 28 8,882 82 2,228

PROBLEM SOLVING

Name ______

Guided Problem Solving 1-4

GPS PROBLEM 12, STUDENT PAGE 25

Six piglets in a litter had an average weight of 8 lb. Find two possibilities for the weight of each pig.

— Understand —

1. What is another term for "average weight"? Mean weight.
2. Which range do you think the piglets weight should fall within? b
   a. 0–8 pounds b. 3–13 pounds c. 8–16 pounds

— Plan —

3. An average weight of 8 pounds for the six piglet means that: b
   a. Each piglet weighs 8 pounds.
   b. The total weight of the piglets can be found by multiplying 6 and 8.
4. How much do the six piglets weigh in all? 48 lb

— Solve —

5. Find a set of reasonable weights whose sum is equal to your answer in Item 4.
   Any six numbers that total 48.
6. Find another set of reasonable weights whose sum is equal to your answer in Item 4.
   Any six numbers that total 48.

— Look Back —

7. How can you check to see if your answer is reasonable?
   Add the weights. Divide by 6. The average weight should be 8 lb.

SOLVE ANOTHER PROBLEM

Seven golden retriever puppies had an average weight of 12 lb. Find two possibilities for the weight of each dog.
Any seven numbers that total 84.

ENRICHMENT

Name ______

Extend Your Thinking 1-4

Critical Thinking

Dunston Data Company's ten employees made the following salaries during the past year.

$17,000, $17,000, $25,000, $25,000, $25,000, $27,000, $32,000, $32,000, $83,000, $102,000

1. For the salaries listed above, find each of the following.
   a. mean $38,500 b. median $26,000
   c. mode $25,000 d. range $85,000
2. How should the company's advertisement for new employees describe salaries? Should it use the mean, median, mode, or range?
   Possible answer: mean, because it is the highest salary and would appear more attractive to prospective employees.
3. Suppose a newspaper article states that $38,500 is the "average" salary of Dunston employees. Would the article be accurate? Could it be misleading? How?
   It is accurate. However, it could be misleading because it implies that most employees make about $38,500.
4. Recently, CompuData Corporation claimed that Dunston's employees are overpaid for the work they perform. In an article defending against such claims, which number would most likely be used? Explain.
   Possible answer: mode, because it is the lowest salary and it would appear that workers are not overpaid.
5. If you worked for the Dunston Data Company, which number would you use to describe the typical earnings of its employees? Explain.
   Possible answers: mode, because more employees earn $25,000 than any other salary; median, because half the salaries are greater and half are lower.

Exercise Notes

Exercise 10

Error Prevention Remind students to include numbers that appear more than once and not to omit the stem digits.

Exercise 15

Social Studies While the population density of Alaska is the least in the U.S., New Jersey's is the highest, with over 1000 people per square mile.

Exercise Answers

7. a. about 6,008,000 people
   b. No, the range is very large, so several data values are very far from the mean. Median might be better.
8. Answers will vary.
9. Mean: about 11.87; Median: 10; Mode: 6.
10. 35
11. C
12. Possible answer: Each piglet weighed 8 lb; three piglets weighed 6 lb each and three weighed 10 lb each.
13. Some sets of data have no repeated values, so there is no mode.
14. No; the median salary is the middle level. If Carlotta is just starting out with the company, her salary probably will be lower.
15. Possible answer: If you divide the total population by the total of square miles, the quotient is 0.99, or about 1 person per square mile.

Alternate Assessment

Interview Ask each student to give examples of three real-life situations in which they would use the mean, median, or mode to summarize a set of data. Have them explain why they would use that measure in the particular situation.

Quick Quiz

Find the mean, median, mode, and range for each set of data.

1. 3, 5, 7, 10, 8, 2, 7 Mean: 6; Median: 7; Mode: 7, Range: 8
2. 14, 21, 12, 18, 15, 17, 15, 16 Mean: 16; Median: 15.5; Mode: 15; Range: 9

Available on Daily Transparency 1-4

Technology

Using a Data Analysis Package • Box-and-Whisker Plots

The Point

Students use technology to create box-and-whisker plots that will help them analyze data.

Materials

Data analysis software or a graphing calculator

Resources

Interactive CD-ROM Spreadsheet/Grapher Tool

Teaching Tool Transparency 23: Graphing Calculator TI-82

About the Page

- The viewing window is important when using a graphing calculator. The Xmin must be less than the minimum value, and Xmax must be greater than the maximum value. The y-axis must have some depth in order for the box plot to be displayed.
- Use the TRACE feature to see the minimum and maximum values, and the median (at the vertical line in the box).

Ask ...

- How do you enter a list of data values into your graphing calculator? Answers may vary.
- How do you access the box plot capability of your graphing calculator? Answers may vary.
- What is an outlier? A data value that seems to lie excessively far from either side of the box, relative to the width of the box.

On Your Own

The response to Question 2 depends upon one's interpretation of the box. A fairly narrow box would indicate that minimum and maximum values likely are outliers. A relatively wide box would indicate that the data is more evenly scattered, and that the extreme values likely are not outliers.

TECHNOLOGY

Using a Data Analysis Package • Box-and-Whisker Plots

Problem: During the first seven days of the school year, a store sold 8, 12, 23, 5, 8, 15, and 3 calculators and 8, 8, 7, 10, 15, 9, and 2 computers. Construct a box-and-whisker plot for each data set. Which set is more "spread out"? Which points seem to be outliers?

You can use a data analysis package to help answer these questions. Data analysis packages are part of statistics programs and are featured on graphing calculators.

1 Enter each data set. If you use a graphing calculator, enter each set as a list. With a data analysis package, enter each data set in a column.

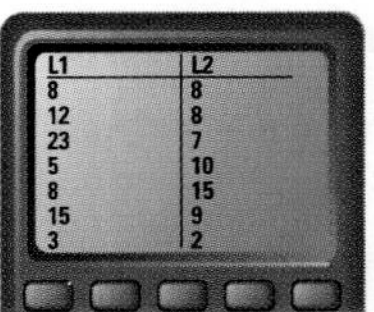

2 On your graphing calculator, select your statistics plotting menu. For your first plot, graph L1 as a box plot; for your second, graph L2 as a box plot. If you are using a data analysis package, select the box plot icon.

3 Interpret your box plots. The line in the middle of the box shows the median of the data. The ends of the box are *quartiles*—the medians of the lower and upper half of the data. The ends of the whiskers show the least and greatest values in the data set.

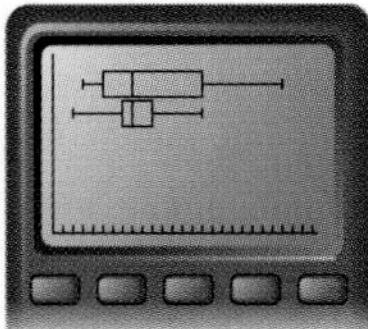

Solution: In step 3, the top box plot (calculators) appears to be more spread out. In the top plot, 23 seems to be an outlier. In the bottom plot, both 2 and 15 computers seem to be outliers.

TRY IT

Construct a box-and-whisker plot and answer the questions in the problem for the following data sets:

a. 33, 38, 43, 30, 29, 40, 51, 27, 42, 23, 31

b. 11, 14, 18, 5, 16, 8, 19, 10, 17, 20, 34

ON YOUR OWN

- How does a graphing calculator or data analysis package make it easier to interpret data?
- What would a box with extremely long whiskers tell you about a data set?
- Suppose two data sets have the same median and equally long whiskers. If the box of one box plot is longer, what can you say about the two data sets?

Answers for Try It

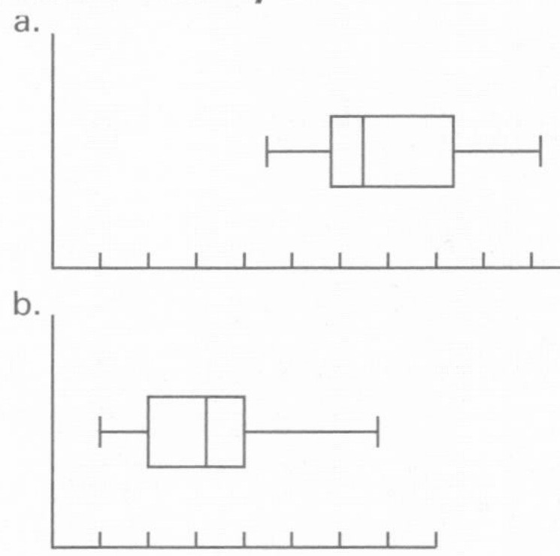

Answers for On Your Own

1. They can graph and analyze data quickly.
2. There are values that are far from the bulk of the data; these are probably outliers.
3. The data set with the longer box probably has more evenly spaced data.

Section 1A Connect

You saw at the beginning of this section that geography is used to help people make better sense of the world. Now you will have a chance to make decisions about displaying and summarizing geographic data.

A World of Geography

Materials: Art supplies for creating a display

1. Study the table. What relationships among data values do you see? When you have discovered something in the data that might help others make better sense of the world, write a sentence or two describing your discovery.

Country	People (per mi^2)	Annual Population Increase (%)	Life Expectancy at Birth (yr)	Annual Income per Inhabitant ($)	Percent Living in Cities
Belgium	854	0.2	76	15,440	95
Brazil	48	1.9	65	2,680	74
Egypt	151	2.4	60	600	45
Guinea	86	2.5	42	480	22
Haiti	636	2.9	45	370	29
Nepal	383	2.5	50	170	8
Poland	320	0.4	71	1,700	61
Singapore	14,206	1.4	75	12,310	100
S. Africa	93	2.6	64	2,520	56
S. Korea	1,190	1.1	71	5,400	74

2. Create two different types of graphs or plots that help communicate relationships that you have noticed among data values.

3. Calculate the mean, median, and mode for each of your two data collections. Decide which summaries of the data will help others better understand what you are showing. Explain.

27

A World of Geography

The Point

In *A World of Geography* on page 5, students discussed how mathematics can be used to describe data in many ways. Now they will determine how to display and summarize data about various countries in the most effective way.

Materials

Art supplies for creating a display

About the Page

- Review the types of graphs or plots that students might use to display data.
- Suggest that students select two columns of data that interest them and graph or plot the data.
- Have students compare, contrast, and analyze the information. Then suggest they summarize and draw conclusions about the relationships they discover.
- Students can use colored paper and other art supplies to make creative displays of the data.

Ongoing Assessment

Check that students accurately display a specific relationship among the chosen data.

Extension

Using the information in the table have students make one or more comparisons, different from that in Question 2, such as comparing (1) life expectancy at birth with annual income per inhabitant, (2) life expectancy with population increase, or (3) density of population with annual income. After students make the comparison, ask them to draw conclusions about the standards of living in the countries they compared.

Answers for Connect

1. Possible relationships include: The higher the percent living in cities, the higher the income tends to be; The higher the life expectancy, the less the population increase.
2. Answers may vary.
3. People per mi^2: Mean 1796.7; Median 351.5; No mode.

   Annual population increase: Mean 1.79%; Median 2.15%; Mode 2.5%.

   Life expectancy: Mean 61.9 yr; Median 64.5 yr; Mode 71 yr.

   Annual income: Mean $4167; Median $2110; No mode.

   Percent living in cities: Mean 56.4%; Median 58.8%; Mode 74%.

1A Review

Review Correlation

Item(s)	Lesson(s)
1, 2	1-1
3	1-3
4	1-4
5	1-3
6	1-2
7	1-1
8–10	1-4

Test Prep

Test Taking Tip

Tell students that sometimes they can substitute similar numbers to help them solve a problem. Here, $\frac{(26 + 26 + 26 + 26 + 26)}{5} = 26$, so they can find the sum of 26 + 26 + 26 + 26 + 26 or multiply 26 × 5.

Answers for Review

5.

Stem	Leaf
3	1 2 2 2 2 3 4 4 6 6 7 8 9
2	3 3 3 6 6 7 7 8 8 9 9 9
1	9

6.

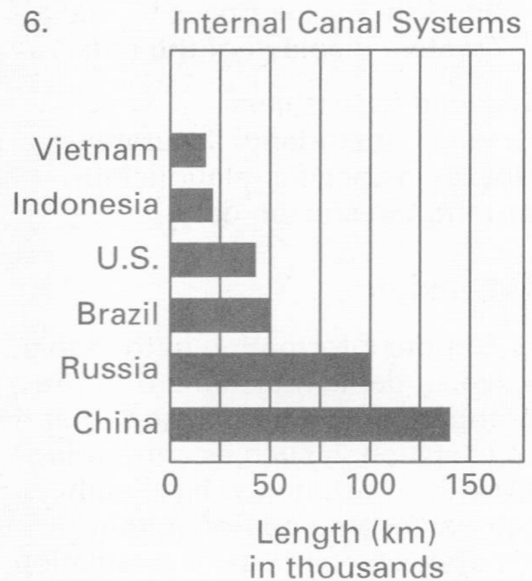

Section 1A Review

REVIEW 1A

Use the graphs for Exercises 1 and 2.

Canadian Labor Force (1996)

% of labor force: 100, 50, 0; Services, Manufacturing, Unemployment, Other

Canadian Labor Force (1996)

Unemployment, Other, Manufacturing, Services

1. About what percent of the labor force in Canada is not employed in services? 25%

2. Which graph best shows the fraction of people in manufacturing? Circle graph

The line plot shows temperatures in several U.S. cities. Use it for Exercises 3–5.

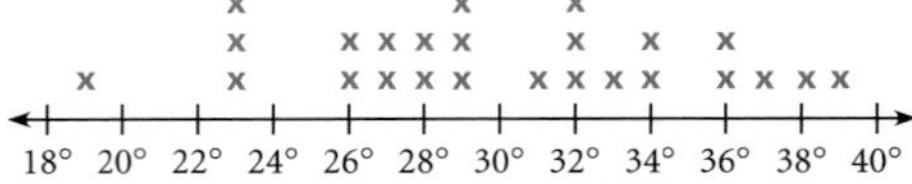

18° 20° 22° 24° 26° 28° 30° 32° 34° 36° 38° 40°

Average December Temperatures in Some U.S. Cities

3. Are any outliers shown? Yes

4. Find the median and mode for the temperatures shown. Median 30°, mode 32°

5. Make a stem-and-leaf diagram of this data.

Geography **Use the table for Exercises 6–9.**

6. Make a horizontal bar graph to show the data.

7. Which country has the longest canal system? China

8. Find the mean length of the canals in the table. 61,534.8 km

9.  If France's 15,000-km canal system is included, how will it affect the answer to Exercise 8? It would lower the mean to 54,887 km.

Internal Canal Systems

Country	Length (km)
China	138,600
Russia	100,000
Brazil	50,000
United States	41,009
Indonesia	21,600
Vietnam	18,000

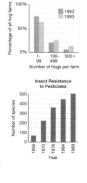

Test Prep

On a multiple-choice test, if you are given the mean for a number of unlisted data values, and asked to find the total of the data values, multiply the mean by the number of items.

10. A set of five data values has a mean of 26. What is the total of the data values? C

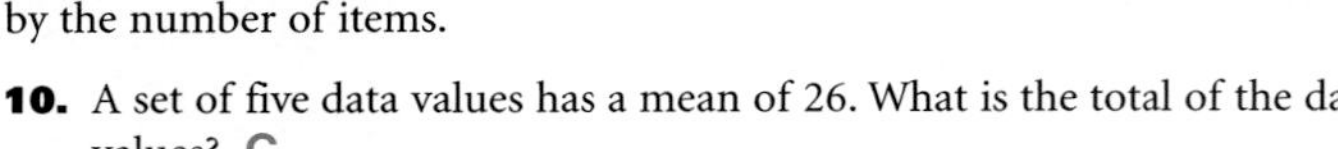

Ⓐ 26 Ⓑ 31 Ⓒ 130 Ⓓ 265

Resources

Practice Masters
Section 1A Review

Assessment Sourcebook
Quiz 1A

 *TestWorks*
Test and Practice Software

PRACTICE

Name

Practice

Section 1A Review

The line plot shows the number of students in classes at Pike Elementary School. Use it for Exercises 1–3.

27 28 29 30 31 32 33

1. Name the outliers, if any. None

2. Find the mean, median, and mode(s) for the data.

mean 30 median 30 mode(s) 30, 31

3. Make a stem-and-leaf diagram of the data.

stem	leaf
2	78899
3	0000111123

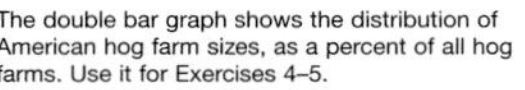

The double bar graph shows the distribution of American hog farm sizes, as a percent of all hog farms. Use it for Exercises 4–5.

Size of Hog Farms (1983, 1993; Percentage of all hog farms: 0%, 50%, 100%; Number of hogs per farm: 1-99, 100-499, 500+)

4. Would you say the average hog farm in 1993 was larger, smaller, or about the same size as the average hog farm in 1983? Larger

5. How could circle graphs be used to display this information? Make one circle graph for 1983, and another circle graph for 1993.

6. **Science** As more pesticides are used, they become less effective because insects become resistant to them. The table shows the number of insect species that were resistant to pesticides from 1956 to 1989. Make a vertical bar graph to show the data.

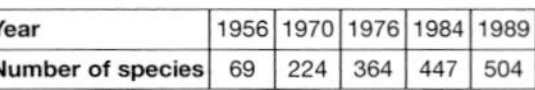

Year	1956	1970	1976	1984	1989
Number of species	69	224	364	447	504

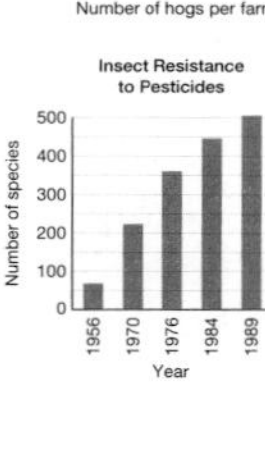

7. **Geography** The summit of Mt. Whitney in California is 14,494 ft above sea level. A mountain climber is at a height of 11,677 ft above sea level. How much higher does the climber need to go in order to reach the summit of Mt. Whitney? *[Previous Course]* 2,817 ft

Section 1B

Trends and Relationships in Data

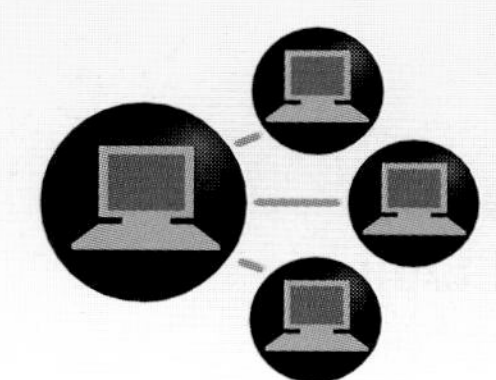

Visit www.teacher.mathsurf.com for links to lesson plans from teachers and other professionals, NCTM information, and other sites.

LESSON PLANNING GUIDE

Student Edition				Ancillaries*	
LESSON		MATERIALS	VOCABULARY	DAILY	OTHER
	Section 1B Opener				
1-5	**Line Graphs**	graphing utility	line graph, trend, double-line graph	1-5	Teaching Tool Trans. 7 Lesson Enhancement Trans. 7 Technology Master 3 *WW Math*—Algebra *Interactive CD-ROM Spreadsheet/Grapher Tool*
1-6	**Scatterplots and Relationships**		scatterplot, positive relationship, negative relationship, no relationship	1-6	Teaching Tool Trans. 7 Lesson Enhancement Trans. 8 Ch. 1 Project Master Technology Master 4
1-7	**Trend Lines**		trend line	1-7	Teaching Tool Trans. 7 Technology Master 5
	Connect				Teaching Tool Trans. 7 Interdisc. Team Teaching 1B
	Review				Practice 1B; Quiz 1B; *TestWorks*
	Extend Key Ideas				
	Chapter 1 Summary and Review				
	Chapter 1 Assessment				Ch. 1 Tests Forms A–F *TestWorks*; Ch. 1 Letter Home
	Cumulative Review Chapter 1	set of four number cubes			Cumulative Review Ch. 1

* Daily Ancillaries include Practice, Reteaching, Problem Solving, Enrichment, and Daily Transparency. Teaching Tool Transparencies are in *Teacher's Toolkits.* Lesson Enhancement Transparencies are in *Overhead Transparency Package.*

SKILLS TRACE

LESSON	SKILL	FIRST INTRODUCED			DEVELOP	PRACTICE/ APPLY	REVIEW
		GR. 5	GR. 6	GR. 7			
1-5	**Reading and interpreting line graphs.**	✘			pp. 30–32	pp. 33–34	pp. 49, 59, 114, 200
1-6	**Making scatterplots.**	✘			pp. 35–37	pp. 38–39	pp. 49, 64, 119, 152, 243
1-7	**Constructing trend lines.**	✘	✘		pp. 40–42	pp. 43–44	pp. 49, 70, 247

CONNECTED MATHEMATICS

The unit *Variables and Patterns (Introducing Algebra),* from the **Connected Mathematics** series, can be used with Section 1B.

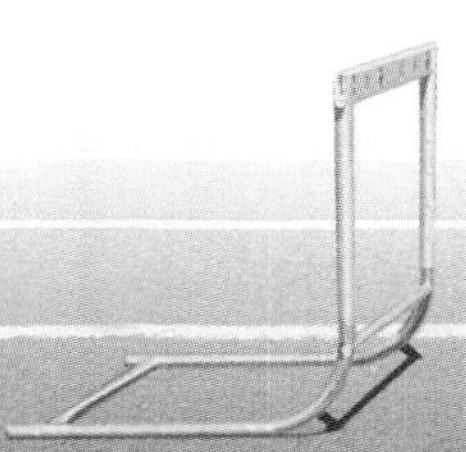

INTERDISCIPLINARY TEAM TEACHING

Math and Social Studies

(Worksheet pages 3–4: Teacher pages T3–T4)

In this lesson, students use trend lines with Olympic data.

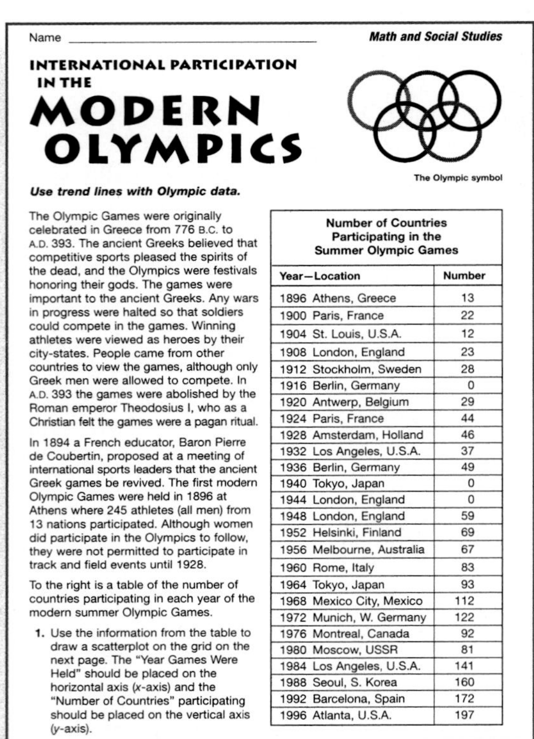

Name ____________________ ***Math and Social Studies***

INTERNATIONAL PARTICIPATION IN THE

MODERN OLYMPICS

The Olympic symbol

Use trend lines with Olympic data.

The Olympic Games were originally celebrated in Greece from 776 B.C. to A.D. 393. The ancient Greeks believed that competitive sports pleased the spirits of the dead, and the Olympics were festivals honoring their gods. The games were important to the ancient Greeks. Any wars in progress were halted so that soldiers could compete in the games. Winning athletes were viewed as heroes by their city-states. People came from other countries to view the games, although only Greek men were allowed to compete. In A.D. 393 the games were abolished by the Roman emperor Theodosius I, who as a Christian felt the games were a pagan ritual.

In 1894 a French educator, Baron Pierre de Coubertin, proposed at a meeting of international sports leaders that the ancient Greek games be revived. The first modern Olympic Games were held in 1896 at Athens where 245 athletes (all men) from 13 nations participated. Although women did participate in the Olympics to follow, they were not permitted to participate in track and field events until 1928.

To the right is a table of the number of countries participating in each year of the modern summer Olympic Games.

Number of Countries Participating in the Summer Olympic Games

Year—Location	Number
1896 Athens, Greece	13
1900 Paris, France	22
1904 St. Louis, U.S.A.	12
1908 London, England	23
1912 Stockholm, Sweden	28
1916 Berlin, Germany	0
1920 Antwerp, Belgium	29
1924 Paris, France	44
1928 Amsterdam, Holland	46
1932 Los Angeles, U.S.A.	37
1936 Berlin, Germany	49
1940 Tokyo, Japan	0
1944 London, England	0
1948 London, England	59
1952 Helsinki, Finland	69
1956 Melbourne, Australia	67
1960 Rome, Italy	83
1964 Tokyo, Japan	93
1968 Mexico City, Mexico	112
1972 Munich, W. Germany	122
1976 Montreal, Canada	92
1980 Moscow, USSR	81
1984 Los Angeles, U.S.A.	141
1988 Seoul, S. Korea	160
1992 Barcelona, Spain	172
1996 Atlanta, U.S.A.	197

1. Use the information from the table to draw a scatterplot on the grid on the next page. The "Year Games Were Held" should be placed on the horizontal axis (x-axis) and the "Number of Countries" participating should be placed on the vertical axis (y-axis).

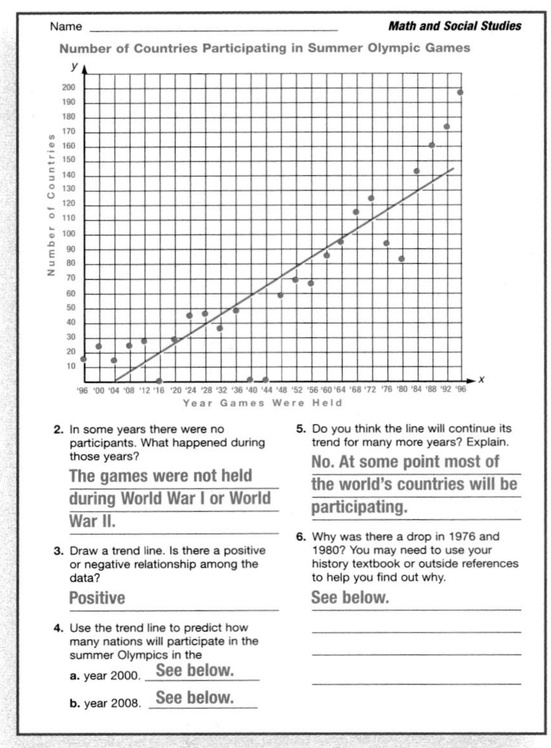

Name ____________________ ***Math and Social Studies***

Number of Countries Participating in Summer Olympic Games

2. In some years there were no participants. What happened during those years?
   The games were not held during World War I or World War II.
3. Draw a trend line. Is there a positive or negative relationship among the data?
   Positive
4. Use the trend line to predict how many nations will participate in the summer Olympics in the
   a. year 2000. **See below.**
   b. year 2008. **See below.**
5. Do you think the line will continue its trend for many more years? Explain.
   No. At some point most of the world's countries will be participating.
6. Why was there a drop in 1976 and 1980? You may need to use your history textbook or outside references to help you find out why.
   See below.

Answers

4. a. and b. Answers will vary, but graphs should show a positive trend. According to the trend line there might be about 150 countries in the year 2000 and about 163 countries in the year 2008. These estimates are probably low because the trend line reflects the years when there was no participation.

6. Answers will vary. Political disputes caused 30 nations to withdraw their teams just before the Montreal games began in 1976. The United States, Canada, and 52 other nations and territories either boycotted or did not participate in the 1980 games in Moscow in protest of the Russian invasion of Afghanistan. In response, the Soviet Union and 14 other nations boycotted the games in Los Angeles in 1984.

BIBLIOGRAPHY

FOR TEACHERS

Guinness Book of Sports Records. New York, NY: Facts on File, 1996.

Hunter, Brian, ed. *The Statesman's Year-Book.* New York, NY: St. Martin's Press, 1996–1997.

Jarrett, William S. *Timetables of Sports History.* New York, NY: Facts on File, 1993.

Spangler, David. *Math for Real Kids.* Glenview, IL: Good Year Books, 1997.

FOR STUDENTS

Berger, Melvin. *Sports.* New York, NY: Watts, 1983.

Feinberg, Jeremy. *Reading the Sports Page.* Columbus, OH: New Discovery Books/Burdett Press, 1992.

Gutman, Bill. *Smitty.* Seattle, WA: Turman, 1988.

Meserole, Mike. *The Information Please Sports Almanac.* Boston, MA: Houghton Mifflin, 1994.

Section 1B

SECTION 1B

Trends and Relationships in Data

▶ Health Link ▶ Career Link ▶ www.mathsurf.com/7/ch1/sports

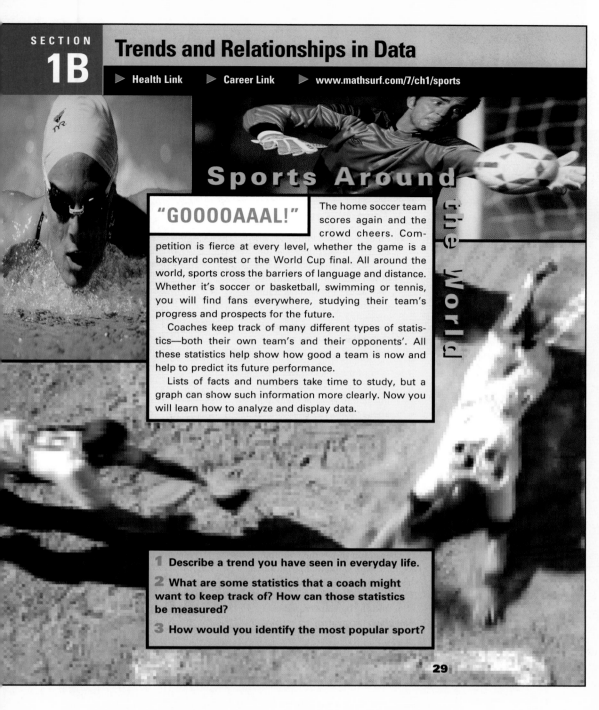

Sports Around the World

"GOOOOAAAL!" The home soccer team scores again and the crowd cheers. Competition is fierce at every level, whether the game is a backyard contest or the World Cup final. All around the world, sports cross the barriers of language and distance. Whether it's soccer or basketball, swimming or tennis, you will find fans everywhere, studying their team's progress and prospects for the future.

Coaches keep track of many different types of statistics—both their own team's and their opponents'. All these statistics help show how good a team is now and help to predict its future performance.

Lists of facts and numbers take time to study, but a graph can show such information more clearly. Now you will learn how to analyze and display data.

1 Describe a trend you have seen in everyday life.

2 What are some statistics that a coach might want to keep track of? How can those statistics be measured?

3 How would you identify the most popular sport?

29

Where are we now?

In Section 1A students read and compared data from graphs.

They learned how to

- make bar and double-bar graphs.
- use diagrams to show how frequently values occur and how they are distributed.
- decide if the mean, median, or mode best summarizes a set of data.

Where are we going?

In Section 1B, students will

- read and interpret line graphs.
- read, interpret, and make scatterplots.
- construct trend lines.
- recognize relationships and trends, and use relationships and trends to make predictions.

Theme: Sports Around the World

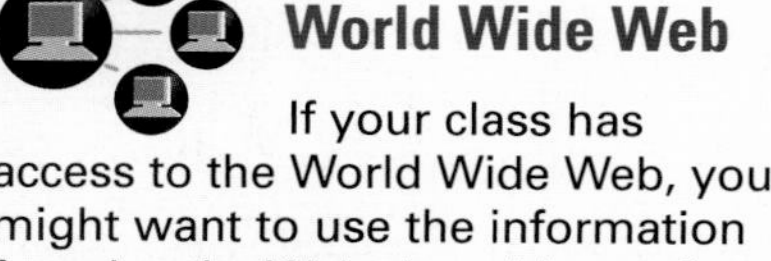

World Wide Web

If your class has access to the World Wide Web, you might want to use the information found at the Web site address given. The interdisciplinary links relate to topics discussed in this section.

About the Page

This page introduces the theme of this section, sports around the world, and shows how sports statistics are analyzed and used to make predictions.

Ask ...

- Why do you think a team's past performance is helpful in predicting its future performance?
- Why do coaches keep statistics about a team and its members?

Extensions

The following activities do not require access to the World Wide Web.

Health
Students may investigate the role of exercise in a healthy lifestyle.

Careers
Title IX, part of the Educational Amendments of 1972, prohibited sex discrimination in athletic programs in schools. This has led to many more opportunities for women in sports. Ask students to research professional careers available to female athletes.

Answers for Questions

1. Possible answer: Clothes keep getting more expensive.
2. Possible answer: Runs per player; goals scored in a season, number of games played. Could use percents.
3. Possible answer: Find out which sport was played by the most people.

Connect

On page 45, students will make scatterplots of sports data, determine relationships, and make predictions.

1-5 Lesson Organizer

Objectives

- Read and interpret line graphs.
- Recognize trends.

Vocabulary

- Line graph, trend, double-line graph

Materials

- Explore: Graphing utility

NCTM Standards

- 1–4, 7, 10

Review

Create a bar graph from the data showing the amount of precipitation in Northfield for 6 months of 1995. January: 13 in.; February, 8 in.; March, 12 in.; April, 7 in.; May, 9 in.; June, 6 in.

Possible answer:

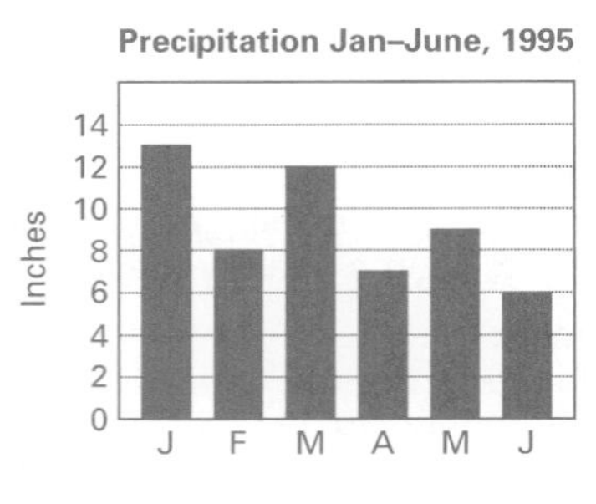

Available on Daily Transparency 1-5

1 Introduce

Explore

The Point
Students see how line graphs can show trends. They also see how to use a trend in a line graph to make predictions.

Ongoing Assessment
Check that students are able to use the graphing utility and that they have input the correct data for their graphs.

1-5 Line Graphs

You'll Learn ...

- to read and interpret line graphs
- to recognize trends

... How It's Used

Physical therapists can quickly see how a patient's performance is improving by checking a line graph of his or her statistics.

Vocabulary

line graph
trend
double-line graph

▶ Lesson Link In the last section, you learned to create displays of data. Now you will see how to display data that changes over time, and to use your displays to predict the future behavior of data. ◀

Explore Line Graphs

A Trendy Tournament

Materials: Graphing utility

1. Enter the first column of data on a graphing utility. Decide on a scale. Then create a line graph of the first column of data. Enter the second column of data.
2. Describe both lines. How are they alike? How are they different?
3. One of the lines shows a trend. Which is it? How can you use this line to make a prediction about future values of the data?
4. Predict the expected total attendance at the 1998 World Cup in France. Explain how you made your prediction.

Men's World Cup Soccer Tournament

Year	Attendance (millions)	Goals (per game)
1962	0.8	2.8
1966	1.6	2.8
1970	1.7	3.0
1974	1.8	2.6
1978	1.6	2.7
1982	1.8	2.8
1986	2.4	2.5
1990	2.5	2.2
1994	3.7	2.7

Learn Line Graphs

The bar graph shows the winning height for the women's high jump at the Olympics from 1968 through 1996. If the tops of the bars are connected by a line and the bars are erased, a **line graph** is created.

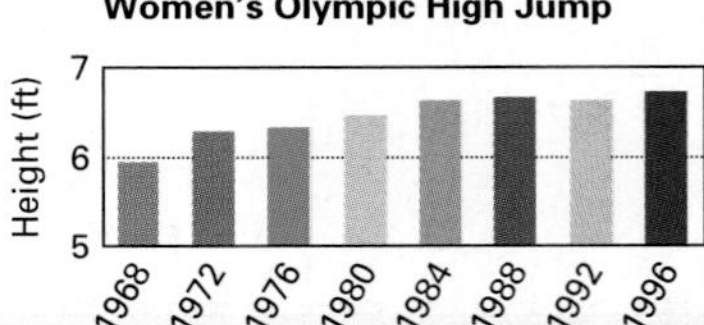

MEETING INDIVIDUAL NEEDS

Resources

1-5 Practice
1-5 Reteaching
1-5 Problem Solving
1-5 Enrichment
1-5 Daily Transparency
Problem of the Day
Review
Quick Quiz
Teaching Tool Trans. 7
Lesson Enhancement Transparency 7
Technology Master 3

Interactive CD-ROM Spreadsheet/Grapher Tool

Wide World of Mathematics
Algebra: Saving our Resources

Learning Modalities

Kinesthetic If students experience difficulty reading the values in the line graphs, encourage them to use a ruler or the edge of a notecard to align the point with the appropriate axis.

Social Have students work in pairs to generate the computer graphs.

English Language Development

Students with limited English proficiency can benefit from creating graphs, as they can communicate information graphically and read and understand information from graphs. Encourage these students to work on data-collection projects and to create graphs to share with their classmates.

A line graph shows how data changes over time. A **trend** is a clear direction in a graph that suggests how the data will behave in the future. The line graph shows that the winning heights have an increasing trend.

If you extend a line graph, the direction of the data can be used to predict the future behavior of the data.

Women's Olympic High Jump

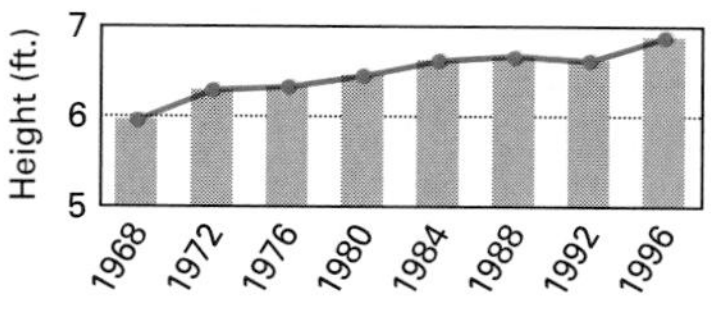

Examples

1 Make a line graph of the following data.

Number of Teams in the NBA							
Year	Teams	Year	Teams	Year	Teams	Year	Teams
1960	8	1970	14	1980	22	1990	27
1965	9	1975	18	1985	23	1995	29

Step 1 Draw and label the axes. Time lines are usually horizontal, so put units of time on the horizontal axis. Decide on the scale for the vertical axis.

Have the scale run from zero to a number that ends in zero, if possible. Divide the scale into intervals that are easy to read and understand.

Step 2 Plot a point for each data value. Then connect the points.

Step 3 Give the graph a title.

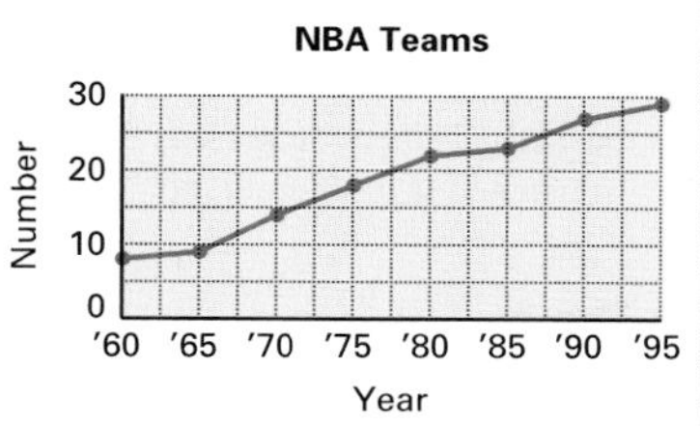

2 Use the graph to predict the number of NBA teams in the year 2010.

NBA Teams

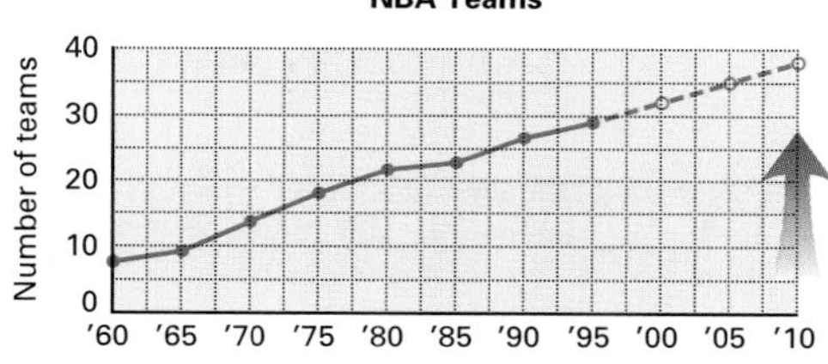

To predict the number of teams in 2010, extend the graph in a reasonable way. The extension shown gives a prediction of about 38 teams. Keep in mind that the prediction will be true only if the trend continues.

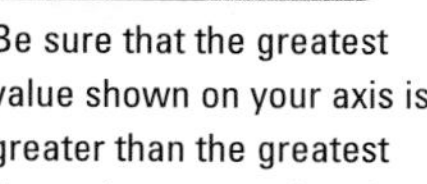

Be sure that the greatest value shown on your axis is greater than the greatest data value you need to show.

History Link

In 1891, a physical education teacher named James Naismith nailed two peach baskets to the gym balcony and asked his students to try tossing a ball into them. Basketball was born!

MATH EVERY DAY

Problem of the Day

The distance around the earth's equator is about 25,000 miles. A one-dollar bill is 6 inches long. If a billion one-dollar bills were laid end to end, about how many times would they circle the earth? About 4 times: 1,000,000,000 one-dollar bills laid end to end is approximately 94,697 miles.
94,697 ÷ 25,000 = 3.78

Available on Daily Transparency 1-5

An Extension is provided in the transparency package

Fact of the Day

In 1996 the U.S. Olympic women's basketball team won a gold medal. The medal game was their 60th straight win in games played on four continents.

Estimation

Estimate each sum or difference.

1. 372 + 891 1300
2. 609 − 387 200
3. 550 + 349 900
4. 422 − 68 350
5. 26 + 258 290

Answers for Explore

1.

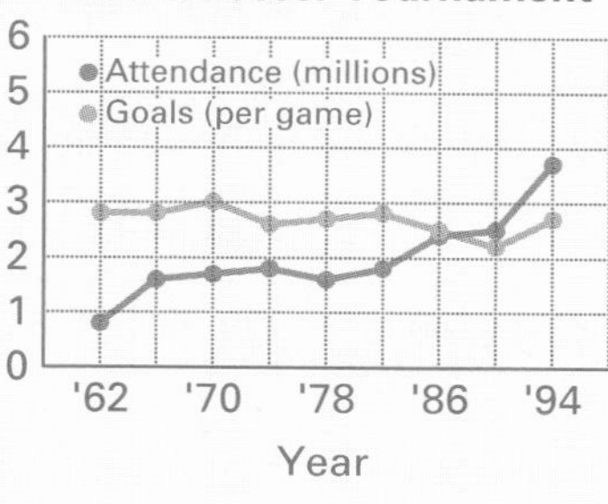

2. Both show increases and decreases. Attendance nearly always increased.
3. Attendance; Extend the line to project future data values.
4. About 5 million; Extend the line to be directly above 1998.

2 Teach

Learn

Lesson Enhancement Transparency 7 and Teaching Tool Transparency 7: $\frac{1}{4}$-Inch Graph Paper may be used with **Learn.**

Alternate Examples

1. Make a line graph of the following data.

Major League Baseball Teams					
Year	1950	1960	1970	1980	1990
Teams	16	20	24	26	26

Step 1 Draw and label the axes, using a scale of zero to 30 with intervals of 5.

Step 2 Plot a point for each data value. Connect the points.

Step 3 Give the graph a title.

Major League Baseball Teams

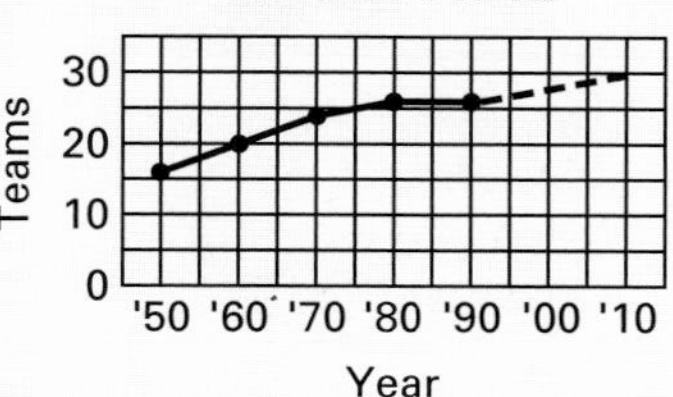

2. Predict how many major league baseball teams there will be in the year 2010.

Extend the graph in a reasonable way. One possible extension gives a prediction of about 30 teams.The broken line on the above graph shows this extension.

Alternate Examples

3. Make a double-line graph and describe the graph.

Average Monthly Temperatures						
Month	J	M	M	J	S	N
Minneapolis	11	29	59	73	61	33
Tampa	60	66	77	82	81	67

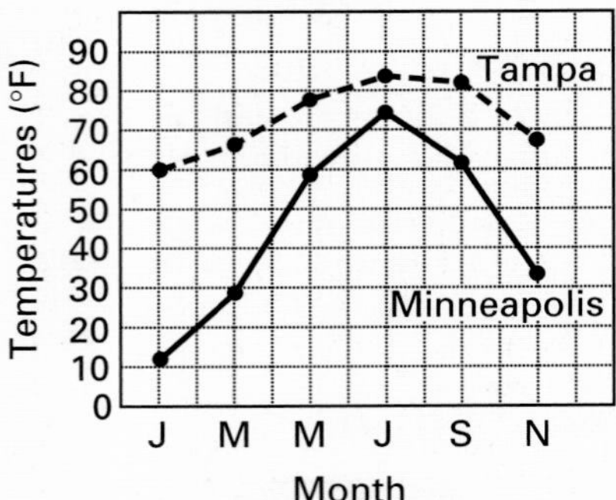

The graph shows that the temperatures in each city rose from January to July and then decreased. Minneapolis had a much greater range of temperatures than Tampa.

Answers for Try It

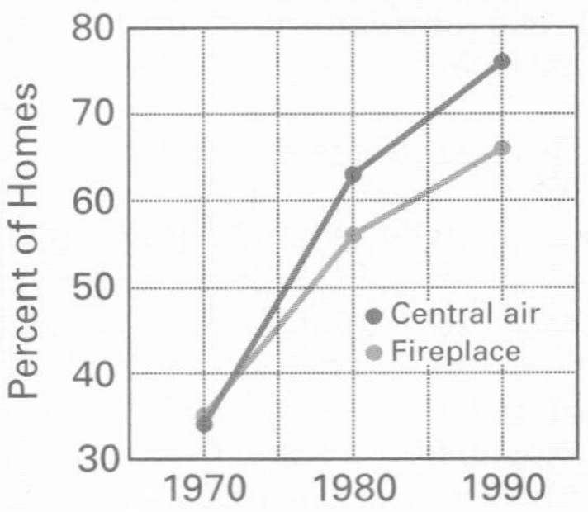

3 Practice and Assess

Check

Answers for Check Your Understanding

1. Possible answer: Because it shows you the direction of change, you may be able to project future (or describe past) values. A line graph shows whether the data values are increasing or decreasing and if so, how fast they are changing.
2. Possible answer: Any data that is not numeric, such as people's favorite colors

A line graph can be misleading if the scale is broken or begins at a number other than zero. The scale of this graph extends from 8% to 11%. As a result, it shows a sharp increase that one with a scale from 0% to 11% would not.

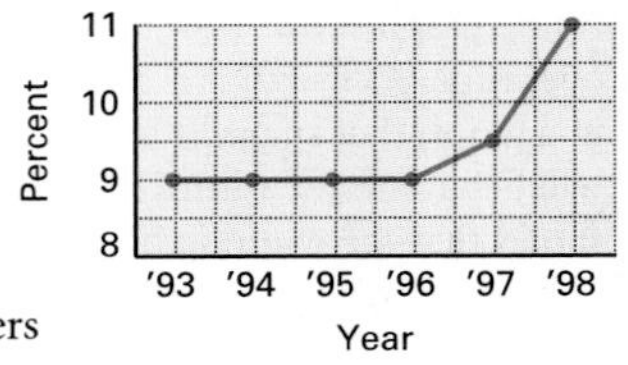

Be alert for misleading line graphs in newspapers and magazines. Be sure that any changes you make in your own line graphs are clearly marked.

You can graph two sets of related data on a **double-line graph**.

Remember

You need to color-code the lines to avoid confusion.

Example 3

Make a double-line graph and describe the graph.

U.S. Athletic Shoe Sales								
	1987	1988	1989	1990	1991	1992	1993	1994
Basketball Shoes ($ millions)	169	226	293	428	449	456	407	407
Aerobic Shoes ($ millions)	401	327	425	389	381	376	318	305

One line is drawn to represent each set of data and the lines are labeled. The graph shows that as the sales of basketball shoes increased, the sales of aerobic shoes decreased.

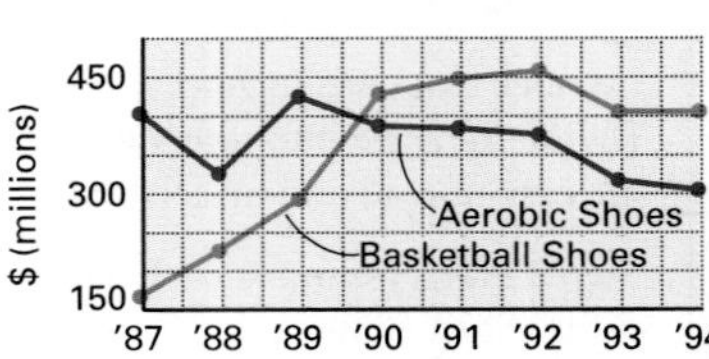

Try It

Make a double-line graph of the data and describe the graph.

Features of New Homes			
	1970	1980	1990
Central Air-Conditioning (%)	34	63	76
At Least One Fireplace (%)	35	56	66

Check Your Understanding

1. Why is a line graph a good way to display data that changes with time? How do line graphs show trends?
2. Give an example of a data set for which a bar graph could be used, but a line graph couldn't be used.

MEETING MIDDLE SCHOOL CLASSROOM NEEDS

Tips from Middle School Teachers

When working with statistics, I find that students are more involved if the data and questions are important to them. I always try to suggest projects that are of personal interest to them. Surveys of classmates are usually popular.

Team Teaching

Have the physical education teachers supply you with multi-year data collected from track-and-field days or scoring records from school teams. Then have students use the data to create line graphs.

History Connection

Because of World War I, there were no Olympic games in 1916. There were no games in 1940 and 1944 because of World War II.

1-5 Exercises and Applications

Practice and Apply

Getting Started **The graph shows the number of countries taking part in the summer Olympic games from 1948 through 1972.**

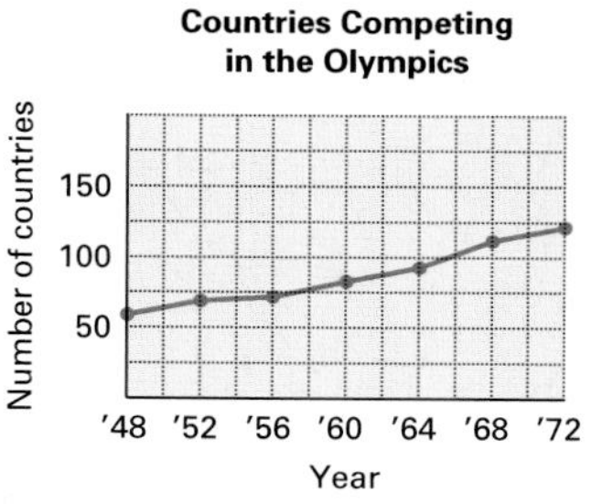

Countries Competing in the Olympics

(Number of countries: 50, 100, 150; Year: '48 '52 '56 '60 '64 '68 '72)

1. What trend do you notice in the graph?

2. What is the interval on the horizontal axis? The vertical?

3. Sports The table shows Josie's total score after each frame of bowling. Make a line graph to show this information.

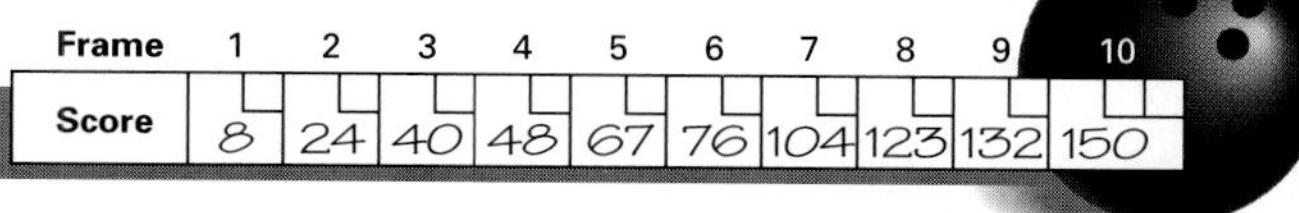

Frame	1	2	3	4	5	6	7	8	9	10
Score	8	24	40	48	67	76	104	123	132	150

Technology **Use the graph of Internet hosts (computer sites where Web pages are stored) for Exercises 4 and 5.**

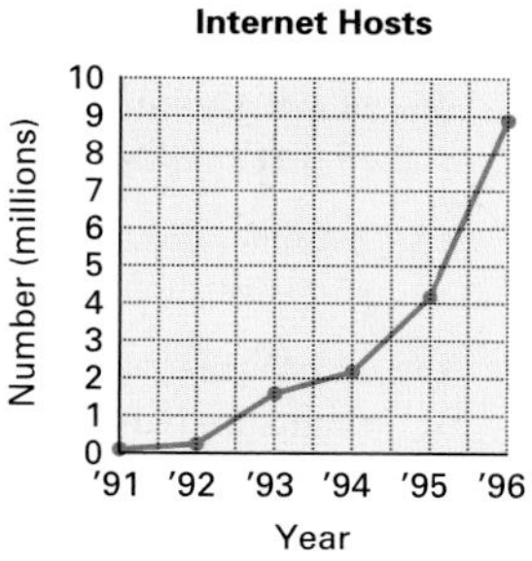

Internet Hosts

(Number (millions): 0–10; Year: '91 '92 '93 '94 '95 '96)

4. Predict the number of hosts in 1998.

5. What other kind of graph could be used to show this data?

Social Studies **Use the table of the mean number of people per household in the United States from 1850 through 1980 for Exercises 6 and 7.**

Year	1850	1860	1870	1880	1890	1900	1910	1920	1930	1940	1950	1960	1970	1980
Mean	5.50	5.28	5.09	5.04	4.93	4.76	4.54	4.34	4.11	3.67	3.37	3.33	3.14	2.75

6. Make a line graph to show this data.

7. Describe any trend you see in the graph.

8. Use the data in the table to make a double-line graph. Describe the graph.

Transportation Used by Commuters	1960	1970	1980	1990
Private Vehicles (%)	69	81	86	88
Public Transportation (%)	13	8	6	5

PRACTICE 1-5

PRACTICE

Name ______________________ Practice 1-5

Line Graphs

Use the graph of the number of pieces of mail sent in the United States for Exercises 1–3.

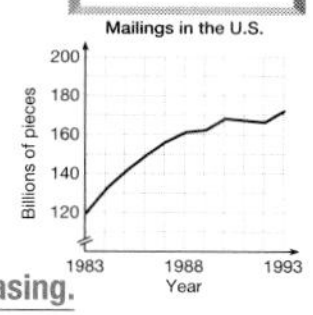

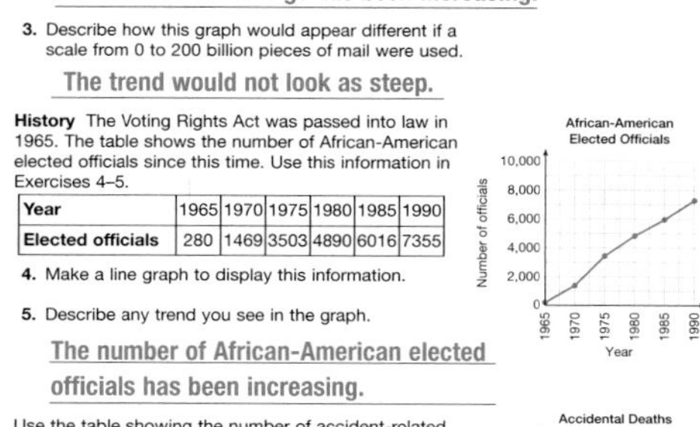

Mailings in the U.S. (Billions of pieces; Year 1983, 1988, 1993)

1. Predict the number of pieces of mail in 1997.
   About 180 billion
2. Describe any trend you see in the graph.
   The number of mailings has been increasing.
3. Describe how this graph would appear different if a scale from 0 to 200 billion pieces of mail were used.
   The trend would not look as steep.

History The Voting Rights Act was passed into law in 1965. The table shows the number of African-American elected officials since this time. Use this information in Exercises 4–5.

Year	1965	1970	1975	1980	1985	1990
Elected officials	280	1469	3503	4890	6016	7355

African-American Elected Officials

4. Make a line graph to display this information.
5. Describe any trend you see in the graph.
   The number of African-American elected officials has been increasing.

Use the table showing the number of accident-related deaths (in thousands) in the United States for Exercises 6–7.

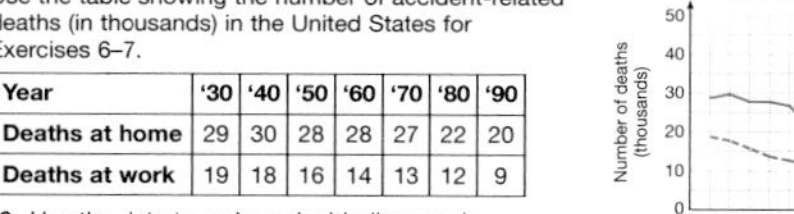

Year	'30	'40	'50	'60	'70	'80	'90
Deaths at home	29	30	28	28	27	22	20
Deaths at work	19	18	16	14	13	12	9

Accidental Deaths (At home; At work)

6. Use the data to make a double-line graph.
7. Describe any trend you see in the graph.
   The number of accidents has been falling steadily, both at home and at work.

RETEACHING

Name ______________________ Alternative Lesson 1-5

Line Graphs

A **line graph** shows how data changes over time. A **trend** is a clear direction in a graph that suggests how the data will behave in the future.

Example

The line graph on the right shows the number of foreign exchange students in Walsen County for the years 1991–1996. In what year will the number of foreign exchange students exceed 25?

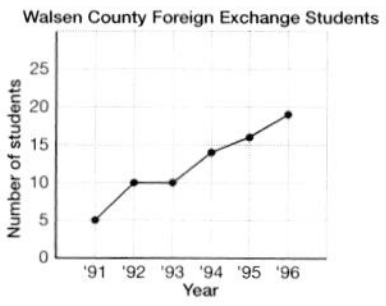

Walsen County Foreign Exchange Students

The trend of the line shows that the number of foreign exchange students is increasing each year. It would be reasonable to expect that by the year 2000 there would be more than 25 foreign exchange students.

Try It Follow these steps to help you make a line graph of the data in the table.

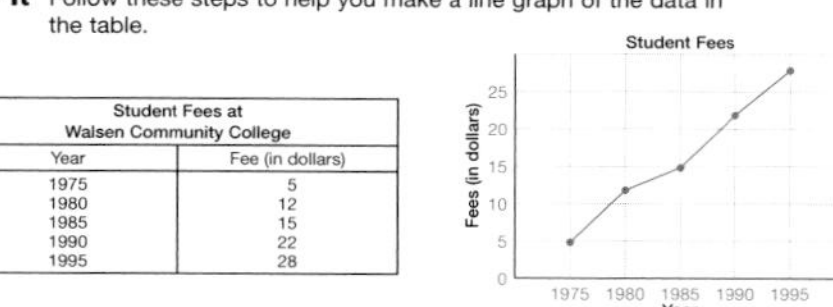

Year	Fee (in dollars)
1975	5
1980	12
1985	15
1990	22
1995	28

Student Fees at Walsen Community College

Student Fees

a. Use the vertical axis for the fee amount. Which interval is better to use: an interval of 2, an interval of 5, or an interval of 20? Explain.
   Intervals of 5 because data using an interval of 2 will not fit on the grid. Using an interval of 20 on the graph would make reading the graph very difficult.

b. What interval will you use along the horizontal axis?
   An interval of 5.

c. Plot a point to represent the fee for each year. Connect the points.

d. What trend do you notice in your graph?
   Possible answer: A steady increase in student fees.

1-5 Exercises and Applications

Assignment Guide

- **Basic** 1, 2, 5, 8, 9, 11, 13–15, 19
- **Average** 3, 4, 6, 7, 9–12, 16–18, 20–22
- **Enriched** 3, 4, 6, 7, 9–12, 16–18, 20–24

Exercise Notes

Exercise 1

Sports Have students use the graph to predict the number of nations taking part in the summer Olympic games in 1984.
140 nations took part.

Exercise Answers

Answers for Exercises 1–8 on page C2.

Reteaching

Activity

- This graph shows the number of golfers and tennis players in the U.S. for each year from 1986 through 1990. Use the graph to answer the questions.

Participants in Golf and Tennis

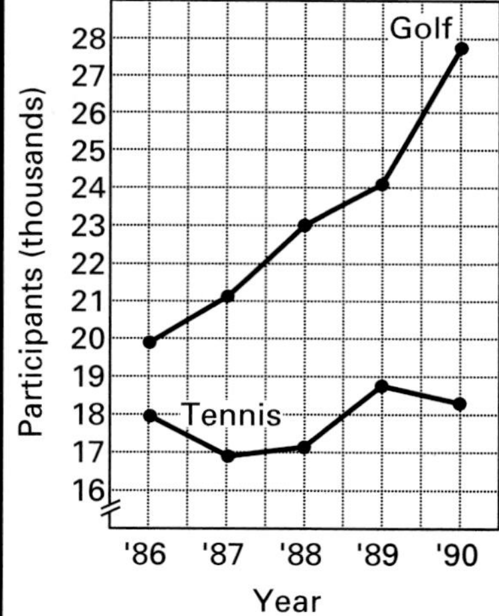

- In what year was the number of golfers closest to the number of tennis players? 1986
- In what year was the difference in the number of participants the greatest? 1990
- Which sport shows a definite trend toward increase in number of participants? golf
- Which sport had only a few more participants in 1990 than in 1986? tennis

Exercise Notes

■ Exercise 9

Error Prevention Be sure that students recognize that a decreasing graph "falls" from left to right.

Exercise Answers

10. Possible answers: Most points scored, about 27–28; Least points allowed, 3–4.
11. 4; Because the line for points scored is higher. A tie game would have a point where the two lines cross.
12. No; It will be accurate only if all conditions remain the same.
19. Possible answer: Scale 100–700, interval 50.
20. Possible answer: Scale: 0–3500, interval 500.
21. Possible answer: Scale: 0–150, interval 10.
22. Possible answer: Scale: 0–1500, interval 250.
23. Possible answer: Scale: 0–50, interval 5.
24. Possible answer: Scale: 1000–1500, interval 50.

Alternate Assessment

Interview Ask each student to pick a real-world situation in which they might want to create a line graph or a double-line graph. Have them explain how they would draw the graph.

Quick Quiz

Make a line graph of the data, and describe any trend.

Bicycles Shipped (millions)				
Year	'87	'88	'89	'90
Imports	7.4	5.4	5.4	4.8

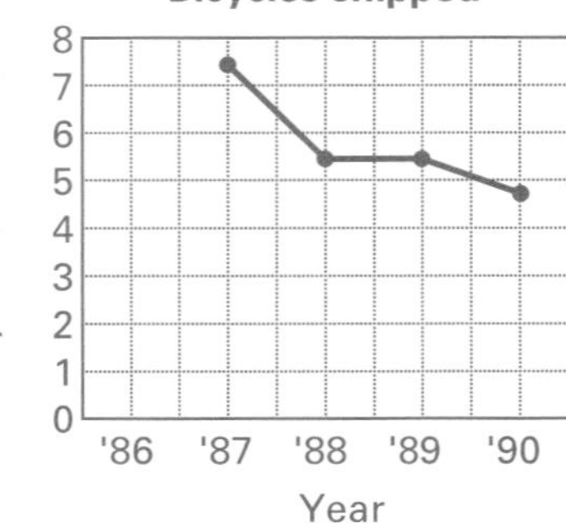

Each year the number of bicycles shipped stays the same or decreases.

Available on Daily Transparency 1-5

PROBLEM SOLVING 1-5

9. **Test Prep** The world record time for the 4 × 400 meter relay has been decreasing over the years. Which of these graphs could represent this? **C**

Ⓐ

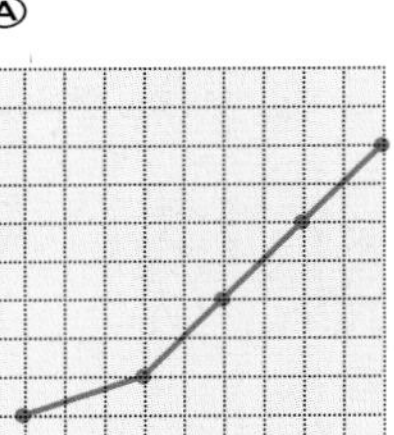

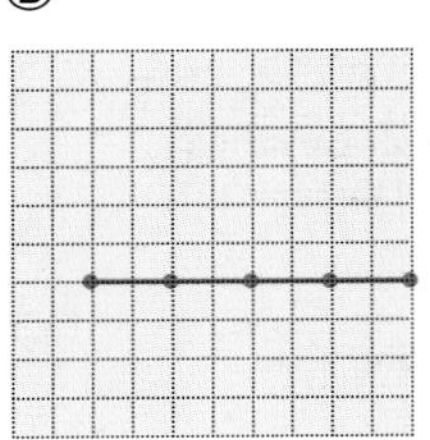

Ⓒ

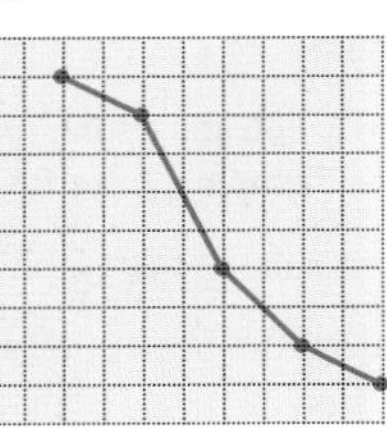

Ⓓ

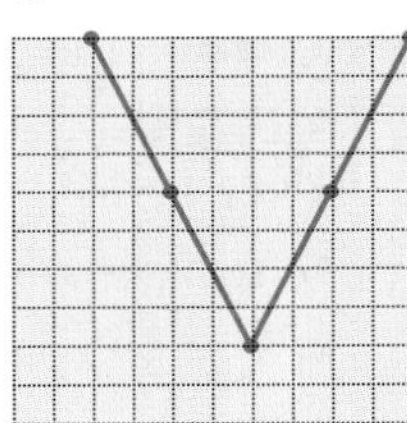

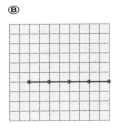

Problem Solving and Reasoning

Critical Thinking The Carolina Panthers joined the NFL in 1995. The double-line graph shows the number of points scored and allowed by the Panthers in the first nine games of their first season. Use the graph for Exercises 10 and 11.

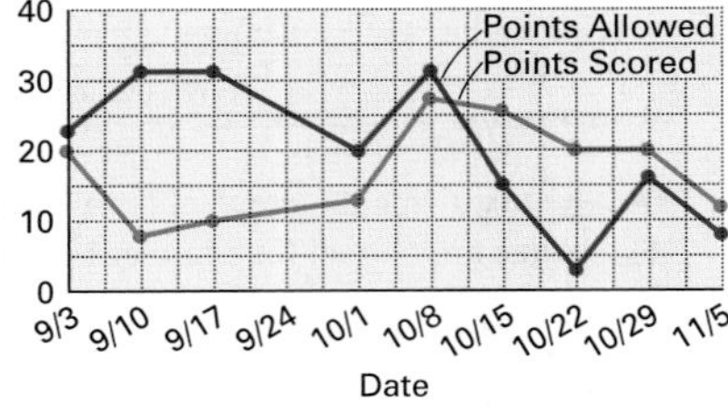

10. Estimate the most points scored by the Panthers in a game. Estimate the fewest points allowed in a game.

11. GPS In how many games did the Panthers score more points than their opponents? How can you tell? How could you tell if there was a tie game?

12. **Communicate** A line graph is useful in predicting future data values. Will your prediction necessarily be accurate? Explain.

Mixed Review

Add or subtract. *[Previous course]*

13. 4,512 + 9,439 **13,951**
14. 6,302 − 2,154 **4,148**
15. 34,293 + 67,262 **101,555**
16. 89,684 − 56,158 **33,526**
17. 452,972 + 318,964 **771,936**
18. 579,532 − 417,359 **162,173**

Choose a convenient scale and interval to use for making a bar graph of the data. *[Lesson 1-2]*

19. 270, 100, 430, 650, 280
20. 1300, 2400, 3400, 400
21. 20, 110, 90, 130
22. 1000, 1500, 750, 250
23. 21, 12, 35, 47
24. 1138, 1257, 1049, 1317

34 *Chapter 1 • Making Sense of the World of Data*

PROBLEM SOLVING

Name ____________

Guided Problem Solving 1-5

GPS PROBLEM 11, STUDENT PAGE 34

The Carolina Panthers joined the NFL in 1995. The double-line graph shows the number of points scored and allowed by the Panthers in the first nine games of their first season. In how many games did the Panthers score more points than their opponents? How can you tell? How could you tell if there was a tie game?

Carolina Panthers 1995 (graph: Points allowed, Points scored; Points 0–40; Date 9/3–11/5)

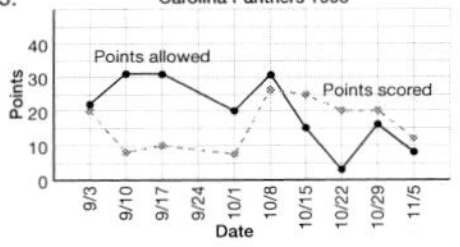

— Understand —

1. Look at the broken line to find how many points the Panthers scored on 9/3. **20 points**
2. Look at the solid line to find how many points they allowed the opposing team to score on 9/3. **22 points**
3. If the line for points scored is below the line for points allowed, did the Panthers win or lose? **Lose**

— Plan —

4. How many times is the line for points scored above the line for points allowed. **4 times**

— Solve —

5. In how many games did the Panthers score more points than their opponents? How can you tell? **4 games, because the line for points scored is above the line for points allowed for only the last 4 games.**
6. Suppose both teams score 10 points. Describe what happens to the lines. Who wins the game? **Since the lines meet at the same point, the game is a tie.**

— Look Back —

7. Write a number sentence to show that the Panther wins and the Panther losses equal the total games played. **Possible answer: 4 + 6 = 10**

SOLVE ANOTHER PROBLEM

In how many games did the Panthers score 10 or more points less than their opponents? Give the dates of these games.
3 games; 9/10, 9/17, 9/24

ENRICHMENT

Name ____________

Extend Your Thinking 1-5

Decision Making

Amalia Ruiz works for the El Paso County Health Department. Each of the graphs below shows the number of reported flu cases during a ten-year period. Which of the graphs should she use to encourage getting flu shots? Why?

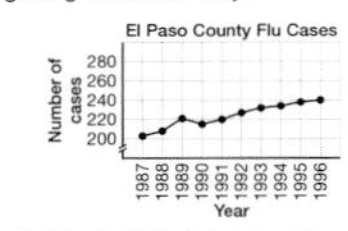

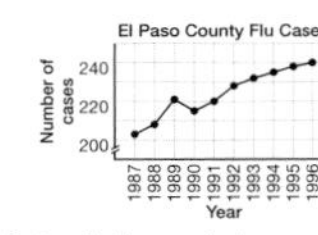

1. What is it that Amalia wishes to communicate with the graph she chooses for her presentation? **She wants to encourage people to get flu shots.**
2. What type of change does the graph on the left show? **A slow gradual increase in the number of flu cases.**
3. What type of change does the graph on the right show? **A sharp rise in the number of flu cases.**
4. Which graph would tend to imply that the incidence of flu is increasing dramatically? Why? **The second graph, because of the steepness of the line on the graph.**
5. To encourage the local community to get flu shots, which graph should Amalia use? Why? **The second graph, because it appears that flu cases are dramatically increasing.**

Scatterplots and Relationships

1-6

▶ Lesson Link You have drawn double-bar graphs and double-line graphs to compare related data values. Now you will see a type of graph that can be used to explore those relationships. ◀

You'll Learn ...

- to read and interpret scatterplots
- to make scatterplots
- to recognize relationships in data

... How It's Used

Chemists often make scatterplots to study how physical factors affect chemicals and chemical reactions.

Vocabulary

scatterplot

positive relationship

negative relationship

no relationship

Explore Scatterplots

Plots of Lots of Shots

The U.S. women's fast-pitch softball team won the 1994 World Championship. The graph shows data for some players in this tournament.

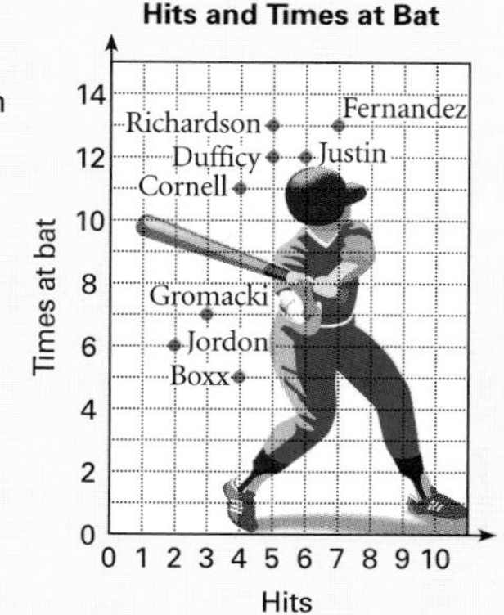

1. Who had the most hits? How many did she have?
2. Which players had the same number of hits? How many did they have?
3. Which players had the same number of times at bat? How many did they have?
4. What would a point on the vertical axis represent? Explain.
5. Imagine a line from the point representing 0 hits and 0 times at bat to 10 hits and 10 times at bat. Why are there no points below the line?

Learn Scatterplots and Relationships

You can investigate the relationship between two sets of data by drawing a **scatterplot**. Each set of data is represented by an axis with its own scale. Each pair of values is represented by a point.

To plot a point, find the value of the data on each axis. Extend a horizontal line from one axis and a vertical line from the other axis. Put a point where the lines meet.

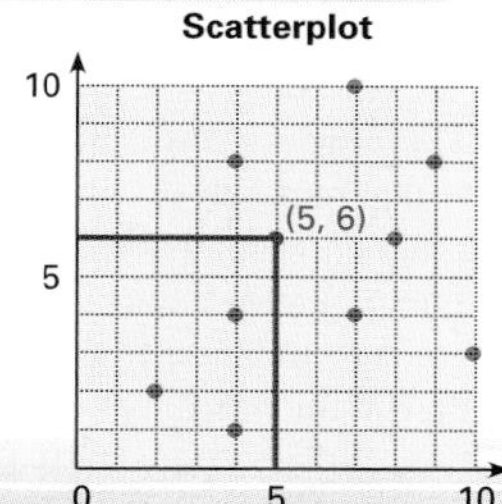

1-6 Lesson Organizer

Objectives

- Read and interpret scatterplots.
- Make scatterplots.
- Recognize relationships in data.

Vocabulary

- Scatterplot, positive relationship, negative relationship, no relationship

NCTM Standards

- 1–4, 7, 8, 10

▶ Review

Tell what number each point corresponds to on the horizontal and vertical axis.

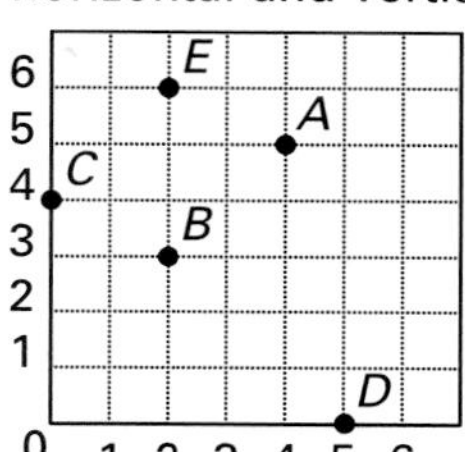

1. A horizontal, 4; vertical, 5
2. B horizontal, 2; vertical, 3
3. C horizontal, 0; vertical, 4
4. D horizontal, 5; vertical, 0
5. E horizontal, 2; vertical, 6

Available on Daily Transparency 1-6

MEETING INDIVIDUAL NEEDS

Resources

- **1-6** Practice
- **1-6** Reteaching
- **1-6** Problem Solving
- **1-6** Enrichment
- **1-6** Daily Transparency
  - Problem of the Day
  - Review
  - Quick Quiz
- Teaching Tool Transparency 7
- Lesson Enhancement Transparency 8
- Chapter 1 Project Master
- Technology Master 4

Learning Modalities

Verbal Encourage students to verbalize their concepts of scatterplots and types of relationships. Encourage discussion of the various types of graphs studied in this chapter and their widespread use in the real world.

Logical One way to determine whether sets of data show a relationship in a scatterplot is to try to enclose all the points in a symmetric oval. If the oval is long and narrow, the sets of data are related. If the oval is nearly circular, they are not related. You might have students apply this test to their scatterplots.

English Language Development

To help limited-English-speaking students to understand the term *scatterplot*, you might use a large grid, labeled like the one on page 35 and scatter a dozen or so grains of rice or dried peas or beans over it. This scatterplot can be likened to that in the text and the students can identify positions of individual grains of rice or peas or beans.

1 Introduce

Explore

You may use Teaching Tool Trans. 7: Graph Paper with this lesson.

The Point

Students see how representing paired data on a coordinate grid can help show relationships between the data values.

Ongoing Assessment

Encourage students to tell what the axes numbers and labels represent.

Answers for Explore on next page.

Answers for Explore

1. Fernandez, 7.
2. Boxx and Cornell, 4; Dufficy and Richardson, 5.
3. Dufficy and Justin, 12; Richardson and Fernandez, 13.
4. A player who had no hits.
5. Because a player cannot make more hits than the number of times she is at bat.

2 Teach

Learn

You may wish to use Lesson Enhancement Transparency 8 with **Learn**.

Alternate Examples

1. Make a scatterplot of the data, and describe the scatterplot.

Month	Altitude (ft)	Record High Temp. (°F)
Jan.	421	98
March	735	108
May	168	108
Oct.	685	116
Nov.	1759	105
Dec.	539	100

Most of the temperatures are more than 105°F. Altitudes are distributed evenly from 150 ft to 750 ft, except for 1759 ft.

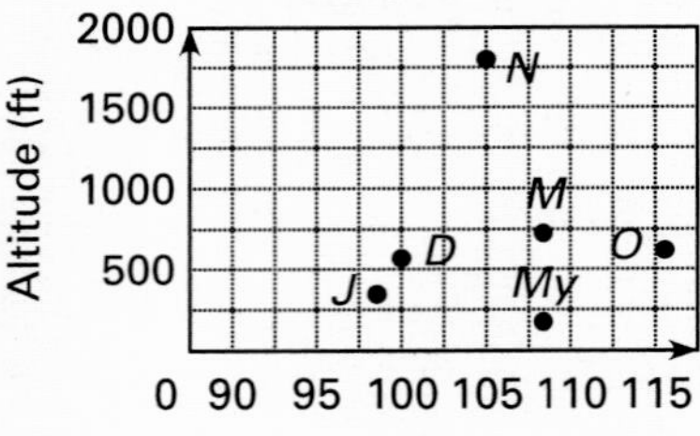

Answers for Try It

Most bridge lengths are clustered around 4000. Number of lanes cluster around 10.0

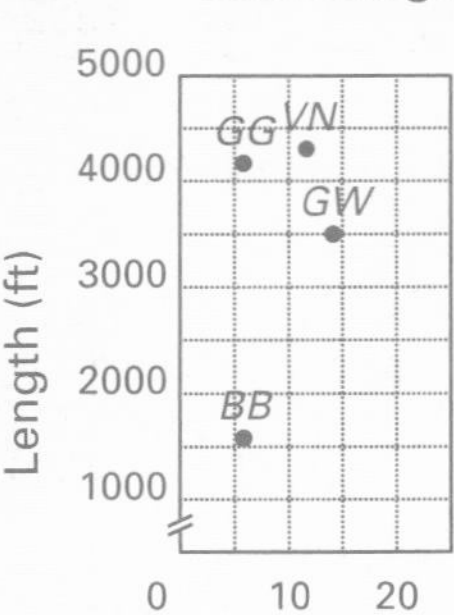

Example 1

Science Link

The Fahrenheit scale of temperature is named after its inventor, Gabriel Daniel Fahrenheit, who lived from 1686 to 1736.

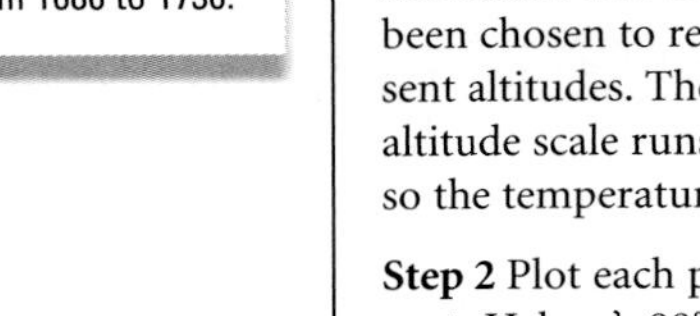

Make a scatterplot of the data. Describe the scatterplot.

City	Altitude (ft)	Highest Temperature (°F)
Denver, CO	5283	99
Helena, MT	4157	98
Phoenix, AZ	1092	113
Reno, NV	4500	102
Spokane, WA	1898	101
Syracuse, NY	408	88

Step 1 Choose the axes and scale. The horizontal axis has been chosen to represent altitudes. The altitude scale runs from 0 to 6000 feet. There are no temperatures below 88°F, so the temperature scale begins at 85°F.

Step 2 Plot each point. Point *H* represents Helena's 98°F temperature and 3828 ft altitude.

Step 3 Label the scatterplot.

Most of the temperatures are clustered around 100°F. Altitudes are distributed fairly evenly from 0 ft to 6000 ft.

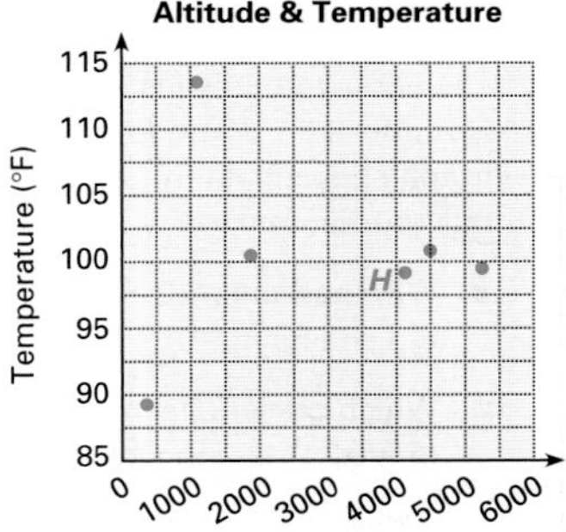

Study TIP

Always make sure that you will have room to show all the data points on your plot.

Try It

Make a scatterplot of the data and describe the result.

Famous U.S. Bridges		
Bridge	**Length (ft)**	**Width (no. of lanes)**
Brooklyn	1595	6
George Washington	3500	14
Golden Gate	4200	6
Verrazano Narrows	4260	12

Career Goals (through 1995–96 season)

Goals scored: 0, 500, 1000; Games played: 1000, 2000; WG, GH, PE, MD, BH, MG, MB, JK

This scatterplot displays data on goals and games played by the National Hockey League players with the most career goals. The plot shows that a player's goal total tends to increase as the number of games played increases.

MATH EVERY DAY

Problem of the Day

Abdul has a 3-liter pitcher and a 5-liter pitcher. How can he use these pitchers to measure exactly 4 L of water?

Possible answer: Fill the 5-liter pitcher and use it to fill the 3-liter pitcher. Empty the 3-liter pitcher and pour the remaining 2 liters from the 5-liter pitcher into the 3-liter pitcher. Refill the 5-liter pitcher and pour 1 liter into the 3-liter pitcher that already holds 2 liters. There are 4 liters remaining in the 5-liter pitcher.

Available on Daily Transparency 1-6

An Extension is provided in the transparency package

Fact of the Day

In 1995, Cal Ripken, Jr. set a record by playing in 2153 consecutive baseball games through several seasons.

Estimation

Estimate each product or quotient.

1. 3652 ÷ 39 90
2. 521 × 23 10,000
3. 439 ÷ 82 5
4. 809 × 681 560,000

When two sets of data increase at the same time, the sets show a **positive relationship**. A scatterplot of a positive relationship slants upward to the right.

When one set of data increases as the other decreases, the sets show a **negative relationship**. A scatterplot of a negative relationship slants downward to the right.

When two sets of data neither increase nor decrease together, they show **no relationship**.

Positive Relationship

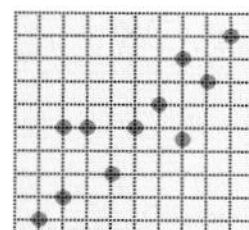

Negative Relationship

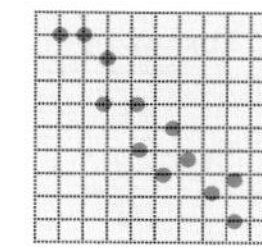

No Relationship

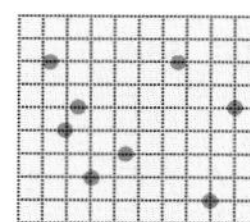

Examples

Decide whether each set of data would show a positive, a negative, or no relationship.

2 The number of students doing a job and the length of time it takes.

The *greater* the number working, the *less* time the job takes: *negative.*

3

Student's Age	11	18	7	13	15	10	9
Student's Area Code	205	302	408	508	914	610	818

The scatterplot shows a random arrangement of points. There is *no relationship* between the sets.

Age and Area Code

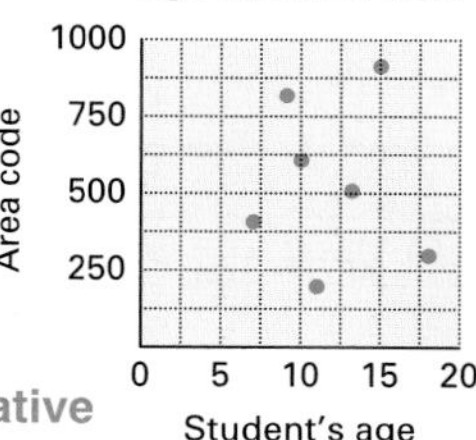

Try It

Decide whether the sets would show a positive, a negative, or no relationship.

a. The number of hours you've been awake and the number of hours until you go to bed. Negative

b. The number of magazines you buy and the total price you pay. Positive

Study TIP

It is better to get a full night's sleep before an important test than to stay up late studying.

Check Your Understanding

1. How are scatterplots and line plots alike? How are they different?
2. Why is it sometimes better to choose a scale that does not begin at zero?

Alternate Examples

2. Decide whether people's heights and their ages would show a positive, a negative, or no relationship.

   Generally, as people grow older they grow taller, until they reach a maximum height. Until that height is reached, the relationship is positive.

3. Decide whether these two data sets would show a positive, a negative, or no relationship.

   The scatterplot slants downward to the right. There is a *negative relationship.*

Runner's Speed (mph)	15	10	12	8	6
Time for Race (min)	8	13	10	15	18

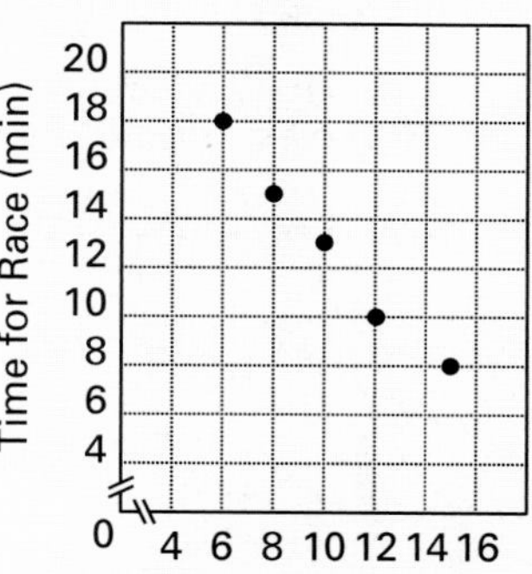

3 Practice and Assess

Check

Be sure students recognize that (1) pairs of values that increase together indicate a positive relationship; (2) pairs of values in which one increases as the other decreases indicate a negative relationship; (3) pairs of values whose plots are randomly scattered indicate no relationship.

Answers for Check Your Understanding

1. Possible answers: Alike: Both show all individual data values; Different: Scatterplots show how two sets of data vary together.
2. Possible answer: Because all values may cluster around a high number so the graph would be too big.

MEETING MIDDLE SCHOOL CLASSROOM NEEDS

Tips from Middle School Teachers

Now that students have a variety of methods to display data, I provide them with data from a science lab or with statistical information from a social studies topic. Since they have all the data at hand, they can concentrate on the appropriateness of different types of graphs. I have the class work in groups to construct graphs and share their choice of representation with the class.

Science Connection

The six record high temperatures for October–March were recorded in Texas, Arizona, and California. The record high temperatures for the remaining six months of the year were all recorded in California, at altitudes below sea level.

Team Teaching

Gather and tabulate data related to the social studies topic that the class is currently studying.

1-6 Exercises and Applications

Assignment Guide

- **Basic** 1–4, 7–10, 13, 14–17, 20
- **Average** 1–9, 11, 12–17, 21
- **Enriched** 1–9, 11–13, 17–21

Exercise Notes

Exercises 6–8

Error Prevention If students are experiencing difficulty with these exercises, suggest that they think of several number pairs that fit each situation and imagine them in a scatterplot.

Project Progress

You may want to have students use Chapter 1 Project Master.

Exercise Answers

1.

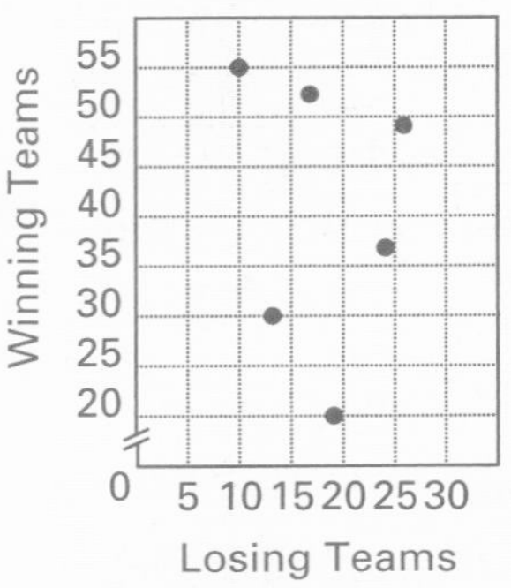

e. No relationship.

Answers for Exercises 4 and 5 on page C2.

Reteaching

Activity

- If the desks in your classroom are arranged in rows and columns, think of this arrangement as a grid.
- Face the front and use the desk in the last row farthest to your left as the starting point. Number both the rows and columns beginning at that point.
- Give the location of your desk in terms of a horizontal (column) number and a vertical (row) number.

1-6 Exercises and Applications

PRACTICE 1-6

Practice and Apply

1. **Getting Started** Follow the steps to draw a scatterplot.
   a. Choose a scale for both axes.
   b. Mark the interval on each axis.
   c. Label both axes.
   d. Plot the points.
   e. What kind of a relationship does the scatterplot show?

Points Scored in Super Bowl, 1990–95

Winning Team	55	20	37	52	30	49
Losing Team	10	19	24	17	13	26

Science Use the scatterplot showing the life expectancies and sizes of some African animals for Exercises 2 and 3.

Life Expectancy and Weight

Weight (lb): 0, 1000, 2000, 3000, 4000, 5000, 6000
Life expectancy (yr): 25, 50, 75, 100
Rhinoceros, Hippopotamus, Lion, Gorilla, Ostrich, Tortoise

2. Which animal has the longest life expectancy? The shortest? **Tortoise; Lion.**
3. What is the life expectancy of a gorilla? A rhinoceros? **Gorilla: 50; Rhinoceros: 72.**
4. **Sports** Make a scatterplot to show the data. Determine if there is any relationship between the two sets of data.

Games Played	4	7	9	14	15	18	20	23
Total Service Aces	13	20	28	44	47	56	59	70

5. The table shows the heights in inches of some students and of their mothers. Make a scatterplot to show this information.

	A	B	C	D	E	F	G	H	I	J
Mother	54	52	60	56	60	66	60	66	64	62
Student	54	58	58	60	62	62	66	66	68	60

Decide whether the sets would show a positive, a negative, or no relationship.

6. The time it takes a parachutist to land and the altitude of the plane when the parachutist jumps. **Positive**
7. The time it takes to run 400 meters and the speed of the runner. **Negative**
8. The time spent waiting in line and the length of the movie. **No relationship**

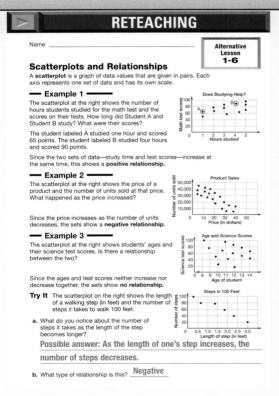

PRACTICE

Name ______________________

Practice 1-6

Scatterplots and Relationships

Use the scatterplot showing weights and maximum speeds of animals for Exercises 1–3.

Weights and Speeds of Animals

Speed (mi/hr): 0, 20, 40, 60, 80, 100
Weight (lb): 100, 200, 300, 400, 500

1. Which is the heaviest of these animals? **Lion**
   the lightest? **Cat**
2. Which is the fastest of these animals? **Cheetah**
   the slowest? **Cat**
3. What is the weight of a reindeer? **250 lb**
   the maximum speed of a cheetah? **70 mi/hr**

The table shows the number of passengers (millions) and the number of paid passenger-miles (billions) flown for the top 9 U.S. airlines in 1993. Use this information for Exercises 4–5.

Airline	Delta	American	US Air	United	Northwest
Passengers	84	83	70	54	44
Paid miles	82.9	99.0	101	35.3	58

Airline	Southwest	Continental	TWA	America West
Passengers	38	37	19	15
Paid miles	16.7	39.9	22.7	11.2

Top Nine U.S. Airlines

Paid passenger-miles (billions): 0, 20, 40, 60, 80, 100
Passengers (millions): 20, 40, 60, 80, 100

4. Make a scatterplot of the data.
5. What kind of relationship is shown? **Positive**

Describe whether the sets would show a positive relationship, a negative relationship, or no relationship.

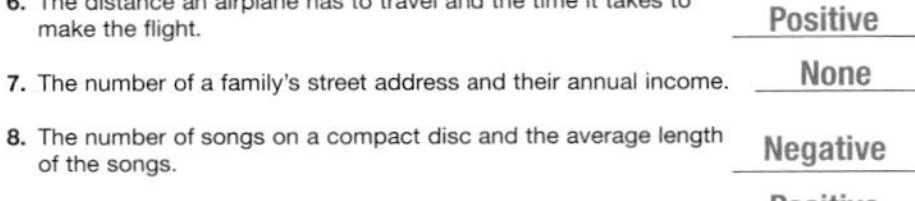

6. The distance an airplane has to travel and the time it takes to make the flight. **Positive**
7. The number of a family's street address and their annual income. **None**
8. The number of songs on a compact disc and the average length of the songs. **Negative**
9. The number of bedrooms in a house and the price of the house. **Positive**

RETEACHING

Name ______________________

Alternative Lesson 1-6

Scatterplots and Relationships

A **scatterplot** is a graph of data values that are given in pairs. Each axis represents one set of data and has its own scale.

Example 1

The scatterplot at the right shows the number of hours students studied for the math test and the scores on their tests. How long did Student A and Student B study? What were their scores?

Does Studying Help?

Math test scores: 0, 20, 40, 60, 80, 100
Hours studied: 1, 2, 3, 4, 5

The student labeled A studied one hour and scored 65 points. The student labeled B studied four hours and scored 90 points.

Since the two sets of data—study time and test scores—increase at the same time, this shows a **positive relationship.**

Example 2

The scatterplot at the right shows the price of a product and the number of units sold at that price. What happened as the price increased?

Product Sales

Number of units sold: 0, 10,000, 20,000, 30,000, 40,000, 50,000
Price (in dollars): 10, 20, 30, 40, 50

Since the price increases as the number of units decreases, the sets show a **negative relationship.**

Example 3

The scatterplot at the right shows students' ages and their science test scores. Is there a relationship between the two?

Age and Science Scores

Science test scores: 0, 20, 40, 60, 80, 100
Age of student: 8, 9, 10, 11, 12, 13, 14

Since the ages and test scores neither increase nor decrease together, the sets show **no relationship.**

Try It The scatterplot on the right shows the length of a walking step (in feet) and the number of steps it takes to walk 100 feet.

Steps in 100 Feet

Number of steps: 0, 20, 40, 60, 80, 100
Length of step (in feet): 0.5, 1.0, 1.5, 2.0, 2.5, 3.0

a. What do you notice about the number of steps it takes as the length of the step becomes longer?
   Possible answer: As the length of one's step increases, the number of steps decreases.

b. What type of relationship is this? **Negative**

9. **Test Prep** Which point on the scatterplot represents a perfect score on a test? **D**

Ⓐ P Ⓑ Q Ⓒ R Ⓓ S

10. **Sports** Which of these scatterplots might show the length of stride against the number of strides taken in a 100-meter sprint? **The third**

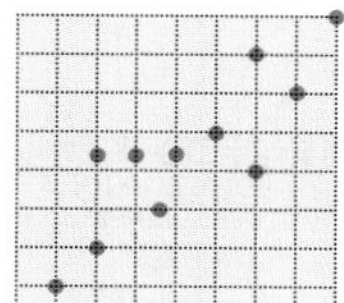

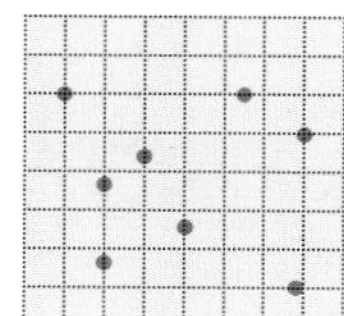

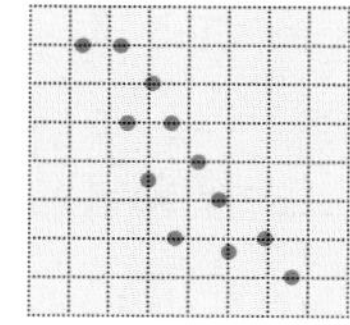

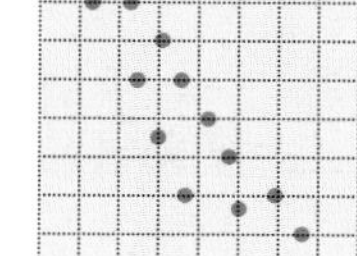

Incorrect answers / Correct answers

11. **Communicate** Describe a set of paired data that has a negative relationship.

Problem Solving and Reasoning

12. **Critical Thinking** The scatterplot shows total goals scored in a series of soccer matches plotted against the total number of attempts. Is there anything surprising about the plot? Explain your thinking.

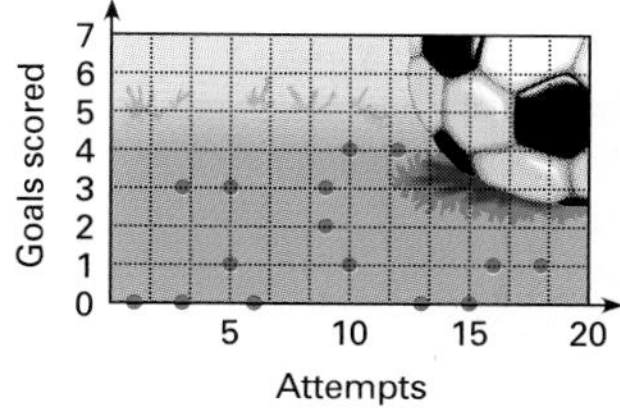

13. **Critical Thinking** The scatterplot shows the number of cars crossing a toll bridge on the different days in May. Describe any patterns you see.

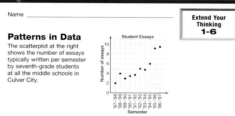

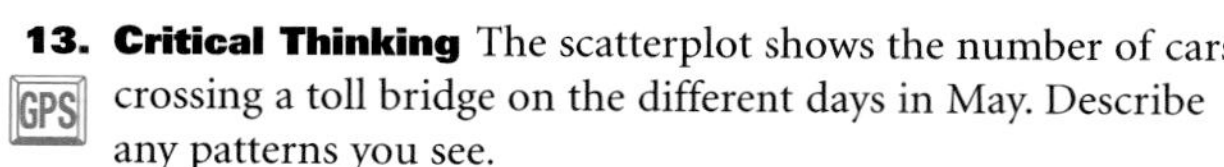

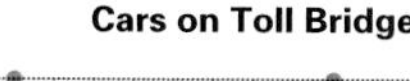

Cars on Toll Bridge

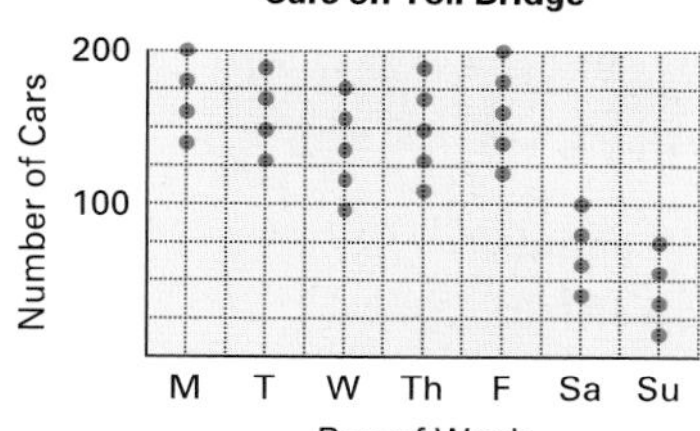

Mixed Review

Multiply or divide. *[Previous course]*

14. 345 × 531 **183,195**
15. 842 ÷ 22 **38 R6**
16. 6,241 × 390 **2,433,990**
17. 5,924 ÷ 50 **118 R24**
18. 7,238 × 942 **6,818,196**
19. 6,319 × 2,733 **17,269,827**

Make a stem-and-leaf diagram for each set of data. *[Lesson 1-3]*

20. 23, 32, 24, 34, 32, 31, 25, 36, 28, 27, 21, 41, 29
21. 7, 4, 8, 12, 14, 9, 21, 23, 17, 21, 10, 11, 16, 19, 12

Project Progress

After all of your events have been completed, look at the data you collected for each event. Decide which type of graph would best show the event's results, and make the graph. Find the winner of each event. You may wish to have a closing ceremony in which all the winners are announced.

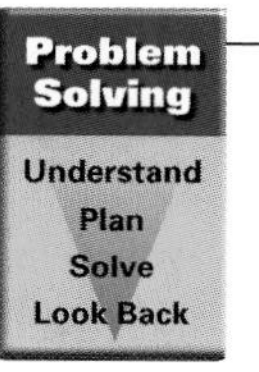

PROBLEM SOLVING

Name ______

Guided Problem Solving 1-6

GPS PROBLEM 13, STUDENT PAGE 39

The scatterplot shows the number of cars crossing a toll bridge on the different days in May. Describe any patterns you see.

— Understand —

1. Underline what you are asked to find.
2. Does the scatterplot show a positive, negative, or no relationship? What does this tell you about the trend? **No relationship, no trends.**

— Plan —

3. On which day(s) were the number of cars between 100 and 200? Between 0 and 100? **Monday through Friday; Saturday and Sunday.**
4. On which days does the number of cars seem to be about the same? **Monday through Friday and Saturday through Sunday.**

— Solve —

5. What pattern do you notice in the scatterplot? **Possible answer: There is heavier traffic on weekdays.**

— Look Back —

6. Is your answer to Item 5 reasonable? Explain. **Yes, because 100–200 cars cross the bridge on weekdays, and only between 0–100 cars cross the bridge on the weekend.**

SOLVE ANOTHER PROBLEM

The scatterplot shows the number of people that visited an amusement park on the different days of June. What do you think might account for any patterns that you see?

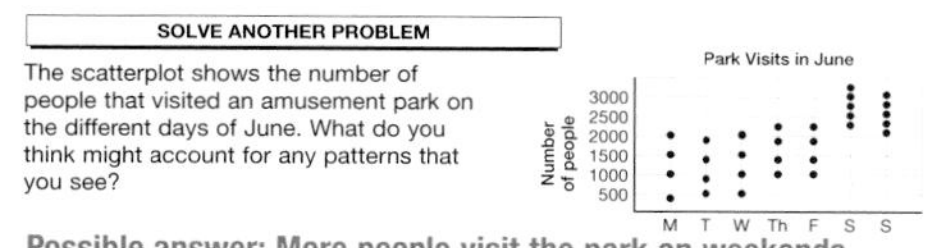

Possible answer: More people visit the park on weekends because they do not have to go to school or to work.

ENRICHMENT

Name ______

Extend Your Thinking 1-6

Patterns in Data

The scatterplot at the right shows the number of essays typically written per semester by seventh-grade students at all the middle schools in Culver City.

Student Essays

1. What pattern do you notice over the ten-year period? **There is an increase in the number of essays.**
2. In what year do you think that more teachers began to emphasize writing in their classes? Explain. **1995–1996; shows a significant increase over previous years.**
3. Suppose that during the 1996–1997 semester, the schools received news that they had a three-year grant to pay for a specialist to teach students to write in all subject areas.
   a. How do you think the grant will affect the pattern the scatterplot shows for the year 1997–1998? Explain. **Possible answer: The number of essays will be 10 or more because that year is one during the three-year grant.**
   b. What do you predict might happen to the pattern for the year 2000-2001? Explain. **Possible answer: The number of essays may drop off since the specialist will no longer be there.**
4. Suppose that during the three years that the specialist was in the school system, she trained all of the middle school teachers to use writing in their subject areas. What pattern might this show for the school years 1998-1999 through 2002-2003? Explain. **Possible answer: A continued increase since the process will be continued by the teachers in the system.**

Exercise Answers

11. Possible answer: The more money you have saved, the less additional money you need to save to reach a financial goal.
12. There is not a clear connection between number of attempts and number of goals scored. One match had 3 goals out of 3 attempts, while another had no goals out of 15 attempts.
13. Most cars on weekdays, then fewer on Saturday, least on Sunday.

20.

Stem	Leaf
4	1
3	1, 2, 2, 4, 6
2	1, 3, 4, 5, 7, 8, 9

21.

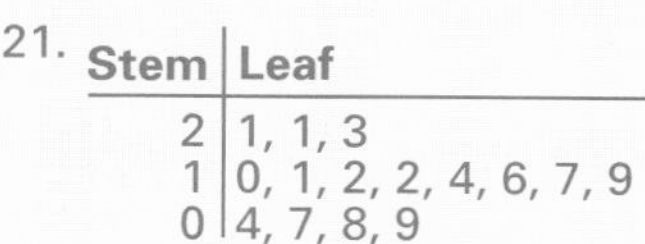

Stem	Leaf
2	1, 1, 3
1	0, 1, 2, 2, 4, 6, 7, 9
0	4, 7, 8, 9

Alternate Assessment

Portfolio Have students put an example in their portfolios of each of the three types of relationships possible between two sets of data.

Quick Quiz

Make a scatterplot of the data, and tell whether there is a positive, negative, or no relationship.

Age (yr)	1	2	3	4	5
Wt (lb)	21	30	37	43	50

There is a positive relationship.

Age and Weight

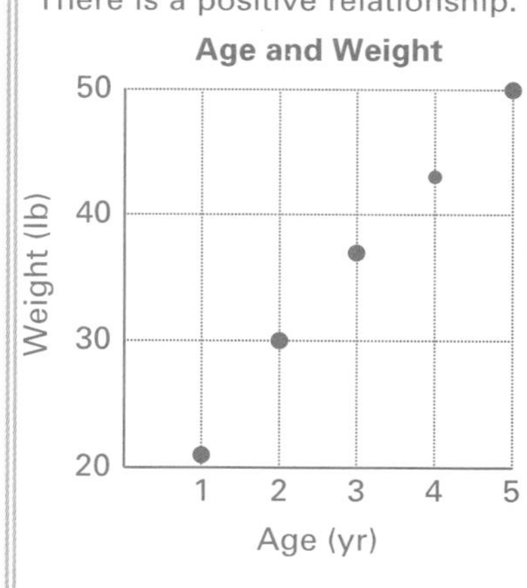

Available on Daily Transparency 1-6

1-7 Lesson Organizer

Objectives

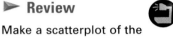

- Construct trend lines.
- Use trend lines to make predictions.

Vocabulary

- Trend line

NCTM Standards

- 1–4, 8, 10

➤ Review

Make a scatterplot of the data, and tell whether there is a positive, a negative, or no relationship.

Age (yr)	20	40	60	80
Pulse rate (beats per min)	85	72	60	56

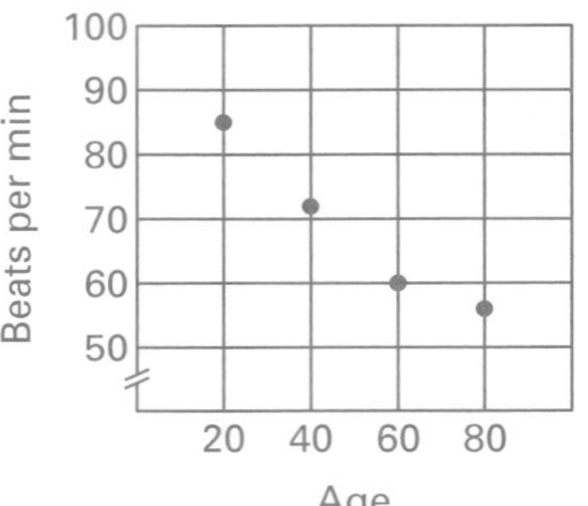

There is a negative relationship.

Available on Daily Transparency 1-7

1 Introduce

Explore

You may wish to use Teaching Tool Transparency 7: $\frac{1}{4}$-Inch Graph Paper with this lesson.

The Point
Students see how they can use a trend in a scatterplot to make predictions.

Ongoing Assessment
Circulate throughout the class to check that students are able to construct the scatterplots correctly.

Answers for Explore on page C3.

1-7 Trend Lines

You'll Learn ...

- to construct trend lines
- to use trend lines to make predictions

... How It's Used

Coaches need to see whether the training schedules they are using are having the desired results. One way to see this is to make a scatterplot and check the trend.

Vocabulary

trend line

► Lesson Link You know how to construct a scatterplot to display the relationship between two sets of data. Now you will see how to use that relationship to make predictions about the data. ◄

Explore Trend Lines

Trends and Relations

Use the box score from the 1996 NCAA Women's Basketball Championship game to answer each question.

University of Tennessee Boxscore				
Player	**Height (ft-in)**	**Minutes**	**Assists**	**Points**
Holdsclaw	6-2	34	3	16
Conklin	6-3	23	3	14
Johnson	6-4	28	1	16
Marciniak	5-9	37	5	10
Davis	5-6	32	8	8
Jolly	5-10	10	1	2
Laxton	6-0	12	0	4
Thompson	6-1	21	0	12

1. Make a scatterplot using "Minutes Played" and "Points" data. Make a second scatterplot using "Assists" and "Height" data.
2. Describe the difference between the shapes of the scatterplots. Is there anything special about the data that might account for this?
3. Do players who are tall tend to have a lot of assists? Do players who play for many minutes tend to score a lot of points?
4. Suppose a player played for 40 minutes. What would be a good prediction for the number of points she scored? Explain.
5. Suppose a player had 10 assists. What would be a good prediction for her height? Explain.
6. Describe the method you used to make your predictions. What are some factors that determine if the prediction is likely to come true?

MEETING INDIVIDUAL NEEDS

Resources

- 1-7 Practice
- 1-7 Reteaching
- 1-7 Problem Solving
- 1-7 Enrichment
- 1-7 Daily Transparency
  - Problem of the Day
  - Review
  - Quick Quiz
- Teaching Tool Transparency 7
- Technology Master 5

Learning Modalities

Verbal Now that students have studied a wide range of graphical representations, present different kinds of data and discuss which types of representations would be most appropriate for purposes of displaying data and projecting trends.

Kinesthetic If students do not have access to clear plastic rulers, you might substitute uncooked spaghetti as an aid for making trend lines.

Challenge

Have students choose one of the types of graphs described in this chapter and construct two graphs with different points of view for the following data. One graph should show that attendance remained about the same at Water World from 1990 to 1995; the other should show a sharp drop in attendance. Have the students share their strategies.

Water World Attendance

Year	Attendance	Year	Attendance
1990	135,000	1993	94,000
1991	131,000	1994	90,000
1992	118,000	1995	83,000

Learn Trend Lines

When sets of data show a positive or negative relationship, you can draw a **trend line** to approximate the data. A trend line should have about the same number of data points above and below it. By extending the trend line, you can make predictions about the data.

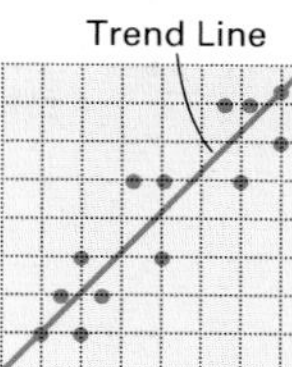

Examples

1 Draw a scatterplot and a trend line for the number of wins and years of coaching for the eight college football coaches with the most total wins.

Years	30	44	27	30	38	33	57	23
Wins	259	319	234	278	323	238	314	231

The scatterplot shows a positive relationship between wins and years of coaching.

To draw a trend line, take a clear plastic ruler and position it until an equal number of points lie above and below the trend line. Then, draw the line.

Wins and Years Coached

Wins: 200, 225, 250, 275, 300, 325

Years: 20, 30, 40, 50, 60, 65

2 Use the trend line to predict the number of wins for a coach who coached for 35 years.

The point on the trend line directly above 35 (years) is approximately 270 (wins). So, the trend line suggests that a coach would win 270 games in 35 years.

Try It

a. Draw a scatterplot and a trend line for this data:

Hours Watching TV (average per day)	2.4	5.1	1.8	3.3	3.9	4.7
Books Read (average per year)	11	3	12	6	6	2

b. Use the trend line to predict the number of daily hours watching TV for someone who reads 14 books per year. About 1

Test Prep

It is better to use a clear ruler than a wooden straightedge so that you can see where all the data points are.

History Link

Television was invented in 1923. The first TV broadcast that could be seen all over the United States was on September 4, 1951, when President Truman spoke in San Francisco.

2 Teach

Learn

Alternate Examples

1. Draw a scatterplot and a trend line for the given winning times for Olympics men's 1500-meter freestyle swimming.

Year	'56	'68	'80	'92	'96
Time (min)	18.0	16.7	15.0	15.0	14.6

The scatterplot shows a negative relationship.

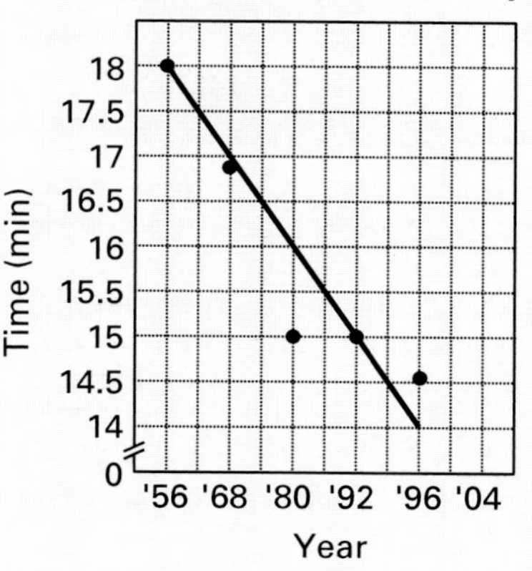

2. Use the trend line in Alternate Example 1 to predict the winning Olympic time for the men's 1500-meter freestyle in the year 2004. About 13.8 min.

Answers for Try It

a.

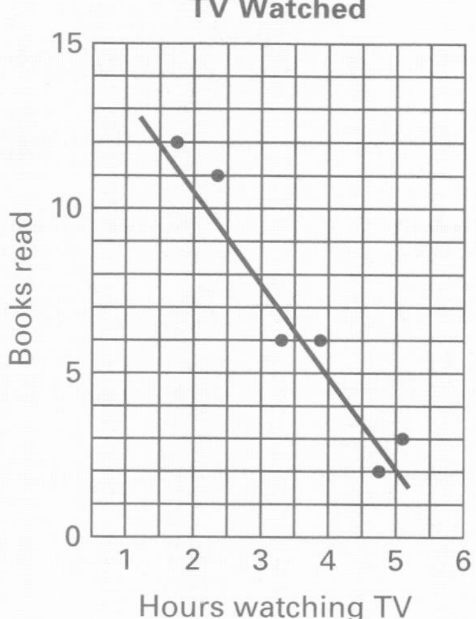

MATH EVERY DAY

Problem of the Day

Pentominos are made by connecting 5 squares. Each square shares at least one side with another square. How many different pentominos can you draw? Hint: Flips and slides count as one shape.

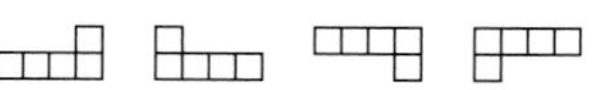

Same Shape

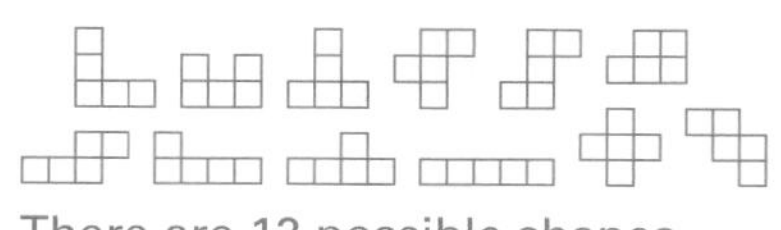

There are 12 possible shapes.

Available on Daily Transparency 1-7

An Extension is provided in the transparency package.

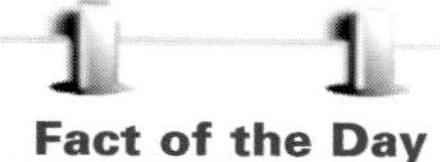

Fact of the Day

In 1995, the University of Connecticut women's basketball team won the most games of any NCAA basketball team—men's or women's.

Mental Math

Solve each equation mentally.

1. $x + 8 = 15$ $x = 7$
2. $y \div 3 = 6$ $y = 18$
3. $a - 9 = 5$ $a = 14$
4. $4 \cdot c = 24$ $c = 6$

Students see how two different graphic representations can be used to make a prediction. The first is a line graph which is extended, and the second is a scatterplot and its trend line.

Answers for What Do You Think?

1. If the trends do not continue.
2. The scatterplot trend line; The line graph takes less of the data into account, so it is more of a guess.

3 Practice and Assess

Check

Emphasize that a trend line showing a negative relationship can be as descriptive as one showing a positive relationship. Also, be sure students know that there may be no data points on a trend line.

Answers for Check Your Understanding

1. The line should be drawn so that there are about as many data points above the line as below it.
2. Yes; there is more than one way to judge the data.

Taro and Melissa wanted to estimate a fair price for a 10-year-old snowmobile. Here is the data they found in the classified ads.

Used Snowmobile Prices

Age (yr)	2	5	3	8	6
Price ($)	4800	3700	4000	2300	3000

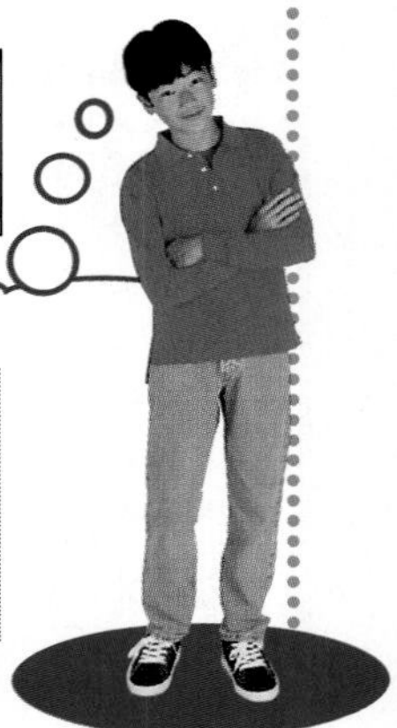

Taro thinks . . .

I'll make a line graph of the data and extend the line.

From the trend of the graph, I estimate a price of $1,500.

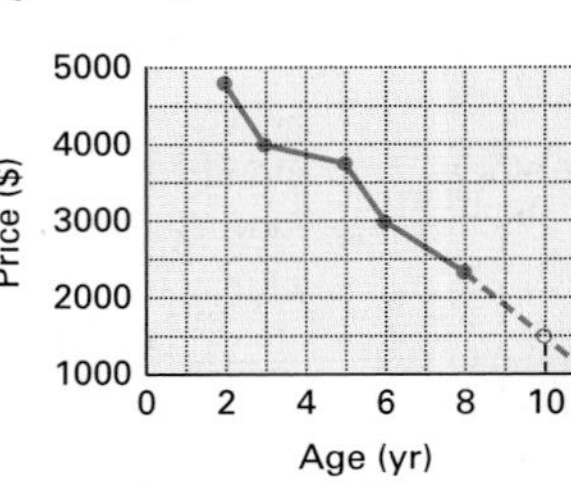

Melissa thinks . . .

I'll make a scatterplot of the data and draw a trend line.

From the trend line, I estimate a price of $1,500.

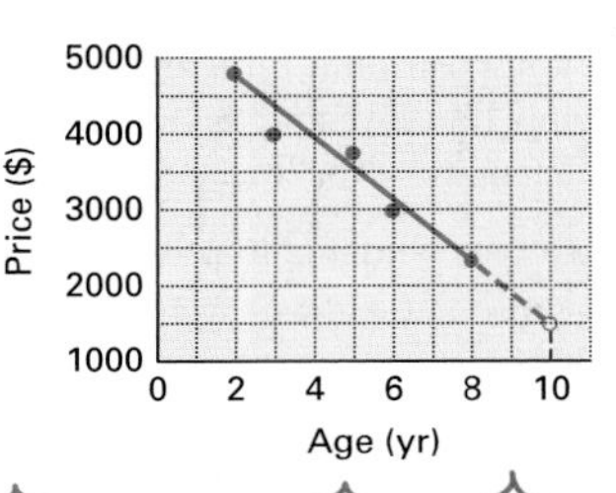

What do you think?

1. What might cause either estimate to be far off the mark?
2. Which method is more certain? Which involves more of a guess?

Check Your Understanding

1. How do you decide where to draw a trend line?
2. For a given scatterplot, is more than one trend line possible? Explain.

MEETING MIDDLE SCHOOL CLASSROOM NEEDS

Tips from Middle School Teachers

I have students try to find examples of scatterplots and display them on the classroom bulletin board. Students try to identify trend lines and then write brief descriptions of the graphs.

Team Teaching

Have the science or social studies teachers provide you with real data that your class can use to create a variety of graphical representations. If available, have students use computer graphing programs or graphing calculators.

Cultural Connection

In Athens in 1896, 311 athletes from 13 countries participated in the first of the modern Olympic games. The ancient Olympic games were religious festivals. The festivals probably started before 1400 B.C., and at first consisted only of foot races.

1-7 Exercises and Applications

Practice and Apply

1. **Getting Started** The Sybox Open Golf Tournament increased ticket prices each of the last 4 years. Use the table to make a scatterplot for the average daily attendance for each ticket price.

Sybox Open Golf Tournament Average Daily Attendance

Ticket Price ($)	Average Attendance
14	5261
15	4706
16	3968
17	3350

   a. Choose a scale for both axes.
   b. Mark the intervals on your axes.
   c. Label both axes and plot the points.
   d. Place your ruler so that about an equal number of data points are above and below its edge.
   e. Draw the trend line.

2. The scatterplot shows the number of fish caught and the time spent fishing. Copy the graph and draw a trend line. Predict the number of fish you might catch in 6 hours.

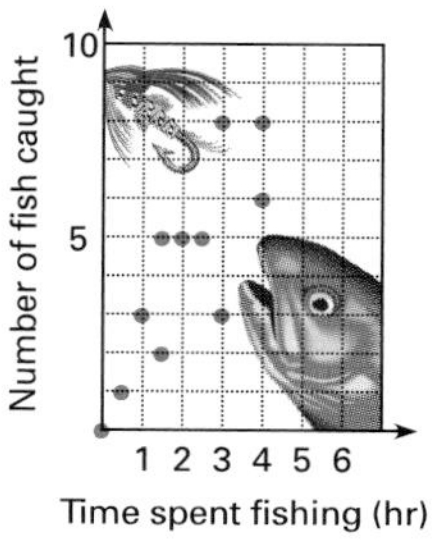

Number of fish caught
10
5
1 2 3 4 5 6
Time spent fishing (hr)

3. **Consumer** Make a scatterplot of the data shown in the table. Draw the trend line.

Price of CD ($)	13.99	12.99	11.99	17.99	19.99	21.99	22.99
Number of Songs	15	23	18	14	25	16	22

4. **Test Prep** The graph shows attempted shots at goal and goals scored by the players on a hockey team. If the trend continues, which of these numbers is a good prediction of how many goals might be scored by a player making 15 attempts?

   Ⓐ 0   Ⓑ 2   Ⓒ 5   Ⓓ 8

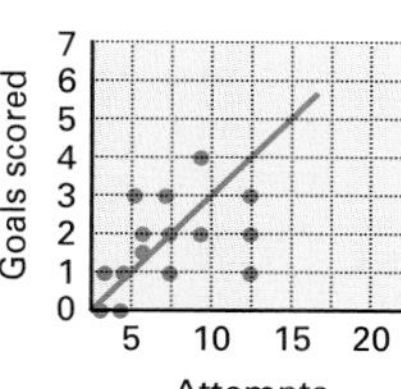

5. **Nutrition** The table shows the grams of fat and number of calories in one 8-ounce serving of milk.
   a. Make a scatterplot and draw a trend line.
   b. Use your trend line to predict how many calories there are in milk with 6.0 grams of fat.

Fat and Calories in Milk

Type of milk	Fat (g)	Calories
Whole	8.5	150
2% Low-Fat	4.7	120
1% Low-Fat	2.5	100
Skim	0.4	85

PRACTICE 1-7

1-7 Exercises and Applications

Assignment Guide

- **Basic**
  1, 2, 4, 5–8, 11–14, 17
- **Average**
  1–4, 6, 8–10, 15–16, 18
- **Enriched**
  1–4, 6, 8–10, 15–19

Exercise Answers

1. a–e.

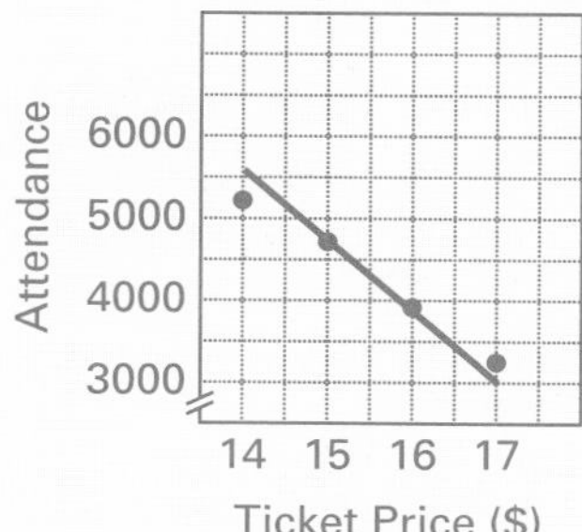

2. Should be in range 10–12.

3–5. See page C3.

Reteaching

Activity

- The chart below shows temperatures for one day in different cities. Make a scatterplot and draw a trend line for the data.

City	Temp. (°F)	Latitude (°N)
Calcutta	97	23
Cairo	83	30
Tokyo	63	35
Rome	68	42
London	56	52
Moscow	47	56

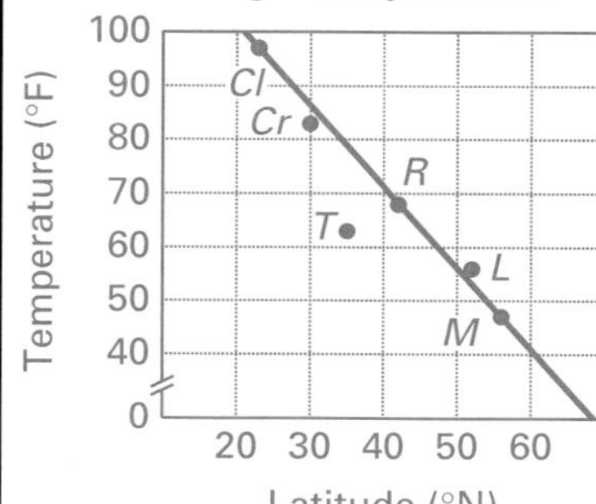

- Predict a temperature for Copenhagen, which is at north latitude 56°. Around 50°F

PRACTICE

Name ______________________

Practice 1-7

Trend Lines

1. **Consumer** The table shows prices of packages containing 100-megabyte computer disks. Make a scatterplot of the data. Draw the trend line.

Number of disks	1	2	3	6	10
Price ($)	20	37	50	100	150

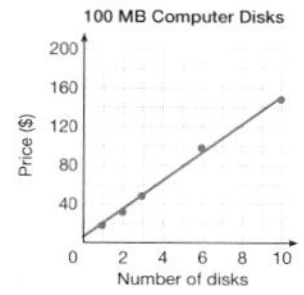

100 MB Computer Disks
Price ($)
200
160
120
80
40
0
2 4 6 8 10
Number of disks

Careers The scatterplot shows the 1989 median income of male year-round workers and the number of years of school. The trend line is shown. Use this scatterplot for Exercises 2–3.

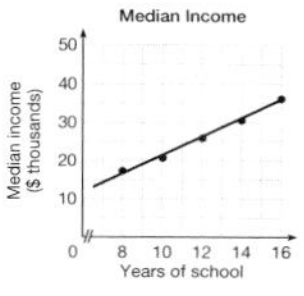

Median Income
Median income ($ thousands)
50
40
30
20
10
0
8 10 12 14 16
Years of school

2. Predict the median income for men who have spent 20 years in school.

   About $46,000

3. Do you think you can use this scatterplot to predict the median salary for women who have spent 20 years in school? Explain.

   Answers will vary.

The table shows average monthly temperatures in degrees Fahrenheit for American cities in January and July. Use this information for Exercises 4–6.

City	Seattle	Baltimore	Boise	Chicago	Dallas	Miami	LA
Jan.	39.1	32.7	29.9	21.4	44.0	67.1	56.0
Jul.	64.8	76.8	74.6	73.0	86.3	82.5	69.0

City	Anchorage	Honolulu	New York	Portland	New Orleans
Jan.	13.0	72.6	31.8	21.5	52.4
Jul.	58.1	80.1	76.4	68.1	82.1

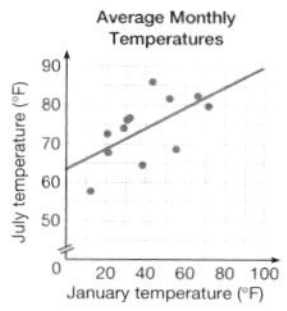

Average Monthly Temperatures
July temperature (°F)
90
80
70
60
50
0
20 40 60 80 100
January temperature (°F)

4. Make a scatterplot and draw a trend line.

5. Use your trend line to predict the July temperature of a city whose average January temperature is 10°F.

   About 66°F

6. Use your trend line to predict the January temperature of a city whose average July temperature is 75°F.

   About 43°F

RETEACHING

Name ______________________

Alternative Lesson 1-7

Trend Lines

When sets of data show a positive or negative relationship, you can draw a **trend line** to approximate the data. A trend line should have about the same number of data points above and below it. By extending the trend line, you can make predictions about the data.

Example

The scatterplot below shows the number of square feet in a house and the cost of the house. The trend line drawn through the data points has five points above it, five points below it, and one point on the line. What can you conclude from the scatterplot?

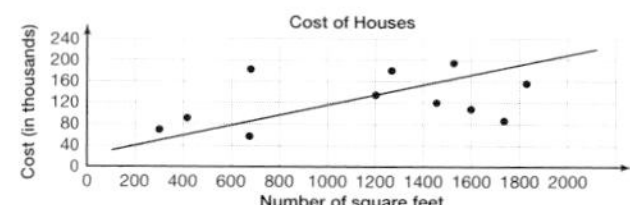

Since the trend line is going up, it indicates that the more square feet in a house, the more expensive the house is.

Try It The scatterplot shows the number of hours needed to rake leaves and the number of trees on the property.

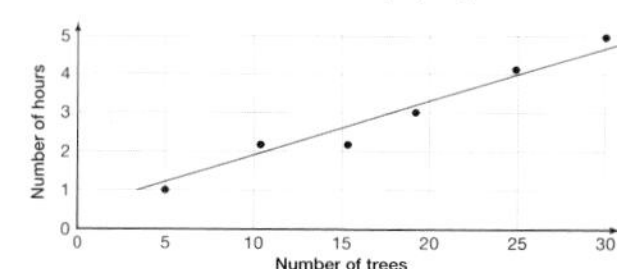

a. Use a straightedge to draw a trend line. Remember, there should be an equal number of points above and below the line.

b. Does the trend line indicate a positive or a negative relationship between the points? Explain.

Possible answer: Positive relationship, because the trend line is moving up from left to right showing an increase in time when there are more trees.

Exercise Notes

■ Exercise 7

Sports In 1992 the U.S. won 108 Olympic medals; 37 of them were gold. In 1988 the U.S. won 94 medals, of which 36 were gold.

Exercise Answers

6. a. Possible answer: Smaller states have smaller populations.
   b. No, because the points are fairly scattered.
7. a. See page C3.
   b. About 75
8. a. Yes; there appears to be a positive relationship.
   b. 10 yr, $40,000; 15 yr, $20,000
9. Possible answer: Positive trend; The more games played, the more points scored.
10. Possible answer: If you make a scatterplot, you can see the direction the data is taking. You can extend the trend line to predict other values.
17. Mean, ≈ 34.67; median, 36.5; mode 38
18. Mean, 28; median, 32.5; mode, 37
19. Mean, 101; median, 98; no mode

Alternate Assessment

Self Assessment Have students evaluate their performance and list any questions they may have about the content of this lesson.

▶ Quick Quiz

Tell if the scatterplot for each set of data would show a positive, a negative, or no trend.

1. Length of hair and age
   No trend
2. Glove size and height
   Positive trend
3. Size of an ice cube on a dish and temperature in the room Negative trend

Available on Daily Transparency 1-7

PROBLEM SOLVING 1-7

6. Communicate The scatterplot shows areas of some states and their 1996 populations.

GPS

a. Describe the plot.

b. Could you use the plot to make any predictions?

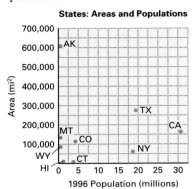

States: Areas and Populations

Area (mi²): 700,000; 600,000; 500,000; 400,000; 300,000; 200,000; 100,000
AK, TX, CA, MT, CO, NY, WY, CT, HI
0 5 10 15 20 25 30
1996 Population (millions)

7. Sports The table shows the number of medals won by six countries at the 1996 Olympics.

a. Make a scatterplot and draw a trend line.

b. Use your trend line to predict how many gold medals could be expected for a country that won a total of 200 medals.

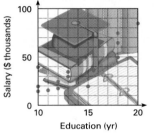

XXVI OLYMPIAD ATLANTA 1996

1996 Olympic Medals		
Country	Gold	Total
United States	44	101
Germany	20	65
Russia	26	63
China	16	50
Australia	9	41
France	15	37

Problem Solving and Reasoning

8. Critical Thinking The scatterplot shows the years of education completed and average income for the employees in a company.

a. Is there an overall trend?

b. Which points appear to go against the overall trend?

Salary and Education of Employees

Salary ($ thousands): 0, 50, 100
Education (yr): 10, 15, 20

9. Critical Thinking Would you expect a scatterplot showing the number of basketball games played to the total number of points scored by a player to show a positive or a negative trend? Why?

10. Journal Describe how scatterplots and trend lines are used to make predictions about future values of data.

Mixed Review

Add, subtract, multiply, or divide. *[Previous course]*

11. 349 + 468 + 2713 3530 **12.** 47,362 × 25 1,184,050 **13.** 60,042 − 5,476 54,566

14. 23)4839 210 R9 **15.** 3748 × 406 1,521,688 **16.** 9,365 − 8,715 650

Find the mean, median, and mode(s) for each data set. *[Lesson 1–4]*

17. 38, 28, 35, 29, 38, 40 **18.** 11, 37, 28, 37, 37, 18 **19.** 109, 98, 92, 94, 112

44 *Chapter 1 • Making Sense of the World of Data*

PROBLEM SOLVING

Name ______________________

Guided Problem Solving 1-7

GPS PROBLEM 6, STUDENT PAGE 44

The scatterplot shows the areas of some states and their 1996 population.

a. Describe the scatterplot.
b. Could you use the scatterplot to make any predictions?

States: Areas and Populations

— Understand —

1. Underline what you are asked to find.

— Plan —

2. Identify the relationship shown in the scatterplot. C

a. positive relationship b. negative relationship c. no relationship

3. Would a trend line help you make a prediction? Explain.
No. Since there is no relationship, there will be no trend line.

— Solve —

4. Describe the scatterplot. Tell how area and population relate. Possible answer: There is no relationship between area and population.

5. Could you use the scatterplot to predict the population of a state with an area of 57,918 square miles? No

— Look Back —

6. Does your answer make sense? Explain. Possible answer: Yes. No relationship between data, no prediction can be made.

SOLVE ANOTHER PROBLEM

The scatterplot shows the population of some states and the number of representatives from that state.

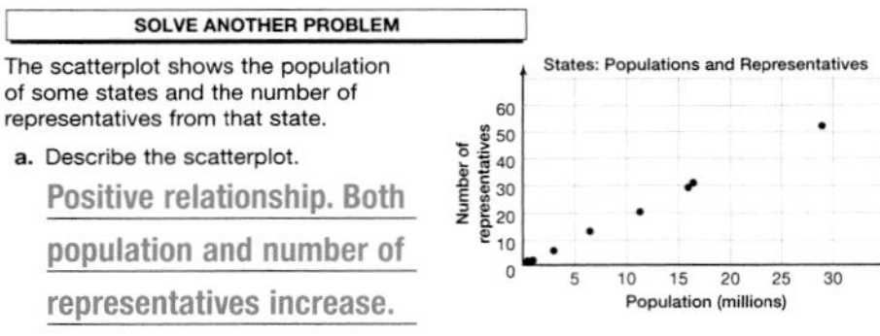

a. Describe the scatterplot.
Positive relationship. Both population and number of representatives increase.

b. Could you use the scatterplot to make any predictions? Explain.
Yes. More populous states have more representatives.

ENRICHMENT

Name ______________________

Extend Your Thinking 1-7

Patterns in Data

Bookends is a three-year-old chain of bookstores on the West Coast. The scatterplot at the right shows the average price of one share of Bookends stock for January through June of 1996.

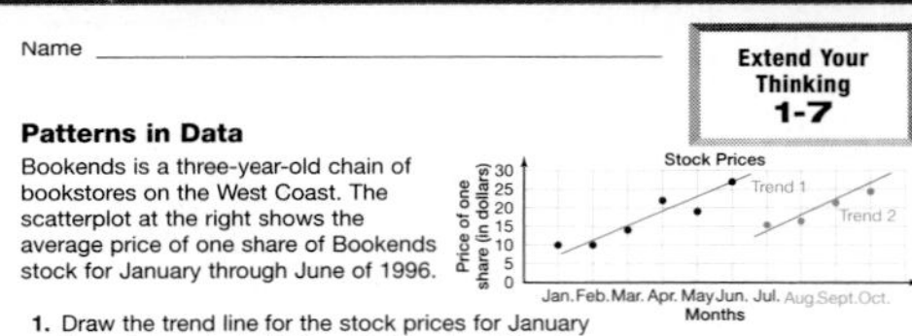

1. Draw the trend line for the stock prices for January through June. Label it *Trend 1*. Based on this pattern, what would you expect the average price to be in July? Explain.
Possible answer: $30, because the data shows a positive relationship, and the trend line shows a $30 price for July.

2. Suppose the average stock price for July was $16, August $17, September $22, and October $25. Plot the points on the graph. What can you assume about the future pattern of stock prices for this company? Explain.
Possible answer: Although the stock prices decreased between June and July, the overall trend is an increase in price as time passes. So the stock price will probably continue to increase.

3. When a 2-for-1 stock split occurs, each stock owner owns twice as many shares of stock as before the split, but each share is worth half as much. In this way, a company can keep its stock affordable. Suppose you learn that Bookends had a 2-for-1 stock split in July.

a. How would that change your prediction of the future pattern of its stock prices? Explain.
The stock prices will be half as much but they will continue to increase at about the same rate as in January through June.

b. Draw a trend line on the scatterplot above to show your new prediction. Label it *Trend 2*. How does it compare with the trend line you drew in Exercise 1?
The new trend line is parallel to the old one and shows stock prices increasing at a steady rate.

Section 1B Connect

In this section, you have seen that sets of data are sometimes related, and you have learned ways to discover and analyze those relationships. Now you will use what you have learned to look for relationships in baseball statistics.

Sports Around the World

The Florida Marlins baseball team has players that have the power to hit home runs and the speed to steal bases. *Home runs* (HR) are usually balls hit over the outfield fence. *Runs batted in* (RBI) are runs that happen as a result of the batter's actions. *Stolen bases* (SB) happen when a base runner runs to the next base as the ball is pitched. The 1995 season totals for the Florida starting lineup are given.

Player	HR	RBI	SB
Gary Sheffield	16	46	19
Jeff Conine	25	105	2
Terry Pendleton	14	78	1
Greg Colbrunn	23	89	11
Quilvio Veras	5	32	56
Andre Dawson	8	37	0
Kurt Abbott	17	60	4
Charles Johnson	11	39	0
Chuck Carr	2	20	25

1. Make a scatterplot with home runs on the horizontal axis and runs batted in on the vertical axis.
2. Determine if there is a positive, a negative, or no relationship between home runs and runs batted in. If there is a relationship, draw a trend line.
3. Make a scatterplot with home runs on the horizontal axis and stolen bases on the vertical axis.
4. Determine if there is a relationship between home runs and stolen bases. If there is, draw a trend line.
5. Predict the number of runs batted in for a Marlins player who hits 30 home runs. Explain how you made your prediction.
6. Predict the number of stolen bases for a Marlins player who hits 30 home runs. Explain.

45

Answers for Connect

1–2. Positive relationship

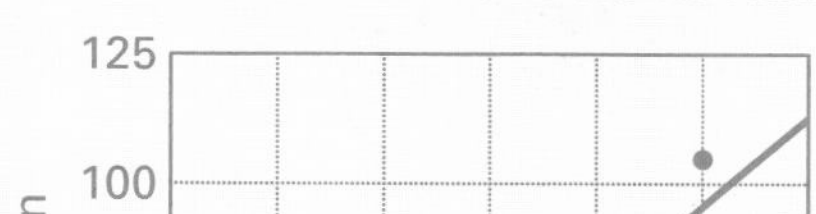

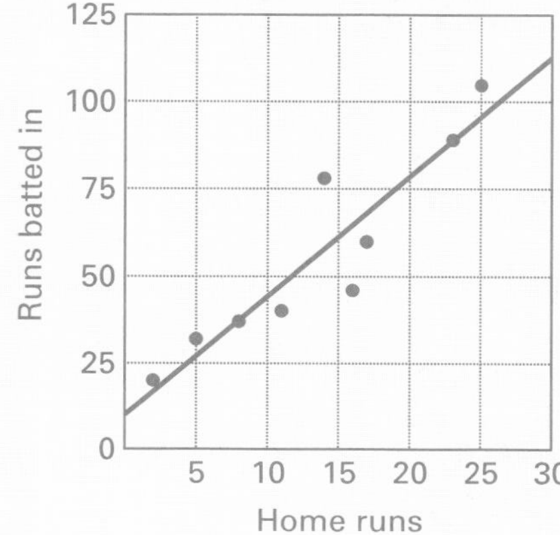

3–4. No relationship

5. Possible answer: 112–113 RBI; Extend trend line and read value for 30.
6. No relationship, so no relationship based on a trend.

1B Connect

Sports Around the World

The Point

Students discussed various sports in *Sports Around the World* on page 29. Now they use scatterplots to identify trends in sports data and to make predictions.

Materials

Graph Paper

Resources

Teaching Tools Transparency 7: $\frac{1}{4}$-Inch Graph Paper

About the Page

Review baseball terms and their abbreviations for students who may not be familiar with the game.

- Have students read the page and try to predict the relationship between home runs and runs batted in, and home runs and stolen bases.
- Ask students what information they think would help them make predictions about a team and its players.
- After students complete their scatterplots, discuss the validity of their predictions

Ongoing Assessment

Check students' scatterplots to determine if they have drawn an acceptable trend line.

Extension

Newspapers carry a variety of statistics in the sports section every day. Have students select a set of statistics about their favorite team or player, display it, and use their display to show a relationship or to make a prediction.

1B Review

Review Correlation

Item(s)	Lesson(s)
1	1-6
2, 3	1-5
4	1-5, 1-6
5–7	1-5, 1-7
8	1-5

Test Prep

Test-Taking Tip

Tell students to check that data points are correctly located on a graph. Here the data points are not correctly graphed in A and B.

Answers for Review

1. a. Possible answers:

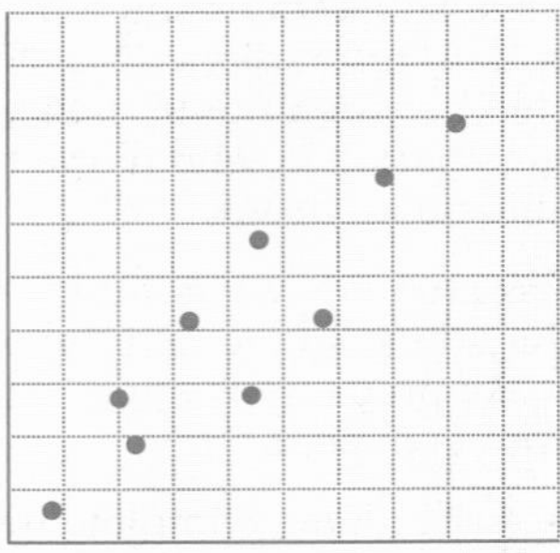

b. Possible answers:

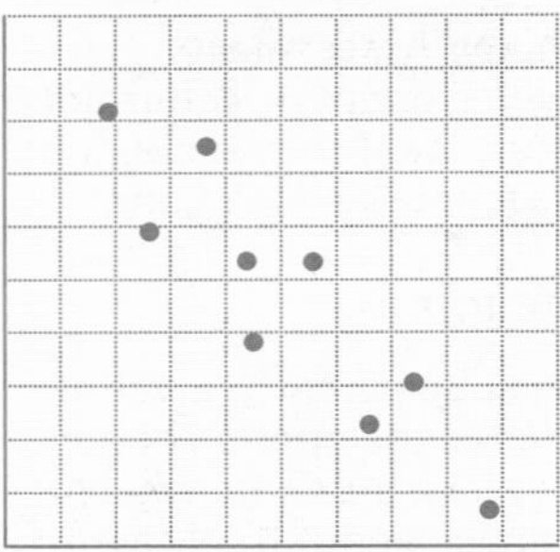

c. Possible answers:

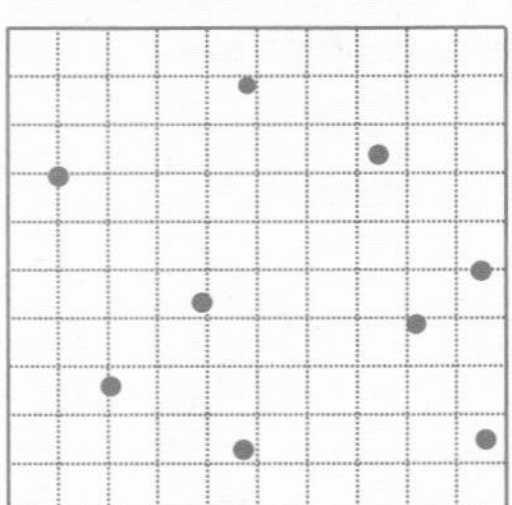

Answers for Exercises 2–8 on page C3.

Section 1B Review

REVIEW 1B

1. Sketch an example of a scatterplot showing:
   a. a positive relationship. b. a negative relationship.
   c. no relationship.
2. The table gives the total braking distance for a car at various speeds. Make a line graph of the data. Use your line graph to predict the braking distance for a car traveling 70 mi/hr.
3. **Communicate** If the braking distance for 50 mi/hr changed to 200 ft, how would your prediction change? Explain.
4. Journal Describe the difference between a line graph and a scatterplot.

Braking Distance

Speed (mi/hr)	Braking Distance (ft)
50	188
20	45
30	78
10	20
40	125

Use the table for Exercises 5–7.

5. Make a scatterplot of the data.
6. Draw a trend line on your scatterplot.
7. Use your trend line to predict the expected average attendance for a team with 110 wins.

American League West Attendance, 1995

Team	Wins	Average Attendance
Minnesota	56	14,690
Cleveland	100	40,038
Milwaukee	65	15,318
Kansas City	70	17,614
Chicago	68	22,673

Test Prep

You are often asked to match data sets to graphs. It is a good idea to make a quick sketch of just enough data points to recognize a match. It also helps to check for any easily identified features, such as repeated data values.

8. Which of these could be the graph for this set of data?

Year	1990	1991	1992	1993	1994	1995	1996
Wins	19	22	25	18	20	24	23

Ⓐ

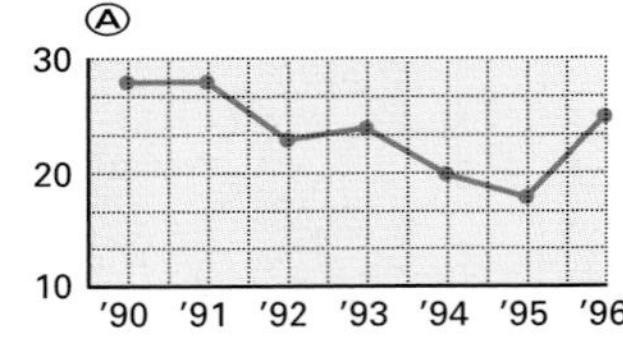

Ⓑ

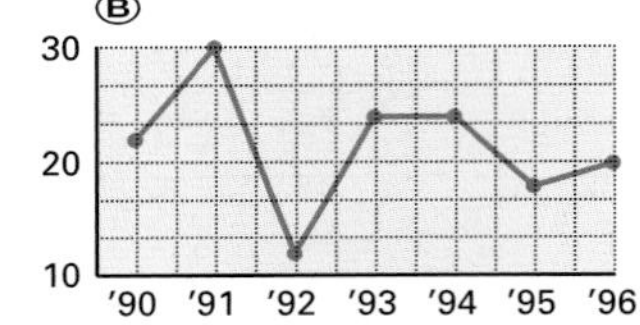

Ⓒ

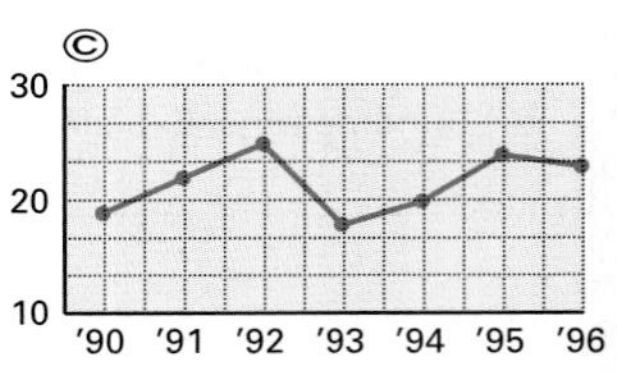

Resources

Practice Masters
Section 1B Review

Assessment Sourcebook
Quiz 1B

TestWorks
Test and Practice Software

PRACTICE

Name ______________

Practice

Section 1B Review

Use the data in the table for Exercises 1–2.

Year	1994	1995	1996	July 1996
Unemployment rate	6.5%	5.3%	5.3%	5.1%

1. Make a line graph of the data in the table.
2. Use your line graph to predict the unemployment rate in 1997.
   About 5%

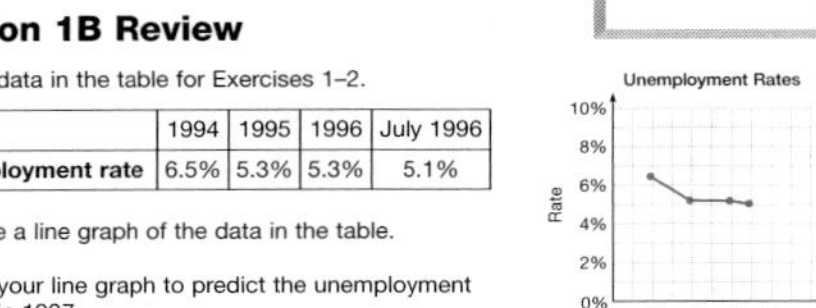

Ron's Bookstore is having a sale. The table shows the regular and sale prices for several books. Use the data for Exercises 3–5.

Regular price ($)	5.00	7.50	10.00	15.00	25.00	35.00
Sale price ($)	4.00	6.00	7.50	12.00	19.00	25.00

3. Make a scatterplot of the data.
4. Draw a trend line on your scatterplot.
5. Use your trend line to predict the sale price of a book whose regular price is $50.00.
   About $36

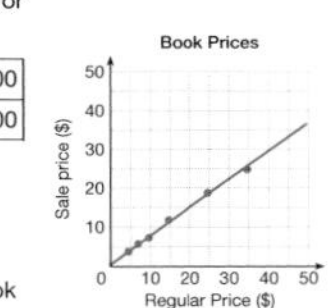

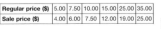

The graph shows the top five largest-grossing movies from 1990–1995. Use this information for Exercises 6–7. *[Lesson 1-1]*

6. List these movies in order from the most sales to the least sales.
   Jurassic Park, Lion King, Home Alone, Ghost, Aladdin
7. Give the dollar amount of ticket sales for *Home Alone*.
   About $285,000,000

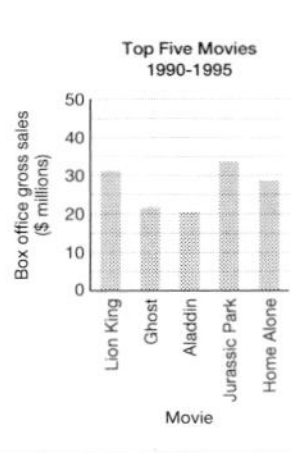

Extend Key Ideas · Statistics

Histograms

You've displayed data in several different ways. A histogram is another commonly used way to illustrate numerical data.

A radio station surveyed 100 people in each of five different age groups to find out how many enjoyed rap music. The frequency table shows the results of the survey. The frequency column shows how many from each age group said they enjoy rap music.

Age Group	Frequency
50–59	5
40–49	9
30–39	18
20–29	40
10–19	28

You can display this data in a bar graph called a histogram. In a histogram, there is no space between the bars.

The age groups are shown at the bottom of the histogram. The height of each bar indicates the number of people in each group.

Notice that the number of years in each age group is the same. When you display data in a histogram, all of the groups must be the same size.

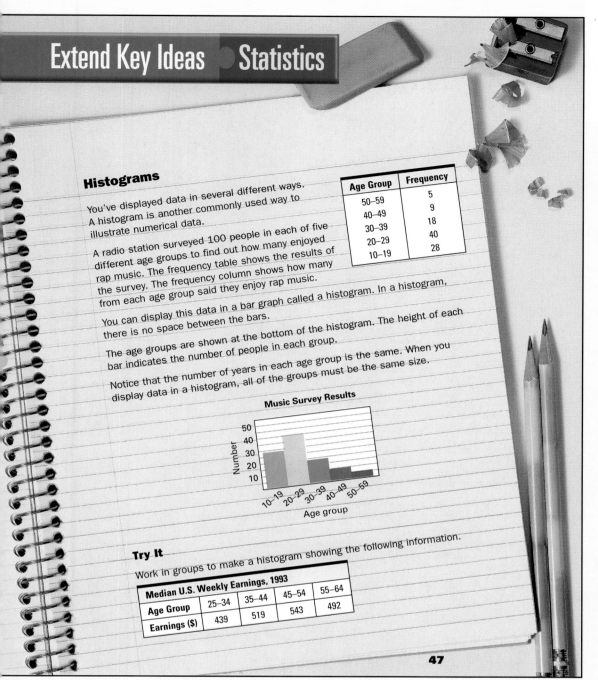

Music Survey Results

Number: 10, 20, 30, 40, 50

Age group: 10–19, 20–29, 30–39, 40–49, 50–59

Try It

Work in groups to make a histogram showing the following information.

Median U.S. Weekly Earnings, 1993				
Age Group	25–34	35–44	45–54	55–64
Earnings ($)	439	519	543	492

47

Extend Key Ideas

Histograms

The Point

Students use a histogram to display data for consecutive and equal groups.

About the Page

- A histogram is useful when comparing groups within continuous data, such as consecutive ages, so no space is left between the bars. A bar graph is used for comparing discrete, or discontinuous, data, therefore a space is left between the bars.

Ask ...

- For the data in **Try It**, why can the data of the 1993 weekly earnings be represented by a histogram? The age groups are in equal intervals and are continuous.
- What data should be along the horizontal axis? the vertical axis? The age groups along the horizontal axis; the earnings along the vertical axis.

Extension

Have students discuss reasons for the steady increase, and then the decrease, in earnings. Sample: Between ages 25 and 54, many people experience growth in their careers. Between ages 55 and 64, people begin to retire.

Answer for Try It

Median U.S. Weekly Earnings, 1993

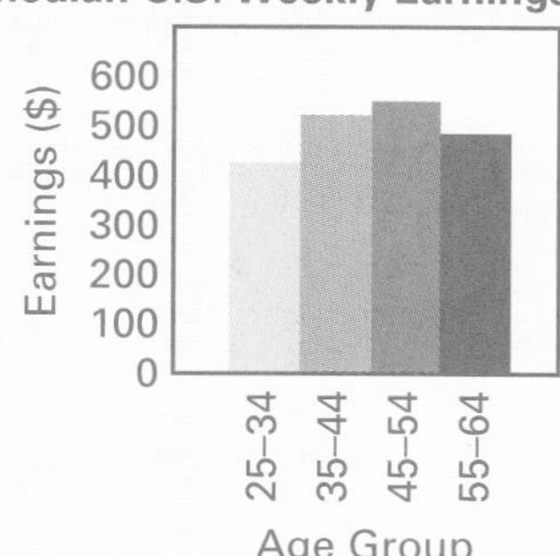

Chapter 1 Summary and Review

Review Correlation

Item(s)	Lesson(s)
1	1-2
2	1-4
3	1-3
4, 5	1-1
6	1-2
7	1-3
8	1-6
9	1-5
10	1-7

For additional review, see page 672.

Answers for Review

1.

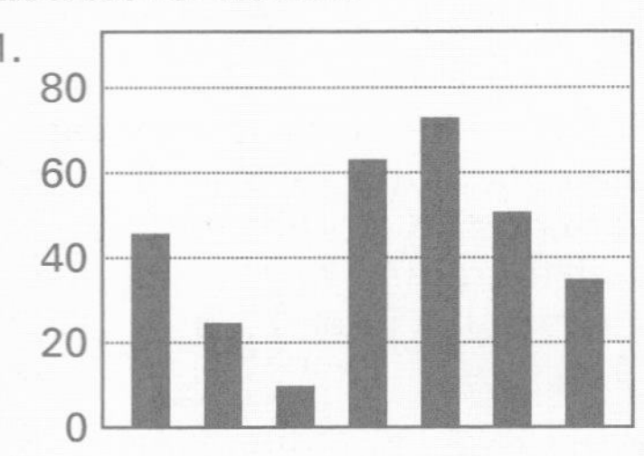

2. Mean: 20.3; Median 21; Mode 23; Range: 44.

3.

Stem	Leaf
2	2 3 8
3	2 3 4 7
4	1 2 5

4. A circle graph

5. Asia and Africa

Chapter 1 Summary and Review

Graphic Organizer

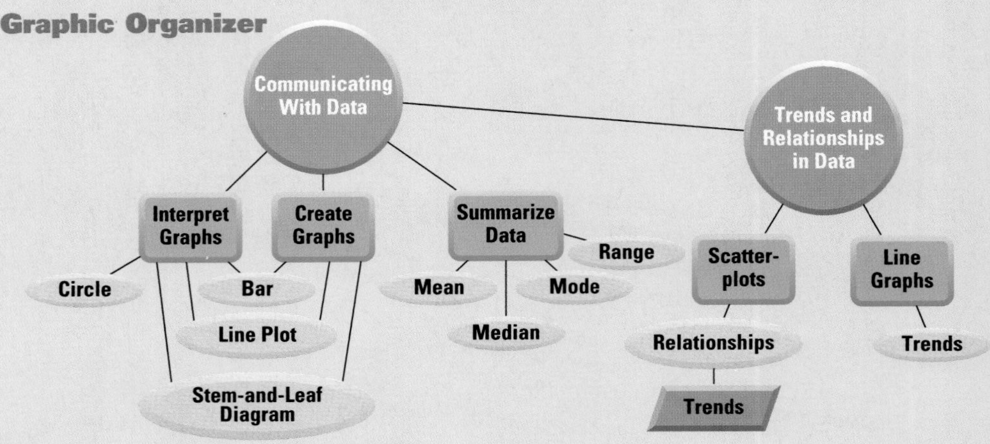

Section 1A Communicating with Data

Summary

- A **circle graph** uses **sectors** of a circle to represent data.
- Data is represented in a **bar graph** by the length of each bar. Bars may be **horizontal** or **vertical**. A **scale** and an **interval** must be chosen to make a bar graph. **Double-bar graphs** show two sets of data on the same graph.
- In a **line plot**, columns of ×'s show how frequently data values occur. It is easy to see which items appear most often and which are **outliers**.
- Use a **stem-and-leaf diagram** to show how data values are distributed.
- The **mean** of a data set is the sum of the data values divided by the number of data values. The **mode** is the number(s) that appears most often. The **median** is the middle value in an ordered set of data. The **range** is the difference between the highest and lowest data values.

Review

1. Make a bar graph to show the data.
45, 23, 10, 62, 73, 50, 35

2. Find the mean, median, mode(s), and range.
14, 23, 7, 25, 23, 19, 7, 51, 11, 23

3. Make a stem-and-leaf diagram to show:
32, 22, 45, 23, 33, 37, 41, 28, 34, 42

4. What type of graph best displays the varieties of music among a student's CDs?

Resources

Practice Masters
Cumulative Review Chapter 1

PRACTICE

Name ____________

Practice

Cumulative Review Chapters 1–7

Find the GCF and LCM. *[Lesson 3-7]*

1. 57, 76 GCF: 19 LCM: 228
2. 60, 100 GCF: 20 LCM: 300
3. 84,144 GCF: 12 LCM: 1008
4. 25, 35 GCF: 5 LCM: 175
5. 64, 112 GCF: 16 LCM: 448
6. 126, 56 GCF: 14 LCM: 504

Solve each equation. *[Lesson 4-3]*

7. $t - 4\frac{6}{7} = 3\frac{2}{7}$ t = $8\frac{1}{7}$
8. $c - 2\frac{1}{2} = 5\frac{3}{7}$ c = $7\frac{13}{14}$
9. $p - 3\frac{2}{9} = 21\frac{4}{9}$ p = $24\frac{2}{3}$
10. $u + 12\frac{1}{6} = 21\frac{19}{24}$ u = $9\frac{5}{8}$

Classify each figure in as many ways as you can. *[Lesson 5-3]*

11. Quadrilateral, trapezoid
12. Obtuse isosceles triangle
13. Right scalene triangle

A model train is 30 in. long. Use each scale to find the length of the actual train. *[Lesson 7-2]*

14. scale: 1 in. = 8 ft actual length: 240 ft
15. scale: 1 in. = 12 ft actual length: 360 ft
16. scale: 2 in. = 15 ft actual length: 225 ft

Find the missing side lengths in each pair of similar figures. *[Lesson 7-9]*

17. $ABCD \sim EFGH$ x = 64
18. $\triangle IJK \sim \triangle LMN$ p = 36 q = 45
19. $PQRS \sim TUVW$ a = 20 b = 50 c = 30

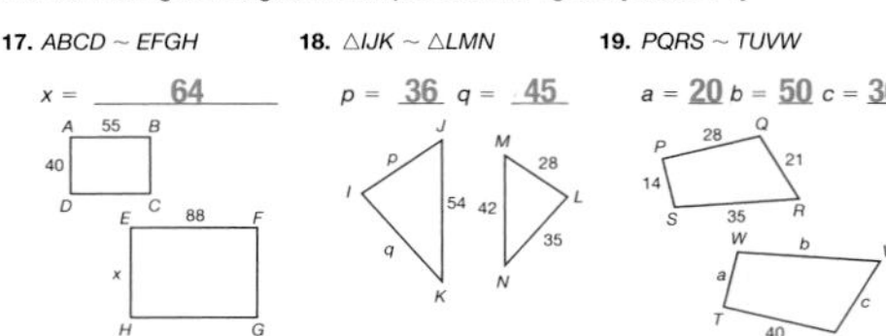

Section 1A Communicating with Data *(continued)*

5. Which two continents cover about half the land in the world between them?

Areas of Continents

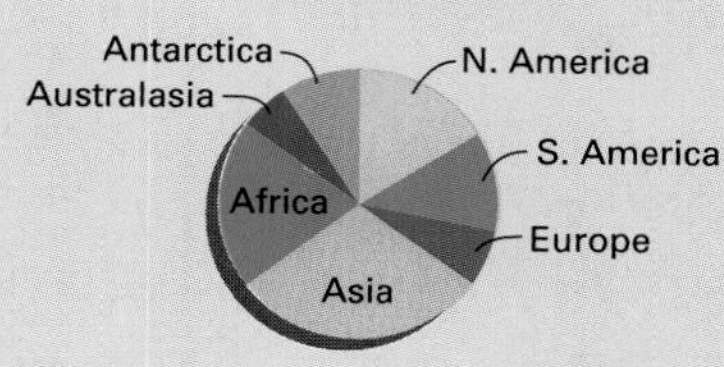

6. Make a bar graph with a broken vertical axis to display the world's four busiest airports in 1994. Explain why your graph could be misleading.

Airport	Passengers (millions)
Chicago O'Hare	66
Atlanta Hartsfield	54
Dallas/Ft. Worth	53
London Heathrow	52

7. Make a line plot to show the times of finishers in a race.

Minutes	30	50	60	70	80	90	120
Finishers	5	4	8	7	6	3	2

Section 1B Trends and Relationships in Data

Summary

- A **line graph** shows data plotted as points and then connected with a line. Two sets of related data can be displayed using a **double-line graph**. The **trend** of the data can be seen from a line graph.
- **Scatterplots** show if paired data has a **positive relationship**, a **negative relationship**, or **no relationship**. A **trend line** can be drawn on a scatterplot and used to make predictions about data values.

Review

8. Which scatterplot shows a positive relationship?

a. 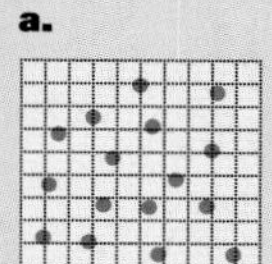

b. 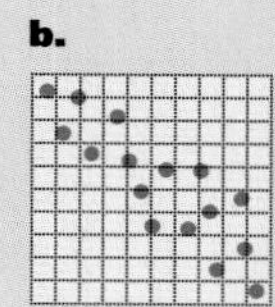

c. 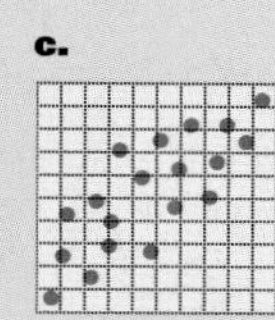

9. The table gives the singles ranking of professional tennis player Conchita Martinez at the end of each year. Make a line graph to display the data.

Year	1991	1992	1993	1994	1995
Ranking	9	8	4	3	2

10. Make a scatterplot of the data for players on a volleyball team. Draw a trend line and use it to predict the expected number of service errors for a player with 20 aces.

Service Aces	4	5	8	10	15
Service Errors	7	12	16	21	33

Answers for Review

6.

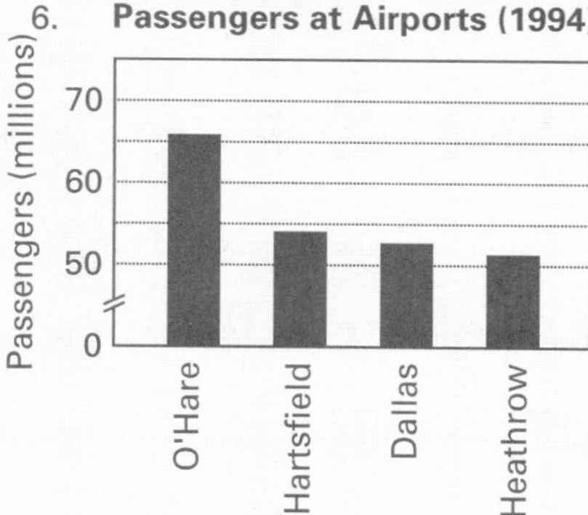

Because of the broken scale, it looks as though O'Hare carries more than twice as many passengers as the others. The range is really only 52,000,000 to 66,000,000.

7.

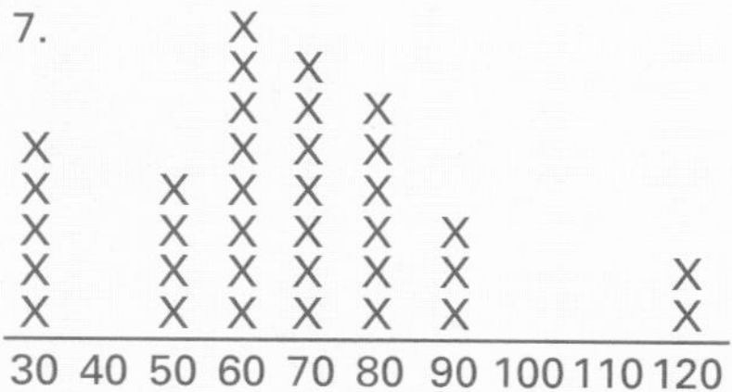

8. C

9.

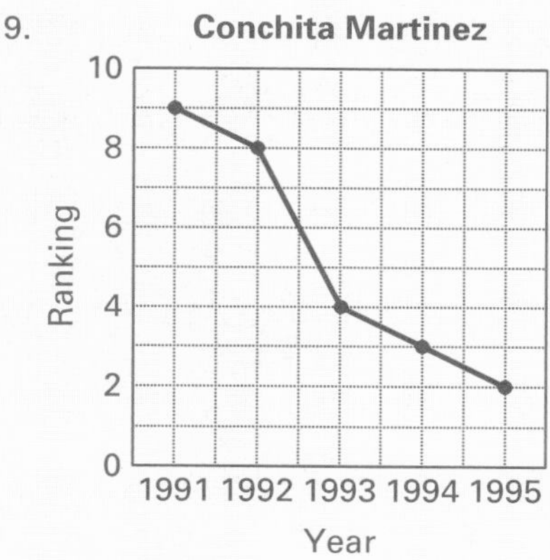

10.

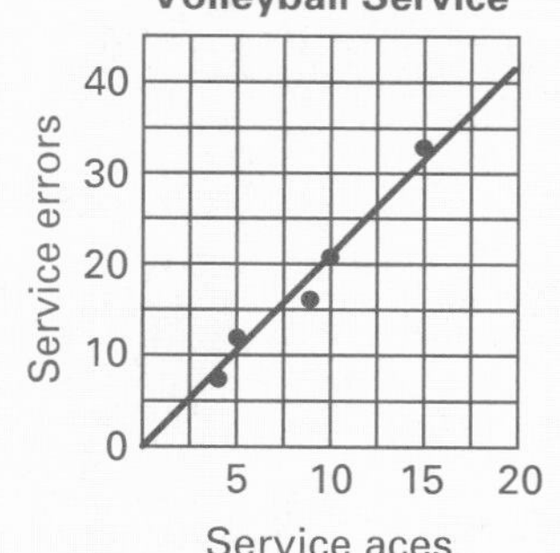

Chapter 1 Assessment

Assessment Correlation

Item(s)	Lesson(s)
1, 2	1-1
3	1-1
4, 5	1-3
6	1-4
7	1-6, 1-7

Answers for Assessment

1. 20–45
2. 45–60 and Over 60
3. Possible answers: Because one graph has a vertical scale that starts at 0 and the other one starts at 40.
4. 7; 71
5. 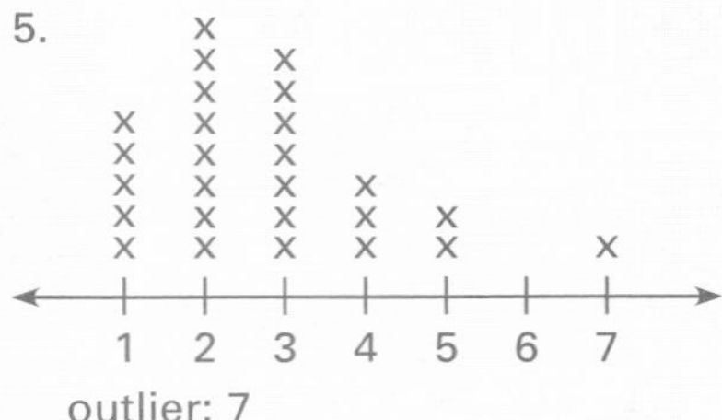

outlier: 7
6. Mean 2.73; Median 2.5; Mode 2; Range, 6. Answers may vary
7. 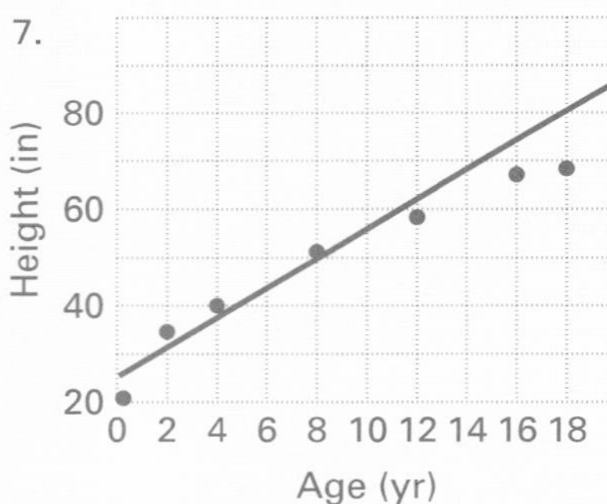

Possible answer: No, because men do not keep growing taller all their lives.

Answers for Performance Task on page C3.

Chapter 1 Assessment

Social Studies **Use the circle graph showing the 1990 U.S. population by age for Questions 1 and 2.**

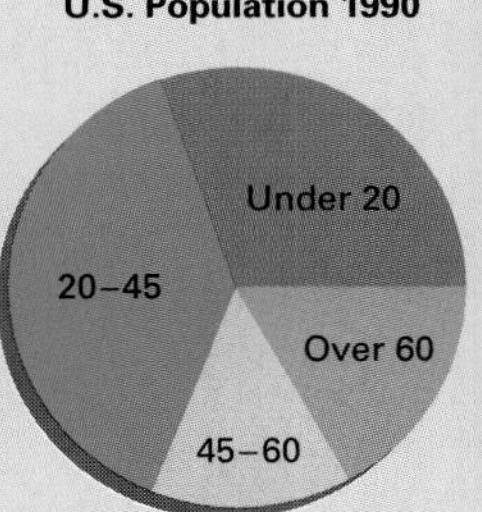

1. Which age group forms the largest part of the 1990 U.S. population?
2. Which two age groups together are about the same size as the Under 20 age group?
3. Explain why these two graphs of the average monthly temperatures in Dallas–Fort Worth look so different.

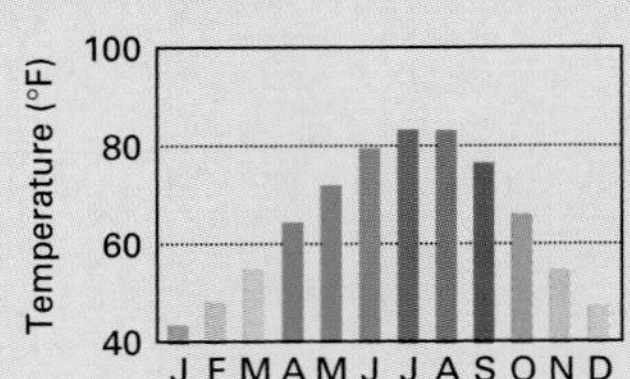

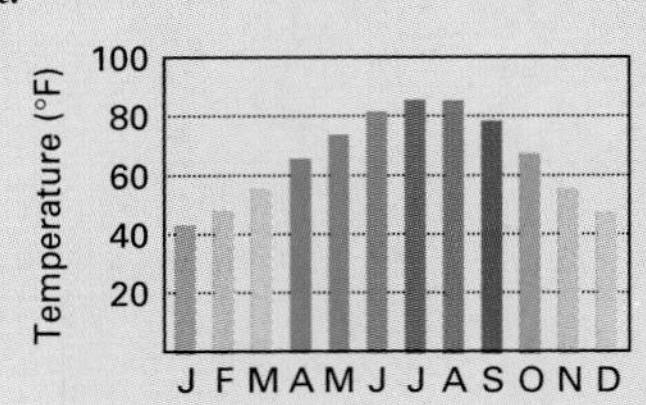

Use the table for Questions 4–6.

Children in Family	1	2	3	4	5	6	7
Number of Families	5	8	7	3	2	0	1

4. How many children are there in the largest family? How many children are there all together?
5. Make a line plot of the data. Use it to name any outliers.
6. Find the mean, median, mode(s), and range for the data. Which best summarizes the information about the families—mean, median, or mode?
7. Make a scatterplot of the data in the table. Draw the trend line and use it to predict the height of a 25-year-old man. Does this prediction make sense?

Age (yr)	Birth	2	4	8	12	16	18
Height (in.)	20	34	40	51	59	68	69

Performance Task

Oceania is the name given to Australia, Melanesia, New Zealand, and Papua New Guinea. Make two types of displays of the data in the table and describe how each helps you understand the data.

	Australia	Melanesia	New Zealand	Papua New Guinea
1995 Population	18,100,000	5,800,000	3,600,000	4,300,000
2015 Population (estimate)	29,000,000	10,100,000	4,400,000	7,500,000

50 *Chapter 1 • Making Sense of the World of Data*

Performance Assessment Key

See key on page 3.

Resources

Assessment Sourcebook
Chapter 1 Tests
- Form A and B (free response)
- Form C (multiple choice)
- Form D (performance assessment)
- Form E (mixed response)
- Form F (cumulative chapter test)

TestWorks
Test and Practice Software

Home and Community Connections
Letter Home for Chapter 1 in English and Spanish

Suggested Scoring Rubric

4
- Accurately displays the given data in two different ways.
- Clearly explains of how each type of display aids in understanding.

3
- Adequately displays the given data in two different ways.
- Explains how each type of display aids in understanding.

2
- Displays data in two different ways with some inaccuracies.
- Explains how at least one display aids in understanding.

1
- Displays data with many inaccuracies and lack of labeling.
- Does not explain how either display aids in understanding.

Cumulative Review Chapter 1

Test Prep

Performance Assessment

Choose a problem.

Popular Pets

Pets are often important parts of our lives. Whether they swim in a bowl or curl up on the rug, they require care and attention. Make a survey to find out which types of pets are most popular in your class. Find out the average cost of keeping each type and the amount of time spent in caring for them. Make a poster to show your results. Be sure to display your data in some of the ways you have learned in this chapter.

Capital Capers

Our nation is made up of 50 states, each of which has a capital. Make a list of the capitals. Count the letters each state capital has in its name. Show your results in a line plot. Does it seem as if there are any outliers? Do they appear to cluster about any particular number of letters? Choose a typical capital to represent the states. Find out how it got its name and how long it has been the state capital. Is it older or younger than the capital of your state?

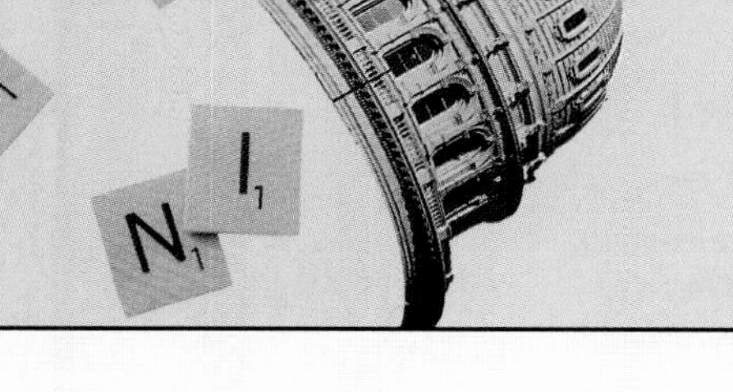

Roll a Score!

Roll a set of four number cubes 100 times and record the total shown each time. Make a stem-and-leaf diagram to show your results. Describe any patterns you see. Choose another way to show your data and compare the two graphs. Explain what your second display shows that the stem-and-leaf diagram does not.

WHAT DO THEY WATCH?

A television network wants to sell advertising time for four of its programs. The network conducted a poll to determine the number of viewers. Numbers represent millions of viewers.

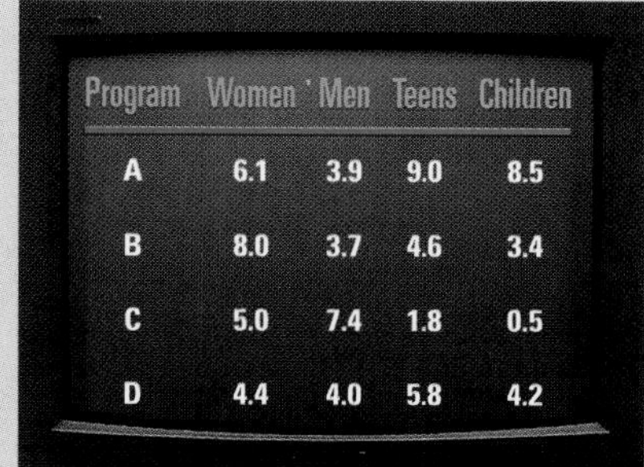

Program	Women	Men	Teens	Children
A	6.1	3.9	9.0	8.5
B	8.0	3.7	4.6	3.4
C	5.0	7.4	1.8	0.5
D	4.4	4.0	5.8	4.2

Make a double-bar graph to use when selling advertising in TV programs that would appeal to adults. Make a second to use when selling advertising in programs for teens and children. As a manufacturer of a new skateboard, use the graphs to decide in which programs you would probably buy advertising time. Explain your choices.

Cumulative Review Test Prep

About Performance Assessment

The Performance Assessment options ...

- provide teachers with an alternate means of assessing students.
- address different learning modalities.
- Teachers may encourage students to choose the most challenging problem.

Learning Modalities
Popular Pets **Visual** Students display data in a poster.
Capital Capers **Interpersonal** Students discuss material and follow their instincts.
Roll a Score! **Logical** Students identify patterns.
What Do They Watch? **Linguistic** Students explain conclusions.

Answers for Assessment on page C4.

Performance Assessment Key

See key on page 53.

Suggested Scoring Rubric

Popular Pets

4
- Summarizes data.
- Poster contains clearly labeled bar graph, circle graph, and stem-and-leaf diagram.

3
- Summarizes most data.
- Poster has two labeled graphs.

2
- Limited data is displayed.
- Poster has an incomplete graph.

1
- Poster displays little data.
- Student shows little understanding of graphing.

Capital Capers

4
- Accurately shows line plot.
- All research is completed.

3
- Line plot includes most required data and/or labels.
- Most research is completed.

2
- Line plot is incomplete.
- Some details of research omitted.

1
- Line plot is largely incorrect.
- Research is inadequate.

Roll a Score!

4
- Stem-&-leaf diagram is accurately drawn and labeled.
- Clearly explains advantages of second graph.

3
- Stem-&-leaf diagram includes most necessary details.
- Attempts to explain advantage of second graph.

2
- Stem-&-leaf diagram is incomplete.
- Second graph is inaccurate.

1
- Makes little attempt to draw a stem-&-leaf diagram.
- Cannot explain a second graph.

What Do They Watch?

4
- Data is displayed in two clearly labeled double bar graphs.
- Clearly explains why the chosen graphs are effective.

3
- Attempts to display data in two double bar graphs
- Understands why graphs are effective.

2
- Uses incorrect data to compile graphs.
- Incomplete understanding of graphs.

1
- Makes only one graph.
- Shows little understanding of graphing.

The Language of Algebra

≤ × ≈ > =

Formulas, Expressions, and Equations

Section 2A

Formulas: Students learn to show relationships using variables. They learn to apply the order of operations and the properties. Students create tables of values and generate formulas.

2-1 Formulas and Variables

2-2 Order of Operations

2-3 Formulas and Tables

Section 2B

Expressions and Equations: Students learn to express problems using algebraic terms and to translate algebraic expressions into words. Students use inverse operations to solve equations with one or more steps.

2-4 Inverse Operations

2-5 Translating Words to Expressions

2-6 Solving Addition and Subtraction Equations

2-7 Solving Multiplication and Division Equations

2-8 Problem Solving with Two-Step Equations

Meeting NCTM Standards

Curriculum Standards

STANDARD			pages
1	**Problem Solving**	Skills and Strategies	54, 59, 66, 74, 81, 85, 90
		Applications	58–59, 63–64, 69–70, 76–77, 80–81, 84–85, 89–90, 93–94, 95
		Exploration	56, 60, 66, 74, 78, 82, 86, 91
2	**Communication**	Oral	55, 58, 62, 68, 73, 75, 79, 83, *85*, 88, 92
		Written	*54*, 59, 64, *66*, 70, 72, 77, 81, 85, *90*, 93, 94, 96
		Cooperative Learning	*52, 56, 60, 62, 66, 70, 74, 78, 82, 86, 91*
3	**Reasoning**	Critical Thinking	59, 64, 70, 77, 81, 85, 90, 94
4	**Connections**	Mathematical	See Standards 6, 7, 8, 9, 12 below.
		Interdisciplinary	Career 80; Industry *55, 73,* 80, 85; Geography 76, 89; Literature 52, 84; Sports 52; Science *52,* 53, 57, 58, 69, 77, 80, 84, 89, 93, 96; Social Studies *52,* 53; Health 58, 70; Fine Arts 81; Consumer 64, *68,* 69; History *55,* 87, 89
		Technology	*52, 55,* 60, 61, 65, 66, 67, *73, 83*
		Cultural	52, *88*
6	**Number Systems and Number Theory**		63, 76
7	**Computation and Estimation**		62, 64, *67*, 71, 77, *79*, 81, 83, 85, *87*, 90, *92*
8	**Patterns and Functions**		66, 97
9	**Algebra**		55–101
12	**Geometry**		58, 89

Italic type indicates Teacher Edition reference.

Teaching Standards

Focus on Respect

An important ingredient for a successful learning environment is the respect of students for each other. In a positive learning environment students

- justify their ideas without becoming hostile or defensive.
- question other students' ideas without demeaning them or ridiculing them.

Assessment Standards

Focus on Inferences

Projects The Inferences Standard promotes the use of a variety of assessment instruments to show a greater range of evidence about students' learning. A project may provide information about mastery of topics, and give insight into students' reasoning ability and facility with previously learned topics. A Chapter 2 project has students

- determine costs of running a business.
- use formulas and equations to help in making decisions.

TECHNOLOGY

For the Teacher

- **Teacher Resource Planner CD-ROM**
  Use the teacher planning CD-ROM to view resources available for Chapter 2. You can prepare custom lesson plans or use the default lesson plans provided.

- **World Wide Web**
  Visit **www.teacher.mathsurf.com** for links to lesson plans from teachers and other professionals, NCTM information, and other sites.

- **TestWorks**
  TestWorks provides ready-made tests and can create custom tests and practice worksheets.

For the Parent

- **World Wide Web**
  Parents can use the web site at **www.parent.mathsurf.com.**

For the Student

- **Interactive CD-ROM**
  Lessons 2-6 and 2-7 have an *Interactive CD-ROM Lesson.* The *Interactive CD-ROM Journal* and *Interactive CD-ROM Spreadsheet/Grapher Tool* are also used in Chapter 2.

- **Wide World of Mathematics**
  Lesson 2-1 Algebra: Ticker-Tape Parade
  Lesson 2-3 Algebra: Bank Debit Cards
  Lesson 2-6 Middle School: The Census

- **World Wide Web**
  Use with Chapter and Section Openers; Students can go online to the Scott Foresman-Addison Wesley Web site at **www.mathsurf.com/7/ch2** to collect information about chapter themes.

STANDARDIZED - TEST CORRELATION

SECTION 2A

LESSON	OBJECTIVE	ITBS Form M	CTBS 4th Ed.	CAT 5th Ed.	SAT 9th Ed.	MAT 7th Ed.	Your Form
2-1	• Use formulas to show relationships among quantities.	✘	✘	✘	✘	✘	
	• Use variables to represent quantities.	✘	✘	✘	✘	✘	
	• Substitute values for variables.	✘	✘	✘	✘	✘	
2-2	• Use the order of operations to find the value of expressions.		✘	✘		✘	
	• Use the associative, commutative, and distributive properties.			✘	✘	✘	
2-3	• Use a formula to make a table of values.		✘				
	• Find a formula when given a table of values.		✘	✘	✘	✘	

SECTION 2B

LESSON	OBJECTIVE	ITBS Form M	CTBS 4th Ed.	CAT 5th Ed.	SAT 9th Ed.	MAT 7th Ed.	Your Form
2-4	• Use inverse operations.			✘	✘	✘	
2-5	• Translate words and phrases into algebraic expressions.		✘	✘	✘	✘	
	• Translate algebraic expressions into words and phrases.			✘	✘		
2-6	• Solve addition and subtraction problems using inverse operations.			✘	✘	✘	
2-7	• Solve multiplication and division equations using inverse operations.			✘		✘	
2-8	• Use more than one inverse operation to solve an equation.			✘		✘	

Key: ITBS - Iowa Test of Basic Skills; CTBS - Comprehensive Test of Basic Skills; CAT - California Achievement Test; SAT - Stanford Achievement Test; MAT - Metropolitan Achievement Test

ASSESSMENT PROGRAM

	QUICK QUIZZES	SECTION REVIEW	CHAPTER REVIEW	CHAPTER ASSESSMENT FREE RESPONSE	CHAPTER ASSESSMENT MULTIPLE CHOICE	CUMULATIVE REVIEW
Traditional Assessment	TE: pp. 59, 64, 70, 77, 81, 85, 90, 94	SE: pp. 72, 96 *Quiz 2A, 2B	SE: pp. 98–99	SE: p. 100 *Ch. 2 Tests Forms A, B, E	*Ch. 2 Tests Forms C, E	SE: p. 101 *Ch. 2 Test Form F

	INTERVIEW	JOURNAL	ONGOING	PERFORMANCE	PORTFOLIO	PROJECT	SELF
Alternate Assessment	TE: p. 85	SE: pp. 64, 72, 77, 81, 85, 93 TE: pp. 54, 64, 90	TE: pp. 56, 61, 66, 74, 78, 82, 86, 91	SE: p. 100 TE: p. 59 *Ch. 2 Tests Form D, E	TE: pp. 77, 94	SE: pp. 64, 77 TE: p. 53	TE: p. 81

*Tests and quizzes are in *Assessment Sourcebook*. Test Form E is a mixed response test. Forms for Alternate Assessment are also available in *Assessment Sourcebook*.

TestWorks: Test and Practice Software

MIDDLE SCHOOL PACING CHART

REGULAR PACING

Day	5 classes per week
1	Chapter 2 Opener; Problem Solving Focus
2	Section **2A** Opener; Lesson **2-1**
3	Lesson **2-2**; Technology
4	Lesson **2-3**
5	**2A** Connect; **2A** Review
6	Section **2B** Opener; Lesson **2-4**
7	Lesson **2-5**
8	Lesson **2-6**
9	Lesson **2-7**
10	Lesson **2-8**
11	**2-B** Connect; **2B** Review; Extend Key Ideas
12	Chapter 2 Summary and Review
13	Chapter 2 Assessment Cumulative Review, Chapter 1

BLOCK SCHEDULING OPTIONS

Block Scheduling for Complete Course

Chapter 2 may be presented in

- eight 90-minute blocks
- ten 75-minute blocks

Each block consists of a combination of

- Chapter and Section Openers
- Explores
- Lesson Development
- Problem Solving Focus
- Technology
- Extend Key Ideas
- Connect
- Review
- Assessment

For details, see *Block Scheduling Handbook*.

Block Scheduling for Interdisciplinary Course

Each block integrates math with another subject area.

In Chapter 2, interdisciplinary topics include

- Cars
- Machines

Themes for Interdisciplinary Team Teaching 2A and 2B are

- Acceleration
- Automobile Air Bags

For details, see *Block Scheduling Handbook*.

Block Scheduling for Lab-Based Course

In each block, 30–40 minutes is devoted to lab activities including

- Explores in the Student Edition
- Connect pages in the Student Edition
- Technology options in the Student Edition
- Reteaching Activities in the Teacher Edition

For details, see *Block Scheduling Handbook*.

Block Scheduling for Course with *Connected Mathematics*

In each block, investigations from **Connected Mathematics** replace or enhance the lessons in Chapter 2.

Connected Mathematics topics for Chapter 2 can be found in

- *Variables and Patterns*
- *Moving Straight Ahead*

For details, see *Block Scheduling Handbook*.

INTERDISCIPLINARY BULLETIN BOARD

Set Up

Have students compare the amounts of electrical power required to run different appliances for varying amounts of time. List appliances and include an incomplete table of values for each. Indicate the power each needs to operate for one hour.

Procedure

- Have small groups of students choose one of the appliances. Have students draw a picture of the appliance and hang the drawing above the appropriate table.
- Ask the groups to fill in the table beneath the appliance to show how many kilowatts (kW) of power each uses during different time periods.

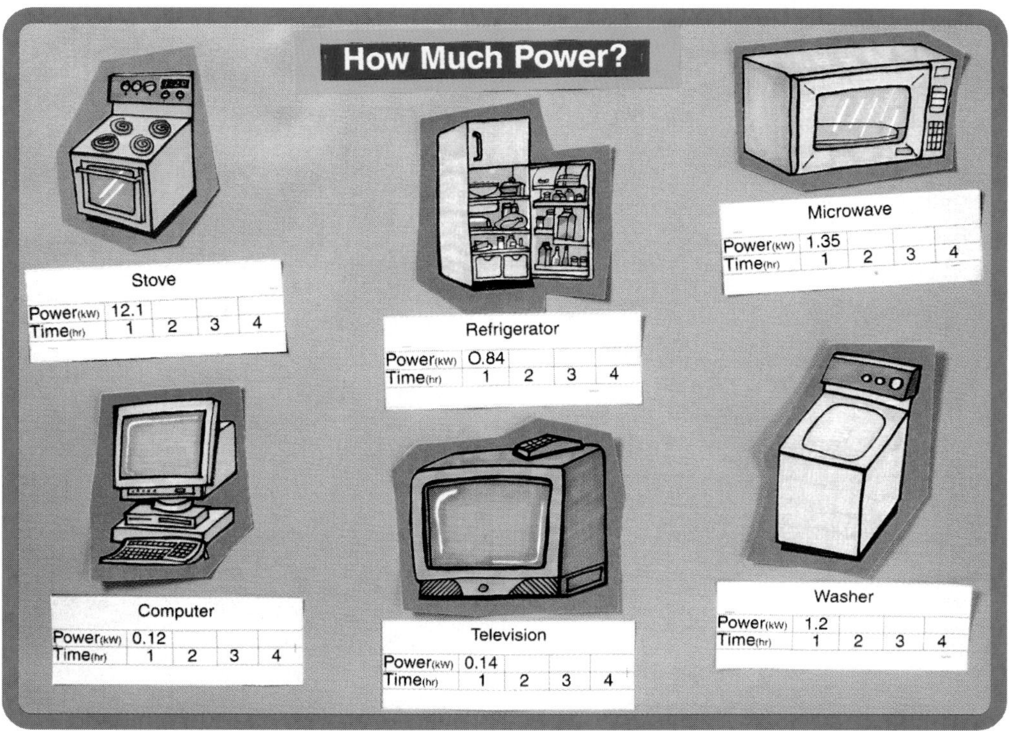

How Much Power?
Stove
Power(kW) 12.1
Time(hr) 1 2 3 4
Refrigerator
Power(kW) 0.84
Time(hr) 1 2 3 4
Microwave
Power(kW) 1.35
Time(hr) 1 2 3 4
Computer
Power(kW) 0.12
Time(hr) 1 2 3 4
Television
Power(kW) 0.14
Time(hr) 1 2 3 4
Washer
Power(kW) 1.2
Time(hr) 1 2 3 4

Chapter 2

The information on these pages shows how formulas are used in real-life situations.

World Wide Web

If your class has access to the World Wide Web, you might want to use the information found at the Web site addresses given.

Extensions

The following activities do not require access to the World Wide Web.

Entertainment
Have students investigate sports events that make up the summer and winter Olympics and how various events are scored.

People of the World
Have students find the origin of the words *algebra* and *equal.* Algebra is from *al-jabr*, an Arabic word for "the reduction"; Equal is from *aequus*, a Latin word for "level."

Arts & Literature
Ask students to find a copy of *David Copperfield* or another book written by Charles Dickens. Have them estimate the number of words on a page, determine the number of pages in the book, and estimate the total number of words in the book.

Science
Ask students if they know any similar ways to describe the occurrences of natural events. Possible answer: Determine how far away a storm is by counting the number of seconds between the lightning and the thunder.

Social Studies
Ask students to work with partners to find out how to use an abacus. They might also research the Asian origin of the abacus. Have each group demonstrate their findings for the class.

2 The Language of Algebra: Formulas,

Entertainment Link
www.mathsurf.com/7/ch2/ent

Arts & Literature Link
www.mathsurf.com/7/ch2/arts

Entertainment

An Olympic diver's score equals the scores from the judges multiplied by the degree of difficulty of the dive.

Arts & Literature

When writing *David Copperfield,* Charles Dickens was paid according to a formula based on the number of words he wrote. *David Copperfield* was one of his longest works.

People of the World

In 1700 B.C. Ahmes, an Egyptian priest, was the first person to use a symbol for equality.

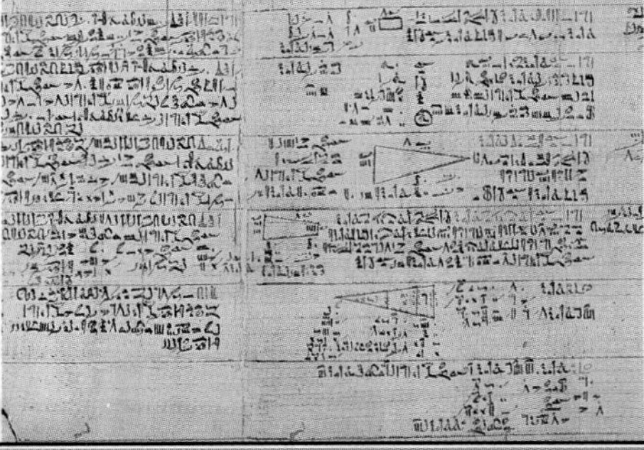

52

TEACHER TALK

Meet Sharon Butler

Twin Creeks Middle School
Spring, Texas

An activity that I use with order of operations I call "Be Seated If ..." I give each student an expression involving the variables, *a*, *b*, and *c*, such as: $a + b \cdot c$, $a \cdot b + c$, $b + c \div a$, $b - a + c$, $a^2 - b$, $b^2 + c^2$, $a \cdot b - c$, $(b + c) \div a$, and so on. Then I write $a = 2$, $b = 3$, and $c = 1$ on the board and have students evaluate their expressions. For this chapter, I make sure only positive numbers occur.

After evaluating their expressions, students stand. I tell them to be seated if the value of their expression is, for example, the quotient $21 \div 7$, greater than 6, an odd number, a factor of 10, and so on. Before a student sits down, I have the class check that the expression has been correctly evaluated. I continue until only one student is left standing.

Expressions, and Equations

Social Studies Link
www.mathsurf.com/7/ch2/social

Science

You can use the chirps of the snowy tree cricket to determine the temperature.

Social Studies

The abacus from ancient China was one of the first calculators. Electronic calculators that performed the order of operations automatically didn't come until the 1900s.

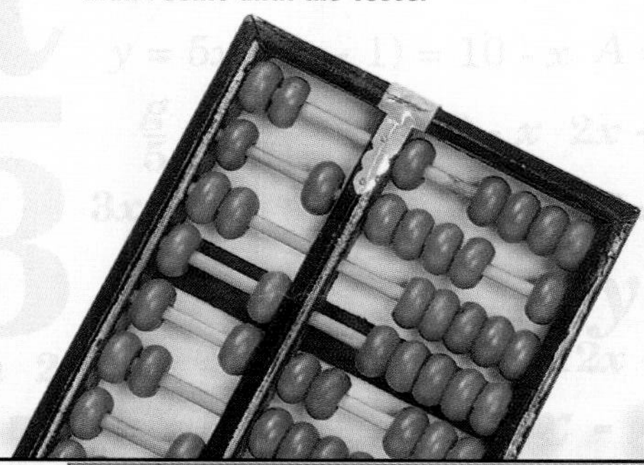

KEY MATH IDEAS

A **variable** is a symbol that represents one or more numerical values.

A **formula** shows how several variables are related. Formulas describe real-world relationships.

The **order of operations** tells what to do first, second, and so on when you find the value of an expression.

When you **solve** an equation or inequality, you find the value(s) of the variable that makes the equation or inequality true.

An **inverse operation** undoes an operation. When you solve an equation or inequality, you use inverse operations to isolate the variable.

CHAPTER PROJECT

Problem Solving

Understand
Plan
Solve
Look Back

In this project, you will make a plan for running a business. Begin the project by thinking about the type of business you would like to run. You might consider mowing lawns, baby-sitting, pet care, or other services.

53

PROJECT ASSESSMENT

You may choose to use this project as a performance assessment for the chapter.

Performance Assessment Key

Level 4 Full Accomplishment

Level 3 Substantial Accomplishment

Level 2 Partial Accomplishment

Level 4 Little Accomplishment

Suggested Scoring Rubric

4
- Students research their business and identify most costs involved.
- Suggested charge to customers is appropriate and justified in a well organized report.

3
- Students research their business and identify some costs involved.
- Suggested charge to customers is acceptable but the report omits some important factors.

2
- Students identify one or two costs of running their business.
- A charge to customers is suggested but not adequately justified.

1
- Students guess rather than research costs involved.
- Students cannot suggest an appropriate charge to customers.

Chapter Project

Students select a business they would like to run, determine what issues they would have to address if they ran the business, and how mathematics might help them.

Resources
Chapter 2 Project Master

Introduce the Project
- Talk about kinds of businesses that teenagers might be able to run. Ask if any students have a business of their own.
- Discuss what issues are involved in running a business, such as making schedules, buying equipment, paying for services, and so on.
- Ask how mathematics might be used in running a business. Possible answer: Determining a payment schedule for purchases, determining what to charge for services, taxes, and so on.

Project Progress
Section A, page 64 Students list things that they would need for their business and determine what it would cost to run the business.

Section B, page 77 Students look at their list of costs and write an equation to determine how much they would need to charge customers. They write a report explaining and justifying their charges.

Community Project

A community project for Chapter 2 is available in *Home and Community Connections*.

Cooperative Learning

You may want to use Teaching Tool Transparency 1: Cooperative Learning Checklist with **Explore** and other group activities in this chapter.

Problem Solving Focus

Finding Unnecessary Information

The Point

Students focus on determining which of the given facts are needed to solve a problem.

Resources

Teaching Tool Transparency 16: Problem-Solving Guidelines

 *Interactive CD-ROM Journal*

About the Page

Using the Problem-Solving Process

In order to solve a problem, students must be able to determine which of the given facts are needed and which information is unnecessary. Discuss these suggestions for evaluating the given information:

- Read the problem several times to determine what the problem is asking you to find.
- Decide what kind of information is needed to solve the problem and determine if this information is given.
- Disregard any information that is not needed.

Ask ...

- In Problem 1, how would you decide what information is extra? The problem asks for the total number of times a pied woodpecker drums in 15 seconds, so the information about the number of woodpecker species is not needed.
- In Problem 4, how do you know the cost of the bird is unnecessary information? The problem asks how long the macaw will live, not the cost.

Answers for Problems

1. There are 209 different species.
2. Roadrunner is 600 cm long.
3. No unnecessary information.
4. Hyacinth macaws sell for $12,000; This bird costs $7,000.

Journal

Have students describe a situation in which they asked a simple question but got a lengthy answer. Suggest that they tell if the original question was answered and if the additional information was useful.

Problem Solving

Understand
Plan
Solve
Look Back

Finding Unnecessary Information

Sometimes a problem contains more information than you need. To better understand the problem, you need to sort through all of the information and decide which of the facts are necessary to solve the problem.

Problem Solving Focus

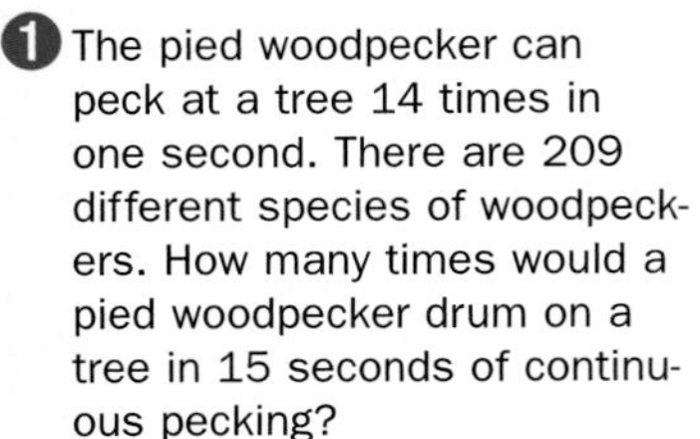

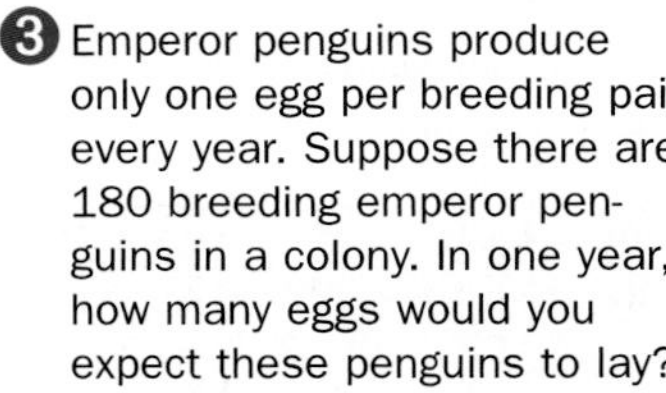

For each problem, identify the unnecessary numerical information. Some problems may not have unnecessary information. (You do not need to solve the problem.)

1. The pied woodpecker can peck at a tree 14 times in one second. There are 209 different species of woodpeckers. How many times would a pied woodpecker drum on a tree in 15 seconds of continuous pecking?
2. An adult roadrunner is about 600 centimeters long. Over short distances, a roadrunner can run at a speed of 20 kilometers per hour. If a roadrunner ran for 2 hours, how far would it run?
3. Emperor penguins produce only one egg per breeding pair every year. Suppose there are 180 breeding emperor penguins in a colony. In one year, how many eggs would you expect these penguins to lay?
4. The most expensive domesticated bird is the hyacinth macaw. These birds can cost up to $12,000, and live an average of 50 years in captivity. A hyacinth macaw in an exotic-bird park is 7 years old. It cost the park $7,000. How much longer would you expect this macaw to live?

54

Additional Problem

Kacey is a plumber. When she started her business 5 years ago, she had one employee. For a service call she charged a $25 flat fee plus $37.50 an hour. Now she has five employees and charges a $35 flat fee plus $45 an hour for her time. How much does Kacey charge now for a service call that takes 2 hours?

1. What does the problem ask you to find? The charge for a service call that takes 2 hours.
2. What information do you need to solve the problem? The current flat fee and the hourly rate for a service call.
3. What information was not needed? When Kacey started her business, what she charged then, the number of employees she had then, and the number of employees she has now.
4. How much does Kacey charge now for a 2-hour service call? $125

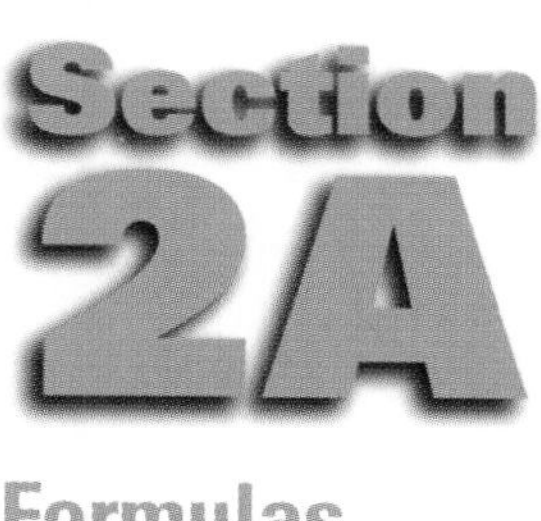

Formulas

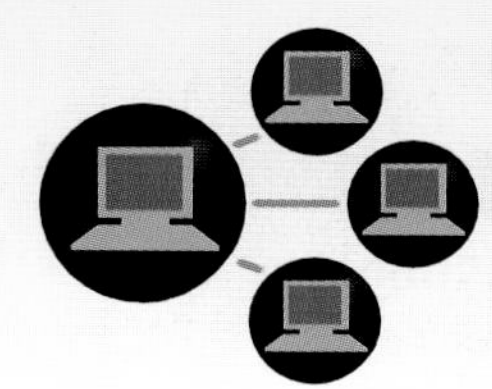

Visit **www.teacher.mathsurf.com** for links to lesson plans from teachers and other professionals, NCTM information, and other sites.

LESSON PLANNING GUIDE

Student Edition / Ancillaries*

LESSON		MATERIALS	VOCABULARY	DAILY	OTHER
	Chapter 2 Opener				Ch. 2 Project Master Ch. Community Project Teaching Tool Trans. 1
	Problem Solving Focus				Teaching Tool Trans. 16 *Interactive CD-ROM Journal*
	Section 2A Opener				
2-1	**Formulas and Variables**		formula, variable, substitute	2–1	Technology Master 6 *WW Math*—Algebra
2-2	**Order of Operations**	scientific calculator	expression, commutative property, associative property, distributive property	2–2	Teaching Tool Trans. 22 Technology Master 1 Ch. 2 Project Master
	Technology	spreadsheet software			*Interactive CD-ROM Spreadsheet/Grapher Tool*
2-3	**Formulas and Tables**	spreadsheet software		2–3	Technology Master 8 *Interactive CD-ROM Spreadsheet/Grapher Tool* *WW Math*—Algebra
	Connect				Interdisc. Team Teaching 2A
	Review				Practice 2A; Quiz 2A; *TestWorks*

* Daily Ancillaries include Practice, Reteaching, Problem Solving, Enrichment, and Daily Transparency. Teaching Tool Transparencies are in *Teacher's Toolkits*. Lesson Enhancement Transparencies are in *Overhead Transparency Package*.

SKILLS TRACE

LESSON	SKILL	FIRST INTRODUCED GR. 5	GR. 6	GR. 7	DEVELOP	PRACTICE/ APPLY	REVIEW
2-1	**Showing relationships using formulas.**	✘			pp. 56–57	pp. 58–59	pp. 81, 98, 182, 277
	Substituting values for variables.		✘				
2-2	**Applying order of operations.**		✘		pp. 60–62	pp. 63–64	pp. 85, 96, 99, 124, 281
	Using the commutative, associative, and distributive properties.	✘					
2-3	**Making tables from formulas and writing formulas from tables.**			✘ p. 66	pp. 66–68	pp. 69–70	pp. 94, 99, 156, 297

CONNECTED MATHEMATICS

The unit *Variables and Patterns (Introducing Algebra)*, from the **Connected Mathematics** series, can be used with Section 2A.

INTERDISCIPLINARY TEAM TEACHING

Math and Science/Technology

(Worksheet pages 5–6: Teacher pages T5–T6)

In this lesson, students use formulas and variables to explore acceleration.

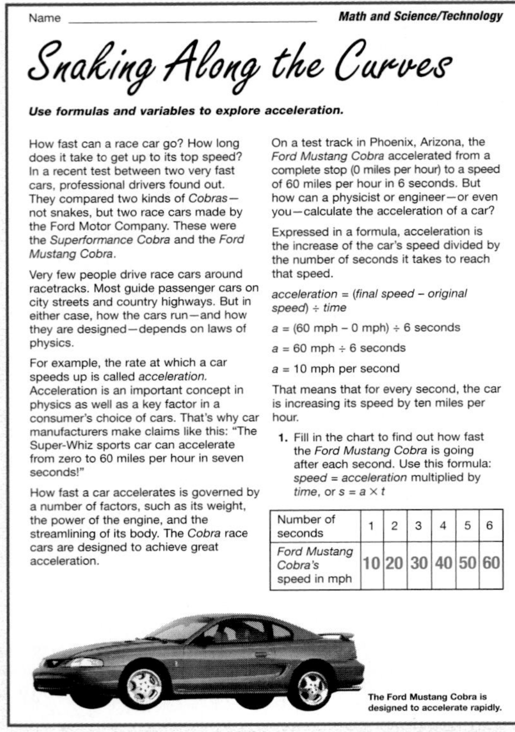

Name ________________ *Math and Science/Technology*

Snaking Along the Curves

Use formulas and variables to explore acceleration.

How fast can a race car go? How long does it take to get up to its top speed? In a recent test between two very fast cars, professional drivers found out. They compared two kinds of *Cobras*—not snakes, but two race cars made by the Ford Motor Company. These were the *Superformance Cobra* and the *Ford Mustang Cobra*.

Very few people drive race cars around racetracks. Most guide passenger cars on city streets and country highways. But in either case, how the cars run—and how they are designed—depends on laws of physics.

For example, the rate at which a car speeds up is called *acceleration*. Acceleration is an important concept in physics as well as a key factor in a consumer's choice of cars. That's why car manufacturers make claims like this: "The Super-Whiz sports car can accelerate from zero to 60 miles per hour in seven seconds!"

How fast a car accelerates is governed by a number of factors, such as its weight, the power of the engine, and the streamlining of its body. The *Cobra* race cars are designed to achieve great acceleration.

On a test track in Phoenix, Arizona, the *Ford Mustang Cobra* accelerated from a complete stop (0 miles per hour) to a speed of 60 miles per hour in 6 seconds. But how can a physicist or engineer—or even you—calculate the acceleration of a car?

Expressed in a formula, acceleration is the increase of the car's speed divided by the number of seconds it takes to reach that speed.

acceleration = (final speed – original speed) ÷ time

a = (60 mph – 0 mph) ÷ 6 seconds

a = 60 mph ÷ 6 seconds

a = 10 mph per second

That means that for every second, the car is increasing its speed by ten miles per hour.

1. Fill in the chart to find out how fast the *Ford Mustang Cobra* is going after each second. Use this formula: *speed = acceleration* multiplied by *time*, or $s = a \times t$

Number of seconds	1	2	3	4	5	6
Ford Mustang Cobra's speed in mph	10	20	30	40	50	60

The Ford Mustang Cobra is designed to accelerate rapidly.

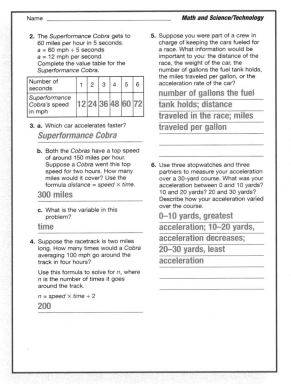

Name ________________ *Math and Science/Technology*

2. The *Superformance Cobra* gets to 60 miles per hour in 5 seconds.
a = 60 mph ÷ 5 seconds
a = 12 mph per second
Complete the value table for the *Superformance Cobra*.

Number of seconds	1	2	3	4	5	6
Superformance Cobra's speed in mph	12	24	36	48	60	72

3. a. Which car accelerates faster?
Superformance Cobra

b. Both the *Cobras* have a top speed of around 150 miles per hour. Suppose a *Cobra* went this top speed for two hours. How many miles would it cover? Use the formula *distance = speed × time*.
300 miles

c. What is the variable in this problem?
time

4. Suppose the racetrack is two miles long. How many times would a *Cobra* averaging 100 mph go around the track in four hours?

Use this formula to solve for n, where n is the number of times it goes around the track.

n = *speed × time ÷ 2*

200

5. Suppose you were part of a crew in charge of keeping the cars fueled for a race. What information would be important to you: the distance of the race, the weight of the car, the number of gallons the fuel tank holds, the miles traveled per gallon, or the acceleration rate of the car?

number of gallons the fuel tank holds; distance traveled in the race; miles traveled per gallon

6. Use three stopwatches and three partners to measure your acceleration over a 30-yard course. What was your acceleration between 0 and 10 yards? 10 and 20 yards? 20 and 30 yards? Describe how your acceleration varied over the course.

0–10 yards, greatest acceleration; 10–20 yards, acceleration decreases; 20–30 yards, least acceleration

BIBLIOGRAPHY

FOR TEACHERS

Boschung, Herbert Jr. et al. *The Audubon Society Field Guide to North American Fishes, Whales, and Dolphins*. New York, NY: Knopf, 1983.

Hughes, James, ed. *The Larousse Desk Reference*. New York, NY: Larousse, 1995.

Wagner, Sigrid, ed. *Research Ideas for the Classroom*. New York, NY: Macmillan, 1993.

FOR STUDENTS

Andretti, Michael. *Michael Andretti at Indianapolis*. New York, NY: Simon & Schuster Books for Young Readers, 1992.

Chimits, Xavier. *The Williams-Renault Formula One Motor Racing Book*. London, England: Dorling Kindersley, 1994.

Siegel, Alice and Basta, Margo McLoone. *The Information Please Kids', Almanac*. Boston, MA: Houghton Mifflin, 1992.

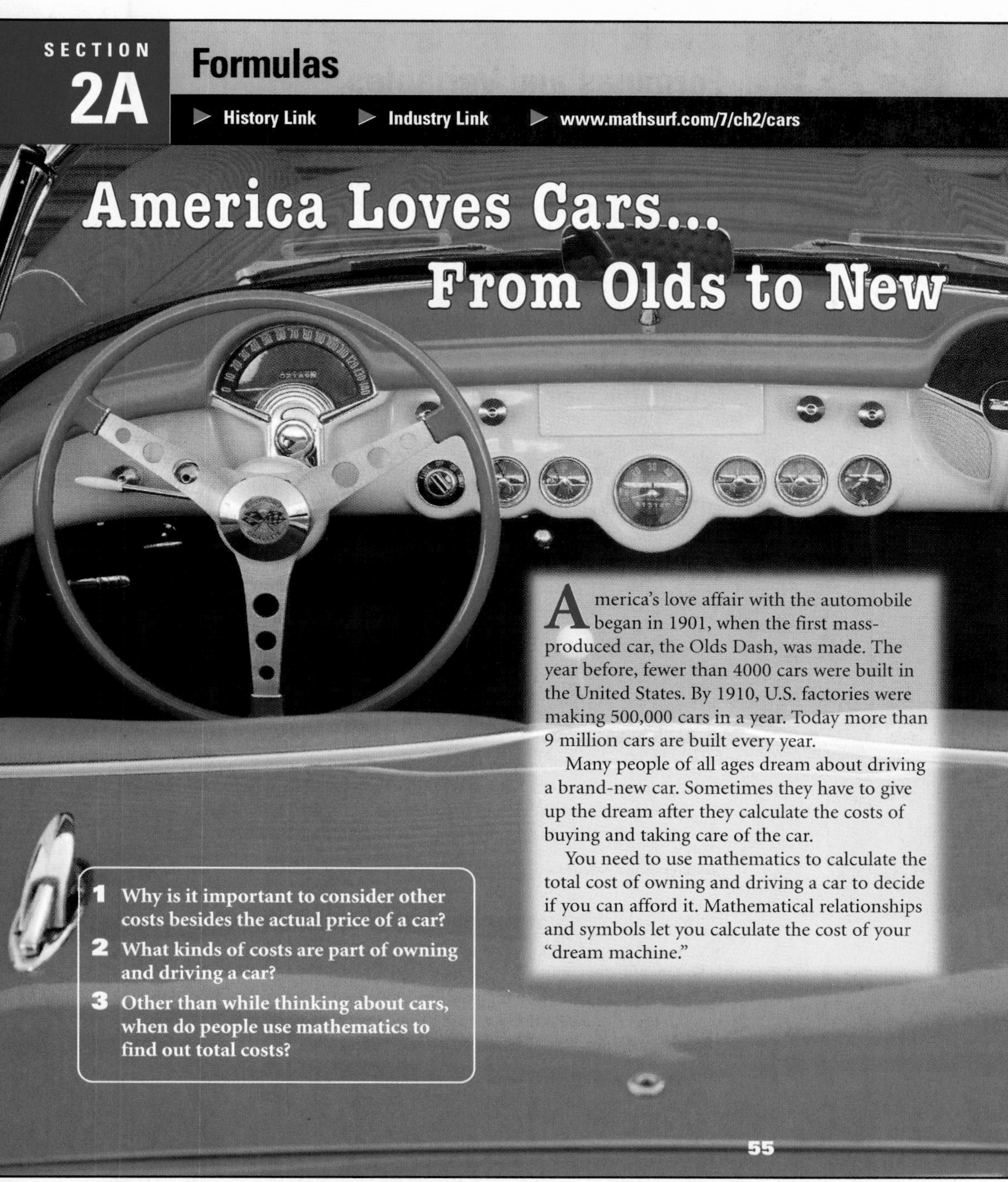

SECTION
2A
Formulas
History Link
Industry Link
www.mathsurf.com/7/ch2/cars
America Loves Cars...
From Olds to New
America's love affair with the automobile began in 1901, when the first mass-produced car, the Olds Dash, was made. The year before, fewer than 4000 cars were built in the United States. By 1910, U.S. factories were making 500,000 cars in a year. Today more than 9 million cars are built every year.
Many people of all ages dream about driving a brand-new car. Sometimes they have to give up the dream after they calculate the costs of buying and taking care of the car.
You need to use mathematics to calculate the total cost of owning and driving a car to decide if you can afford it. Mathematical relationships and symbols let you calculate the cost of your "dream machine."
1 Why is it important to consider other costs besides the actual price of a car?
2 What kinds of costs are part of owning and driving a car?
3 Other than while thinking about cars, when do people use mathematics to find out total costs?
55

Section 2A

Theme: Cars

World Wide Web

If your class has access to the World Wide Web, you might want to use the information found at the Web site address given. The Interdisciplinary links relate to topics discussed in this section.

About the Page

This page introduces the theme of this section, cars, and discusses the cost of owning and operating a car.

Ask ...

- If you were going to buy a car, what type would you buy?
- What should you think about when you are planning to purchase a car?

Extensions

The following activities do not require access to the World Wide Web.

History
Students might like to investigate the history of the automobile and describe the changes that have taken place since Henry Ford and other pioneers in the industry made cars available to the general public.

Industry
Have students do research to find the number of cars produced in the United States in a recent year. They might also find the number of cars imported in the same year.

Answers for Questions

1. Possible answer: Because the price is not the only cost. Running, insuring, and maintaining a car will all cost money.
2. Possible answers: Service, fuel, insurance, and so on.
3. Possible answers: Paying taxes, shopping, and so on.

Connect

On page 71 students use tables and formulas to analyze the costs of operating a car.

Where are we now?

In Grade 6 students learned how to

- use formulas to show geometric relationships.
- use order of operations to evaluate expressions.
- make tables, given algebraic expressions.
- use the distributive property to compute mentally.

Where are we going?

In Grade 7 Section 2A, students will

- use formulas to show relationships.
- apply the order of operations.
- use the associative, commutative, and distributive properties.
- make a table of values when given a formula and find a formula when given a table of values.

Lesson Organizer

Objectives

- Use formulas to show relationships among quantities.
- Use variables to represent quantities.
- Substitute values for variables.

Vocabulary

- Formula, variable, substitute

NCTM Standards

- 1–4, 9, 12

Review

Evaluate each when $t = 16$.

1. $8 \times t$ 128
2. $\frac{t}{4}$ 4

Find a when $b = 5$.

3. $a = 7 + b$ 12
4. $a = \frac{(9 + b)}{2}$ 7

Available on Daily Transparency 2-1

1 Introduce

Explore

The Point
Students explore formulas by completing a table and writing an equation to describe the relationship found in the table.

Ongoing Assessment
Some students may have trouble using symbols to describe the relationship in Step 2. Encourage them to describe the relationship in words and then replace these words with symbols.

For Groups That Finish Early
Estimate the average speed that you could ride a bicycle. Write an equation describing a relationship between the average speed (s), the total distance (d), and the time the bicycle is ridden (t). Possible answers: $d = s \cdot t$, $s = \frac{d}{t}$, $t = \frac{d}{s}$

2-1 Formulas and Variables

You'll Learn ...

- to use formulas to show relationships among quantities
- to use variables to represent quantities
- to substitute values for variables

... How It's Used

Environmental analysts use formulas to determine the amount of acid found in rain.

Vocabulary

formula
variable
substitute

▶ **Lesson Link** In the last chapter, you used line graphs and scatterplots to display relationships among quantities. Now you will learn how to show relationships by using symbols. ◀

Explore Formulas

Start Your Engines!

1. The 24 Hours of Daytona is an automobile race held each year in Daytona Beach, Florida. Teams of 3 to 5 drivers drive their cars as many miles as possible in 24 hours. The table shows the average speeds, in mi/hr, of several cars that finished the 1996 race. You can calculate the number of miles that a car is driven in the race if you multiply the car's average speed by 24. Copy and complete the table.

Average Speed	103	96	95	93	90	88	82
Miles							

2. Use symbols to give a relationship among the average speeds of cars, the distance, and the time it takes to complete the race.
3. Explain how you could use the relationship alone to find the number of miles driven by a car with an average speed of 110 mi/hr.
4. The first Daytona race, in 1962, was only 3 hours long. Dan Gurney drove a Lotus Ford at an average speed of 104 mi/hr to win. Change your relationship to find the number of miles traveled by Gurney's Lotus Ford. Explain the change in the relationship.

Learn Formulas and Variables

A **formula** is a rule showing relationships among quantities. A **variable** is used to represent a quantity whose values may change or vary. Formulas usually contain variables.

Letters are often used to represent variables. Choose letters that remind you of what they represent.

MEETING INDIVIDUAL NEEDS

Resources

2-1 Practice
2-1 Reteaching
2-1 Problem Solving
2-1 Enrichment
2-1 Daily Transparency
Problem of the Day
Review
Quick Quiz
Technology Master 6

Wide World of Mathematics
Algebra: Ticker-Tape Parade

Learning Modalities

Verbal Have students write a definition of *variable* and describe why variables are used in formulas.

Individual Have students write a formula using y for the current year, b for their year of birth, and a for their age. $y = b + a$, $b = y - a$, or $a = y - b$

Visual Draw pictures to illustrate formulas involving geometric concepts.

English Language Development

To help students understand the meaning of formulas, have students write a complete sentence that tells what the formula means. For example, $p = 4s$ means, "The perimeter of a square is equal to 4 times the length of a side." Ask students who are learning English to give their native language equivalents for the three vocabulary words: *formula, variable,* and *substitute.*

To find the relationship between the perimeter of (distance around) a square and the length of a side, let the variable s represent the length of a side of a square and the variable p represent the perimeter of the square. The relationship is the formula $p = 4 \cdot s$. Notice that $4 \times s$ is written as $4 \cdot s$. It can also be written as just $4s$.

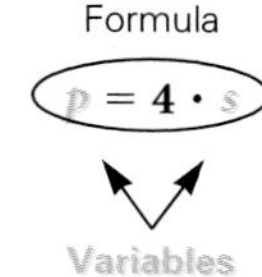

Sometimes you know the values of some of the variables in a formula. You can replace these variables with the values you know. Replacing variables with values is called **substituting**.

Examples

1 The formula for the cost (C) of a tank of gas is $C = p \cdot g$. Find the cost of a tank of gas if the price per gallon (p) is $1.70 and the number of gallons (g) is 12.

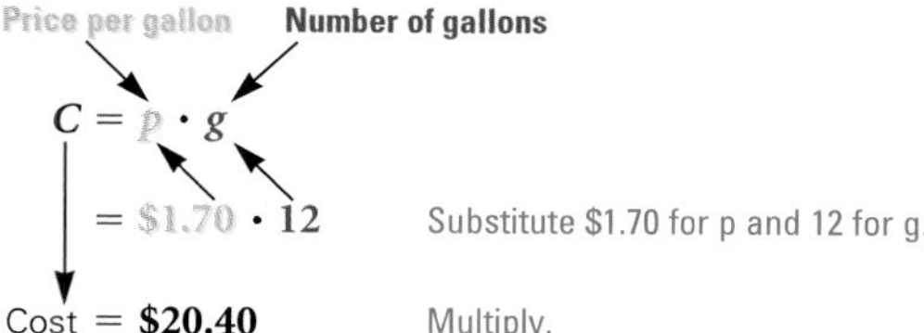

$C = p \cdot g$

$= \$1.70 \cdot 12$ Substitute $1.70 for p and 12 for g.

Cost $= \$20.40$ Multiply.

The cost of the tank of gas is $20.40.

2 Jeremy is a cook at the Home Cooking Restaurant. He uses the formula $c = \frac{f}{8}$ to change fluid ounces (f) into cups (c). Find out how many cups are equal to 32 fluid ounces.

$c = \frac{f}{8} = \frac{32}{8}$ Substitute 32 for f.

$= 4$ Divide.

Four cups are equal to 32 fluid ounces.

Try It

a. The formula for the average (A) of two numbers (a and b) is $A = \frac{a + b}{2}$. Use the formula to find the average of 10 and 18. 14

b. The cost of a tune-up (C), the hourly charge (h), and the number of hours worked (n) are related by the formula $C = h \times n$. If the hourly charge is $40, find the cost of a tune-up that takes 4 hours. $160

DID YOU KNOW?

A gallon of unleaded regular gasoline cost $0.61 in 1976.

Science Link

The metric system of measurement is used by scientists around the world. A liter is about the same as 34 fluid ounces, or a little more than a quart.

Answers for Explore

1. 2472, 2304, 2280, 2232, 2160, 2112, 1968
2. $d = s \cdot 24$
3. Multiply 110 by 24.
4. New relationship is $d = s \cdot 3$. He traveled $104 \cdot 3$, or 312 miles.

2 Teach

Learn

Alternate Examples

1. The formula for the distance (D) that can be driven on one tank of gas is $D = m \cdot g$. Find the distance that can be driven if the average miles per gallon (m) is 24 and the number of gallons (g) is 15.

$D = m \cdot g$

$D = 24 \cdot 15$

Distance = 360 miles

2. Juan works at the Wall-to-Wall Carpet Store. He uses the formula $y = \frac{f}{9}$ to change square feet (f) into square yards (y). Find how many square yards are equal to 72 square feet.

$y = \frac{f}{9} = \frac{72}{9}$

$y = 8$

Eight square yards are equal to 72 square feet.

MATH EVERY DAY

Problem of the Day

If Gear 1 turns in the direction of the arrow, which way will Gears 3 and 5 turn? Describe the pattern you see.

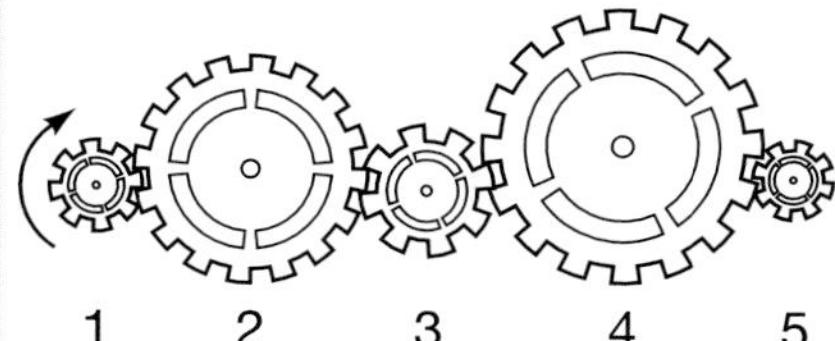

Gears 3 and 5 will both turn in the same direction, clockwise, as Gear 1. Every odd-numbered gear will turn in a clockwise direction.

Available on Daily Transparency 2-1

An Extension is provided in the transparency package.

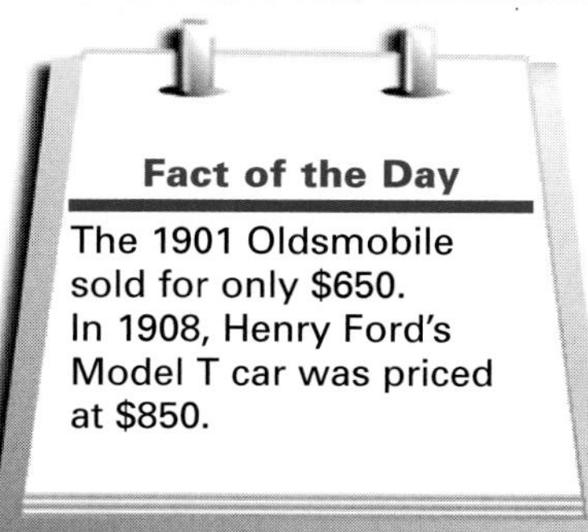

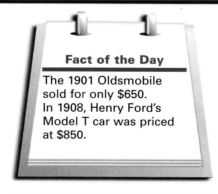

Fact of the Day

The 1901 Oldsmobile sold for only $650. In 1908, Henry Ford's Model T car was priced at $850.

Mental Math

Do these mentally.

1. 3×40 120
2. 3×400 1200
3. 3×4000 12,000

2-1 Exercises and Applications

Assignment Guide

- Basic
  1–10, 13–14, 17–29
- Average
  1–11, 13–15, 17–22,
  23–29 odds
- Enriched
  1–9 odds, 10–16, 20–30 evens

3 Practice and Assess

Check

Answers for Check Your Understanding

1. Possible answer: l to represent the length of a rectangle.
2. Possible answer: To share a bag of candy $C = n \div p$ where C is the number of candies each person gets, n is the total number of candies in the bag, and p is the number of people sharing.

Reteaching

Activity

Materials: Small containers, counters

When 3 children go to a movie, the total cost (C) of buying an item for all 3 can be found by using the formula $C = 3 \cdot p$, where p is the price of an individual item.

- The price of a candy bar is \$2. Use 3 small containers to represent $3 \cdot p$.
- Place 2 counters in each container. What is the cost of the 3 candy bars? \$6
- To show the cost of three \$5 movie tickets, place 5 counters in each of 3 containers.
- Use the formula to find the cost of the movie tickets. \$15

Check Your Understanding

1. Give an example of a variable and explain what it represents.
2. Give an example of a formula you use in everyday life.

2-1 Exercises and Applications

PRACTICE 2-1

Practice and Apply

1. **Getting Started** The formula $p = 2 \cdot l + 2 \cdot w$ can be used to find the perimeter of a rectangle.
   a. Name the variables in this formula. l and w
   b. Use the formula to find the perimeter of a rectangle with length (l) 6 cm and width (w) 4 cm. 20 cm

Geometry You can use the formula $A = l \cdot w$ to find the area of a rectangle. Substitute the given values into the formula. Then use the formula to find A.

2. $l = 15$ cm, $w = 5$ cm 75 cm^2
3. $l = 10$ m, $w = 23$ m 230 m^2
4. $l = 8$ in., $w = 14$ in. 112 in^2
5. $l = 12$ ft, $w = 20$ ft 240 ft^2

Science The formula $r = \frac{d}{t}$ is used to find rate or average speed when you know d (distance) and t (time). Substitute the values for d and t into the formula. Then use the formula to find r.

6. $d = 150$ mi, $t = 3$ hr 50 mi/hr
7. $d = 10$ km, $t = 23$ hr $\approx$ 0.435 km/hr
8. $d = 800$ mi, $t = 1$ hr 800 mi/hr
9. $d = 12$ km, $t = 20$ hr 0.6 km/hr

Science Use the table for Exercises 10 and 11.

Animal	Cheetah	Lion	Zebra	Giraffe	Elephant	Chicken
Maximum Speed (mi/hr)	70	50	40	32	25	9

10. At these speeds, how far would a cheetah travel in 30 min? An elephant? Cheetah: 35 mi; Elephant: 12.5 mi
11. How much farther than a giraffe could a lion travel in 30 min? 9 miles
12. **Health** The formula $C = 13m$ relates calories "burned" (C) and minutes of running (m). Find the number of calories "burned" in 30 minutes of running. 390 calories

PRACTICE

Name ______________________

Practice 2-1

Formulas and Variables

Geometry You can use the formula $A = \frac{1}{2}bh$ to find the area of a triangle. Substitute the given values into the formula. Then use the formula to find A.

1. $b = 8$ in., $h = 5$ in., $A =$ 20 in^2
2. $b = 18$ cm, $h = 10$ cm, $A =$ 90 cm^2
3. $b = 4$ m, $h = 3$ m, $A =$ 6 m^2
4. $b = 3$ ft, $h = 8$ ft, $A =$ 12 ft^2
5. $b = 3$ mi, $h = 8$ mi, $A =$ 12 mi^2
6. $b = 12$ km, $h = 3$ km, $A =$ 18 km^2

Science The formula $t = \frac{d}{v}$ is used to find t (time) when you know d (distance) and v (rate or average speed). Substitute the values for d and v into the formula. Then use the formula to find t.

7. $d = 465$ km, $v = 93$ km/hr
   $t =$ 5 hr
8. $d = 180$ mi, $v = 45$ mi/hr
   $t =$ 4 hr
9. $d = 200$ ft, $v = 25$ ft/sec
   $t =$ 8 sec
10. $d = 85$ km, $v = 85$ km/hr
   $t =$ 1 hr

Use the table for Exercises 11–12.

Street	Main St	Harbor Blvd	Oak Hwy	River Fwy
Speed Limit (mi/hr)	25	35	50	65

11. How far can you travel in 3 hours on Harbor Blvd? 105 mi
    On Oak Hwy? 150 mi On River Fwy? 195 mi
12. How much farther can you travel in 5 hours on Harbor Blvd than on Main St? 50 mi

13. **Geometry** You can use the formula $A = \frac{h}{2}(b_1 + b_2)$ to find the area of a trapezoid with bases b_1 and b_2 and height h. Find the area of a trapezoid with bases 9 cm and 13 cm, and height 7 cm. 77 cm^2
14. **Health** Sheri's pulse rate is 150 beats per minute when she exercises. The formula $b = 150t$ relates the number of beats (b) to the time (t) in minutes. Find the number of beats in 8 minutes of exercise. 1200 beats

RETEACHING

Name ______________________

Alternative Lesson 2-1

Formulas and Variables

A **formula** is a rule showing relationships among quantities. A **variable** is used to represent a quantity whose values may change or vary. Formulas usually contain variables.

Example 1

When flying a plane, the airspeed of a plane (a) is decreased by the head wind speed (h) to give the ground speed (g). The formula used to show this relationship is $g = a - h$.

Suppose the airspeed of a plane is 210 miles per hour and the head wind speed is 35 miles per hour. Find the plane's ground speed.

Substitute 210 for a and 35 for h.

$$g = a - h = 210 - 35 = 175$$

The ground speed is 175 mi/hr.

Try It Substitute the values for a and h into the formula to find the ground speed.

a. $a = 342$, $h = 47$ 295 mi/hr
b. $a = 412$, $h = 28$ 384 mi/hr
c. $a = 278$, $h = 39$ 239 mi/hr
d. $a = 315$, $h = 45$ 270 mi/hr
e. $a = 395$, $h = 28$ 367 mi/hr
f. $a = 278$, $h = 32$ 246 mi/hr

Example 2

When investing money, the interest earned (I) is the product of the principal (P), the rate (R), and the time the money is invested (T). The formula used to show this relationship is $I = PRT$.

Suppose the principal is \$500, the rate is 6% or 0.06, and time is 2 years. Find the interest earned.

Substitute 500 for P, 0.06 for R, and 2 for T.

$$I = PRT = 500 \cdot 0.06 \cdot 2 = 30 \cdot 2 = 60$$

The interest is \$60.

Try It Substitute the values for P, R, and T into the formula to find the interest.

g. $P = \$1000$, $R = 0.08$, $T = 2$ years \$160
h. $P = \$3000$, $R = 0.12$, $T = 1$ year \$360
i. $P = \$10{,}000$, $R = 0.04$, $T = 4$ years \$1600
j. $P = \$750$, $R = 0.03$, $T = 3$ years \$67.50
k. $P = \$1050$, $R = 0.07$, $T = 5$ years \$367.50
l. $P = \$300$, $R = 0.045$, $T = 2$ years \$27

13. **Test Prep** Use the formula $g = \frac{c}{16}$ to convert cups (c) to gallons (g). How many gallons are equal to 64 cups? B

Ⓐ $\frac{1}{4}$ gal   Ⓑ 4 gal   Ⓒ 48 gal   Ⓓ 1024 gal

Problem Solving and Reasoning

14. You have to get your car stereo fixed. The repair shop charges \$10 per hour, plus \$30 for the visit. Use the formula $C = 10h + 30$, where C is cost and h is hours. GPS

a. How much will it cost if the repairs take 3 hours?

b. Choose a Strategy Is this the same amount you would pay if you brought the stereo in once for 1 hour and once for 2 hours? Explain your reasoning.

15. Communicate Think of a formula that you have used before. Write a real-world problem for which you would use this formula.

16. Critical Thinking Some formulas that were used in the past have become obsolete. Units called palms (p), digits (d), and spans (s) were once used to measure lengths.

a. For $p = d \div 4$ and $s = p \div 3$, how many spans long is an object that measured 24 digits?

b. Where do you think the words *digits, palms,* and *spans* (and feet) came from?

Problem Solving STRATEGIES

- Look for a Pattern
- Make an Organized List
- Make a Table
- Guess and Check
- Work Backward
- Use Logical Reasoning
- Draw a Diagram
- Solve a Simpler Problem

PROBLEM SOLVING 2-1

Mixed Review

Round each number as indicated. *[Previous course]*

17. 23,685; nearest 1,000 24,000
18. 45,684; nearest 10 45,680
19. 7,466; nearest 100 7,500
20. 754,391; nearest 1,000 754,000
21. 295,972; nearest 100 296,000
22. 1,864; nearest 10 1,860
23. 74,614; nearest 100 74,600
24. 8,397; nearest 10 8,400
25. 146,199; nearest 1,000 146,000
26. 187,243; nearest 10,000 190,000
27. 3,824,341; nearest 10,000 3,820,000
28. 4,179,486; nearest 10,000 4,180,000

Make a line graph to show each set of data. *[Lesson 1-5]*

29.

Year	'90	'91	'92	'93
Height (in.)	42	46	47	49

30.

Year	'80	'85	'90	'95
Profit (\$1000)	328	625	763	947

Exercise Notes

Exercise 13

Test Prep If students selected A, they reversed the terms when substituting 64 for c in the formula or when simplifying.

Exercise Answers

14. a. \$60.00

b. No; You would have to pay the per-visit charge twice.

15. Possible answer: $P = 4s$. Find the perimeter of a square.

16. a. 2 spans

b. Possible answer: Ancient measures based on the width of a finger, breadth of the palm of the hand, and the stretch from thumb to pinkie.

29.

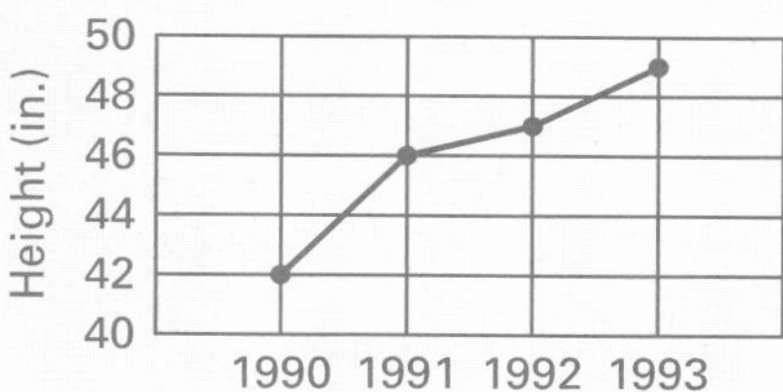

30.

Profit (\$1000): 1000, 900, 800, 700, 600, 500, 400, 300
1980 1985 1990 1995

Alternate Assessment

Performance Have students use words to describe a relationship between two quantities and then write the formula.

Quick Quiz

In Items 1 and 2, use the formula $h = \frac{m}{60}$ to convert minutes (m) to hours (h).

1. How many hours are equal to 240 minutes? 4 hours

2. How many hours are equal to 480 minutes? 8 hours

3. What formula would you use to convert hours to days? $d = \frac{h}{24}$

Available on Daily Transparency 2-1

PROBLEM SOLVING

Name ______________

Guided Problem Solving 2-1

GPS PROBLEM 14, STUDENT PAGE 59

You have to get your car stereo fixed. The repair shop charges \$10 per hour, plus \$30 for the visit. Use the formula $C = 10h + 30$, where C is cost and h is hours.

a. How much will it cost if the repairs take 3 hours?
b. Is this the same amount you would pay if you brought the stereo in once for 1 hour and once for 2 hours? Explain your reasoning.

Understand

1. Circle the information you need.

2. What value will you substitute for h in the formula if the repairs take

a. 1 hour? 1   **b.** 2 hours? 2   **c.** 3 hours? 3

Plan

3. Make a table to organize the data. What will be the labels on the table? Cost; Hours

Solve

4. Substitute values for h into the formula to complete the table.

Cost	40	50	60
Hours	1	2	3

5. How much will it cost if the repairs take 3 hours? \$60

6. How much will it cost if the repairs take 1 hour during one service call and 2 hours during another service call? \$90

7. Does it cost the same amount for a service call of 3 hours as it does for two service calls taking 1 hour and 2 hours? Explain.
No. Although the hours spent repairing the stereo are the same, there is an additional charge for each visit.

Look Back

8. What other strategies could you have used to solve the problem?
Possible answer: Look for a Pattern; Use Logical Reasoning.

SOLVE ANOTHER PROBLEM

How much will it cost if the repairs take 6 hours? \$90

ENRICHMENT

Name ______________

Extend Your Thinking 2-1

Patterns in Algebra

You can find patterns in the perimeters and areas of rectangles.

1. The formula $P = 2 \cdot l + 2 \cdot w$ can be used to find the perimeter of a rectangle. Complete the table to show the perimeter of each rectangle.

Width	3	6	9	12	15	18	21	24
Length	5	10	15	20	25	30	35	40
Perimeter	16	32	48	64	80	96	112	128

2. What pattern describes the widths and lengths in the table? Possible answer: They are multiples of the first number in each row.

3. Write a rule for the change in the perimeter of a rectangle when its width and the length are increased by the same factor.
Possible answer: The perimeter increases by the same factor as the length and width increase.

4. Predict how many times greater the perimeter will be if you multiply the length and width of a rectangle by each factor.

a. By 10 10 times   **b.** By 50 50 times   **c.** By 125 125 times

5. The formula $A = l \cdot w$ can be used to find the area of a rectangle. Complete the table to show the area of each rectangle.

Width	3	6	9	12	15	18	21	24
Length	5	10	15	20	25	30	35	40
Area	15	60	135	240	375	540	735	960

6. What pattern describes the widths and lengths in the table? Possible answer: They are multiples of the first number in each row.

7. Write a rule for the change in the area of a rectangle when its width and the length are increased by the same factor.
Possible answer: The area increases by the square of the factor used to increase the length and width.

8. Predict how many times greater the area will be if you multiply the length and width of a rectangle by each factor.

a. By 10 100   **b.** By 50 2500   **c.** By 125 15,625

2-2 Lesson Organizer

Objectives

- Use the order of operations to find the values of expressions.
- Use the associative, commutative, and distributive properties.

Vocabulary

- Expression, commutative property, associative property, distributive property

Materials

- Explore: Scientific calculator

NCTM Standards

- 1–4, 6, 7, 9

Review

Perform the computation mentally. Check by using a calculator.

1. 30 + 22 + 70 122
2. 204 × 2 408
3. 306 × 3 918

Available on Daily Transparency 2-2

Lesson Link

Have students tell how they decided in which order to perform the operations in the formula for the perimeter of a rectangle in Lesson 2-1.

1 Introduce

Explore

You may wish to use Teaching Tool Transparency 22: Scientific Calculator with **Explore**.

The Point
Students explore order of operations by evaluating expressions using calculators and by determining which operation was performed first.

2-2 Order of Operations

You'll Learn ...

- to use the order of operations to find the values of expressions
- to use the associative, commutative, and distributive properties

... How It's Used

Astronomers use the associative, commutative, and distributive properties to solve and simplify complicated equations describing the motions of stars and planets.

Vocabulary

expression
Commutative Property
Associative Property
Distributive Property

Lesson Link You've used formulas to show relationships among quantities. Now you'll see how to use formulas that involve several operations. ◄

Explore Order of Operations

May I Take Your Order?

Materials: Scientific calculator

1. Enter 12 [+] 9 [÷] 3. What answer do you get? Which of the operations—addition or division—does your calculator do first?
2. Some calculators give an answer of 7 to Step 1. How might these calculators do the problem?
3. Enter (12 [+] 9) [÷] 3. What answer do you get? How did your calculator find the answer?
4. Use your calculator to find the value of each expression. Tell which operation it performed first.
   a. $4 + 3 \times 2$ **b.** $(4 + 3) \times 2$ **c.** $16 - 4 \div 2$ **d.** $(16 - 4) \div 2$
5. Suppose you are using a scientific calculator and a formula with three operations. One of the operations is addition or subtraction. One is multiplication or division. One is done inside parentheses. Which operation will your calculator do first? Second? Third?

Learn Order of Operations

An **expression** is a mathematical phrase that can be made up of variables and/or numbers and operations. $4 + 3 \cdot 2$ and $b + 4$ are both expressions.

The value of an expression can depend on the order in which you do operations. Here are two ways that could be used to find the value of $7 + 3 \times 2$:

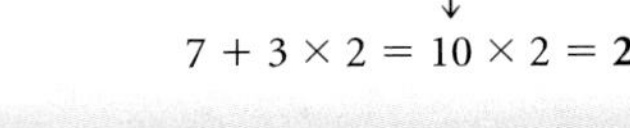

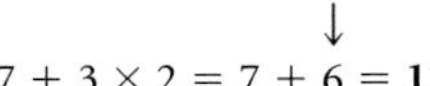

Add 7 + 3 first.	Multiply 3 × 2 first.
↓	↓
$7 + 3 \times 2 = 10 \times 2 = \mathbf{20}$	$7 + 3 \times 2 = 7 + 6 = \mathbf{13}$

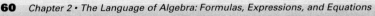

MEETING INDIVIDUAL NEEDS

Resources

2-2 Practice
2-2 Reteaching
2-2 Problem Solving
2-2 Enrichment
2-2 Daily Transparency
  Problem of the Day
  Review
  Quick Quiz
Teaching Tool Transparency 22
Technology Master 1
Chapter 2 Project Master

Learning Modalities

Verbal Have students make a table or poster that displays the addition and multiplication properties.

Kinesthetic Have students use counters to model the addition and multiplication properties.

Inclusion

Have students who need help remembering the standard order of operations write the following questions on an index card.

Are there any
(1) parentheses or division bars?
(2) multiplications or divisions?
(3) additions or subtractions?

Include this reminder: For each *yes* answer do the operations in order from left to right and for each *no* answer go to the next step.

Have students add new vocabulary to their reference books.

The result of evaluating a formula such as $D = a + b \cdot c$ also depends on the order in which you do the operations.

To indicate which order to use, sometimes we need to use grouping symbols. Parentheses and division bars are two kinds of grouping symbols.

ORDER OF OPERATIONS	$2 + 3^2 \times (4 + 3)$
1. Simplify inside parentheses or above or below the division bar.	$2 + 3^2 \times (7)$
2. Simplify exponents.	$2 + 9 \times 7$
3. Multiply and divide from left to right.	$2 + 63$
4. Add and subtract from left to right.	65

There are many ways to show multiplication.

3 times n can be written $3 \times n$, $3 \cdot n$, $3(n)$, or $3n$, and $a \cdot b$ is also written ab.

On a spreadsheet, an asterisk (*) is used to show multiplication: 3 * n.

Technology Link

Scientific calculators normally follow the order of operations. Many basic calculators, sometimes called "four-function calculators," do not follow the order of operations, so you must enter the operations in a special order to get a correct answer.

Remember

3^2 is read as three squared.
$3^2 = 3 \cdot 3$ or 9

[Previous course]

Examples

1 Find the value of $2(6 + 4) - 3 \cdot 5$.

$2(6 + 4) - 3 \cdot 5 = 2(10) - 3 \cdot 5$ Do operations within grouping symbols first.

$= 20 - 15$ Multiply 2(10) and $3 \cdot 5$.

$= 5$ Subtract.

2 An auto mechanic ordered eight car spark plugs and four truck spark plugs. Car spark plugs cost \$0.75, and truck spark plugs cost \$3.00. Find the value of $8 \cdot 0.75 + 4 \cdot 3$, the total cost of these parts.

$8 \cdot 0.75 + 4 \cdot 3 = 6 + 12$ Multiply $8 \cdot 0.75$ and $4 \cdot 3$.

$= 18$ Add.

The cost of the parts is \$18.

Try It

Find the value of each expression.

a. $3 + 8 \div 2$ **7**

b. $\frac{6 + 3}{3} - 1$ **2**

c. $(2 \times 5) - 1 + 5^2 \div 5$ **14**

d. $14 \div 7 + 8(3)$ **26**

Ongoing Assessment

Check that students are deciding which of the two operations have been performed first by the calculator and are not just finding the value of each expression.

For Groups That Finish Early

Write two expressions using the same numbers and the same operations, one using parentheses and one without parentheses. Decide whether or not the two expressions have the same value.

Follow Up

Discuss students' answers to Step 5. Have students explain how the order that they suggest would produce the results that they found in Step 4.

Answers for Explore

1. 15; Division
2. They do the addition first, then the division: $12 + 9 = 21$; $21 \div 3 = 7$.
3. 7; Addition first, then division.
4. a. 10; Multiplication
   b. 14; Addition
   c. 14; Division
   d. 6; Subtraction
5. 1st: Parentheses; 2nd: Multiplication or division; 3rd: Addition or subtraction.

2 Teach

Learn

Alternate Examples

1. Find the value of $3(4^2 - 8) - 3 \cdot 4$

   Do operations within grouping symbols first. Next, multiply, then, subtract.

   $3(4^2 - 8) - (3 \cdot 4) = 3(8) - 3 \cdot 4$
   $= 24 - 12$
   $= 12$

2. Mia had \$8. After spending \$2, she divided the rest into 3 equal parts for herself and her two sisters. Today she worked for 7 hours, earning \$5 per hour. How much money does Mia have now?

   $\frac{8-2}{3} + 7 \cdot 5 = \frac{6}{3} + 7 \cdot 5$
   $= 2 + 35$
   $= 37$

   Mia has \$37 now.

MATH EVERY DAY

Problem of the Day

Put three + signs and one − sign between the following digits so that the answer is 100. Do not change the order of the digits.

9 8 7 6 5 4 3 2 1

98 − 76 + 54 + 3 + 21

Available on Daily Transparency 2-2

An Extension is provided in the transparency package.

Fact of the Day

The first automobile trip across the United States began on May 23, 1903, in San Francisco. It ended 10 weeks later, in New York.

Mental Math

Do these mentally.

1. 120 + 700 820
2. 450 + 430 880
3. 222 + 333 555

Alternate Examples

3. Tickets for the school play were sold for $3 each. The formula $M = 3T$ relates the amount of money collected (M) to the number of tickets sold (T). If 203 tickets were sold, how much money was collected for these tickets?

   Substitute 203 for T. Rewrite 203 as 200 + 3 and use the distributive property.

   $M = 3(203)$

   $= 3(200 + 3)$

   $= 3 \cdot 200 + 3 \cdot 3$

   $= 600 + 9$

   $= 609$

   $609 was collected.

3 Practice and Assess

Check

Answers for Check Your Understanding

1. No; Order of operations already tells you to do the division first.
2. No; No; 8 − 3 is not equal to 3 − 8, 12 ÷ 4 is not equal to 4 ÷ 12.

Along with order-of-operation rules, the **commutative**, **associative**, and **distributive** properties will help you find values of expressions.

PROPERTY	EXAMPLE (numbers)	EXAMPLE (variables)
Commutative Property of Addition	$2 + 7 = 7 + 2$	$a + b = b + a$
Commutative Property of Multiplication	$4 \cdot 9 = 9 \cdot 4$	$ab = ba$
Associative Property of Addition	$3 + (5 + 1) = (3 + 5) + 1$	$a + (b + c) = (a + b) + c$
Associative Property of Multiplication	$8 \cdot (2 \cdot 9) = (8 \cdot 2) \cdot 9$	$a(bc) = (ab)c$
Distributive Property	$5(7 + 2) = 5 \cdot 7 + 5 \cdot 2$	$a(b + c) = ab + ac$

- The commutative properties state that *order* doesn't matter when you add or multiply.
- The associative properties state that *grouping* doesn't matter when you add or multiply.
- The Distributive Property states that multiplying a sum of two numbers by a third number is the same as multiplying each number in the sum by the third number, then adding.

Example 3

MENTAL MATH

When multiplying a large number by a small one, split the large number into two numbers that are easier to multiply and use the distributive property to multiply in your head.

Only 104 Dual-Ghia automobiles were ever built. The formula $T = 4D$ relates the number of tires (T) to the number of Dual-Ghias (D). How many tires were needed for all the Dual-Ghias?

$T = 4(104)$	Substitute.
$= 4(100 + 4)$	Rewrite 104 as 100 + 4.
$= 4 \cdot 100 + 4 \cdot 4$	Use the distributive property.
$= 400 + 16$	Multiply.
$= 416$	Add.

416 tires were needed.

Try It

Evaluate. **a.** 6(405) 2430 **b.** $307 \cdot 8$ 2456 **c.** $12 \cdot 205$ 2460

Check Your Understanding

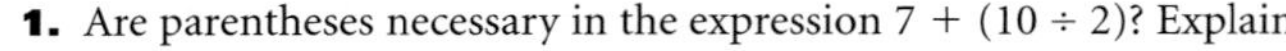

1. Are parentheses necessary in the expression 7 + (10 ÷ 2)? Explain.
2. Is there a commutative property for subtraction? For division? Explain.

MEETING MIDDLE SCHOOL CLASSROOM NEEDS

Tips from Middle School Teachers

To help students distinguish between the associative and the commutative properties of addition, I like to have them use counters so that they can change the order or the grouping of the numbers visually.

Team Teaching

Working with the physical education teacher, have students calculate the average number of push-ups or sit-ups completed per student on a particular day. Have students write the expression, correctly using order of operations.

Cooperative Learning

Have students play this game in pairs. Each student should make up an expression using at least three numbers from 1 through 10 and at least two different operations. The expression must represent a whole number. Parentheses and/or division bars may be used. Have partners exchange papers and find the value. The first student to find the correct value earns a point. Repeat the process 4 times, for a total of 5 rounds.

2-2 Exercises and Applications

Practice and Apply

Getting Started Name the operation that should be done first.

1. $12 - 6 \times 2$ Multiplication
2. $18(24 + 36)$ Addition
3. $64 \div 2 \cdot 3$ Division
4. $\frac{16 + 4}{5}$ Addition

Does the expression contain grouping symbols? What are they?

5. $24 \div (6 - 5)$ Yes; Parentheses
6. $24 \div 12 + 2$ No
7. $\frac{14 + 4}{9}$ Yes; Division bar
8. $20 \cdot 3 \div 2$ No

Find the value of each expression.

9. $16 - 12 \div 4$ 13
10. $3^2 \cdot 2 - (8 - 2) \div 3$ 16
11. $83 + 2(4 - 1)$ 89
12. $11(3 + 1) \div 2^2 + 3$ 14
13. $72 - 30 \div (2 + 3)$ 66
14. $7^2 - \frac{5^2 + 1}{2} \cdot 3$ 10
15. **Test Prep** Find the value of $a + 2 \cdot b$ if b is 4 and a is 3. B

    Ⓐ 10 Ⓑ 11 Ⓒ 18 Ⓓ 20

Operation Sense Copy each statement below. Insert parentheses to make each sentence true.

16. $18 + 12 \div 3 + 1 = 11$ $(18 + 12) \div 3 + 1 = 11$
17. $18 + 12 \div 3 + 1 = 21$ $18 + 12 \div (3 + 1) = 21$
18. $7 \times 2 + 3 \times 6 = 102$ $(7 \times 2 + 3) \times 6 = 102$
19. $7 \times 2 + 3 \times 6 = 140$ $7 \times (2 + 3 \times 6) = 140$

Which property is being shown?

20. $12 + 48 = 48 + 12$
21. $12 \cdot (14 \cdot 16) = (12 \cdot 14) \cdot 16$
22. $28 + (30 + 34) = (28 + 30) + 34$
23. $47 \cdot 39 = 39 \cdot 47$
24. $5(3 + 4) = 5 \cdot 3 + 5 \cdot 4$
25. $(6 + 2) \cdot (5 + 7) = (5 + 7) \cdot (6 + 2)$
26. You are organizing a pet show. Forty dogs will be shown the first morning. You need to allow 4 minutes for each dog to be shown and 1 minute for cleanup after each dog. How long will the morning session be? What property could you use to find the answer?

PRACTICE 2-2

2-2 Exercises and Applications

Assignment Guide

- Basic
  1–28, 31–33, 39
- Average
  1–25, 27–39 odds
- Enriched
  1–15 odds, 16–30, 32–40 evens

Exercise Notes

Exercise 15

Test Prep If students select A, they have transposed the values of a and b when substituting. If they choose D, they have added first instead of multiplying first.

Exercise Answers

20. Commutative Property of Addition.
21. Associative Property of Multiplication.
22. Associative Property of Addition.
23. Commutative Property of Multiplication.
24. Distributive Property.
25. Commutative Property of Multiplication.
26. 200 minutes; Distributive Property.

Reteaching

Activity

Materials: Scientific calculator

Work with a partner. For each pair of expressions, find the value of one expression, while your partner finds the value of the other. Compare answers.

1. $3 \times 4 + 7$; $(3 \times 4) + 7$ 19; 19
2. $(2 + 5)9$; $2 + 5 \times 9$ 63; 47
3. $(6 - 1)3$; $6 - 1 \times 3$ 15; 3
4. $9 + 6 \cdot 2$; $9 + (6 \cdot 2)$ 21; 21
5. $8(4 - 2)$; $8 \cdot 4 - 2$ 16; 30

- When was multiplication or division done first? When inside parentheses or when there were no parentheses. Addition or subtraction? Only when inside parentheses.
- When was the operation inside the parentheses done first? Always

PRACTICE

Name ______________________ **Practice 2-2**

Order of Operations

Does the expression contain grouping symbols? What are they?

1. $\frac{10 + 6}{7 + 1}$ Yes, fraction bar
2. $8 \cdot 4 - 2 \cdot 3$ No
3. $8 - 3 + 7$ No
4. $17(3 + 5)$ Yes, parentheses
5. $(5 + 3) \div 4$ Yes, parentheses
6. $4 \div 2 - 5$ No

Find the value of each expression.

7. $6 + 8 \times 9$ 78
8. $10(8 - 3)$ 50
9. $\frac{2 \cdot 3 + 8}{5 + 2}$ 2
10. $\frac{25}{5} + \frac{18}{3}$ 11
11. $4 + \frac{8 + 10}{2}$ 13
12. $\frac{15}{8 - 7} + 6$ 21
13. $5 \times \frac{4}{4 - 2}$ 10
14. $\frac{5 \cdot 10}{25} + 4 \div 2$ 4

Operation Sense Insert parentheses to make each sentence true.

15. $(3 + 7) \times (4 - 2) = 20$
16. $10 - (3 + 7) + 4 = 4$
17. $300 \div 50 \div (2 \times 3) = 1$
18. $24 \div (2 + 30 \div 3) = 2$
19. $6 + (4 \div 2) \div 2 = 7$
20. $(4 - 2) \times (9 - 4) = 10$

Which property is being shown?

21. $11 \cdot (12 \cdot 13) = (11 \cdot 12) \cdot 13$ Associative property of multiplication
22. $8(3 + 7) = (8 \cdot 3) + (8 \cdot 7)$ Distributive property
23. $13 + 18 = 18 + 13$ Commutative property of addition
24. $(3 + 5) + 8 = 3 + (5 + 8)$ Associative property of addition
25. $11 \cdot (12 + 13) = (11 \cdot 12) + (11 \cdot 13)$ Distributive property
26. To calculate a distance, Herb used the formula $d = rt$. Sal used the formula $d = tr$. What property assures that Herb and Sal should get the same answer?

    Commutative property of multiplication

RETEACHING

Name ______________________ **Alternative Lesson 2-2**

Order of Operations

An **expression** is a mathematical phrase that can be made up of variables and/or numbers and operations. Here are two expressions.

$8 - 3 \times 5$ $x + 7$

When more than one operation is used, we need to have rules to tell us in which order to do the operations so that everyone will get the same answer.

Order of Operations
1. Simplify inside parentheses or above or below the division bar.
2. Multiply and divide from left to right.
3. Add and subtract from left to right.

Example

Find the value of $9 + (13 - 5) \times 7$.	$9 + (13 - 5) \times 7$
Simplify inside parentheses first.	$9 + (8) \times 7$
Multiply.	$9 + 56$
Add.	65

The value of $9 + (13 - 5) \times 7$ is 65.

Try It Find the value of $(7 + 19) \div 2 - 2 \times 3$. $(7 + 19) \div 2 - 2 \times 3$

a. Simplify inside parentheses. $26 \div 2 - 2 \times 3$
b. Divide and multiply. $13 - 6$
c. Subtract. 7

Find the value of each expression.

d. $8 - 3 \times 2$ 2
e. $7 + 8 \div 4$ 9
f. $6 \div 3 + 8$ 10
g. $2 \times 6 - 4$ 8
h. $13 + 2(8 - 6)$ 17
i. $12 - (10 - 5) \div 5$ 11
j. $18 - 12 \div (1 + 3)$ 15
k. $10(9 - 6) \div 6$ 5
l. $9 \div 3 + (8 + 6)$ 17
m. $6 + 2(4 - 1)$ 12
n. $16 + \frac{6}{2} + 4$ 23
o. $2 + \frac{8}{4} \times 4$ 10

Project Progress

You may want to have students use Chapter 2 Project Master.

Exercise Answers

27. a. $65.10
 b. $71.40
 c. Possible answer: If you use the distributive property on the second one, you get the first.

28. Possible answer: $(4 + 4) \div (4 + 4)$, $4 \times 4 \div (4 \times 4)$, $4 - 4 + 4 \div 4$

29. Yes. By the distributive property, $2(l + w) = 2l + 2w$

30. 5 salads + 5 drinks or 5 times the cost of a salad and a drink. The distributive property.

39. 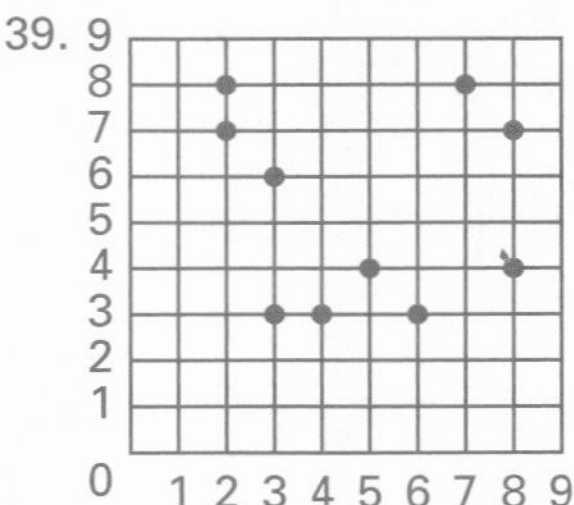

There is no relationship.

40. 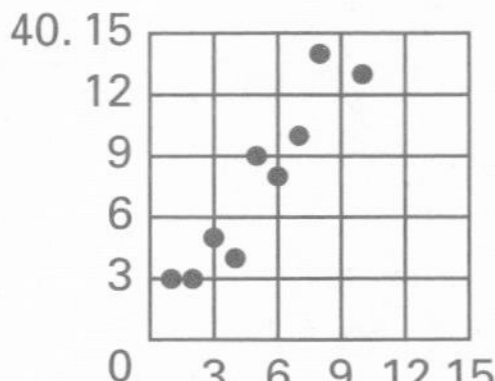

As more games are played, more hits are made.

Alternate Assessment

You may want to use the *Interactive CD-ROM Journal* with this assessment.

Journal Have students write a paragraph about using order of operations and the properties to help them compute mentally.

Quick Quiz

Find the value of each expression.

1. $32 - 4(1 + 3)$ 16
2. $9 \cdot 4 \div 3 + 1$ 13

Which property is being shown?

3. $8 + (5 + 7) = (8 + 5) + 7$ Associative property of addition

Available on Daily Transparency 2-2

---

27. **Consumer** The formula $C = p + ip$ gives the total cost (C) of an item where p is the cost of the item before tax and i is the tax rate.
 a. What is the total cost of a $62 car battery if the tax rate is 5% (0.05)?
 b. The formula $C = p(1 + i)$ will also give you the total cost. Use this formula to find the total cost of a $62.00 battery at the same tax rate.
 c. How are the two formulas related?

Problem Solving and Reasoning

28. **Critical Thinking** Use exactly four 4's and a combination of $+, -, \times, \div$, and parentheses to write three different expressions that equal 1.

29. Journal Jose uses the formula $p = 2l + 2w$ to find the perimeter (p) of a rectangle with length (l) and width (w). Phan uses the formula $p = 2(l + w)$. Will both find the correct perimeter? Explain.

30. **Critical Thinking** Wanda invites four friends to lunch. Each one orders a salad and a drink. There are two ways to compute the bill. What are they? Which property is illustrated by the fact that both methods give the same result?

PROBLEM SOLVING 2-2

Mixed Review

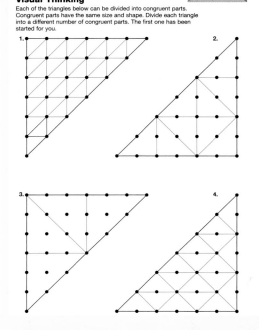

Estimate each sum. *[Previous course]*

31. 48 + 27 80
32. 275 + 305 580
33. 89 + 38 + 61 190
34. 7,846 + 4,874 13,000
35. 32 + 61 + 78 170
36. 3,275 + 2,305 5,600
37. 97 + 78 + 35 220
38. 15,321 + 26,453 41,000

Make a scatterplot to show the data. Describe the relationship. *[Lesson 1-6]*

39.

Child's age	2	6	3	4	8	5	7	3	8	2
Cousins	7	3	6	3	4	4	8	3	7	8

40.

Games	5	2	7	8	4	1	6	10	3
Hits	9	3	10	14	4	3	8	13	5

Project Progress

Think about the costs of starting and running your business. Make a chart that lists the things you would need for your business and how much it would cost to serve the number of customers you expect.

Problem Solving
Understand
Plan
Solve
Look Back

PROBLEM SOLVING

Name ____________

Guided Problem Solving 2-2

GPS PROBLEM 27, STUDENT PAGE 64

The formula $C = p + ip$ gives the total cost (C) of an item where p is the cost of the item before tax and i is the tax rate.

a. What is the total cost of a $62 car battery if the tax rate is 5% (0.05)?
b. The formula $C = p(1 + i)$ will also give you the total cost. Use this formula to find the total cost of a $62.00 battery at the same tax rate.
c. How are the two formulas related?

— Understand —

1. Circle the information you need. Possible answers: Items 6 and 7

— Plan —

2. Which numbers will you substitute for p and i to find the cost of the $62 battery? 62; 0.05
3. Which operation will you do first in order to solve
 a. $C = p + ip$? Multiplication. b. $C = p(1 + i)$? Addition.

— Solve —

4. Use the formula $C = p + ip$ to find the total cost of a $62 car battery if the tax rate is 5% (0.05). $65.10
5. Use the formula $C = p(1 + i)$ to find the total cost of a $62.00 battery at the same rate. $65.10
6. The two formulas give the same answer, so $p + ip = p(1 + i)$. How do you know this is true and that the formulas are related?
 If you use the Distributive Property of multiplication on the second formula, you get the first.

— Look Back —

7. Which formula is easier to use? Explain.
 $C = p + ip$, You can use mental math to solve the problem.

SOLVE ANOTHER PROBLEM

The formulas $A = s + t$ and $A = t + s$ give the area of the rectangle.

a. What is the area of the rectangle if s is 10 and t is 5? 15 square units
b. How are the formulas related? Possible answer: The formulas are examples of the Commutative Property of Addition.

ENRICHMENT

Name ____________

Extend Your Thinking 2-2

Visual Thinking

Each of the triangles below can be divided into congruent parts. Congruent parts have the same size and shape. Divide each triangle into a different number of congruent parts. The first one has been started for you.

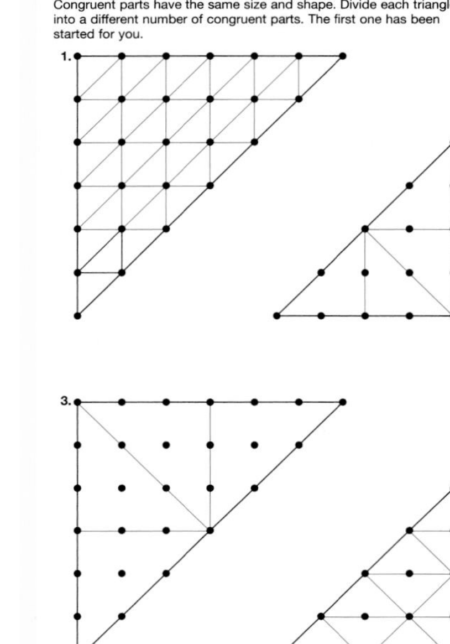

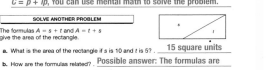

TECHNOLOGY

Using a Spreadsheet • Formulas and Operations

Problem: Your basketball team has scored 85, 90, 73, 100, 76, 92, 87, and 75 points in its last eight games. How many points did your team score in all? What is your team's average score?

You can use your spreadsheet's built-in formulas to answer these questions.

1 Enter the scores into the spreadsheet as shown:

	A	B	C	D	E	F	G	H	I
1	Points Scored	85	90	73	100	76	92	87	75
2	Total =								
3	Average =								

2 In cell B2, enter your spreadsheet's built-in summing formula. This may have an icon that looks like Σ.

	A	B	C	D	E	F	G	H	I
1	Points Scored	85	90	73	100	76	92	87	75
2	Total =	678							
3	Average =								

3 In cell B3, enter your spreadsheet's built-in averaging formula.

	A	B	C	D	E	F	G	H	I
1	Points Scored	85	90	73	100	76	92	87	75
2	Total =	678							
3	Average =	84.75							

Solution: The total is 678 points. The average is 84.75 points.

TRY IT

a. Find the sum and average of 721, 789, 765, 345, 234, 143, 908, and 709.

b. Find the sum and average of 23, 34, 67, 88, 54, 27, 28, 21, 41, and 55.

ON YOUR OWN

- Why do you think spreadsheets have built-in formulas?
- What are the advantages and disadvantages of using a spreadsheet to find an average? Explain.
- Enter the customized formula "=(B1+C1+D1+E1+F1+G1+H1+I1)/8" in cell B4. Compare the answer with the average in cell B3. Explain what you see.

65

Technology

Using a Spreadsheet • Formulas and Operations

The Point

Students use built-in formulas to find the sum and then the average of a set of data values.

Materials

Spreadsheet software

Resources

Interactive CD-ROM Spreadsheet/Grapher Tool

About the Page

The symbol Σ is the Greek letter sigma, and in mathematics it is used to represent a summation.

Ask ...

- How do you enter a built-in formula into a cell? Answers may vary.
- How does the built-in formula for averaging take decimal places into account ? Answers may vary.

Answers for Try It

a. sum = 4,614; average = 576.75

b. sum = 438; average = 43.8

On Your Own

For the second question, one advantage that students may overlook is the ease of changing data values and the subsequent recalculation of the average.

Answers for On Your Own

- So that people can find important values such as sums and averages quickly.
- Advantages: Speed and accuracy if the numbers are entered correctly. Disadvantages: it may be faster to find an average by hand if there are only a few numbers.
- The numbers in cells B3 and B4 are equal; The formula entered in B4 is the formula for the average of the 8 numbers in B1 through I1.

2-3 Lesson Organizer

Objectives

- Use a formula to make a table of values.
- Find a formula when given a table of values.

Materials

- Explore: Spreadsheet software

NCTM Standards

- 1–4, 7, 8, 9

Review

For each sequence of numbers, find a pattern and write three more terms of the sequence.

1. 2, 4, 6, 8 10, 12, 14
2. 1, 4, 7, 10 13, 16, 19
3. 30, 60, 90, 120 150, 180, 210

Available on Daily Transparency 2-3

1 Introduce

Explore

The Point
Students explore formulas and tables by examining spreadsheet tables and writing formulas to show the relationships between the quantities shown.

Ongoing Assessment
Check students' work to make sure that they are entering formulas into the spreadsheet, not just numbers. Encourage students to discuss how entries in one column could be obtained by using entries in the other column.

For Groups That Finish Early
Make a spreadsheet giving data on your earnings for 1–4 hours at a part-time job, or your allowance for 1–4 weeks.

2-3 Formulas and Tables

You'll Learn ...

- to use a formula to make a table of values
- to find a formula when you are given a table of values

... How It's Used

When insurance agents analyze claims, they use tables of values that are based on formulas.

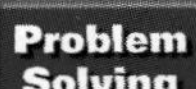

Problem Solving TIP

Look for a pattern to find out the relationships among the values in a table or on a spreadsheet. Notice how the values in each column change.

▶ Lesson Link You know how to substitute values when you are given a formula. Now you will create tables from formulas and find formulas from tables. ◀

Explore Formulas and Tables

Auto Biographies

Materials: Spreadsheet software

On a spreadsheet, if you want to multiply the number in cell A2 by 5 and store the result in C2, type "=A2*5" into C2 and press Enter.

The spreadsheet gives data on the Motorette, a car sold from 1946 to 1948.

	A	B
1	Number of Cars	Number of Wheels
2	1	3
3	2	6
4	3	9
5	4	

1. What pattern do you see relating the values in columns A and B? What formula would you use for cell B5?
2. Enter the Motorette information on a spreadsheet. Complete the next 4 rows.

This data is for a 1983 car, the Thrust 2.

	A	B
1	Distance (mi)	Time (hr)
2	633	1
3	1266	2
4	1899	3
5	2532	

3. What pattern do you see relating the values in columns A and B? What formula would you use for cell B5?
4. Enter the Thrust 2 information on a spreadsheet. Complete the next 7 rows.
5. Make a spreadsheet for the 1955 Eshelman roadster. Complete the next 2 rows.

	A	B	C	D
1	Number of Cars	Weight (lb)	Distance (mi)	Gas (gal)
2	1	250	70	1
3	2	500	140	2

6. What was unusual about the Motorette, the Thrust 2, and the Eshelman?

MEETING INDIVIDUAL NEEDS

Resources

- 2-3 Practice
- 2-3 Reteaching
- 2-3 Problem Solving
- 2-3 Enrichment
- 2-3 Daily Transparency
  - Problem of the Day
  - Review
  - Quick Quiz
- Technology Master 8

Interactive CD-ROM Spreadsheet/ Grapher Tool

Wide World of Mathematics Algebra: Bank Debit Cards

Learning Modalities

Verbal Have students write a description of the relationship between the variables in a table.

Visual Have students make a graph of the data presented in a table and then compare the graph and the formula.

Challenge

Transpo Car Rental allows 200 free miles. The charges are $35.00 per day, plus $0.30 for every mile over 200. Write a formula to figure the amount charged (C) for driving a car m miles in d days.

$C = 35d + 0.30(m - 200)$

Learn Formulas and Tables

You can use a formula to make a table of values. The rows and columns of a table need to be labeled. The values come from substituting into the formula.

Example 1

The sales tax formula in Nebraska is $t = 0.05 \times c$, where c is the cost of goods or services and t is the sales tax. Use the formula to make a sales tax table for services offered by Sparkling Car Wash.

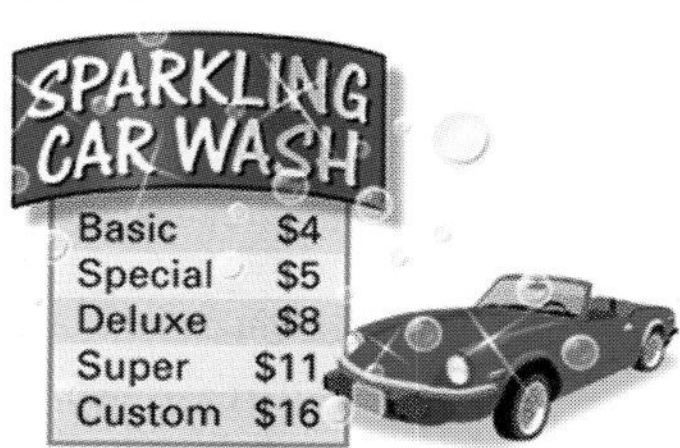

Multiply the cost of each service by 0.05.

Services	Basic	Special	Deluxe	Super	Custom
Cost (c)	$4.00	$5.00	$8.00	$11.00	$16.00
Sales Tax (t)	$0.20	$0.25	$0.40	$0.55	$0.80

Try It

The area of a square can be found using the formula $A = s \cdot s$, where A is the area and s is the length of a side. Use the formula to make a table for the areas of squares with sides of length 2, 3, 5, 8, 10, and 12 in.

If you *begin* with a table of values, you can use your number sense to find the formula that was used to make the table.

Example 2

Find a formula relating t and d.

Time (t)	1	2	3	4	5	6
Distance Driven (d)	50	100	150	200	250	300

Study the table. Notice that in each column, the distance driven is equal to the time multiplied by 50.

The formula is $d = 50t$.

Try It

Find a formula relating the variables.

a.

x	1	2	3	4
y	8	16	24	32

$y = 8x$

b.

m	6	7	8	9
n	2	3	4	5

$n = m - 4$

HINT

The constant function on many calculators can help you find and check values in a table. For $D = 30g$, you might

Enter 1 [×] 30 [=]

then 2 [=]

3 [=]

MATH EVERY DAY

Problem of the Day

Keisha put a wire fence around her square garden. She started with 60 meters of fencing and has 4.6 meters left over. How long is each side of her garden? 13.85 meters

Available on Daily Transparency 2-3

An Extension is provided in the transparency package.

Fact of the Day

In 1994, the most popular compact sports car color was white. Green was the second most popular. About 15% of buyers chose white and about 13% chose green.

Estimation

Estimate.

1. 37×8 320
2. 4×72 280
3. 11×65 650

Answers for Explore

1. Column B is 3 times column A; B5 = A5 * 3
2.

	A	B
1	Number of Cars	Number of Wheels
2	1	3
3	2	6
4	3	9
5	4	12
6	5	15
7	6	18
8	7	21
9	8	24

3. Column A is 633 times column B; B5 = A5 ÷ 633

Answers for Steps 4–6 on page C4.

2 Teach

Learn

Alternate Examples

1. The time it takes Janet to walk a given distance can be found by using the formula $t = 15d$, where d is the distance in miles and t is the time in minutes. Use the formula to complete the following table.

   Multiply each distance by 15.

d	2	4	5	7
t	30	60	75	105

   The formula $t = 15d$ is used to calculate the values in the bottom row.

2. Find a formula relating n and p where n is the number of pencils and p is the price.

n	1	2	3	4
p	15	30	45	60

   Notice that in each column, the price is equal to the number of pencils multiplied by 15.

   The formula is $p = 15n$.

Answers for Try It

Example 1

s (in.)	2	3	5	8	10	12
A (in^2)	4	9	25	64	100	144

Students see two ways of looking at the information in the table. One way focuses on the total number of members and describes how the number of representatives can be determined. The other way focuses on the number of representatives and describes how the total number of members can be determined. Students see that both ways produce useful formulas.

Answers for What Do You Think?

1. Yes; Jacob's method.
2. Yes; Kimberly's method.

3 Practice and Assess

Check

Students should recognize that the way in which the information is presented in the table does not affect the information itself. Students should also recognize that not all sets of numbers are related. For example, the number of representatives that a state has is not related to the number of senators, since all states have two senators.

Answers for Check Your Understanding

1. No; The same information is in a different position.
2. Possible answer: No; Some numbers may have no relationship to one another (for example, tosses of a number cube).

The table gives data on the number of representatives (r) a state might have in the House of Representatives, and the total number of members of Congress (t) the state would have. Find a formula relating r and t.

Representatives (r)	1	2	3	4	5	6
Total Members (t)	3	4	5	6	7	8

Kimberly thinks ...

In each column, the value of t is 2 more than the value of r.

The formula is $t = r + 2$.

Jacob thinks ...

In each column the value of r is 2 less than the value of t.

The formula is $r = t - 2$.

What do you think?

1. Will both methods allow you to find r if you know t? Which one is easier to use if you know t?
2. Will both methods allow you to find t if you know r? Which one is easier to use if you know r?

Check Your Understanding

1. Suppose the rows and columns of a table are switched. Does the new table show different information? Explain.
2. Do you think there is a formula relating *any* two sets of numbers? Explain.

MEETING MIDDLE SCHOOL CLASSROOM NEEDS

Tips from Middle School Teachers

I find that some students are not comfortable making and using tables and need extra encouragement. As students continue to solve problems, I try to point out when a table will be useful.

Team Teaching

Work with a science teacher to introduce the concepts of variable expressions and formulas used in science.

Consumer Connection

All but five states in the United States have a sales tax on goods or services. The rates vary, but some are 8% or more. Some states exempt food and medicine. Have students research the sales tax rate for their state.

2-3 Exercises and Applications

Practice and Apply

1. **Getting Started** The formula $H = 24 \cdot D$ relates the number of hours (H) to the number of days (D).
   - **a.** Substitute 3 for D to find the number of hours in 3 days.
   - **b.** Substitute 4 for D to find the number of hours in 4 days.
   - **c.** Use your answers to **a** and **b** to begin filling in the table. Fill in the rest of the table.

Days	3	4	5	6	7	8
Hours						

2. **Consumer** In 1973, the average price for regular gasoline in the United States was $0.39 per gallon. The formula $C = 0.39G$ relates cost (C) to the number of gallons bought (G). Make a table that shows the cost of 2, 5, 7, 9, and 12 gallons of gasoline in 1973.

3. **Science** The Kelvin temperature scale is sometimes used in science. The formula $K = 273 + C$ relates degrees Kelvin (K) to degrees Celsius (C). Make a table that shows the Kelvin temperatures for the Celsius temperatures of 0°, 20°, 40°, 60°, 80°, and 100°. GPS

Find a formula relating the variables.

4.

u	1	2	3	4
v	5	6	7	8

$v = u + 4$

5.

x	3	4	5	6
y	15	20	25	30

$y = 5x$

6.

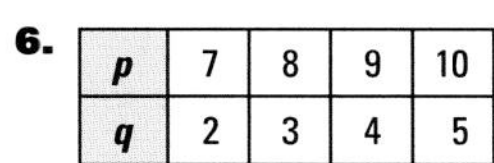

p	7	8	9	10
q	2	3	4	5

$q = p - 5$

7.

m	2	3	4	5
n	12	18	24	30

$n = 6m$

8.

x	5	6	7	8
y	50	60	70	80

$y = 10x$

9.

w	11	12	13	14
v	1.1	1.2	1.3	1.4

$v = 0.1w$

PRACTICE 2-3

PRACTICE

Name ______________________

Practice 2-3

Formulas and Tables

1. The formula $P = 4s$ gives the perimeter (P) of a square, where s is the length of a side. Use this formula to make a table of the perimeters of squares with sides of length 1, 2, 4, 6, 9, 12, and 18 cm.

Side (s)	1	2	4	6	9	12	18
Perimeter (P)	4	8	16	24	36	48	72

Find a formula relating the variables.

2. Formula: $y = 4x$

x	2	3	4	5
y	8	12	16	20

3. Formula: $t = s + 8$

s	4	5	6	7
t	12	13	14	15

4. Formula: $r = h - 4$

h	11	12	13	14
r	7	8	9	10

5. Formula: $v = u + 10$

u	5	6	7	8
v	15	16	17	18

6. Formula: $z = 7x$

x	2	3	4	5
z	14	21	28	35

7. Formula: $b = a - 5$

a	8	9	10	11
b	3	4	5	6

8. For a given distance, the formula $i = 12f$ relates the number of inches (i) to the number of feet (f). Make a table that shows the number of inches equal to 1, 2, 5, 8, 10, 12, and 20 feet.

Number of feet (f)	1	2	5	8	10	12	20
Number of inches (i)	12	24	60	96	120	144	240

9. **Science** The formula $d = 16 \cdot t \cdot t$ gives the distance (d) in feet that a ball has fallen t seconds after it has been dropped. Make a table to show the distance the ball has fallen after 0, 1, 2, 3, 4, 5, and 6 seconds.

Time (t), sec	0	1	2	3	4	5	6
Distance (d), ft	0	16	64	144	256	400	576

RETEACHING

Name ______________________

Alternative Lesson 2-3

Formulas and Tables

You can use a formula to make a table of values. The rows and columns of a table need to be labeled. The values come from substituting into the formula.

Example 1

The formula for the total cost of mailing a two-day package is $c = 3 \times p$ where c is the cost of the packages and p is the number of packages sent. Make a table of the total cost of mailing 2, 3, 4, 5, and 6 packages.

Multiply the number of packages by 3.

Number of packages (p)	2	3	4	5	6
Total cost of mailing (c)	6	9	12	15	18
Think:	$3 \times 2 = 6$	$3 \times 3 = 9$	$3 \times 4 = 12$	$3 \times 5 = 15$	$3 \times 6 = 18$

The formula $c = 3 \times p$ is used to calculate the values in the bottom row.

Try It The perimeter of a square can be found using the formula $P = 4 \cdot s$, where P is the perimeter and s is the length of a side. Use the formula to make a table for the perimeters of squares with sides of length 1, 4, 7, 8, 10, and 15 inches.

a. Multiply the length of the sides by 4.

b. Complete the table.

Length of side (in.)	1	4	7	8	10	15
Perimeter (in.)	4	16	28	32	40	60

c. What formula was used to calculate the values in the bottom row? $P = 4 \cdot s$

Example 2

Find a formula that relates the values in the table.

Think: In each column the value of b is 4 more than the value of a.

a	1	2	3	4	5
b	5	6	7	8	9

The formula is $b = a + 4$.

Try It

p	10	9	8	7	6	5
b	7	6	5	4	3	2

d. In each column, how are the values of b related to the values of p?

Possible answers: The value of p is 3 more than the value of b. The value of b is 3 less than the value of p.

e. Write a formula relating p and b. Possible answers: $p = b + 3$; $b = p - 3$

2-3 Exercises and Applications

Assignment Guide

- **Basic** 1–3, 6–10, 12, 14–22 evens
- **Average** 1–10, 12, 14–22 evens
- **Enriched** 2–7, 10–13, 15–23 odds

Exercise Notes

Exercise 3

Science The Kelvin temperature scale was created by Lord Kelvin, a British physicist and mathematician who lived from 1824 to 1904.

Exercise Answers

1. a. 72

   b. 96

   c.

Days	3	4	5	6	7	8
Hours	72	96	120	144	168	192

2.

G	2	5	7	9	12
C ($)	0.78	1.95	2.73	3.51	4.68

3.

C	0°	20°	40°	60°	80°	100°
K	273°	293°	313°	333°	353°	373°

Reteaching

Activity

Materials: Counters

- Use counters to help write a formula relating the variables.

s	3	4	5	6	7
t	6	7	8	9	10

- Take 3 counters, the first value of s. What could you do to the counters to obtain 6, the first value of t? Add 3 counters.
- Continue for each value of s. Take the number of counters that is the value of s and add counters to obtain the value of t.
- Describe in words what you did for each value of s. Take s counters. Add 3 counters. Now I have t counters.
- Write the formula that relates s and t. $t = s + 3$

Exercise Answers

Answers for Exercises 11–13 on page C4.

22. $y = 8$

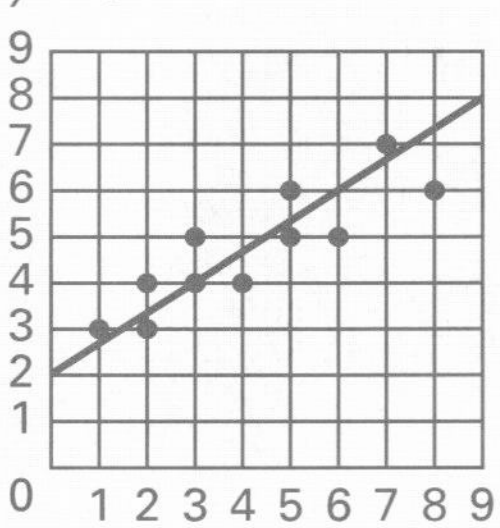

23. $y = 1$

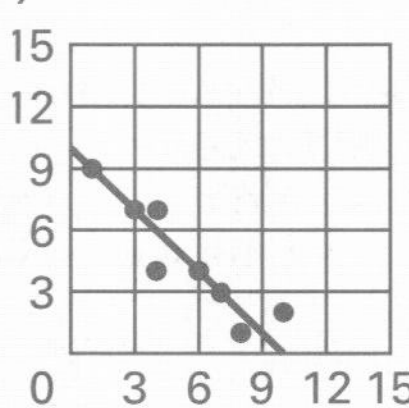

Alternate Assessment

Performance Have students work together in pairs. Give each student two of the following formulas and five different values for x.

1. $y = x + 4$ 2. $y = 3x$
3. $y = x + 3$ 4. $y = 5x$

Have students complete a table of x and y values for each of their given formulas. Then have partners exchange their completed tables without the formulas and write the formulas for each table.

Observe how students determine the entries for the tables and how they determine the formulas.

Quick Quiz

1. Use the formula $D = 7W$ to complete the following table.

W	1	2	3	4
D	7	14	21	28

Find a formula relating the variables.

2.

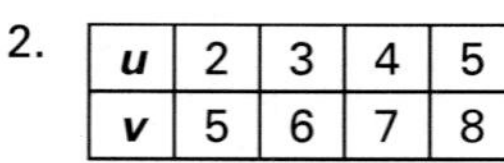

u	2	3	4	5
v	5	6	7	8

$v = u + 3$

3.

a	9	12	15	18
b	3	4	5	6

$a = b \times 3$ or $b = \frac{a}{3}$

Available on Daily Transparency 2-3

PROBLEM SOLVING 2-3

10. **Test Prep** Which formula gives the relationship of the variables in the table? **C**

k	4	6	8	12
j	2	3	4	6

Ⓐ $j = 2k$ Ⓑ $j = 2 + k$ Ⓒ $k = 2j$ Ⓓ $k = 2 + j$

11. **Health** To decide how much adult medicine to give a child, some doctors use the formula $C = \frac{Y}{Y + 12} \cdot A$, where C is the amount of medicine to give the child, Y is the child's age in years, and A is the amount of medicine normally given to an adult. Make a table for a 4-year-old child to show the amount of medicine to give the child when the adult dose is 4 g, 8 g, 12 g, and 16 g.

Problem Solving and Reasoning

12. **Communicate** Sound travels at about 1480 meters per second in 20°C water. The formula $D = 1480s$ relates distance (D) and seconds (s).

a. Make a table of values to see how far sound travels in 0 to 10 seconds.

b. In 10°C water, sound travels 1450 meters per second. How does this change the values in the table? The formula?

13. **Critical Thinking** The intensity of sound decreases quickly as you move away from the source of the sound. The formula $I = \frac{100}{d \cdot d}$ gives the intensity (I) of a sound that has 100 watts of power at a given distance (d) from the source of the sound. How many times more intense is this sound at 1 foot away than at 10 feet away?

Mixed Review

Estimate each difference. *[Previous course]*

14. 52 − 24 **25** **15.** 81 − 32 **50** **16.** 625 − 238 **400** **17.** 499 − 328 **170**

18. 81 − 47 **30** **19.** 572 − 297 **270** **20.** 8324 − 7632 **700** **21.** 7811 − 3236 **4600**

Make a scatterplot to show the data. Draw a trend line and predict the value of y when $x = 9$. *[Lesson 1-7]*

22.

x	2	5	3	7	3	8	2	5	1	6	4
y	4	6	5	7	4	6	3	5	3	5	4

23.

x	10	8	3	4	7	1	4	6
y	2	1	7	7	3	9	4	4

PROBLEM SOLVING

Name ______________________

Guided Problem Solving 2-3

GPS PROBLEM 3, STUDENT PAGE 69

The Kelvin temperature scale is sometimes used in science. The formula $K = 273 + C$ relates degrees Kelvin (K) to degrees Celsius (C). Make a table that shows the Kelvin temperatures for the Celsius temperatures of 0°, 20°, 40°, 60°, 80°, and 100°.

— Understand —

1. Circle the data you need to make the table showing Kelvin and Celsius temperatures.
2. How do you use the formula to find degrees Kelvin?
   Add 273 to the Celsius temperature.

— Plan —

3. What labels will you use to show the two sets of information?
   Degrees Kelvin; Degrees Celsius
4. Which data will go on the top row of your table? Degrees Celsius

— Solve —

5. Complete the table below, including labels.

Degrees Celsius	0	20	40	60	80	100
Degrees Kelvin	273	293	313	333	353	373

— Look Back —

6. How can you use subtraction to check your answer?
   Subtract 273 from the Celsius temperature to find the Kelvin temperature.

SOLVE ANOTHER PROBLEM

The formula $C = \frac{5}{9}(F - 32)$ relates degrees Fahrenheit (F) to degrees Celsius (C). Make a table that shows the Celsius temperatures for the Fahrenheit temperatures of 50°, 68°, 77°, 95°, 104°, and 149°.

Degrees Fahrenheit	50	68	77	95	104	149
Degrees Celsius	10	20	25	35	40	65

ENRICHMENT

Name ______________________

Extend Your Thinking 2-3

Patterns in Geometry

A diagonal of a polygon is a line that is drawn from one vertex (corner) of the polygon to another nonadjacent vertex.

vertex no diagonals

vertex 1 diagonal

Draw all possible diagonals from one vertex to divide each polygon into triangles.

1.

2.

3.

4.

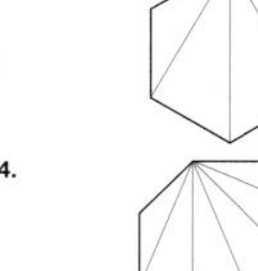

5.

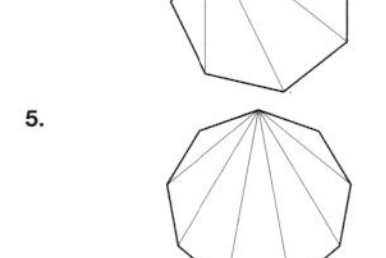

6.

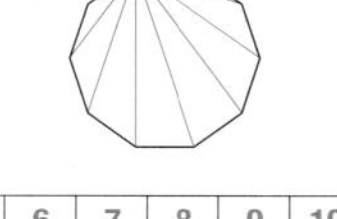

7. Use all the polygons above to make a table.

Number of sides	3	4	5	6	7	8	9	10
Number of triangles	1	2	3	4	5	6	7	8

8. Write a formula relating the data in your table. Be sure to define the variables.
   $t = s - 2$ where t is the number of triangles and s is the number of sides.

9. Suppose that all the possible diagonals from one vertex are drawn for polygons below. Use your formula to find the number of triangles that would be in each polygon.

   a. Eleven sides 9 triangles **b.** Fifty sides 48 triangles

In this section you've seen how variables and formulas can help you understand relationships among real-world quantities. Now you'll have a chance to apply what you have learned to a situation that could occur: You have just turned 16 and someone has given you a new car. The question is, can you afford to operate it?

America Loves Cars ... From Olds to New

You've just been given a new four-cylinder Freebie. The car was free, but the day-to-day expenses are your responsibility. There are brakes to maintain, gas to buy, and an engine to keep up. The American Automobile Association estimates that for a four-cylinder car, costs average about $0.08 per mile.

1. Complete the table for a four-cylinder car.

Miles Driven (m)	10	20	50	100	500	1000	2000
Cost (c)							

2. Write a formula relating the two variables in the table.

3. Estimate the average distance you would drive each day. How much would it cost you to operate your car for one day? For one year?

The table shows that the day-to-day costs of operating your car depend on how far you drive. But there are other *fixed costs* that you must pay whether you drive or not—insurance, license and registration fees, taxes, and so on. These can amount to thousands of dollars a year.

4. Suppose the fixed costs for your car are $3000 per year. Complete the table to show the total annual cost, including the $3000.

Annual Mileage (m)	6,000	9,000	12,000	18,000	24,000
Annual Cost (a)					

5. Write a formula relating the annual mileage (m) and the annual cost (a).

6. Using your estimate from Step 3, find how much it will cost you to operate your car for one year.

Answers for Connect

1.

Miles Driven (m)	10	20	50	100	500	1000	2000
Cost (c)	0.80	1.60	4.00	8.00	40.00	80.00	160.00

2. $c = 0.08m$

3. Possible answer: 30 mi; $2.40; $876.00.

4.

Annual Mileage (m)	6,000	9,000	12,000	18,000	24,000
Annual Cost (a)	3,480	3,720	3,960	4,440	4,920

5. $a = 0.08m + 3000$

6. Possible answer: $3,876.

America Loves Cars ... From Olds to New

The Point

In *America Loves Cars ... From Olds to New* on page 55, students discussed costs involved in owning a car. Now they will use tables and formulas to analyze the annual cost of operating a car.

About the Page

- If necessary, have students express the problem represented by each table in words before they try to write a formula. Then assist them in translating the words into an equation.
- Help students understand day-to-day costs by asking if they know how often they would buy gas and what it would cost.
- Help students understand fixed costs by asking if they know how much insurance will cost for a year.
- Discuss why it is important to consider both the fixed and day-to-day costs when owning a car.

Ongoing Assessment

Check that students have completed the tables and written the formulas correctly.

Extension

Most people are not given free cars; usually they borrow some of the money and make monthly payments to repay the loan. Ask students to determine the annual cost of driving the car for one year if they also had to make a monthly payment of $250 for a car loan. It will cost 12×250, or $3000 more than the amount calculated for Question 6.

2A Review

Review Correlation

Item(s)	Lesson(s)
1–9	2-2
10, 11	2-1
12–14	2-3
15	2-1, 2-2
16	2-2

Test Prep

Test-Taking Tip

Tell students not to guess on multiple-choice tests, unless they can eliminate one or more choices, since some tests deduct for incorrect answers. In this problem, students are given the hint to work the problem out step by step. Then, if they do not arrive at one of the answers given, it will be easier to check for errors.

Answers for Review

14.

Speed (*s*) in mi/hr	5	8	10	20
Travel Time (*t*) in hr	32	20	16	8

15. Possible answer: Replace the variables with the values, then follow the order of operations to evaluate the expression.

Section 2A Review

REVIEW 2A

Evaluate each expression.

1. $9 + 12 \div 3 - 3$ 10

2. $\frac{3^2 + 3}{3 \cdot 2^2}$ 1

3. $14 \div 7 \cdot 4 - 1$ 7

4. $42 \cdot 2 - 2.1$ 81.9

5. $\frac{2 + 6}{2} + 3 \cdot 4$ 16

6. $6^2 \div 4 + 5 \cdot 3 + 1$ 25

Place parentheses to make each statement true.

7. $9 \times 9 - 9 \div 9 = 0$
$9 \times (9 - 9) \div 9 = 0$

8. $9 \times 9 - 9 \div 9 = 8$
$(9 \times 9 - 9) \div 9 = 8$

9. $9 \times 9 - 9 \div 9 = 80$
$(9 \times 9) - (9 \div 9) = 80$

Evaluate each formula for the given values.

10. $t = \frac{D}{r}$, $D = 1000$, $r = 50$ 20

11. $C = ph$, $p = 12$, $h = 10$ 120

Find a formula relating the variables.

12. $v = u + 9$

u	1	2	3	4
v	10	11	12	13

13. $y = 3x$

x	2	4	5	6
y	6	12	15	18

14. The formula $t = \frac{d}{s}$ measures a storm's travel time in hours. A major storm is located 160 miles from Miami. Complete the table to estimate the number of hours it will take to reach Miami for the different speeds.

Speed (*s*) in mi/hr	5	8	10	20
Travel Time (*t*) in hr				

15. 

Describe the steps you use to substitute values into a formula.

Test Prep

When you are asked to find the value of an expression that has several operations in it, it is a good idea to write the expression on a separate sheet of paper and carefully use the order of operations in a step-by-step manner.

16. Find the value of $12 + 3 \cdot 4^2(7 - 5) + \frac{4 + 2}{3}$. B

Ⓐ 62 Ⓑ 110 Ⓒ 146 Ⓓ 482

Resources

Practice Masters
Section 2A Review
Assessment Sourcebook
Quiz 2A
TestWorks
Test and Practice Software

PRACTICE

Name ____________________ Practice

Section 2A Review

Evaluate each expression.

1. $6 + 8 \div 2 - 4$ 6
2. $2 \times 3 + 4 \times 5$ 26
3. $7 + 3 \cdot 8 \div 6$ 11
4. $\frac{7 + 8}{5 - 2}$ 5
5. $3 + \frac{10 - 2}{4}$ 5
6. $2 \times 5 - \frac{3 + 9}{5 - 1}$ 7

Place parentheses to make each sentence true.

7. $(4 + 6) \div (2 - 1) = 10$
8. $(7 \times 7 - 7) \div 7 = 6$
9. $40 + 20 \div (10 - 5) = 44$
10. $7 \times (10 - 8) \div 2 = 7$

Evaluate each formula for the given values.

11. $A = \ell w$, $\ell = 3$, $w = 7$; $A =$ 21
12. $d = rt$, $r = 30$, $t = 2$; $d =$ 60
13. $P = 2\ell + 2w$, $\ell = 6$, $w = 5$; $P =$ 22
14. $r = \frac{d}{t}$, $d = 150$, $t = 3$; $r =$ 50

Find a formula relating the variables.

15. $y = 3x$

x	2	3	4	5
y	6	9	12	15

16. $v = u - 8$

u	11	12	13	14
v	3	4	5	6

17. The formula $r = \frac{d}{t}$ gives the average speed of travel for a distance *d* and time *t*. New Orleans, Louisiana, is a 400-mile drive from Memphis, Tennessee. Complete the table to find the average speed if the trip from Memphis to New Orleans is made in different times.

Time (*t*) in hours	2	4	8	10	20
Speed (*r*) in mi/hr	200	100	50	40	20

18. The per capita public debt (in thousands of dollars) of the United States for the years 1940 to 1990 appears below. Create a scatterplot and determine a trend line. Based on your scatterplot, what do you expect the per capita public debt to be in 2020? *[Lesson 1-7]*

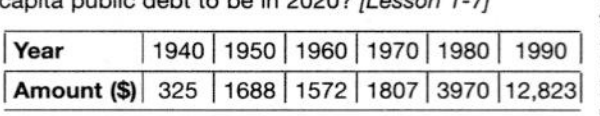

Year	1940	1950	1960	1970	1980	1990
Amount ($)	325	1688	1572	1807	3970	12,823

About 14,600

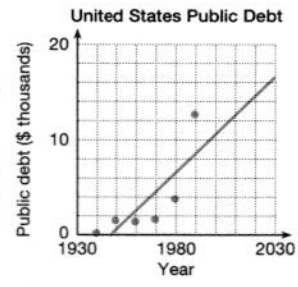

Expressions and Equations

Visit www.teacher.mathsurf.com for links to lesson plans from teachers and other professionals, NCTM information, and other sites.

LESSON PLANNING GUIDE

Student Edition | **Ancillaries***

LESSON		MATERIALS	VOCABULARY	DAILY	OTHER
	Section 2B Opener				
2-4	**Inverse Operations**		inverse operations	2–4	Ch. 2 Project Master
2-5	**Translating Words to Expressions**		algebraic expression	2–5	
2-6	**Solving Addition and Subtraction Equations**		equation, solve, solution	2–6	Teaching Tool Trans. 2, 3 *Interactive CD-ROM Lesson* *WW Math*—Middle School
2-7	**Solving Multiplication and Division Equations**			2–7	*Interactive CD-ROM Lesson*
2-8	**Problem Solving with Two-Step Equations**			2–8	Technology Master 9
	Connect				Lesson Enhancement Trans. 9 Interdisc. Team Teaching 2B
	Review				Practice 2B; Quiz 2B; *TestWorks*
	Extend Key Ideas				
	Chapter 2 Summary and Review				
	Chapter 2 Assessment				Ch. 2 Tests Forms A–F *TestWorks*; Ch. 2 Letter Home
	Cumulative Review, Ch. 1–2				Cumulative Review Ch. 1–2

* Daily Ancillaries include Practice, Reteaching, Problem Solving, Enrichment, and Daily Transparency. Teaching Tool Transparencies are in *Teacher's Toolkits*. Lesson Enhancement Transparencies are in *Overhead Transparency Package*.

SKILLS TRACE

LESSON	SKILL	FIRST INTRODUCED GR. 5	GR. 6	GR. 7	DEVELOP	PRACTICE/ APPLY	REVIEW
2-4	**Using inverse operations.**		✘		pp. 74–75	pp. 76–77	pp. 85, 99, 129, 302
2-5	**Translating words and phrases into algebraic expressions and vice versa.**		✘		pp. 78–79	pp. 80–81	pp. 90, 99, 109, 307
2-6	**Solving addition and subtraction equations using inverse operations.**		✘		pp. 82–83	pp. 84–85	pp. 94, 99, 114, 312
2-7	**Solving multiplication and division equations using inverse operations.**		✘		pp. 86–88	pp. 89–90	pp. 99, 119, 148, 340, 348
2-8	**Using more than one inverse operation to solve equations.**			✘ p. 91	pp. 91–92	pp. 93–94	pp. 99, 124, 177

CONNECTED MATHEMATICS

Investigation 7 in the unit *Moving Straight Ahead (Linear Relationships)*, from the **Connected Mathematics** series, can be used with Section 2B.

INTERDISCIPLINARY TEAM TEACHING

Math and Science/Technology

(Worksheet pages 7–8: Teacher pages T7–T8)

In this lesson, students write algebraic equations using automobile air bag data.

Name ______________________________ ***Math and Science/Technology***

Puff! The Magic Air Bag

Write algebraic equations using automobile air bag data

Moving north at a moderate speed, Mrs. Smith directs her car toward an intersection. To her horror, a truck moving south swerves into her lane. Both drivers stamp down on their brake pedals. Too late! There's going to be a crash!

The car and truck collide. Obeying Sir Isaac Newton's first law of motion, which among other things states that an object in motion tends to remain in motion unless a force acts on it, every object in the car—including Mrs. Smith—continues to move forward. Mrs. Smith's seatbelts restrain her plunge forward, but her chest and head are on a collision course for the steering wheel and windshield, which represent forces that, according to Newton, will act on Mrs. Smith to stop her motion.

All this happens in the tiniest fraction of a second. However, something else is happening at the same time—something that will prevent serious injury to Mrs. Smith. A sensor in the front of the car has detected the crash. A switch turns on. A tiny explosion triggers the release of nitrogen gas into a bag stored in the steering wheel. Puff! The bag pops out and inflates. Mrs. Smith's body crashes into the soft, inflated bag instead of the hard surfaces of the car. An instant later, the bag deflates, and Mrs. Smith—safe and sound—breathes a sigh of relief.

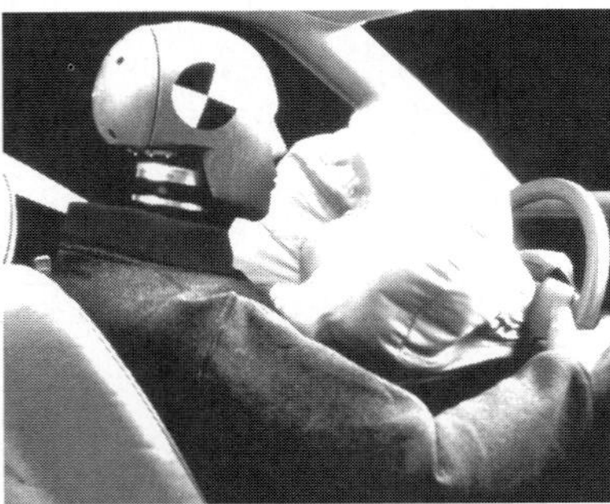

Crash dummies, like this one, are used to test the effectiveness of air bags. The photo shows the dummy beginning to move forward as the air bag deploys and inflates.

Name ______________________________ ***Math and Science/Technology***

1. a. Mrs. Smith's driver's seat air bag inflated quickly at the rate of 120 miles per hour. To calculate how much time it took for the air bag to reach her body, what variable would you have to know if *time = distance* divided by *speed*?

the distance the air bag traveled from its compartment to Mrs. Smith's body

b. If the air bag traveled 1 foot, could you easily solve for time using the rate of 120 miles per hour? What other math operation would you have to do?

No, because the distance is in feet and the rate is in miles. You would have to convert one of the measurements.

2. One mile per hour equals about 1.5 feet per second. What operation do you have to do to calculate the speed of the air bag's movement in feet per second? Show the answer.

Multiply 120 by 1.5 feet per second for a rate of 180 feet per second.

3. If Mrs. Smith's air bag traveled 1 foot, how long did it take to reach her body? (Your answer will be a fraction of a second.)

time = *distance* ÷ *speed*
time = 1 foot ÷ 180 feet per second
time = 1/180 of a second

4. Mrs. Smith's car was traveling at 30 miles per hour (mph) when it entered the intersection. Three seconds later—after Mrs. Smith had applied the brakes— her car struck the truck at 18 mph. What was the mean rate of Mrs. Smith's reduction of speed during those three seconds? Write an equation to show your work.

(30 mph – 18 mph) ÷ 3 = 4 mph

5. Although air bags save many lives, they may injure or be deadly for some people. Do some research to find out how (and to whom) air bags can be dangerous. Find out how this danger can be decreased. Write your findings on a separate sheet of paper.

Air bags can be dangerous to young children and infants. Sensors that can sense weights of passengers and alter the rate of inflation might reduce injuries.

6. Research the current controversies regarding air bags. Then, on a separate sheet of paper, give your opinions of the following questions: Should laws requiring air bags in all cars be changed? Should people be allowed to disconnect air bags?

Opinions will vary. However, students should address questions such as freedom of choice vs. safety.

BIBLIOGRAPHY

FOR TEACHERS

Boschung, Herbert Jr. et al. *The Audubon Society Field Guide to North American Fishes, Whales, and Dolphins*. New York, NY: Knopf, 1983.

Hughes, James, ed. *The Larousse Desk Reference*. New York, NY: Larousse, 1995.

Wagner, Sigrid, ed. *Research Ideas for the Classroom*. New York, NY: Macmillan, 1993.

FOR STUDENTS

Marzio, Peter C. *Rube Goldberg: His Life and Work*. New York, NY: Harper, 1973.

Parker, Steve. *The Random House Book of How Things Work*. New York, NY: Random House, 1991.

SECTION **2B**

Expressions and Equations

▶ Industry Link ▶ www.mathsurf.com/7/ch2/machines

An Efficient Machine?

Is it a compliment to call an invention a "Rube Goldberg" machine? Cartoonist Rube Goldberg (1881–1970) enjoyed poking fun at America's love of machines. He "invented" many complicated but useless machines. Here, a cartoon shows an invention used to avoid oversleeping.

His "inventions" became so widely known that *Webster's New World Dictionary* added "Rube Goldberg" to its listing. *Webster's* defines it as "any very complicated invention…contrived to perform a seemingly simple operation." Goldberg's machines involve a series of actions done in a certain order.

Mathematical operations, too, can often be described in terms of a series of actions. In this section you'll learn about some of these operations. You'll see how both doing and "undoing" operations can help you solve problems much more easily than Rube Goldberg's machine can wake a person up!

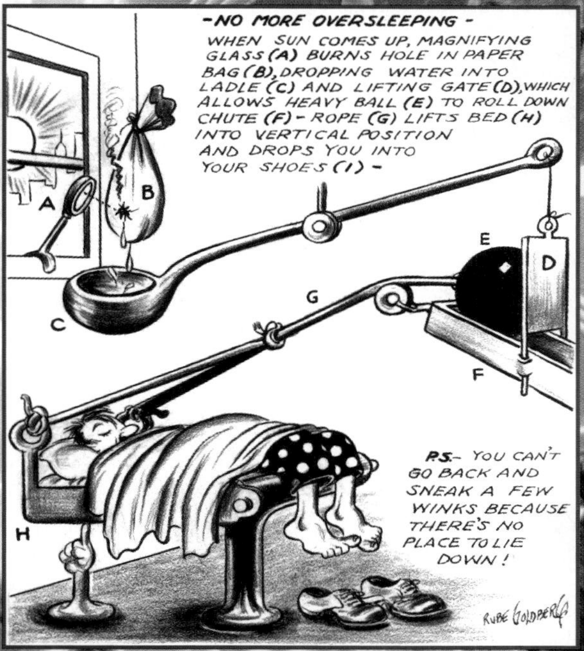

1 How do you write "triple five, then add two" mathematically?

2 Describe a mathematical formula that involves several steps.

73

Where are we now?

In Section 2A, students learned how to

- use formulas to show relationships.
- apply the order of operations.
- use the associative, commutative, and distributive properties.
- make a table of values when given a formula and find a formula when given a table of values.

Where are we going?

In Section 2B, students will

- translate words into algebraic expressions.
- solve addition and subtraction problems using inverse operations.
- solve multiplication and division problems using inverse operations.
- use more than one inverse operation to solve an equation.

Section 2B

Theme: Machines

World Wide Web

If your class has access to the World Wide Web, you might want to use the information found at the Web site address given. The interdisciplinary link relates to topics discussed in this section.

About the Page

This page introduces the theme of this section, machines, and discusses the machines Rube Goldberg drew in his cartoons.

Ask …

- What wakes you up in the morning? How many steps are involved?
- What do you think Goldberg was trying to show in his cartoons?

Industry

Have students research the work of Rube Goldberg and find out how it affected the cartoon industry. A suggested source would be his biography, *Rube Goldberg, His Life and Work*, by Peter C. Marzio.

Answers for Questions

1. $3 \times 5 + 2$
2. Possible answer: $P = 2(l + w)$

Connect

On page 95, students use a successive set of equations to work through the steps of a multiple-step problem.

2-4 Lesson Organizer

Objective

- Use inverse operations.

Vocabulary

- Inverse operations

NCTM Standards

- 1–4, 6, 9

Review

Find each answer.

1. 5 + 7 − 7 5
2. 2 × 9 ÷ 9 2
3. 8 − 6 + 6 8
4. 6 ÷ 3 • 3 6

Available on Daily Transparency 2-4

1 Introduce

Explore

The Point
Students explore the *working backward* strategy by solving a problem that gives information about the end of a process and asks what was true at the beginning.

Ongoing Assessment
Check to see that students understand that they can find a day's output from the next day's output. Ask questions such as: What was Thursday's output? How can you find Wednesday's output?

For Groups That Finish Early
What could you do to check your answer? How will you decide that the answer is correct? Work forward beginning with the answer. If the number of doggles on Friday is 23, the answer is probably correct.

Follow Up
Have students take turns explaining the steps that they performed to solve the problem.

2-4 Inverse Operations

You'll Learn ...

- to use inverse operations

... How It's Used

A computer game designer often has to work backward and undo the steps of a game to fix errors and make improvements.

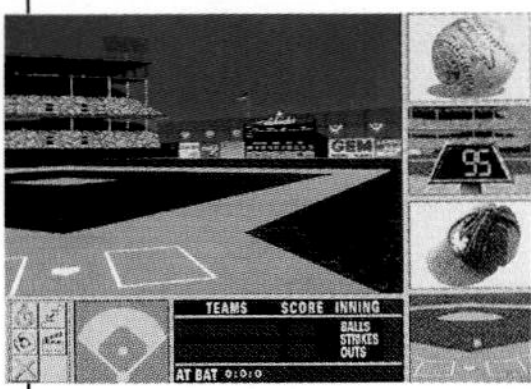

Vocabulary

inverse operations

Lesson Link You have used formulas, variables, and the order of operations to express relationships and find the values of expressions. Now you will *reverse* the order of operations to solve problems. ◄

Explore Working Backward

Friday, Thursday, Wednesday ...

An inventor has created a machine that makes swim goggles for dogs. The following clues describe the "doggle" (dog-ull) machine's first week of operation.

A. Monday went well except for telephone interruptions from pet store owners wanting to find out when they could order doggles.

B. Tuesday was a success. The machine produced twice as many doggles as it did on Monday.

C. On Wednesday a bottle of glue fell into the machine, gumming it up for 2 hours. The day's output was 4 fewer than the previous day.

D. On Thursday, two workers called in sick. The day's output was only half Wednesday's.

E. On Friday, 23 pairs of doggles were produced, 5 more than on Thursday.

1. Begin with the last clue and work backward to find how many pairs of doggles were produced on Monday.

2. Explain how you solved the problem.

Problem Solving TIP

Make a table to keep track of the doggles made on each day.

Learn Inverse Operations

Suppose you ride your bike north for 4 miles and decide that you need to return to where you started. You need to ride your bike south for 4 miles. Riding north and riding south are inverse actions because they "undo" each other.

MEETING INDIVIDUAL NEEDS

Resources

- 2-4 Practice
- 2-4 Reteaching
- 2-4 Problem Solving
- 2-4 Enrichment
- 2-4 Daily Transparency
  - Problem of the Day
  - Review
  - Quick Quiz
- Teaching Tool Transparency 21
- Chapter 2 Project Master

Learning Modalities

Musical Play a simple musical passage forward and backward. Describe the changes from note to note in the forward passage and the backward passage.

Kinesthetic Have students use counters to show the result of performing an operation and the result of performing the inverse operation.

Challenge

Ben wanted to buy a $10 tape, but he did not have that much money. He told Ken, "Lend me the same amount of money as I have, and I will buy the tape." Ken agreed, and Ben bought the tape. At a bookstore Ben made the same request, got the loan, and bought a $10 book. Now he has no money left. How much did he have before the loan for the tape? $7.50

Suppose you add 5 to a number and want to return to the number you started with. You would subtract 5. Addition and subtraction are called **inverse operations**. So are multiplication and division. The inverse of the action of multiplying by 4 is dividing by 4. Inverse operations "undo" each other.

2 [+ 5] = 7   7 [− 5] = 2

2 [• 4] = 8   8 [÷ 4] = 2

Sometimes more than one action needs to be undone. The order in which the actions are done affects the order in which they are undone. You may have put on a sock, then a shoe, in the morning before school. To undo those actions, you need to take off the shoe first, then take off the sock. Inverse operations work the same way.

Examples

1 The machine below is an inverse operation machine. If 9 is entered, what will be the result?

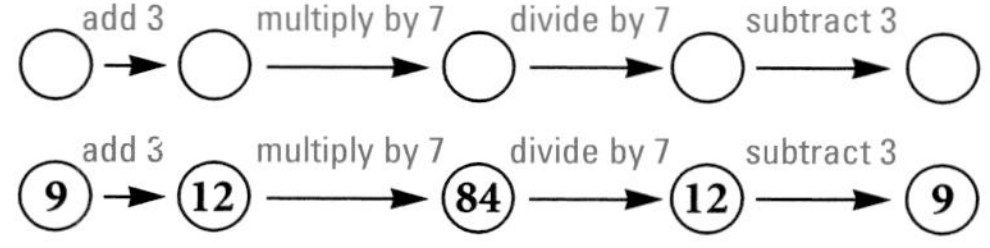

The result is 9.

2 A number is multiplied by 4, then 5 is subtracted from the result. What operations are needed to return to the original number?

Five needs to be added to undo the subtraction, then the sum needs to be divided by 4 to undo the multiplication.

Try It

a. If 12 is entered in the machine in Example 1, what will be the result? 12

b. A number is divided by 2, then 3 is added to the quotient. What operations are needed to return to the original number?
Subtract 3, then multiply by 2

Check Your Understanding

1. How can you use inverse operations to check a sum? A product?

2. How does an inverse operation "undo" an operation?

MATH EVERY DAY

Problem of the Day

Copy this picture of nine dots in a square. Draw two more squares to separate the large square into nine sections with exactly one dot in each section.

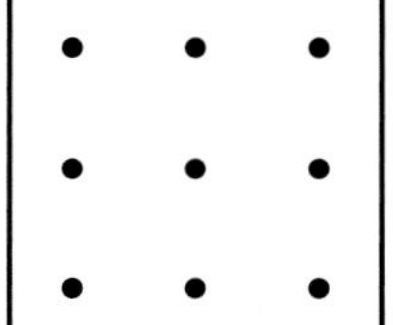

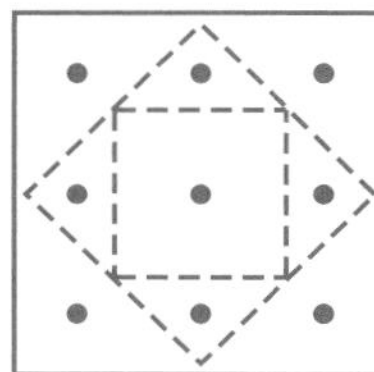

Available on Daily Transparency 2-4

An Extension is provided in the transparency package.

Fact of the Day

The steerable bicycle was invented in Germany about 180 years ago, in 1818.

Mental Math

Do these mentally.

1. 4 • 25 100
2. 6 • 25 150
3. 9 • 25 225

Answers for Explore

1. There were 20 doggles produced on Monday.
2. I worked backwards: 23 is 5 more than Thursday, so Thursday was 18. Wednesday was twice that, or 36. Tuesday was 4 more, or 40. Monday's total was half of Tuesday's, so the answer is 20.

2 Teach

Learn

Alternate Examples

1. The machine below is an inverse operation machine. If 7 is entered, what will be the result?

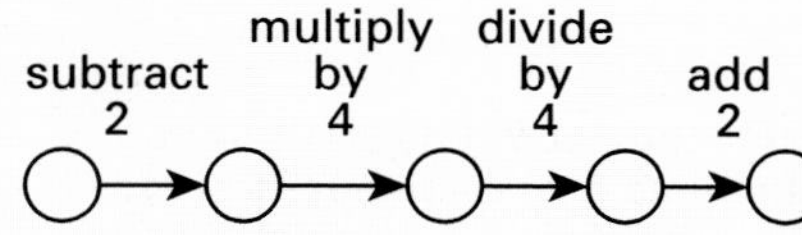

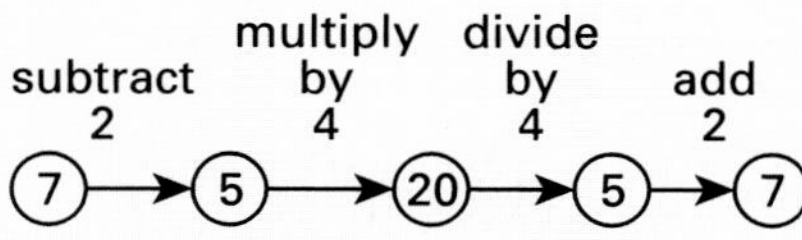

The result is 7.

2. A number is divided by 3, then 9 is added to the result. What operations are needed to return to the original number?

Nine needs to be subtracted to undo the addition, then the result needs to be multiplied by 3 to undo the division.

3 Practice and Assess

Check

Answers for Check Your Understanding

1. Subtract one of the addends from the sum—your answer should be the other addend; Divide the product by one factor—your answer should be the other factor.
2. Possible answer: An inverse operation does the exact opposite of the original operation.

2-4 Exercises and Applications

Assignment Guide

- Basic
  1–9, 12–13, 15, 18–31
- Average
  1–17, 22–26, 30–33
- Enriched
  1–9 odds, 10–18, 23–35

Exercise Notes

Exercise 13

Geography In the continental United States, there are four time zones—Eastern, Central, Mountain, and Pacific. As a result, adjustments in clock times must be made in moving from one zone to another.

Exercise 14

Extension You may wish to use Teaching Tool Transparency 21: Map of United States with this exercise. Have students plan other routes through the same cities mentioned.

Exercise Answers

10. m; $m + 5$; $8(m + 5) = 8m + 40$; $(8m + 40) \div 8 = m + 5$; $m + 5 - 5 = m$

11. Multiply by 4, subtract 7.

13. Set his watch ahead 3 hours.

14. South from Seattle to San Francisco, then southeast to Dallas, northeast to Pittsburgh, and southeast to Baltimore.

Reteaching

Activity

Materials: Counters

- Start with 5 counters. Add 3 counters. Double the number of counters. Take away 2 counters. How many counters do you now have? 14
- What should you do to the set of counters to undo the operations that you performed? Add 2 counters, halve the number of counters, and take away 3 counters.

2-4 Exercises and Applications

Practice and Apply

Getting Started Name the inverse action of each.

1. Drive 5 mi east Drive 5 mi west
2. Turn on a heater Turn off the heater
3. Run up three flights of stairs Run down 3 flights of stairs
4. Subtract 643 Add 643
5. Add $4.50 Subtract $4.50
6. Divide by 65 Multiply by 65

The machine below is an inverse operation machine. What will be the result when each is entered into the machine? Record each step.

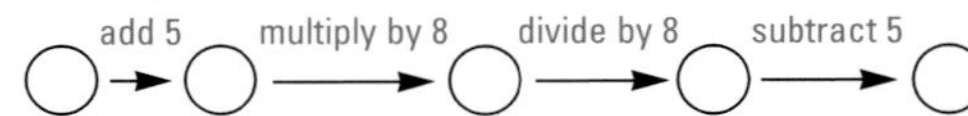

7. 25 25, 30, 240, 30, 25
8. 12 12, 17, 136, 17, 12
9. 44 44, 49, 392, 49, 44
10. m

11. **Operation Sense** What labels does the machine below need so that the output will be the same as the input?

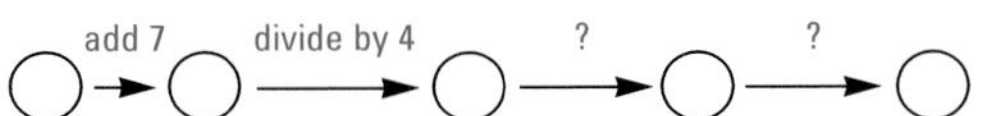

12. **Test Prep** A number is multiplied by 5, then 7 is added to the result. What operations are needed to return to the original number? A

Ⓐ Subtraction and division
Ⓑ Addition and multiplication
Ⓒ Division and addition
Ⓓ None of these

13. **Geography** When Les flew from Ohio to Oregon, he set his watch back 3 hours. What should he do to his watch when he flies back to Ohio?

14. **Geography** Pilot Denny Zimmerman flies all over the United States delivering overnight mail. On one trip, he traveled from Baltimore northwest to Pittsburgh, then southwest to Dallas. The following night, he flew from Dallas northwest to San Francisco and then north to Seattle. What route would Captain Zimmerman need to follow if he wants to return to Baltimore by going through the same cities?

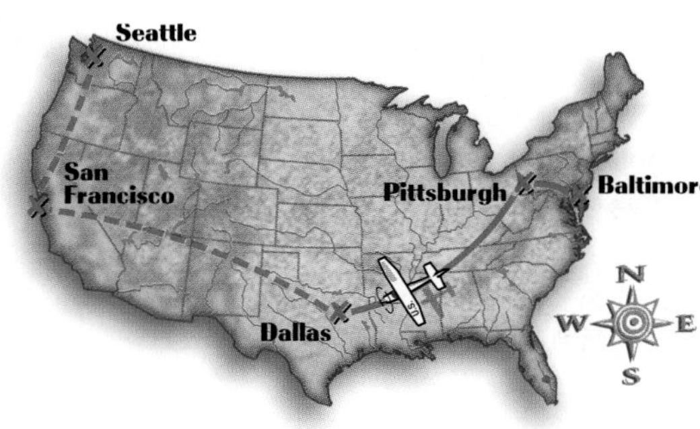

PRACTICE

Name ______________ Practice 2-4

Inverse Operations

The machines below are inverse operation machines. What will be the result when the given number is entered into each machine? Record each step.

1. 10 — Add 7, Multiply by 5, Divide by 5, Subtract 7: 10, 17, 85, 17, 10
2. 16 — Divide by 4, Add 10, Subtract 10, Multiply by 4: 16, 4, 14, 4, 16
3. 23 — Subtract 3, Divide by 5, Multiply by 5, Add 3: 23, 20, 4, 20, 23
4. 5 — Multiply by 8, Subtract 13, Add 13, Divide by 8: 5, 40, 27, 40, 5

Add labels to each machine below so that the output will be the same as the input.

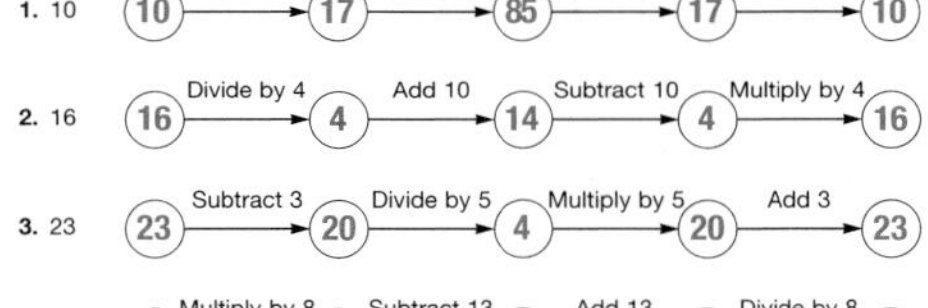

7. Maxine locked the door when she left her apartment. What will she need to do to get back inside?
Unlock the door

8. At the mall, Tony went from his car to the shoe store, then the music store, then the card shop, and finally the video arcade. Suddenly he realized that he had lost his wallet, so he decided to retrace his steps back to his car. What route did he take going back?
From the video arcade, he went to the card shop, then the music store, then the shoe store, and finally back to his car.

RETEACHING

Name ______________ Alternative Lesson 2-4

Inverse Operations

Inverse operations "undo" each other. The order in which the actions are done affects the order in which they are undone.

Example 1

How can you "undo" a move of 3 steps to the right?

To return to the starting point, you would move 3 steps to the left.

Try It

a. If you loan $5 to a friend, what would "undo" that action? Being paid back $5.

b. If you drive 17 miles east, what would "undo" that action? Driving 17 miles west.

Example 2

Addition and subtraction are inverse operations. Multiplication and division are also inverse operations.

Name the inverse operation.

a. Add 6.
You can find the inverse operation by "undoing" *Add 6*.
The inverse operation of *Add 6* is *Subtract 6*.

b. Multiply by 8.
You can find the inverse operation by "undoing" *Multiply by 8*.
The inverse operation of *Multiply by 8* is *Divide by 8*.

Try It Name the inverse operation.

c. Add 9. Subtract 9.
d. Subtract 6. Add 6.
e. Multiply by 2. Divide by 2.
f. Divide by 3. Multiply by 3.
g. Subtract 16. Add 16.
h. Multiply by 3. Divide by 3.
i. Divide by 7. Multiply by 7.
j. Add 5. Subtract 5.
k. Multiply by 30. Divide by 30.
l. Subtract 45. Add 45.
m. Divide by 34. Multiply by 34.
n. Multiply by 50. Divide by 50.
o. Add 72. Subtract 72.
p. Subtract 100. Add 100.
q. Multiply by 8 Divide by 8.
r. Divide by 7. Multiply by 7.

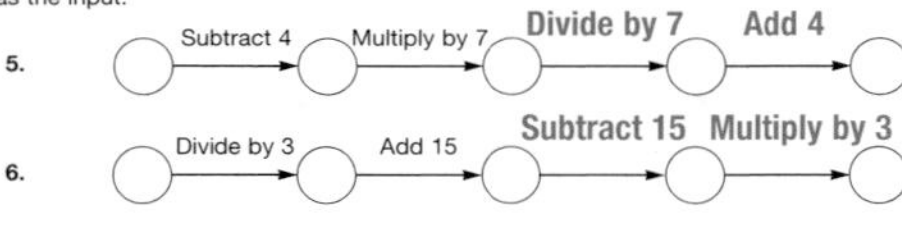

15. Science A wolf had 10 pups in her third litter. The number of pups was twice as many as in her second litter, and her second litter had 3 more pups than her first. Find the number of pups in her first litter. 2

GPS

Problem Solving and Reasoning

16. Journal Suppose you lost your wallet or purse. How can inverse operations or actions help you find it? Give an example.

17. Communicate Write a set of actions and then describe the steps you would do to undo these actions.

18. Critical Thinking Copy and complete the table. Explain how you found the missing numbers.

n	Add 8	Subtract 8
4	12	4
12	20	?
18	?	18
?	10	?
?	?	10
n	?	?

Mixed Review

Estimate each product. *[Previous course]*

19. 31×8 240 **20.** 14×58 900 **21.** 28×52 1500 **22.** 715×16 14,000

23. 129×419 52,000 **24.** 318×104 32,000 **25.** 4792×617 3,000,000 **26.** 4122×108 400,000

Multiply. *[Previous course]*

27. $10 \times 10 \times 10$ 1000 **28.** $4 \times 4 \times 4 \times 4$ 256 **29.** $5 \times 5 \times 5$ 125

30. $7 \times 7 \times 7 \times 7$ 2401 **31.** $10 \times 10 \times 10 \times 10$ 10,000 **32.** $2 \times 2 \times 2 \times 2 \times 2$ 32

33. $10 \times 10 \times 10 \times 10 \times 10$ 100,000 **34.** $3 \times 3 \times 3 \times 3 \times 3 \times 3$ 729 **35.** $8 \times 8 \times 8 \times 8 \times 8$ 32,768

Project Progress

Look at the costs you listed earlier. As you learn more about equations, write and solve an equation to find how much to charge each customer to meet your costs. Then decide how much you will charge for your service. Prepare a report describing your business and explaining how you decided on the price you will charge.

PROBLEM SOLVING 2-4

PROBLEM SOLVING

Name ______________________

Guided Problem Solving 2-4

GPS PROBLEM 15, STUDENT PAGE 77

A wolf had 10 pups in her third litter. The number of pups was twice as many as in her second litter, and her second litter had 3 more pups than her first. Find the number of pups in her first litter.

— Understand —

1. What is it you are asked to find? The number of pups in the wolf's first litter.
2. Has the number of pups been increasing or decreasing since her first litter? Increasing
3. How many litters has she had including her first? 3 litters

— Plan —

4. The litter of 10 pups she just had was twice the number of pups in her second litter. How would you use this fact to find the number of pups in her second litter? Divide 10 by 2.
5. The number of pups in the wolf's second litter was 3 more than in her first litter. How would you use this fact to find the number of pups in her first litter, once you found the number of pups in her second litter? Subtract 3.

— Solve —

6. Find the number of pups in her second litter. 5 pups
7. Find the number of pups in her first litter. 2 pups

— Look Back —

8. How can you check your answer? Possible answer: Start with the answer. Add 3. Then multiply by 2. This answer should equal 10.

SOLVE ANOTHER PROBLEM

There are 17 members in the three-year-old computer club. This is 2 more members than last year. Last year there were three times as many members as there were in the first year. How many members were in the computer club the first year? 5 members

ENRICHMENT

Name ______________________

Extend Your Thinking 2-4

Decision Making

The seventh-grade orienteering club was given a destination point and a set of directions that led to a given location. From this information, they needed to tell how to get from the starting point to the destination.

The information they were given is listed below.

- You are at the red cabin.
- The cabin is 3 miles due north of the river.
- The river is $2\frac{1}{2}$ miles northeast of Founders' Rock.
- Founders' Rock is 5 miles north of the waterfall.
- The waterfall is $3\frac{3}{4}$ miles southwest of the parking lot.

1. What would be the inverse of 3 miles due north? 3 miles due south
2. What would be the inverse of $2\frac{1}{2}$ miles northeast? $2\frac{1}{2}$ miles southwest
3. What would be the inverse of 5 miles north? 5 miles south
4. What would be the inverse of $3\frac{3}{4}$ miles southwest? $3\frac{3}{4}$ miles northeast
5. Draw a diagram to show the path you took to the red cabin.

red cabin
river
Founders' Rock
parking lot
waterfall

6. List the directions to get from the red cabin to the parking lot. Possible answer: Go 3 miles south to the river, turn southwest and travel $2\frac{1}{2}$ miles to Founders' Rock. Walk 5 miles south to the waterfall and $3\frac{3}{4}$ miles northeast to the parking lot.
7. You can use an alternate path to get to the red cabin. It goes by the covered bridge, the old mill, Goldenrod Field, and Harmony Lake. Add these sites to your diagram. Then list the directions to get from the red cabin to the parking lot using this path. Check student's work.

Exercise Notes

Exercise 18

Error Prevention Some students will say that the first missing number in Column 3 is 4 instead of 12. Point out that they must subtract 8 from the number in the second column instead of the first column.

Project Progress

You may want to have students use Chapter 2 Project Master.

Exercise Answers

16. Possible answer: Retrace your steps in hopes of finding it. You shopped at the supermarket and then at the drugstore, and then you stopped for lunch and missed your wallet. You go back to the drugstore and then to the supermarket.

17. Possible answer: I pick up my backpack, strap it on, start hiking, stop hiking, unstrap my backpack, put down my backpack.

18.

n	Add 8	Subtract 8
4	12	4
12	20	12
18	26	18
2	10	2
10	18	10
n	$8 + n$	n

I followed the directions at the top and used the inverse operations when necessary.

Alternate Assessment

Portfolio From this lesson, have each student select an exercise or problem that demonstrates his or her understanding of inverse operations or working backward.

Quick Quiz

Name the inverse action of each.

1. Add 15. Subtract 15.
2. Walk south 2 blocks. Walk north 2 blocks.
3. Multiply by 7. Divide by 7.

Available on Daily Transparency 2-4

2-5 Lesson Organizer

Objectives

- Translate words and phrases into algebraic expressions.
- Translate algebraic expressions into words and phrases.

Vocabulary

- Algebraic expression

NCTM Standards

- 1–4, 7, 9

► Review

Find each answer.

1. Five more than 7 12
2. The product of 8 and 4 32
3. Two less than 12 10
4. Half of 36 18

Available on Daily Transparency 2-5

1 Introduce

Explore

The Point
Students explore translating words into expressions by performing a number trick.

Ongoing Assessment
In Step 4, check that students used a variable to represent their original number.

For Groups That Finish Early
Use variables, operations, and numbers to translate your number trick from Step 5 into an expression.

Answers for Explore

1. Possible answers: 3; $3 \times 2 = 6$; $6 - 5 = 1$; $1 + 5 = 6$; Half of $6 = 3$.
2. Students should always finish with the number with which they started.
3. I always get back to the number I started with; Because each operation I do gets undone later.

2-5 Translating Words to Expressions

You'll Learn ...

- to translate words and phrases into algebraic expressions
- to translate algebraic expressions into words and phrases

... How It's Used

Inventors must be able to explain their inventions clearly. They often use mathematical symbols rather than written descriptions.

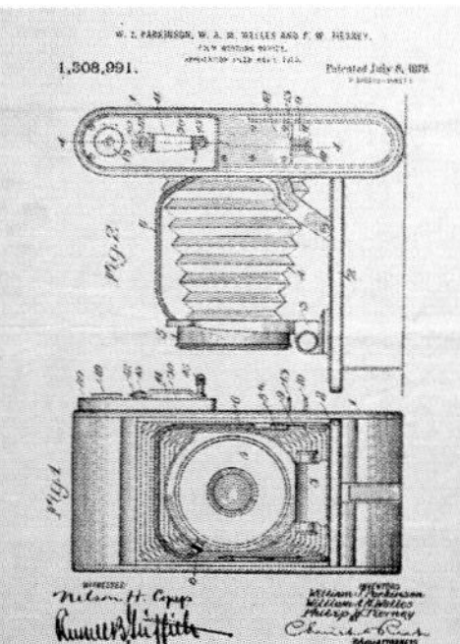

Vocabulary

algebraic expression

► Lesson Link You have learned to find the value of a given expression. Now you will write expressions by translating words into mathematical symbols. ◄

Explore Number Tricks

Next Time, I'll Make a Rabbit Disappear

1. [Pick a number. Write it down.] → [Double the number.] → [Subtract 5.] → [Add 5.] → [Halve the number. Write the result.]
2. Repeat Step 1 three times using a different starting number each time.
3. What do you notice about your results? Why do you think this happens?
4. Use variables, operations, and numbers, to translate this "number trick" into symbols.
5. Make up a number trick like this one. Use at least four words that describe number operations. (The trick above uses *double*, *subtract*, *add*, and *halve*.) Try out your trick on another student.

Learn Translating Words to Expressions

An **algebraic expression** is an expression that contains a variable, like x, $b - 4$, and $5(n + 3)$. When solving a real-world problem, you may have to translate words or phrases into algebraic expressions. The chart shows the operations that may be suggested by words or phrases.

Addition	Subtraction	Multiplication	Division
plus	minus	times	divided by
sum	difference	product	quotient
more than	less than	double	half of
increased by	decreased by	by	separate equally
gain of	less	of	per

MEETING INDIVIDUAL NEEDS

Resources

- 2-5 Practice
- 2-5 Reteaching
- 2-5 Problem Solving
- 2-5 Enrichment
- 2-5 Daily Transparency
  - Problem of the Day
  - Review
  - Quick Quiz

Learning Modalities

Verbal Have students work in pairs, read the phrase aloud, discuss the meaning of the phrase, then write the appropriate algebraic expression.

Kinesthetic Have students use algebra tiles or counters and cups to model algebraic expressions to help them translate expressions into words.

English Language Development

Have students work in pairs and translate these word phrases into symbols: 4 more than a number x, $x + 4$, a number y decreased by 7, $y - 7$, 3 times a number b, $3b$, and half of a number s, $\frac{s}{2}$. Then have them write as many word phrases as they can for each expression.

Examples

Write an algebraic expression for each phrase.

1 Five less than a number c

$c - 5$

2 Four times the sum of a number n and 3

$4(n + 3)$ 4 times the sum of n and 3: $4 \cdot \boxed{n + 3}$

Try It

Write an algebraic expression for each phrase.

a. Half of a number h $h \div 2$

b. d dollars more than a price of \$25 $\$25 + d$

c. The product of a number d and the difference of a number v and 5 $d(v - 5)$

Study TIP

Be careful when you translate subtraction phrases. Sometimes you will need to switch the word order: *5 less than 7* means $7 - 5$, not $5 - 7$.

You can also translate algebraic expressions into phrases.

Examples

Write a phrase for each algebraic expression.

3 $x + 7$

One answer is "a number x increased by 7." Others are possible.

4 $4n - 5$

One answer is "five less than four times a number n." Others are possible.

Try It

Write a phrase for each algebraic expression.

a. $12 - g$ **b.** $3a + 4b$ **c.** $11(5 - r)$

Remember

An expression is a mathematical phrase made up of variables and/or numbers and operations. **[Page 60]**

Check Your Understanding

1. Are the expressions $a + 2$ and $2 + a$ equal? Explain.
2. Are the expressions $x - 4$ and $4 - x$ equal? Explain.
3. Give a phrase in which "of" suggests multiplication.
4. Give a phrase in which "quotient" suggests division.

MATH EVERY DAY

Problem of the Day

At 7:34 on a digital clock, the hours digit is equal to the sum of the minutes digits. How many times will this happen when the hours digit is 9? 6 times: 9:09, 9:18, 9:27, 9:36, 9:45, and 9:54

Available on Daily Transparency 2-5

An Extension is provided in the transparency package.

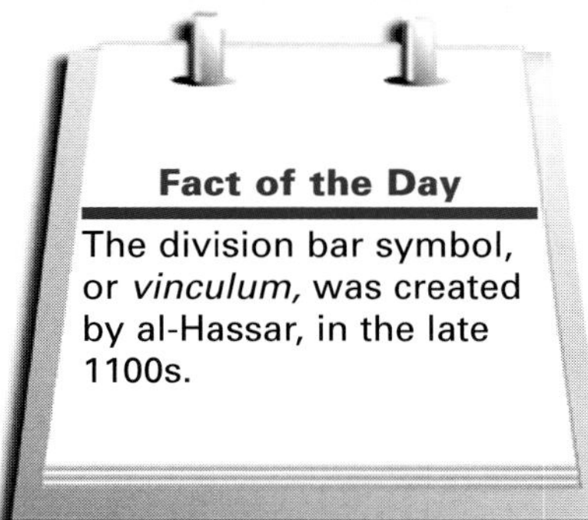

Fact of the Day

The division bar symbol, or *vinculum,* was created by al-Hassar, in the late 1100s.

Estimation

Estimate.

1. $462 \div 9$ 50
2. $3610 \div 5$ 700
3. $7310 \div 8$ 900

Answers for Explore

4. Steps are x; $2x$; $2x - 5$; $(2x - 5) + 5 = 2x$; $2x \div 2 = x$.
5. Possible answer: Think of a number. Multiply it by 4. Add 8. Divide by 4. Your answer is 2 more than the number you thought of.

2 Teach

Learn

Alternate Examples

Write an algebraic expression for each phrase.

1. 9 more than a number s.

   $s + 9$

2. 6 times 4 less than a number t.

   $6(t - 4)$

Write a phrase for each algebraic expression.

3. $y - 5$

   One answer is "a number y decreased by 5." Others are possible.

4. $8b + 2$

   One answer is "2 more than 8 times a number b." Others are possible.

Answers for Try It

Possible answers:

a. Twelve decreased by a number g.

b. The sum of the products of 3 and a number a and 4 and a number b.

c. The product of 11 and the difference between 5 and r.

3 Practice and Assess

Check

Answers for Check Your Understanding

1. Yes; Addition is commutative so the sum of a and 2 is the same as the sum of 2 and a.
2. No; $x - 4$ means 4 less than x, but $4 - x$ means x less than 4.
3. Possible answer: $\frac{3}{4}$ of a number h.
4. Possible answer: The quotient of 12 and a number g is 4.

2-5 Exercises and Applications

Assignment Guide

- **Basic**
  1–18, 24–28, 30, 32–35, 40–41
- **Average**
  1–13, 14–42 evens
- **Enriched**
  1–23 odds, 24–31, 33–43 odds

Exercise Answers

14. The product of 2 and a number m.
15. 6 decreased by a number x.
16. Twice the difference of a number b and 5.
17. The sum of twice a number r and 3.
18. 4 less than a number n.
19. Half a number f.
20. The sum of 4 times a number a and twice a number b.
21. The product of 3 and the sum of a number d and 3.
22. The quotient of a number w decreased by 4 and the sum of a number u and 3.
23. 4 more than the quotient of 3 and the sum of a number c and 2.

Reteaching

Activity

Materials: Common classroom objects

- Choose an object to represent a variable. You will need at least three of whatever object you choose.
- Use these objects and some counters to show the quantities described. Then write the algebraic expression.
- For example, to show the quantity "4 more than twice a number m," use 2 of the objects and 4 counters. The expression would be $2m + 4$.

1. Three times a number b $3b$
2. The sum of a number t and 5 $t + 5$
3. Twice a number x plus 3 $2x + 3$

2-5 Exercises and Applications

Practice and Apply

Getting Started Tell what operation the action suggests.

1. Loses 18 yards **Subtraction**
2. Deposits $25 **Addition**
3. Gains 25 lb **Addition**

Write an algebraic expression for each phrase.

4. 6 more than a number x $x + 6$
5. Double a number k $2k$
6. Half of a number y $\frac{y}{2}$
7. 4 less than a number u $u - 4$
8. The product of a number w and 4 $4w$
9. 8 more than twice a number c $2c + 8$
10. A number p decreased by 6 $p - 6$
11. Four times the difference of a number n and 6 $4(n - 6)$
12. 6 times a number m $6m$
13. 3 times the sum of a number x and 15 $3(x + 15)$

Write a phrase for each algebraic expression.

14. $2m$
15. $6 - x$
16. $2(b - 5)$
17. $2r + 3$
18. $n - 4$
19. $\frac{f}{2}$
20. $4a + 2b$
21. $3(d + 3)$
22. $\frac{w - 4}{u + 3}$
23. $\frac{3}{c + 2} + 4$

24. **Test Prep** Choose the correct algebraic expression for the phrase "three times the sum of a number and 6." **A**
    Ⓐ $3(n + 6)$ Ⓑ $3 + 6n$ Ⓒ $3n + 6$ Ⓓ $6 + 3n$

25. **Industry** A machine can produce 267 bolts in one hour. Write an expression to describe:
    a. The number of bolts produced in n hours. $267n$
    b. The number of usable bolts produced in n hours if 25 had to be thrown away because they were defective. $267n - 25$

26. **Career** A dentist earns twice as much as she did in her last job, 3 years before. If her salary 3 years ago was p, write an algebraic expression for her current salary. $2p$

27. **Science** A 5-ft pine tree was planted and grew 2 ft each year. Write an algebraic expression for the height after y years. $5 + 2y$

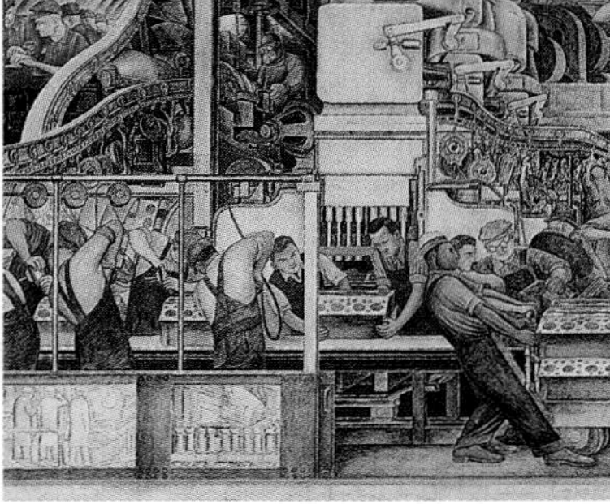

Detroit Industry (detail), 1932–1933, mural by Diego Rivera.

PRACTICE 2-5

PRACTICE

Name ______________________ **Practice 2-5**

Translating Words to Expressions

Write an algebraic expression for each phrase.

1. the product of a number (x) and 3 $x \cdot 3$ or $3x$
2. 13 less than a number (m) $m - 13$
3. the quotient of a number (s) and 7 $s \div 7$
4. 7 less than twice a number (d) $2d - 7$
5. the difference between three times a number (k) and 4 $3k - 4$
6. 15 more than one-third of a number (m) $\frac{m}{3} + 15$

Write a phrase for each algebraic expression.

7. $r + 12$ a number (r) increased by 12
8. $3(x + 4)$ the product of 3 and the sum of a number (x) and 4
9. $c - 18$ a number (c) decreased by 18
10. $\frac{12}{u}$ the quotient of 12 and a number (u)
11. $7z - 5$ 5 less than the product of 7 and a number (z)
12. $\frac{m}{n}$ the quotient of a number (m), and a number (n)
13. **Career** Miguel earns $8.00 per hour at his job. Write an expression for the number of dollars he earns for working n hours. $8n$
14. Thomas likes to paint bird houses in his garage on Saturday. He spends a total of one hour setting up and cleaning up, and during the rest of the day he can paint 3 bird houses every hour.
    a. If Thomas spends n hours in his garage, how many hours can he spend actually painting? $n - 1$
    b. Write an expression for the number of bird houses Thomas can paint if he is in his garage for n hours. $3(n - 1)$

RETEACHING

Name ______________________ **Alternative Lesson 2-5**

Translating Words to Expressions

An **algebraic expression** is an expression that contains a variable. Algebraic expressions translate words into mathematical symbols. The chart shows the operations that may be suggested by words or phrases.

Addition	Subtraction	Multiplication	Division
plus sum more than increased by gain of	minus difference less than decreased by less	times product double by of	divided by quotient half of separate equally per

Example

Write an algebraic expression for each phrase. Each expression will have a number, an operation, and a variable. The number and the variable are given. Refer to the table to help determine the operation.

6 **more than** a number n → $n + 6$
9 **less than** a number r → $r - 9$
the **product** of 7 and a number x → $7x$
twice a number p → $2p$
16 **divided by** a number a → $16 \div a$

Try It Match each of the phrases on the left with its algebraic expression on the right.

a. 2 **more than** a number x 6 — 1 $x - 10$
b. 8 **times** a number x 7 — 2 $\frac{15}{x}$
c. 15 **divided by** a number x 2 — 3 $6x$
d. 3 **less than** a number x 4 — 4 $x - 3$
e. a number x **multiplied by** 6 3 — 5 $x \div 2$
f. a number x **minus** 10 1 — 6 $x + 2$
g. **half** of a number x 5 — 7 $8x$

Write an expression for each phrase.

h. a number g **increased by** 9 $g + 9$
i. 10 **more than** a number c $c + 10$
j. a number f **decreased by** 5 $f - 5$

28. Fine Art This sculpture is made of cars and concrete. Each row contains four cars. Write an algebraic expression for the number of cars in x rows of the sculpture. $4x$

Long Term Parking, 1975–1983, sculpture by Arman.

Problem Solving and Reasoning

29. Critical Thinking Geometric figures can be used to model algebraic expressions. The figure below is a model for $x + 3$.

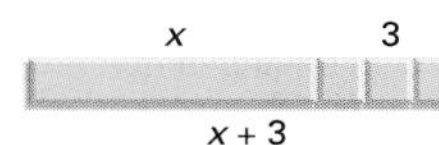

a. Write an algebraic expression for the figure below.

b. Write another algebraic expression for the figure.

c. Can the expressions in **a** and **b** be shown to be equal without the model? Explain.

30. Choose a Strategy GPS The area of a rectangle is equal to its length times its width. Write an algebraic expression to describe the area of the shaded portion of the large rectangle. Explain your reasoning.

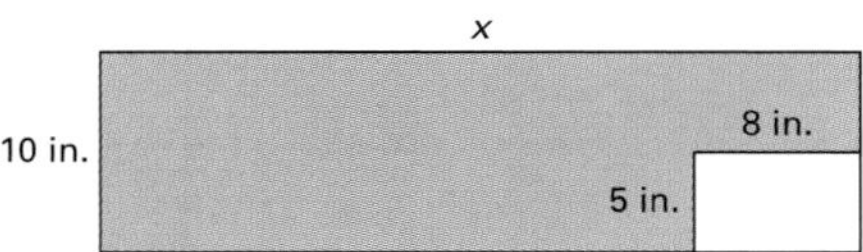

31. Journal Write an algebraic expression using each of these three words or phrases: product, sum, and less than. Explain what each word or phrase means.

Problem Solving STRATEGIES

- Look for a Pattern
- Make an Organized List
- Make a Table
- Guess and Check
- Work Backward
- Use Logical Reasoning
- Draw a Diagram
- Solve a Simpler Problem

PROBLEM SOLVING 2-5

Mixed Review

Estimate each quotient. *[Previous course]*

32. $65 \div 8$ 8 **33.** $83 \div 5$ 16 **34.** $49 \div 11$ 5 **35.** $66 \div 16$ 4

36. $144 \div 11$ 13 **37.** $784 \div 39$ 20 **38.** $4843 \div 528$ 10 **39.** $6324 \div 157$ 40

You can use the formula $P = 2l + 2w$ to find the perimeter of a rectangle. Substitute the given values into the formula. Then use the formula $A = lw$ to find the area. *[Lesson 2-1]*

40. $l = 11$ in., $w = 7$ in. **41.** $l = 31$ ft, $w = 20$ ft

42. $l = 18$ cm, $w = 12$ cm **43.** $l = 62$ m, $w = 40$ m

Exercise Notes

Exercise 29

Extension Have students draw a diagram similar to the one in Exercise 29a. Have students write two expressions for their diagram. Discuss how this is an example of the distributive property.

Exercises 32–39

Estimation Remind students that it is helpful to use compatible numbers when estimating quotients.

Exercise Answers

29. a. $2x + 6$

 b. $2(x + 3)$

 c. Possible answer: By using the distributive property.

30. $10x - 40$; Area of large rectangle minus area of small rectangle.

31. Possible answer: $3(g + 7) - 2$. Product: the result of multiplying 2 factors; sum: the result of adding numbers; less than: subtracting one number from another.

40. $P = 36$ in.; $A = 77\ in^2$

41. $P = 102$ ft; $A = 620\ ft^2$

42. $P = 60$ cm; $A = 216\ ft^2$

43. $P = 204$ m; $A = 2480\ m^2$

Alternate Assessment

Self Assessment Have students write a paragraph describing any difficulties they encountered in writing phrases to indicate the four operations.

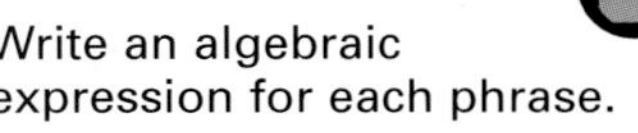

Quick Quiz

Write an algebraic expression for each phrase.

1. 5 less than a number v $v - 5$
2. The product of a number d and 7 $7d$

Write a phrase for each algebraic expression.

3. $b + 8$ 8 more than a number b
4. $2(x - 3)$ Twice the difference of 3 less than a number x

Available on Daily Transparency 2-5

PROBLEM SOLVING

Name ______________________

Guided Problem Solving 2-5

GPS **PROBLEM 30, STUDENT PAGE 81**

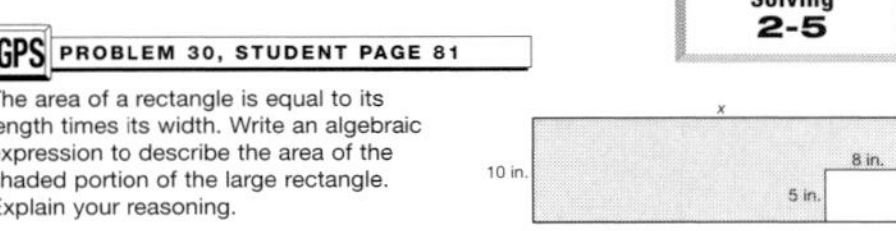

The area of a rectangle is equal to its length times its width. Write an algebraic expression to describe the area of the shaded portion of the large rectangle. Explain your reasoning.

— Understand —

1. What are the dimensions of the large rectangle?
 Length: x Width: 10 in.
2. What are the dimensions of the small rectangle?
 Length: 8 in. Width: 5 in.

— Plan —

3. Will the shaded area be larger or smaller than the area of the large rectangle? Smaller than
4. What is the relationship between the areas of the large rectangle, the small rectangle, and the shaded area?
 The difference between the area of the large and small rectangles equals the area of the shaded area.

— Solve —

5. Write an expression for the area of the large rectangle. $10x$
6. Find the area of the small rectangle. $40\ in^2$
7. Write an algebraic expression to describe the area of the shaded portion of the large rectangle. $10x - 40$

— Look Back —

8. How can you check your answer? Possible answer: Assign a value to x. Find the area of the shaded portion. Substitute the value of x into the formula (expression) $10x - 40$ and solve. Compare your two answers.

SOLVE ANOTHER PROBLEM

Write an algebraic expression for the area of a sheet of paper 12 in. by 9 in. with a rectangle 4 in. by x in. cut out of its center. $108 - 4x$

ENRICHMENT

Name ______________________

Extend Your Thinking 2-5

Decision Making

Next semester Webster's schedule will include seven subjects, study hall, and lunch. The days and times that these "courses" are offered is listed below. A course must be taken at the same time each day it is offered. For example, the science class can be taken from 10–12 on Tuesday and Thursday or from 1–3 on both days. It cannot be taken from 10–12 on Tuesday and from 1–3 on Thursday.

What might Webster's schedule look like for the next semester?

Course	Hours Weekly	Days and Times Offered
Science	4	Tues and Thurs, 10–12 or 1–3
Math	5	Daily, 8, 10, or 1
Study Hall	3	Mon, Wed, and Fri, 10 or 1
Lang. Arts	5	Daily, 9 or 2
Lunch	5	Daily, 11, 12, or 1
Social Studies	5	Daily, 11 or 2
Gym	3	Mon, Wed, and Fri, 8, 10, or 2
Art	2	Tues and Thurs, 8, 11, or 1
Music	3	Mon, Wed and Fri, 10, 11, or 2

Possible answer:	Monday	Tuesday	Wednesday	Thursday	Friday
8–9	Math	Math	Math	Math	Math
9–10	Lang Arts	Lang Arts	Lang Arts	Lang Arts	Lang Arts
10–11	Gym	Science	Gym	Science	Gym
11–12	Music	Science	Music	Science	Music
12–1	Lunch	Lunch	Lunch	Lunch	Lunch
1–2	Study Hall	Art	Study Hall	Art	Study Hall
2–3	Soc Stud	Soc Stud	Soc Stud	Soc Stud	Soc Stud

INTERACTIVE LESSON

2-6 Lesson Organizer

Objective

- Solve addition and subtraction equations using inverse operations.

Vocabulary

- Equation, solve, solution

NCTM Standards

- 1–4, 7, 9

Review

Write an expression for each phrase.

1. 4 more than y $y + 4$
2. 7 less than m $m - 7$
3. r decreased by 3 $r - 3$
4. The sum of b and 9 $b + 9$

Available on Daily Transparency 2-6

1 Introduce

Explore

The Point
Students explore addition and subtraction equations by picturing a balanced scale as a model. By deciding how to remove weights to get the x-weight alone, they discover how subtraction is used to solve addition equations.

Ongoing Assessment
Check students' answers for Step 2 to be sure they understand the need for removing weights from each side of the scale.

For Groups That Finish Early
Sketch a balanced scale that shows $x + 4 = 6$. Describe what you would do to get x by itself on one side. Remove 4 weights from each side. What is the value of x? $x = 2$

Follow Up
Ask students to show their sketch for Step 3 and describe what they did to find the value of x. Removed 7 weights from each side.

2-6 Solving Addition and Subtraction Equations

You'll Learn ...

- to write and solve addition and subtraction equations

... How It's Used

Chemists use addition and subtraction equations when they plan and experiment with chemical reactions.

Vocabulary

equation

solve

solution

Lesson Link You've learned that addition and subtraction are inverse operations. Now you'll use that fact to solve equations involving addition and subtraction.

Explore Addition and Subtraction Equations

More or Less

You can use a balanced scale to represent an equation.

1. The balanced scale represents the equation $x + 3 = 7$.
2. What would you do to get x by itself on one side of the scale and still keep the scale in balance? What is the value of x?
3. Sketch a balanced scale that shows $x + 7 = 9$. What is the value of x?
4. What inverse operation did you use to get x by itself on one side of the equation $x + 7 = 9$? Why did it make sense to use this operation?

Learn Solving Addition and Subtraction Equations

An **equation** is a statement that two expressions are equal.

Expressions		→ Equation
$3 + 5$	8	$3 + 5 = 8$
$x + 6$	10	$x + 6 = 10$

To **solve** an equation containing a variable means to find the value(s) of the variable that make(s) the equation true.

$x = 4$ is a **solution** to the equation $x + 6 = 10$ because $\boxed{4} + 6 = 10$ is true.

$x = 11$ is *not* a solution because $\boxed{11} + 6$ is not equal to 10.

$x + 6 \stackrel{?}{=} 10$	$x + 6 \stackrel{?}{=} 10$
$\boxed{4} + 6 \stackrel{?}{=} 10$	$\boxed{11} + 6 \stackrel{?}{=} 10$
$10 = 10$	17 is not equal to 10.

MEETING INDIVIDUAL NEEDS

Resources

2-6 Practice
2-6 Reteaching
2-6 Problem Solving
2-6 Enrichment
2-6 Daily Transparency
  Problem of the Day
  Review
  Quick Quiz
Teaching Tool Transparencies 2, 3

Interactive CD-ROM Lesson

Wide World of Mathematics Middle School: The Census

Learning Modalities

Verbal Have students write a paragraph describing the process for solving addition and subtraction equations.

Social Have students work together in groups of 4 to take turns explaining how addition and subtraction equations have been solved.

Inclusion

For students who might benefit from a hands-on approach, prepare a set of simple addition equations such as $x + 3 = 8$. Have students place an object and 3 counters on one side of their desks and 8 counters on the other side. Explain that (1) the two collections are equal, and (2) removing 3 counters from each side will keep them equal, so the object (x) must represent 5.

Using inverse operations, you solve an addition equation using subtraction and a subtraction equation using addition. When you change one side of an equation, you must change the other side in the same way to keep it "in balance."

$$x + 3 = 8$$
$$x + 3 \boxed{-3} = 8 \boxed{-3}$$

The equation $x + 3 = 8$ can represent many situations. Here are two. If 3 more cars were sold, for a total of 8 cars, how many were there originally? Or, what quantity added to 3 equals 8?

Examples

1 Solve $x - 5 = 12$.

$x - 5 + 5 = 12 + 5$	To undo subtracting 5, add 5 to *both* sides.
$x = 17$	Add.

Check: $\boxed{17} - 5 \stackrel{?}{=} 12$

$12 = 12$ ✓ The solution checks.

2 In 1940, a farmer using modern machinery could produce food for 13 people. This was 9 more people than a farmer in 1860 could feed. How many people could a farmer feed in 1860?

Let n = the number a farmer could feed in 1860.	Choose a variable.
$13 = n + 9$	Translate the phrases into an equation.
$13 - 9 = n + 9 - 9$	To undo adding 9, subtract 9 from both sides.
$4 = n$	Subtract.

A farmer could feed 4 people in 1860.

Try It

a. Solve $148 = x - 33$. $x = 181$

b. The price of a product includes the materials and labor cost plus the markup. A breadmaker, marked up $67, sold for $122. Write and solve an equation to find the materials and labor cost.
$b + 67 = 122$; $b = 55$; $55

Threshing is the process that separates the grain from the chaff. In ancient times, this was done by beating the cut crops with tools called *flails.* This was a very hard and lengthy chore.

Check Your Understanding

1. How are the equations $7 = y + 3$ and $7 - 3 = y + 3 - 3$ related?

2. Write a problem for $x - 8 = 17$ and describe how to solve it.

3. Can $x + 4$ take on the value of 100? Explain.

Answers for Explore

2. Remove 3 weights from both sides of the scale; $x = 4$
3. Student's sketch should show x and 7 weights on one side of the scale and 9 weights on the other side; $x = 2$
4. Subtraction; Because subtraction undoes addition.

2 Teach

Learn

Alternate Examples

1. Solve $y - 3 = 10$.

   $y - 3 + 3 = 10 + 3$

   $y = 13$

   Check: $13 - 3 = 10$

   $10 = 10$

   The solution checks.

2. The first model of the Boeing 777 airplane holds 375 passengers. This is 85 more passengers than the Boeing 767 airplane can hold. How many passengers can the Boeing 767 hold?

   Let p = the number of passengers that the Boeing 767 can hold.

   375 is 85 more than p.

   $375 = p + 85$

   $375 - 85 = p + 85 - 85$

   $290 = p$

   The Boeing 767 can hold 290 passengers.

3 Practice and Assess

Check

Answers for Check Your Understanding

1. To solve the first equation, you need to subtract 3 from each side. This results in the second equation.
2. Possible answer: Eight less than a number is 17. What is the number? Add 8 to each side of the equation.
3. Yes, when $x = 25$.

MATH EVERY DAY

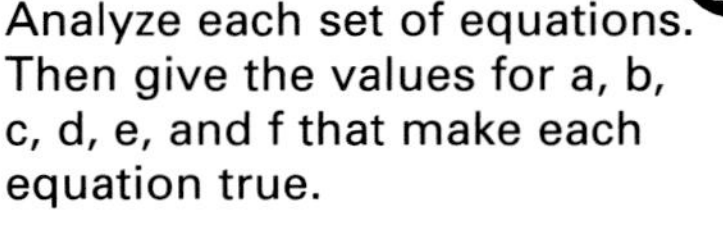

Problem of the Day

Analyze each set of equations. Then give the values for a, b, c, d, e, and f that make each equation true.

$b - a = a$	$d + e = f$
$b + c = 20$	$f - d = 6$
$a + a = 14$	$d + d = 10$

$a = 7$, $b = 14$, $c = 6$, $d = 5$, $e = 6$, $f = 11$

Available on Daily Transparency 2-6

An Extension is provided in the transparency package.

Fact of the Day

The electronic pocket calculator was invented in 1972. This was 330 years after the invention of the adding machine.

Mental Math

Do these mentally.

1. $5000 \div 2$ 2500
2. $5000 \div 20$ 250
3. $5000 \div 200$ 25

2-6 Exercises and Applications

Assignment Guide

- Basic
  1–16, 25–29, 32–36, 39–51 odds
- Average
  1–7 odds, 9–16, 25–37, 39, 41–52
- Enriched
  1–25 odds, 26–40, 42–52 evens

Exercise Notes

Exercise 25

Test Prep If students choose *B*, they are not considering the inverse of the operation in the equation.

Exercise 28

Science Aluminum is the most abundant metal. It comprises 8% of the earth's crust.

Exercise Answers

1. Add 80 to both sides: $d - 80 + 80 = 70 + 80$
2. Subtract 89 from both sides: $s + 89 - 89 = 154 - 89$
3. Subtract 16 from both sides: $f + 16 - 16 = 32 - 16$
4. Add 80 to both sides: $a - 80 + 80 = 320 + 80$

30. Possible answer: A herd of zebras was drinking at the waterhole. After 16 zebras galloped off, there were 28 left. How many zebras were in the original herd?

Reteaching

Activity

Materials: Cups, counters

- To solve $x + 2 = 6$, place a cup and 2 counters on one side of your desk and 6 counters on the other side. How many counters will you place in the cup so that there are the same number of counters on both sides? 4
- Solve $n + 4 = 9$. Place a cup and 4 counters on one side of your desk and 9 counters on the other side. Remove 4 counters from each side. How many counters does the cup represent? 5

2-6 Exercises and Applications

Practice and Apply

Getting Started Write the first step in solving each equation.

1. $d - 80 = 70$ 2. $s + 89 = 154$ 3. $f + 16 = 32$ 4. $a - 80 = 320$

Tell if the given number is a solution to the equation.

5. $x - 19 = 84$; 103 Yes 6. $y + 26 = 78$; 56 No 7. $25 + r = 129$; 156 No 8. $u - 47 = 29$; 18 No

Solve each equation. Check your answer.

9. $d + 83 = 92$ $d = 9$ 10. $r - 77 = 99$ $r = 176$ 11. $45 = 36 + f$ $f = 9$ 12. $102 = v - 66$ $v = 168$

13. $x - 22 = 66$ $x = 88$ 14. $987 = 16 + m$ $m = 971$ 15. $1.5 = p + 1.5$ $p = 0$ 16. $w - 56 = 560$ $w = 616$

17. $55 = h - 13$ $h = 68$ 18. $48 = d + 23$ $d = 25$ 19. $937 = f - 63$ $f = 1000$ 20. $0 = y - 87.4$ $y = 87.4$

21. $138 + g = 150$ $g = 12$ 22. $2098 = k - 536$ $k = 2634$ 23. $651 + c = 800$ $c = 149$ 24. $71 = s - 583$ $s = 654$

25. **Test Prep** Which is the first step in solving $x - 3 = 3$? D
   Ⓐ Add 3 to the left side. Ⓑ Subtract 3 from both sides.
   Ⓒ Subtract 3 from the left side. Ⓓ Add 3 to both sides.

PRACTICE 2-6

Write an equation for each statement.

26. The number of hours (h) increased by 12 equals 54. $h + 12 = 54$
27. The amount of profit (p) decreased by $25 is $180. $p - 25 = 180$
28. **Science** The chemical element aluminum was discovered in 1825 by Hans Christian Oersted. This was 18 years after Sir Humphry Davy discovered the element sodium. Write and solve an equation to find the year (y) that sodium was discovered. $y + 18 = 1825$; $y = 1807$
29. **Literature** In Douglas Adams's five-book trilogy, *The Hitchhiker's Guide to the Galaxy,* the answer to Life, the Universe, and Everything is a number. This number (n) is 17 less than 59. Write and solve an equation to find n. $n = 59 - 17$; $n = 42$
30. Write a word problem that would be solved by the equation $z - 16 = 28$.

Aluminum

Sodium

PRACTICE

Name ______________

Practice 2-6

Solving Addition and Subtraction Equations

Tell if the given number is a solution to the equation.

1. $x + 18 = 99$; 80 No 2. $u - 3 = 56$; 53 No 3. $17 + t = 74$; 57 Yes
4. $k - 12 = 84$; 96 Yes 5. $r - 5 = 10$; 15 Yes 6. $w + 15 = 40$; 20 No

Solve each equation. Check your answer.

7. $y + 15 = 23$ $y =$ 8 8. $27 + s = 51$ $s =$ 24 9. $w - 31 = 25$ $w =$ 56
10. $64 + q = 123$ $q =$ 59 11. $41 = d - 28$ $d =$ 69 12. $37 = 11 + g$ $g =$ 26

Write an equation for each statement.

13. The number of students (x) decreased by 15 equals 81. $x - 15 = 81$
14. The revenue (r) increased by $3,200 is $38,500. $r + 3,200 = 38,500$
15. The number of hours (h) decreased by 12 equals 64. $h - 12 = 64$

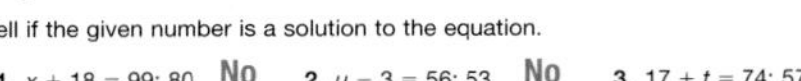

Estimate a solution to each equation.

16. $m - 483 = 1703$ $m \approx$ 2200 17. $6309 = 4120 + p$ $p \approx$ 2200
18. $3240 + y = 7735$ $y \approx$ 4500 19. $v - 847 = 1256$ $v \approx$ 2100

20. **Career** Xochitl is a real estate agent. This month she earned commissions of $6240, which is $3460 more than she earned last month. Write and solve an equation to find last month's commissions.
    $x + 3460 = 6240$; $x = 2780$; she earned $2780 last month
21. **History** Thomas Edison invented the phonograph in 1887, 98 years before the introduction of the compact disc (CD). Write and solve an equation to find the year (y) that CDs were introduced.
    $1887 = y - 98$; $y = 1985$; CDs were introduced in 1985

RETEACHING

Name ______________

Alternative Lesson 2-6

Solving Addition and Subtraction Equations

An **equation** is a statement that two expressions are equal. To **solve** an equation containing a variable means to find the value(s) of the variable that make(s) the equation true. One value is called a **solution**.

Example

Solve $x + 4 = 15$.
To solve an equation, you must "undo" what was done to the variable.

4 was added to the variable (x).	$x + 4 = 15$
To "undo" addition of 4, subtract 4 from both sides.	$x + 4 - \mathbf{4} = 15 - \mathbf{4}$
So $x = 11$ is the solution to the equation $x + 4 = 15$.	$x = 11$
Check your work by substituting 11 for x in the equation and solving.	$11 + 4 \stackrel{?}{=} 15$
Since $15 = 15$, the solution is correct.	$15 = 15$

Try It Solve $m - 34 = 57$.

a. What was done to the variable? 34 was subtracted.
b. What must you do to both sides? Add 34.
c. What is the solution? $m = 91$

Solve $22 = d + 8$.

d. What was done to the variable? 8 was added.
e. What must you do to both sides? Subtract 8.
f. What is the solution? $d = 14$

Solve each equation.

g. $81 = x - 20$ $x = 101$ h. $b + 25 = 72$ $b = 47$
i. $y + 12 = 35$ $y = 23$ j. $z - 16 = 18$ $z = 34$
k. $92 = g - 41$ $g = 133$ l. $45 = 19 + j$ $j = 26$
m. $p + 21 = 38$ $p = 17$ n. $5 + r = 12$ $r = 7$
o. $28 + s = 42$ $s = 14$ p. $57 = x - 19$ $x = 76$

31. **Industry** Arty's Auto is suffering a slump. Last month Arty's salespeople sold a record 250 cars. The number of cars sold this month is 127 less than last month's number. Write and solve an equation to find the number of cars sold this month (n). $n + 127 = 250$; $n = 123$

Estimation Estimate a solution to each equation.

32. $673 = x + 104$ $x \approx 570$ **33.** $1{,}789 - t = 391$ $t \approx 1400$ **34.** $c - 9{,}422 = 3{,}207$ $c \approx 12{,}600$ **35.** $12{,}949 + s = 19{,}323$ $s \approx 6000$

Problem Solving and Reasoning

Communicate Explain what was done to the first equation to get the second.

36. $x + 21 = 27 \rightarrow x = 6$ **37.** $16 = q - 13 \rightarrow q = 29$

38.  You have learned to write algebraic expressions and equations. Explain the difference between the two.

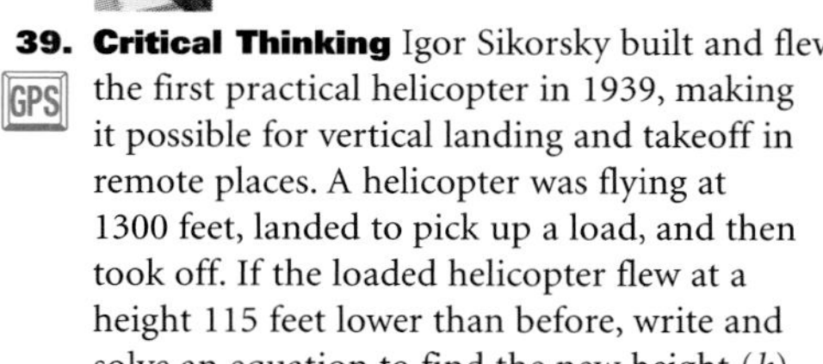

39. Critical Thinking Igor Sikorsky built and flew the first practical helicopter in 1939, making it possible for vertical landing and takeoff in remote places. A helicopter was flying at 1300 feet, landed to pick up a load, and then took off. If the loaded helicopter flew at a height 115 feet lower than before, write and solve an equation to find the new height (h).

40. Choose a Strategy You have been told that there is buried treasure somewhere due north of your house. You also know that it is exactly 3 miles from a large oak tree that is 12 miles due north of your house. How could you use equations to decide where to dig?

Problem Solving STRATEGIES
- Look for a Pattern
- Make an Organized List
- Make a Table
- Guess and Check
- Work Backward
- Use Logical Reasoning
- Draw a Diagram
- Solve a Simpler Problem

Mixed Review

Name the inverse action of each. *[Lesson 2-4]*

41. Subtract 17 Add 17 **42.** Divide by 4 Multiply by 4
43. Multiply by 20 Divide by 20 **44.** Add 32 Subtract 32

Find the value of each expression. *[Lesson 2-2]*

45. $6 \div (12 - 9) + 5$ 7 **46.** $4 + 3 \times 7 - 5$ 20 **47.** $1 + 2 \times 3 - 4$ 3 **48.** $2 \times 32 - 8 \div 4$ 62

49. $9 + 8 - 7 + 6$ 16 **50.** $23 - 48 \div 6$ 15 **51.** $12 \div 2 \times 3$ 18 **52.** $12 - (2 + 6) \div 4$ 10

PROBLEM SOLVING 2-6

Exercise Notes

Exercise 40

Problem-Solving Tip You may wish to use Teaching Tool Transparencies 2 and 3: Guided Problem Solving, pages 1 and 2.

Exercise Answers

36. 21 was subtracted from both sides.
37. 13 was added to both sides.
38. Possible answer: An algebraic expression is an expression that contains a variable, like x, $b - 4$, and $5(n + 3)$. An equation sets two expressions equal to each other, like $x - 5 = 3$.
39. $1300 = h + 115$; $h = 1185$; The new height was 1185 feet.
40. There are two possible equations: (d is the distance from your home): $d = 12 + 3$ and $d = 12 - 3$. You should dig holes at 9 miles and 15 miles due north of your house.

Alternate Assessment

Interview Have students solve the following equations. While students are solving them, ask individual students to explain to you how they are solving one equation.

1. $y + 15 = 43$ $y = 28$
2. $n - 36 = 17$ $n = 53$
3. $t - 28 = 54$ $t = 82$
4. $w + 19 = 62$ $w = 43$
5. $b - 41 = 26$ $b = 67$

Quick Quiz

Solve each equation.

1. $x + 47 = 82$ $x = 35$
2. $m - 51 = 23$ $m = 74$
3. $110 = s + 65$ $s = 45$

Available on Daily Transparency 2-6

PROBLEM SOLVING

Name ____________ **Guided Problem Solving 2-6**

GPS PROBLEM 39, STUDENT PAGE 85

Igor Sikorsky built and flew the first practical helicopter in 1939, making it possible for vertical landing and takeoff in remote places. A helicopter was flying at 1300 feet, landed to pick up a load, and then took off. If the loaded helicopter flew at a height 115 feet lower than before, write and solve an equation to find the new height (h).

— Understand —
1. Underline what you are asked to do.
2. Circle the information you need.
3. Is 1300 feet more or less than the new height (h)? More than

— Plan —
4. How much would you need to add to the new height to get to 1300 feet? 115 feet
5. Which is a reasonable solution? a
 a. 1200 ft b. 1800 ft c. 1400 ft

— Solve —
6. Write an equation to show the information. Possible answer: $1300 = h + 115$
7. What will you need to do to both sides of your equation to find the solution? Possible answer: Subtract 115.
8. Solve your equation. Show your work. $h = 1185$
 $1300 = h + 115$
 $1300 - 115 = h + 115 - 115$
 $1185 = h$

— Look Back —
9. Draw a picture to show that your answer makes sense.
 Possible answer: 1300
 115
 1185

SOLVE ANOTHER PROBLEM

The technology center has 25 computers, 28 monitors and 37 keyboards. If the number of monitors they have now is 7 more than the number they had last year (n), write and solve an equation to find how many monitors they had last year.
$n + 7 = 28$; $n = 21$

ENRICHMENT

Name ____________ **Extend Your Thinking 2-6**

Visual Thinking

Circle the letter of the figure on the right that matches the figure on the left. The figures may be flipped or turned.

1.

a. b. (c.) d.

2.
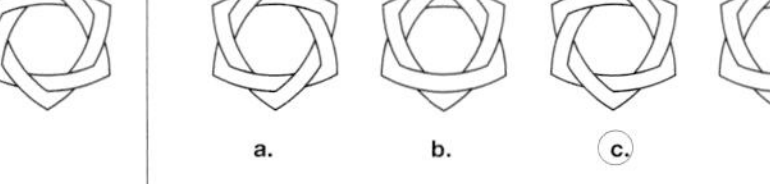
a. b. c. (d.)

3.
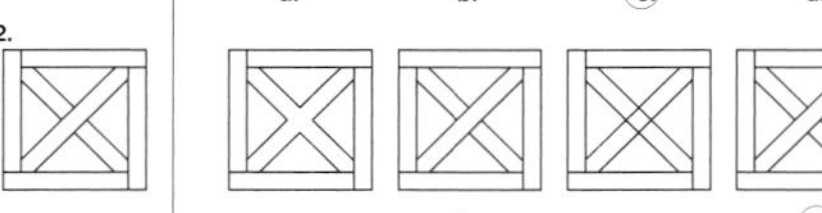
a. b. (c.) d.

4.
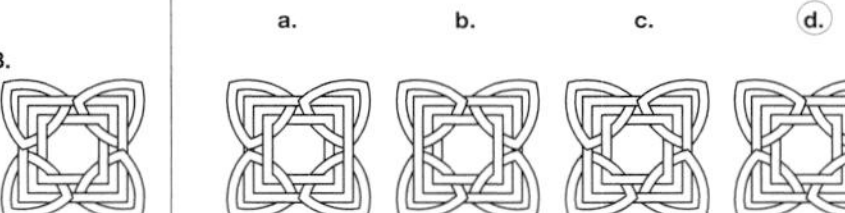
a. (b.) c. d.

5.
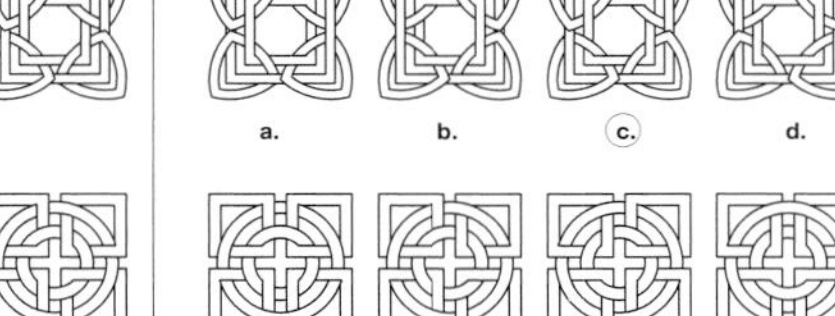
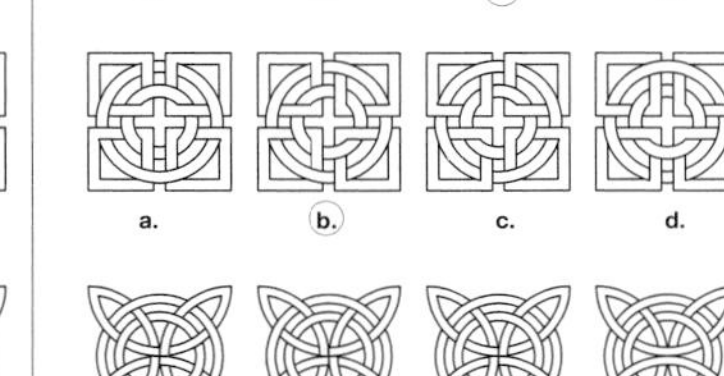
(a.) b. c. d.

INTERACTIVE LESSON

2-7 Lesson Organizer

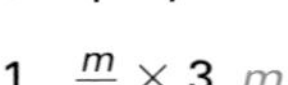
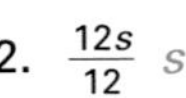

Objective

- Solve multiplication and division equations using inverse operations.

NCTM Standards

- 1–4, 7, 9, 12

Review

Simplify.

1. $\frac{m}{3} \times 3$ *m*
2. $\frac{12s}{12}$ *s*
3. $y \div 7 \times 7$ *y*

Available on Daily Transparency 2-7

Lesson Link

Have students give an example of an addition or subtraction equation. Have them explain how an inverse operation is used to solve the equation. Discuss the fact that multiplication and division are inverse operations.

1 Introduce

Explore

The Point
Students explore multiplication and division equations by picturing a balanced scale. As they describe how to get one *x*-weight alone, they translate to the use of inverse operations.

Ongoing Assessment
Check students' answers for Step 2 to see that students are thinking in terms of division and removing 2 equal groups, not just 2 weights.

For Groups That Finish Early
Work with a partner and take turns modeling equations by sketching balanced scales. The partner can then write and solve the equation.

Follow Up
Have a volunteer explain how the answer is found for Step 5.
$\frac{1}{2}x$ must be doubled to get *x*, so 7 must be doubled.

2-7 Solving Multiplication and Division Equations

You'll Learn ...

- to write and solve multiplication and division equations

... How It's Used

Scientists use multiplication and division equations to help analyze the growth of organisms.

Lesson Link In the last lesson, you used inverse operations to solve addition and subtraction equations. Now you will see how inverse operations can help you solve multiplication and division equations. ◄

Explore Multiplication and Division Equations

Matching Equals

1. The balanced scale represents the equation $3x = 12$.

2. What would you do to get just one *x* by itself on one side of the scale and still keep the scale in balance? What is the value of *x*?
3. Sketch a balanced scale that shows $2x = 6$. What is the value of *x*?
4. How did you use an inverse operation to get *x* by itself on one side of the equation $2x = 6$?
5. Sketch a balanced scale that shows $\frac{1}{2}x = 7$ or $x \div 2 = 7$. What is the value of *x*?

Learn Solving Multiplication and Division Equations

Because multiplication and division are inverse operations, you can solve a multiplication equation using division. To solve division equations, use multiplication. When you change one side of an equation by multiplication or division, you must change the other side the same way to keep the "balance."

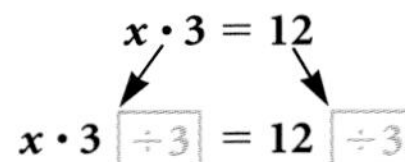

MEETING INDIVIDUAL NEEDS

Resources

- 2-7 Practice
- 2-7 Reteaching
- 2-7 Problem Solving
- 2-7 Enrichment
- 2-7 Daily Transparency
  - Problem of the Day
  - Review
  - Quick Quiz

Interactive CD-ROM Lesson

Learning Modalities

Logical Have students explain how the process of removing equal groups models division.

Social Have students work together to create a collection of problems which could be solved by writing and solving multiplication and division equations.

English Language Development

Have students work in pairs, with one writing a sentence which means the same as a given multiplication or division equation and the other translating the sentence back into symbols. Have the students compare the completed equation with the original one and decide if they are equivalent. Pair each student who is learning English with one who is proficient in English.

Examples

1 Solve: $\frac{x}{4} = 5$

$\frac{x}{4} \times 4 = 5 \times 4$ To undo dividing by 4, multiply both sides by 4.

$x = 20$ Multiply.

Check: $\boxed{20} \div 4 \stackrel{?}{=} 5$

$5 = 5$ ✓ The solution checks.

2 In 1793, Eli Whitney invented a cotton gin for separating cotton fiber from its seed. A person using a gin could work 50 times faster than a person working by hand. Suppose a person with a gin can clean 400 lb of cotton. In the same amount of time, how much could a person clean by hand?

Let c = the amount a person could clean by hand. Choose a variable.

Using a gin cleans 50 times as much as cleaning by hand. Describe the situation.

$400 = 50 \cdot c$ Write an equation.

$\frac{400}{50} = \frac{50c}{50}$ To undo multiplying by 50, divide ***both*** sides by 50.

$8 = c$ Divide.

A person working by hand could clean 8 pounds of cotton.

3 In 1993, 7 times as many cars were manufactured in the United States as were manufactured in Mexico. If there were about 5,950,000 cars made in the United States that year, how many were made in Mexico?

Let m = number of cars made in Mexico. Choose a variable.

Number of U.S. cars was 7 times cars made in Mexico. Describe the situation.

$5{,}950{,}000 = 7 \cdot m$ Write an equation.

$\frac{5{,}950{,}000}{7} = \frac{7m}{7}$ To undo multiplying by 7, divide by 7.

$850{,}000 = m$ Divide.

About 850,000 cars were made in Mexico.

Try It

a. Solve: $x \div 35 = 7$ $x = 245$

b. Solve: $4s = 888$ $s = 222$

c. The cost of running an appliance equals the number of kilowatts of power used times the cost per kilowatt. The cost is $0.15 per kilowatt. How many kilowatts did Stacey use if the cost of running her air conditioner was $18? 120

Study TIP

Always remember to check your solution.

History Link

In about 1764, James Hargreaves, an Englishman, invented the Spinning Jenny. Samuel Slater brought the new methods to the United States and, together with Americans Francis Lowell and Eli Whitney, revolutionized the cotton industry.

MATH EVERY DAY

Problem of the Day

Jamie has 10 white marbles and 10 red marbles in a bag. She chooses marbles from the bag without looking. How many times must she choose a marble to be sure she will have two marbles of the same color? 3 times

Available on Daily Transparency 2-7

An Extension is provided in the transparency package.

Fact of the Day

A single-row machine picks about 500 pounds of cotton per hour. A person can pick about 15 pounds per hour.

Mental Math

Do these mentally.

1. 21×5 105
2. 34×5 170
3. 62×5 310

Answers for Explore

2. Remove 2 x-weights from the left side. Remove 2 of the 3 equal layers of weights from the right side; $x = 4$.
3. Student's sketch should show a scale with 2 x-weights on one side and 6 weights on the other side; $x = 3$.
4. I divided both sides by 2.
5. Student's sketch should show a scale with one half of an x-weight on one side and 7 weights on the other side. $x = 14$

2 Teach

Learn

Alternate Examples

1. Solve: $\frac{b}{3} = 7$

   $\frac{b}{3} \times 3 = 7 \times 3$

   $b = 21$

   Check: $21 \div 3 \stackrel{?}{=} 7$

   $7 = 7$

2. A person weighs about 6 times as much on Earth as on the moon. Eric weighs 120 pounds on Earth. How much would he weigh on the moon?

   Let w = Eric's weight on the moon.

   Eric's Earth weight is 6 times as much as his moon weight.

   $120 = 6 \cdot w$

   $\frac{120}{6} = \frac{6w}{6}$

   $20 = w$

   Eric would weigh 20 pounds on the moon.

3. Ms. Pell bought a computer with 60 times the memory of her old computer. If the new computer has 2400 megabytes of memory, how much memory did the old one have?

   Let m = amount of memory for the old computer.

   $60 \cdot m = 2400$

   z $= \frac{2400}{60}$

   $m = 40$

   The old computer had 40 megabytes of memory.

Students see two methods of solving a problem. One method uses a table and the other uses an equation. Students can see that for this problem both methods are easy to use. Students can decide which method they prefer for certain types of problems.

Answers for What Do You Think?

1. Possible answer: It makes sense when there are not very many data values to fill in the table. It does not when you have to deal with large numbers of values.
2. Possible answer: He had to undo the multiplication on the left side. Division undoes multiplication.

3 Practice and Assess

Check

Answers for Check Your Understanding

1. To solve the first equation, you must undo the division by 4. To do this, you need to multiply both sides of the equation by 4, which gives you the second equation.
2. When you solve a multiplication equation, you are finding what number can be added to itself a certain number of times to equal the product.

In 1986, cyclist Fred Markham set the world speed record for bicycles, 65 mi/hr. Wendy and Luis want to know how long it would take for a rider to travel the 260 miles from Cincinnati to Detroit if he could sustain that rate.

Wendy thinks ...

I'll make a table of values.

Time (hr)	1	2	3	4
Distance (mi)	65	130	195	260

It would take 4 hours.

Luis thinks ...

I'll write and solve an equation. I'll let t = the time it will take.

The equation is $65t = 260$ because rate times time equals distance.

To undo multiplying by 65, I'll divide both sides by 65: $\frac{65t}{65} = \frac{260}{65}$

Then I'll get: $t = 4$

It would take 4 hours.

What do you think?

1. When does it make sense to use Wendy's method? When doesn't it make sense?
2. Why did Luis divide 260 by 65 rather than multiply by 65?

Check Your Understanding

1. How are the equations $k \div 4 = 9$ and $k \div 4 \times 4 = 9 \times 4$ related?
2. How are solving a multiplication equation and an addition equation alike?

MEETING MIDDLE SCHOOL CLASSROOM NEEDS

Tips from Middle School Teachers

When I introduce the writing of equations for the first time, I stress that the variable is the number name for a certain quantity. The variable might be the number name that tells how many people in a group, an amount of money, the number of hours, the distance traveled, or the age of a person.

Team Teaching

Working with the social studies teacher, have students write equations regarding changes in population, stock market prices, U.S. income levels, unemployment rates, immigration rates, and so on.

Cultural Connection

Bicycles outnumber automobiles worldwide by two to one. A large part of these 800 million bicycles are located in India and China. In China, the city of Beijing has some 3 million bicycles. To tourists, it appears that the streets belong to the bicycle riders. On some major streets, the lane closest to the curb is reserved for bicycles.

2-7 Exercises and Applications

Practice and Apply

Getting Started **What is the first step in solving each equation?**

1. $15d = 1200$ **2.** $m \div 43 = 2$ **3.** $\frac{f}{16} = 32$ **4.** $80k = 4.80$

Is the given number a solution to the equation?

5. $k \div 19 = 76$; 4 No **6.** $j \cdot 25 = 75$; 3 Yes **7.** $25m = 125$; 3125 No

8. **Test Prep** Which equation shows the next step in solving $3g = 33$? C

Ⓐ $3g - 3 = 33 - 3$ Ⓑ $3g + 3 = 33 + 3$ Ⓒ $3g \div 3 = 33 \div 3$ Ⓓ None of these

Solve each equation. Check your answer.

9. $m \cdot 45 = 90$ $m = 2$ **10.** $\frac{s}{77} = 11$ $s = 847$ **11.** $36 = 36p$ $p = 1$ **12.** $100 = \frac{w}{66}$ $w = 6600$

13. $60 \div 4 = d$ $d = 15$ **14.** $216 = n \div 2$ $n = 432$ **15.** $1.5 = y \cdot 1.5$ $y = 1$ **16.** $33j = 198$ $j = 6$

17. $7r = 147$ $r = 21$ **18.** $\frac{t}{17} = 16$ $t = 272$ **19.** $268 = \frac{h}{13}$ $h = 3484$ **20.** $352 = 8z$ $z = 44$

21. **Test Prep** Which of these numbers is the solution to $72x = 936$? A

Ⓐ 13 Ⓑ 864 Ⓒ 1008 Ⓓ 67,392

22. **Science** A winch raises a weight 6 feet for each turn of the handle. Write an equation that shows how many turns it would take to raise a weight 20 feet. $6t = 20$

23. **Geometry** Two rectangles each have an area of 12 square centimeters. What is the height of each rectangle if the base of one is 4 cm and the base of the other is 6 cm?

24. **History** A league was an early measure of distance. A league is about 3 miles long. A horse was traveling at 9 leagues per hour. Write an equation to show how many leagues the horse could travel in 2 hours. $d = 2 \times 9$

25. **Geography** The average area of each state in the United States is about 75,500 square miles. What is the area of the United States? about 3,775,000 mi²

26. James bakes some cookies and gives 8 to each of his 9 friends. Write and solve an equation to find the number of cookies (c) that James baked. $c \div 9 = 8$; $c = 72$

PRACTICE 2-7

PRACTICE

Name ______________________

Practice 2-7

Solving Multiplication and Division Equations

Tell if the given number is a solution to the equation.

1. $5x = 20$; 100 No 2. $t \div 3 = 7$; 21 Yes 3. $\frac{u}{9} = 36$; 4 No
4. $8m = 88$; 11 Yes 5. $\frac{b}{5} = 5$; 30 No 6. $r \div 4 = 10$; 40 Yes
7. $3x = 81$; 9 No 8. $6c = 42$; 7 Yes 9. $\frac{d}{11} = 1$; 11 Yes

Solve each equation. Check your answer.

10. $12 = s \div 4$ $s =$ 48 11. $17x = 85$ $x =$ 5 12. $63 = p \cdot 3$ $p =$ 21
13. $6u = 222$ $u =$ 37 14. $\frac{w}{11} = 22$ $w =$ 242 15. $13 = \frac{z}{5}$ $z =$ 65
16. $38 = 19t$ $t =$ 2 17. $9q = 108$ $q =$ 12 18. $\frac{c}{5} = 35$ $c =$ 175
19. $\frac{k}{18} = 72$ $k =$ 1296 20. $21j = 294$ $j =$ 14 21. $y \cdot 4 = 168$ $y =$ 42

Estimate a reasonable solution to each equation.

22. $210x = 4119$ $x \approx$ 20 23. $64{,}382 = 39y$ $y \approx$ 1600 24. $\frac{m}{98} = 43$ $m \approx$ 4000 25. $295 = \frac{r}{51}$ $r \approx$ 15,000

26. A 7-inch phonograph record turns at a rate of 45 revolutions per minute. Write and solve an equation to find the number of minutes to complete 315 revolutions.
$45x = 315$; $x = 7$; it takes 7 minutes

27. **Geometry** A rectangle has area 50 in² and base 10 in. Write and solve an equation to find the height of the rectangle.
$10h = 50$; $h = 5$; height is 5 in.

RETEACHING

Name ______________________

Alternative Lesson 2-7

Solving Multiplication and Division Equations

Multiplication and division are inverse operations.
To solve multiplication equations, use division.
To solve division equations, use multiplication.

Example

Solve $5x = 35$.
To solve an equation, you must "undo" what was done to the variable.

The variable (x) was multiplied by 5. $5x = 35$

To "undo" multiplication by 5, divide both sides by 5. $\frac{5x}{5} = \frac{35}{5}$

So $x = 7$ is the solution to the equation $5x = 35$. $x = 7$

Check your work by substituting 7 for x in the equation and solving. $5 \cdot 7 \stackrel{?}{=} 35$

Since $35 = 35$, the solution is correct. $35 = 35$

Try It Solve $8c = 96$.

a. What was done to the variable? It was multiplied by 8.
b. What must you do to both sides? Divide by 8.
c. What is the solution? $c = 12$

Solve $\frac{k}{9} = 11$.

d. What was done to the variable? It was divided by 9.
e. What must you do to both sides? Multiply by 9.
f. What is the solution? $k = 99$

Solve each equation.

g. $72 = 8x$ $x = 9$ h. $b \div 25 = 4$ $b = 100$
i. $y \div 8 = 5$ $y = 40$ j. $z \cdot 18 = 18$ $z = 1$
k. $9 = g \div 3$ $g = 27$ l. $150 = 3 \cdot j$ $j = 50$
m. $\frac{p}{15} = 6$ $p = 90$ n. $7r = 84$ $r = 12$
o. $3c = 96$ $c = 32$ p. $21 = d \div 2$ $d = 42$

2-7 Exercises and Applications

Assignment Guide

- **Basic** 1–16, 21, 22, 26, 27–43 odds
- **Average** 2–20 evens, 21–31, 32–44 evens
- **Enriched** 5–8 odds, 9–43 odds

Exercise Notes

Exercises 1–4

Error Prevention Watch for students who name the operation used in the equation rather than its inverse. Remind them that the goal is to undo that operation and get the variable by itself on one side.

Exercise 24

Extension Write an equation to show how many miles the horse could travel in 4 hours.

Exercise Answers

1. Divide both sides by 15: $15d \div 15 = 1200 \div 15$
2. Multiply both sides by 43: $m \div 43 \times 43 = 2 \times 43$
3. Multiply both sides by 16: $\frac{f}{16} \times 16 = 32 \times 16$
4. Divide both sides by 80: $80k \div 80 = 4.80 \div 80$

23. Rectangle with 4-cm base has a height of 3 cm and rectangle with 6-cm base has a height of 2 cm.

Reteaching

Activity

Materials: Cups, counters

- To solve $4x = 12$, place 4 cups on one side of your desk and 12 counters on the other side. Drop 12 more counters into the cups, 1 at a time, until all are used. How many are in each cup? 3 Are there any left over? No What is the value of x? $x = 3$
- Use the same process to solve $2x = 14$. $x = 7$

Exercise Answers

32. Possible answer: $\frac{y}{8} = 26$, multiply both sides by 8; $23p = 230$, divide both sides by 23.

33. No unique solution; Since multiplying any number by 0 results in 0, j can represent any number.

34. A pizza; For every 811 Turkish lira, there was 1 Japanese yen. For every 110 Japanese yen, there was one U.S. dollar. $1{,}000{,}000 \div (811 \times 110) \approx 11.21$. So, 1,000,000 Turkish lira was about \$11.21.

35. $n = 1235 \div 36$; $n \approx 34.31$; Hua must buy 35 rolls of film

36. Possible answer: About 15 ft

37. Possible answer: About $\frac{1}{8}$ mi

38. Possible answer: About 6 in.

39. Possible answer: About 12 ft

Alternate Assessment

You may want to use the *Interactive CD-ROM Journal* with this assessment.

Journal Have students write a paragraph describing how inverse operations are used to solve equations. They should include examples.

Quick Quiz

Solve each equation.

1. $c \cdot 3 = 45$ $c = 15$
2. $\frac{t}{12} = 3$ $t = 36$
3. $33 = 11v$ $v = 3$

Available on Daily Transparency 2-7

PROBLEM SOLVING 2-7

Estimation Estimate a reasonable solution to each equation.

27. $9320 = 321k$ $k \approx 30$ **28.** $\frac{t}{487} = 3$ $t \approx 1{,}500$ **29.** $\frac{t}{5} = 3979$ $t \approx 20{,}000$ **30.** $7{,}943p = 15{,}887$ $p \approx 2$

Problem Solving and Reasoning

31. Choose a Strategy Fingernails grow about 1.5 inches per year. The world record for the longest fingernails is 37 inches. Which equation shows how long it might take to grow nails 37 inches long? **C**

Ⓐ $1.5 + y = 37$ Ⓑ $\frac{y}{1.5} = 37$
Ⓒ $1.5y = 37$ Ⓓ $y = 1.5 \cdot 37$

Problem Solving STRATEGIES
- Look for a Pattern
- Make an Organized List
- Make a Table
- Guess and Check
- Work Backward
- Use Logical Reasoning
- Draw a Diagram
- Solve a Simpler Problem

32. Communicate Write an equation that can be solved using multiplication and another that can be solved using division. Explain how to solve the equations.

33. Critical Thinking What is the solution to the equation $0 \cdot j = 0$? Explain.

34. Communicate In September 1996, one U.S. dollar was worth 110 Japanese yen, and one yen was worth 811 Turkish lira. If you had a million Turkish lira, would you be able to buy a house, a car, a pizza, or a newspaper? Explain how you decided.

35. Critical Thinking Each roll of Hua's film allows her to take 36 photographs. Write an equation to calculate how many rolls (n) of film she needs to take a picture of each member of a school with 1235 students. Use your equation to find out how many rolls of film she must buy.

Mixed Review

Use mental math to estimate each measurement. *[Previous course]*

36. The height of a house **37.** The length of a city block

38. The height of a soda can **39.** The height of an elephant

Write an algebraic expression for each phrase. *[Lesson 2-5]*

40. Seven more than a number x $x + 7$ **41.** Three less than twice a number c $2c - 3$

42. A number n increased by 5 $n + 5$ **43.** A number r decreased by 10 $r - 10$

44. Triple the sum of 2 and a number d $3(2 + d)$

PROBLEM SOLVING

Name ____________

Guided Problem Solving 2-7

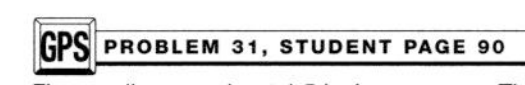

GPS PROBLEM 31, STUDENT PAGE 90

Fingernails grow about 1.5 inches per year. The world record for the longest fingernails is 37 inches. Which equation shows how long it might take to grow nails 37 inches long?

(A) $1.5 + y = 37$ **(B)** $\frac{y}{1.5} = 37$ **(C)** $1.5y = 37$ **(D)** $y = 1.5 \times 37$

— Understand —

1. Circle what you are asked to find.
2. What does y represent in the equations? Number of years.

— Plan —

3. What operation can you use to find the answer? Multiplication.
4. Explain how your answer to Item 3 would allow you to eliminate some of the equations. You can eliminate answers A and B because they do not have 1.5 as a factor.

— Solve —

5. Which equation would show that the total growth was 37 inches? C

— Look Back —

6. Solve the equation. Why is your answer to Item 5 reasonable?
$y = 24.6$; Possible answer: Growth rate of 1.5 in. per year is between 1 and 2. So, it should take between 18 and 37 years to grow the nails. 25 is reasonable.

SOLVE ANOTHER PROBLEM

There were 920 statistics textbooks ordered this year. This was 2.3 times the number that were ordered five years ago. Which equation shows how many statistics textbooks were ordered five years ago? Explain.

(A) $920 = s + 2.3$ **(B)** $\frac{s}{2.3} = 920$ **(C)** $920 - 2.3 = s$ **(D)** $2.3s = 920$

D; Possible answer: A and C are not reasonable since you need to use multiplication or division to find the answer. B is not reasonable because it will give an answer higher than the increased sales.

ENRICHMENT

Name ____________

Extend Your Thinking 2-7

Critical Thinking

The equation $d = r \times t$ relates rate (r), time (t) and distance (d).

1. If you are traveling at 55 miles per hour, what formula would you use to find the distance you will travel over various lengths of time? $d = 55 \times t$

2. Sometimes you are given distances and need to know how long it would take to travel at various rates. Complete the table to find the time it would take to travel 500 miles at speeds of 40, 55, 60, 65, and 70 miles per hour. Round your times to the nearest quarter hour, if necessary.

Rate (in mi/hr)	40	55	60	65	70
Time (in hours)	$12\frac{1}{2}$	9	$8\frac{1}{4}$	$7\frac{3}{4}$	$7\frac{1}{4}$
Distance (in miles)	500	500	500	500	500

3. What operation did you use to find the time? Rewrite the equation so that t stands alone on one side of the equal sign.
Division: $t = \frac{d}{r}$

4. Rewrite the equation so that r stands alone on one side of the equal sign? Explain your reasoning.
$r = \frac{d}{t}$; Possible answer: To find the rate, divide the distance by the time.

5. How is rewriting an equation like solving an equation? Possible answer: You use inverse operations to isolate the variable.

6. Why would you want to rewrite an equation?
Possible answer: If you needed to find many solutions using the same equation, it would be faster to have the variable isolated before doing each calculation.

7. The equation to find the perimeter of a regular polygon can be written as $P = n \times s$ where P is the perimeter, n is the number of sides and s is the length of each side. How could you rewrite the equation to find the length of a side? $s = \frac{P}{n}$

Problem Solving with Two-Step Equations

2-8

▶ Lesson Link You've solved equations by using inverse operations. Now you'll use inverse operations to solve equations with more than one operation. ◀

You'll Learn ...

- to use more than one inverse operation to solve an equation

... How It's Used

Contractors need to understand equations that have more than one operation because they have to work with fixed costs and variable costs.

Explore Two-Step Equations

Watch Your Balance

1. The balanced scale represents the equation $2x + 3 = 13$.
2. What steps would you take to get one x alone on one side of the scale and still keep the scale in balance? What is the value of x?
3. Sketch a balanced scale that shows $3x + 1 = 7$. What is the value of x?
4. How did you use inverse operations to get x by itself on one side of $3x + 1 = 7$?
5. When you solve an equation like $3x + 1 = 7$, would you first try to find out what $3x$ without the 1 equals, or first find out what x equals? Explain.

Learn Problem Solving with Two-Step Equations

If an equation involves two operations, you need to use inverse operations one at a time. The order of operations says to do multiplication and division before addition and subtraction. So you need to undo any addition or subtraction first. Then undo any multiplication or division.

$2w \boxed{+ 3} = 9$ Undo addition first.

$2w + 3 \boxed{- 3} = 9 \boxed{- 3}$ Undo by subtracting 3.

$\frac{2w}{2} = \frac{6}{2}$ Undo multiplication by dividi..g.

$w = 3$

MEETING INDIVIDUAL NEEDS

Resources

- 2-8 Practice
- 2-8 Reteaching
- 2-8 Problem Solving
- 2-8 Enrichment
- 2-8 Daily Transparency
  - Problem of the Day
  - Review
  - Quick Quiz
- Technology Master 9

Learning Modalities

Kinesthetic Have students use algebra tiles or counters and cups to model the solution of two-step algebraic equations.

Social Have groups of students do a presentation for the class on solving equations. Encourage the students to use examples, models, and overhead transparencies to create an interesting presentation.

Challenge

There are 310 books on a shelf. There are twice as many math books as geography books and 10 more science books than math books. How many of each kind are on the shelf? 60 geography books, 120 math books, and 130 science books

2-8 Lesson Organizer

Objective

- Use more than one inverse operation to solve an equation

NCTM Standards

- 1–4, 7, 9

▶ Review

Evaluate each expression when $n = 4$.

1. $2n - 3$ 5
2. $\frac{n}{2} + 5$ 7
3. $7 + 4n$ 23

Available on Daily Transparency 2-8

1 Introduce

Explore

The Point

Students explore two-step equations by picturing a balanced scale. As they find how to get one x-weight alone, they discover the order in which inverse operations are used when solving equations.

Ongoing Assessment

Check to see that students understand the importance of order. Review order of operations and remind students to work in reverse order when undoing operations.

For Groups That Finish Early

Think of situations that might be represented by the equation $3x + 1 = 7$. Possible Answer: Jake earned $3 per hour and was given a tip of $1; x = the number of hours he worked for a total of $7.

Answers for Explore

2. Remove 3 unit weights from each side. Then separate the unit weights on the right into 2 equal groups. Remove one x-weight from the left side and one group of unit weights from the right. $x = 5$

Answers continued on next page.

Answers for Explore

3. Student's sketch should show 3 x-weights and 1 unit weight on one side and 7 unit weights on the other side. $x = 2$
4. Subtract 1 from both sides, then divide both sides by 3.
5. First find out what $3x$ equals. In $3x + 1$, the multiplication would be done first. Since we are undoing the operations, 1 is subtracted first.

2 Teach

Learn

Alternate Examples

1. Solve $4d - 9 = 3$.

$4d - 9 + 9 = 3 + 9$

$4d = 12$

$\frac{4d}{4} = \frac{12}{4}$

$d = 3$

Check: $4 \cdot 3 - 9 \stackrel{?}{=} 3$

$12 - 9 = 3$

The solution checks.

2. Jennifer plays on the seventh-grade basketball team. During one game, she scored 27 points. She made 5 free throws (worth 1 point each). How many field goals (worth 2 points each) did she make?

Let f = the number of field goals.

27 points is 5 points more than twice the number of field goals.

$27 = 5 + 2f$

$27 - 5 = 5 + 2f - 5$

$22 = 2f$

$\frac{22}{2} = \frac{2f}{2}$

$11 = f$

Jennifer made 11 field goals.

3 Practice and Assess

Check

Answers for Check Your Understanding

1. It is the exact reverse.
2. 897 [−] 412 [=] 485 [÷] 34 [=] 14.26
3. Yes, when $x = 4$.

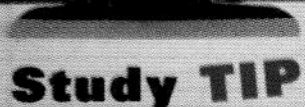

Study TIP

Always make sure that you write each step on a different line and that the equal signs are directly under one another.

DID YOU KNOW?

The Wrights' 1903 plane traveled just 120 ft through the air. If it had taken off inside a Boeing 747 at the nose end, it would have touched down 111 ft from the tail—still inside the plane!

Examples

1 Solve: $3p - 10 = 8$

$3p - 10 + 10 = 8 + 10$	To undo subtracting 10, add 10 to *both* sides.
$3p = 18$	Add.
$\frac{3p}{3} = \frac{18}{3}$	To undo multiplying by 3, divide *both* sides by 3.
$p = 6$	Divide.

Check: $3(6) - 10 \stackrel{?}{=} 8$

$18 - 10 = 8$ ✓ The solution checks.

2 Orville and Wilbur Wright began experimenting with a glider in 1900. The 40-foot wings of their 1903 airplane were 8 feet longer than twice the length of the wings of the glider. How long were the glider's wings?

Let w = the length of the glider's wings. Choose a variable.

$40 = 8 + 2 \cdot w$	Write an equation.
$40 - 8 = 8 + 2w - 8$	To undo adding 8, subtract 8 from *both* sides.
$32 = 2w$	Subtract.
$\frac{32}{2} = \frac{2w}{2}$	To undo multiplying by 2, divide *both* sides by 2.
$16 = w$	Divide.

The glider's wings were 16 feet long.

Try It

a. Solve: $\frac{x}{3} - 12 = 5$ $x = 51$

b. Chris earns $5 per hour as a waiter. One evening, he took home his regular earnings plus $48 in tips, for a total of $73. How many hours did he work? 5 hours.

Check Your Understanding

1. When you use inverse operations, how is their order related to the order of operations?
2. Describe how you would solve $897 = 34x + 412$ using a calculator.
3. Can $3x + 5$ ever take on the value of 17? Explain.

MATH EVERY DAY

Problem of the Day

Giant pandas live only in the bamboo forests of central China and are listed as endangered animals. They weigh twenty times as much as the lesser pandas who live in western China. The average weight of a giant panda is 360 lb. Write and solve an equation to find the weight of the lesser panda. Let x = the weight of the lesser panda. $20x = 360$; $x = 18$ 18 pounds

Available on Daily Transparency 2-8

An Extension is provided in the transparency package.

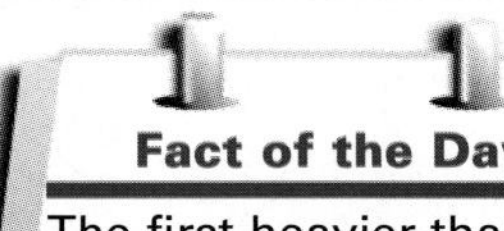

Fact of the Day

The first heavier-than-air flight to carry human passengers took place in 1783 when a hot-air balloon reached an altitude of 80 feet and was aloft for 5 minutes.

Estimation

Estimate.

1. 722 − 413 300
2. 1135 − 197 900
3. 2625 − 841 1800

2-8 Exercises and Applications

Practice and Apply

Getting Started For each equation, tell which operation you would undo first.

1. $2x + 3 = 10$ Addition **2.** $6x - 3 = 33$ Subtraction **3.** $\frac{x}{4} - 6 = 10$ Subtraction

4. **Test Prep** Which of the following have a solution of $m = 16$? C and D

Ⓐ $m + 8 = 8$ Ⓑ $\frac{m}{16} = 256$ Ⓒ $2m - 10 = 22$ Ⓓ $4m + 4 = 68$

Solve each equation. Check your answer.

5. $45n + 45 = 90$ $n = 1$ **6.** $\frac{k}{7} + 11 = 11$ $k = 0$ **7.** $36 = 6u + 30$ $u = 1$ **8.** $10 = \frac{t}{66} + 9$ $t = 66$

9. $60 \div 4 = 2m$ $m = 7.5$ **10.** $216 = \frac{r}{2} + 214$ $r = 4$ **11.** $10 = 15s - 5$ $s = 1$ **12.** $4h - 8 = 8$ $h = 4$

13. $5u - 7 = 13$ $u = 4$ **14.** $14 = 6t + 2$ $t = 2$ **15.** $12s - 10 = 50$ $s = 5$ **16.** $23 = 8g + 7$ $g = 2$

17. $7x + 2 = 51$ $x = 7$ **18.** $9k - 3 = 78$ $k = 9$ **19.** $15 = \frac{s}{4} + 11$ $s = 16$ **20.** $14 = 5 + 3b$ $b = 3$

21. RGP Marco is making a mobile like the one in the photograph. Write an equation to show the mobile is balanced. What should each of the small boxes weigh? $8 = 4 + 2x$; 2 oz.

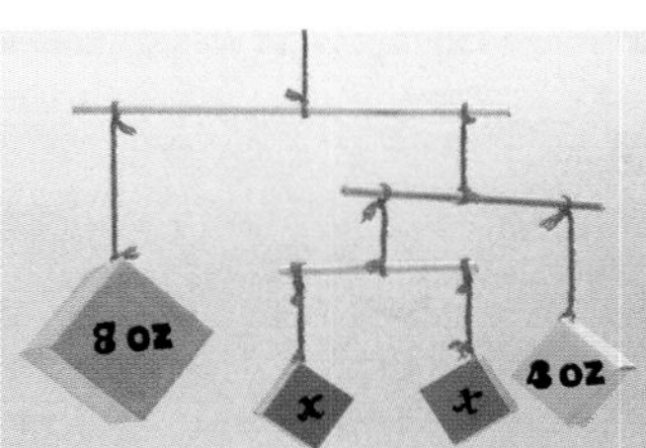

22. Journal When you solve an equation, you must do the same operation to both sides. Explain why this is true.

23. **Science** Crickets chirp faster as the temperature rises. The formula $F = \frac{c}{4} + 40$ can be used to find the number of chirps. F stands for temperature in degrees Fahrenheit and c for the number of chirps per minute.

a. How many times will crickets chirp if the temperature is 84°F? 176 chirps per minute

b. How many times will crickets chirp if the temperature is 44°F? 16 chirps per minute

Acheta domestica

PRACTICE 2-8

PRACTICE

Name ____________

Practice 2-8

Problem Solving with Two-Step Equations

Solve each equation. Check your answer.

1. $3x + 7 = 37$ $x =$ 10
2. $31 = 7x - 11$ $x =$ 6
3. $11k - 84 = 92$ $k =$ 16
4. $4r + 13 = 57$ $r =$ 11
5. $\frac{z}{4} + 16 = 21$ $z =$ 20
6. $7 = \frac{t}{6} - 3$ $t =$ 60
7. $6q - 18 = 30$ $q =$ 8
8. $\frac{w}{15} + 26 = 42$ $w =$ 240
9. $15u + 18 = 18$ $u =$ 0
10. $9 = 7b - 12$ $b =$ 3
11. $\frac{x}{11} + 21 = 35$ $x =$ 154
12. $\frac{s}{7} - 11 = 17$ $s =$ 196

Explain what was done to the first equation to get the second equation.

13. $\frac{x}{5} - 3 = 12 \rightarrow x = 75$
Add 3 to both sides, then multiply both sides by 5.

14. $6x + 7 = 31 \rightarrow x = 4$
Subtract 7 from both sides, then divide both sides by 6.

15. $\frac{x}{3} + 2 = 4 \rightarrow x = 6$
Subtract 2 from both sides, then multiply both sides by 3.

16. Hideki baked 41 cookies. He gave the same number of cookies to each of 5 friends, saving 11 cookies for himself. How many cookies did each friend receive? 6 cookies

17. **Consumer** Estelle is buying dresses by mail. She pays $65 for each dress, plus a shipping and handling charge of $8 for the entire order. If her order costs $268, how many dresses did she buy? 4 dresses

18. Ms. Juarez planted a 7-ft-tall tree. The height (h) of the tree, in feet, after n years is given by the equation $h = 4n + 7$. In how many years will the height be 39 feet? 8 years

RETEACHING

Name ____________

Alternative Lesson 2-8

Problem-Solving with Two-Step Equations

Some equations involve more than one operation. To solve them, you must "undo" each operation. Always "undo" any addition or subtraction before you "undo" any multiplication or division.

Example

Solve $2d + 1 = 9$.
To solve an equation, you must "undo" what was done to the variable.

The variable (d) was multiplied by 2. Then 1 was added.	$2d + 1 = 9$
"Undo" addition/subtraction first. To "undo" addition of 1, subtract 1 from both sides.	$2d + 1 - \mathbf{1} = 9 - \mathbf{1}$
"Undo" multiplication/division next. To "undo" multiplication by 2, divide both sides by 2.	$\frac{2d}{\mathbf{2}} = \frac{8}{\mathbf{2}}$
So $d = 4$ is the solution to the equation $2d + 1 = 9$.	$d = 4$
Check your work by substituting 4 for d in the equation and solving.	$2 \cdot 4 + 1 \stackrel{?}{=} 4$
Since $9 = 9$, the solution is correct.	$9 = 9$

Try It Solve $7x - 5 = 16$.

a. What must you first do to both sides? Add 5.

b. What must you next do to both sides? Divide by 7.

c. What is the solution? $x = 3$

Solve $12 = \frac{t}{5} + 8$.

d. What must you first do to both sides? Subtract 8.

e. What must you next do to both sides? Multiply by 5.

f. What is the solution? $t = 20$

Solve.

g. $7y - 6 = 8$ $y = 2$ **h.** $81 = 3x - 6$ $x = 29$

i. $\frac{c}{8} + 10 = 15$ $c = 40$ **j.** $2f - 6 = 4$ $f = 5$

k. $4k + 20 = 24$ $k = 1$ **l.** $\frac{e}{5} + 100 = 120$ $e = 100$

2-8 Exercises and Applications

Assignment Guide

- Basic
  1–16, 21–41 odds
- Average
  2–20 evens, 21–25, 28–33, 38–39
- Enriched
  1–4, 5–19 odds, 21–29, 34–41

Exercise Notes

Exercise 4

Test Prep If students selected A, they used subtraction instead of addition after substituting 16 for m. If they selected B, they used multiplication instead of division.

Exercise 23

Science Male ground-dwelling crickets make a chirping sound by rapidly rubbing together the front edge of their wing covers.

Exercise Answers

22. Responses should include the following idea: An equation states that two expressions are equal. If you change one of the expressions, you must change the other in the same way so that they will still be equal.

Reteaching

Activity

Materials: Cups, counters

- Use cups and counters to show the equation $3m = 9$. 3 cups on left, 9 counters on right
- Add 2 counters to each side. What equation is shown now? $3m + 2 = 11$
- What is the first step you would take with the cups and counters to get m by itself? Remove 2 counters from each side. What operation does this represent? Subtract 2
- What is the next step you would take and what operation does it represent? Separate the 9 counters into 3 equal groups, remove 2 of the groups and remove 2 cups from the left side. Divide by 3.
- What is the value of m? $m = 3$

Exercise Answers

25. No; s cannot equal both $3x - 25$ and $3x - 22$ for the same value of x.
26. y should have been 4. Kim probably added 5 on the right instead of subtracting.
27. 4 days
28. First 1 was subtracted from both sides, then both sides were divided by 2.
29. First 6 was subtracted from both sides, then both sides were multiplied by 4.

Alternate Assessment

Portfolio Have students select a problem from this lesson that demonstrates their understanding of using an equation to solve problems.

▶ Quick Quiz

Solve each equation.

1. $10t - 5 = 25$ $t = 3$
2. $\frac{v}{4} + 3 = 9$ $v = 24$
3. $32 = 3x + 5$ $x = 9$

Available on Daily Transparency 2-8

PROBLEM SOLVING 2-8

24. Sara helps sell strawberries at her family's fruit stand. The family pays \$10 a day to rent the stand, and they earn \$0.80 for each basket of strawberries they sell. How much does the family make on a day when they sell 90 baskets of strawberries? \$62

Problem Solving and Reasoning

25. Critical Thinking A man's shoe size (s) is determined by the formula $s = 3x - 25$, where x is the length of the foot in inches. The formula for a woman is $s = 3x - 22$. Is there any value for x that would give the same size for a man and a woman? Explain.

26. Communicate Kim solved this equation for y: $6y + 5 = 29$. She got the answer 5.67, which was incorrect. What should the answer have been and what mistake do you think Kim made?

27. Critical Thinking New skis have been invented to help skiers turn more easily. They are called parabolic, or hourglass, skis. Renting these skis costs \$22 per day plus a flat fee of \$10 for insurance. If Hawke's rental bill was \$98, for how many days did he rent the skis?

Communicate Explain what was done to the first equation to get the second.

28. $2x + 1 = 5 \rightarrow x = 2$ **29.** $\frac{x}{4} + 6 = 10 \rightarrow x = 16$

Mixed Review

Solve each equation. *[Lesson 2-6]*

30. $3 + x = 7$ $x = 4$ **31.** $x - 11 = 15$ $x = 26$ **32.** $6 + x = 13$ $x = 7$ **33.** $123 - x = 47$ $x = 76$

34. $32 - x = 27$ $x = 5$ **35.** $x + 34 = 97$ $x = 63$ **36.** $234 = x + 107$ $x = 127$ **37.** $106 = 963 - x$ $x = 857$

Find a formula relating the variables. *[Lesson 2-3]*

38. $g = 3f$

f	3	4	5	6
g	9	12	15	18

39. $e = d + 4$

d	11	12	13	14
e	15	16	17	18

40. $q = p - 6$

p	7	8	9	10
q	1	2	3	4

41. $y = 9x$

x	2	3	4	5
y	18	27	36	45

PROBLEM SOLVING

Name ______

Guided Problem Solving 2-8

GPS PROBLEM 21, STUDENT PAGE 93

Marco is making a mobile like the one in the diagram. Write an equation to show the mobile balanced. What should each of the small boxes weigh?

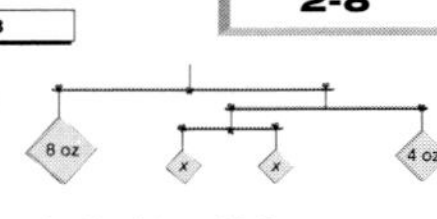

— Understand —

1. What is the total weight of the boxes on each side of the mobile? Explain how you know.
   8 oz, because that is the weight on one side of the mobile and all sides must weigh the same for the mobile to balance.
2. Since the two small boxes are both labeled x, can their weights be different? Explain.
   No. They have the same variable, and a variable can only represent one value in the same problem.

— Plan —

3. What number will stand alone on one side of the equation? 8
4. How many x variables will you have in your equation? 2

— Solve —

5. Write an equation to show that the mobile is balanced. $8 = 2x + 4$
6. What operation will you need to undo first? Addition.
7. What operation will you need to undo second? Multiplication.
8. Solve your equation. What will each of the small boxes weigh? 2 oz

— Look Back —

9. How can you check to see if your answer is reasonable? Possible answer: Use 2 for x and solve the equation to see if it is true.

SOLVE ANOTHER PROBLEM

An adult that weighs 175 lb balances four children on a seesaw. One child weighs 70 lb. The other children weigh the same amount. Write and solve an equation to find the weight of the other children.
$3x + 70 = 175$; $x = 35$; The other children each weigh 35 lb.

ENRICHMENT

Name ______

Extend Your Thinking 2-8

Critical Thinking

Booster Club members are planning a homecoming party. Eula Mae sells twice as many tickets as Carol. Andy sells 4 fewer than Eula Mae. Marcia sells half as many as Carol. Donita sells 3 more than Eula Mae. Alex sells 8 more than Carol. Martha Jane sells 2 fewer than Marcia.

1. Let x represent the number of tickets that Carol sells. Write an expression that shows how many tickets each member sells.
   a. Eula Mae $2x$ b. Andy $2x - 4$
   c. Marcia 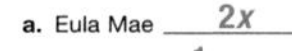 $\frac{1}{2}x$ d. Donita $2x + 3$
   e. Alex $x + 8$ f. Martha Jane $\frac{1}{2}x - 2$
2. Write the expression for the total number of tickets sold.
   $x + 2x + 2x - 4 + \frac{1}{2}x + 2x + 3 + x + 8 + \frac{1}{2}x - 2$

Suppose Carol sold 10 tickets.

3. How many tickets did each of these students sell?
   a. Eula Mae 20 tickets b. Andy 16 tickets
   c. Marcia 5 tickets d. Donita 23 tickets
   e. Alex 18 tickets f. Martha Jane 3 tickets
4. How many tickets were sold in all? 95 tickets

Suppose Eula Mae sold 24 tickets.

5. How many tickets did each of these students sell?
   a. Carol 12 tickets b. Andy 20 tickets
   c. Marcia 6 tickets d. Donita 27 tickets
   e. Alex 20 tickets f. Martha Jane 4 tickets
6. How many tickets were sold in all? 113 tickets

You have learned to solve a variety of equations. Now you will solve a problem using an equation and a Rube Goldberg–type machine.

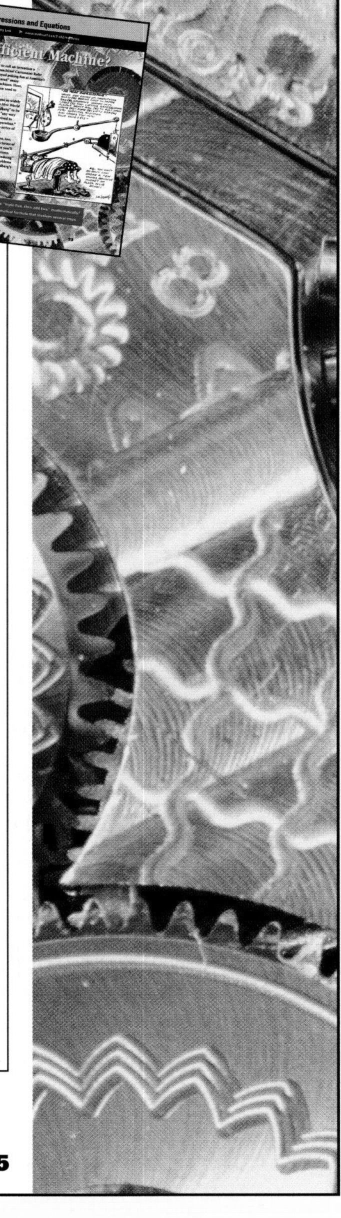

Check It Out!

The last digit in a 12-digit bar code "checks" the accuracy of the first 11 digits. Here's how it works:

M = sum of digits in odd positions

N = sum of digits in even positions (except for the check digit)

4 51702 00836 6

In the bar code shown:

$M = 4 + 1 + 0 + 0 + 8 + 6 \quad M = 19$

$N = 5 + 7 + 2 + 0 + 3 \quad N = 17$

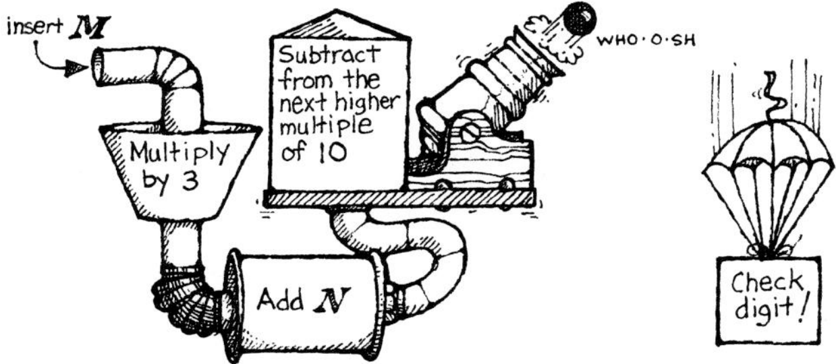

1. Check that the machine sends out the correct check digit for the bar code above. $3 \times 19 + 17 = 74; 80 - 74 = 6$
2. Find the check digit for these bar codes.
   a. 3 21635 00481 ? 3 **b.** 5 90335 26648 ? 1
3. One digit is missing from this bar code: 1 32832 69?25 6
   a. Find N for the bar code. $N = 24$
   b. The sum of $3M$ and N is 84. Write and solve an equation using M, the number 84, and the value of N you found above. $3M + 24 = 84; M = 20$
   c. Explain how you found the missing digit. The sum of M is 20. The sum of the known odd digits is 17. $M = 17 + d$ (d = missing digit) So $d = 3$.

An Efficient Machine?

The Point

In *An Efficient Machine?* on page 73, students discussed machines that involve several actions and likened them to mathematical formulas. Now they will use a set of equations to work through a multiple-step problem.

Resources

Lesson Enhancement Transparency 9

About the Page

- Ask the students where they have seen bar codes and what they think their use is.
- Ask students to list the digits in the odd positions on the bar code and those in the even positions.

Ongoing Assessment

Check that students are able to correctly identify "the next higher multiple of 10."

Extension

Students might enjoy designing a "Rube Goldberg" machine. They might draw and describe one that does homework, cleans up after dinner, hangs up clothes, or turns the lights off. Students with artistic talent might draw a sketch, while others could write a set of directions.

2B Review

Review Correlation

Item(s)	Lesson(s)
1	2-4
2–8	2-5
9–12	2-2
13	2-5
14, 15, 17	2-6
16, 18, 19	2-8
20, 21	2-7
22	2-8
23	2-7
24	2-8

Test Prep

Test-Taking Tip

Tell students to stay as relaxed as possible during a test. In this problem, one of the four answers must be correct, and students can test one value at a time until a true sentence results.

Answers for Review

1. She unfastens her seatbelt, opens the door, stands up, gets out of the car, closes the door.
5. 28 decreased by the number *f*.
6. The sum of the products of 4 and a number *c* and 3 and a number *d*.
7. The product of 6 and the difference of *g* and 8.
8. The quotient of the difference of a number *s* and 3 and the difference of 8 and a number *t*.
13. Possible response: $h + \frac{5}{2} - 4$.

Section 2B Review

REVIEW 2B

1. A driver opens the car door, gets in, sits down, closes the door, and fastens her seatbelt before driving home. Describe the inverse operations she would use after arriving home and turning the engine off.

Write an algebraic expression for each phrase.

2. Seven less than a number *p* $p - 7$

3. *y* dollars more than a price of \$32 $32 + y$

4. The product of a number *h* and the sum of a number *j* and 9 $h(j + 9)$

Write a phrase for each algebraic expression.

5. $28 - f$ **6.** $4c + 3d$ **7.** $6(g - 8)$ **8.** $(s - 3) \div (8 - t)$

Find the value of each expression.

9. $15 - 4 \times 3 - 2$ 1 **10.** $\frac{11 - 3}{2} + 4 \cdot 5$ 24 **11.** $5 \cdot 4 + 3 - 2$ 21 **12.** $12 - \frac{8}{4}$ 10

13.  Write an algebraic expression using each of these three phrases: "increased by," "difference," and "half of."

Solve each equation.

14. $g - 8 = 12$ $g = 20$ **15.** $k + 6 = 14$ $k = 8$ **16.** $16 + 5y = 51$ $y = 7$ **17.** $27 = z - 11$ $z = 38$

18. $6t + 18 = 18$ $t = 0$ **19.** $3x - 5 = 1$ $x = 2$ **20.** $21 = 3q$ $q = 7$ **21.** $7 = \frac{k}{7}$ $k = 49$

22. Ken went rowing. The rental was \$6.00 for the first hour and \$4.50 for each hour after that. If Ken's rental was \$24.00, how long did he row? 5 hours

23. Science Physicists use the formula $F = ma$ to relate force (F), mass (m), and acceleration (a). Substitute 20 for F and 5 for a, then solve to find the mass. $m = 4$

Test Prep

When you are asked to find the correct solution to an equation, it may be quickest to substitute each of the given values into the equation and see which one works.

24. Which of these numbers is the solution to $8w - 9 = 15$? C

Ⓐ 24 Ⓑ 1 Ⓒ 3 Ⓓ 0.75

Resources

Practice Masters
Section 2B Review

Assessment Sourcebook
Quiz 2B

 *TestWorks*
Test and Practice Software

PRACTICE

Name ____________________ Practice

Section 2B Review

1. Before gym class, Scott takes off his boots, takes off his jeans, puts on his shorts, and puts on his shoes. Describe the inverse operations he would use after class.
take off shoes, take off shorts, put on jeans, put on boots

Write an algebraic expression for each phrase.

2. Fourteen less than a number (*g*) $g - 14$
3. Eight more than the product of a number (*k*) and ten $10k + 8$

Write a phrase for each algebraic expression.

4. $15x$ the product of fifteen and a number (*x*)
5. $d + 17$ the sum of a number (*d*) and 17

Find the value of each expression.

6. $3 + 6 \times 4 =$ 27 7. $\frac{23 - 5}{4 + 2} =$ 3 8. $3 \times 4 - \frac{35}{5} =$ 5

Solve each equation.

9. $5s = 45$ $s =$ 9 10. $y - 12 = 31$ $y =$ 43 11. $2x + 8 = 46$ $x =$ 19 12. $\frac{w}{7} - 3 = 10$ $w =$ 91

13. An online service charges \$10.00 for the first 5 hours in a month, and \$2.50 for each additional hour. If Seth's bill is \$22.50, how many hours did he use the service?
10 hours

14. Draw a bar graph to show the number of registered motorcycles (in thousands) in several states in 1990. *[Lesson 1-2]*

State	CA	FL	NY	TX	WA
Reg. motorcycles	627	206	196	175	216

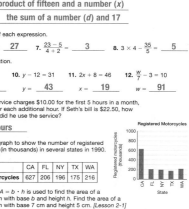

15. The formula $A = b \cdot h$ is used to find the area of a parallelogram with base *b* and height *h*. Find the area of a parallelogram with base 7 cm and height 5 cm. *[Lesson 2-1]*
35 cm^2

Extend Key Ideas Algebra

Functions

A function is a relationship between numbers. You can think of the function as taking a number and transforming it into another number.

Function machines can be a useful way to think about functions. This machine seems to be using the rule "double it" to decide which number it puts out.

The equation that represents the "double it" function can be written as $y = 2x$. The input number is x and the output number is y.

When you know the equation for the function, you can substitute an input (x) value to find the output (y) value that goes with it.

If $y = 3x + 5$, what's the y-value for an x-value of 2?

$y = 3(\mathbf{2}) + 5$ Substitute 2 for x.
$y = 6 + 5$ Multiply.
$y = 11$ Add.

Try It

Evaluate each function for the given values.

1. $y = 5x$ for $x = 1, 2,$ and 3
2. $y = x + 2$ for $x = 6, 8,$ and 10
3. $y = 2x - 1$ for $x = 5, 7,$ and 9
4. $y = 4x + 2$ for $x = 2, 3,$ and 4

Think of each table as a function machine. Copy and complete each one. Then write an equation for the table.

5.

x	1	2	3	4	5
y	5	10	15		

6.

x	1	2	3	4	5
y	3	5	7		

97

Extend Key Ideas

Functions

The Point

Students learn that a function can be thought of as a rule that is applied to one number to get another number.

About the Page

- Make sure students understand that the input number, x, is substituted in the equation to obtain the output number, y.
- Explain that for each input number, a function will yield exactly one output number.

Ask ...

- How would you write the "triple it" function? When the input is 4, what is the output? $y = 3x$; 12
- How would you write the "add 5" function? When the input is 2, what is the output? $y = x + 5$; 7

Extension

Explain that the notation "f(x)" can be used to write a function. For example, $f(x) = 2x + 5$ is the algebraic way of writing "Multiply the number x by 2 and then add 5." To evaluate this function when x is 9, write $f(9) = 2(9) + 5 = 23$. Have students evaluate $f(x) = 8x - 5$ for f(3), f(2), and f(1). 19; 11; 3

Answers for Try It

1. $x = 1, y = 5; x = 2, y = 10; x = 3, y = 15$
2. $x = 6, y = 8; x = 8, y = 10; x = 10, y = 12$
3. $x = 5, y = 9; x = 7, y = 13; x = 9, y = 17$
4. $x = 2, y = 10; x = 3, y = 14; x = 4, y = 18$
5.

x	1	2	3	4	5
y	5	10	15	20	25

Equation: $y = 5x$

6.

x	1	2	3	4	5
y	3	5	7	9	11

Equation: $y = 2x + 1$

Chapter 2 Summary and Review

Review Correlation

Item(s)	Lesson(s)
1, 2	2-1
3–6	2-2
7, 8	2-3
9, 12	2-4
10, 14, 16	2-7
11, 13, 15, 17	2-6
18, 19, 21	2-8
20, 22	2-5

For additional review, see page 673.

Answers for Review

1. 20 ft^2
2. It will cost $20 to travel 6 miles.

Chapter 2 Summary and Review

Graphic Organizer

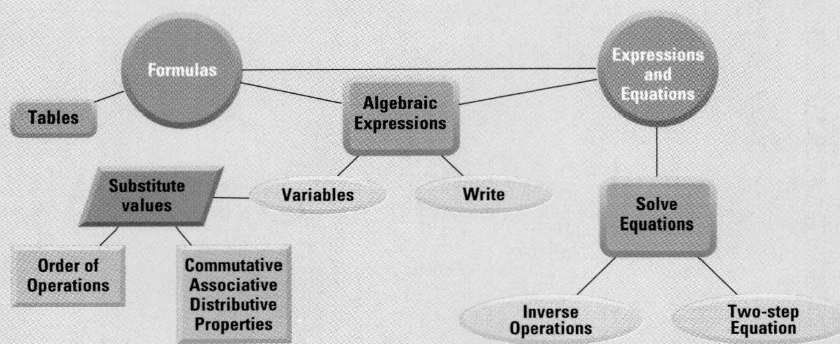

Section 2A Formulas

Summary

- A **formula** is a rule showing relationships among quantities. A **variable** represents a quantity whose values may change. Formulas usually contain variables.
- An **expression** can be made up of variables and/or numbers and operations.
- You must do operations in the correct order. First do operations in parentheses, or above or below a division bar, then multiplication and division, from left to right, and finally addition and subtraction from left to right.
- Along with order-of-operation rules, the **commutative, associative,** and **distributive properties** will help you find the values of expressions.
- You can use a formula to make a table of values.

Review

1. The formula $A = \frac{1}{2}bh$ gives the area of a triangle. Find the area of a triangle with base (b) 8 ft and height (h) 5 ft.

2. A taxi ride costs $2 plus $3 for each mile. Let $C = 3m + 2$, where C is the cost and m is the number of miles. How much will it cost to travel 6 miles?

Resources

Practice Masters
Cumulative Review Chapters 1–2

PRACTICE

Name ______________________ **Practice**

Cumulative Review Chapters 1–2

Use the circle graph to answer each question. *[Lesson 1-1]*

1. About what percent of American kids are white? 67%
2. List the ethnic groups in order from the largest to the smallest. White, African American, Latino Asian/Pacific Islander, Native American

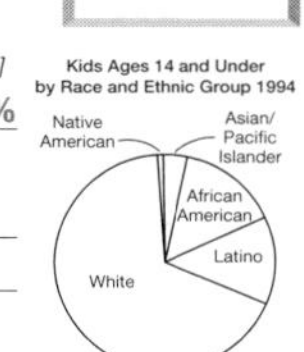

Find the mean, median, and mode(s) for each set of data. *[Lesson 1-4]*

3. 35, 26, 28, 26, 31, 35, 29
   Mean 30
   Median 29
   Mode(s) 26, 35
4. 161, 163, 186, 163, 172, 193
   Mean 173
   Median 167.5
   Mode(s) 163

Find the value of each expression. *[Lesson 2-2]*

5. $7 \times 4 - 6 \times 3$ 10
6. $7(6 - 5) + 2$ 9
7. $(8 - 3) \div (4 + 1)$ 1
8. $\frac{12}{3} - \frac{18}{9}$ 2
9. $\frac{20 + 10}{10 - 5}$ 6
10. $25 - 3 \cdot \frac{33}{11}$ 16

Write a phrase for each algebraic expression. *[Lesson 2-5]*

11. $2 + 7t$ the sum of 2 and the product of 7 and a number (t)
12. $\frac{4}{5 + x}$ the quotient of 4 and the sum of 5 and a number (x)
13. $3(8 + r)$ the product of 3 and the sum of 8 and a number (r)

Solve each equation. Check your answer. *[Lesson 2-8]*

14. $3x - 10 = 35$ $x =$ 15
15. $12 = 7c - 9$ $c =$ 3
16. $62 = 6g + 14$ $g =$ 8
17. $10k - 18 = 32$ $k =$ 5
18. $\frac{m}{6} + 5 = 21$ $m =$ 96
19. $11 = \frac{z}{4} - 10$ $z =$ 84

Section 2A Formulas *continued*

3. Find the value of $3 + 4 \times 5$.

4. Find the value of $5 \times (6 - 2) \div 2$.

5. Tell which operation you would do first to evaluate $\frac{(5+4) \times 6}{18}$.

6. Which property is suggested by the formulas $P = 2l + 2w$ and $P = 2(l + w)$?

7. Find a formula relating the variables.

x	1	2	3	4	5	6	7
y	4	8	12	16	20	24	28

8. Use the formula $d = rt$ to make a table of values showing the distance (d) traveled in 0, 1, 2, 3, 4, and 5 hours (t) at a rate (r) of 40 mi/hr.

Section 2B Expressions and Equations

Summary

- Addition and subtraction and, likewise, multiplication and division are called **inverse operations** because they undo each other.
- An **algebraic expression** is an expression that contains a variable.
- An **equation** is a statement that two expressions are equal.
- To **solve** an equation containing a variable means to find the value of the variable that makes the equation true.
- You can use inverse operations to solve addition, subtraction, multiplication, and division equations.
- Some equations contain more than one operation, so you will need to use two or more inverse operations to solve them.

Review

9. Name the inverse of flying 260 miles north.

10. Tell if 35 is a solution to $p \div 5 = 7$.

11. Write and solve an equation for the statement: The number of dogs (d) increased by 7 is 23.

12. A number is divided by 11. What operation is needed to return to the original number?

13. Tell if 18 is a solution to $x + 6 = 26$.

14. Solve $25x = 325$. Check your solution.

15. Solve $a + 15 = 32$. Check your solution.

16. Solve $8 = \frac{n}{12}$. Check your solution.

17. Solve $108 = x - 27$. Check your solution.

18. Solve $\frac{x}{5} - 3 = 21$. Check your solution.

19. Eighteen is added to a number. The result is multiplied by 3. What operations are needed to return to the original number?

20. Write algebraic expressions for
a. 21 more than a number (k).
b. The product of 10 and a number (u).

21. Solve $3x - 5 = 16$. Check your solution.

22. Write a phrase for
a. $5z$ **b.** $12(j - 4)$ **c.** $\frac{d + 5}{14}$

Answers for Review

3. 23
4. 10
5. Addition
6. The Distributive Property
7. $y = 4x$
8.

Time (t) in hr	0	1	2	3	4	5
Distance (d) in mi	0	40	80	120	160	200

9. Flying 260 miles south.
10. Yes, $p = 35$
11. $d + 7 = 23$; $d = 16$ dogs
12. Multiplication by 11.
13. No, $x \neq 18$
14. $x = 13$
15. $a = 17$
16. $n = 96$
17. $x = 135$
18. $x = 120$
19. Divide by 3, then subtract 18.
20. a. $k + 21$
    b. $10u$
21. $x = 7$
22. a. The product of 5 and a number z.
    b. The product of 12 and 4 less than a number j.
    c. The quotient of a number d increased by 5 divided by 14.

Chapter 2 Assessment

Assessment Correlation

Item(s)	Lesson(s)
1, 13	2-1
2, 6	2-3
3, 11	2-2
4, 7	2-5
5, 12	2-4
8, 10	2-8
9	2-6, 2-7
14	2-7
15–18	2-2

Answers for Assessment

1. $V = 480\text{ in}^3$
2.

Time (t) in hr	0	1	2	3	4
Distance (d) in km	0	15	30	45	60

3. 52
4. The sum of x and 12, divided by 8.
5. 18
6. $y = x - 6$
7. a. $k - 32$ b. $3(g - 5)$
8. No; There is no number that, after multiplying by 3, can have the same result when 11 is added to it and when 7 is subtracted from it.
9. a. $x = 38$ b. $x = 84$
10. a. $a = 13$ b. $k = 360$
11. Multiplication
12. Multiplication by 12, then addition of 23.
13. $102
14. $3m = 2100$; $m = 700$
15. $10 + 14 \div (2 + 5) = 12$
16. $(10 + 14) \div 2 + 5 = 17$
17. $(36 \div 6 + 6) \div 2 = 6$
18. $36 \div (6 + 6 \div 2) = 4$

Answers for Performance Task on page 101.

Chapter 2 Assessment

1. You can use the formula $V = lwh$ to find the volume of a box. Find the volume (V) of a box with length (l) 12 in., width (w) 8 in., and height (h) 5 in.

2. Shelly is riding a bicycle at a rate (r) of 15 km/hr. Use the formula $d = rt$ to make a table of values showing the distance (d) traveled in 0, 1, 2, 3, and 4 hours (t).

3. Find the value of $8 \times 7 - 20 \div 5$.

4. Write a phrase for $\frac{x + 12}{8}$.

5. If 18 is entered into this inverse operation machine, what will be the result?

6. Find a formula relating the variables.

x	10	11	12	13	14	15
y	4	5	6	7	8	9

7. Write algebraic expressions for

a. Thirty-two less than a number k.

b. Three times the difference between a number g and five.

8. Can you find one value for the variable w that will make both equations true?

$3w + 11 = 20$ $\quad$ $3w - 7 = 20$

Explain your thinking.

9. Solve and check your solution.

a. $65 = x + 27$ $\quad$ **b.** $x \div 3 = 28$

10. Solve and check your solution.

a. $4a - 15 = 37$ $\quad$ **b.** $23 = \frac{k}{12} - 7$

11. Which operation would you do first?

$\frac{100}{18 \times 2} - 26$

12. Twenty-three is subtracted from a number. The result is divided by 12. What operations are needed to return to the original number?

13. A mail-order company sells compact discs for $14 each, with a $4 shipping charge for the entire order. Let $C = 14d + 4$, where C is the cost and d is the number of discs. Athena placed an order for 7 discs. How much will she have to pay?

14. Raul drove 2100 miles in 3 days. He drove the same number of miles each day. Write and solve an equation to find the number of miles he drove each day.

Copy each statement. Insert parentheses to make each sentence true.

15. $10 + 14 \div 2 + 5 = 12$

16. $10 + 14 \div 2 + 5 = 17$

17. $36 \div 6 + 6 \div 2 = 6$

18. $36 \div 6 + 6 \div 2 = 4$

Performance Task

Consider the expression $3 + 5 \times 4 - 1 \times 2$. Find all possible ways to insert a single pair of parentheses and evaluate the expression. For example, $3 + (5 \times 4 - 7) \times 2 = 29$. How many different ways of evaluating the expression can you find?

100 *Chapter 2 • The Language of Algebra, Formulas, Expressions, and Equations*

Performance Assessment Key

See key on page 53.

Resources

Assessment Sourcebook

Chapter 2 Tests
- Forms A and B (free response)
- Form C (multiple choice)
- Form D (performance assessment)
- Form E (mixed response)
- Form F (cumulative chapter test)

TestWorks
Test and Practice Software

Home and Community Connections
- Letter Home for Chapter 2 in English and Spanish

Suggested Scoring Rubric

4
- Correctly shows 10 different placements of parentheses.
- Follows the order of operations to correctly evaluate each expression.

3
- Correctly shows 6–9 different placements of parentheses.
- Follows the order of operations to correctly evaluate each expression written.

2
- Correctly shows 3–5 different placements of parentheses.
- Attempts to follow the order of operations, but has some difficulty.

1
- Correctly shows 2 or fewer different placements of parentheses.
- Does not follow the order of operations.

Cumulative Review Chapters 1–2 Test Prep

Multiple Choice

Choose the best answer.

1. Which type of graph is the best choice for displaying a corporation's profits over the last five years? *[Lessons 1-1, 1-3, 1-5]*

Ⓐ Circle graph Ⓑ Line graph
Ⓒ Line plot Ⓓ Stem-and-leaf plot

2. Consider the data 2, 5, 3, 7, 5, 4, 3, 6, 3, 7. Which of the following is 4.5? *[Lesson 1-4]*

Ⓐ Mean Ⓑ Mean and median
Ⓒ Mode and mean Ⓓ Median

3. The scatterplot shows the daily high and low temperatures in Junction City over a 2-week period. The low temperature the next day was 43°. Use the scatterplot to give the best estimate of the high temperature on that day. *[Lesson 1-7]*

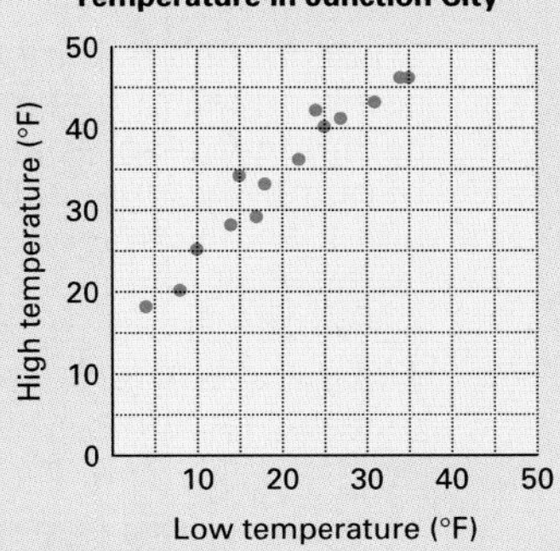

Ⓐ 30° Ⓑ 45° Ⓒ 55° Ⓓ 70°

4. Use the formula $h = \frac{m}{60}$ to relate minutes (m) and hours (h). How many hours are equal to 240 minutes? *[Lesson 2-1]*

Ⓐ 4 hr Ⓑ 180 hr
Ⓒ 300 hr Ⓓ 14,400 hr

5. What property is suggested by the equation $(3 + 4) + 5 = 3 + (4 + 5)$? *[Lesson 2-2]*

Ⓐ Distributive property
Ⓑ Associative property of addition
Ⓒ Order of operations
Ⓓ Commutative property of addition

6. Which formula was used to create the table? *[Lesson 2-3]*

x	3	4	5	6	7
y	9	12	15	18	21

Ⓐ $x = 3y$ Ⓑ $y = x + 6$
Ⓒ $y = \frac{x}{3}$ Ⓓ $y = 3x$

7. Thirty-five is added to a number. What operation is needed to return to the original number? *[Lesson 2-4]*

Ⓐ Divide by 35 Ⓑ Multiply by 35
Ⓒ Subtract 35 Ⓓ Subtract from 35

8. Which expression shows 5 less than twice a number (n)? *[Lesson 2-5]*

Ⓐ $2n - 5$ Ⓑ $2 \times (n - 5)$
Ⓒ $5 - 2n$ Ⓓ $n - 2 \times 5$

9. Solve $x + 15 = 53$. *[Lesson 2-6]*

Ⓐ 705 Ⓑ 62
Ⓒ 38 Ⓓ 32

10. Solve $2y - 3 = 17$. *[Lesson 2-7]*

Ⓐ $y = 10$ Ⓑ $y = 7$
Ⓒ $y = 40$ Ⓓ $y = 25.5$

Answers for Performance Task (page 100)

The ten possible ways are:

$(3 + 5) \times 4 - 1 \times 2 = 30$

$3 + (5 \times 4) - 1 \times 2 = 21$

$3 + 5 \times (4 - 1) \times 2 = 33$

$3 + 5 \times 4 - (1 \times 2) = 21$

$(3 + 5 \times 4) - 1 \times 2 = 21$

$3 + (5 \times 4 - 1) \times 2 = 41$

$3 + 5 \times (4 - 1 \times 2) = 13$

$(3 + 5 \times 4 - 1) \times 2 = 44$

$3 + (5 \times 4 - 1 \times 2) = 21$

$(3 + 5 \times 4 - 1 \times 2) = 21$

Cumulative Review Test Prep

About Multiple-Choice Tests

The Cumulative Review, found at the end of Chapters 2, 4, 6, 8, 10, and 12, can be used to prepare students for standardized tests.

Students sometimes do not perform as well on standardized tests as they do on other tests. There may be several reasons for this that are related to the format and content of the test.

- **Format**
Students may have limited experience with multiple-choice tests. For some questions, such tests are harder because having options may confuse the student.

- **Content**
A standardized test may cover a broader range of content than normally covered on a test, and the relative emphasis given to various strands may be different from that given in class. Also, some questions may assess general aptitude or thinking skills and not include specific pieces of mathematical content.

It is important not to let the differences between standardized tests and other tests shake your students' confidence.

Answers for Review

1. B
2. B
3. C
4. A
5. B
6. D
7. C
8. A
9. C
10. A

Chapter 3

▶ OVERVIEW

Number Sense

Decimals and Fractions

Section 3A

Decimal Concepts: Estimating and Solving Equations: Students compare, order, and round decimals and solve equations containing decimals. Students write numbers in scientific notation.

3–1 Place Value: Comparing and Ordering Decimals

3–2 Estimating by Rounding

3–3 Problem Solving: Sums and Differences of Decimals

3–4 Problem Solving: Products and Quotients of Decimals

3–5 Powers of 10 and Scientific Notation

Section 3B

Fraction Concepts: Students find the greatest common factor and least common multiple of pairs of numbers, write equivalent fractions in lowest terms, order fractions, convert fractions to decimals, and convert decimals to fractions.

3–6 Divisibility and Prime Factorization

3–7 GCF and LCM

3–8 Equivalent Fractions and Lowest Terms

3–9 Comparing and Ordering Fractions

3–10 Converting Between Fractions and Decimals

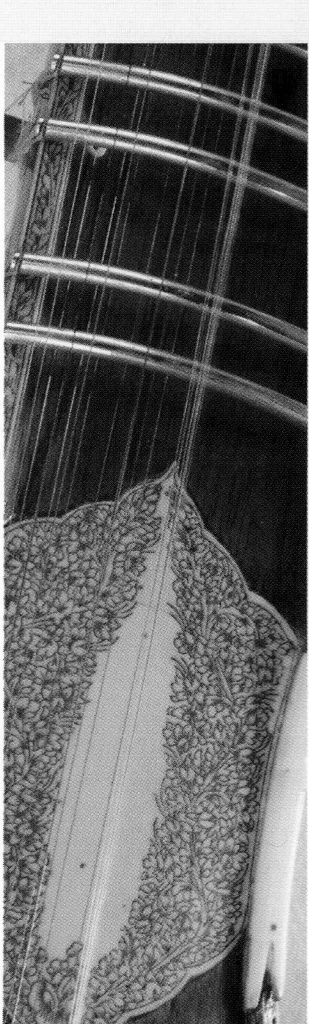

Meeting NCTM Standards

Curriculum Standards

STANDARD

Standard			pages
1	**Problem Solving**	Skills and Strategies	104, 114, 121, 129, *137,* 138, 148, 150, *152*
		Applications	108–109, 113–114, 118–119, 123–124, 128–129, 131, 137–138, 142–143, 147–148, 151–152, 155–156
		Exploration	106, 110, 115, 120, 125, 134, 139, 144, 149, 153
2	**Communication**	Oral	105, 108, *109,* 112, 117, 122, 127, 133, 136, 142, 146, *148,* 151, 154
		Written	104, 109, *114,* 118, 119, 124, *129,* 132, 138, 143, 152, 156, 158
		Cooperative Learning	*106, 110, 115, 120, 125, 133, 134, 136, 139, 144, 149, 153*
3	**Reasoning**	Critical Thinking	109, 114, 119, 124, 129, 138, 143, 148, 152, 156
4	**Connections**	Mathematical	See Standards 5–10, 13 below.
		Interdisciplinary	Language 102, 145, 154; Industry 147; History 107, 122, 136; Consumer 108, *119,* 132; Social Studies 103, 113, 129; Career 114, 142; Sports 118, *148*; Literature 103, *122,* 129; Music 133, *136,* 140, 143, *146,* 149, 151, 155, 157, 158; Science 102, *105,* 108, *112,* 114, 116, *117,* 118, 123, 124, 127, 128, 132, 136, 137, 141, 148, 151, 155
		Technology	*105,* 112, 116, 125, 130, *133,* 145, 153, 155
		Cultural	102, *127*
5	**Number and Number Relationships**		106, 137, 153–156
6	**Number Systems and Number Theory**		106–109, 115–129, 134–152, 159
7	**Computation and Estimation**		110–124, 126, 129, 132, *140,* 143, 148
8	**Patterns and Functions**		129, 134, 142, *153, 155,* 159
9	**Algebra**		109, 115–124
10	**Statistics**		131, 148
13	**Measurement**		123

Italic type indicates Teacher Edition reference.

Teaching Standards

Focus on Tools for Discourse

Teachers should value and encourage the use of a variety of tools for exploring mathematics. This includes having students use

- computers, calculators, and other technology.
- concrete materials such as models.
- pictures, diagrams, tables, and graphs.

Assessment Standards

Focus on Equity

Journals Equitable assessment practices give each student the opportunity to display his or her own learning. Written journal responses give students the chance to explain their reasoning, provide partial solutions to problems or formulate new problems which extend the question being asked. Journal writing in Chapter 3 has students

- use scientific notation.
- find prime factorizations.
- convert fractions to decimals.

TECHNOLOGY

For the Teacher

- **Teacher Resource Planner CD-ROM**
  Use the teacher planning CD-ROM to view resources available for Chapter 3. You can prepare custom lesson plans or use the default lesson plans provided.

- **World Wide Web**
  Visit **www.teacher.mathsurf.com** for links to lesson plans from teachers and other professionals, NCTM information, and other sites.

- **TestWorks**
  TestWorks provides ready-made tests and can create custom tests and practice worksheets.

For the Parent

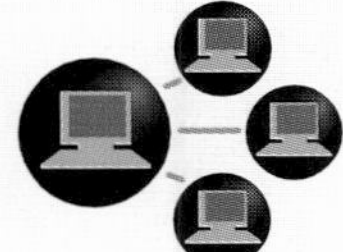

- **World Wide Web**
  Parents can use the Web site at **www.parent.mathsurf.com.**

For the Student

- **Interactive CD-ROM**
  Lesson 3-6 has an *Interactive CD-ROM Lesson*. The *Interactive CD-ROM Journal* and *Interactive CD-ROM Spreadsheet/Grapher Tool* are also used in Chapter 3.

- **Wide World of Mathematics**
  Lesson 3-1 Middle School: In 0.01 Second
  Lesson 3-5 Middle School: Hubble Telescope
  Lesson 3-5 Algebra: Breaking the German Code

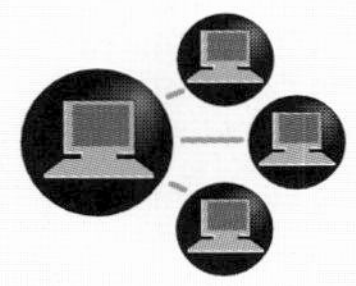

- **World Wide Web**
  Use with Chapter and Section Openers; Students can go online to the Scott Foresman-Addison Wesley Web site at **www.mathsurf.com/7/ch3** to collect information about chapter themes.

STANDARDIZED - TEST CORRELATION

SECTION 3A

LESSON	OBJECTIVE	ITBS Form M	CTBS 4th Ed.	CAT 5th Ed.	SAT 9th Ed.	MAT 7th Ed.	Your Form
3–1	• Compare and order decimals.	✘		✘	✘	✘	
3–2	• Round to the nearest decimal place.	✘	✘	✘	✘	✘	
	• Estimate by rounding to whole numbers.	✘	✘		✘	✘	
	• Use front-end estimation and compatible numbers to estimate.	✘	✘	✘	✘	✘	
3–3	• Solve addition and subtraction equations containing decimals.	✘	✘	✘	✘	✘	
3–4	• Multiply and divide decimal numbers.	✘	✘	✘	✘	✘	
	• Solve multiplication and division equations containing decimals.	✘	✘	✘		✘	
3–5	• Use exponents to write powers of 10.	✘	✘		✘		
	• Write large numbers in scientific notation.						

SECTION 3B

LESSON	OBJECTIVE	ITBS Form M	CTBS 4th Ed.	CAT 5th Ed.	SAT 9th Ed.	MAT 7th Ed.	Your Form
3–6	• Test for divisibility.	✘	✘	✘	✘	✘	
	• Write any number as a product of primes.		✘		✘	✘	
3–7	• Find the greatest common factor of a pair of numbers.				✘	✘	
	• Find the least common multiple of a pair of numbers.			✘	✘	✘	
3–8	• Write equivalent fractions.	✘	✘	✘	✘	✘	
	• Rewrite fractions in lowest terms.	✘	✘	✘	✘	✘	
3–9	• Compare the values of fractions.	✘		✘	✘	✘	
	• Order fractions.	✘		✘	✘	✘	
3–10	• Convert fractions to decimals.			✘		✘	
	• Convert decimals to fractions.			✘		✘	

Key: ITBS - Iowa Test of Basic Skills; CTBS - Comprehensive Test of Basic Skills; CAT - California Achievement Test; SAT - Stanford Achievement Test; MAT - Metropolitan Achievement Test

ASSESSMENT PROGRAM

Traditional Assessment

QUICK QUIZZES	SECTION REVIEW	CHAPTER REVIEW	CHAPTER ASSESSMENT FREE RESPONSE	CHAPTER ASSESSMENT MULTIPLE CHOICE	CUMULATIVE REVIEW
TE: pp. 109, 114, 119, 124, 129, 138, 143, 148, 152, 156	SE: pp. 132, 158 *Quiz 3A, 3B	SE: pp. 160–161	SE: p. 162 *Ch. 3 Tests Forms A, B, E	*Ch. 3 Tests Forms C, E	SE: p. 163 *Ch. 3 Tests Form F Quarterly Test Ch. 1–3

Alternate Assessment

INTERVIEW	JOURNAL	ONGOING	PERFORMANCE	PORTFOLIO	PROJECT	SELF
TE: pp. 109, 148	SE: pp. 109, 114, 118, 132, 138, 152, 156, 158 TE: pp. 114, 129, 138, 143, 156	TE: pp. 106, 110, 115, 120, 125, 134, 139, 144, 149, 153	SE: pp. 162, 163 TE: p. 124 *Ch. 3 Tests Forms D, E	TE: p. 152	SE: pp. 124, 143 TE: p. 103	TE: p. 119

*Tests and quizzes are in *Assessment Sourcebook*. Test Form E is a mixed response test. Forms for Alternate Assessment are also available in *Assessment Sourcebook*.

TestWorks: Test and Practice Software

MIDDLE SCHOOL PACING CHART

REGULAR PACING

Day	5 classes per week
1	Chapter 3 Opener; Problem Solving Focus
2	Section **3A** Opener; Lesson **3–1**
3	Lesson **3–2**
4	Lesson **3–3**
5	Lesson **3–4**
6	Lesson **3–5**; Technology
7	**3A** Connect; **3A** Review
8	Section **3B** Opener; Lesson **3–6**
9	Lesson **3–7**
10	Lesson **3–8**
11	Lesson **3–9**
12	Lesson **3–10**
13	**3B** Connect; **3B** Review; Extend Key Ideas
14	Chapter 3 Summary and Review
15	Chapter 3 Assessment
16	Cumulative Review, Chapters 1–3

BLOCK SCHEDULING OPTIONS

Block Scheduling for Complete Course

Chapter 3 may be presented in

- ten 90-minute blocks
- thirteen 75-minute blocks

Each block consists of a combination of

- Chapter and Section Openers
- Explores
- Lesson Development
- Problem Solving Focus
- Technology
- Extend Key Ideas
- Connect
- Review
- Assessment

For details, see *Block Scheduling Handbook*.

Block Scheduling for Interdisciplinary Course

Each block integrates math with another subject area.

In Chapter 3, interdisciplinary topics include

- Astronomy
- Music

Themes for Interdisciplinary Team Teaching 3A and 3B are

- Asteroids
- Musical Instruments

For details, see *Block Scheduling Handbook*.

Block Scheduling for Lab-Based Course

In each block, 30–40 minutes is devoted to lab activities including

- Explores in the Student Edition
- Connect pages in the Student Edition
- Technology options in the Student Edition
- Reteaching Activities in the Teacher Edition

For details, see *Block Scheduling Handbook*.

Block Scheduling for Course with *Connected Mathematics*

In each block, replacement units including activities from **Connected Mathematics** replace or enhance the lessons in Chapter 3.

Connected Mathematics topics for Chapter 3 can be found in

- *Data Around Us*
- *Comparing and Scaling*
- *Moving Straight Ahead*

For details, see *Block Scheduling Handbook*.

INTERDISCIPLINARY BULLETIN BOARD

Set Up

On a bulletin board draw musical scores for the beginning measures of simple tunes. Explain the fraction at the left: the top number indicates beats per measure, the bottom number tells which type of note has one beat. In other words, in $\frac{4}{4}$ time, a measure has 4 beats and a quarter note gets one beat. Include a table showing a whole note, half note, quarter note, and eighth note.

Procedure

- Have pairs of students choose a measure from one of the songs and write in the appropriate fraction for each note.
- Have the students add the fractional parts of the notes in the measure to see if they equal the number of beats indicated by the top number of the meter signature found at the beginning of the score.

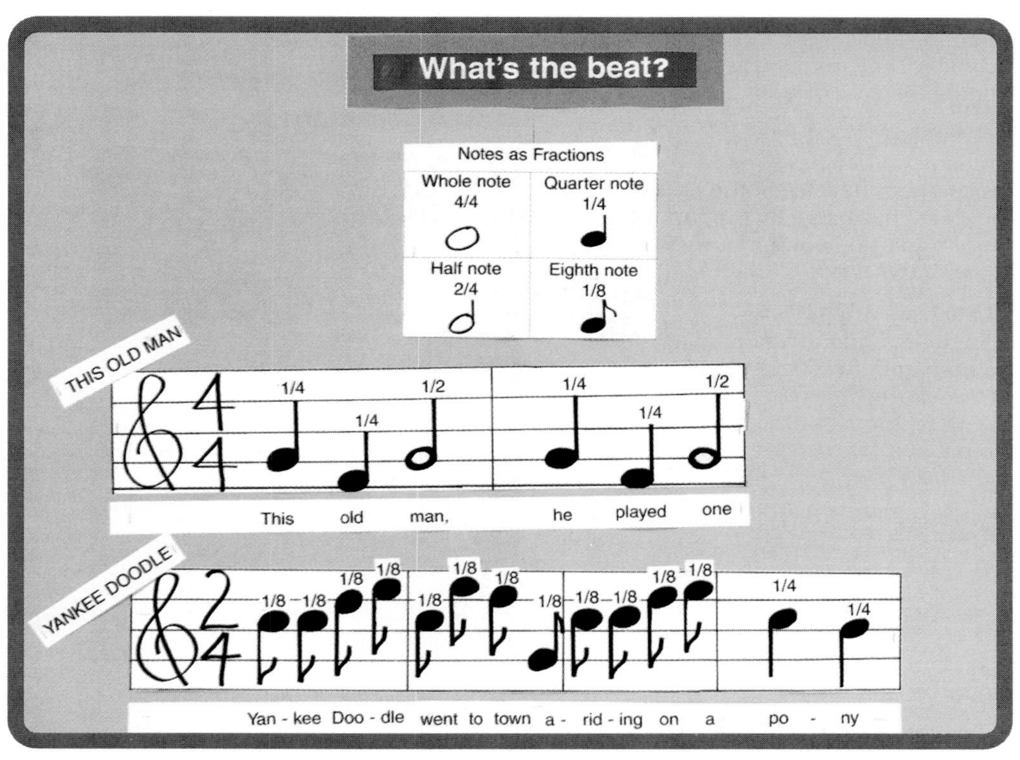

Chapter 3

The information on these pages shows how very large numbers are used in real-world situations.

World Wide Web

If your class has access to the World Wide Web, you might want to use the information found at the Web site addresses given.

Extensions

The following activities do not require access to the World Wide Web.

Entertainment
Suggest that students work in groups and investigate the letters in a Scrabble game, noting their values and how many of each letter there are. Challenge them to compete among themselves to create words with up to seven letters that have the greatest value.

Science
Have interested students interview an engineer to find out his or her specialty, what kind of work the job entails, and how mathematics is used.

People of the World
Ask students to find out how they would make an international direct dial telephone call to a country of their choice. They might also investigate the cost of such a call.

Arts & Literature
Ask students if they have read *Jurassic Park* or have seen the movie. Have these students report on their impressions of the book or movie to the class.

Social Studies
Have students find Calcutta, India, on the map and investigate facts about the city, such as its population, climate, tourist attractions, and so on.

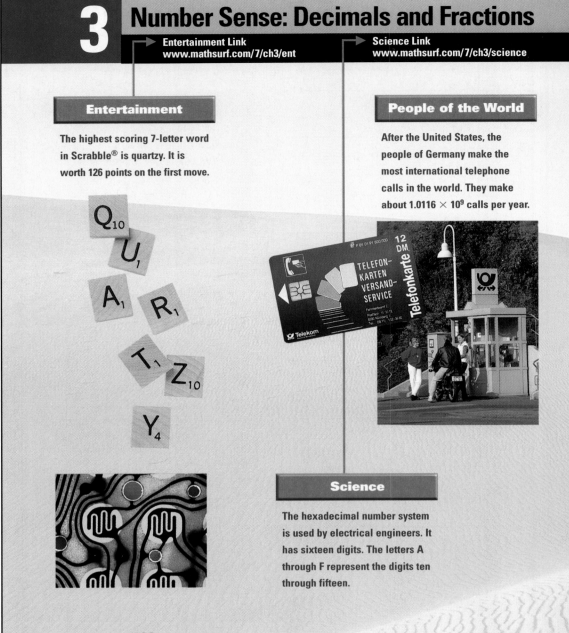

3 Number Sense: Decimals and Fractions

Entertainment Link
www.mathsurf.com/7/ch3/ent

Science Link
www.mathsurf.com/7/ch3/science

Entertainment

The highest scoring 7-letter word in Scrabble® is quartzy. It is worth 126 points on the first move.

People of the World

After the United States, the people of Germany make the most international telephone calls in the world. They make about 1.0116×10^9 calls per year.

Science

The hexadecimal number system is used by electrical engineers. It has sixteen digits. The letters A through F represent the digits ten through fifteen.

102

TEACHER TALK

Meet Allison Harris

Seattle Public Schools
Seattle, Washington

Often students have difficulty connecting their work with fractions to similar situations involving decimals. To develop good number sense about the relationships between decimals and fractions, and to help students create a model they can use for reference, I use their prior knowledge about money.

As part of daily warm-up exercises, I ask students to estimate the decimal representation for fractions of a dollar. Since they know that $\frac{1}{4}$ of a dollar is a quarter and can be recorded as $0.25, I challenge them to estimate the decimal notation for $\frac{1}{8}$ of a dollar using what they already know about the relationship between $\frac{1}{4}$ and $\frac{1}{8}$. To increase the challenge, I may name a coin and ask for both the fraction and the decimal it represents.

Arts & Literature Link
www.mathsurf.com/7/ch3/arts

Arts & Literature

Michael Crichton's best-selling novel, *Jurassic Park,* has sold over 10^6 copies.

Social Studies

The world's largest university is the University of Calcutta, India. It has 300,000 students.

KEY MATH IDEAS

When multiplying or dividing decimal numbers, you must be careful to locate the **decimal point** in the answer correctly.

Scientific notation uses decimal numbers and powers to express very large or very small numbers conveniently.

One number is a factor of another if it divides that number with no remainder. A **prime number** has only two factors, one and itself.

To compare two fractions, first write them with a **common denominator**. The fraction with the larger numerator is greater.

CHAPTER PROJECT

In this project, you will make a display that shows the number of animals of a certain type (species) that might exist after several generations. Begin the project by thinking of an animal species you would like to research.

103

PROJECT ASSESSMENT

You may choose to use this project as a performance assessment for the chapter.

Performance Assessment Key

Level 4 Full Accomplishment

Level 3 Substantial Accomplishment

Level 2 Partial Accomplishment

Level 1 Little Accomplishment

Suggested Scoring Rubric

4	• Research is accurate and generational diagram is clear. • Use of exponents and scientific notation is correct and appropriate.
3	• Research and diagram are acceptable, but portions may be incomplete. • Some use of exponents and scientific notation may not be correct.
2	• An attempt is made to research information and make a diagram, but much of it is incomplete. • Students have difficulty expressing the numbers in exponential and scientific notation.
1	• No attempt is made to put information into an appropriate diagram. • Numbers are not expressed in exponential or scientific notation.

Chapter Project

Students research an animal of interest to them, learn how many offspring a pair of these animals might produce, and then predict the number of offspring that might exist after several generations.

Resources
Chapter 3 Project Master

Introduce the Project

- Discuss the types of animals students might wish to investigate for this project.
- Talk about things that might affect the number of animals of a species in future generations, such as the frequency with which babies are born, environmental factors that may affect the animals' survival, and the number of predators that prey on the species.
- Talk about where students might find information about their chosen animals, such as encyclopedias, books, and the Internet.

Project Progress

Section A, page 124 Students start with one set of animal parents and draw a diagram showing possible future generations, based on the number of offspring a set of parents might have.

Section B, page 143 Students use exponents to show how many animals can result from the original pair of animals. They express large numbers using scientific notation.

Community Project

A community project for Chapter 3 is available in *Home and Community Connections.*

Cooperative Learning

You may want to use Teaching Tool Transparency 1: Cooperative Learning Checklist with **Explore** and other group activities in this chapter.

Problem Solving Focus

Reading the Problem

The Point

Students focus on reading and understanding problems.

Resources

Teaching Tool Transparency 16: Problem-Solving Guidelines

 *Interactive CD-ROM Journal*

About the Page

Using the Problem-Solving Process

It is important that students be able to read a problem and identify how they will use the given information to solve it. Discuss the following suggestions.

- Read the problem and decide what it is asking you to do or find. Reread the problem to be sure you are correct.
- Determine how the given information relates to the question being asked.

Ask ...

- How will you use the information given in Problem 1? Answers may vary.
- Who has the greatest number of sponsors? The least number? Lou; Greg
- In Problem 2, how do you know WAFT donates more time? WAFT donates the same amount of time per day as WEBC, but for three extra days.

Answers for Problems

1. a. Fund raising at a walkathon.
   b. Who earned the most money
   c. $2.00
   d. Greg and June.
   e. Possible answer: How much did the three children earn in all? $224
2. a. Time donated by radio stations.
   b. How much time WEFG donated.
   c. 20
   d. 120
   e. Possible answer: Which station donated twice as much time as WEBC? WAFT

Journal

Ask students to write about a situation in which they did not read information carefully. Have them explain the consequences.

Problem Solving

Understand
Plan
Solve
Look Back

Reading the Problem

Before you can solve a problem, you need to understand it. Some problems look harder than they are because they have unexpected twists. Going back over a problem a second time may help you understand what the problem is really asking.

Problem Solving Focus

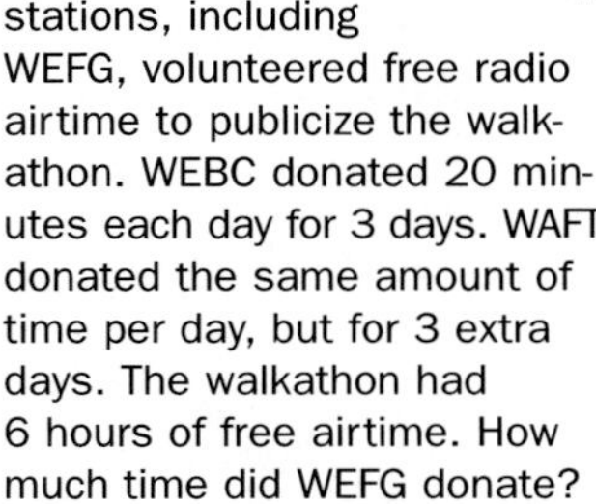

Read each problem, and answer the questions about the problem.

1. The children's clinic held a walkathon. Each sponsor paid walkers $2.00 a mile. June got 8 sponsors and walked 4 miles. Greg walked twice as far as June did, but had half as many sponsors. Lou had 3 times as many sponsors as Greg and walked as far as June did. Who earned the most money?

   a. What is the problem about?

   b. What is the problem asking for?

   c. How much did each sponsor pay for a mile walked?

   d. Which two walkers earned the same amount of money?

   e. Write and answer a question of your own that can be solved using the information in this problem.

2. Three radio stations, including WEFG, volunteered free radio airtime to publicize the walkathon. WEBC donated 20 minutes each day for 3 days. WAFT donated the same amount of time per day, but for 3 extra days. The walkathon had 6 hours of free airtime. How much time did WEFG donate?

   a. What is the problem about?

   b. What is the problem asking for?

   c. How many minutes of airtime did WEBC donate each day?

   d. How many total minutes did WAFT donate?

   e. Write and answer a question of your own that can be solved using the information in this problem.

104

Additional Problem

The Tucson Racewalkers planned a race to raise money for charity. Two hundred people from Tucson signed up and paid $20 each to enter the race. Twice as many people from other parts of Arizona signed up for the race and paid the same $20 entry fee. The number of participants from outside Arizona was half the number from Tucson, but to enter the race, they had to pay twice as much as the people from Tucson. How much money was raised from entry fees?

1. What is the problem about? What does the problem ask? The number of participants in a race and the entry fees they paid. The total amount of money raised from entry fees.
2. Organize the information in a way that will help you solve the problem. Possible answer: 200 people from Tucson paid $20 each; 400 people from other parts of Arizona paid $20 each; 100 people from outside Arizona paid $40 each.
3. What is the answer? How did you find it? $16,000; Possible method: Multiply 200 by 20, multiply 400 by 20, multiply 100 by 40, and add the products.

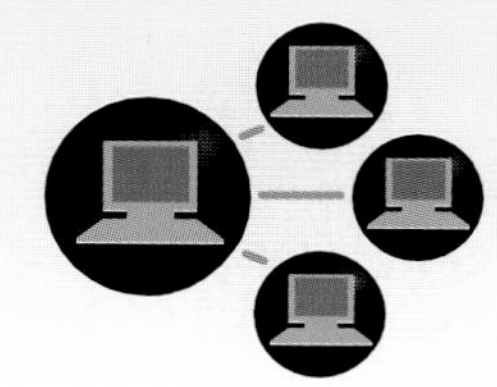

Visit www.teacher.mathsurf.com for links to lesson plans from teachers and other professionals, NCTM information, and other sites.

Estimating and Solving Equations

LESSON PLANNING GUIDE

Student Edition / Ancillaries

LESSON		MATERIALS	VOCABULARY	DAILY	OTHER
	Chapter 3 Opener				Ch. 3 Project Master Ch. 3 Community Project Teaching Tool Trans. 1
	Problem Solving Focus				Teaching Tool Trans. 16 *Interactive CD-ROM Journal*
	Section 3A Opener				
3–1	**Place Value: Comparing and Ordering Decimals**	graph paper, colored pencils		3–1	Teaching Tool Trans. 4, 7 *WW Math*—Middle School
3–2	**Estimating by Rounding**			3–2	Teaching Tool Trans. 2, 3
3–3	**Problem Solving: Sums and Differences of Decimals**			3–3	
3–4	**Problem Solving: Products and Quotients of Decimals**	spreadsheet software		3–4	*Interactive CD-ROM Spreadsheet/Grapher Tool* Ch. 3 Project Master
3–5	**Powers of 10 and Scientific Notation**	scientific or graphing calculator	exponent, base, power, standard form, scientific notation	3–5	Teaching Tool Trans. 22 *WW Math*—Middle School
	Technology	scientific calculator			Teaching Tool Trans. 22
	Connect				Interdisc. Team Teaching 3A
	Review				Practice 3A; Quiz 3A; *TestWorks*

SKILLS TRACE

LESSON	SKILL	FIRST INTRODUCED GR. 5	GR. 6	GR. 7	DEVELOP	PRACTICE/ APPLY	REVIEW
3–1	**Comparing and ordering decimals.**	✘			pp. 106–107	pp. 108–109	pp. 138, 160, 172, 216
3–2	**Rounding through thousandths.** **Using rounding to estimate.**	✘ ✘			pp. 110–112	pp. 113–114	pp. 148, 160, 177, 221
3–3	**Solving addition and subtraction equations containing decimals.**		✘		pp. 115–117	pp. 118–119	pp. 129, 160, 182, 226
3–4	**Multiplying and dividing decimals.** **Solving multiplication and division equations containing decimals.**	✘ ✘			pp. 120–122	pp. 123–124	pp. 143, 160, 190, 231
3–5	**Using exponents to write powers of 10.** **Writing large numbers in scientific notation.**		✘	✘ p. 125	pp. 125–127	pp. 128–129	pp. 152, 160, 195, 352

CONNECTED MATHEMATICS

The unit *Data Around Us (Number Sense)*, from the **Connected Mathematics** series, can be used with Section 3A.

INTERDISCIPLINARY TEAM TEACHING

Math and Science/Technology

(Worksheet pages 9–10: Teacher pages T9–T10)

In this lesson, students use decimals and scientific notation with astronomical distances.

Name ______________________ *Math and Science/Technology*

Doomsday Rock

Use decimals and scientific notation with astronomical distances.

Doomsday Rock Hurtling Toward Earth
Asteroid on Collision Course

Could these be real headlines, or are they just science fiction? The truth is, sooner or later an asteroid will collide with Earth. It's happened before—there are huge craters on Earth where asteroids have crashed—and it's likely to happen again. This may not happen for thousands of years or it may happen much sooner. And someday we may be able to spot incoming asteroids early enough to push them off course.

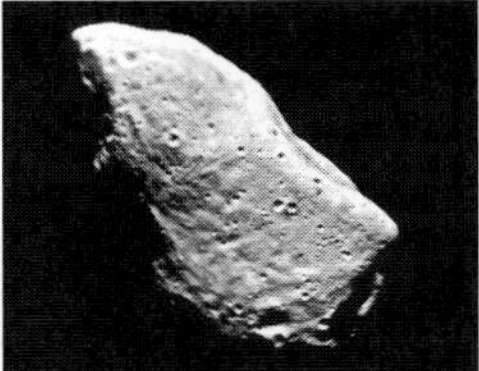

Asteroids are chunks of rock that hurtle through space. They range in size from pebbles and boulders to about 1000 km in diameter. A large one crashing into Earth could do serious damage.

What are asteroids anyway? Asteroids are sometimes called minor planets. They are the "leftovers" of the rocky material which formed our solar system. Some are very small. Others are quite large, up to 1,000 km in diameter. All orbit the Sun. Most asteroids move in an orbit between the planets Mars and Jupiter. We don't have to worry about bumping into these. However, others have unusual orbits that cross the orbit of Earth. These are the asteroids we have to look out for.

In February, 1996, a space probe was launched by NASA to study one of these asteroids. On its 1.3 billion-mile mission, the space probe—called NEAR for Near Earth Asteroid Rendezvous—will get within 20 miles of the asteroid Eros, which is a potato-shaped rock twice the length of Manhattan Island. Instruments aboard the probe will take photographs of Eros and collect data about it. The data will provide scientists with clues about the composition and behavior of Eros. NEAR is to reach Eros in February, 1999. When it does, we may get a better idea of whether it will collide with Earth at some distant point in the future. Such a collision could cause a huge explosion.

1. What could be some of the dangers if an asteroid or part of an asteroid struck land on Earth?

   Answers will vary, but with the information provided in the introduction, students can conclude that depending on the size of the asteroid, the impact could destroy large areas.

Name ______________________ *Math and Science/Technology*

2. a. Asteroid Eros is 37.5 kilometers long. If there are 1.6 kilometers in 1 mile, how long is Eros in miles? Tell how you got your answer.

   Divide 37.5 by 1.6 to get 23.4 miles.

   b. If Asteroid Eros is 17.5 miles in diameter, what is its diameter in kilometers?

   Multiply 17.5 by 1.6 to get 28 km.

   c. How does the length of Eros compare with its diameter? Give your answer in miles.

   $23.4 - 17.5 = 5.9$ miles longer than the diameter

3. a. The last time Eros came close to Earth was in 1931. It came within 24,135,000 kilometers of Earth. Round this distance to the nearest million.

   24 million; 24,000,000

   b. Use scientific notation to express this distance.

   2.4×10^7 km

4. Sometimes scientists express distance in space in astronomical units (AU), where the distance between Earth and the Sun is given as 1.00 AU. Asteroid Vesta is the third largest asteroid. It is 2.360 AU from the Sun.

   a. Jupiter is 5.203 AU from the Sun. Saturn is 9.555 AU from the Sun and Mars is 1.524 AU from the Sun. Between which two planets is the Asteroid Vesta found?

   between Mars and Jupiter

   b. Suppose other asteroids come within these distances from the Sun (in AU):

   2.173; 0.9412; 1.6275; 0.8417

   Which of these asteroids should we be worried about? Why?

   Those that come within less than 1.0 AU from the Sun. They cross Earth's orbit and could collide with it.

5. A number of suggestions have been made about how to keep an asteroid that is on a collision course with Earth from hitting it. Do some research to find out what those suggestions are. Write a report of your findings on a separate sheet of paper. Explain which suggestion you would support and why.

   Students might access NASA's Internet site for information or obtain copies of magazine and newspaper articles on the subject.

BIBLIOGRAPHY

FOR TEACHERS

Seymour, Dale and Beardslee, Ed. *Critical Thinking Activities*. Palo Alto, CA: Dale Seymour, 1996.

Spangler, David. *Math for Real Kids*. Glenview, IL: Good Year Books, 1997.

Williams, Wayne. *Quizzes*. Palo Alto, CA: Dale Seymour, 1996.

FOR STUDENTS

Baird, Anne. *Space Camp*. New York, NY: Morrow Junior Bks, 1992.

Collins, Michael. *Flying to the Moon*. New York, NY: Farrar, Straus & Giroux, 1994.

Herbst, Judith. *Animal Amazing*. New York, NY: Atheneum, 1991.

Pearl, Mary Corliss. *The Illustrated Encyclopedia of Wildlife*. Lakeville, CT: Grey Castle Press, 1991.

Decimal Concepts: Estimating and Solving Equations

▶ Science Link ▶ www.mathsurf.com/7/ch3/astronomy

The Lonely Planets

When astronauts Neil Armstrong and Buzz Aldrin landed on the moon in 1969, they were the first people ever to visit another celestial body. Over the next three years, 10 more astronauts walked on the moon. At that time, many people believed that traveling to the moon and even to other planets would be common by the year 2000.

However, in the 25 years since then, no one has been back to the moon and no one has visited another planet. Many scientists believe that no one ever will. The reason is that our solar system is so huge. Armstrong and Aldrin took four days to get to the moon. At the speed they traveled, it would take nearly two *years* to reach Mars, the nearest planet with conditions that humans could stand. The planet Jupiter is 20 years farther than that, and Pluto, the most distant planet, 100 years farther yet.

Working with huge numbers is something astronomers and space explorers do every day. They carefully measure time and distance as they try to make the dream of understanding and visiting other worlds come true. Keeping these records and making calculations with large numbers is made simpler by using decimal notation.

1 How many times as far away from Earth is Pluto than the moon? Explain.

2 Give examples of things you can find on Earth that need very large or very small numbers to express.

3 The moon is about 240,000 miles from Earth. Estimate Armstrong and Aldrin's average speed in mi/hr. How does their speed compare with typical speeds on Earth?

105

Where are we now?

In Section 2B, students wrote and solved equations involving whole numbers.

They learned how to

- translate words into algebraic expressions.
- solve addition and subtraction problems using inverse operations.
- solve multiplication and division problems using inverse operations.
- use more than one inverse operation to solve an equation.

Where are we going?

In Section 3A, students will

- compare and order decimals.
- estimate by rounding and using compatible numbers.
- solve equations containing decimals.
- write numbers in scientific notation.

Theme: Astronomy

World Wide Web

If your class has access to the World Wide Web, you might want to use the information found at the Web site address given. The interdisciplinary link relates to topics discussed in the section.

About the Page

This page introduces the theme of this section, astronomy, and describes the first human visit to the moon. The possibility of visiting other planets is discussed.

Ask ...

- Do you think that interplanetary travel will become a reality in your lifetime?
- If humans ever visit another planet, which one do you think it would be? Why?

Extension

The following activity does not require access to the World Wide Web.

Science

In 1996, Dr. Shannon Lucid broke the record for the longest space flight by a woman and the U.S. space-endurance record. Dr. Lucid is a 53-year-old biochemist astronaut who is also the mother of three. Students might research the amount of time Dr. Lucid and others have spent in space. They might also investigate how astronauts prepare for space travel.

Answers for Questions

1. About 11,100 times as far; Convert 100 + 20 + 2 years to days, then divide by 4.
2. Large: Number of cells in the body, grains of sand on a beach; Small: Size of a bacterium, width of a hair.
3. About 2500 mi/hr; Very much faster—only SSTs approach this level of speed.

Connect

On page 131, students use decimals and scientific notation to compare data about the planets.

3-1 Lesson Organizer

Objective

- Compare and order decimals.

Materials

- Explore: Graph paper, colored pencils

NCTM Standards

- 1–6

Review 

In the number 135,479

1. 3 represents 3 ______. ten thousands
2. 5 represents 5 ______. thousands
3. 4 represents 4 ______. hundreds
4. 7 represents 7 ______. tens

Available on Daily Transparency 3-1

Lesson Link

You might review whole-number place value and comparing and ordering a set of 4 or 5 whole numbers as a lead-in to the lesson.

1 Introduce

Explore  

You may wish to use Teaching Tool Transparency 7: $\frac{1}{4}$-inch Graph Paper with **Explore**.

The Point

Students explore decimal representation with grid models and then extend their work with whole numbers to compare and order decimal numbers.

Ongoing Assessment

Check that students understand how to construct the grid models for the six decimals.

For Groups That Finish Early

You and your partner each think of a decimal number in tenths or hundredths. Make a model of it on grid paper, then exchange papers and write the decimal shown.

3-1 Place Value: Comparing and Ordering Decimals

You'll Learn ...

- to compare and order decimals

... How It's Used

Environmental scientists need to compare the decimal values of pollutants that they find in the air or in water.

Lesson Link You have worked with whole numbers. Now you'll begin to study decimals by deciding which of two decimals is greater. ◄

Explore Comparing and Ordering Decimals

Model Behavior

Materials: Graph paper, Colored pencils

Modeling Decimals

The graph paper shows a model of the number 1.47. To model a decimal:

- Color a complete 10-by-10 grid for each whole in the decimal.
- Draw another 10-by-10 grid next to the last complete grid.
- In this grid, color one 10-by-1 strip for each tenth in the decimal. Color a small square for each hundredth.

1.47

1. Draw a grid model for each decimal.
   a. 1.3 **b.** 1.29 **c.** 0.8 **d.** 1.30 **e.** 0.51 **f.** 0.99
2. What do you notice about the models for 1.3 and 1.30? What does this tell you about these numbers? Explain.
3. Rank the decimals from smallest to largest. Explain your reasoning.
4. The number 51 is greater than 8. Why is 0.8 greater than 0.51?
5. Could you use this method to model 1.354? Explain.

Learn Comparing and Ordering Decimals

The place value of each digit of a whole number is one-tenth of the value of the place to its left. Moving to the right of a decimal point, you can create the place values *tenths, hundredths, thousandths,* and so on.

MEETING INDIVIDUAL NEEDS

Resources

- 3-1 Practice
- 3-1 Reteaching
- 3-1 Problem Solving
- 3-1 Enrichment
- 3-1 Daily Transparency
  - Problem of the Day
  - Review
  - Quick Quiz

Teaching Tool Transparencies 4, 7

 *Wide World of Mathematics* Middle School: In 0.01 Second

Learning Modalities

Logical Write the number 56,782.314 on the chalkboard. Have students identify the place in which each digit is located, starting with the 5. Ask how each place is related to the place to its left. Each place is $\frac{1}{10}$ the place to its left. Students should recognize the 3 as being in the tenths place. The 1 is in the $\frac{1}{10}$ of $\frac{1}{10}$, or $\frac{1}{100}$ (hundredths) place; and the 4 is in the $\frac{1}{10}$ of $\frac{1}{100}$ (thousandths) place.

Social Have students work in pairs and use grid models to pose comparisons of decimals.

English Language Development

For students with limited English proficiency, point out the symmetry of the place values around the ones place and the similarity of the names of the corresponding places. That is, *thousands* corresponds to *thousandths*, *hundreds* corresponds to *hundredths*, and *tens* corresponds to *tenths*.

Place	thousands	hundreds	tens	ones	•	tenths	hundredths	thousandths
Place Value	1000	100	10	1		$\frac{1}{10}$ or 0.1	$\frac{1}{100}$ or 0.01	$\frac{1}{1000}$ or 0.001

As with whole numbers, the value of each digit in a decimal is the product of the digit and its place value.

Examples

1 Read 8052.468.

The number is read "eight thousand fifty-two *and* four hundred sixty-eight thousandths."

2 Give the value of each 8 in 8052.468.

The first 8 is in the thousands place. Its value is $8 \times 1000 = 8000$.

The second 8 is in the thousandths place. Its value is $8 \times \frac{1}{1000} = \frac{8}{1000}$ or 0.008.

> **Remember**
>
> The symbol $<$ means *less than.* The symbol $>$ means *greater than.* **[Previous course]**

To compare and order decimals, write the numbers with their decimal points lined up. Then compare the digits in each place, moving left to right. Sometimes one number has more decimal places than another. *Annex* zeros to the right of the decimal part of each number so that each number has the same number of digits after the decimal point.

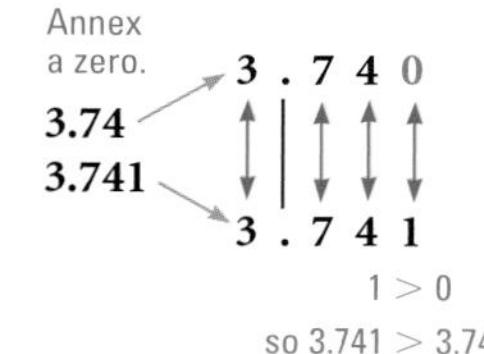

Example 3

America's first two manned space flights that orbited Earth took place in 1962. Compare the time in orbit of the two astronauts.

4 . 9 2 3 0 Annex a zero.
4 . 9 3 4 7 Compare digits in each place.
2 < 3

Astronaut	Time in Orbit
John Glenn	4.923 hr
Scott Carpenter	4.9347 hr

Glenn's time of 4.923 hr was less than Carpenter's time of 4.9347 hr.

Try It

Compare using $<$, $>$, or $=$.

a. 58.7351 [>] 58.73 **b.** 3.24 [=] 3.240

> **History Link**
>
> The first woman in space was Valentina Tereshkova, of the U.S.S.R. Between June 16 and 19, 1963, she made 48 orbits of Earth in 70.83 hours.

MATH EVERY DAY

Problem of the Day

Suppose an anonymous benefactor donates $1 each minute of every day until a total of $10,000,000 is reached. To the nearest year, how long will it take to collect all the money? About 19 years; $60 \times 24 = 1440$ per day, $1440 \times 365 = 525{,}600$ per year, $10{,}000{,}000 \div 525{,}600 = 19.02588$

Available on Daily Transparency 3-1

An Extension is provided in the transparency package.

Fact of the Day

Since the moon rotates on its axis once during its 29-day cycle, the same side is always seen from Earth.

Mental Math

Give the value of the 8 in each number.

1. 83,555 80,000
2. 20,849 800
3. 486,302 80,000
4. 728 8

Follow Up

To help students understand why zeros can be annexed to write equal decimals, write 3 tenths and 30 hundredths as fractions and show that they are equal. Repeat with 5 tenths and 50 hundredths.

Answers for Explore

1. See page C5.
2. The same area is shaded. The numbers are equal.
3. 0.51, 0.8, 0.99, 1.29, 1.3 or 1.30; Possible answer: They are ordered from least amount of shading in the grid to the most amount of shading.
4. 0.8 = 0.80 and 80 is greater than 51.
5. Possible answer: Yes; Use grids with 100 rows and 10 columns. Color a complete grid for the 1. In another grid, color 3 columns for 3 tenths. Then, in the fourth column, color 50 boxes for 5 hundredths and 4 more boxes for 4 thousandths.

2 Teach

Learn

You may want to use Teaching Tool Transparency 4: Place Value Charts with **Learn.**

Refer to the chart on this page. Discuss the relationship between the fraction and the decimal representations for the place values to the right of the decimal point.

Alternate Examples

1. Read 5204.72.

   The number is read "five thousand two hundred four and seventy-two hundredths."

2. Give the value of each 2 in 5204.72.

   The first 2 is in the hundreds place, so its value is $2 \times 100 = 200$. The second 2 is in the hundredths place, so its value is $2 \times \frac{1}{100} = \frac{2}{100}$ or 0.02.

3. The first and second U.S. manned space flights lasted 0.2561 hr and 0.2603 hr, respectively. Which flight lasted longer?

   0.2 5 6 1
   0.2 6 0 3
   6 > 5

   The second flight lasted longer.

3-1 Exercises and Applications

Assignment Guide

- **Basic**
  1–2, 5–6, 10–13, 18–21, 23, 25–26, 29–35 odds
- **Average**
  3–4, 7–10, 14–28, 30–36 evens
- **Enriched**
  3–4, 7–10, 14–28, 29–35 odds

3 Practice and Assess

Check

Answers for Check Your Understanding

1. Each row and column = 0.1; each small square = 0.01.
2. No; 0.3 > 0.27 because $0.3 = \frac{30}{100}$ and $0.27 = \frac{27}{100}$.

Exercise Answers

1. Thirty-six and five tenths.
2. One hundred twenty-four and eighty-four hundredths.
3. Four thousand, seven hundred ninety-two and six hundred thirty-nine thousandths.
4. Three hundred six and three hundred six thousandths.
5. $\frac{6}{100}$
6. 6; $\frac{6}{1000}$
7. $\frac{6}{10}$
8. 600; $\frac{6}{100}$
9. 6000; 600; $\frac{6}{10}$; $\frac{6}{100}$

17. Greatest: 1993; Least: 1991.

19. a. Country Yogurt; It contains more for the same cost.
    b. Big Y is lower in fat per serving, Country Yogurt is lower in fat per ounce.

Reteaching

Activity

Materials: Red and yellow counters

- Draw a place value table. Then use red counters to model 8.562 and yellow counters to model 8.59.
- Compare the numbers of counters in each place from left to right. The third column has more yellow counters than red, so 8.59 > 8.562.
- Repeat with other pairs.

Check Your Understanding

1. Explain the relationship between place values in a decimal and a grid model.
2. You know that 3 is less than 27. Is 0.3 less than 0.27? Explain.

3-1 Exercises and Applications

PRACTICE 3-1

Practice and Apply

Getting Started Write each decimal in words.

1. 36.5
2. 124.84
3. 4792.639
4. 306.306

Give the value of each 6.

5. 125.067
6. 16.136
7. 42.68
8. 634.16
9. 46,600.66

10. **Test Prep** Which of these numbers has the same value as the 5 in this number: 247.358? D

    Ⓐ 50 Ⓑ 5.0 Ⓒ 0.5 Ⓓ 0.05

Compare using <, >, or =.

11. 0.034 [<] 0.340
12. 1.01 [<] 1.013
13. 487.835 [<] 487.838
14. 16.2 [<] 16.201
15. 5.831 [<] 6.813
16. 196.789 [<] 196.987

17. **Science** The table shows levels of ozone-depleting chemicals in the air. Which year had the greatest level? The least?

Year	1991	1992	1993	1994	1995
Level (parts per billion)	2.981	3.133	3.148	3.138	3.124

18. **Test Prep** Which of these numbers is the smallest? D

    Ⓐ 36.397 Ⓑ 36.400
    Ⓒ 36.399 Ⓓ 3.700

19. **Consumer** You are deciding which of two brands of yogurt to buy. Both brands cost $1.69 per container.
    a. Which is the better deal? Explain.
    b. Which brand is lower in fat? Explain.

PRACTICE

Name ______________________

Practice 3-1

Place Value: Comparing and Ordering Decimals

Give the value of each 1.

1. 316.24 — 10
2. 587.13 — 0.1
3. 201.473 — 1
4. 17,364.9 — 10,000
5. 8,447.301 — 0.001
6. 8,139.64 — 100
7. 9.4321 — 0.0001
8. 3,142,864.3 — 100,000

Give the value of each 8.

9. 384.29 — 80
10. 506.83 — 0.8
11. 84,163.2 — 80,000
12. 1841.67 — 800

Give the value of each 3.

13. 1,203.7 — 3
14. 382.87 — 300
15. 610.731 — 0.03
16. 53,042.75 — 3,000

Use the symbols < or > to show which number is larger.

17. 387.65 (>) 387.56
18. 72.83 (<) 73.73
19. 0.005 (>) 0.0005
20. 58.006 (<) 58.060
21. 17.341 (>) 17.3409
22. 312.745 (<) 312.746

23. **Health** One cup of canned orange juice has 1.1 mg of iron. A 10-oz package of frozen peaches has 1.05 mg of iron. Which has more iron? Orange juice

24. The table shows the top 5 earned-run averages in the history of major league baseball. Who had the highest of these averages? Rube Waddel

    Who had the lowest of these averages? Ed Walsh

Player	Mordecai Brown	Addie Joss	Christy Mathewson	Rube Waddel	Ed Walsh
Earned-run average	2.06	1.88	2.13	2.16	1.82

RETEACHING

Name ______________________

Alternative Lesson 3-1

Place Value: Comparing and Ordering Decimals

A place-value chart can help you read decimals. Always remember to read the decimal point as "and."

Example 1

Write 3507.206 in words.

The decimal in the place-value chart is written as "three thousand, five hundred seven *and* two hundred six thousandths."

Try It Write each decimal in the place-value chart. Then write each decimal in words.

thousands 1000	hundreds 100	tens 10	ones 1	.	tenths 0.1 or 1/10	hundredths 0.01 or 1/100	thousandths 0.001 or 1/1000
3	5	0	7	.	2	0	6
		2	5	.	0	7	1
	1	0	2	.	0	9	6

a. 25.071 Twenty-five and seventy-one thousandths

b. 102.096 One hundred two and ninety-six thousandths

Example 2

Compare 345.73 and 345.732.

To compare two decimals, you can write each decimal in a place-value chart.

hundreds 100	tens 10	ones 1	.	tenths 0.1 or 1/10	hundredths 0.01 or 1/100	thousandths 0.001 or 1/1000
3	4	5	.	7	3	0
3	4	5	.	7	3	2

same; 0 < 2

345.73 < 345.732
345.732 > 345.73

Step 1: Annex a zero to 345.73 so that both have the same number of decimal places.

Step 2: Check each place value beginning from the left. The first place value where their digits differ will determine which decimal is greater. The two numbers differ in the thousandths place.

Since 0 is less than 2, 345.73 is less than 345.732 and 345.732 is greater than 345.73.

Try It Circle the greater decimal.

c. 63.095 and (63.41)
d. (127.75) and 127.739
e. (23.495) and 23.4
f. 49.278 and (49.287)
g. 64.057 and (64.570)
h. (389.321) and 389.042

Problem Solving and Reasoning

20. Critical Thinking Here is a decimal with some missing digits: GPS ☐ 3. ☐ 8 ☐. If no two digits of this number are alike, what is the largest possible number this can be? The smallest? Fill in the missing digits to make the closest possible number to $53\frac{1}{2}$.

21. Communicate Write three decimals that are greater than 3.71 but less than 3.72. Order them from the least to the greatest. Could you write more than three of these numbers? Is there a limit to how close you can get to 3.72 without actually reaching it? Explain your answers.

22. Journal Explain how you would put the three numbers 1.01, 1.029, and 1.103 in order from least to greatest.

23. Critical Thinking Number lines can be used to display and order decimals. Compare 3.2, 3.4, and 4.3 by plotting each on a number line. How can you tell the order of the three decimals?

24. Critical Thinking The books in a library are arranged according to *call number;* the lower call numbers are on the left side of the shelf and the higher numbers are on the right. The call numbers for six books on planetary astronomy are lettered a–f. Give the order in which they should appear on the shelf.

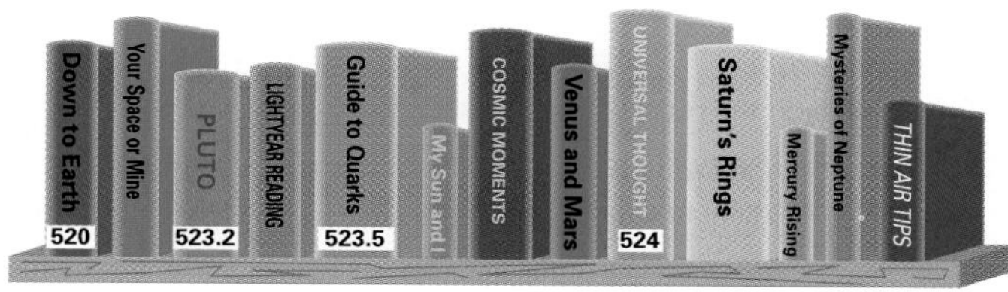

a. 523.1 **b.** 523.70 **c.** 523.43 **d.** 523.45 **e.** 523.4 **f.** 523.449

Mixed Review

Order each data set from least to greatest. Then find the median for each set. *[Lesson 1-4]*

25. 34, 65, 23, 78, 46, 45, 89, 43, 29

26. 164, 215, 432, 653, 671, 564

27. 3, 6, 8, 5, 3, 4, 6, 8, 5, 3, 2, 7, 9, 6

28. 65, 67, 73, 83, 53, 65, 75, 49, 71

Write a phrase for each algebraic expression. *[Lesson 2-5]*

29. $x - 7$ **30.** $63c$ **31.** $8(n - 4)$ **32.** $42k + 17$

33. $\frac{d + 3}{4}$ **34.** $4 - 3y$ **35.** $5 - n$ **36.** $12c + 16w$

PROBLEM SOLVING 3-1

PROBLEM SOLVING

Name ______________________

Guided Problem Solving 3-1

GPS **PROBLEM 20, STUDENT PAGE 109**

Here is a decimal with some missing digits: ☐3.☐8☐. If no two digits of this number are alike, what is the largest possible number this can be? The smallest? Fill in the missing digits to make the closest possible number to $53\frac{1}{2}$.

— Understand —

1. Can you use a digit more than once? No.
2. What number must be in the tens place? The hundredths place? 5, 8

— Plan —

3. Which digits can you use to make the decimals? 0, 1, 2, 4, 5, 6, 7, 9
4. Which three digits will you use to make the largest possible number? The smallest possible number? 6, 7, 9; 0, 1, 2
5. To find the number closest to $53\frac{1}{2}$, rewrite $53\frac{1}{2}$ as 53.500. Write 5 in the tens place. Decide which of the remaining digits make the decimal closest to 0.500.
   5 3 . 5 0 0
   5 3 . 4 8 9

— Solve —

6. Write the greatest possible number. 93.786
7. Write the least possible number. 13.082
8. What number is closest to $53\frac{1}{2}$? 53.489

— Look Back —

9. Why do you think your answer to Item 8 is reasonable?
   Possible answer: The fraction $\frac{489}{1000}$ is very close to $\frac{500}{1000}$ or $\frac{1}{2}$.

SOLVE ANOTHER PROBLEM

Here is a decimal with some missing digits: ☐4.☐8☐. If no two digits of this number are alike, what is the largest possible number this can be? The smallest? Fill in the missing digits to make the closest possible number to $34\frac{1}{2}$.
94.786; 14.082; 34.581

ENRICHMENT

Name ______________________

Extend Your Thinking 3-1

Critical Thinking

Our place-value system is based on tens. Each place value is 10 times greater than the one at its right. The number 34,567 is shown in a **base ten** place-value chart.

10,000s (10 × 10 × 10 × 10)	1000s (10 × 10 × 10)	100s (10 × 10)	10s (10)	1s (1)
3	4	5	6	7

To find the value of the number 34,567, add the values of each of its digits:

$(3 \times 10{,}000) + (4 \times 1000) + (5 \times 100) + (6 \times 10) + (7 \times 1) = 34{,}567$

Other place-value systems are based on numbers other than ten. The place-value chart below is based on fours. Notice that each value is 4 times greater than the one at its right. The number in the **base four** place-value chart below can be written as 31232_{four}. ← Base of system

256s (4 × 4 × 4 × 4)	64s (4 × 4 × 4)	16s (4 × 4)	4s (4)	1s (1)
3	1	2	3	2

To find the value of the number 31232_{four}, add the values of each of its digits:

$(3 \times 256) + (1 \times 64) + (2 \times 16) + (3 \times 4) + (2 \times 1) = 878$

Sketch a place-value chart for the indicated base of each number. Then find the value of the number.

Place-value chart / **Value**

1. 4503_{seven} a.

343	49	7	1
4	5	0	3

b. 1620

2. 210121_{three} a.

243	81	27	9	3	1
2	1	0	1	2	1

b. 583

3. 71462_{eight} a.

4096	512	64	8	1
7	1	4	6	2

b. 29,490

4. 10110111_{two} a.

128	64	32	16	8	4	2	1
1	0	1	1	0	1	1	1

b. 183

Exercise Answers

20. Largest: 93.786; Smallest: 13.082; 53.489.
21. Possible answer: 3.711, 3.712, 3.713; Yes; No—as long as the hundredths digit is still 1, you will never reach 3.72.
22. 1.01, 1.029, 1.103. Possible answer: Match the decimal places from left to right and check the first place that was greater.
23. 3.2 < 3.4 < 4.3; Larger numbers are to the right.

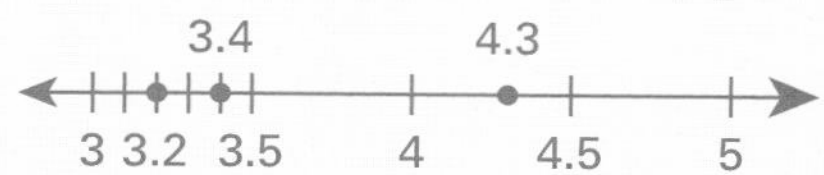

24. a, e, c, f, d, b
25. 23, 29, 34, 43, 45, 46, 65, 78, 89; Median is 45.
26. 164, 215, 432, 564, 653, 671; Median is 498.
27. 2, 3, 3, 3, 4, 5, 5, 6, 6, 6, 7, 8, 8, 9; Median is 5.5.
28. 49, 53, 65, 65, 67, 71, 73, 75, 83: Median is 67.
29. 7 less than a number *x*.
30. The product of 63 and a number *c*.
31. The product of 8 and 4 less than a number *n*.
32. The sum of 17 and the product of 42 and a number *k*.
33. The quotient of 3 more than a number *d* and 4.
34. 4 decreased by the product of 3 and a number *y*.
35. 5 reduced by a number *n*.
36. The product of 12 and a number *c* increased by the product of 16 and a number *w*.

Alternate Assessment

Interview Ask students to tell you how comparing decimals is similar to comparing whole numbers.

Quick Quiz

Use these three numbers: 443.6, 402.03, 356.29.

1. Give the value of each 3.
   443.6, 3; 402.03, $\frac{3}{100}$; 356.26, 300
2. Arrange the numbers in order from least to greatest.
   356.29, 402.03, 443.6

Available on Daily Transparency 3-1

3-2 Lesson Organizer

Objectives

- Round to the nearest place.
- Round to whole numbers to estimate.
- Use front-end estimation and compatible numbers to estimate.

NCTM Standards

- 1–4, 7

▶ Review

Round each number to the indicated place.

1. 567, nearest ten
   570
2. 3498, nearest thousand
   3000
3. 5084, nearest hundred
   5100
4. 413, nearest ten
   410

Available on Daily Transparency 3-2

▶ Lesson Link

Ask students for examples of numbers in daily life that are frequently rounded. Possibilities are populations, attendances at sporting events, and so on.

1 Introduce

Explore

The Point
Students explore a decimal number given to three different levels of precision. They investigate the possible uses for each.

Ongoing Assessment
Check that students recognize that the three numbers given all represent the same distance. They may need to express the first and third in standard notation.

3-2 Estimating by Rounding

You'll Learn ...

- to round to the nearest decimal place
- to estimate by rounding to whole numbers
- to use front-end estimation and compatible numbers to estimate

... How It's Used

Contractors need to estimate costs in order to make a realistic bid for a job. They often have to round quantities and expenses to give a customer a quote.

▶ Lesson Link You have rounded whole numbers when you didn't need exact answers or when you wanted to estimate. Now you'll see how to round decimal numbers. ◀

Explore Estimating by Rounding

How Far Is Mars?

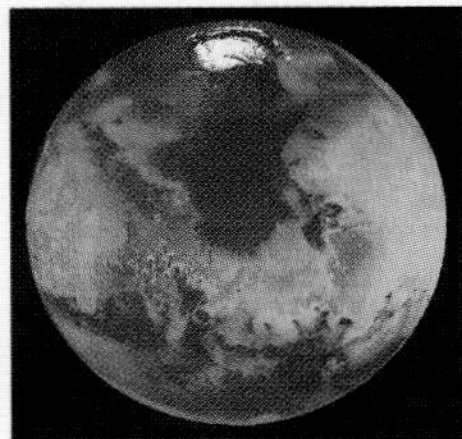

Gail was writing a report on space probes. In 1971, NASA engineers placed the *Mariner 9* space probe in orbit around the planet Mars. Gail needed to find the distance from Earth to Mars. Three sources of information gave three different distances:

40 million miles **36,862,000 miles** **36.9 million miles**

1. A NASA report said, "At the moment it went into Martian orbit, *Mariner 9* was ____ from Earth." Which of the three distances was probably in the report? Why do you think so?
2. A World Wide Web page said, "Mars is about ____ from Earth." Which of the three distances probably was given? Why?
3. In 1978, the *Pioneer 12* probe was placed in orbit around the planet Venus. A newspaper report said, "*Pioneer 12* is 7.3 million miles closer to Earth than *Mariner 9*'s ____ when it went into Martian orbit in 1971." Which distance did the newspaper probably give? Why?
4. Give another distance from Earth to Mars Gail might have found and where she might have found it. Why would the source give that distance?

Learn Estimating by Rounding

Sometimes decimals are more exact than you really need to give a useful answer. Or you may want to estimate an answer by using numbers simple enough for mental math. In both cases, you can simplify your work by *rounding*.

MEETING INDIVIDUAL NEEDS

Resources

3-2 Practice
3-2 Reteaching
3-2 Problem Solving
3-2 Enrichment
3-2 Daily Transparency
- Problem of the Day
- Review
- Quick Quiz

Teaching Tool Transparencies 2, 3

Learning Modalities

Logical For Exercises 9–12, have students find the actual product and compare it with the estimate. They should see that rounding both factors up produces an estimate greater than the actual product and that rounding both down produces an estimate less than the actual product. Remind them to use this logic when deciding if an answer is reasonable based on an estimate.

Visual Have students draw and use number lines to round decimals to the nearest tenth or the nearest one.

English Language Development

To help students with limited English proficiency, as well as others, relate the term *compatible numbers* to the term *compatible* as applied to people who get along well together.

Compatible is a cognate with Spanish and French. Ask students who speak other languages for additional equivalents.

5.3485 to nearest tenth — **34.287 to nearest hundredth**

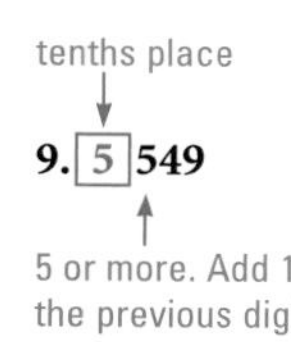

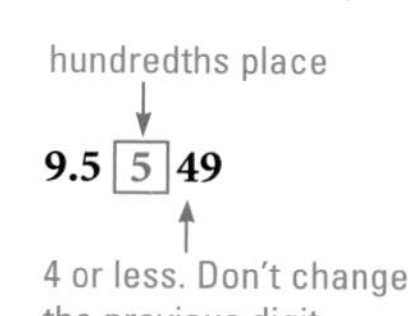

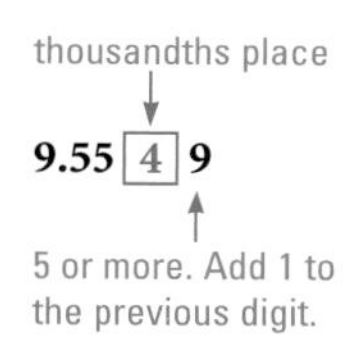

5.3485 to nearest tenth		34.287 to nearest hundredth
5.[3]485	Find the place value.	34.2[8]7
5.[3]485	Look at the digit to the right.	34.2[8]7
5.[3]485 (no change)	If the digit is 5 or greater, add 1 to the place value digit. If it is less than 5, do not change the place value digit.	34.2[8]7 (add 1)
5.3	Delete all digits to the right.	34.29

Study TIP

When you round 5.3485 to the nearest *tenth*, think: Is it closer to 5.3 or 5.4?

Example 1

The planet Saturn is 9.5549 times as far from the sun as Earth is. Round 9.5549 to the nearest tenth, hundredth, and thousandth.

tenths place	hundredths place	thousandths place
9.[5]549	9.5[5]49	9.55[4]9
5 or more. Add 1 to the previous digit	4 or less. Don't change the previous digit.	5 or more. Add 1 to the previous digit.
To the nearest tenth, 9.5549 rounds to 9.6.	To the nearest hundredth, 9.5549 rounds to 9.55.	To the nearest thousandth, 9.5549 rounds to 9.555.

Try It

Round 7.865 to the nearest tenth, hundredth, and thousandth. 7.9; 7.87; 7.865

DID YOU KNOW?

Although Jupiter is the largest planet in the solar system, with a mass that is 318 times that of Earth, it spins around its axis faster than any other planet. A day on Jupiter is only 9.9 hours long!

There are several ways to use rounding to estimate answers to problems that contain decimals.

One way to estimate is to round each number to the highest place value. Then add, subtract, multiply, or divide.

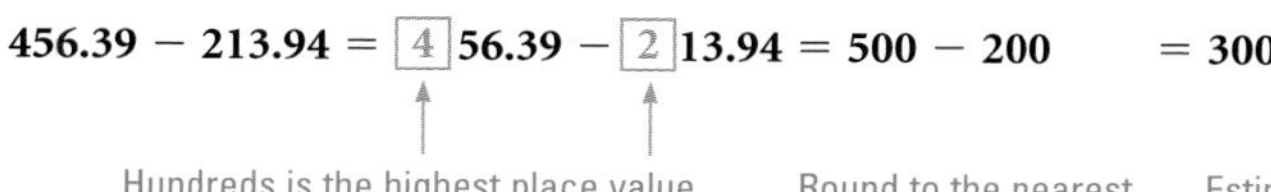

456.39 − 213.94 = [4]56.39 − [2]13.94 = 500 − 200 = 300

Hundreds is the highest place value. Round to the nearest hundred place. Estimate.

To estimate using *compatible numbers,* replace the numbers with the nearest numbers that are easy to use.

356.4 ÷ 84.7

Round 356.4 to 360. If you replace 84.7 with 80, it is not compatible with 360. Instead, replace 84.7 with 90. 360 ÷ 90 = 4.

For Groups That Finish Early

Find *Pioneer 12's* distance from Earth. 29.6 million miles

Follow Up

Have volunteers explain their reasoning for their answers to the questions.

Answers for Explore

1. 36,862,000 miles; the NASA report would need to have the exact distance.
2. 40 million miles; the WWW page says "about," which suggests approximation.
3. 36.9 million miles; the other number in the newspaper article is written in this form.
4. Possible answers: About 37,000,000 miles; In a student's report on Mars. Rounded to the nearest million.

2 Teach

Learn

Explain that the rounding methods used with whole numbers can be applied to rounding decimals as well.

Alternate Examples

1. The orbital velocity of Mercury is 1.6072 times that of Earth. Round 1.6072 to the nearest tenth, hundredth, and thousandth.

   Tenths place: 1.6072 rounds to 1.6, because the digit to the right of the tenths place is less than 5.

   Hundredths place: 1.6072 rounds to 1.61, because the digit to the right of the hundredths place is 5 or greater.

   Thousandths place: 1.6072 rounds to 1.607, because the digit to the right of the thousandths place is less than 5.

MATH EVERY DAY

Problem of the Day

Janine's little sister stacked blocks using this pattern. How many blocks will she need in order to make the tenth figure?

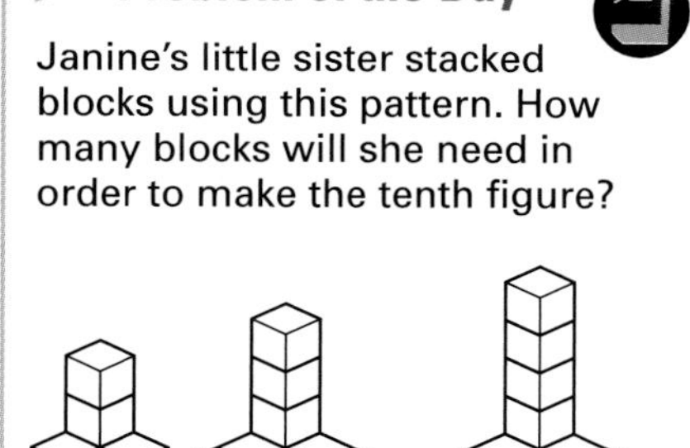

32 blocks

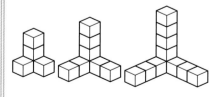

Available on Daily Transparency 3-2

An Extension is provided in the transparency package.

Fact of the Day

As the *Galileo* probe approached Jupiter in 1995, Jupiter's tremendous gravitational pull made the probe accelerate to a speed of 106,000 miles per hour.

Estimation

Estimate each answer.

1. 563 + 732 1300
2. 893 − 401 500
3. 239 × 48 10,000
4. 893 ÷ 32 30

Alternate Examples

2. Estimate 5.97 + 14.3.

   5.97 rounds to 6.
   14.3 rounds to 14.
   Estimate: 6 + 14 = 20

3. Estimate 46.22 × 61.985.

   Round to the highest place value, the tens place.
   46.22 rounds to 50.
   61.985 rounds to 60.
   Estimate: 50 × 60 = 3000

4. Estimate 434.71 ÷ 68.49.

   Use compatible numbers. Round 434.71 to 420 rather than 430, and 68.49 to 70.
   Estimate: 420 ÷ 70 = 6

5. Posters at the Stargazer Planetarium cost $2.49 each, including tax. Estimate how many posters you can buy with $12.

   Round 2.49 to a number compatible with 12.
   The nearest compatible number is 2, but 12 ÷ 2 = 6, and 6 posters would cost $14.94. To be sure the cost of the posters doesn't exceed $12, round $2.49 to $3.
   12 ÷ 3 = 4, and 4 posters would cost $9.96.

3 Practice and Assess

Check

Discuss with students the value of estimating answers to calculations, especially when using a calculator, to be sure the answers are reasonable.

Answers for Check Your Understanding

1. So that you can check whether your answer is reasonable. Sometimes this can help you spot an error.
2. Possible answer: When rounding small numbers like 0.2 and 0.001; rounding to the nearest whole number would round both to 0.

Examples

Estimate.

2 14.779 + 20.24

14.779 rounds to 15. 20.24 rounds to 20. Estimate: 15 + 20 = 35

3 23.12 × 37.627

Round to the nearest ten. 23.12 rounds to 20.
37.627 rounds to 40. Estimate: 20 × 40 = 800

4 319.24 ÷ 68.93

Use compatible numbers. 319.24 rounds to 320.
Replace 68.93 with 80 instead of 70. Estimate: 320 ÷ 80 = 4

Technology Link

When you use your calculator, it is important to estimate your answer first. Then you will know if you have pressed the wrong keys.

Try It

Estimate. **a.** 67.54 − 32.45 ≈ 68 − 32 = 36 **b.** 12.5 × 58.44 ≈ 10 × 60 = 600 **c.** 428.9 ÷ 88.3 ≈ 450 ÷ 90 = 5

In some situations, rounding to the nearest place does not make sense. Suppose you have $6 in your pocket and want to buy as many comic books as possible. The cost of each comic book is $2.39 with tax. If you round $2.39 to $2 (the nearest whole number) you will estimate that you could buy three comic books (6 ÷ 2 = 3). But three comic books will cost more money than you have. It is better to replace $2.39 with $3 and estimate two comic books (6 ÷ 3 = 2).

Example 5

Your astronomy club plans to wash cars to raise money for a new telescope. With tax, the telescope costs $317.19. Estimate how many cars will have to be washed if you charge $5.00 per car.

Replace 317.19 with a compatible number to make dividing by 5 easier. The nearest compatible number is 300. To be sure the club makes enough money to buy a telescope, however, it is better to replace 317.19 with 350. Estimate: 350 ÷ 5 = 70.

About 70 cars should be washed.

Study TIP

When you choose compatible numbers, keep the math as simple as possible: 320 and 350 can both be divided by 5; it is easier to divide 350 by 5.

Check Your Understanding

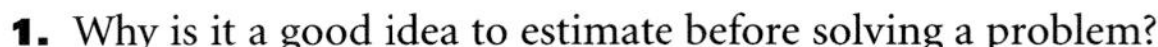

1. Why is it a good idea to estimate before solving a problem?

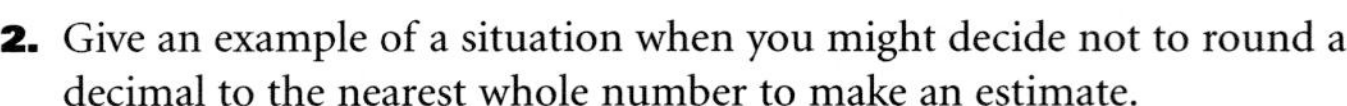

2. Give an example of a situation when you might decide not to round a decimal to the nearest whole number to make an estimate.

MEETING MIDDLE SCHOOL CLASSROOM NEEDS

Tips from Middle School Teachers

I find that students understand the concept of rounding more readily when I use measurements and money. I have them bring in grocery-store receipts and have them round the weights of produce and the prices.

Team Teaching

You might work with the language-arts teachers to have students investigate Jules Verne's books, in many of which the events described have since become fact.

Science Connection

In 1979, the U.S. satellite *Pioneer II* neared Saturn after a $6\frac{1}{2}$-year journey of 3.2 billion kilometers.

3-2 Exercises and Applications

Practice and Apply

Getting Started Round each number to the nearest tenth by looking at the digit to the *right* of the tenths digit.

1. 3.084 3.1 **2.** 22.247 22.2 **3.** 17.458 17.5 **4.** 138.985 139.0

Round each number to the nearest whole number.

5. 15.2 15 **6.** 2.43 2 **7.** 10.39 10 **8.** 158.942 159

Round each number to the nearest whole number and multiply.

9. 14.92×0.98 ≈ 15, ≈ 1; 15 **10.** 21.94×1.34 ≈ 22, ≈ 1; 22 **11.** 1.68×9.4 ≈ 2, ≈ 9; 18 **12.** 72.8×19.68 ≈ 73, ≈ 20; 1460

Estimate.

13. 163.2×5.4 ≈ 815 **14.** $37.19 + 100.94$ ≈ 138 **15.** $\frac{45.4}{4.75}$ ≈ 9 **16.** $47.49 - 16.85$ ≈ 30

17. $39.23 + 246.49$ ≈ 290 **18.** 6343.2×2.57 ≈ 18,900 **19.** $376.82 - 139.28$ ≈ 240 **20.** $37.19 \div 8.18$ ≈ 5

21. 42.3×239.23 ≈ 9600 **22.** $731.37 - 36.48$ ≈ 700 **23.** $\frac{289.29}{42.52}$ ≈ 7 **24.** $5893.4 + 2169.3$ ≈ 8100

25. $\frac{5314.3}{2128.2}$ ≈ 2 **26.** 942.94×3.184 ≈ 2700 **27.** $842.4 - 294.31$ ≈ 550 **28.** 739.12×423.9 ≈ 280,000

Round each number to the nearest: (a) hundredth (b) tenth (c) thousandth

29. 23.3825 **30.** 312.5504 **31.** 19.0096 **32.** 99.9999

33. 0.0464 **34.** 81.8181 **35.** 43.4343 **36.** 67.6767

37. Your astronomy club wants to buy five different eyepieces for a new telescope. The 6-, 12-, and 20-millimeter lenses cost $42.95 each, and the 32- and 40-millimeter lenses cost $58.95 each. Estimate the total cost of the lenses. ≈ $240

38. Social Studies GPS A social service agency finds that, on the average, 2.87 of every 100 families need help from the agency. About how many families can they expect to help in a town of 966 families? ≈ 29 families

PRACTICE 3-2

3-2 Exercises and Applications

Assignment Guide

- **Basic** 1–35 odds, 38–41, 44–45, 47–50
- **Average** 2–36 evens, 37–39, 41–44, 46, 51–54
- **Enriched** 1–35 odds, 37–39, 41–44, 46, 51–54

Exercise Notes

Exercises 13–28

Estimation Estimates may vary depending upon the places to which students round.

Exercises 23 and 25

Error Prevention Students may need help in determining compatible numbers. Ask volunteers to give possible pairs of compatible numbers, such as 280 and 40 for Exercise 23 and 5000 and 2500 for Exercise 25.

Exercise Answers

29.	a. 23.38	b. 23.4	c. 23.383
30.	a. 312.55	b. 312.6	c. 312.550
31.	a. 19.01	b. 19.0	c. 19.010
32.	a. 100.00	b. 100.0	c. 100.000
33.	a. 0.05	b. 0.0	c. 0.046
34.	a. 81.82	b. 81.8	c. 81.818
35.	a. 43.43	b. 43.4	c. 43.434
36.	a. 67.68	b. 67.7	c. 67.677

PRACTICE

Name ____________

Practice 3-2

Estimating by Rounding

Round each number to the nearest whole number.

1. 3.874 4 **2.** 5.132 5 **3.** 21.635 22 **4.** 17.5 18

5. 36.498 36 **6.** 163.094 163 **7.** 843.17 843 **8.** 562.63 563

Round each number to the nearest whole number and multiply.

9. 8.37×12.13 96 **10.** 9.76×4.173 40 **11.** 16.53×2.75 51 **12.** 15.84×3.14 48

13. 18.5×6.19 114 **14.** 8.137×2.071 16 **15.** 5.384×3.481 15 **16.** 7.36×30.08 210

Estimate.

17. 3.76×28.4 ≈ 120 **18.** $238.4 - 88.3$ ≈ 150 **19.** $19.47 + 3.21$ ≈ 22 **20.** $\frac{81.37}{8.65}$ ≈ 9

21. 6.83×98.6 ≈ 700 **22.** $361.238 - 23.7$ ≈ 340 **23.** $835.4 + 173.2$ ≈ 1000 **24.** $157.3 \div 42.4$ ≈ 4

Round to (a) the nearest hundredth (b) the nearest tenth (c) the nearest thousandth

25. 81.3074 (a) 81.31 (b) 81.3 (c) 81.307

26. 123.6855 (a) 123.69 (b) 123.7 (c) 123.686

27. 3.41987 (a) 3.42 (b) 3.4 (c) 3.420

28. During the 1968 Olympic Games, Mamo Wolde of Ethiopia ran 26.21875 miles in 2.341 hours. Estimate the number of miles he ran each hour. About 13 mi

29. At the farmer's market, Saul bought 1.83 lb of broccoli, 0.84 lb of carrots, and 1.23 lb of onions. Estimate the total weight of his purchases. About 4 lb

RETEACHING

Name ____________

Alternative Lesson 3-2

Estimating by Rounding

There are several ways to estimate answers. One way is to round each number to the highest place value before finding the estimate mentally.

Example

Estimate 38.312 + 14.975.

Round both decimals to the highest place value. Then add to find the estimate.

Highest place value / Digit to the right: 38.312 → 40 + Highest place value / Digit to the right: 14.975 → 10 = 50

Since 40 + 10 = 50, then 38.312 + 14.975 is about 50.

Try It Estimate 47.182 − 35.539.

a. Round each decimal to its highest place value: 47.182 ≈ 50 35.539 ≈ 40

b. Subtract. ≈ 10

Estimate 134.29 + 253.74.

c. Round each decimal to its highest place value: 134.29 ≈ 100 253.74 ≈ 300

d. Add. ≈ 400

Estimate 4.9 × 21.375.

e. Round each decimal to its highest place value: 4.9 ≈ 5 21.375 ≈ 20

f. Multiply. ≈ 100

Estimate.

g. 9.135 − 4.621 ≈ 4 **h.** 7.628 + 5.495 ≈ 13

i. 7.9 × 41.348 ≈ 320 **j.** 94.859 − 28.421 ≈ 60

k. 35.713 − 18.299 ≈ 20 **l.** 46.333 + 81.623 ≈ 130

m. 135.135 + 487.999 ≈ 600 **n.** 3.589 × 14.496 ≈ 40

o. 23.732 + 19.218 ≈ 40 **p.** 809.354 − 198.526 ≈ 600

q. 8.2 × 29.6 ≈ 240 **r.** 27.136 + 34.925 ≈ 60

Reteaching

Activity

Materials: 10 × 10 grids

- On a grid, shade 0.38 as shown below. Is the amount you shaded nearer 3 columns of 10 squares or 4 columns? 4 columns
- What amount do the 4 columns represent? 0.4 So, 0.38 rounded to the nearest tenth is 0.4. Repeat with other decimals less than 1.

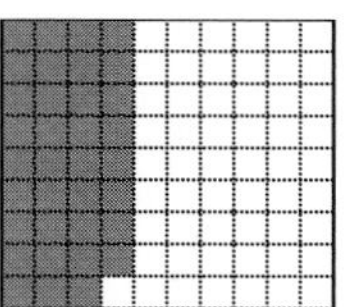

Exercise Notes

■ Exercise 42

Problem-Solving Tip You may wish to use Teaching Tool Transparencies 2 and 3: Guided Problem Solving, pages 1–2.

Exercise Answers

41. Mars: 0.2 year; Jupiter: 1.3 years; Saturn: 2.7 years; Neptune: 9.3 years.

42. Possible answer: 4.75 inches ≈ 5 inches, so the distance is 5 × 150 ≈ 750 miles.

43. Possible answer: $2.00 per hour or part thereof; Fairer way: charge by the minute.

44. Possible answer: To divide the bill fairly and to figure an appropriate tip.

45.

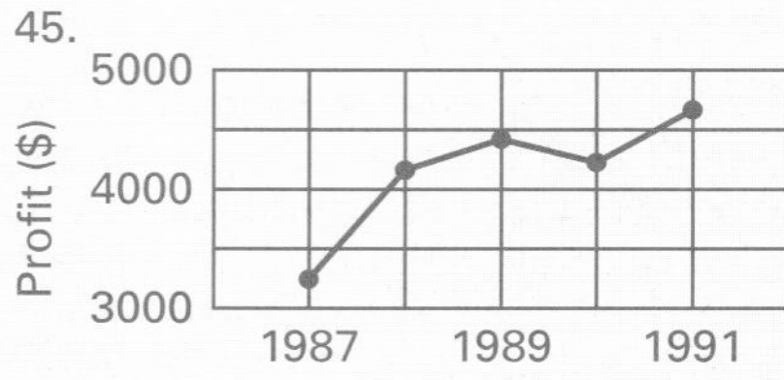

46.

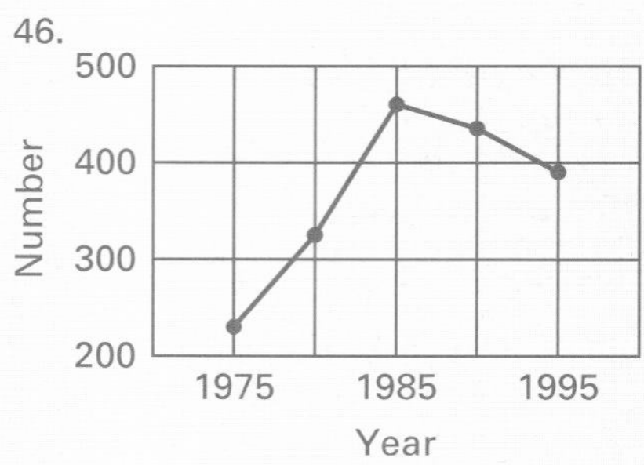

Alternate Assessment

You may want to use the *Interactive CD-ROM Journal* with this assessment.

Journal Have students describe the rounding methods they would use to find sums, differences, products, and quotients of decimal numbers.

Quick Quiz

Round 3049.68 to the given place.

1. Nearest 10 3050
2. Nearest hundred 3000
3. Nearest tenth 3049.7
4. Nearest one 3050

Available on Daily Transparency 3-2

39. **Test Prep** Which would give the best estimate for 483.64 × 29.78? B

Ⓐ 483 × 29 Ⓑ 484 × 30 Ⓒ 400 × 30 Ⓓ 500 × 25

40. **Career** A tailor needs three pieces of fabric, 1.67 yards long, 1.5 yards long, and 1.25 yards long. Estimate how many yards of material he should buy. ≈ 4.5 yards

41. **Science** *Voyager 2* travels at an average speed of about 466.73 million km per year. About how many years would it take to get to each planet in the table?

Planet	Mars	Jupiter	Saturn	Neptune
Distance from Earth (million km)	78.34	628.73	1277.38	4346.47

Problem Solving and Reasoning

42. **Choose a Strategy** Measured on a map with a scale of 150 miles per inch, the distance from Chicago to New York is 4.75 inches. How could you use estimation to find out about how many miles it is from Chicago to New York?

Problem Solving STRATEGIES

- Look for a Pattern
- Make an Organized List
- Make a Table
- Guess and Check
- Work Backward
- Use Logical Reasoning
- Draw a Diagram
- Solve a Simpler Problem

43. **Critical Thinking** An Internet service provider charges $2 per hour of use. A customer called to say that she used the Internet for 1 hour and 1 minute and was charged $4. Her friend, who uses the same Internet service provider, used the Internet for 1 hour and 50 minutes and was also charged $4. How do you think the charge was calculated? Give a more fair way to charge each user.

44. Journal Describe a situation where estimation could be used by a group of friends in a restaurant.

Mixed Review

Make a line graph for each set of data. *[Lesson 1-5]*

45.

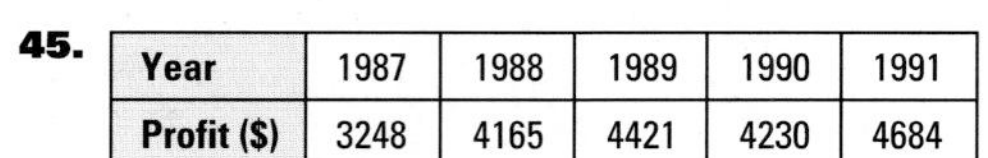

Year	1987	1988	1989	1990	1991
Profit ($)	3248	4165	4421	4230	4684

46.

Year	1975	1980	1985	1990	1995
Number	230	325	460	435	390

Solve each equation. *[Lesson 2-6]*

47. $x - 7 = 15$ $x = 22$ **48.** $u + 19 = 34$ $u = 15$ **49.** $125 = m - 72$ $m = 197$ **50.** $365 = h + 148$ $h = 217$

51. $y + 12 = 15$ $y = 3$ **52.** $16 + u = 23$ $u = 7$ **53.** $45 = n - 10$ $n = 55$ **54.** $145 = p + 76$ $p = 69$

PROBLEM SOLVING 3-2

PROBLEM SOLVING

Name ______

Guided Problem Solving 3-2

GPS PROBLEM 38, STUDENT PAGE 113

A social service agency finds that on the average, 2.87 of every 100 families need help from the agency. About how many families can they expect to help in a town of 966 families?

— Understand —

1. What are you asked to find?
About how many families need help from the social service agency.

2. Do you need to find an exact answer or an estimate? Estimate.

— Plan —

3. Use compatible numbers to estimate about how many 100s there are in 966. Write an equation.
1000 ÷ 100 = 10

4. What number sentence shows about how many can be helped? c
a. 10 × 3000 b. 1000 × 10 c. 10 × 3

— Solve —

5. About how many families can the agency help? 30 families.

— Look Back —

6. What strategy can you use to check your answer? Show an example.
Make a Table.

3	6	9	12	15	18	21	24	27	30
100	200	300	400	500	600	700	800	900	1000

SOLVE ANOTHER PROBLEM

In the seventh grade at Howard Middle School, 2.14 out of every 100 students play the trumpet. There are 400 seventh graders at Howard. About how many students play trumpet?
About 8 students.

ENRICHMENT

Name ______

Extend Your Thinking 3-2

Decision Making

The Johnston Community Center is having a fundraising chili supper and have already sold 953 tickets. This is the recipe they used.

JOHNSTON'S CHILI

9 lb hamburger	3 large cans tomato juice
6 cans chili beans	1 T. salt
3 packages of macaroni	3 T. chili powder
3 large onions	
	Serves 18

1. Estimate how many batches of chili are needed to serve 953 people. Make estimates using front-end estimation, using rounding to estimate, and using compatible numbers to estimate. Show your work.
Front-end: 900 ÷ 10 = 90; Rounding: 1000 ÷ 20 = 50; Compatible numbers: 1000 ÷ 20 = 50.

2. Look at your three estimates. Would all of the estimates be good guides for planning the amount of chili needed? Explain.
Possible answer: No. There would be too many batches made if they use front-end estimation.

3. Suppose they predict that about 200 tickets will be sold at the door. How will this change the estimates?
They will need to make about 10 more batches than originally planned.

4. How would your estimates change if the supper is an "all you can eat" supper? Explain. Possible answer: Reconsider using the front-end estimate.

5. Would it be more desirable to end up with too much chili or with not enough chili to serve the customers? How can they plan to handle each problem?
Possible answers: Donate leftovers to homeless shelters. Give coupons to redeem at next supper.

Problem Solving: Sums and Differences of Decimals

3-3

▶ Lesson Link You have solved addition and subtraction equations with whole numbers. Now you'll see how to solve addition and subtraction equations that contain decimals. ◀

You'll Learn ...

■ to solve addition and subtraction equations containing decimals

... How It's Used

When you balance a checkbook, you have to add and subtract decimal dollar amounts.

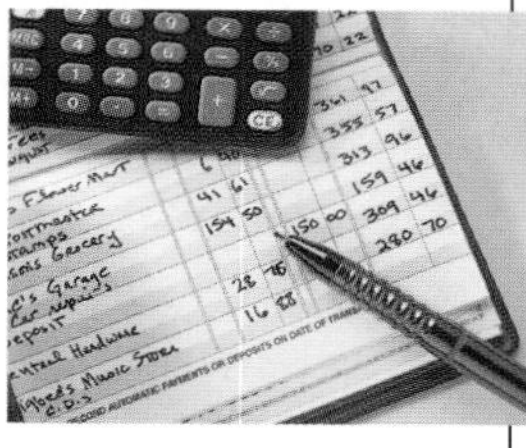

Explore Sums and Differences of Decimals

A Different Walk

Astronaut Mark Lee took part in an "extra-vehicular activity" (EVA) during a 1994 mission of the space shuttle *Discovery*. He wore a propulsion module to "walk" in space 200 miles above the earth.

The propulsion module is stored in an airlock unit aboard the shuttle.

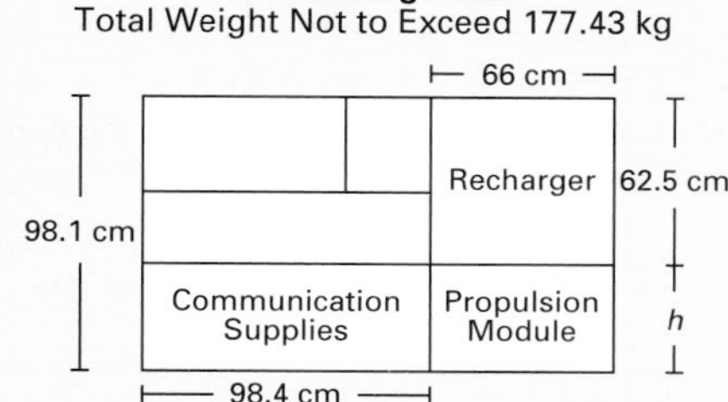

1. Find the length of the EVA propulsion module in storage. How did you get your answer?
2. Let h equal the height of the module. Write an addition equation that you can use to find h. $h + 62.5 = 98.1$
3. Find the height of the module. How did you get your answer?
4. The combined weight of the stored items other than the propulsion module is 139.83 kg. Let w equal the maximum weight of the propulsion module. Write a subtraction equation that you can use to find w. $177.43 - w = 139.83$
5. Find the maximum weight of the propulsion module. How did you get your answer?

MEETING INDIVIDUAL NEEDS

Resources

3-3 Practice
3-3 Reteaching
3-3 Problem Solving
3-3 Enrichment
3-3 Daily Transparency
Problem of the Day
Review
Quick Quiz

Learning Modalities

Logical Write the number 842.1 on the chalkboard. Then write the number 3.456 directly below it, aligning the 1 and the 6. Have students discuss why it would not be correct to add or subtract the numbers in their present arrangement.

Visual You might have students explore adding and subtracting decimals by using 10-by-10 grids or number lines.

Challenge

Have students find the missing measurements.

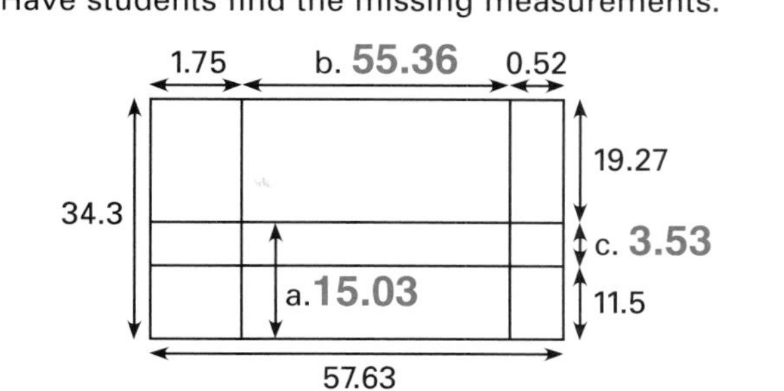

3-3 Lesson Organizer

Objective

■ Solve addition and subtraction equations containing decimals.

NCTM Standards

■ 1–4, 6, 7, 9

▶ Review

Solve each equation.

1. $x + 28 = 47$ $x = 19$
2. $a - 57 = 63$ $a = 120$
3. $18 = c - 42$ $c = 60$
4. $87 = 49 + y$ $y = 38$

Available on Daily Transparency 3-3

▶ Lesson Link

Ask students for examples of situations in which they have had to add and subtract decimals. A likely suggestion is when shopping.

1 Introduce

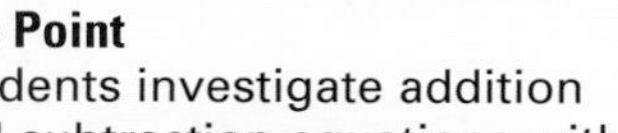

Explore

The Point
Students investigate addition and subtraction equations with decimal numbers.

Ongoing Assessment
Be sure that students remember how to add and subtract decimals correctly by first aligning the decimal points.

For Groups That Finish Early
Find three decimal numbers, x, y, and z, so that 21.84 minus x, then that difference minus y, and then that difference minus z equals 10.39.

Answers for Explore

1. 164.4 cm; Added 98.4 + 66.
3. 35.6 cm; Subtracted 62.5 from both sides of the equation.
5. 37.6 cm; Possible answer: Found a number that added to 139.83 would give the sum: 177.43.

2 Teach

Learn

Review the addition and subtraction of decimals and the solving of addition and subtraction equations involving whole numbers. Stress that it is important to estimate answers and solutions in order to determine reasonableness.

Alternate Examples

The average distance of Neptune from the sun is 29.288 AU more than the average distance of Venus from the sun, 0.723 AU. What is the average distance of Neptune from the sun?

Let x = Neptune's average distance.

Venus's distance + 29.288 = Neptune's distance

$0.723 + 29.288 = x$

Estimate: $1 + 30 = 31$

$$\begin{array}{r} 0.723 \\ \underline{29.288} \\ 30.011 \end{array}$$ Add the digits and place the decimal point.

$x = 30.011$

The estimate was 31, so the solution is reasonable. The average distance of Neptune from the sun is 30.011 AU.

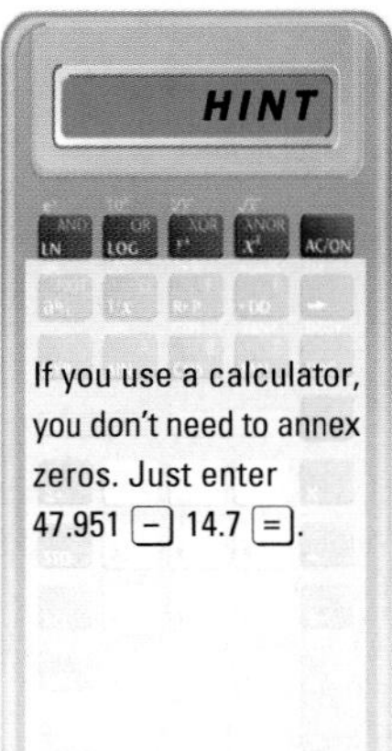

If you use a calculator, you don't need to annex zeros. Just enter 47.951 [−] 14.7 [=].

Learn Sums and Differences of Decimals

To solve addition and subtraction equations that contain decimals, you need to add and subtract decimals.

ADDING AND SUBTRACTING DECIMALS

- Write the numbers with their decimal points lined up.
- Annex zeros as needed.
- Add or subtract the digits.
- Place the decimal point in the answer.

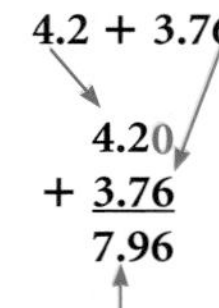

Place decimal point.

Solving decimal equations is very similar to solving whole-number equations. Remember to estimate before finding the exact solution and to check to see if your solution is reasonable.

Example 1

When Halley's comet is at its maximum distance from the sun, it is 25.72 AU (astronomical units) farther from the sun than Saturn is. Saturn's distance from the sun is 9.55 AU. Find the maximum distance of Halley's comet from the sun.

DID YOU KNOW?

Because distances in space are so great, scientists often measure distances in *astronomical units* (AU). 1 AU = 93,000,000 mi, the distance from the earth to the sun.

Let x = Halley's Comet's maximum distance. — Choose a variable.

Saturn's distance plus 25.72 AU equals maximum distance. — Describe the situation.

$9.55 + 25.72 = x$ — Write an equation.

$$\begin{array}{r} {}^{1} \\ 9.55 \\ +\underline{25.72} \\ 35.27 \end{array}$$

Estimate: $10 + 26 = 36$

Add the digits and place the decimal point.

$35.27 = x$

The estimate was 36, so the solution is reasonable.

Halley's comet's maximum distance from the sun is 35.27 AU.

Try It

Solve. **a.** $x - 4.5 = 8.6$ $x = 13.1$ **b.** $x + 16.05 = 37.4$ $x = 21.35$

MATH EVERY DAY

Problem of the Day

Several dancers in place for a Mexican hat dance are arranged evenly in a circle. The fifth person is directly opposite the eleventh person. How many dancers are there in the circle? 12 dancers

Available on Daily Transparency 3-3

An Extension is provided in the transparency package.

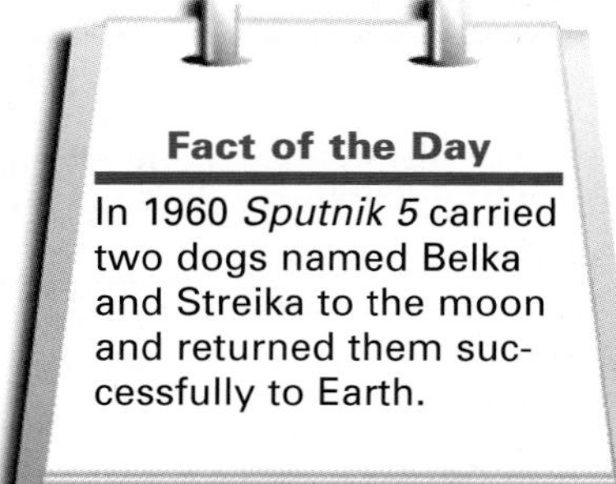

Fact of the Day

In 1960 *Sputnik 5* carried two dogs named Belka and Streika to the moon and returned them successfully to Earth.

Mental Math

Solve each equation mentally.

1. $x + 4 = 12$ $x = 8$
2. $y - 3 = 10$ $y = 13$
3. $20 = a + 5$ $a = 15$
4. $6 = m - 8$ $m = 14$

Shawon and Nedra are buying a birthday present for their mother that costs $42.95 . Nedra has $18.75 with her. How much money does Shawon have to come up with to get the present?

Shawon thinks ...

I'll let a = the amount I need.

My amount plus Nedra's amount equals the total cost.

$$a + 18.75 = 42.95$$

$$a + 18.75 - 18.75 = 42.95 - 18.75$$

$$\begin{array}{r} 42.95 \\ -\ 18.75 \\ \hline 24.20 \end{array}$$

$$a = 24.20$$

I need to add $24.20 to Nedra's amount to buy the present.

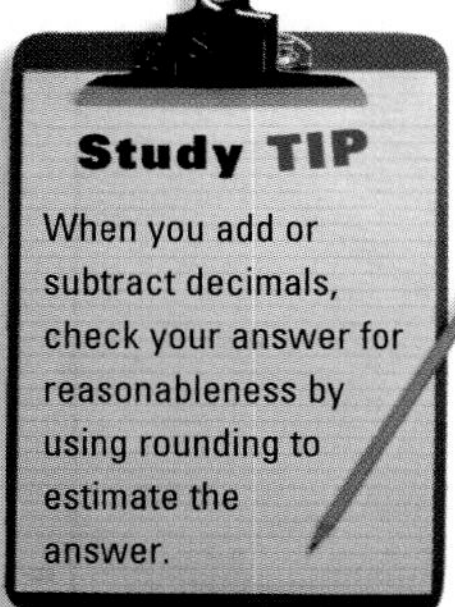

Nedra thinks ...

The amount Shawon has to come up with is the difference between the cost of the birthday present and the amount that I have with me. I'll represent the difference between 42.95 and 18.75 with the expression 42.95 − 18.75.

$$\begin{array}{r} 42.95 \\ -\ 18.75 \\ \hline 24.20 \end{array}$$

Shawon needs to add $24.20 to my amount to buy the present.

What do you think?

1. How are the two ways of finding the solution alike?
2. Would it have been helpful for Shawon and Nedra to estimate first?

Study TIP

When you add or subtract decimals, check your answer for reasonableness by using rounding to estimate the answer.

Check Your Understanding

1. Why do you line up decimal points when you add or subtract decimals?
2. How is solving a decimal equation like solving a whole-number equation?

Students see two methods of solving a problem. One involves solving an addition equation, and the other involves a subtraction calculation. Students should see that both solutions involve finding the difference of the same numbers.

Answers for What Do You Think?

1. Each method represents the situation with an equation. Shawon used a variable and wrote a sum. Nedra used an expression for a difference.
2. Yes; it would have been a way to check if their answer was reasonable.

3 Practice and Assess

Check

Be sure students understand that aligning the decimal points when adding or subtracting decimals is analogous to aligning the ones digits when adding or subtracting whole numbers.

Answers for Check Your Understanding

1. So that place values are aligned.
2. The solution methods are identical. Inverse operations are used in both cases.

MEETING MIDDLE SCHOOL CLASSROOM NEEDS

Tips from Middle School Teachers

I have students bring in information involving Olympic records that include decimals and have them write problems using addition and subtraction of decimals. We display the Olympic data and the problems on the bulletin board.

Team Teaching

Work with the science teachers to have students investigate how Earth months are related to the phases of the moon.

Science Connection

In 1949, Fred L. Whipple, an American astronomer, suggested that practically all of a comet's mass is contained in the nucleus, which is really like a "dirty snowball." That is, it consists of dust, frozen gases, and water. As the comet nears the sun, some gases escape from the nucleus and form a coma (a cloudlike mass around the nucleus) and a tail. Whipple's ideas were confirmed by the 1986 study of Halley's comet.

3-3 Exercises and Applications

Assignment Guide

- **Basic** 1–17 odds, 20–22, 25, 28–29, 31–34
- **Average** 1, 2–18 evens, 21, 23, 25–29, 35–38
- **Enriched** 3–19 odds, 21, 23–30, 35–38

Exercise Notes

Exercises 2–13

Extension Have students find the actual sums and differences. They might use calculators.

Exercise 20

Science The zero point of the Kelvin scale is absolute zero—the temperature at which molecules stop moving.

Exercise Answers

20. $384.9 = 273 + C$, 111.9°C; $K = 273 + 37.2$, 310.2K
22. 0.96; Possible answer: I thought of each number as hundredths, then added.
23. 2.3125 points
24. $731.54 million

Reteaching

Activity

Materials: 10 × 10 grids, colored pencils

- Use grids to model the equation $x + 1.4 = 3.2$. With one color, shade 3.2. Then on that model, double-shade 1.4 in another color. The amount that is shaded in only the original color represents x. Count the ones and tenths to find x. $x = 1.8$
- Use grids to model the equation $y - 0.29 = 1.3$. With one color, shade 1.3. Then shade an additional 0.29 in another color. The amount that is shaded altogether represents y. Count the ones, tenths, and hundredths to find y. $y = 1.59$

3-3 Exercises and Applications

Practice and Apply

1. **Getting Started** Follow the steps to find the difference between 42.4 and 42.268.
   a. Decide which of the two numbers is greater, and put it on top. 42.4 > 42.268
   b. Align the decimal points.
   c. Annex zeros.
   d. Subtract to find the difference. 0.132

Estimate each sum or difference.

2. $12.3 + 32.1$ ≈ 44
3. $119.07 + 53.3$ ≈ 170
4. $148 + 147.99$ ≈ 296
5. $0.066 + 0.183 + 0.10$ ≈ 0.4
6. $16.9 - 16.09$ ≈ 1
7. $1.333 - 0.667$ ≈ 0.6
8. $0.00882 - 0.00679$ ≈ 0.002
9. $0.00726 + 0.00251$ ≈ 0.010
10. $68.28 + 931.2$ ≈ 1000
11. $0.0386 - 0.003$ ≈ 0.036
12. $634.2 - 428.34$ ≈ 200
13. $0.049 + 0.134 + 0.082$ ≈ 0.26

Solve each equation.

14. $121.4 + x = 437.734$ $x = 316.334$
15. $x - 53.204 = 31.1$ $x = 84.304$
16. $34.02 = x + 9.881$ $x = 24.139$
17. $4.095 = x - 12.3$ $x = 16.395$
18. $x + 0.047 = 0.176$ $x = 0.129$
19. $0.0073 = x - 0.008367$ $x = 0.015667$
20. **Science** The formula that relates degrees Kelvin (K) to degrees Celsius (C) is $K = 273 + C$. Write and solve an equation to find the degrees Celsius for 384.9 K. Write and solve an equation to find the degrees Kelvin for 37.2°C.
21. **Test Prep** Which is the solution to the equation $13.5 = d + 5.027$? A
    Ⓐ 8.473 Ⓑ 8.527 Ⓒ 13.5 Ⓓ 18.527
22. **Journal** Find the sum $0.2 + 0.07 + 0.08 + 0.1 + 0.01 + 0.3 + 0.2$ mentally. Explain the strategy you used to find your answer.
23. **Sports** In the 1995 National Football League regular-season games, the Dallas Cowboys averaged 27.1875 points, and the Miami Dolphins averaged 24.875 points. How many more points did the Cowboys average?
24. The top ten money-earning films of 1994 included *The Lion King,* at $298.88 million; *Forrest Gump,* at $298.10 million; and *The Santa Clause,* at $134.56 million. How much did these three films earn all together?

Forrest Gump

PRACTICE 3-3

PRACTICE

Name ______________________ **Practice 3-3**

Problem-Solving: Sums and Differences of Decimals

Estimate each sum or difference.

1. $63.7 + 24.3$ ≈ 80
2. $841.63 - 124.8$ ≈ 700
3. $364.78 - 37.2$ ≈ 320
4. $53.87 + 81.3$ ≈ 130
5. $738.2 - 18.37$ ≈ 720
6. $98.76 - 21.3$ ≈ 80
7. $8.7388 + 9.01$ ≈ 18
8. $31.49 + 63.9$ ≈ 90
9. $38.754 - 21.4$ ≈ 20
10. $3.7 + 8.4 + 9.2$ ≈ 21
11. $9.3 + 1.4 + 8.9$ ≈ 19
12. $2.8 + 1.3 + 0.6$ ≈ 5
13. $87.43 + 9.06$ ≈ 96
14. $53.21 - 8.7$ ≈ 44
15. $321.846 + 0.049$ ≈ 322
16. $68.037 - 5.9$ ≈ 62

Solve each equation.

17. $x + 0.37 = 9.42$ $x =$ 9.05
18. $x - 6.43 = 8.7$ $x =$ 15.13
19. $3.841 = x + 1.2$ $x =$ 2.641
20. $8.93 = x - 0.41$ $x =$ 9.34
21. $x + 2.75 = 11.3$ $x =$ 8.55
22. $x - 5.2 = 10.17$ $x =$ 15.37
23. $3.6 = x - 8.471$ $x =$ 12.071
24. $5.2 = x + 2.13$ $x =$ 3.07
25. $88.43 = x + 1.8$ $x =$ 86.63
26. $x - 12.87 = 3.6$ $x =$ 16.47
27. $x + 37.4 = 91.6$ $x =$ 54.2
28. $63.24 = x - 9.3$ $x =$ 72.54
29. **Career** A designer needs 4.83 yards of a certain fabric to make curtains. If the designer already has 1.9 yards of the fabric, how much additional fabric must be purchased? 2.93 yd
30. The Lucky Seven Discount Store calculates the retail price (R) of every item using the formula $R = W + 7.77$, where W is the wholesale price. If a chair retails for $61.23, what is the wholesale price? $53.46

RETEACHING

Name ______________________ **Alternative Lesson 3-3**

Problem-Solving: Sums and Differences of Decimals

Solving decimal equations is very similar to solving whole-number equations. Remember to add or subtract the same number on both sides of an equation when you need to "undo" an operation. Remember also, that when adding and subtracting with decimals, write the numbers with their decimal points lined up. Annex zeros as needed. Add or subtract and place the decimal point in the answer.

Example 1

Solve $x + 23.498 = 132.76$.

$x + 23.498$	=	132.760	Annex a zero.
$- 23.498$		$- 23.498$	Subtract 23.498 from both sides.
x	=	109.262	

Example 2

Solve $x - 37.435 = 18.6$.

$x - 37.435$	=	18.600	Annex 2 zeros.
$+ 37.435$		$+ 37.435$	Add 37.435 to both sides.
x	=	56.035	

Try It Solve $x + 49.762 = 78.95$.

a. What must you do to both sides? Subtract 49.762.
b. Show your "undo" step at the right.
c. Solve the equation. $x = 29.188$

$x + 49.762$	=	78.950
$- 49.762$		$- 49.762$
		$x = 29.188$

Solve $x - 216.8 = 46.2$.

d. What must you do to both sides? Add 216.8.
e. Show your "undo" step at the right.
f. Solve the equation. $x = 263$

$x - 216.8$	=	46.2
$+ 216.8$		$+ 216.8$
x		= 263.0

Solve each equation.

g. $x - 9.382 = 12.38$ $x = 21.762$
h. $x + 12.762 = 27.934$ $x = 15.172$
i. $x + 32.766 = 45.314$ $x = 12.548$
j. $x - 25.871 = 37.443$ $x = 63.314$
k. $x - 25.321 = 38.199$ $x = 63.52$
l. $x + 92.7 = 135.842$ $x = 43.142$
m. $x + 28.315 = 47.6$ $x = 19.285$
n. $x - 32.1 = 58.977$ $x = 91.077$

Problem Solving and Reasoning

25. Critical Thinking GPS Planetary probes have small engines that technicians on Earth can use to correct the path of a probe while it is traveling between planets. A probe to Jupiter started with 55.7 kg of fuel for its engine. The engine has been used three times. Use the table to calculate how much fuel has been used and how much is remaining.

Engine Firing	1	2	3
Fuel Used (kg)	12.87	9.3	11.22

26. Critical Thinking At a fruit stand, Green Valley apples are \$0.75 each, Del-Ray apples are \$0.85 each, and pears are \$0.65 each. Kim buys one of each and pays with a \$20 bill. The cash register has just broken. Write and solve an equation to help the clerk determine how much change he owes Kim.

27. Communicate In some cases it's wise to round a very small decimal value to 0, and in some cases it's not. For each of the following, tell whether you would round 0.001 to 0 and explain why or why not.

a. $0.009 - 0.001 + 0.0007$

b. $131.10085 + 143.9784 + 0.001 + 5.3534$

28. Test Prep Jennifer is following directions to Suki's house. The directions say, "At the corner of Route 9 and Bancroft, turn right and go exactly 4.8 miles on Bancroft. The driveway will be on your left." At the corner, Jennifer's odometer reads 47,253.8. What odometer reading should she watch for in order to find Suki's driveway? D

Ⓐ 8.6 Ⓑ 47,259.0 Ⓒ 47,244.8 Ⓓ 47,258.6

Mixed Review

Draw a scatterplot and trend line for each set of data. *[Lesson 1-6]*

29.

x	1	5	7	2	5	8	3	6
y	2	4	5	3	3	6	4	4

30.

x	6.4	3.2	7.1	9.1	4.3	8.1	2.9	8.3
y	4.2	7.1	3.9	1.8	5.5	2.7	7.0	2.6

Solve each equation. Check your solution. *[Lesson 2-7]*

31. $6v = 72$ $v = 12$ **32.** $195 = x \cdot 16$ $x = 12.1875$ **33.** $7 = c \div 20$ $c = 140$ **34.** $j \div 42 = 6$ $j = 252$

35. $\frac{w}{5} = 12$ $w = 60$ **36.** $211 = y \cdot 12$ $y = 17.58\overline{3}$ **37.** $9 = \frac{d}{8}$ $d = 72$ **38.** $23e = 368$ $e = 16$

PROBLEM SOLVING 3-3

PROBLEM SOLVING

Name ______________________

Guided Problem Solving 3-3

GPS PROBLEM 25, STUDENT PAGE 119

Planetary probes have small engines that technicians on Earth can use to correct the path of a probe while it is traveling between planets. A probe to Jupiter started with 55.7 kg of fuel for its engine. The engine has been used three times. Use the table to calculate how much fuel has been used and how much is remaining.

Engine Firing	1	2	3
Fuel Used (kg)	12.87	9.3	11.22

Understand

1. How much fuel did the probe start with? 55.7 kg
2. How many times has the engine been fired? 3 times.

Plan

3. Write an expression that shows how much fuel the probe has used during the trip? 12.87 + 9.3 + 11.22
4. How much fuel has the probe used? 33.39 kg
5. What operation will you use to find how much fuel is left? Subtraction.

Solve

6. Write a sentence that tells how much fuel the probe has left? The probe has 22.31 kg of fuel left after three firings.

Look Back

7. Could you have found the amount of fuel remaining after the three trips by finding the fuel left after each trip? Explain. Yes. Subtracting fuel used from remaining fuel will give, after three calculations, the same answer. 55.7 – 12.87 = 42.83; 42.83 – 9.3 = 33.53; 33.53 – 11.22 = 22.31

SOLVE ANOTHER PROBLEM

How much fuel has been used and how much is remaining after two firings? 22.17 kg; 33.53 kg

ENRICHMENT

Name ______________________

Extend Your Thinking 3-3

Critical Thinking

Ramona's dog walked across her math homework with his muddy paws. She reconstructed the problem like this.

3☐.2☐ + ☐19.☐0 = 4☐1.87 → 3[2].2[7] + [4]19.[6]0 = 4[5]1.87

There is a 0 in the hundredths place in the second number, so the missing digit must be **7**.

In the tenths place, 6 added to 2 is 8. The missing digit must be **6**.

The sum shows a 1 as the sum in the ones place. So the actual sum must have been 11. Add **2** to 9 to get 11.

In the tens place, the sum of the 1 ten from the ones column, 3 tens and 1 ten is **5** tens.

There is no digit in the hundreds place in the first number. So the missing digit must be **4**.

Ramona's reconstructed problem is 32.27 + 419.6 = 451.87.

Complete to help Ramona reconstruct the rest of the problems.

1. 99.999 + [8][7].[6][5][5] = 187.654
2. 23[5].0[0]9 + [9]7.[8]9[2] = [3]32.901
3. 7[0]8.6[2]9 + [4]30.[9]8[6] = 113[9].615
4. [8]27.3[4]0 – 6[3][6].05[9] = 191.[2]81
5. [8]2.6[6]1 – 7[5].57[9] = 7.[0]82
6. [4][6]9.[3]9[4] – 9[8].9[9]9 = 370.395

Exercise Notes

■ **Exercise 28**

Consumer Explain that an odometer in a car measures distance covered while a speedometer measures speed.

Exercise Answers

25. Fuel used = 33.39 kg; fuel remaining = 22.31 kg
26. Possible equation: $x + 0.75 + 0.85 + 0.65 = 20.00$, $x = \$17.75$
27. Possible answers: a. No; all three numbers are very small and two of them, 0.001 and 0.0007, would round to zero, resulting in a significant amount to omit. b. Yes; all quantities are much greater than 0.001, so rounding to zero will not make a significant difference.
29. 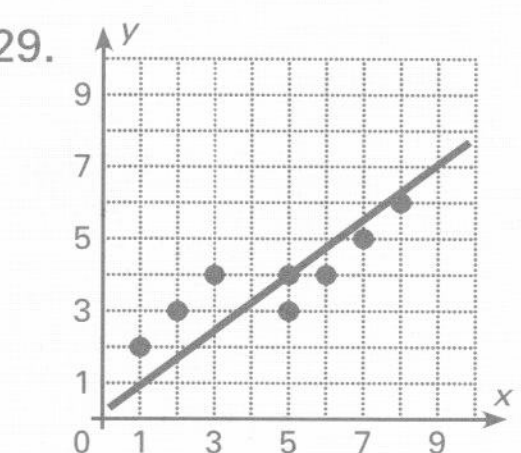
30. 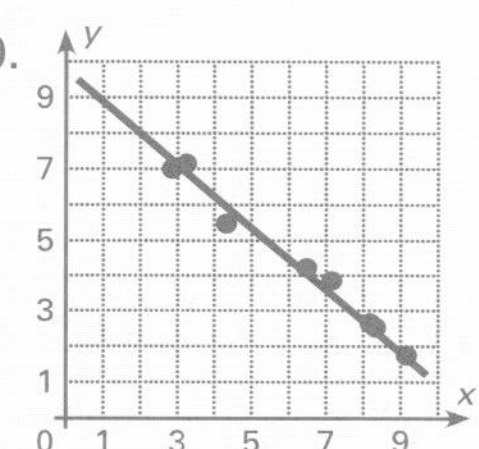

Alternate Assessment

Self Assessment Have students solve the following two equations, including explanations for each step in the solutions. Then have them show a check to demonstrate the correctness of the solutions.

1. $x + 13.29 = 20.1$ $x = 6.81$
2. $y - 16.89 = 3.514$ $y = 20.404$

Explanations may vary.

Quick Quiz

Solve each equation.

1. $a + 1.25 = 3.7$ $a = 2.45$
2. $c - 5.6 = 9.78$ $c = 15.38$
3. $12 = x + 4.82$ $x = 7.18$
4. $3.01 = y - 7.896$ $y = 10.906$

Available on Daily Transparency 3-3

3-4 Lesson Organizer

Objectives

- Multiply and divide decimal numbers.
- Solve multiplication and division equations containing decimals.

Materials

- Spreadsheet software

NCTM Standards

- 1–4, 6, 7, 9, 13

▶ Review

Solve each equation.

1. $x \cdot 8 = 96$ $x = 12$
2. $a \div 7 = 12$ $a = 84$
3. $105 = 15c$ $c = 7$
4. $7 = \frac{y}{9}$ $y = 63$

Available on Daily Transparency 3-4

▶ Lesson Link

Ask students for examples of situations in which they have had to multiply and divide decimals. As in the previous lesson, a likely suggestion is when shopping.

1 Introduce

Explore

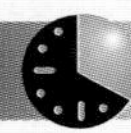

The Point
Students use spreadsheet software to explore multiplication of decimals.

Ongoing Assessment
Check that students realize that B2*B3 means *the contents of cell B2 times the contents of cell B3.*

For Groups That Finish Early
The pull of gravity for Pluto is 0.16 of that on Earth. Find the weight of a 9.4-lb probe on Pluto.
About 1.5 lb

Follow Up
Have students determine their own weights on each of the given planets.

3-4 Problem Solving: Products and Quotients of Decimals

You'll Learn ...

- to multiply and divide decimal numbers
- to solve multiplication and division equations containing decimals

... How It's Used

Caterers must purchase food in large quantities. Because recipes and packages do not always use measures that are whole numbers, a caterer must be able to multiply and divide decimals.

▶ Lesson Link You've solved addition and subtraction equations containing decimals. Now you'll solve multiplication and division equations containing decimals. ◀

Explore Products and Quotients of Decimals

Lighten Up!

Materials: Spreadsheet software

Objects on Venus weigh 0.9 times what they weigh on Earth. A space probe that weighs 9.4 pounds on Earth has landed on Venus.

	A	B
1		Venus
2	Pull of gravity	0.9
3	Probe weight on Earth	9.4
4	Probe weight on planet	

1. Set up your spreadsheet as shown. To find the weight of the probe on Venus, enter the formula "=B2*B3" into cell B4. How much does the probe weigh on Venus?
2. The table compares the force of gravity on other planets with that on Earth. Enter the planet names in row 1 and their gravity factors in row 2 of your spreadsheet. Then use the spreadsheet to calculate the weight on each planet of a probe that weighs 9.4 lb on Earth.

Body	Mars	Jupiter	Saturn	Neptune
Pull of Gravity	0.38	2.58	1.11	1.4

3. Without finding the answer, how can you tell whether a probe's weight on a planet will be greater or less than its Earth weight?

Learn Products and Quotients of Decimals

You can use models to multiply decimals. The large square represents 1. Each row and column represents one-tenth of the large square, or 0.1. Each small square represents 0.01.

Each factor in 0.4×0.2 has 1 decimal place, but the product 0.08 has 2 places.

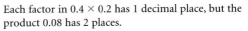

MEETING INDIVIDUAL NEEDS

Resources

- 3-4 Practice
- 3-4 Reteaching
- 3-4 Problem Solving
- 3-4 Enrichment
- 3-4 Daily Transparency
  - Problem of the Day
  - Review
  - Quick Quiz
- Chapter 3 Project Master

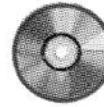

Interactive CD-ROM Spreadsheet/ Grapher Tool

Learning Modalities

Logical Have students use whole numbers greater than zero and calculators to explore whether the quotient is *less than 1, equal to 1,* or *greater than 1* in each of the following cases: A number greater than 1 is divided by a number less than 1. Greater than 1. A number less than 1 is divided by a number greater than 1. Less than 1. A number less than 1 is divided by a number less than 1. Could be less than 1, equal to 1, or greater than 1.

Social Have students work in groups of 3 or 4 to estimate the weight of common objects on Earth and then compute the weights on other planets.

English Language Development

To help students with limited English proficiency conceptualize dividing with decimals, use the idea of dividing with money. For instance, you could ask how many quarters are in \$1.50; that is, $1.5 \div 0.25$. After students give the correct answer, 6, you can write the long division on the chalkboard, showing the movement of the decimal point.

MULTIPLYING DECIMALS

- Multiply as with whole numbers.
- Place the decimal point in the product so that it has the same number of decimal places as the sum of the decimal places in the factors.

$$\begin{array}{r l} 4.36 & \text{2 decimal places} \\ \times\ 2.1 & \text{1 decimal place} \\ \hline 436 & \\ 872 & \\ \hline 9.156 & \text{3 decimal places} \end{array}$$

9.156

Example 1

A *year* is the time it takes a planet to orbit the sun. An Earth year lasts 365.3 days. A year on Mars is 1.88 times as long. Find the length of a year on Mars.

Let $x =$ the length of a Martian year. — Choose a variable.

A Martian year is 1.88 times an Earth year. — Describe the situation.

$x = 1.88 \times 365.3$ — Write an equation.

$$\begin{array}{r l} 365.3 & \text{1 decimal place} \\ \times\ 1.88 & \text{2 decimal places} \\ \hline 29224 & \\ 29224 & \\ 3653 & \\ \hline 686.764 & \text{3 decimal places} \end{array}$$

Estimate: $2 \times 400 = 800$

$x = 686.764$

The estimate was 800, so the solution is reasonable.

A Martian year is 686.764 Earth days.

Try It

Solve. **a.** $x = 0.3 \times 5.391$ $x = 1.6173$ **b.** $x = 23.41 \times 6.5$ $x = 152.165$

You can also use models to divide decimals. The model shows $0.3 \div 6$. Notice that if the decimal point is moved one place to the right in both the dividend (0.3) and the divisor (6), you get the same quotient ($3 \div 60 = 0.05$).

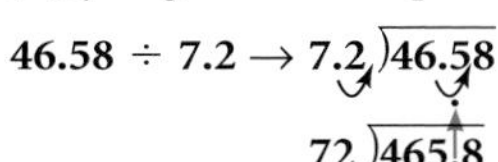

$46.58 \div 7.2 \rightarrow 7.2\overline{)46.58}$

$72\overline{)465.8}$

DIVIDING DECIMALS

- Move the decimal point the same number of places to the right in both the divisor and the dividend until the divisor is a whole number.
- Divide as you divide by a whole number.

Problem Solving TIP

Because the problem asks you to find the length of a year on Mars, you should make the variable (x) equal to the length of a year on Mars. When you solve the equation, you will have the solution to the problem.

DID YOU KNOW?

The planet with the longest year is Pluto. You would have to wait 248.5 Earth years between birthdays if you lived on Pluto!

Answers for Explore

1. 8.46 lb
2. Mars: 3.572 lb; Jupiter: 24.252 lb; Saturn: 10.434 lb; Neptune: 13.16 lb.
3. If the pull of gravity on a planet is less than 1, the weight will be less than its Earth weight. If the pull of gravity is greater than 1, the weight will be greater than its Earth weight.

2 Teach

Learn

Alternate Examples

1. A year on Venus is about 0.62 times an Earth year of 365.3 days. Find the length of a year on Venus.

   Choose a variable, describe the situation, and write an equation.

   Let $x =$ days in Venus year. A Venus year is 0.62 times an Earth year.

   $x = 0.62 \times 365.3$

   Estimate: $0.5 \times 400 = 20$

   $$\begin{array}{r l} 365.3 & \text{1 decimal place} \\ \times\ 0.62 & \text{2 decimal places} \\ \hline 7306 & \\ 21918 & \\ \hline 226.486 & \text{3 decimal places} \end{array}$$

   $x = 226.486$

   The estimate was 200, so the solution is reasonable. A Venus year is about 226.486 Earth days.

MATH EVERY DAY

Problem of the Day

A printer uses 234 pieces of type to number the pages in Jesse's book. The pages are numbered consecutively with the first page numbered 1. One piece of type is required for each digit in a page number. How many pages are in Jesse's book? 114 pages

Available on Daily Transparency 3-4

An Extension is provided in the transparency package

Fact of the Day

Mars has two small moons. Phobos has a diameter of about 13 miles, and Deimos is only about 7.5 miles in diameter.

Mental Math

Solve each equation mentally.

1. $4x = 12$ $x = 3$
2. $\frac{y}{3} = 10$ $y = 30$
3. $4a = 36$ $a = 9$
4. $6 = \frac{m}{7}$ $m = 42$

Alternate Examples

2. Divide: 36.4 ÷ 1.3
   Estimate: 36 ÷ 1 = 36

   1.3)36.4

   13)364 = 28
   26
   104
   104

3. Divide: 15.96 ÷ 4.56
   Estimate: 15 ÷ 5 = 3

   4.56)15.96

   456)1596.0 = 3.5
   1368
   2280
   2280

4. Use the formula $d = rt$ to find the time (t) it takes a space shuttle traveling at an average rate (r) of 17,181 mi/hr to make one orbit of the earth, a distance (d) of 12,543 miles.

   $12{,}543 = 17{,}181t$

   $\frac{12{,}543}{17{,}181} = \frac{17{,}181t}{17{,}181}$

   $12{,}543 \div 17{,}181 = t$
   Estimate: 10,000 ÷ 20,000 = 0.5

   12,543 ÷ 17,181 = 0.7300506

   The estimate was 0.5, so the solution is reasonable. Round to 2 decimal places. The orbit took 0.73 hour.

3 Practice and Assess

Check

Ask students if the product of two decimals greater than 1 is greater or less than 1. Greater than 1
Ask volunteers for examples. Sample: 1.5 × 3.7 = 5.55.

Answers for Check Your Understanding

1. It will be less than both numbers; Multiplying a number by a quantity less than 1 always yields a product that is less than the numbers.
2. The division is carried out in exactly the same way; The difference is that you have to consider the placement of the decimal point in the quotient.

ESTIMATION
An estimate can help you with the placement of the decimal point.

Examples

2 Divide: 11.68 ÷ 0.8

0.8)11.68 — Estimate: 12 ÷ 1 = 12

8)116.8 = 14.6
8
36
32
48
48

The quotient is 14.6.

3 Divide: 16.51 ÷ 2.54

2.54)16.51 — Estimate: 18 ÷ 3 = 6

254)1651 = 6.5
1524
1270
1270

The quotient is 6.5.

Try It

Divide. **a.** 13.8 ÷ 0.4 34.5 **b.** 9.966 ÷ 15.1 0.66

Sometimes you need to multiply or divide by decimals to solve equations.

Example 4

Use the formula $d = rt$ to find the time (t) it took a space probe that traveled at an average rate (r) of 2,342.36 mi/hr to go a distance (d) of 43,143.8 miles.

$43{,}143.8 = 2{,}342.36t$ — Substitute the values for r and d.

$\frac{43{,}143.8}{2{,}342.36} = \frac{2{,}342.36t}{2{,}342.36}$ — Undo multiplication by 2,342.36 by dividing by 2,342.36.

Estimate: 40,000 ÷ 2000 = 20 — **43143.8 [÷] 2342.36 [=] 18.418945**

$18.418945 = t$

The estimate was 20, so the solution is reasonable.

The space probe took about 18.42 hours.

Try It

Solve. **a.** $3.4x = 32.21$ $x \approx 9.47$ **b.** $\frac{n}{4.1} = 48.28$ $n \approx 197.95$

DID YOU KNOW?
On August 20, 1960, two dogs named Strelka and Belka orbited Earth in a Russian satellite. One of their puppies was given to President Kennedy.

Check Your Understanding

1. Two decimals are both less than 1. How does their product compare with the numbers themselves? Explain.
2. How is dividing decimals like dividing whole numbers? How is it different?

MEETING MIDDLE SCHOOL CLASSROOM NEEDS

Tips from Middle School Teachers

Writing and talking about mathematics is one of the best ways to learn it, so I have the students discuss what they have learned about how to calculate with decimals, either orally or in several short paragraphs.

Team Teaching

Work with the science teachers to help students understand the concept of gravity and how weights are affected on different planets.

Literature Connection

The planet Mars is named after the god of war in Roman mythology. Mars was the son of Jupiter—the king of gods. His mother was Juno. Since Mars was the father of Romulus, the legendary founder of Rome, he was thought to be the father of Roman people. Mars was often identified with Ares, the Greek god of war.

3-4 Exercises and Applications

Practice and Apply

1. **Getting Started** Follow these steps to solve $\frac{x}{9.1} = 4.2$.
   a. Round and estimate. $\approx \frac{x}{9} = 4$; $x = 36$
   b. Undo division by 9.1 by multiplying. 38.22
   c. Compare the answer to your estimate. Is it reasonable? 38.22 and 36 are close, so the answer is reasonable.

Estimate each product or quotient.

2. 2.3×32 ≈ 60 3. $11.7 \times 3.3 \approx 36$ 4. $2.47 \times 3.5 \approx 10$ 5. 4.98×2.46 ≈ 12.5 6. 37.2×2.6 ≈ 111

7. $\frac{4.6}{2.3}$ 2 8. $\frac{2.3}{4.6}$ 0.5 9. $\frac{0.046}{0.0023}$ 20 10. $\frac{0.0046}{0.023}$ 0.2 11. $\frac{0.0023}{0.0046}$ 0.5

12. $3.6 \times 1.2 \approx 4$ 13. $3.6 \times 0.12 \approx 0.4$ 14. 0.36×0.012 ≈ 0.004 15. 0.036×0.12 ≈ 0.004 16. $4.3 \times 5.07 \approx 20$

17. $\frac{8.47}{0.35} \approx 20$ 18. $\frac{0.36}{7.2}$ 0.05 19. $\frac{2.42}{0.108} \approx 24$ 20. $\frac{36.18}{0.048} \approx 720$ 21. $\frac{0.0038}{0.0689} \approx 0.05$

Solve each equation.

22. $0.12x = 0.432$ $x = 3.6$ 23. $5.06 = \frac{u}{0.092}$ $u = 0.46552$ 24. $\frac{c}{1.23} = 14.568$ $c = 17.91864$ 25. $4.785 = 1.7x$ $x \approx 2.8147$

26. $3.278s = 2.34$ $s \approx 0.71$ 27. $0.28 = \frac{a}{3.56}$ $a = 0.9968$ 28. $45.3 = 4.7x$ $x \approx 9.64$ 29. $\frac{k}{12.67} = 0.04$ $k = 0.5068$

30. **Measurement** The formula $c = 2.54i$ relates the number of inches (i) and the number of centimeters (c). Find how many inches are in 15 centimeters. 15 cm $\approx$ 5.9 in.

31. **Test Prep** Juice boxes cost \$3.89 for a six-pack. Which is the best estimate for the price of one juice box? B

    Ⓐ \$23.34 Ⓑ \$0.65 Ⓒ \$0.80 Ⓓ \$1.54

32. **Science** The number of times a telescope magnifies an image is equal to its length divided by the focal length of the eyepiece. If a 0.996-m-long telescope has a 0.0125-m eyepiece, what is the telescope's magnification? How many decimal places are there in your answer? Do you think you need to describe the magnification to this number of decimal places? Explain.

PRACTICE 3-4

PRACTICE

Name ____________

Practice 3-4

Problem-Solving: Products and Quotients of Decimals

Estimate each product or quotient.

1. 0.05×0.86 ≈ 0.045 2. 0.809×1.2 ≈ 0.8 3. 3.54×0.07 ≈ 0.28 4. $\frac{21.44}{13.4}$ ≈ 2

5. $\frac{0.1944}{0.9}$ ≈ 0.2 6. $\frac{4.716}{3.6}$ ≈ 1.25 7. 13.9×0.35 ≈ 5.6 8. 7.5×0.41 ≈ 3.2

9. 0.348×0.3 ≈ 0.09 10. $\frac{64.32}{13.4}$ ≈ 5 11. $\frac{9.4325}{0.686}$ ≈ 13 12. $\frac{161.56}{8.8}$ ≈ 18

13. 0.009×80 ≈ 0.72 14. 2.9×0.1 ≈ 0.3 15. 14.58×0.2 ≈ 3 16. $\frac{0.1572}{0.4}$ ≈ 0.4

Solve each equation.

17. $8.5d = 112.2$ $d =$ 13.2 18. $\frac{a}{0.29} = 8.9$ $a =$ 2.581 19. $0.1n = 0.313$ $n =$ 3.13 20. $\frac{b}{0.7} = 8.953$ $b =$ 6.2671

21. $\frac{s}{11.39} = 0.48$ $s =$ 5.4672 22. $1.13f = 0.2712$ $f =$ 0.24 23. $\frac{k}{4.1} = 15$ $k =$ 61.5 24. $9.2d = 30.222$ $d =$ 3.285

25. $\frac{x}{8.5} = 9.378$ $x =$ 79.713 26. $2.1d = 6.3$ $d =$ 3 27. $\frac{m}{4.33} = 1.5$ $m =$ 6.495 28. $\frac{u}{15.5} = 4.79$ $u =$ 74.245

29. $4.7z = 19.458$ $z =$ 4.14 30. $\frac{u}{3.155} = 6.4$ $u =$ 20.192 31. $2.08m = 5.3456$ $m =$ 2.57 32. $\frac{v}{4.4} = 8.37$ $v =$ 36.828

33. **Measurement** The formula $p = 2.2k$ relates the mass (k) in kilograms and the weight (p) in pounds. Find the mass, in kilograms, of a casserole weighing 1.474 pounds. 0.67 kg

34. Find the price of 1.83 lb of cauliflower costing \$0.63 per pound. Round your answer to the nearest cent. \$1.15

RETEACHING

Name ____________

Alternative Lesson 3-4

Problem Solving: Products and Quotients of Decimals

You can multiply and divide decimals using the techniques you learned for multiplying and dividing whole numbers. Placing the decimal in the answer is an important key in getting a correct answer.

Example 1

Find 0.0321 x 0.47.

Multiply as with whole numbers.

```
  0.0321
 × 0.47
   2247
  12840
  15087
```

Write the decimal point in the product.

```
  0.0321  ← 4 decimal places
 × 0.47   ← 2 decimal places
   2247
  12840
0.015087  ← 6 decimal places
 ↑ Annex a zero.
```

So $0.0321 \times 0.47 = 0.015087$.

Try It Find the products.

a. 0.09×8.65 0.7785 b. $0.08 \times 0.479 =$ 0.03832
c. 0.008×0.306 0.002448 d. 0.037×0.4 0.0148
e. 0.02×0.089 0.00178 f. 0.019×0.05 0.00095

Example 2

Find $1.2 \div 0.06$.

Multiply the divisor by a power of 10 that will make it a whole number. (× 100) 0.06)1.2

Multiply the dividend by the same number. Annex zeros if needed. (× 100) 0.06)1.20

Divide as with whole numbers. Place the decimal point above its new position in the dividend.

```
   20.
 6)120.
   12
    00
     0
```

So $1.2 \div 0.06 = 20$.

Try It Find the quotients.

g. $6.768 \div 7.2$ 0.94 h. $12.992 \div 2.03$ 6.4
i. $0.37185 \div 5.55$ 0.067 j. $5.1 \div 0.003$ 1700
k. $2.7 \div 0.009$ 300 l. $0.4992 \div 3.12$ 0.16

3-4 Exercises and Applications

Assignment Guide

- **Basic** 1–19 odds, 22–25, 30–31, 33–34, 35–47 odds
- **Average** 1, 2–28 evens, 31–35, 36–46 evens
- **Enriched** 1–29 odds, 31–35, 37–38, 40–46 evens

Exercise Notes

Exercises 2–21

Extension Have students find the actual products and quotients. You may wish to have them use calculators.

Exercise Answers

32. 79.68; 2 decimal places; No; Your eyes cannot tell the difference between 79.68 times and 80 times magnification.

Reteaching

Activity

Materials: Graph paper, calculator

- Find the product 8.4×12.3 using graph paper to help you align the numbers correctly. First, estimate: $8 \times 10 = 80$.
- Write one digit in each square as shown below. Then multiply as with whole numbers and use your estimate to place the decimal point. Could the product be 10,332? No 1033.2? No 103.32? Yes 10.332? No 1.0332? No

			1	2.	3		
	x			8.	4		
			4	9	2		
		9	8	4			
	1	0	3	3	2		

- Check your answer with your calculator.
- Use the same method to find the quotient $15.4 \div 1.4$. $15.4 \div 1.4 = 11$

Exercise Notes

■ Exercise 34

Science Ganymede is the largest moon in the solar system. It is larger even than the planets Pluto and Mercury.

Project Progress

You may want to have students use Chapter 3 Project Master.

Exercise Answers

33. \$10.68; Divided 41.7 by 27.3 to find number of gallons per day, multiplied result by \$1.39 to find cost per day, multiplied by 5 to find cost per week.

34.

Moon	Io	Ganymede	Callisto
Orbital Radius (km x 1,000,000)	0.42	1.07	1.88
Periods (days)	1.77	7.15	16.69
Orbital distance (radius x 6.28)	2.6376	6.7196	11.8064
Speed $\frac{\text{distance}}{\text{period}}$	1.490	0.94	0.7074

35. $4.3w - 3.7 + 3.7 = 9.5 + 3.7$; undo subtraction by adding. $\frac{4.3w}{4.3} = \frac{13.2}{4.3}$; perform addition and undo multiplication by dividing.

$w \approx 3.0697 \approx 3.07$; divide and round to nearest hundredth.

Alternate Assessment

Performance Have students solve the following two equations, including explanations for each step in the solutions.

1. $x \cdot 12.3 = 9.84$ $x = 0.8$
2. $\frac{y}{4.2} = 3.55$ $y = 14.91$

Explanations may vary.

➤ Quick Quiz

Solve each equation.

1. $a \cdot 1.25 = 3$ $a = 2.4$
2. $c \div 5.6 = 0.9$ $c = 5.04$
3. $8.54 = 6.1x$ $x = 1.4$
4. $3.1 = \frac{y}{7.8}$ $y = 24.18$

Available on Daily Transparency 3-4

Problem Solving and Reasoning

33. Communicate Ilse's mother commutes 41.7 miles every day. If her car averages 27.3 miles per gallon and gasoline costs \$1.399 per gallon, how much are her gasoline costs for one 5-day work week? Explain how you found your answer.

34. Critical Thinking GPS As part of her research in astronomy, Nava has been calculating the speed of travel of the moons in the solar system. Here is some of the data she has collected for some of the moons of Jupiter:

Copy and complete the table.

Moon	Io	Ganymede	Callisto
Orbital Radius (km × 1,000,000)	0.42		
Period (days)	1.77	7.15	16.69
Orbital Distance (radius × 6.28)		6.7196	11.8064
Speed $\left(\frac{\text{distance}}{\text{period}}\right)$		0.94	

Io, a moon of Jupiter

35. Critical Thinking Use inverse operations to solve $4.3w - 3.7 = 9.5$. Give a reason for each step.

Mixed Review

Find the value of each expression. *[Lesson 2-2]*

36. $43 + 15 \div 5$ 46 **37.** $7 \times (84 - 32)$ 364 **38.** $\frac{96 - 18 \times 3}{12 - (3 + 2)}$ 6 **39.** $\frac{45 \div (8 - 3)}{2 \times 4 + 1}$ 1

Solve each equation. Check your answer. *[Lesson 2-8]*

40. $3y + 7 = 28$ $y = 7$ **41.** $12g - 13 = 71$ $g = 7$ **42.** $8x - 17 = 63$ $x = 10$ **43.** $339 = 23x + 17$ $x = 14$

44. $\frac{k}{12} + 24 = 73$ $k = 588$ **45.** $100 = \frac{w}{7} - 18$ $w = 826$ **46.** $\frac{x}{4} - 3 = 32$ $x = 140$ **47.** $\frac{c}{17} + 39 = 57$ $c = 306$

PROBLEM SOLVING 3-4

Project Progress

Draw a picture or diagram of one set of animal parents (the *first* generation). Do library research to find out how many babies this pair might have at one time (the *second* generation). Indicate the number of babies on your picture.

Problem Solving
Understand
Plan
Solve
Look Back

PROBLEM SOLVING

Name ____________

Guided Problem Solving 3-4

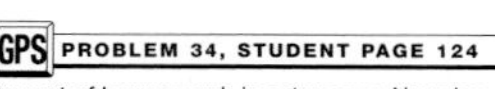

GPS PROBLEM 34, STUDENT PAGE 124

As part of her research in astronomy, Nava has been calculating the speed of travel of the moons in the solar system. Here is some of the data she has collected for some of the moons of Jupiter. Complete the table.

Moon	Io	Ganymede	Callisto	Europa
Orbital Radius (km × 1,000,000)	0.42	1.07	1.88	0.67
Period (days)	1.77	7.15	16.69	3.55
Orbital Distance (radius × 6.28)	2.6376	6.7196	11.8064	4.2076
Speed $\left(\frac{\text{distance}}{\text{period}}\right)$	1.490	0.94	0.707	1.1852

— Understand —

1. What formula is used to find the orbital distance? radius × 6.28
2. What formula is used to find the speed? distance ÷ period

— Plan —

3. Write an expression for finding the orbital radius when you know the orbital distance. $d \div 6.28$

— Solve —

4. Complete the table.
   a. Use the formulas to complete the data for Io.
   b. For Ganymede, you know the orbital distance. Find the orbital radius.
   c. Find the orbital radius for Callisto. Then find the speed.

— Look Back —

5. Would it be easier to complete the table by finding all orbital radii, then all the orbital distances, and so on? Explain. Possible answer: Yes, you would not need to alternate formulas.

SOLVE ANOTHER PROBLEM

Europa, another of Jupiter's moons has an orbital radius of 0.67 and a period of 3.55 days. Extend the table above and add the data. Then complete the table to find the missing data.

ENRICHMENT

Name ____________

Extend Your Thinking 3-4

Patterns in Numbers

Find each product.

1. 26×3 78; 26×0.3 7.8; 26×0.03 0.78; 26×0.003 0.078
2. 26×3 78; 2.6×3 7.8; 0.26×3 0.78; 0.026×3 0.078
3. What pattern do you notice in the products? Possible answer: Adjacent products are the same because there are the same number of decimal places in the factors of each problem.
4. Use the digits 3 and 26 as factors. Find three different pairs of numbers using any combination of decimal places whose product is 0.0000078. Possible answer: (3)0.0000026; (0.3)0.000026; (0.03)0.00026

Find each quotient.

5. $408 \div 12$ 34; $408 \div 1.2$ 340; $408 \div 0.12$ 3400; $408 \div 0.012$ 34,000
6. $408 \div 12$ 34; $40.8 \div 12$ 3.4; $4.08 \div 12$ 0.34; $0.408 \div 12$ 0.034
7. What pattern do you notice in the quotients? Possible answer: Decreasing divisor by power of ten increases quotient by same; decreasing dividend by power of ten decreases quotient by same.
8. Use the digits 12 as the divisor and 408 as the dividend. Find three different pairs of numbers using any combination of decimal places whose quotient is 0.000034. Possible answer: $0.000408 \div 12$; $0.00408 \div 120$; $0.0408 \div 1200$

Powers of 10 and Scientific Notation

3-5

▶ Lesson Link You've seen that some numbers are too large to be written down easily. Now you'll use a method created by scientists that makes it easier to write and work with very large numbers. ◀

Explore Expressing Numbers as Powers of 10

Table for 10

Materials: Scientific or graphing calculator

1. Copy and complete the table.

Multiply	10	10 · 10	10 · 10 · 10	10 · 10 · 10 · 10	10 · 10 · 10 · 10 · 10
Result	10	100			
No. of 0s	1	2			

Study the patterns in the table. Then answer the following questions.

2. How is the number of zeros related to the number of 10s multiplied?
3. How many times must you multiply 10 by itself to get 100,000,000,000,000,000,000,000,000?

Now use the patterns in the first two columns to complete this table.

2×100	$7.2 \times 10{,}000$	3.5×1000		$36.8 \times 1{,}000{,}000{,}000$
200	72,000		4,800,000	

4. How does your calculator display the result in the last column?

You'll Learn ...

- to use exponents to write powers of 10
- to write large numbers in scientific notation

... How It's Used

Scientific notation helps scientists write and calculate with huge numbers that are involved in distances and speeds related to space.

Vocabulary

exponent
base
power
standard form
scientific notation

Learn Powers of 10 and Scientific Notation

A number like 1000 can be written as $10 \times 10 \times 10$. When factors are repeated, you can use an **exponent** and a **base**. You can write $10 \times 10 \times 10$ as 10^3 because there are three 10s multiplied together. The product (1000) is called a **power** of 10. 10, 100, and 10,000 are also powers of 10.

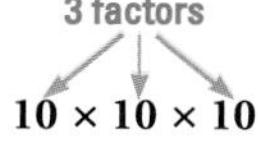

MEETING INDIVIDUAL NEEDS

Resources

3-5 Practice
3-5 Reteaching
3-5 Problem Solving
3-5 Enrichment
3-5 Daily Transparency
Problem of the Day
Review
Quick Quiz

Teaching Tool Transparency 22

Wide World of Mathematics Middle School: Hubble Telescope

Learning Modalities

Verbal The concept of scientific notation can be a difficult one. Help students to verbalize orally or in writing the meanings of the new terms in this lesson.

Social Have students complete **Explore** in pairs. It would be a good experience for pairs to have access to both scientific and graphing calculators if they are available.

English Language Development

You might relate the term *base* to the base of a statue, which is its lower part, just as the base of a power is its lower part. To help students understand *standard form*, remind them that *standard* means normal or usual, and that standard form is the normal, or usual, form in which they see numbers.

When doing the **Social** activity above, pair English language learners with students more proficient in English.

3-5 Lesson Organizer

Objectives

- Use exponents to write powers of 10.
- Write large numbers in scientific notation.

Vocabulary

- Exponent, base, power, standard form, scientific notation

Materials

- Explore: Scientific or graphing calculator

NCTM Standards

- 1–4, 6, 7, 8

▶ Review

Find each product.

1. $4 \times 4 \times 4$ 64
2. 10×35 350
3. $3 \times 3 \times 3 \times 3$ 81
4. 62×100 6200
5. 2000×30 60,000

Available on Daily Transparency 3-5

1 Introduce

Explore

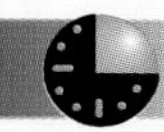

You may want to use Teaching Tool Transparency 22: Scientific Calculator with **Explore**.

The Point
Students use a calculator to find patterns for powers of 10, then apply those patterns to multiplication, which leads to the use of scientific notation.

Ongoing Assessment
Students should recognize that the number of zeros in a product is the same as the number of times that 10 is used as a factor.

Answers for Explore on next page.

For Groups That Finish Early
With your partner, take turns making up multiplication problems involving powers of 10 and decimal numbers. The products can be checked by using a calculator.

Answers for Explore

1. See page C5.
2. They are equal.
3. 26 times; See page C5 for table.
4. Possible answer: 3.68E10

2 Teach

Learn

Write 3^4 on the chalkboard and ask students to identify the base and the exponent in the expression. 3, 4 Then ask them what the expression means and to evaluate it. 3 is used as a factor 4 times for a product of 81.

Alternate Examples

1. Evaluate 4^6.

   $4^6 = 4 \times 4 \times 4 \times 4 \times 4 \times 4$
   $= 4096$

2. Multiply 3.072×10^5.

   Move decimal point 5 places to the right and annex zeros. Write as a whole number.

   $3.072 \times 10^5 = 307200.0$
   $= 307,200$

Example 1

Evaluate 3^5.

$3^5 = 3 \cdot 3 \cdot 3 \cdot 3 \cdot 3$ — Use the meaning of an exponent.

$= 243$ — Multiply.

You can multiply a decimal or a whole number by a power of 10 simply by moving the decimal point. A calculator or pencil-and-paper calculation will show that $3.2 \times 10,000 = 32,000$.

If you annex zeros, you can see that the decimal point in 32,000.0 is four places to the right of the decimal point in 3.20000.

3.2 → 3.20000 (1 2 3 4)
32,000 → 32000.0

If 10,000 is written as 10^4, you can see that the exponent (4) tells you the number of places to the right to move the decimal point.

MENTAL MATH

When you multiply numbers that end with zeros, multiply the other digits and put all the zeros at the end.

Example 2

Multiply 5.47×10^6.

$5.47 \times 10^6 = 5.470000.0$ — Move the decimal point six places to the right and annex zeros.

$= 5,470,000$ — Write as a whole number.

Scientists use an understanding of powers of 10 to help them write very large numbers.

The numbers you have used so far have been written in **standard form**. The number 88,000 is written in standard form.

88,000 can be expressed many ways using powers of 10.

$8,800 \times 10$ $\quad$ 880×100, or 880×10^2

88×1000, or 88×10^3 $\quad$ $8.8 \times 10,000$, or 8.8×10^4

The last notation, 8.8×10^4, is called **scientific notation**. Scientific notation is a way of writing large numbers. A number written in scientific notation has three parts:

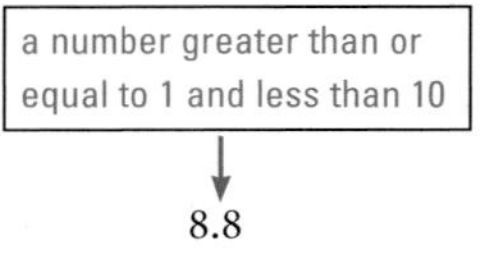

×
×

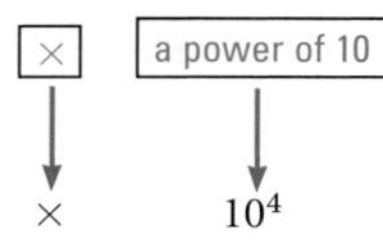

MATH EVERY DAY

Problem of the Day

A stack of 100 sheets of paper is about 0.7 mm high. How many kilometers high would a stack of 1,000,000,000,000 sheets of paper be? 7,000 km high;

Stacks of 100 sheets: 1,000,000,000,000 ÷ 100 (sheets in a stack) = 10,000,000,000;
Height in mm: 10,000,000,000 × 0.7 = 7,000,000,000;
Height in km: 7,000,000,000 ÷ 1,000,000 (mm in a kilometer) = 7,000

Available on Daily Transparency 3-5

An Extension is provided in the transparency package.

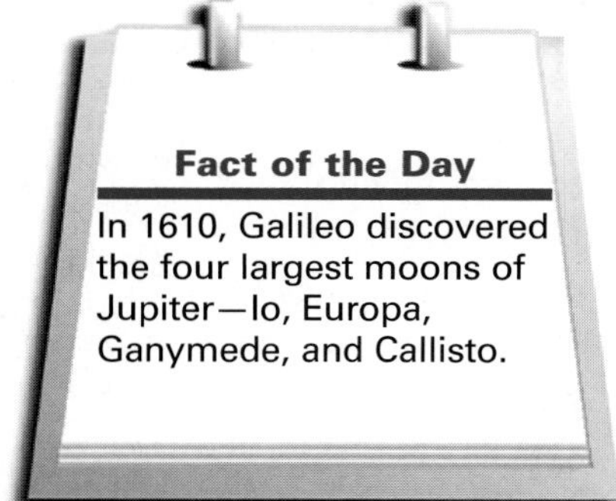

Fact of the Day
In 1610, Galileo discovered the four largest moons of Jupiter—Io, Europa, Ganymede, and Callisto.

Mental Math

Give each expression using exponents.

1. $2 \times 2 \times 2$ 2^3
2. $3 \times 3 \times 3 \times 3$ 3^4
3. 9×9 9^2
4. $15 \times 15 \times 15$ 15^3

To write a number in scientific notation, count how many places you must move the decimal point to get a number greater than or equal to 1 and less than 10. The number of places you move the decimal point is the power of 10.

$24{,}000.0 = 24{,}000.0$ 4 places, 2.4 is between 1 and 10.

$2.4000.0 \times 10^4$

Examples

3 The average distance of Jupiter's moon Callisto from Jupiter is 1,880,000 km. Write the distance in scientific notation.

$1{,}880{,}000.0 \rightarrow 1.88 \times 10^6$ ← number of places decimal point moved

Check: $1.88 \times 10^6 = 1.88 \times 1{,}000{,}000 = 1{,}880{,}000$

The distance in scientific notation is 1.88×10^6 km.

Galileo's observations of Jupiter's moons.

4 The total number of cars, trucks, and buses in the world in 1992 was about 6.13×10^8. Write the number in standard form.

Reverse the procedure you use to write a number in scientific notation.

6.13×10^8 ← number of places *to move* the decimal point to the right

$6.13000000.0$ (8 places right) → 613,000,000

The number of vehicles was about 613,000,000, or 613 million.

Try It

Write in scientific notation. **a.** 31,700,000,000 3.17×10^{10} **b.** 9,600.5 9.6005×10^3

Write in standard form. **c.** 4.1×10^5 410,000 **d.** 2.894×10^{12} 2,894,000,000,000

Science Link

Astronomers have so far discovered 16 moons of Jupiter, ranging in size from the tiny Leda, with a diameter of 16 km, to the giant Ganymede, which is 5,260 km across. Four of Jupiter's moons are larger than the planet Pluto.

Check Your Understanding

1. What advantages does scientific notation have over standard notation?
2. Is 52.6×10^4 written in scientific notation? Is 1×10? Explain both answers.

Alternate Examples

3. The average distance from Mars to the sun is about 141,750,000 miles. Write this distance in scientific notation.

   $1.41{,}750{,}000.0 \rightarrow 1.4175 \times 10^8$

   Check: $1.4175 \times 10^8 = 1.4175 \times 100{,}000{,}000 = 141{,}750{,}000$

4. Light from the sun reaches Earth in about 4.99012×10^2 seconds. Write this time in standard form.

   $4.99.012 \times 10^2 \rightarrow 499.012$

   Light from the sun reaches Earth in about 499.012 seconds.

3 Practice and Assess

Check

Ask students how many digits come before the decimal point in any number greater than or equal to 1 and less than 10. 1 Stress that when a number is written in scientific notation, the part which is *not* the power of 10 has exactly 1 digit preceding the decimal point.

Answers for Check Your Understanding

1. Possible Answer: Numbers can be much easier to write and work with; the notation can be shorter.
2. No; 52.6 is not between 1 and 10; Yes. The first number is 1, and 10 is the same as 10^1.

MEETING MIDDLE SCHOOL CLASSROOM NEEDS

Tips from Middle School Teachers

I pose this problem to be solved using a calculator: Light travels at the speed of about 186,282 miles per second. Find the distance light travels in 1 day. When the students calculate $186{,}282 \times 60 \times 60 \times 24$, their calculators may display an error message or a number in scientific notation: 1.6095 10, which is 1.6095×10^{10} or around 16 billion miles.

Team Teaching

Work with the science teachers in your team to reinforce the use of numbers in scientific notation.

Cultural Connections

In 1984 Svetlana Savitskaya of Russia became the first woman to walk in space. The space shuttle was *Soyuz T-12.*

The Quechua of Bolivia and the Maya of Mexico had observatories to study astronomy prior to the arrival of Christopher Columbus.

3-5 Exercises and Applications

Assignment Guide

- Basic
  1, 2–18 evens, 19, 20–28 evens, 34–35, 38–48 evens
- Average
  1, 3–29 odds, 30–34, 35–47 odds
- Enriched
  2–18 evens, 19, 28–36, 40–48 evens

Exercise Notes

Exercise 28

Error Prevention Students should be able to order the masses by first arranging them in order of the powers of 10 and then further ordering within the powers by the corresponding factors.

Exercise Answers

20. 8,000,000
21. 600,000,000
22. 520,000,000
23. 1,200,000,000,000
24. 135
25. 498,000
26. 23,680,000,000
27. 5,690,000
28. Pluto: 1.32×10^{22}; Mercury: 3.30×10^{23}; Mars: 6.42×10^{23}; Venus: 4.87×10^{24}; Earth: 5.98×10^{24}; Uranus: 8.69×10^{25}; Neptune: 1.02×10^{26}; Saturn: 5.69×10^{26}; Jupiter: 1.90×10^{27}.

Reteaching

Activity

Materials: Calculator

- Use your calculator to write the number 156,892 in scientific notation. How many times must you divide by 10 in order to get a quotient between 1 and 10? 5 This is the exponent of 10.
- What is the quotient? 1.56892 The quotient is the other factor, so 156,892 = 1.56892×10^5. Try this method with other numbers.

3-5 Exercises and Applications

Practice and Apply

1. **Getting Started** Follow these steps to write 16,120,000 in scientific notation.
   a. Move the decimal point to the left until it is between the first two digits. 1.6120000
   b. Count how many spaces the decimal point moved. 7
   c. Use that number as the exponent of 10. 16,120,000 = _____ × 10— 1.612×10^7

Evaluate.

2. 2^3 8 3. 3^2 9 4. 5^3 125 5. 10^4 10,000 6. 2^6 64

Write each number in scientific notation.

7. 9,370,000,000 9.37×10^9
8. 8,500 8.5×10^3
9. 175 1.75×10^2
10. 93,000 9.3×10^4
11. 1,010,000,000 1.01×10^9
12. 10,100,000 1.01×10^7
13. 36,540,000 3.654×10^7
14. 384,200 3.842×10^5
15. 990,000,000,000,000,000 9.9×10^{17}
16. 96,500 9.65×10^4
17. 243,000,000 2.43×10^8
18. 439,300,000 4.393×10^8
19. **Test Prep** In scientific notation, 40,240,000,000 is written: C
    Ⓐ 40.240×10^6 Ⓑ 40.240×10^9 Ⓒ 4.024×10^{10} Ⓓ 4.024×10^{11}

Write each number in standard form.

20. 8×10^6
21. 6×10^8
22. 5.2×10^8
23. 1.2×10^{12}
24. 1.35×10^2
25. 4.98×10^5
26. 2.368×10^{10}
27. 5.69×10^6
28. **Science** The illustration shows the masses of the nine planets in the solar system in kilograms. List their masses in order from least to greatest.

PRACTICE 3-5

PRACTICE

Name ______________________

Practice 3-5

Powers of 10 and Scientific Notation

Evaluate.

1. 4^2 16
2. 5^4 625
3. 3^3 27
4. 9^2 81

Write each number in scientific notation.

5. 30 3×10^1
6. 84,000 8.4×10^4
7. 400 4×10^2
8. 390 3.9×10^2
9. 3,820 3.82×10^3
10. 470 4.7×10^2
11. 976,000 9.76×10^5
12. 3,740,000 3.74×10^6

Write each number in standard form.

13. 3.5×10^3 3500
14. 7.8×10^6 7,800,000
15. 6.38×10^4 63,800
16. 1.87×10^7 18,700,000
17. 3.41×10^2 341
18. 3.841×10^3 3,841
19. 8.4×10^4 84,000
20. 9.3×10^6 9,300,000
21. 5.1×10^{11} 510,000,000,000
22. 9×10^{13} 90,000,000,000,000

23. **Social Science** The table shows estimated 1995 populations of some eastern Asian nations. List the populations, in standard form, in order from least to greatest.

Nation	China	Hong Kong	Japan	North Korea	South Korea	Mongolia
Population	1.22×10^9	5.9×10^6	1.25×10^8	2.39×10^7	4.5×10^7	2.4×10^6

2,400,000, 5,900,000, 23,900,000, 45,000,000, 125,000,000, 1,220,000,000

24. The average person has about 1×10^4 taste buds. Use your calculator and the information in Exercise 23 to estimate the number of human taste buds in China. Give your answer in scientific notation. 1.22×10^{13}

RETEACHING

Name ______________________

Alternative Lesson 3-5

Powers of 10 and Scientific Notation

The number 72,000 is written in **standard form.** Another way of writing large numbers is **scientific notation.** The number 72,000 written in scientific notation has three parts.

a number greater than or equal to 1 and less than 10 × a power of ten

7.2 × 10^4

Example 1

Write 68,000,000 in scientific notation.

68,000,000.

Move decimal point in 68,000,000 **seven** places to the left to get a number greater than or equal to 1 and less than 10.

Use **7** as the exponent to show a power of ten. 6.8×10^7

So 68,000,000 written in scientific notation is 6.8×10^7.

Try It Write each number in scientific notation.

a. 2300 2.3×10^3
b. 190,000 1.9×10^5
c. 2,334,000 2.334×10^6
d. 40,240,000 4.024×10^7
e. 42,000 4.2×10^4
f. 871,000,000 8.71×10^8
g. 5,004,000 5.004×10^6
h. 325,000 3.25×10^5

Example 2

Write 4.3×10^5 in standard form.

4.30000.

The power of ten is **5.** Annex zeros and move the decimal point in 4.3 **five** places to the right to show the result of multiplying by 10^5 or 100,000.

So 4.3×10^5 written in standard form is 430,000.

Try It Write each number in standard notation.

i. 6.41×10^4 64,100
j. 2.9×10^3 2900
k. 3.120×10^7 31,200,000
l. 4.7×10^5 470,000
m. 4.8×10^3 4800
n. 2.59×10^4 25,900
o. 1.7×10^2 170
p. 3.7×10^4 37,000

29. Social Studies In 1994, the U.S. national debt (the amount of money owed by the U.S. government) was 4.721 trillion dollars. There were 260 million people in the country. Use your calculator to determine how much money each person in the U.S. would have had to contribute that year to pay off the national debt. **\$18,157.69**

30. Patterns How many zeros are there in a billion? In 10^{10}? In 10^{20}? In 10^{100}? **9; 10; 20; 100**

Problem Solving and Reasoning

31. Literature In 1994, about 2,274,400,000 books were sold in the United States. Express this number in scientific notation.

32. Critical Thinking Use your calculator to divide 2.50×10^{14} by 1.25×10^{14}. Explain why the result is not in scientific notation.

33. Social Studies During the 1994–1995 school year, there were about 43.9 million students in United States public schools. States spent a total of 239.1 billion dollars on these schools. What was the average spent per pupil? Round your answer to the nearest dollar.

34. Communicate Large corporations and countries keep track of budgets that total billions or even trillions of dollars, but they never use scientific notation to express these numbers. Explain when and why scientific notation is not useful to express some very large numbers.

35. Choose a Strategy GPS In a laboratory experiment, two colonies of bacteria are being observed. One is growing at the rate of 1.5×10^5 bacteria per half-hour. The other is growing at the rate of 3.2×10^5 bacteria per hour. Which is growing faster? How do you know?

Problem Solving STRATEGIES

- Look for a Pattern
- Make an Organized List
- Make a Table
- Guess and Check
- Work Backward
- Use Logical Reasoning
- Draw a Diagram
- Solve a Simpler Problem

36. Critical Thinking Describe how you can add two numbers that are in scientific notation. Consider the case where the exponents are the same and the case where the exponents are different.

Mixed Review

Give the inverse of each action. *[Lesson 2-4]*

37. Add 5 **Subtract 5** **38.** Multiply by 7 **Divide by 7** **39.** Stand up **Sit down** **40.** Go up 4 steps **Go down 4 steps**

Estimate, then add. *[Lesson 3-3]*

41. 4.23 + 7.821 **12.051** **42.** 8.471 + 3.196 **11.667** **43.** 3.645 + 2.946 **6.591** **44.** 3.4 + 0.34 + 0.034 **3.774**

45. 14.7 + 93.74 **108.44** **46.** 5.23 + 4.2 + 0.039 **9.469** **47.** 3.856 + 84.28 **88.136** **48.** 4.8943 + 3.541 **8.4353**

PROBLEM SOLVING 3-5

PROBLEM SOLVING

Name ______ Guided Problem Solving 3-5

GPS PROBLEM 35, STUDENT PAGE 129

In a laboratory experiment, two colonies of bacteria are being observed. One is growing at the rate of 1.5×10^5 bacteria per half-hour. The other is growing at the rate of 3.2×10^5 bacteria per hour. Which is growing faster? How do you know?

— Understand —

1. Are both rates given for the same length of time? No.

— Plan —

2. Why will you need to double the first number in order to compare? Hourly rate will be twice as great as that for a half-hour.

3. Which number is greater, 1.5×10^5 or 3.2×10^5? 1.5×10^5, 3.2×10^5 — The power of 10 is the same. Compare 1.5 and 3.2. 3.2×10^5 is greater than 1.5×10^5 since 3.2 > 1.5.

4. Which of these pairs of numbers will you need to compare to decide which product is greater for $2(1.5 \times 10^5)$ and 3.2×10^5. a
   a. 2(1.5) and 3.2 b. 2(3.2) and 1.5 c. 1.5 and 3.2

— Solve —

5. Compare the rates. Explain. 3.2×10^5 per hour is a faster rate than 1.5×10^5 per half-hour because 3.2 > 3.0.

— Look Back —

6. How could you find the answer using another method of solving? Write each number in standard notation and compare.

SOLVE ANOTHER PROBLEM

One colony of bacteria is growing at the rate of 2.59×10^7 times per half hour. The other is growing at the rate of 2.79×10^7 times per hour. Which is growing faster? How do you know?

The first colony. Power of ten is same, and 2(2.59) > 2.79.

ENRICHMENT

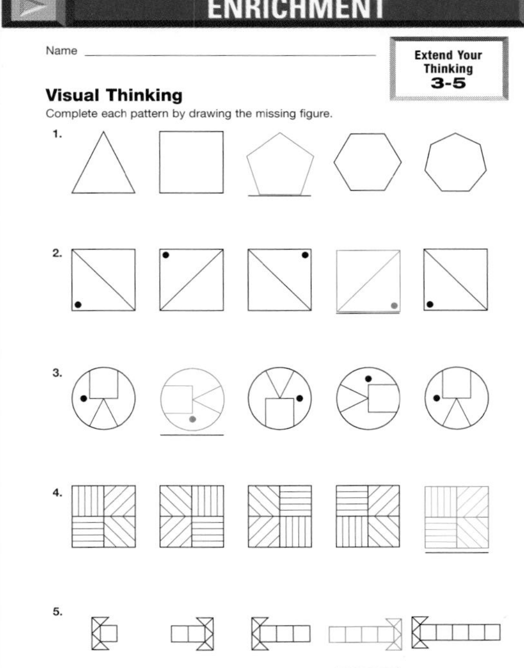
Name ______ Extend Your Thinking 3-5

Visual Thinking

Complete each pattern by drawing the missing figure.

1.

2.

3.

4.

5.

Exercise Notes

Exercise 32

Error Prevention Students may need to use parentheses around each product to do the division. You may need to explain how to enter the powers of 10 using the exponent key.

Exercise Answers

31. 2.2744×10^9

32. 2; because 2.50 is twice 1.25 and $10^{14} \div 10^{14} = 1$, so the problem is really $(2.50 \div 1.25) \times 1 = 2$.

33. \$5446

34. Possible answer: When working with money, they may not want to drop any digits, so there is no advantage in scientific notation. For instance, \$3,456,789,102 would become 3.456789102×10^9, which is no simpler.

35. The second one grows faster. The first one grows at an hourly rate of $2 \times (1.5 \times 10^5) = 3.0 \times 10^5$ bacteria per hour.

36. Possible answer: If the exponents are the same, you can simply add the decimal parts and keep the power of ten the same. If the exponents are different, you must first adjust one exponent so they match, and then add as above.

Alternate Assessment

You may want to use the *Interactive CD-ROM Journal* with this assessment.

Journal Have students write a paragraph or two describing with examples how to write a number in scientific notation and vice versa. Students demonstrate that they can write a standard-form number in scientific notation, and vice versa.

Quick Quiz

Write each number in scientific notation.

1. 56,321 5.6321×10^4
2. 435.62 4.3562×10^2

Write each number in standard form.

3. 3.682×10^5 368,200
4. 7.032561×10^3 7032.561

Available on Daily Transparency 3-5

Technology

Using a Scientific Calculator • Scientific Notation

The Point
Students explore the scientific notation capabilities of their calculator.

Materials
Calculator with scientific notation capability

Resources
Teaching Tool Transparency 22: Scientific Calculator

About the Page
- Students using graphing calculators should consult their manuals about entering numbers in scientific notation and computing in scientific notation.
- Students with calculators that have 8-digit displays may not be able to enter the numbers in **Try It**. The third question in **On Your Own** deals with the capacity of calculators.

Answers for Try It
a. 111,457,135,120,000 = $1.1145713512 \times 10^{14}$

b. 36,281 = 3.6281×10^{4}

On Your Own
For the third question, in addition to the number of significant digits exceeding the length of the display, calculators cannot accept numbers in scientific notation with an exponent greater than 99.

Answers for On Your Own
- There are too few digits in the display to show the whole number.
- Look at the exponent in the answer. Move the decimal point in the answer that many places to the right.
- Yes, on most calculators any number greater than 1×10^{100} is too large for the calculator to handle.

TECHNOLOGY

Using a Scientific Calculator • Scientific Notation

Problem: What is the product of 106,000,000,000,000 and 22,220,000,000,000,000?

You can use your scientific calculator's built-in exponential notation key to help simplify this problem.

1. **Express each number in scientific notation as shown:**
   106,000,000,000,000 = 1.06 • 10^{14}
   22,220,000,000,000,000 = 2.222 • 10^{16}
2. **Enter the first number into your scientific calculator as [1] [.] [0] [6] [EE] [1] [4]. Press the [×] key, then enter the second number as [2] [.] [2] [2] [2] [EE] [1] [6]. (Note: Your calculator may use [E] instead of [EE].)**
3. **Press the [=] key to find the product.**

Solution: The product of 106,000,000,000,000 and 22,220,000,000,000,000 is 2.35532×10^{30}, which equals 2,355,320,000,000,000,000,000,000,000,000.

TRY IT

a. What is the sum of 345,901,120,000 and 111,111,234,000,000?

b. What is the quotient of 145,124,000,000,000,000 and 4,000,000,000,000?

ON YOUR OWN

- ▶ When you enter a large number into your calculator, why is it sometimes necessary to express the number in scientific notation?
- ▶ If your calculator gives an answer that uses an exponent, how can you change it to standard notation?
- ▶ Are there some very large numbers that you could not enter into a scientific calculator? If so, explain why and give an example. If not, explain why not.

130

You've seen how decimals can be used to better understand the solar system. Now you'll use decimals to describe a planet.

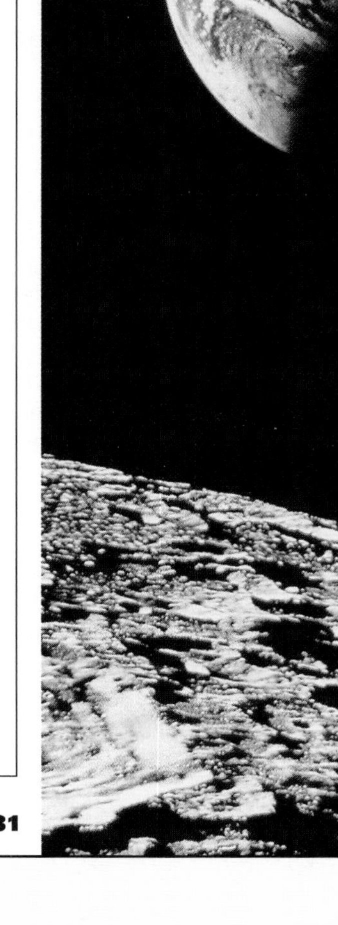

The Lonely Planets

1. Column 2 shows how the mass of each planet compares with Earth's. Order the masses from least to greatest.

Planet	Mass Compared with Earth's	Distance from Sun (mi)	Distance from Sun Compared with Earth's	Day (hr)	Length of Year Compared with Earth's
Mercury	0.0553	3.59×10^7	0.39	1407.6	0.24
Venus	0.8150	6.72×10^7	0.72	5832.2	0.62
Mars	0.1074	1.42×10^8	1.53	24.6	1.88
Jupiter	317.89	4.84×10^8	5.21	9.9	11.86
Saturn	95.18	8.87×10^8	9.55	10.7	29.46
Uranus	14.54	1.78×10^9	19.20	17.2	84.01
Neptune	17.15	2.79×10^9	30.10	16.1	164.76
Pluto	0.002	3.67×10^9	39.46	153.3	247.65

Choose a planet. Use data on your planet to answer these questions.

2. Write your planet's distance from the sun in standard notation. Let d = Earth's average distance from the sun. Use data on your planet's distance from the sun (columns 3–4) to write an equation you can solve to find Earth's distance from the sun.

3. Solve the equation you wrote in Question 2. What is Earth's distance from the sun to the nearest million miles? Write the answer in both standard and scientific notation.

4. Earth's *rotation* period is 23.9 hr. How much longer or shorter is a "day" on your planet than it is on Earth?

5. Earth's *revolution* period—the length of one Earth year—is 365.3 days. How long is your planet's year in Earth days?

6. Write a paragraph that compares your planet with Earth.

131

Answers for Connect

1. Masses: Pluto 0.002, Mercury 0.0553, Mars 0.1074, Venus 0.8150, Uranus 14.54, Neptune 17.15, Saturn 95.18, Jupiter 317.89.

   The remainder of the answers will depend on planet chosen. Answers for Mars are given.

2. 142,000,000 mi; $1.53d = 1.42 \times 10^8$.
3. $d = 93{,}000{,}000$; $d = 9.3 \times 10^7$
4. 0.7 hr longer
5. 686.764 days
6. Possible answer: Mars is about 49,000,000 miles farther from the sun than Earth. Its day is slightly longer than an Earth day.

The Lonely Planets

The Point

In *The Lonely Planets* on page 131, students discussed data about the planets. Now they will use their understanding of decimal operations and scientific notation to analyze data about the planets.

About the Page

- Review the column descriptions to be sure that students understand the meaning of the data presented.
- In Question 2, ask students to express the problem in words before they write the equation.
- Students may confuse rotation period and revolution period. Demonstrate with a globe or other round object that rotation means the planet turns on its axis, while revolution means the planet is moving around the sun. Explain that rotation and revolution are occurring simultaneously.

Ongoing Assessment

Check that students have written the equation for Question 2 correctly.

Extension

Ask students to determine the revolution period (the number of days it takes to travel around the sun) of each planet. They can use the data in the last column of the table and the fact that the revolution period of Earth is 365.3 days. Mercury, 87.672 days; Venus, 226.486 days; Mars, 686.764 days; Jupiter, 4,332.458 days; Saturn, 10,761.738 days; Uranus, 30,688.853 days; Neptune, 60,186.828 days Pluto, 90,466.545 days.

3A Review

Review Correlation

Item(s)	Lesson(s)
1	3-1
2–10	3-2
11–14	3-3, 3-4
15, 16	3-5
17	3-2
18	3-4
19	3-3
20, 21	3-2

Test Prep

Test-Taking Tip

Tell students to eliminate answers that they know cannot be correct. For example, in Exercise 20 they are asked to find a sum. One addend is about 72, so the sum must be greater than 72.

Answers for Review

11. $x \approx 9$; $x = 8.96$
12. $x \approx 40$; $x = 40.8$
13. $x \approx 5$; $x = 4.90$ to the nearest hundredth
14. $x \approx 8$; $x = 8.13$
15. a. 1.21×10^4
    b. 5.206×10^6
    c. 4.86×10^9
16. a. 5000
    b. 700,000
    c. 72,000,000
    d. 160,000,000,000,000
17. Possible answer: By rounding dollar amounts and weights it is easier to make direct comparisons. Estimating can help you keep a running total of your bill as you shop.
18. Yes; $(6.75 \times 72) \div 16 = 30.375$; $30.375 < 50$
19. He can spend about $6.00.

Section 3A Review

REVIEW 3A

Compare using <, >, or =.

1. **a.** 9.501 [>] 9.5 **b.** 0.067 [<] 0.670 **c.** 756.38 [=] 756.380

2. Round to the underlined place value. **a.** 10.6<u>7</u>4 **10.67** **b.** 5.<u>8</u>19 **5.8** **c.** 56.09<u>8</u>6 **56.099**

Estimate.

3. 23×3.2 ≈ **69** **4.** $153.3 - 9.07$ ≈ **140** **5.** $13.34 + 32.01 + 36.8$ ≈ **82** **6.** 652.3×7.57 ≈ **5200**

7. $\frac{5.6}{2.8}$ **2** **8.** 5.52×4.91 ≈ **30** **9.** $\frac{0.0038}{0.019}$ **0.2** **10.** $37.48 - 29.93$ ≈ **7**

Solve each equation. Estimate the solution first.

11. $\frac{x}{3.2} = 2.8$ **12.** $x - 23.5 = 17.3$ **13.** $3.24x = 15.86$ **14.** $15.76 + x = 23.89$

15. Write in scientific notation. **a.** 12,100 **b.** 5,206,000 **c.** 4,860,000,000

16. Write in standard form. **a.** 5×10^3 **b.** 7×10^5 **c.** 7.2×10^7 **d.** 1.6×10^{14}

17. Journal Describe the way you can use rounding and estimation of decimals when shopping for groceries to decide which items have the best value.

18. **Science** A space probe can carry 50 lb of scientific instruments on its journey. Can 72 identical instruments, each weighing 6.75 oz, be carried? Explain. (Hint: 1 lb = 16 oz.)

19. **Consumer** After spending the morning shopping, Joe has $14.37 left. He needs $2.65 bus fare to get home, and he needs to keep $5.00 to pay back a debt. About how much can he afford to spend on lunch?

Test Prep

On a multiple choice test, when you are asked to find the answer to a decimal calculation or the solution to a decimal equation, a reasonable estimate can often help you eliminate some choices right away.

20. Find the sum of 3.89, 72.076, and 2.6. **C**

Ⓐ 0.78566 Ⓑ 7.8566 Ⓒ 78.566 Ⓓ 785.66

21. Find the difference of 97.24 and 1.308. **C**

Ⓐ 9.5932 Ⓑ 84.16 Ⓒ 95.932 Ⓓ 971.092

Resources

Practice Masters
Section 3A Review

Assessment Sourcebook
Quiz 3A

TestWorks
Test and Practice Software

PRACTICE

Name ______________________

Practice

Section 3A Review

Put the correct symbol (<, >, or =) to make a true statement.

1. 17.651 (>) 17.65 2. 2.940 (>) 2.904 3. 37.84 (<) 38.74

Estimate.

4. $143.74 - 31.2$ ≈ 110 5. 4.631×9.31 ≈ 45 6. $87.4 \div 10.9$ ≈ 8

Solve each equation. Estimate the solution first.

7. $2.83x = 13.301$ $x =$ 4.7 8. $x + 5.3 = 8.241$ $x =$ 2.941 9. $x - 8.972 = 7.6$ $x =$ 16.572 10. $\frac{x}{12.3} = 4.89$ $x =$ 60.147

Write in scientific notation.

11. 16,430 1.643×10^4 12. 370,000 3.7×10^5 13. 94,300,000 9.43×10^7

Write in standard form.

14. 4.91×10^3 4910 15. 3×10^6 3,000,000 16. 1.8×10^8 180,000,000

17. Shagufta is going on a backpacking trip. She wants to carry no more than 30 lb. If her backpack weighs 4.87 lb, her food weighs 8.6 lb, and her clothing weighs 7.3 lb, find the maximum weight of other items she can bring. 9.23 lb

18. Monte has $18.60. Can he buy 2 lb of shiitake mushrooms priced at $0.59 per ounce? Explain. (Hint: 1 lb = 16 oz)
No, 2 lb = 32 oz and 32 × $0.59 = $18.88

The line graph shows the number of American newspapers being published from 1920 to 1990. Use the graph for Exercises 19–20.

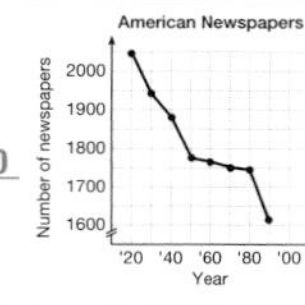

19. Estimate the number of newspapers that were being published in 1940. About 1880

20. Predict the number of newspapers in 2010. About 1400–1500

Fraction Concepts

Visit www.teacher.mathsurf.com for links to lesson plans from teachers and other professionals, NCTM information, and other sites.

LESSON PLANNING GUIDE

Student Edition / Ancillaries

LESSON		MATERIALS	VOCABULARY	DAILY	OTHER
	Section 3B Opener				
3-6	**Divisibility and Prime Factorization**	36 small objects	divisible, factor, prime number, composite number, prime factorization, factor tree	3-6	Teaching Tool Trans. 2, 3 *Interactive CD-ROM Lesson* *WW Math*—Algebra
3-7	**GCF and LCM**	42 small objects	greatest common factor (GCF), common multiple, least common multiple (LCM)	3-7	Technology Master 10 Ch. 3 Project Master
3-8	**Equivalent Fractions and Lowest Terms**	calculator	fraction, numerator, denominator, equivalent, lowest terms	3-8	Lesson Enhancement Trans. 10 Teaching Tool Trans. 2, 3 Technology Master 11
3-9	**Comparing and Ordering Fractions**	graph paper	common denominator	3-9	Lesson Enhancement Trans. 11 Technology Master 12
3-10	**Converting Between Fractions and Decimals**	calculator	terminating decimal, repeating decimal	3-10	Technology Master 13
	Connect				Lesson Enhancement Trans. 12 Interdisc. Team Teaching 3B
	Review				Practice 3B; Quiz 3B; *TestWorks*
	Extend Key Ideas				
	Chapter 3 Summary and Review				
	Chapter 3 Assessment				Ch. 3 Tests Forms A–F; *TestWorks*; Ch. 3 Letter Home
	Cumulative Review, Chapters 1–3				Cumulative Review Ch. 1–3 Quarterly Test Ch. 1–3

SKILLS TRACE

LESSON	SKILL	FIRST INTRODUCED GR. 5	GR. 6	GR. 7	DEVELOP	PRACTICE/APPLY	REVIEW
3-6	**Testing for divisibility.** **Writing numbers as products of primes.**	✘	 ✘		pp. 134–136	pp. 137–138	pp. 161, 200, 252, 459
3-7	**Finding the greatest common factor.** **Finding the least common multiple.**	✘	 ✘		pp. 139–141	pp. 142–143	pp. 161, 216, 257, 465
3-8	**Writing equivalent fractions.** **Rewriting fractions in lowest terms.**	✘ ✘			pp. 144–146	pp. 147–148	pp. 161, 221, 262, 470
3-9	**Comparing and ordering fractions.**	✘			pp. 149–150	pp. 151–152	pp. 161, 226, 285, 356
3-10	**Converting fractions and decimals.**	✘			pp. 153–154	pp. 155–156	pp. 161, 389, 538

CONNECTED MATHEMATICS

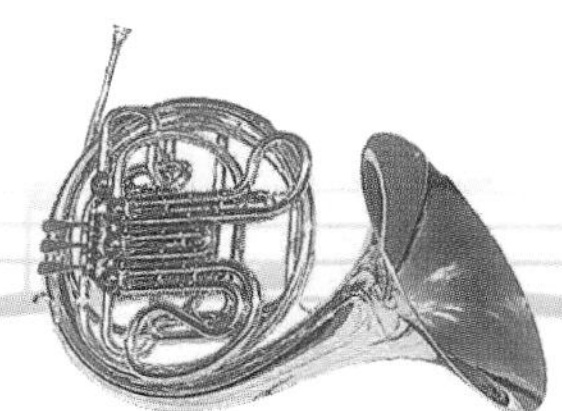

The unit *Comparing and Scaling (Ratio Proportion and Percent)* and Investigation 4 in *Moving Straight Ahead (Linear Relationships)*, from the **Connected Mathematics** series, can be used with Section 3B.

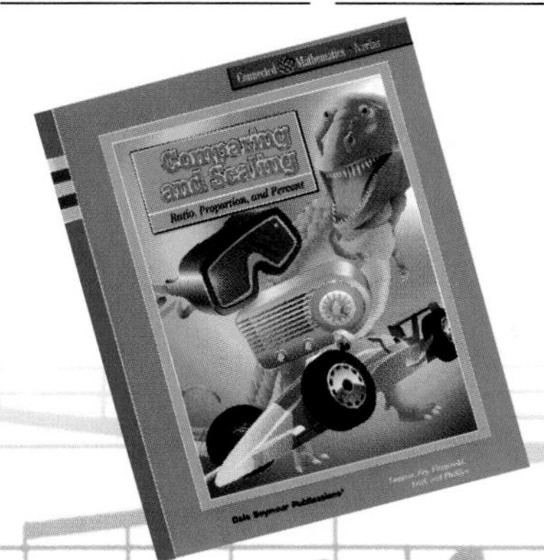

INTERDISCIPLINARY TEAM TEACHING

Math and Music

(Worksheet pages 11–12: Teacher pages T11–T12)

In this lesson, students use factors, fractions, and decimals in music.

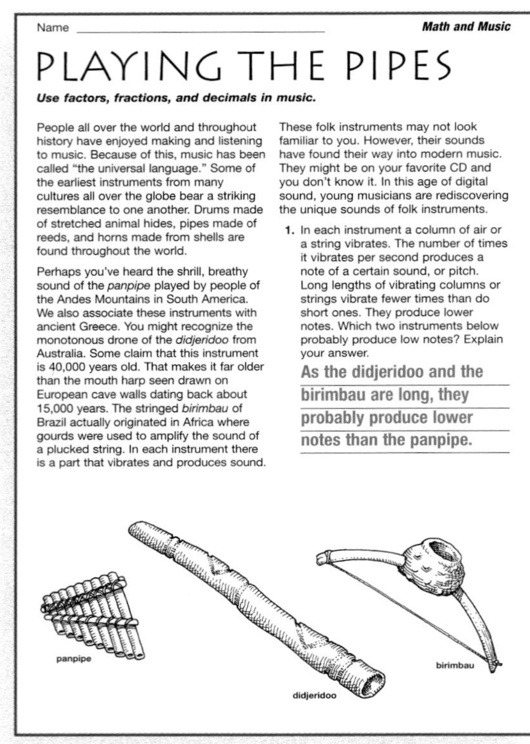

Name ______________________ ***Math and Music***

PLAYING THE PIPES

Use factors, fractions, and decimals in music.

People all over the world and throughout history have enjoyed making and listening to music. Because of this, music has been called "the universal language." Some of the earliest instruments from many cultures all over the globe bear a striking resemblance to one another. Drums made of stretched animal hides, pipes made of reeds, and horns made from shells are found throughout the world.

Perhaps you've heard the shrill, breathy sound of the *panpipe* played by people of the Andes Mountains in South America. We also associate these instruments with ancient Greece. You might recognize the monotonous drone of the *didjeridoo* from Australia. Some claim that this instrument is 40,000 years old. That makes it far older than the mouth harp seen drawn on European cave walls dating back about 15,000 years. The stringed *birimbau* of Brazil actually originated in Africa where gourds were used to amplify the sound of a plucked string. In each instrument there is a part that vibrates and produces sound.

These folk instruments may not look familiar to you. However, their sounds have found their way into modern music. They might be on your favorite CD and you don't know it. In this age of digital sound, young musicians are rediscovering the unique sounds of folk instruments.

1. In each instrument a column of air or a string vibrates. The number of times it vibrates per second produces a note of a certain sound, or pitch. Long lengths of vibrating columns or strings vibrate fewer times than do short ones. They produce lower notes. Which two instruments below probably produce low notes? Explain your answer.

   As the didjeridoo and the birimbau are long, they probably produce lower notes than the panpipe.

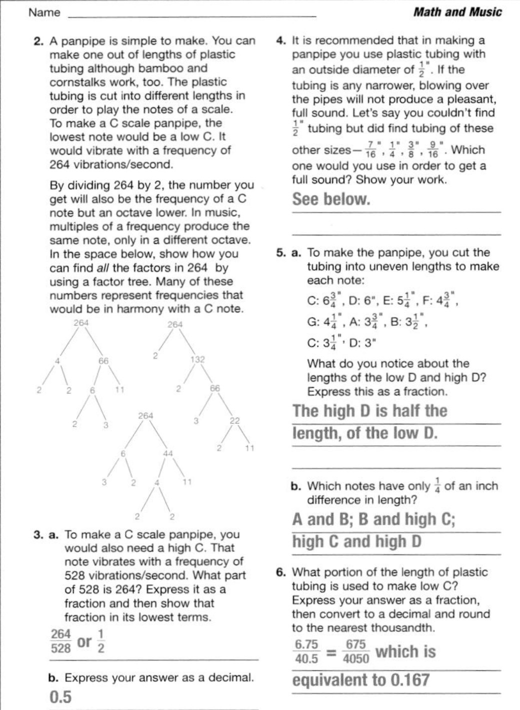

Name ______________________ ***Math and Music***

2. A panpipe is simple to make. You can make one out of lengths of plastic tubing although bamboo and cornstalks work, too. The plastic tubing is cut into different lengths in order to play the notes of a scale. To make a C scale panpipe, the lowest note would be a low C. It would vibrate with a frequency of 264 vibrations/second.

   By dividing 264 by 2, the number you get will also be the frequency of a C note but an octave lower. In music, multiples of a frequency produce the same note, only in a different octave. In the space below, show how you can find *all* the factors in 264 by using a factor tree. Many of these numbers represent frequencies that would be in harmony with a C note.

3. a. To make a C scale panpipe, you would also need a high C. That note vibrates with a frequency of 528 vibrations/second. What part of 528 is 264? Express it as a fraction and then show that fraction in its lowest terms.

   $\frac{264}{528}$ or $\frac{1}{2}$

   b. Express your answer as a decimal.

   0.5

4. It is recommended that in making a panpipe you use plastic tubing with an outside diameter of $\frac{1}{2}$". If the tubing is any narrower, blowing over the pipes will not produce a pleasant, full sound. Let's say you couldn't find $\frac{1}{2}$" tubing but did find tubing of these other sizes—$\frac{7}{16}$", $\frac{1}{4}$", $\frac{3}{8}$", $\frac{9}{16}$". Which one would you use in order to get a full sound? Show your work.

   See below.

5. a. To make the panpipe, you cut the tubing into uneven lengths to make each note:

   C: $6\frac{3}{4}$", D: 6", E: $5\frac{1}{4}$", F: $4\frac{3}{4}$",
   G: $4\frac{1}{4}$", A: $3\frac{3}{4}$", B: $3\frac{1}{2}$",
   C: $3\frac{1}{4}$", D: 3"

   What do you notice about the lengths of the low D and high D? Express this as a fraction.

   The high D is half the length, of the low D.

   b. Which notes have only $\frac{1}{4}$ of an inch difference in length?

   A and B; B and high C; high C and high D

6. What portion of the length of plastic tubing is used to make low C? Express your answer as a fraction, then convert to a decimal and round to the nearest thousandth.

   $\frac{6.75}{40.5} = \frac{675}{4050}$ which is equivalent to 0.167

Answers

4. The greatest common factor of the denominators is 16. Converting these fractions to fractions with a denominator of 16: $\frac{7}{16}, \frac{4}{16}, \frac{6}{16}, \frac{9}{16}$; put them in order: $\frac{4}{16}, \frac{6}{16}, \frac{7}{16}, \frac{9}{16}$. The fraction of $\frac{1}{2}$ is equivalent to $\frac{8}{16}$. The only diameter that is over $\frac{1}{2}$" is $\frac{9}{16}$".

BIBLIOGRAPHY

FOR TEACHERS

Seymour, Dale and Beardslee, Ed. *Critical Thinking Activities*. Palo Alto, CA: Dale Seymour, 1996.

Spangler, David. *Math for Real Kids*. Glenview, IL: Good Year Books, 1997.

Williams, Wayne. *Quizzes*. Palo Alto, CA: Dale Seymour, 1996.

FOR STUDENTS

Baines, Anthony. *The Oxford Companion to Musical Instruments*. Oxford, England: Oxford Press, 1992.

SECTION 3B

Fraction Concepts

▶ Fine Arts Link ▶ www.mathsurf.com/7/ch3/music

One, Two, Three ... Play!

Music and mathematics are closely related. For example, music travels as sound "waves" in the air. The pitch of a musical note depends on the number of waves per second.

Music also involves fractions. Fractions determine the notes of a musical scale, a fact discovered some 2500 years ago by the Greek mathematician Pythagoras. Fractions help musicians keep time, too. Knowing how long a "whole" note should last, the players can determine the length of a "half" note, a "quarter" note, and so on. This allows them to play together as a group.

Some modern music is based almost entirely on mathematics. The Austrian composer Arnold Schönberg (1874–1951) wrote complete pieces using sets of 12-note musical phrases that changed continually according to strict mathematical rules.

Today, computers can replace musicians altogether, using electronically produced digital sounds.

1 How many "eighth" notes would it take to equal a "half" note? Explain how you decided.

2 Give examples of the importance of mathematics to other arts such as theater, writing, dance, or painting.

133

Where are we now?

In Section 3A, students used decimals to solve equations.

They learned how to

- compare and order decimals.
- estimate by rounding and using compatible numbers.
- solve equations containing decimals.
- write numbers in scientific notation.

Where are we going?

In Section 3B, students will

- use divisibility rules.
- write numbers as products of primes.
- find the GFC and LCM of pairs of numbers.
- compare and order fractions.
- simplify fractions.
- convert fractions to decimals.
- convert decimals to fractions.

Theme: Music

World Wide Web

If your class has access to the World Wide Web, you might want to use the information found at the Web site address given at the top of the page. The interdisciplinary link relates to topics discussed in this section.

About the Page

This page introduces the theme of this section, music, and discusses the relationship of music and mathematics.

Ask ...

- What musical instrument do you enjoy playing or listening to? Did you realize that there is mathematics involved in music?
- What is a musical scale? Can you sing the scale?
- How is music written? How are whole, half, and quarter notes shown? What is different about the way each is played?

Extension

The following activity does not require access to the World Wide Web.

Fine Arts

Ask groups of students to study string, brass, woodwind, and percussion instruments and tell how math affects the way each type of instrument is played. Some students might study the contributions of particular ethnic groups to music.

Answers for Questions

1. Half of 8 is 4.
2. Theater: stage and set design. Writing: word and page counts. Dance: formations and patterns. Painting: perspective and design.

Connect

On page 157, students use fractions to identify musical notes.

INTERACTIVE LESSON

3-6 Lesson Organizer

Objectives

- Test for divisibility.
- Write any number as a product of primes.

Vocabulary

- Divisible, factor, prime number, composite number, prime factorization, factor tree

Materials

- Explore: 36 small objects

NCTM Standards

- 1–6, 8

Review

Find each quotient.

1. 24 ÷ 2 12
2. 24 ÷ 3 8
3. 24 ÷ 4 6
4. 24 ÷ 5 4 R4
5. 24 ÷ 6 4
6. 24 ÷ 7 3 R3
7. 24 ÷ 8 3
8. 24 ÷ 9 2 R6

Available on Daily Transparency 3-6

Lesson Link

Ask students to describe situations in which they have needed to know whether a number can be divided by another number with no remainder. One suggestion is the process of sharing a bag of pretzels equally among a group of friends.

1 Introduce

Explore

The Point
Students use objects to model all possible pairs of factors in order to investigate patterns in composite numbers.

Ongoing Assessment
Be sure students realize that in this case they should list both arrangements of factor pairs, that is, $30 = 2 \times 15$ and 15×2.

3-6 Divisibility and Prime Factorization

You'll Learn ...

- to test for divisibility
- to write any number as a product of primes

... How It's Used

Landscape gardeners often arrange plants in rows to display them in an efficient and pleasing way.

Vocabulary

divisible
factor
prime number
composite number
prime factorization
factor tree

Lesson Link You've divided with whole numbers. Now you'll see how to tell whether there is a remainder when one whole number is divided by another.

Explore Factoring and Prime Numbers

Materials: 36 small objects

Row, Row, Row Your Band

Mrs. Buchanan is planning marching routines for the school band. The band might have 30 to 36 members. Band members can march in any number of rows as long as each row has the same number of members.

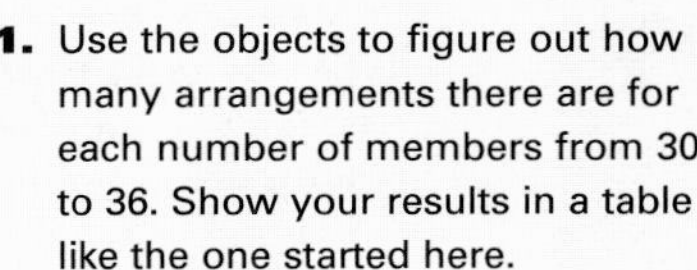

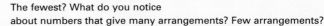

1. Use the objects to figure out how many arrangements there are for each number of members from 30 to 36. Show your results in a table like the one started here.

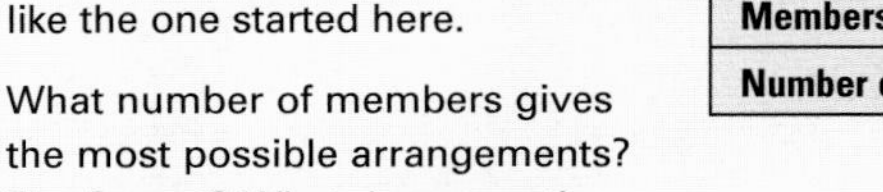

Number of Members	30	30
Members per Row	1	2
Number of Rows	30	15

2. What number of members gives the most possible arrangements? The fewest? What do you notice about numbers that give many arrangements? Few arrangements?

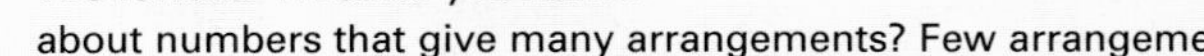

3. Describe patterns that will help you predict whether arrangements of 2, 3, and 6 members per row are possible for other sizes of bands.

Learn Divisibility and Prime Factorization

A music store window displayed 12 trumpets in groups of 4. We say that 12 is **divisible** by 4 because 12 can be divided into groups of 4 with no remainder. 12 is also divisible by 6. We say that 4 and 6 are **factors** of 12 because 12 is divisible by 4 and 6.

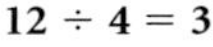

$12 \div 4 = 3$ $\quad$ $12 \div 6 = 2$

Five is not a factor of 12 because $12 \div 5$ equals 2 with a remainder of 2.

MEETING INDIVIDUAL NEEDS

Resources

- 3-6 Practice
- 3-6 Reteaching
- 3-6 Problem Solving
- 3-6 Enrichment
- 3-6 Daily Transparency
  - Problem of the Day
  - Review
  - Quick Quiz

Teaching Tool Transparencies 2, 3

Interactive CD-ROM Lesson

Wide World of Mathematics Algebra: Breaking the German Code

Learning Modalities

Logical Help students to see that the test for divisibility by 6 must involve both 2 and 3. Then ask them to state a rule for divisibility by 12.

Social Have all students in each group complete the table of arrangements for 30 band members. Then have each person complete the tables for two of the remaining numbers 31–36, so that all of the tables are completed.

Inclusion

Some students will not understand the distinction between prime and composite numbers. It is often helpful to have them use counters to model a number and then try to make a rectangular array having two or more rows and columns. If no such array can be made, the number is prime.

Example 1

Give the ways 8 students can be divided into groups of the same size.

Divide 8 by each number from 1 to 8. Look for quotients with remainders of zero.

8 ÷ 1 = 8, remainder 0	**8 ÷ 5 = 1, remainder 3**
8 ÷ 2 = 4, remainder 0	**8 ÷ 6 = 1, remainder 2**
8 ÷ 3 = 2, remainder 2	**8 ÷ 7 = 1, remainder 1**
8 ÷ 4 = 2, remainder 0	**8 ÷ 8 = 1, remainder 0**

Eight students can be divided into groups of 1, 2, 4, and 8.

You can use divisibility rules to help you find the factors of a number.

DIVISIBILITY RULES

A number is divisible by
- 2 if the ones digit is 0, 2, 4, 6, or 8.
- 3 if the sum of the digits is divisible by 3.
- 4 if the number formed by the last two digits is divisible by 4.
- 5 if the ones digit is 0 or 5.
- 6 if the number is divisible by both 2 and 3.
- 8 if the number formed by the last three digits is divisible by 8.
- 9 if the sum of the digits is divisible by 9.
- 10 if the ones digit is 0.

You can use the divisibility rule for 4 to check which years are leap years.

Example 2

Test the number 4320 for divisibility by 2, 3, 4, 5, 6, 8, 9, and 10.

2?	Yes	The last digit is 0.
3?	Yes	4 + 3 + 2 + 0 = 9, which is divisible by 3.
4?	Yes	The number formed by the last two digits (20) is divisible by 4.
5?	Yes	4320 ends in 0.
6?	Yes	4320 is divisible by both 2 and 3.
8?	Yes	The number formed by the last three digits (320) is divisible by 8.
9?	Yes	4 + 3 + 2 + 0 = 9, which is divisible by 9.
10?	Yes	The ones digit is 0.

4320 is divisible by 2, 3, 4, 5, 6, 8, 9, and 10.

Try It

Check each number for divisibility by 2, 3, 4, 5, 6, 8, 9, and 10.

a. 84 **b.** 845 **c.** 128 **d.** 162

84 is divisible by 2, 3, 4, and 6
845 is divisible by 5
128 is divisible by 2, 4, and 8
162 is divisible by 2, 3, 6 and 9

For Groups That Finish Early

Have students list all the numbers less than 36 that yield only two possible arrangements. 2, 3, 5, 7, 11, 13, 17, 19, 23, 29, 31 Ask what they notice about the numbers. Except for the number 2, all are odd numbers.

Answers for Explore

1. See page C5.
2. Most: 36; fewest: 31. Many: they have many different factors; Few: not many factors.
3. The numbers of members would have to be divided by 2, 3, and 6 with no remainder.

2 Teach

Learn

Alternate Examples

1. Give the ways 9 students can be divided into groups of the same size.

   Divide 9 by each number from 1 to 9. Look for quotients with remainders of zero.

   9 ÷ 1 = 9 R0 9 ÷ 2 = 4 R1
   9 ÷ 3 = 3 R0 9 ÷ 4 = 2 R1
   9 ÷ 5 = 1 R4 9 ÷ 6 = 1 R3
   9 ÷ 7 = 1 R2 9 ÷ 8 = 1 R1
   9 ÷ 9 = 1 R0

   Nine students can be divided into groups of 1, 3, and 9.

2. Test the number 3560 for divisibility by 2, 3, 4, 5, 6, 8, 9, and 10.

   2? Yes; the ones digit is zero.

   3? No; 3 + 5 + 6 + 0 = 14, and 14 is not divisible by 3.

   4? Yes; the number formed by the last two digits, 60, is divisible by 4.

   5? Yes; the ones digit is zero.

   6? No; the number is divisible by 2 but not by 3.

   8? Yes; the number formed by the last three digits, 560, is divisible by 8.

   9? No; 3 + 5 + 6 + 0 = 14, and 14 is not divisible by 9.

   10? Yes; the ones digit is zero.

   3560 is divisible by 2, 4, 5, 8, and 10.

MATH EVERY DAY

Problem of the Day

Show how to divide the figure into 2 parts, into 3 parts, and into 4 parts, so that, in each case, the parts have the same shape and size.

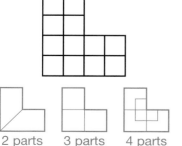

2 parts 3 parts 4 parts

Available on Daily Transparency 3-6
An Extension is provided in the transparency Package

Fact of the Day

In 1955 Marian Anderson became the first African American to sing a leading role at the Metropolitan Opera.

Mental Math

Find the prime factors of each number.

1. 21 3, 7
2. 49 7, 7
3. 15 3, 5
4. 33 3, 11

Alternate Examples

3. Write the prime factorization of 96.

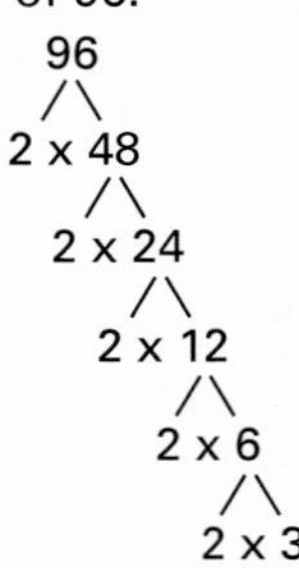

The prime factorization is $2 \times 2 \times 2 \times 2 \times 2 \times 3$. Using exponents, the prime factorization of 96 is $2^5 \times 3$.

3 Practice and Assess

Check

Cooperative Learning Have students work in groups to find the prime numbers from 30 to 50, and verify by testing for divisibility that the numbers are indeed prime. 31, 37, 41, 43, 47

Answers for Check Your Understanding

1. The number itself.
2. A prime number has 2 factors, itself and 1; a composite number has 3 or more factors.
3. Find the product of the factors.

> **Remember**
> Two is the only even prime number. Every other even number is divisible by 2, and so has to be composite. **[Previous course]**

A **prime number** is a whole number greater than 1 that has exactly two factors, 1 and itself. Seven is a prime number because its only factors are 1 and 7.

A **composite number** is a whole number that has more than two factors. Fifteen is a composite number because it has more than two factors—1, 3, 5, and 15.

Composite	Prime
$12 = 1 \cdot 12$	$11 = 1 \cdot 11$
$2 \cdot 6$	2 factors
$3 \cdot 4$	
6 factors	

When you write a composite number as a product of prime numbers, the product is called the **prime factorization** of the composite number. The prime factorization of 18 is $2 \times 3 \times 3$. You should use exponents to write repeated factors, so $2 \times 3 \times 3$ is written 2×3^2.

Example 3

> **History Link**
> An ancient Greek geographer named Eratosthenes studied prime numbers as long ago as 240 B.C.

Write the prime factorization of 84.

You can use a **factor tree** to find a prime factorization. At each "branch," find factors using divisibility rules. You'll get the same prime factorization no matter which factor you begin with.

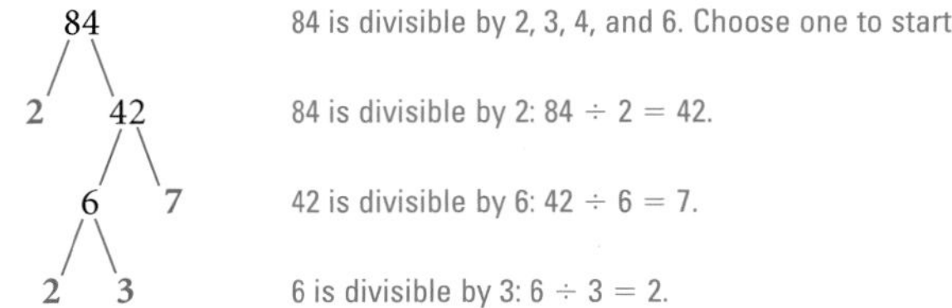

84
2 42
6 7
2 3
84 is divisible by 2, 3, 4, and 6. Choose one to start.
84 is divisible by 2: 84 ÷ 2 = 42.
42 is divisible by 6: 42 ÷ 6 = 7.
6 is divisible by 3: 6 ÷ 3 = 2.

The "leaves" at the ends of the branches give the prime factorization $2 \times 2 \times 3 \times 7$. Use exponents to write this as $2^2 \times 3 \times 7$.

The prime factorization of 84 is $2^2 \times 3 \times 7$.

Try It

Find the prime factorization of each number.

a. 124 $2^2 \times 31$ **b.** 63 7×3^2 **c.** 308 $2^2 \times 7 \times 11$ **d.** 102 $2 \times 3 \times 17$

Check Your Understanding

1. What is the prime factorization of a prime number?
2. Give the difference between a prime number and a composite number.
3. How can you find a number if you know its prime factorization?

MEETING MIDDLE SCHOOL CLASSROOM NEEDS

Tips from Middle School Teachers

To make the situation in **Explore** concrete, I ask the class to think of all the ways we might arrange the desks in rows and columns. We work together to complete a table like the one in the text.

Team Teaching

The physical education teacher might group the class in various formations for marching and exercise drills.

Music Connection

The trumpet is widely used in marching bands. While large conch-shell trumpets were used as ritual instruments in early cultures, the use of silver and bronze trumpets dates back to ancient Egypt. Trumpets have undergone many changes in shape—from S-shaped to an elongated loop. Valves were added to the trumpet in about 1820.

3-6 Exercises and Applications

Practice and Apply

Getting Started **Is the first number divisible by the second number?**

1. 571; 2 No **2.** 3560; 5 Yes **3.** 8394; 3 Yes **4.** 6737; 4 No

5. 675; 9 Yes **6.** 558; 6 Yes **7.** 82240; 8 Yes **8.** 5605; 10 No

Test each number for divisibility by 2, 3, 4, 5, 6, 8, 9, and 10.

9. 291 3 **10.** 582 2, 3, 6 **11.** 585 3, 5, 9 **12.** 592 2, 4, 8

13. 5920 2, 4, 5, 8, 10 **14.** 5921 None **15.** 5922 2, 3, 6, 9 **16.** 5925 3, 5

Determine whether each of these numbers is composite or prime.

17. 63 Composite **18.** 89 Prime **19.** 116 Composite **20.** 201 Composite

21. 152 Composite **22.** 167 Prime **23.** 323 Composite **24.** 153 Composite

Use factor trees to find the prime factorizations of the following numbers. Use exponents to write repeated factors.

25. 18 2×3^2 **26.** 180 $2^2 \times 3^2 \times 5$ **27.** 185 5×37 **28.** 285 $3 \times 5 \times 19$

29. 360 $2^3 \times 3^2 \times 5$ **30.** 864 $2^5 \times 3^3$ **31.** 1125 $3^2 \times 5^3$ **32.** 1512 $2^3 \times 3^3 \times 7$

33. **Test Prep** Which of these numbers is *not* a prime factor of 168? C

Ⓐ 2 Ⓑ 3 Ⓒ 4 Ⓓ 7

34. The longest pipe in many pipe organs is 32 feet long. Find the prime factorization of 32. Use exponents to write repeated factors. 2^5

35. **Science** Eva is analyzing a radio wave. She finds that the waveform repeats every 378 seconds. What other, shorter periods of waveforms divide evenly into 378 seconds?

36. **Number Sense** Find the prime numbers that are less than 30.

37. Find a number between 60 and 90 that has exactly two prime factors.

38. **Test Prep** Satu is evaluating bottle racks for use in a packing plant. The number of bottles in the rack must be divisible by both 6 and 4. Which of the following rack capacities can she use? A

Ⓐ 120 Ⓑ 126 Ⓒ 148 Ⓓ 164

PRACTICE 3-6

3-6 Exercises and Applications

Assignment Guide

- Basic
  1–33 odds, 34–35, 37–39, 41–55 odds
- Average
  2–32 evens, 33–39, 42–54 evens
- Enriched
  2–32 evens, 33–39, 40–54 evens

Exercise Notes

Exercises 17–24

Problem-Solving Tip Remind students to use the divisibility rules for 2, 3, 4, 5, 6, 8, 9, and 10. If none of these are factors, they can divide by 7, then by 11, 13, and so on. The first time a quotient is less than the divisor, but there is still a remainder, it is safe to quit testing and assume the number is prime.

Exercise 38

Test Prep If students choose B they have not tested for divisibility by 4. If they choose C or D they have not tested for 6.

Exercise Answers

35. 1, 2, 3, 6, 7, 9, 14,18, 21, 27, 42, 54, 63, 126, 189 seconds

36. 2, 3, 5, 7, 11, 13, 17, 19, 23, 29

37. Possible answers: 62, 65, 69, 74, 77, 82, 85, 86, 87

Reteaching

Activity

Materials: 24 counters

- Make a rectangular array of counters with dimensions of 2 by 3. Continue making identical arrays until you have used up 24 counters. How many arrays are there? 4
- Write the dimensions and the number of arrays as a product. $2 \times 3 \times 4$ Write it again using prime numbers. $2 \times 3 \times 2 \times 2$ or $2^3 \times 3$ This is the prime factorization of 24.
- Try this method to find the prime factorization of other numbers like 36 and 45. Hint: Start with arrays having dimensions the same as the smallest prime factors of the number.

PRACTICE

Name ________________

Practice 3-6

Divisibility and Prime Factorization

Test each number for divisibility by 2, 3, 4, 5, 6, 8, 9, and 10.

1. 7040 2, 4, 5, 8, 10 **2.** 4532 2, 4 **3.** 250 2, 5 **4.** 554 2

5. 2168 2, 4, 8 **6.** 1992 2, 3, 4, 6, 8 **7.** 3215 5 **8.** 2291 None

9. 2180 2, 4, 5, 10 **10.** 2604 2, 3, 4, 6 **11.** 1197 3, 9 **12.** 873 3, 9

Determine whether each of these numbers is composite or prime.

13. 181 Prime **14.** 674 Composite **15.** 373 Prime **16.** 64 Composite

17. 377 Composite **18.** 345 Composite **19.** 569 Prime **20.** 205 Composite

Use factor trees to find the prime factorization of the following numbers.

21. 144 = $2^4 \times 3^2$ **22.** 385 = $5 \times 7 \times 11$ **23.** 90 = $2 \times 3^2 \times 5$

144 → 12, 12; 12 → 3, 4; 12 → 3, 4; 4 → 2, 2; 4 → 2, 2

385 → 5, 77; 77 → 7, 11

90 → 10, 9; 10 → 5, 2; 9 → 3, 3

24. Zelda wants to divide a 96-inch-long plank into equal sections. If the length of each section is to be a whole number of inches, what lengths can she use?

1 in., 2 in., 3 in., 4 in., 6 in., 8 in., 12 in., 16 in., 24 in., 32 in., 48 in., 96 in.

25. Give the ways 30 students can be divided into groups of the same size.

Groups of 1, 2, 3, 5, 6, 10, 15, or 30

RETEACHING

Name ________________

Alternative Lesson 3-6

Divisibility and Prime Factorization

A divisibility rule is a *shortcut* for determining when one number is divisible by another.

A number is divisible by:
- 2 if the ones digit is 0, 2, 4, 6, or 8.
- 3 if the sum of the digits is divisible by 3.
- 4 if the number formed by the last two digits is divisible by 4.
- 5 if the ones digit is 0 or 5.
- 6 if the number is divisible by both 2 and 3.
- 8 if the number formed by the last three digits is divisible by 8.
- 9 if the sum of the digits is divisible by 9.
- 10 if the ones digit is 0.

Example

Test 170 for divisibility by 2, 3, 4, 5, 6, 8, 9, and 10.

One way: Divide 170 by 2. The quotient is 85. Since there is no remainder, 170 is divisible by 2. Repeat using the other digits.

Another way: Use the divisibility rules. Since the ones digits is 0, 170 is divisible by 2, 5, and 10. None of the other rules apply.

So, 170 is divisible by 2, 5, and 10.

Try It Complete the table. Write *yes* or *no*.

		Divisible by:							
		2	3	4	5	6	8	9	10
a.	630	Yes	Yes	No	Yes	Yes	No	Yes	Yes
b.	351	No	Yes	No	No	No	No	Yes	No
c.	97	No	No	No	No	No	No	No	No
d.	3744	Yes	Yes	Yes	No	Yes	Yes	Yes	No
e.	1720	Yes	No	Yes	Yes	No	Yes	No	Yes
f.	61,776	Yes	Yes	Yes	No	Yes	Yes	Yes	No
g.	22,548	Yes	Yes	Yes	No	Yes	No	No	No
h.	11,216	Yes	No	Yes	No	No	Yes	No	No

Exercise Notes

■ Exercise 40

Problem-Solving Tip You may wish to use Teaching Tool Transparencies 2 and 3: Guided Problem Solving, pages 1–2.

Exercise Answers

39. a. Possible answer: 20 cm × 30 cm × 20 cm, 20 cm × 60 cm × 10 cm, 120 cm × 5 cm × 20 cm

b. Possible answer: The third one.

40. Possible answer: By repeatedly dividing the numbers by greater and greater prime numbers.

41. Possible answer: Start with a different pair of factors; the prime factorization will be the same.

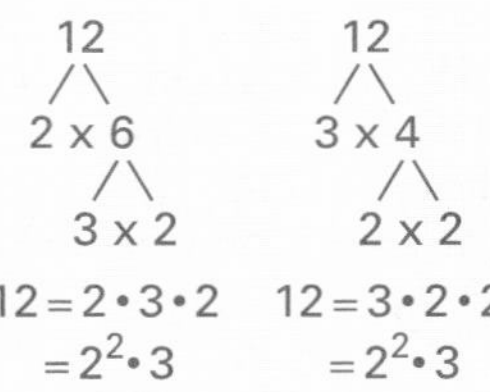

$12 = 2 \cdot 3 \cdot 2 = 2^2 \cdot 3$ $\quad$ $12 = 3 \cdot 2 \cdot 2 = 2^2 \cdot 3$

42. No; 248 is not divisible by 9.

43. 1,758,289,144; Increased last 2 digits until they were divisible by 4.

Answers for Exercises 44–47 on page C5.

Alternate Assessment

You may want to use the *Interactive CD-ROM Journal* with this assessment.

Journal Have students write a paragraph on how to find the prime factorization of a number. Students demonstrate that they can describe the procedure for finding the prime factorization of a number.

➤ Quick Quiz

Give the prime factorization of each number.

1. 64 2^6
2. 120 $2^3 \times 3 \times 5$
3. 225 $3^2 \times 5^2$
4. 200 $2^3 \times 5^2$

Available on Daily Transparency 3-6

Problem Solving and Reasoning

39. Critical Thinking Raoul is building a fish tank. He wants it to hold 12 liters (12,000 mL) of water. The formula $V = lwh$ tells the volume (V) in milliliters of a tank with length (l), width (w), and height (h) in centimeters. He wants the length, width, and height to be whole numbers.

a. List three sets of dimensions that will result in a 12,000 mL tank.

b. Which shape do you think requires the most glass?

40. Choose a Strategy Suggest one way a computer program that tests whether or not large numbers are prime might work.

41. Journal Describe how you can find more than one factor tree for some composite numbers. Will the prime factorization be the same? Give an example.

42. Critical Thinking There are 248 different cards in a fantasy card game. Laura stores her cards in 9-card plastic sheets. Will the last sheet be completely full? Explain how you found the answer.

43. Critical Thinking The number 1,758,289,141 is not divisible by 4. What is the smallest number larger than 1,758,289,141 that *is* divisible by 4? How did you find this number?

Problem Solving STRATEGIES

- Look for a Pattern
- Make an Organized List
- Make a Table
- Guess and Check
- Work Backward
- Use Logical Reasoning
- Draw a Diagram
- Solve a Simpler Problem

Mixed Review

Make a stem-and-leaf diagram for each set of data. *[Lesson 1-3]*

44. 32, 43, 51, 32, 41, 53, 61, 39, 47

45. 17, 23, 31, 43, 15, 29, 41, 38, 26

46. 83, 79, 71, 74, 83, 74, 91, 73, 89

47. 95, 103, 87, 94, 99, 105, 117, 86

Compare using <, >, or =. *[Lesson 3-1]*

48. 1.9999 [>] 1.999 **49.** 0.307 [>] 0.0307 **50.** 12.345 [<] 123.4 **51.** 2.709 [<] 2.71

52. 2.08 [<] 2.123 **53.** 195.5 [>] 19.55 **54.** 4.55 [<] 4.555 **55.** 0.064 [>] 0.0064

PROBLEM SOLVING 3-6

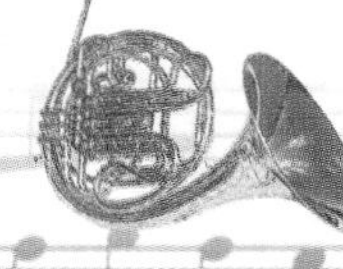

PROBLEM SOLVING

Name ______________________

Guided Problem Solving 3-6

GPS PROBLEM 39, STUDENT PAGE 138

Raoul is building a fish tank. He wants it to hold 12 liters (12,000-mL) of water. The formula $V = lwh$ tells the volume (V) in milliliters of a tank with length (l), width (w), and height (h) in centimeters. He wants the length, width, and height to be whole numbers.

Possible answers: Items 6, 7, 8

a. List three sets of dimensions that will result in a 12,000-mL tank.

b. Which shape do you think requires more glass?

— Understand —

1. What product will lwh produce? Volume of rectangular prism.
2. How many measures will be in each set of dimensions? 3 measures.

— Plan —

3. Write the prime factorization of 12,000. $2^5 \times 3 \times 5^3$
4. How can you use the prime factorization to find three dimensions? Combine factors in different ways to make up three numbers.
5. How will you find the glass needed to make the aquarium? The aquarium will have a glass top. Find area of 6 sides.

— Solve —

6. Find three sets of whole number dimensions that multiply to 12,000. 20 × 30 × 20; 20 × 60 × 10; 120 × 5 × 20
7. Which set of dimensions do you think requires the most glass? 120 × 5 × 20 uses 6200 square units.

— Look Back —

8. What other strategy could you use to find the answer? Guess and Check.

SOLVE ANOTHER PROBLEM

Using only whole numbers for dimensions, find three sets of dimensions that will produce a volume of 23 L (23,000 mL). Possible answers: 23 × 25 × 40; 46 × 25 × 20; 23 × 20 × 50

ENRICHMENT

Name ______________________

Extend Your Thinking 3-6

Patterns In Number Theory

A famous Greek astronomer-mathematician named Eratosthenes discovered a way to find prime numbers. His discovery, called the Sieve of Eratosthenes, enabled people all over the world to identify prime numbers using a systematic approach.

Below is a 10 × 10 grid showing the numbers from 1 to 100. Use the Sieve of Eratosthenes to find all prime numbers less than 100.

Step 1: Cross out 1 (1 is not prime).

Step 2: Cross out all multiples of 2 except 2 (2 is prime).

Step 3: Cross out all multiples of 3 except 3 (3 is prime).

Step 4: Cross out all multiples of 5 except 5 (5 is prime).

Step 5: Cross out all multiples of 7 except 7 (7 is prime).

The numbers not crossed out are prime numbers less than 100.

1	2	3	4	5	6	7	8	9	10
11	12	13	14	15	16	17	18	19	20
21	22	23	24	25	26	27	28	29	30
31	32	33	34	35	36	37	38	39	40
41	42	43	44	45	46	47	48	49	50
51	52	53	54	55	56	57	58	59	60
61	62	63	64	65	66	67	68	69	70
71	72	73	74	75	76	77	78	79	80
81	82	83	84	85	86	87	88	89	90
91	92	93	94	95	96	97	98	99	100

1. How many primes are between 1 and 100? 24 primes.
2. How many primes other than 2 are even numbers? Explain. None. All multiples of 2 were crossed out.
3. How can you find all the prime numbers between 1 and 1000? Make a bigger chart.

GCF and LCM

3-7

▶ Lesson Link You've looked at the factors of whole numbers. Now you'll find which of several factors common to two or more numbers is the greatest. You'll also find which of the multiples common to several numbers is the least. ◀

You'll Learn ...

- to find the greatest common factor of a pair of numbers
- to find the least common multiple of a pair of numbers

... How It's Used

Warehouse management involves using space efficiently. Using GCFs and LCMs can help the workers organize the stacks.

Vocabulary

greatest common factor (GCF)

common multiple

least common multiple (LCM)

Explore Greatest Common Factor

Marching in Prime Time

Materials: 42 small objects

The 12-member Phoenix Middle School marching band is marching in the Thanksgiving Day parade behind the 30-member Jacksonville Middle School marching band. The rows in both bands have to be the same width.

1. Use the objects to find the widest row that can be used by both bands.
2. Find the prime factorizations of 12 and 30 and list them one above the other. Line up equal factors (for example, 2 above 2, 3 above 3, and so on).
3. Using only the factors that are common to both numbers, suggest a rule you could use to find the row width you found in Step 1.
4. Test your rule using bands of 28 and 42 students.

Learn GCF and LCM

Numbers often have *common factors.*

Factors of 42 = [1], [2], [3], [6], 7, 14, 21, 42

Factors of 12 = [1], [2], [3], 4, [6], 12

The common factors of 42 and 12 are **1, 2, 3,** and **6.** The **greatest common factor** (GCF) is **6.**

One way to find the GCF of two or more numbers is to list their common factors. The greatest of these is the GCF.

MEETING INDIVIDUAL NEEDS

Resources

- **3-7** Practice
- **3-7** Reteaching
- **3-7** Problem Solving
- **3-7** Enrichment
- **3-7** Daily Transparency
  - Problem of the Day
  - Review
  - Quick Quiz
- Technology Master 10
- Chapter 3 Project Master

Learning Modalities

Verbal Encourage students to verbalize their notions of *greatest common factor* and *least common multiple* and how these concepts are related to the terms *factor* and *multiple*, respectively.

Visual It may help students when finding a GCF to align the equal prime factors of the two numbers and circle each pair of equal factors as shown.

36: [2] × [2] × 3 × 3
40: [2] × [2] × 2 × 5

Challenge

Have students find the GCF and the LCM of each set of three numbers.

1. 24, 36, 64 4; 576
2. 24, 72, 144 24; 144
3. 12, 15, 36 3; 180
4. 9, 16, 25 1; 3600

3-7 Lesson Organizer

Objectives

- Find the greatest common factor of a pair of numbers.
- Find the least common multiple of a pair of numbers.

Vocabulary

- Greatest common factor (GCF), common multiple, least common multiple (LCM)

Materials

- Explore: 42 small objects

NCTM Standards

- 1–4, 6, 7, 8

▶ Review

Give the prime factorization of each number without using exponents.

1. 36 2 × 2 × 3 × 3
2. 48 2 × 2 × 2 × 2 × 3
3. 56 2 × 2 × 2 × 7
4. 81 3 × 3 × 3 × 3
5. 108 2 × 2 × 3 × 3 × 3

Available on Daily Transparency 3-7

1 Introduce

Explore

The Point

Students use objects to model common factors of a pair of numbers in order to discover a method for finding their GCF.

Ongoing Assessment

Be sure that students are able to write the prime factorizations of the numbers required.

For Groups That Finish Early

Use your rule to find the length of the longest row for bands of 48 and 60 students. Length of longest row is 12 students.

Answers for Explore on next page.

Answers for Explore

1. 6
2. $12 = 2 \times 2 \times 3$
   $30 = \quad 2 \times 3 \times 5$
3. The row width equals the product of the common prime factors.
4. $28 = 2 \times 2 \times 7$
   $42 = 2 \times 3 \times 7$
   Common factors are 2 and 7, so the longest row width is 14.

2 Teach

Learn

Be sure students realize that a pair of numbers may have many common factors, but only one is the *greatest*, and that a pair of numbers has an infinite number of common multiples, but only one is the *least*.

Alternate Examples

1. Find the GCF of 12 and 36.

   Use divisibility rules to find factors of 12 and 36.

   12
   Think: $12 \div 1 = 12$; $12 \div 2 = 6$; $12 \div 3 = 4$.
   36
   Think: $36 \div 1 = 36$; $36 \div 2 = 18$; $36 \div 3 = 12$; $36 \div 4 = 9$; $36 \div 6 = 6$.

   Factors of 12: 1, 2, 3, 4, 6, 12
   Factors of 36: 1, 2, 3, 4, 6, 9, 12, 18, 36

   The common factors are 1, 2, 3, 4, 6, and 12. The *greatest* common factor (GCF) of 12 and 36 is 12. Notice that, in this case, the GCF is one of the numbers.

2. Two pieces of ribbon measuring 48 in. and 72 in. are to be cut into the longest possible strips of equal length. How long will the strips of ribbon be?

   Each piece of ribbon can be cut into lengths that are factors of the total length. The GCF is the longest common strip length.

   Write the prime factorizations. Box the common prime factors.

   $48 = \boxed{2} \times \boxed{2} \times \boxed{2} \times 2 \times \boxed{3}$

   $72 = \boxed{2} \times \boxed{2} \times \boxed{2} \times 3 \times \boxed{3}$

   The GCF is $2 \times 2 \times 2 \times 3 = 24$. The strips of ribbon will be 24 in. long.

Example 1

Find the GCF of 24 and 40.

Use divisibility rules to find factors of 24. Begin with 1 and 24. Divide each factor you find into 24 to get another factor.

Factor: 2 — Think: $24 \div 2 = 12$, so 12 is also a factor.

Factor: 3 — Think: $24 \div 3 = 8$, so 8 is also a factor.

Factor: 4 — Think: $24 \div 4 = 6$, so 6 is also a factor.

Factors of 24: $\boxed{1}$, $\boxed{2}$, 3, $\boxed{4}$, 6, $\boxed{8}$, 12, 24

Factors of 40: $\boxed{1}$, $\boxed{2}$, $\boxed{4}$, 5, $\boxed{8}$, 10, 20, 40

The common factors are 1, 2, 4, and 8.

The *greatest* common factor (GCF) of 24 and 40 is 8.

Music Link

The tuba plays very low notes, but it is not the lowest member of the orchestra. That honor falls to the piano, which also plays the highest notes.

When a musical instrument produces a note, you actually hear many notes at once. The note you hear most clearly is the *fundamental.* But you also hear notes called the *first overtone,* the *second overtone,* and so on. Each note is caused by a vibration, or sound wave.

Here are the prime factorizations of the second overtones of two tuba notes:

$212 = 2^2 \times 53$ $\quad$ $244 = 2^2 \times 61$

You can use prime factorizations to find the GCF. The GCF is the product of the common prime factors. The common prime factors are 2^2, so the GCF is $2^2 = 4$.

Example 2

Two wooden planks measuring 63 in. and 84 in. are to be cut into the longest possible shelves of equal length. How long will the shelves be?

Each plank can be cut into lengths that are factors of the total length. The greatest common factor is the longest common shelf length.

$63 = 3 \times \boxed{3} \times \boxed{7}$ — Write the prime factorizations. Box the common prime factors.

$84 = 2 \times 2 \times \boxed{3} \times \boxed{7}$

The GCF is $3 \times 7 = 21$. The shelves will be 21 in. long.

Try It

Find the GCF. **a.** 18, 36 18 **b.** 144, 168 24 **c.** 78, 91 13 **d.** 20, 26 2

MATH EVERY DAY

Problem of the Day

The people at a meeting of Goodtime Sports Club are forming equal teams. When they form groups of 2, 3, 4, 5, or 6, there is always exactly one person left. What is the smallest number of people that could be at the meeting? 61 people

Available on Daily Transparency 3-7

An Extension is provided in the transparency package.

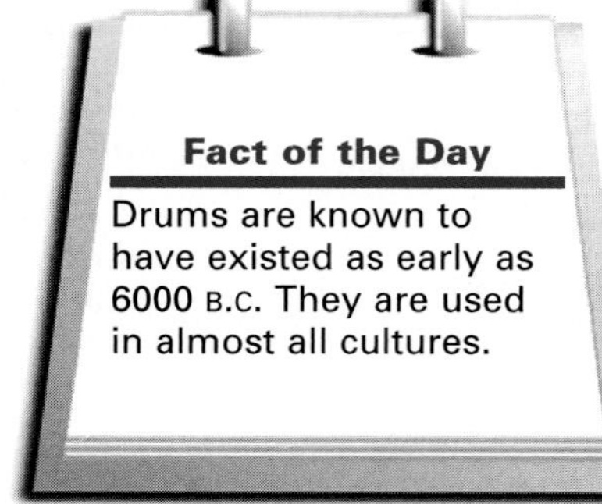

Fact of the Day

Drums are known to have existed as early as 6000 B.C. They are used in almost all cultures.

Estimation

Estimate each product or quotient.

1. 47.2×1.9 100
2. 112×309 30,000
3. $56.84 \div 8.02$ 7
4. $402 \div 81$ 5

A *multiple* of a number is the product of the number and a whole number. The first five non-zero multiples of 5 are 5, 10, 15, 20, and 25.

5 = 5 • 1 10 = 5 • 2 15 = 5 • 3 20 = 5 • 4 25 = 5 • 5

You've seen that numbers can have common factors. They also have **common multiples**. Listed below are some multiples of 4 and 6.

Multiples of 4: 4 (1 • 4), 8 (2 • 4), 12 (3 • 4), 16 (4 • 4), 20 (5 • 4), 24 (6 • 4)

Multiples of 6: 6 (1 • 6), 12 (2 • 6), 18 (3 • 6), 24 (4 • 6)

Common multiples of 4 and 6 include 12 and 24. The **least common multiple** (LCM) of 4 and 6 is 12.

One way to find the LCM of two or more numbers is to list their common multiples. The least of these is the LCM.

Study TIP

Don't list too many multiples of one number before beginning the other list. You may write many more than you need.

Examples

3 Find the LCM of 8 and 10.

	1 • 8	2 • 8	3 • 8	4 • 8	5 • 8	6 • 8	7 • 8
Multiples of 8:	**8**	**16**	**24**	**32**	**[40]**	**48**	**56**

	1 • 10	2 • 10	3 • 10	4 • 10	5 • 10
Multiples of 10:	**10**	**20**	**30**	**[40]**	**50**

The LCM is 40.

4 In one part of a musical composition, the triangle player in an orchestra plays once every 12 beats. The tympani player plays once every 9 beats. How often do they play together?

You need to find the LCM of 12 and 9.

	1 • 12	2 • 12	3 • 12	
Multiples of 12:	**12**	**24**	**[36]**	

	1 • 9	2 • 9	3 • 9	4 • 9
Multiples of 9:	**9**	**18**	**27**	**[36]**

The LCM of 12 and 9 is 36.

The triangle and tympani play together once every 36 beats.

Try It

Find the LCM. **a.** 5, 15 15 **b.** 12, 16 48 **c.** 10, 12 60 **d.** 7, 9 63

▶ Science Link

We have a pair of *tympani* in our heads! Tympanic membrane is the name for an *eardrum*.

Alternate Examples

3. Find the LCM of 18 and 24.

   Multiples of 18:
   1 • 18 2 • 18 3 • 18 4 • 18
   18 36 54 72

   Multiples of 24:
   1 • 24 2 • 24 3 • 24
   24 48 72

   The LCM of 18 and 24 is 72.

4. In one composition, the cymbals are played every 12 beats and the tambourine is struck every 8 beats. How often are the instruments played at the same time?

   Multiples of 12: 1 • 12 2 • 12
   12 [24]

   Multiples of 8: 1 • 8 2 • 8 3 • 8
   8 16 [24]

   The LCM of 12 and 8 is 24, so the instruments will be played at the same time every 24 beats.

MEETING MIDDLE SCHOOL CLASSROOM NEEDS

Tips from Middle School Teachers

To stress the differences between greatest common factor and least common multiple, I give students a variety of pairs of simple numbers and have them find both the GCF and the LCM for each pair.

Team Teaching

The shop teacher or sewing teacher might point out instances where LCD and GCF are used in their subjects. For example, bolts of cloth might come in two different widths. A sewing teacher might want to find the widest strips of equal width into which each bolt can be cut without wasting cloth. This width is the GCF of both original widths.

Science Connection

A synthesizer is a musical instrument that produces sounds electronically. Most synthesizers are played by means of a keyboard. Synthesizers are used in all kinds of music and often replace live musicians. A physicist and an inventor independently developed the first commercially successful synthesizers in the 1960's.

3-7 Exercises and Applications

Assignment Guide

- Basic
  1–9 odds, 10, 11–19 odds, 20–22, 25–37 odds
- Average
  1, 2–22 evens, 23, 24–38 evens
- Enriched
  2–38 evens

3 Practice and Assess

Check

Answers for Check Your Understanding

1. Yes, if the smaller number is a factor of the larger.
2. GCF is 1; LCM is their product.

Exercise Notes

Exercises 2–9

Extension All of these pairs of numbers have a GCF greater than 1. Pairs whose GCF is 1 are said to be *relatively prime*. One such pair is 6 and 35. Have students suggest other pairs of relatively prime numbers. Samples: 12, 49; 9, 16; 8, 18.

Project Progress

You may want to have students use Chapter 3 Project Master.

Reteaching

Activity

Materials: String, inch rulers, scissors

- Cut a 48-in. strip and a 36-in. strip of string. Stretch them out on the floor. Then cut several strips of each of these lengths: 12 in., 16 in., 18 in., and 24 in. Which ones can be used to fill both of the original strips? 6 in.; 12 in. Which is longest? 12 in. This is the GCF of 36 and 48.
- To find the LCM of 36 and 48, use several 36-in. and several 48-in. pieces of string. Stretch out in a straight line as many pieces of each length as necessary to reach the same length. What is this length? 144 in. This is the LCM of 36 and 48.

Check Your Understanding

1. Can the greatest common factor of two numbers be equal to one of the numbers? Explain.
2. What is the GCF of two different prime numbers? What is the LCM?

3-7 Exercises and Applications

Practice and Apply

PRACTICE 3-7

1. **Getting Started** Follow these steps to find the GCF of 42 and 63.
   a. Find all of the factors of 42. 1, 2, 3, 6, 7, 14, 21, 42
   b. Find all of the factors of 63. 1, 3, 7, 9, 21, 63
   c. List the factors that 42 and 63 have in common. 1, 3, 7, 21
   d. Find the greatest factor common to both numbers. 21

Find the GCF by listing all the factors of each number.

2. 54, 90 18 3. 84, 96 12 4. 125, 175 25 5. 323, 391 17

Find the GCF by writing the prime factorization of each number.

6. 54, 81 27 7. 432, 378 54 8. 24, 117 3 9. 405, 486 81

10. **Test Prep** The GCF of 198 and 220 is: A
    Ⓐ 22 Ⓑ 11 Ⓒ 26 Ⓓ 4

Find the LCM of each pair of numbers.

11. 9, 15 45 12. 12, 20 60 13. 15, 20 60 14. 16, 24 48
15. 8, 14 56 16. 15, 24 120 17. 8, 30 120 18. 14, 24 168

19. **Pattern** A local restaurant is offering a free meal to every 25th customer and a free hat to every 12th customer. Which customer will be the first to get both a free meal and a free hat? The 300th customer

20. **Career** Bennie is catering a wedding and is putting finger food on plates. GPS He has 72 cheese puffs and 48 carrot sticks. He wants both kinds of food on each plate. He wants to distribute the food evenly, and he doesn't want any left over. What is the largest number of plates he can use, and how many of each type of food should he put on each plate? 24 plates; 3 cheese puffs and 2 carrot sticks

PRACTICE

Name ______________

Practice 3-7

GCF and LCM

Find the GCF by listing all the factors of each number.

1. 145, 100
   Factors of 145 1, 5, 29, 145
   Factors of 100 1, 2, 4, 5, 10, 20, 25, 50, 100
   GCF: 5

Find the GCF by writing the prime factorization of each number.

2. 243, 54
   243 = $3 \times 3 \times 3 \times 3 \times 3$
   54 = $2 \times 3 \times 3 \times 3$
   GCF = 27
3. 150, 155
   150 = $2 \times 3 \times 5 \times 5$
   155 = 5×31
   GCF = 5
4. 96, 84
   96 = $2 \times 2 \times 2 \times 2 \times 2 \times 3$
   84 = $2 \times 2 \times 3 \times 7$
   GCF = 12
5. 57, 285
   57 = 3×19
   285 = $3 \times 5 \times 19$
   GCF = 57

Find the LCM of each pair of numbers.

6. 11, 5 55 7. 5, 12 60 8. 12, 7 84 9. 5, 9 45
10. 5, 18 90 11. 5, 20 20 12. 7, 10 70 13. 17, 13 221
14. 14, 8 56 15. 11, 23 253 16. 14, 5 70 17. 16, 9 144

18. Cameron is making bead necklaces. He has 90 green beads and 108 blue beads. What is the greatest number of identical necklaces he can make if he wants to use all of the beads? 18

19. A radio station broadcasts a weather forecast every 18 minutes and a commercial every 15 minutes. If the station broadcasts both a weather forecast and a commercial at noon, when is the next time that both will be broadcast at the same time? At 1:30 P.M.

RETEACHING

Name ______________

Alternative Lesson 3-7

GCF and LCM

Numbers often have **common factors.** The **greatest common factor** of two numbers is the greatest number that is a factor of both of them.

Numbers also have **common multiples.** The **least common multiple** is the smallest number that is a common multiple of the given numbers.

Example 1

Find the greatest common factor (GCF) of 8 and 20.

Use divisibility rules to find the factors of 8 and 20.
List the factors. Circle the greatest common factor.

Factors of 8: 1 2 (4) 8 — 1, 2, and 4 are common factors.
Factors of 20: 1 2 (4) 5 10 20 — The GCF is 4.

Try It Find the GCF by listing all the factors of each number.

a. 12: 1 2 3 4 6 12
   18: 1 2 3 6 9 18
   GCF: 6
b. 18: 1 2 3 6 9 18
   30: 1 2 3 5 6 10 15 30
   GCF: 6

Find the GCF for each pair of numbers.

c. 28 and 35 7 d. 16 and 24 8
e. 12 and 72 12 f. 30 and 36 6

Example 2

Find the least common multiple (LCM) of 6 and 8.

List the multiples. Circle the smallest multiple that is on both lists.

6: 6 12 18 (24) 30
8: 8 16 (24) 32 — The LCM is 24.

Try It Find the LCM of each pair of numbers by listing multiples of each number.

g. 12: 12 24 36 48
   16: 16 32 48
   LCM: 48
h. 24: 24 48 72
   36: 36 72
   LCM: 72

Find the LCM of each pair of numbers.

i. 3 and 8 24 j. 4 and 14 28
k. 10 and 25 50 l. 50 and 75 150

21. Music Aaron is composing music for a pair of synthesizers. One instrument's part contains 595 bars of music; the other contains 680 bars of music. What is the greatest number of bars of music that divides evenly into both instruments' parts? **85 bars**

22. Test Prep Find the LCM and the GCF of 18 and 27. **D**

Ⓐ LCM: 108; GCF: 3 Ⓑ LCM: 54; GCF: 3

Ⓒ LCM: 108; GCF: 9 Ⓓ LCM: 54; GCF: 9

Problem Solving and Reasoning

23. Critical Thinking Give a method for finding the LCM of two numbers by using prime factorizations.

Critical Thinking For each number, find three pairs of numbers for which the given number is the GCF.

24. 9 **25.** 14 **26.** 7 **27.** 25

28. Communicate *A* and *B* are two different whole numbers. Their GCF is *A*. Their LCM is *B*. Which one is greater? Explain.

Mixed Review

Make a bar graph for each set of data. *[Lesson 1-2]*

29.

Color	Red	Blue	Green
Number	13	21	9

30.

Student	Ralph	Joan	Liz
Height (in.)	48	39	45

Estimate each product or quotient. *[Lesson 3-4]*

31. 23.4×7.81 ≈ **160** **32.** $20.01 \div 8.7$ ≈ **2** **33.** $6.73 \cdot 0.037$ ≈ **0.28** **34.** $1.68 \div 0.35$ ≈ **5**

35. $\frac{639.9}{161.5}$ ≈ **4** **36.** 281.19×29.42 ≈ **8400** **37.** $214.34 \div 2.45$ ≈ **100** **38.** $0.048 \cdot 4.59$ ≈ **0.25**

Project Progress

Use exponents to show how many animals can result from your original pair in the third through the eighth generation. (Assume each baby survives to find a mate, and that there are always equal numbers of males and females.) Make a poster that shows the growth in the population. Express large numbers in scientific notation.

PROBLEM SOLVING 3-7

PROBLEM SOLVING

Name ______

Guided Problem Solving 3-7

GPS PROBLEM 20, STUDENT PAGE 142

Bennie is catering a wedding and is putting finger food on plates. He has 72 cheese puffs and 48 carrot sticks. He wants both kinds of food on each plate. He wants to distribute the food evenly, and he doesn't want any left over. What is the largest number of plates he can use, and how many of each type of food should he put on each plate?

Understand

1. Underline what you are asked to find.
2. Circle the quantities of food Bennie has to serve.

Plan

3. Write the prime factorization of 72. $2^3 \times 3^2$
4. Write the prime factorization of 48. $2^4 \times 3$

Solve

5. Use the prime factorizations to find the GCF of 72 and 48. **24**
6. What is the largest number of plates Bennie can use? **24 plates.**
7. The remaining factors in the prime factorization tell how many of each item will be on a plate. How many of each item will be on each plate?
   a. cheese puffs **3 cheese puffs.** b. carrot sticks **2 carrot sticks.**

Look Back

8. What is another way you could find the largest number of plates? **Possible answer: Find GCF by listing factors of each number.**

SOLVE ANOTHER PROBLEM

Bennie is catering another party and is putting finger food on plates. He has 60 pigs-in-a-blanket and 45 small tacos. He wants both kinds of food on each plate. He wants to distribute the food evenly, and he doesn't want any left over. What is the largest number of plates he can use, and how many of each type of food should he put on each plate?
15 plates, 4 pigs-in-a-blanket, 3 tacos.

ENRICHMENT

Name ______

Extend Your Thinking 3-7

Decision Making

Use the map to make your decisions on which routes to take. Sometimes you can choose different types of routes between two cities. The route may be mostly toll roads, mostly divided higways, or mostly scenic routes.

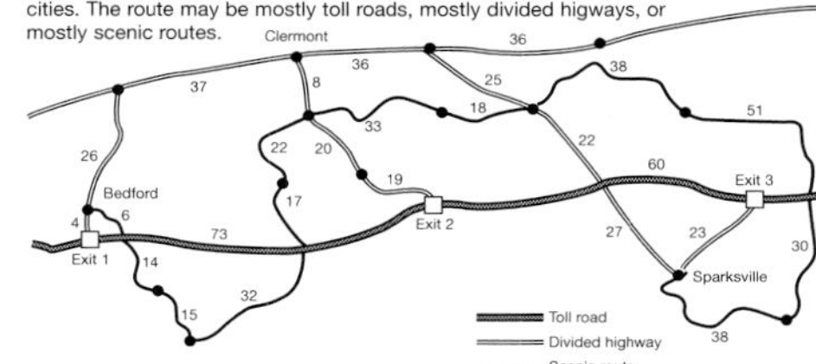

1. Find the total distance in miles between the two given cities for each type of route. Include not only the miles traveled mostly on a specific type of road but also the miles traveled to reach the road. Circle the miles in the route you would rather take.

		Distance in miles when driving mostly:		
		Toll roads	Divided highways	Scenic routes
a.	Bedford to Clermont	124	(63)	114
b.	Clermont to Sparksville	130	(110)	216
c.	Bedford to Sparksville	(160)	173	314

2. Explain why you chose each route.
Possible answers: The route was the shortest—saved time.
The scenery was beautiful—wanted to look at fall leaves.
The drive was easier—didn't want to deal with heavy traffic.

3. Other than looking at different routes on a map, what other factors do you need to know in order to make an informed choice?
Possible answers: Time, gas prices, purpose of trip, toll cost, road construction

Exercise Answers

23. Possible answer: Choose the greater number of times each factor appears in either number. The LCM is the product of all these groups of factors.

24. Possible answer: 18 and 27; 36 and 45; 90 and 99.

25. Possible answer: 28 and 42; 56 and 70; 140 and154.

26. Possible answer: 49 and 21; 28 and 35; 70 and 77.

27. Possible answer: 50 and 75; 100 and 125; 150 and 175.

28. *B* is greater than *A*. The LCM is the least number which is divisible by *A* and *B*. The GCF is the greatest number that divides *A* and *B*. *B* is greater than *A*. The GCF, *A*, must be a factor of *B*, so it is smaller than *B*.

29. Numbers of Each Color

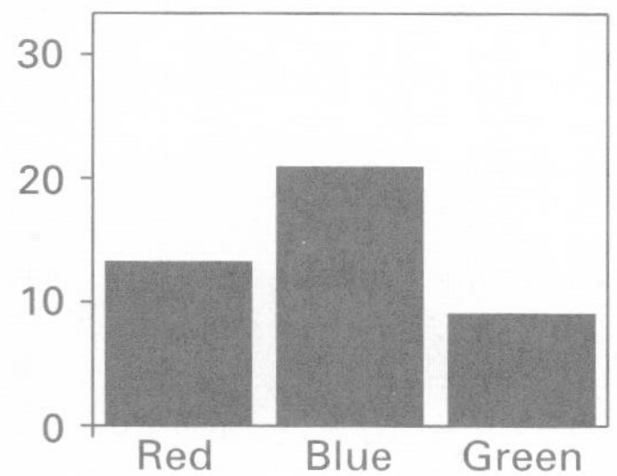

30. Heights of Students

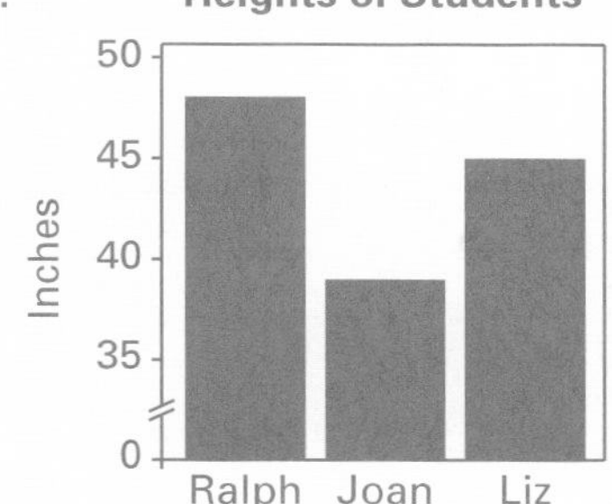

Alternate Assessment

You may want to use the *Interactive CD-ROM Journal* with this assessment.

Journal Have students work in pairs to write procedures for finding the GCF and the LCM of a pair of numbers.

Quick Quiz

Find the GCF and the LCM for each pair of numbers.

1. 48, 64 **16, 192**
2. 72, 108 **36, 216**
3. 50, 125 **25, 250**

Available on Daily Transparency 3-7

3-8 Lesson Organizer

Objectives

- Write equivalent fractions.
- Rewrite fractions in lowest terms.

Vocabulary

- Fraction, numerator, denominator, equivalent, lowest terms

Materials

- Explore: Calculator

NCTM Standards

- 1–4, 6

▶ Review

Find each quotient.

1. 1 ÷ 2 0.5
2. 1 ÷ 4 0.25
3. 1 ÷ 3 0.333...
4. 3 ÷ 4 0.75
5. 2 ÷ 3 0.666...

Available on Daily Transparency 3-8

1 Introduce

Explore

You may wish to use Lesson Enhancement Transparency 10 with **Explore**.

The Point
Students use frequencies of piano keys to identify equal fractions.

Ongoing Assessment
Check that students are computing correctly to express the fractions represented by the frequency comparisons.

For Groups That Finish Early
Have students conjecture the frequency of the C below C1, the F below F1, and the G below G1.
66, 88, 99

3-8 Equivalent Fractions and Lowest Terms

You'll Learn ...

- to write equivalent fractions
- to rewrite fractions in lowest terms

... How It's Used

Brokers sometimes use equivalent fractions to compare prices of stocks and bonds.

Vocabulary

fraction
numerator
denominator
equivalent
lowest terms

▶ Lesson Link You've learned to find the greatest common factor of two numbers. Now you'll use the GCF to write fractions that are equivalent.◂

Explore Equivalent Fractions

The Key to Fractions

Materials: Calculator

When you strike a piano key, a string vibrates. The vibration produces the sound that you hear. Here are the names of 12 piano keys and their *frequencies*—the number of times their strings vibrate each second.

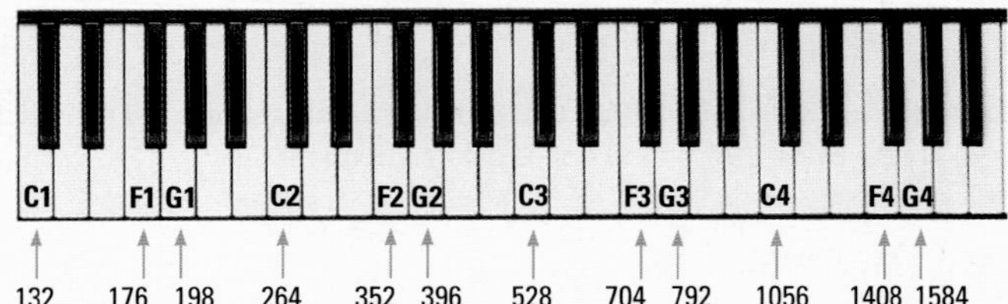

1. Compare the frequency of C1 with C2, C2 with C3, and C3 with C4. What pattern do you find? How is each C-note related to the next one?
2. Repeat Question 1, comparing the F-notes. Repeat again, comparing the G-notes.
3. Compare C1 with F1, C2 with F2, and so on. What do you find?
4. Compare C1 with G1, C2 with G2, and so on. What do you find?
5. Make conjectures about the frequencies of C5, F5, and G5. Explain.

Learn Equivalent Fractions and Lowest Terms

The symbol $\frac{a}{b}$ where a and b are whole numbers and $b \neq 0$ is a **fraction**. The top number is the **numerator**. The bottom number is the **denominator**.

$1 \div 4 = \frac{1}{4}$ ← numerator (1), ← denominator (4)

If two fractions represent the same quantity, they are **equivalent**: $\frac{1}{4}$ and $\frac{2}{8}$ are equivalent.

$\frac{1}{4}$ 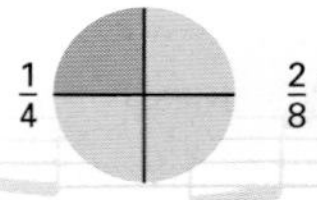 $\frac{2}{8}$ 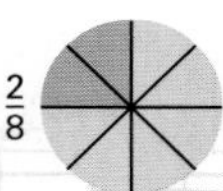

MEETING INDIVIDUAL NEEDS

Resources

3-8 Practice
3-8 Reteaching
3-8 Problem Solving
3-8 Enrichment
3-8 Daily Transparency
  Problem of the Day
  Review
  Quick Quiz
Lesson Enhancement Transparency 10
Teaching Tool Transparencies 2, 3
Technology Master 11

Learning Modalities

Kinesthetic You might have students carefully cut the bottom of egg cartons to create twelfths, sixths, fourths, thirds, and halves. They can use these models to help find equivalent fractions and, in the next lesson, compare fractions.

Social Discuss with students the instruments they play and have volunteers describe the musical scale.

English Language Development

For students with limited English proficiency, relate the term *numerator* to the word *number* and tell them that the numerator tells the *number* of equal parts. Relate the term *denominator* to the word *nominate*, as it gives the *name* of the equal parts.

In the **Social** activity above, group English language learners with students more proficient in English.

You can use a calculator to decide if two fractions are equivalent.

1 [÷] 4 [=] 0.25

2 [÷] 8 [=] 0.25

$\frac{1}{4}$ and $\frac{2}{8}$ both equal 0.25, so they are equivalent.

You can create an equivalent fraction by multiplying or dividing the numerator and denominator of a fraction by the same number.

Example 1

Find two fractions equivalent to $\frac{12}{16}$.

Multiply or divide by any convenient numbers.

$\frac{12 \times 2}{16 \times 2} = \frac{24}{32}$ Multiply by 2. $\frac{12 \div 4}{16 \div 4} = \frac{3}{4}$ Divide by 4.

$\frac{24}{32}$ and $\frac{3}{4}$ are equivalent to $\frac{12}{16}$.

Try It

Find two equivalent fractions for each fraction. **a.** $\frac{6}{9}$ **b.** $\frac{25}{30}$ **c.** $\frac{10}{12}$ **d.** $\frac{15}{21}$

a. $\frac{2}{3}, \frac{12}{18}$ b. $\frac{5}{6}, \frac{50}{60}$ c. $\frac{5}{6}, \frac{30}{36}$ d. $\frac{3}{7}, \frac{30}{42}$

Test Prep

You may sometimes be asked to give a fraction in *simplest form.* Don't be confused! *Simplest form* means the same thing as *lowest terms.*

When 1 is the only common factor of the numerator and the denominator of a fraction, the fraction is in **lowest terms**. The fraction $\frac{10}{15}$ is not in lowest terms because 5 is a common factor of the numerator and the denominator.

$\frac{10}{15} = \frac{10 \div 5}{15 \div 5} = \frac{2}{3}$ 1 is the only common factor of 2 and 3.

You can rewrite a fraction in lowest terms by dividing the numerator and denominator by a common factor several times or by dividing the numerator and denominator by the GCF of both numbers to reach lowest terms in one step.

Example 2

Show that $\frac{8}{10}$ and $\frac{20}{25}$ are equivalent.

Two fractions that are the same in lowest terms are equivalent.

$\frac{8}{10} = \frac{8 \div 2}{10 \div 2} = \frac{4}{5}$ $\frac{20}{25} = \frac{20 \div 5}{25 \div 5} = \frac{4}{5}$

$\frac{8}{10}$ and $\frac{20}{25}$ both equal $\frac{4}{5}$ in lowest terms, so they are equivalent.

Try It

Decide whether the fractions are equivalent.

a. $\frac{3}{4}$ and $\frac{12}{15}$ No **b.** $\frac{9}{10}$ and $\frac{19}{20}$ No **c.** $\frac{10}{30}$ and $\frac{6}{18}$ Yes **d.** $\frac{4}{14}$ and $\frac{6}{21}$ Yes

Language Link

Look at the word *equivalent.* It tells you what it means: *equi-* always means "equal" and *valent* is related to the word *value.* So *equivalent* means "having equal value."

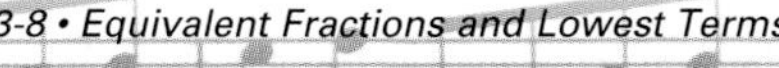

Answers for Explore

1. C4 = 2 • C3, C3 = 2 • C2, C2 = 2 • C1; The frequency of each C-note is half the next one.
2. F4 = 2 • F3, F3 = 2 • F2, F2 = 2 • F1; The frequency of each F-note is half the next one. The frequency of each G-note is half the next one.
3. The frequency of the F-note is always $\frac{4}{3}$ times that of the preceding C-note.
4. G1 ÷ C1 = $\frac{3}{2}$, G2 ÷ C2 = $\frac{3}{2}$, G3 ÷ C3 = $\frac{3}{2}$, G4 ÷ C4 = $\frac{3}{2}$; The frequency of the G-note is always $\frac{3}{2}$ times that of the preceding C-note.
5. From answers 1 and 2, C5 = 2112, F5 = 2816, G5 = 3168; F5 ÷ C5 = $\frac{4}{3}$, G5 ÷ C5 = $\frac{3}{2}$

2 Teach

Learn

Alternate Examples

1. Find two fractions equivalent to $\frac{18}{24}$.

   $\frac{18 \times 2}{24 \times 2} = \frac{36}{48}$ Multiply by 2.

   $\frac{18 \div 6}{24 \div 6} = \frac{3}{4}$ Divide by 6.

   $\frac{36}{48}$ and $\frac{3}{4}$ are equivalent to $\frac{18}{24}$.

2. Show that $\frac{8}{12}$ and $\frac{18}{27}$ are equivalent.

   $\frac{8}{12} = \frac{8 \div 4}{12 \div 4} = \frac{2}{3}$

   $\frac{18}{27} = \frac{18 \div 9}{27 \div 9} = \frac{2}{3}$

   $\frac{8}{12}$ and $\frac{18}{27}$ both equal $\frac{2}{3}$ in lowest terms, so they are equivalent.

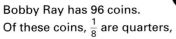

MATH EVERY DAY

Problem of the Day

Bobby Ray has 96 coins. Of these coins, $\frac{1}{8}$ are quarters, $\frac{3}{8}$ are dimes, $\frac{1}{4}$ are nickels, and $\frac{1}{4}$ are pennies. How much money does he have? $8.04

Available on Daily Transparency 3-8

An Extension is provided in the transparency package.

Fact of the Day

Bartolomeo Cristofori of Florence, Italy, is usually credited with inventing the piano in 1709.

Mental Math

Solve each equation mentally.

1. $8x = 64$ $x = 8$
2. $5y = 35$ $y = 7$
3. $7c = 63$ $c = 9$
4. $9a = 45$ $a = 5$
5. $6w = 60$ $w = 10$

Students see two methods for writing a fraction in lowest terms. They are asked to decide when one method is preferred over the other.

Answers for What Do You Think?

1. Brett's method, when the numbers are not too large and it is easy to spot factors; Lorena's method always works, and it is especially useful with large numbers.
2. Brett's method.

3 Practice and Assess

Check

Stress that the numerator and the denominator must be multiplied or divided by the same number to yield an equivalent fraction. Show the class that this procedure is, in effect, multiplying or dividing the fraction by 1, since $\frac{1}{1} = \frac{2}{2} = \frac{3}{3}$ and so on.

Answers for Check Your Understanding

1. No; The numerator and denominator can both be multiplied by any number to produce equivalent fractions.
2. No; If it were, the fraction would not be in lowest terms.

Of the 84 students in the school band, 24 play brass instruments. For an article for the school paper, Brett and Lorena want to know the fraction of band members who play brass instruments.

Brett thinks ...

I need to write $\frac{24}{84}$ in lowest terms.

$\frac{24 \div 2}{84 \div 2} = \frac{12}{42}$ Divide by 2.

$\frac{12 \div 2}{42 \div 2} = \frac{6}{21}$ Divide by 2 again.

$\frac{6 \div 3}{21 \div 3} = \frac{2}{7}$ Divide by 3.

The fraction is $\frac{2}{7}$.

Lorena thinks ...

I need to write $\frac{24}{84}$ in lowest terms. $24 = 2^3 \times 3$

$84 = 2^2 \times 3 \times 7$

The GCF of 24 and 84 is $2^2 \times 3 = 12$.

I'll divide by the GCF: $\frac{24 \div 12}{84 \div 12} = \frac{2}{7}$

The fraction is $\frac{2}{7}$.

What do  think?

1. When does Brett's method work well? When does Lorena's work well?
2. If you're using mental math, whose method is easier?

Check Your Understanding

1. Is there any limit to the number of equivalent fractions one fraction can have? Explain.
2. The numerator of a fraction in lowest terms has 2 as a factor. Is 2 a factor of the denominator? Explain.

MEETING MIDDLE SCHOOL CLASSROOM NEEDS

Tips from Middle School Teachers

To help my students grasp the concept of numerator and denominator, I have them write the word names of fractions as I say them aloud. This helps them to remember that the numerator tells how many pieces and that the denominator indicates the size of the pieces.

Team Teaching

A music teacher might use a keyboard and simple tunes to illustrate the musical notes discussed in **Explore**.

Music Connection

Ragtime is a style of piano playing in which the left hand provides harmony and a firm beat, while the right hand plays the melody. This style of music was a predecessor of jazz, which grew out of the African-American culture of the American South.

3-8 Exercises and Applications

Practice and Apply

1. **Getting Started** Follow these steps to use the GCF to express $\frac{16}{24}$ in lowest terms.
   a. Find all of the factors of 16. 1, 2, 4, 8, 16
   b. Find all of the factors of 24. 1, 2, 3, 4, 6, 8, 12, 24
   c. What is the GCF of 16 and 24? GCF = 8
   d. Divide the numerator and denominator by the GCF. $\frac{2}{3}$

Find an equivalent fraction with (a) a smaller and (b) a larger denominator.

2. $\frac{20}{24}$ $\frac{5}{6}, \frac{40}{48}$
3. $\frac{15}{27}$ $\frac{5}{9}, \frac{30}{54}$
4. $\frac{6}{21}$ $\frac{2}{7}, \frac{12}{42}$
5. $\frac{16}{22}$ $\frac{8}{11}, \frac{32}{44}$
6. $\frac{8}{52}$ $\frac{2}{13}, \frac{16}{104}$

Express each fraction in lowest terms.

7. $\frac{54}{81}$ $\frac{2}{3}$
8. $\frac{36}{68}$ $\frac{9}{17}$
9. $\frac{28}{36}$ $\frac{7}{9}$
10. $\frac{18}{76}$ $\frac{9}{38}$
11. $\frac{32}{40}$ $\frac{4}{5}$
12. $\frac{34}{52}$ $\frac{17}{26}$
13. $\frac{42}{63}$ $\frac{2}{3}$
14. $\frac{21}{69}$ $\frac{7}{23}$
15. $\frac{24}{32}$ $\frac{3}{4}$
16. $\frac{36}{54}$ $\frac{2}{3}$
17. $\frac{36}{48}$ $\frac{3}{4}$
18. $\frac{25}{35}$ $\frac{5}{7}$
19. $\frac{60}{90}$ $\frac{2}{3}$
20. $\frac{90}{108}$ $\frac{5}{6}$
21. $\frac{14}{98}$ $\frac{1}{7}$
22. $\frac{64}{144}$ $\frac{4}{9}$
23. $\frac{117}{243}$ $\frac{13}{27}$
24. $\frac{42}{77}$ $\frac{6}{11}$
25. $\frac{36}{50}$ $\frac{18}{25}$
26. $\frac{60}{72}$ $\frac{5}{6}$
27. $\frac{25}{110}$ $\frac{5}{22}$
28. $\frac{128}{288}$ $\frac{4}{9}$
29. $\frac{96}{212}$ $\frac{24}{53}$
30. $\frac{144}{216}$ $\frac{2}{3}$

31. **Test Prep** Which one of the following fractions is not equivalent to the others? C

   Ⓐ $\frac{24}{96}$ Ⓑ $\frac{8}{32}$ Ⓒ $\frac{25}{97}$ Ⓓ $\frac{23}{92}$

32. **Industry** A saxophone manufacturer made 800 saxophones last year. Of these, 720 passed final quality checks. What fraction of the saxophones passed final quality checks? An order for 20 saxophones came from a music store. How many of the next 20 saxophones made are likely to be "good"? $\frac{9}{10}$; 18

33. **Data** In 1864, 2,218,388 of the 4,031,887 votes in the U.S. presidential election went to Abraham Lincoln. About what fraction of the votes did Lincoln receive? About $\frac{11}{20}$

PRACTICE 3-8

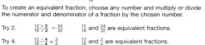

PRACTICE

Name ____________

Practice 3-8

Equivalent Fractions and Lowest Terms

Find an equivalent fraction with (a) a smaller and (b) a larger denominator.

1. $\frac{4}{28}$ (a) $\frac{1}{7}$ (b) $\frac{8}{56}$
2. $\frac{9}{69}$ (a) $\frac{3}{23}$ (b) $\frac{18}{138}$
3. $\frac{7}{35}$ (a) $\frac{1}{5}$ (b) $\frac{14}{70}$
4. $\frac{6}{30}$ (a) $\frac{1}{5}$ (b) $\frac{12}{60}$
5. $\frac{52}{86}$ (a) $\frac{26}{43}$ (b) $\frac{104}{172}$
6. $\frac{45}{75}$ (a) $\frac{3}{5}$ (b) $\frac{90}{150}$
7. $\frac{34}{56}$ (a) $\frac{17}{28}$ (b) $\frac{68}{112}$
8. $\frac{42}{52}$ (a) $\frac{21}{26}$ (b) $\frac{84}{104}$
9. $\frac{30}{38}$ (a) $\frac{15}{19}$ (b) $\frac{60}{76}$
10. $\frac{10}{18}$ (a) $\frac{5}{9}$ (b) $\frac{20}{36}$
11. $\frac{72}{81}$ (a) $\frac{8}{9}$ (b) $\frac{144}{162}$
12. $\frac{12}{22}$ (a) $\frac{6}{11}$ (b) $\frac{24}{44}$

Express each fraction in lowest terms.

13. $\frac{46}{62}$ $\frac{23}{31}$
14. $\frac{5}{60}$ $\frac{1}{12}$
15. $\frac{15}{24}$ $\frac{5}{8}$
16. $\frac{20}{58}$ $\frac{10}{29}$
17. $\frac{12}{14}$ $\frac{6}{7}$
18. $\frac{26}{64}$ $\frac{13}{32}$
19. $\frac{8}{342}$ $\frac{4}{171}$
20. $\frac{30}{46}$ $\frac{15}{23}$
21. $\frac{30}{64}$ $\frac{15}{32}$
22. $\frac{6}{14}$ $\frac{3}{7}$
23. $\frac{18}{98}$ $\frac{9}{49}$
24. $\frac{24}{46}$ $\frac{12}{23}$
25. $\frac{30}{45}$ $\frac{2}{3}$
26. $\frac{14}{24}$ $\frac{7}{12}$
27. $\frac{48}{80}$ $\frac{3}{5}$
28. $\frac{49}{77}$ $\frac{7}{11}$
29. $\frac{123}{171}$ $\frac{41}{57}$
30. $\frac{38}{72}$ $\frac{19}{36}$
31. $\frac{22}{60}$ $\frac{11}{30}$
32. $\frac{8}{10}$ $\frac{4}{5}$
33. $\frac{210}{304}$ $\frac{105}{152}$
34. $\frac{18}{39}$ $\frac{6}{13}$
35. $\frac{42}{104}$ $\frac{21}{52}$
36. $\frac{40}{116}$ $\frac{10}{29}$

37. The city of Austin, Texas, typically has 115 clear days out of the 365 days in a year. What fraction of Austin's days are clear? Write your answer in lowest terms. $\frac{23}{73}$
38. In 1985, American education expenditures totaled \$247.7 billion, of which \$137 billion was spent on public elementary and secondary schools. About what fraction of education expenditures were spent on public elementary and secondary schools? About $\frac{11}{20}$

RETEACHING

Name ____________

Alternative Lesson 3-8

Equivalent Fractions and Lowest Terms

If two fractions represent the same quantity, they are **equivalent**. You can draw models to show the equivalence.

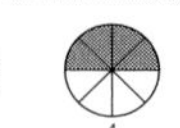

Example 1

Find two fractions equivalent to $\frac{12}{16}$.

To create an equivalent fraction, choose any number and multiply or divide the numerator and denominator of a fraction by the chosen number.

Try 2. $\frac{12 \times \mathbf{2}}{16 \times \mathbf{2}} = \frac{24}{32}$ $\frac{12}{16}$ and $\frac{24}{32}$ are equivalent fractions.

Try 4. $\frac{12 \div \mathbf{4}}{16 \div \mathbf{4}} = \frac{3}{4}$ $\frac{12}{16}$ and $\frac{3}{4}$ are equivalent fractions.

Both $\frac{3}{4}$ and $\frac{24}{32}$ are equivalent to $\frac{12}{16}$.

Try It Find an equivalent fraction with a smaller denominator. Then find one with a larger denominator.

a. $\frac{30}{36}$ $\frac{5}{6}, \frac{60}{72}$ b. $\frac{30}{75}$ $\frac{2}{5}, \frac{60}{150}$

Example 2

Express $\frac{30}{84}$ in lowest terms.

To write a fraction in lowest terms, divide both the numerator and the denominator by the greatest common factor of each number.

The greatest common factor of 30 and 84 is 6.

$\frac{30}{84} = \frac{30 \div 6}{84 \div 6} = \frac{5}{14}$

$\frac{30}{84}$ in lowest terms is $\frac{5}{14}$.

Try It Express each fraction in lowest terms.

c. $\frac{24}{36}$ $\frac{2}{3}$ d. $\frac{8}{12}$ $\frac{2}{3}$ e. $\frac{27}{72}$ $\frac{3}{8}$ f. $\frac{32}{64}$ $\frac{1}{2}$
g. $\frac{15}{95}$ $\frac{3}{19}$ h. $\frac{24}{54}$ $\frac{4}{9}$ i. $\frac{56}{63}$ $\frac{8}{9}$ j. $\frac{60}{75}$ $\frac{4}{5}$
k. $\frac{45}{54}$ $\frac{5}{6}$ l. $\frac{32}{68}$ $\frac{8}{17}$ m. $\frac{10}{25}$ $\frac{2}{5}$ n. $\frac{25}{105}$ $\frac{5}{21}$
o. $\frac{40}{42}$ $\frac{20}{21}$ p. $\frac{36}{72}$ $\frac{1}{2}$ q. $\frac{72}{81}$ $\frac{8}{9}$ r. $\frac{24}{27}$ $\frac{8}{9}$

3-8 Exercises and Applications

Assignment Guide

- **Basic**
  1–31 odds, 32–34, 40, 41–51 odds
- **Average**
  1, 2–30 evens, 31, 32–54 evens
- **Enriched**
  1–39 odds, 40, 41–55 odds

Reteaching

Activity

- Fold a piece of paper in half. Shade the area on one side of the fold line. What fraction of the paper is shaded? $\frac{1}{2}$ Now fold the paper in half the other way. How many parts are made by the fold lines? 4 What fraction is represented by each part? $\frac{1}{4}$ How many fourths are shaded? $\frac{2}{4}$
- Fold the paper once more. Now what fraction is represented by each part? $\frac{1}{8}$ How many eighths are shaded? $\frac{4}{8}$
- Finally, fold the paper one more time. What fraction is represented by each part? $\frac{1}{16}$ How many sixteenths are shaded? $\frac{8}{16}$
- What does your model show? $\frac{1}{2} = \frac{2}{4} = \frac{4}{8} = \frac{8}{16}$

Exercise Notes

■ Exercises 35–38

Problem Solving Tip Students may suggest using cross multiplication to find the value of x in each equation. In Exercise 35, for instance, $18 \times x = 14 \times 27$, and $x = 378 \div 18 = 21$.

■ Exercise 39

Problem-Solving Tip You may wish to use Teaching Tool Transparencies 2 and 3: Guided Problem Solving, pages 1–2.

■ Exercise 40

Sports Discuss with students which player has the best batting average. Ja Ask students what batting averages are common for professional players. Tell them that Rogers Hornsby of the National League had a batting average of .401 in 1922, .424 in 1924, and .403 in 1925. In the American League, Ty Cobb batted .420 in 1911 and .410 in 1912.

Exercise Answers

39. Apply rules of divisibility and divide by any factors; find the prime factorization of each number and divide by the GCF. The reduced fraction is $\frac{17}{18}$.

Alternate Assessment

Interview Have students describe how they would find fractions equivalent to $\frac{30}{36}$ by multiplying and by dividing. Possible answer: By multiplying both the numerator and denominator by 2, for $\frac{60}{72}$; by dividing both the numerator and the denominator by 6, for $\frac{5}{6}$. Ask how they could check that the fractions are equivalent. Possible answer: Use a calculator with each to divide the numerator by the denominator; the quotient is 0.833... for all three fractions.

▶ Quick Quiz

Write each fraction in lowest terms.

1. $\frac{30}{78}$ $\frac{5}{13}$
2. $\frac{72}{108}$ $\frac{2}{3}$
3. $\frac{50}{175}$ $\frac{2}{7}$
4. $\frac{48}{84}$ $\frac{4}{7}$
5. $\frac{19}{76}$ $\frac{1}{4}$

Available on Daily Transparency 3-8

34. Science Over her lifetime, a female green turtle lays an average of 1800 eggs. Of these, about 1395 do not hatch, about 374 young turtles quickly die, and only about 3 live long enough to breed. About what fraction of a green turtle's eggs survive to breed? Write your answer in lowest terms. $\frac{1}{600}$

Problem Solving and Reasoning

Critical Thinking **Fill in the missing number to make the fractions equivalent.**

35. $\frac{14}{18} = \frac{x}{27}$ $x = 21$ **36.** $\frac{72}{84} = \frac{x}{77}$ $x = 66$ **37.** $\frac{51}{85} = \frac{45}{x}$ $x = 75$ **38.** $\frac{48}{216} = \frac{26}{x}$ $x = 117$

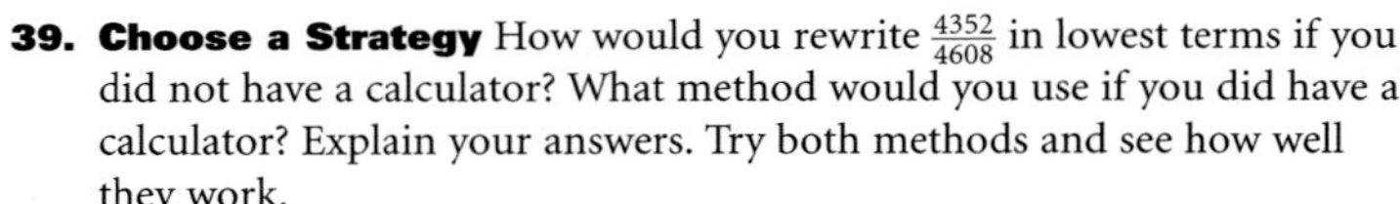

39. Choose a Strategy How would you rewrite $\frac{4352}{4608}$ in lowest terms if you did not have a calculator? What method would you use if you did have a calculator? Explain your answers. Try both methods and see how well they work.

Problem Solving STRATEGIES

- Look for a Pattern
- Make an Organized List
- Make a Table
- Guess and Check
- Work Backward
- Use Logical Reasoning
- Draw a Diagram
- Solve a Simpler Problem

40. Critical Thinking GPS A batting average in softball or baseball is the number of hits divided by the number of times at bat. A batting average of .285 means that the batter would be expected to get a hit 285 times in 1000 at-bats. The fraction $\frac{285}{1000}$ can be used to represent a batting average of .285. Use equivalent fractions to help you complete the following table. Use a calculator to check your answers.

	Maria	Sophie	Ja	Mia
Hits	20	27	24	18
Times at Bat	80	90	60	90
Batting Average	.250	.300	.400	.200

Mixed Review

Solve each equation. Check your solutions. *[Lesson 2-7]*

41. $3t = 27$ $t = 9$ **42.** $8j = 864$ $j = 108$ **43.** $26 = 13x$ $x = 2$ **44.** $162 = z \cdot 27$ $z = 6$

45. $n \div 17 = 12$ $n = 204$ **46.** $31 = \frac{s}{8}$ $s = 248$ **47.** $y \div 51 = 8$ $y = 408$ **48.** $\frac{b}{50} = 374$ $b = 18{,}700$

Use rounding to whole numbers to estimate. *[Lesson 3-2]*

49. $23.7 + 6.872$ 31 **50.** $64.3 - 2.41$ 62 **51.** 46.62×9.63 470 **52.** $\frac{55.86318}{7.236751}$ 8

53. $14.45 + 72.5$ 87 **54.** $179.734 - 22.176$ 158 **55.** $7.13 \cdot 8.449$ 56

PROBLEM SOLVING 3-8

PROBLEM SOLVING

Name ______________________

Guided Problem Solving 3-8

GPS PROBLEM 40, STUDENT PAGE 148

A batting average in softball or baseball is the number of hits divided by the number of times at bat. A batting average of .285 means that the batter would be expected to get a hit 285 times in 1000 at-bats. The fraction $\frac{285}{1000}$ can be used to represent a batting average of .285. Use equivalent fractions to help you complete the following table. Use a calculator to check your answers.

	Maria	Sophie	Ja	Mia	Chim	Que
Hits	20	27	24	18	14	18
Times at Bat	80	90	60	90	40	90
Batting Average	.250	.300	.400	.200	.350	.200

— Understand —

1. What do you need to do? Complete the table.

— Plan —

2. Write the batting average as a fraction for each player $\left(\frac{\text{number of hits}}{\text{number of times at bat}}\right)$.
 Maria $\frac{250}{1000}$ Sophie $\frac{300}{1000}$ Ja $\frac{400}{1000}$ Mia $\frac{200}{1000}$
3. Write a fraction for each blank in the table. Let x represent any unknowns. For example, the number of hits for Maria is $\frac{x}{80}$.
 Sophie $\frac{x}{90}$ Ja $\frac{24}{x}$ Mia $\frac{18}{x}$
4. Write equivalent fractions for each player using information from Items 2 and 3. Maria, $\frac{250}{1000} = \frac{x}{80}$; Sophie, $\frac{300}{1000} = \frac{x}{90}$; Ja, $\frac{400}{1000} = \frac{24}{x}$; Mia, $\frac{200}{1000} = \frac{18}{x}$

— Solve —

5. Complete the table.

— Look Back —

6. Does each girl's batting average equal her hits divided by times at bat? Yes.

SOLVE ANOTHER PROBLEM

Add this information to the table: Chim: hits, 14; batting average, .350; Que: times at bat, 90; batting average .200. Complete the table.

ENRICHMENT

Name ______________________

Extend Your Thinking 3-8

Visual Thinking

For each exercise, the same cube is shown in different positions. Write the letter that appears on the bottom of the fourth cube.

1. 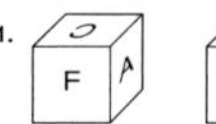 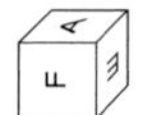 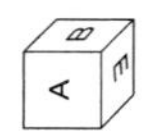 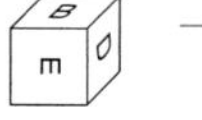 F

2.  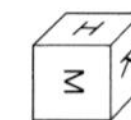 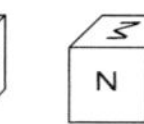 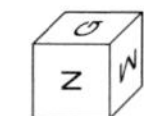 K

3. 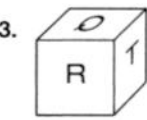 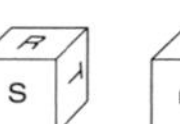 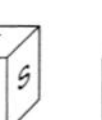 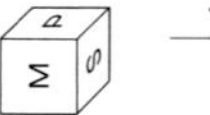 T

4. 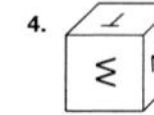 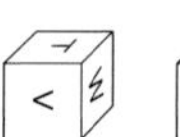 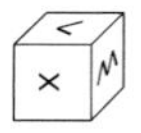 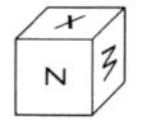  T

5.  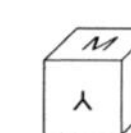  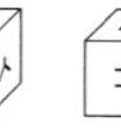  A

Comparing and Ordering Fractions

3-9

▶ Lesson Link You have learned how to decide whether two fractions are equivalent. Now you'll learn how to order a set of fractions that are not equivalent. ◀

Explore Comparing Fractions

As Time Goes By

Materials: Graph paper

A written musical note tells you the length of time the note should be played. If a "whole" note lasts 4 beats, then a "half" note lasts 2 beats, a "quarter" note lasts 1 beat, and so on.

1. Write each of the following notes or sets of notes as a fraction.

2. Using graph paper, model each of the fractions in Step 1. Let an 8 × 8 square (64 squares) represent a whole note.
3. Order the fractions from least to greatest. Explain your method.

You'll Learn ...

- to compare the values of fractions
- to order fractions

... How It's Used

Mechanics need large collections of socket wrenches. It is much easier to find the right wrench for a job if they are organized by size.

Vocabulary

common denominator

Learn Comparing and Ordering Fractions

There are many ways to compare fractions. One way is to use a model.

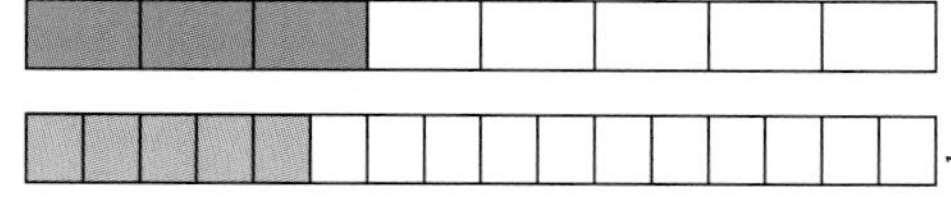

The first model represents $\frac{3}{8}$. The second represents $\frac{5}{16}$. By visually comparing lengths, we can see that $\frac{5}{16}$ is less than $\frac{3}{8}$.

MEETING INDIVIDUAL NEEDS

Resources

- **3-9** Practice
- **3-9** Reteaching
- **3-9** Problem Solving
- **3-9** Enrichment
- **3-9** Daily Transparency
  - Problem of the Day
  - Review
  - Quick Quiz
- Lesson Enhancement Transparency 11
- Technology Master 12

Learning Modalities

Verbal Engage the students in a discussion of when and how they have used and compared fractions and mixed numbers. Suggestions include distances at track meets and measurements in cooking and sewing or crafts.

Kinesthetic You may want to use plastic fraction models of some sort to help students compare fractions. It is important that they see and work with fractions that have different denominators such as 3, 4, 6, and 8.

English Language Development

Students with limited English proficiency can benefit greatly from working with fraction models to compare fractions. They can place one over the other to determine which is greater. You can also help them by writing the fractions on the board with the greater than and less than symbols and then reading the sentences aloud, stressing the symbols.

3-9 Lesson Organizer

Objectives

- Compare the values of fractions.
- Order fractions.

Vocabulary

- Common denominator

Materials

- Explore: Graph paper

NCTM Standards

- 1–4, 6, 8

▶ Review

Rewrite each fraction with the denominator specified.

1. $\frac{1}{2}$, 18 $\frac{9}{18}$
2. $\frac{7}{8}$, 24 $\frac{21}{24}$
3. $\frac{5}{6}$, 12 $\frac{10}{12}$
4. $\frac{7}{12}$, 48 $\frac{28}{48}$

Available on Daily Transparency 3-9

1 Introduce

Explore

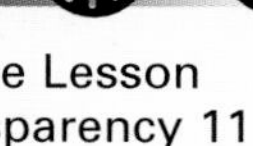

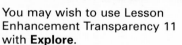

You may wish to use Lesson Enhancement Transparency 11 with **Explore**.

The Point
Students model fractions and find that, among fractions with equal numerators and different denominators, the one with the smaller denominator represents the greatest number.

Ongoing Assessment
Be sure students understand that, when a whole is divided into 4 equal parts, the parts are smaller than if it is divided into 2 equal parts.

Answers for Explore on next page.

For Groups That Finish Early

Use 8 × 8 grids to model $\frac{3}{4}$, $\frac{5}{8}$, and $\frac{9}{16}$. Then write the fractions in order with those in Step 3. Check students' models; $\frac{7}{32}$, $\frac{1}{4}$, $\frac{5}{16}$, $\frac{3}{8}$, $\frac{1}{2}$, $\frac{9}{16}$, $\frac{5}{8}$, $\frac{3}{4}$

Follow Up

Ask volunteers to share their models and explain how they ordered the fractions.

Answers for Explore

1. $\frac{1}{2}$, $\frac{1}{4}$, $\frac{3}{8}$, $\frac{5}{16}$, $\frac{7}{32}$
2. See page C5.
3. $\frac{7}{32}$, $\frac{1}{4}$, $\frac{5}{16}$, $\frac{3}{8}$, $\frac{1}{2}$; I counted the shaded squares.

2 Teach

Learn

After discussing Example 3 and the Problem Solving Tip, ask students if they think it is better to use the LCM as the common denominator and why. They may suggest that it is easier because the numbers are smaller.

Alternate Examples

1. The diameters of two drill bits are $\frac{9}{16}$ in. and $\frac{3}{4}$ in. Which is larger?

   Use fraction models to tell which has the greater diameter.

   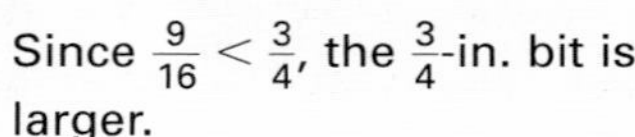

   Since $\frac{9}{16} < \frac{3}{4}$, the $\frac{3}{4}$-in. bit is larger.

2. Compare $\frac{5}{8}$ and $\frac{23}{32}$. Since $8 \times 4 = 32$, change $\frac{5}{8}$ to an equivalent fraction with a denominator of 32.

   $\frac{5}{8} = \frac{5 \times 4}{8 \times 4} = \frac{20}{32}$

   $\frac{20}{32} < \frac{23}{32}$, so $\frac{5}{8} < \frac{23}{32}$.

3. Compare $\frac{7}{8}$ and $\frac{2}{3}$.

   You can get equivalent fractions with a common denominator by multiplying the numerator and the denominator of each fraction by the denominator of the other.

   $\frac{7}{8} = \frac{7 \times 3}{8 \times 3} = \frac{21}{24}$ Multiply by 3.

   $\frac{2}{3} = \frac{2 \times 8}{3 \times 8} = \frac{16}{24}$ Multiply by 8.

   Since $\frac{21}{24} > \frac{16}{24}$, $\frac{7}{8} > \frac{2}{3}$.

Example 1

Martin is building a recorder. He needs to choose the smaller of two drill bits measuring $\frac{3}{4}$ in. and $\frac{5}{8}$ in. Which bit should he choose?

You can use a model to compare fourths and eighths. Since $\frac{5}{8} < \frac{3}{4}$, Martin should choose the $\frac{5}{8}$ in. bit.

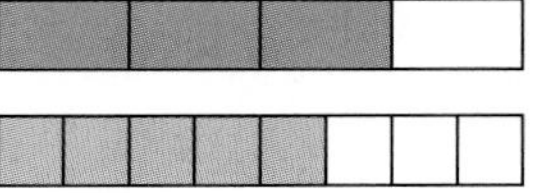

If two fractions have the same denominator, the one with the larger numerator is greater.

$$\frac{8}{11} > \frac{7}{11}$$

Fractions with the same denominator are said to have a **common denominator**. If the denominators are different, you can still compare the fractions by making equivalent fractions that have a common denominator.

Examples

2 Compare $\frac{2}{3}$ and $\frac{11}{18}$.

Look at the denominators. You know that 18 is a multiple of 3. Since $3 \cdot 6 = 18$, change $\frac{2}{3}$ to an equivalent fraction with a denominator of 18.

$\frac{2}{3} = \frac{2 \times 6}{3 \times 6} = \frac{12}{18}$ Multiply the numerator and the denominator by 6.

$\frac{12}{18} > \frac{11}{18}$, so $\frac{2}{3} > \frac{11}{18}$.

Problem Solving TIP

Notice that 12 is the LCM for 6 and 4. You could change the denominators to 12 in your head.

3 Compare $\frac{5}{6}$ and $\frac{3}{4}$.

You can get equivalent fractions with a common denominator by multiplying the numerator and denominator of each fraction by the denominator of the other.

$\frac{5}{6} = \frac{5 \times 4}{6 \times 4} = \frac{20}{24}$ Multiply by 4, the denominator of $\frac{3}{4}$.

$\frac{3}{4} = \frac{3 \times 6}{4 \times 6} = \frac{18}{24}$ Multiply by 6, the denominator of $\frac{5}{6}$.

Using a common denominator of 24, you can see that $\frac{20}{24} > \frac{18}{24}$, so $\frac{5}{6} > \frac{3}{4}$.

Try It

Compare using <, >, or =.

a. $\frac{3}{4}$ [>] $\frac{7}{12}$ **b.** $\frac{3}{5}$ [>] $\frac{4}{7}$ **c.** $\frac{7}{10}$ [<] $\frac{8}{11}$

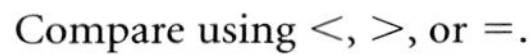

MATH EVERY DAY

Problem of the Day

A professional basketball team won 51 games this year—three times more than they won last year. How many more games did they win this year than last year? 34 games

Available on Daily Transparency 3-9

An Extension is provided in the transparency package.

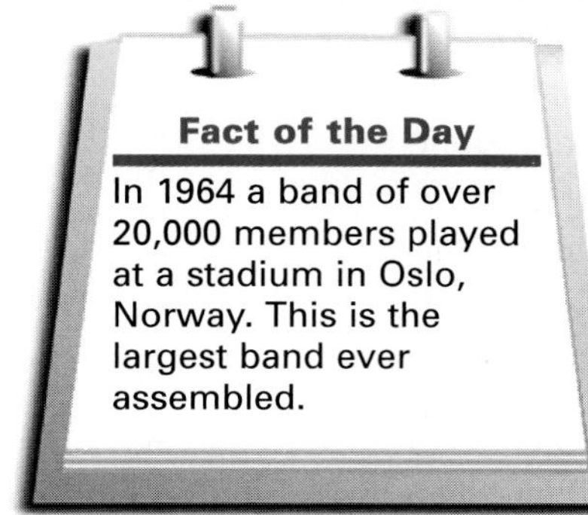

Fact of the Day
In 1964 a band of over 20,000 members played at a stadium in Oslo, Norway. This is the largest band ever assembled.

Mental Math

Give each fraction in lowest terms.

1. $\frac{5}{10}$ $\frac{1}{2}$
2. $\frac{6}{8}$ $\frac{3}{4}$
3. $\frac{4}{12}$ $\frac{1}{3}$
4. $\frac{4}{6}$ $\frac{2}{3}$

Check Your Understanding

1. How can you tell which of two fractions on a ruler is greater?
2. Describe a method for comparing a decimal and a fraction.

3-9 Exercises and Applications

Practice and Apply

1. **Getting Started** Follow the steps to compare $\frac{6}{7}$ and $\frac{7}{8}$.
   a. Multiply the numerator and denominator of $\frac{6}{7}$ by the denominator of $\frac{7}{8}$. $\frac{48}{56}$
   b. Multiply the numerator and denominator of $\frac{7}{8}$ by the denominator of $\frac{6}{7}$. $\frac{49}{56}$
   c. Compare the numerators found in **a** and **b**. Which fraction is larger? $\frac{7}{8} > \frac{6}{7}$

Compare using <, >, or =.

2. $\frac{20}{24}$ [>] $\frac{28}{36}$
3. $\frac{15}{27}$ [=] $\frac{5}{9}$
4. $\frac{6}{7}$ [>] $\frac{18}{22}$
5. $\frac{16}{22}$ [<] $\frac{25}{33}$
6. $\frac{8}{9}$ [<] $\frac{9}{10}$
7. $\frac{22}{30}$ [>] $\frac{7}{10}$
8. $\frac{19}{24}$ [<] $\frac{24}{30}$
9. $\frac{33}{48}$ [>] $\frac{8}{12}$
10. $\frac{21}{25}$ [>] $\frac{20}{26}$
11. $\frac{5}{9}$ [=] $\frac{10}{18}$
12. $\frac{12}{14}$ [=] $\frac{24}{28}$
13. $\frac{16}{24}$ [=] $\frac{8}{12}$
14. $\frac{23}{27}$ [<] $\frac{24}{26}$
15. $\frac{11}{15}$ [=] $\frac{33}{45}$
16. $\frac{22}{55}$ [>] $\frac{3}{10}$
17. $\frac{13}{52}$ [=] $\frac{16}{64}$

18. **Science** Hummingbirds are among the smallest birds in the world. Order the weights of the hummingbirds in the table from least to greatest. $\frac{1}{14}$ oz, $\frac{1}{11}$ oz, $\frac{1}{9}$ oz, $\frac{2}{3}$ oz

actual size = 2 in.

Name	Bee Hummingbird	Giant Hummingbird	Costa's Hummingbird	Calliope Hummingbird
Weight	$\frac{1}{14}$ oz	$\frac{2}{3}$ oz	$\frac{1}{9}$ oz	$\frac{1}{11}$ oz

19. **Music** Theresa is building a guitar for her daughter. The guitar must be between $\frac{1}{2}$ and $\frac{3}{4}$ of the size of a full-sized guitar. Find and list in order, from least to greatest, four fractions in that range. Express the fractions in lowest terms. GPS
   Possible answer: $\frac{4}{7}, \frac{3}{5}, \frac{5}{8}, \frac{2}{3}$

PRACTICE 3-9

PRACTICE

Name ______________________

Practice 3-9

Comparing and Ordering Fractions

Compare.

1. $\frac{16}{21} > \frac{28}{38}$
2. $\frac{12}{40} > \frac{13}{44}$
3. $\frac{5}{22} < \frac{8}{32}$
4. $\frac{12}{26} > \frac{16}{36}$
5. $\frac{12}{35} < \frac{7}{18}$
6. $\frac{7}{16} < \frac{16}{35}$
7. $\frac{10}{20} > \frac{20}{41}$
8. $\frac{4}{6} < \frac{9}{12}$
9. $\frac{4}{9} > \frac{19}{44}$
10. $\frac{4}{6} = \frac{10}{15}$
11. $\frac{21}{25} > \frac{18}{22}$
12. $\frac{20}{24} > \frac{16}{20}$
13. $\frac{20}{25} > \frac{10}{13}$
14. $\frac{4}{13} < \frac{8}{25}$
15. $\frac{26}{45} > \frac{3}{6}$
16. $\frac{23}{27} < \frac{16}{18}$
17. $\frac{4}{12} > \frac{13}{41}$
18. $\frac{4}{11} > \frac{7}{21}$
19. $\frac{4}{8} = \frac{25}{50}$
20. $\frac{6}{24} < \frac{8}{31}$
21. $\frac{4}{6} < \frac{12}{17}$
22. $\frac{22}{25} > \frac{22}{26}$
23. $\frac{11}{26} < \frac{14}{32}$
24. $\frac{7}{12} < \frac{30}{50}$
25. $\frac{11}{20} > \frac{25}{46}$
26. $\frac{13}{47} < \frac{3}{9}$
27. $\frac{19}{21} < \frac{32}{35}$
28. $\frac{16}{22} > \frac{25}{35}$
29. $\frac{4}{6} = \frac{22}{33}$
30. $\frac{4}{42} < \frac{2}{19}$
31. $\frac{8}{38} > \frac{8}{39}$
32. $\frac{4}{7} < \frac{27}{47}$
33. $\frac{6}{32} < \frac{4}{18}$
34. $\frac{22}{33} < \frac{34}{50}$
35. $\frac{39}{48} > \frac{38}{47}$
36. $\frac{4}{15} < \frac{3}{11}$
37. $\frac{4}{6} > \frac{9}{14}$
38. $\frac{38}{46} < \frac{38}{45}$
39. $\frac{20}{48} > \frac{16}{39}$
40. $\frac{9}{21} < \frac{22}{50}$
41. $\frac{4}{18} > \frac{4}{19}$
42. $\frac{15}{19} > \frac{15}{20}$
43. $\frac{6}{18} < \frac{13}{37}$
44. $\frac{15}{42} < \frac{8}{21}$

45. Kenny estimates that the distance from his home to the library is between $\frac{1}{3}$ and $\frac{1}{2}$ mile. Find four fractions in that range and list them in order from least to greatest. Express the fractions in lowest terms.
   Possible answer: $\frac{11}{30}, \frac{2}{5}, \frac{13}{30}, \frac{7}{15}$

46. The table shows the approximate fraction of new books and editions published in 1993 in each of several subjects. Order these fractions from least to greatest.

Art	Biography	Fiction	History	Technology
$\frac{3}{100}$	$\frac{21}{500}$	$\frac{1}{9}$	$\frac{2}{43}$	$\frac{7}{155}$

$\frac{3}{100}, \frac{21}{500}, \frac{7}{155}, \frac{2}{43}, \frac{1}{9}$

RETEACHING

Name ______________________

Alternative Lesson 3-9

Comparing and Ordering Fractions

Fractions with the same denominator are said to have a **common denominator.** If two fractions have a common denominator, the one with the greater numerator is greater. If the denominators are different, you can make equivalent fractions that have a common denominator.

Example

Compare $\frac{5}{8}$ and $\frac{2}{3}$.

Method 1

To find a common denominator, find the LCM. List multiples to find the LCM.

8: 8 16 (24) 32
3: 3 6 9 12 15 18 21 (24)

Write each fraction with a denominator of 24.

$\frac{5}{8} \rightarrow \frac{15}{24}$ $\frac{2}{3} \rightarrow \frac{16}{24}$

15 is less than 16, so $\frac{15}{24} < \frac{16}{24}$.

So $\frac{5}{8} < \frac{2}{3}$.

Method 2

Multiply numerator and denominator of each fraction by the denominator of the other.

$\frac{5}{8} = \frac{5 \times 3}{8 \times 3} = \frac{15}{24}$

$\frac{2}{3} = \frac{2 \times 8}{3 \times 8} = \frac{16}{24}$

16 is greater than 15, $\frac{16}{24} > \frac{15}{24}$.

So $\frac{2}{3} > \frac{5}{8}$.

Try It Compare $\frac{5}{12}$ and $\frac{11}{18}$.

a. Write $\frac{5}{12}$ as an equivalent fraction with a denominator of 36. $\frac{15}{36}$
b. Write $\frac{11}{18}$ as an equivalent fraction with a denominator of 36. $\frac{22}{36}$
c. Compare the numerators. Use <, =, or >. 15 < 22 or 22 > 15
d. Compare $\frac{5}{12}$ and $\frac{11}{18}$. Use <, =, or >. $\frac{5}{12} < \frac{11}{18}$; $\frac{11}{18} > \frac{5}{12}$

Compare using <, > or =.

e. $\frac{1}{2}$ > $\frac{1}{3}$
f. $\frac{5}{8}$ < $\frac{3}{4}$
g. $\frac{5}{7}$ > $\frac{1}{2}$
h. $\frac{1}{3}$ > $\frac{1}{4}$
i. $\frac{3}{4}$ = $\frac{12}{16}$
j. $\frac{1}{2}$ > $\frac{4}{9}$
k. $\frac{3}{4}$ < $\frac{5}{6}$
l. $\frac{5}{8}$ < $\frac{7}{10}$
m. $\frac{2}{3}$ > $\frac{7}{12}$
n. $\frac{4}{10}$ = $\frac{6}{15}$
o. $\frac{3}{5}$ = $\frac{9}{15}$
p. $\frac{2}{3}$ < $\frac{3}{4}$
q. $\frac{8}{15}$ > $\frac{5}{10}$
r. $\frac{18}{24}$ > $\frac{9}{16}$
s. $\frac{4}{15}$ < $\frac{8}{25}$
t. $\frac{15}{28}$ < $\frac{21}{24}$
u. $\frac{1}{2}$ < $\frac{4}{7}$
v. $\frac{9}{10}$ < $\frac{11}{12}$
w. $\frac{13}{20}$ > $\frac{5}{8}$
x. $\frac{4}{5}$ < $\frac{14}{15}$

3-9 Exercises and Applications

Assignment Guide

- **Basic**
  1–19 odds, 20–22, 25–41 odds
- **Average**
  1, 2–18 evens, 19–20, 22–25, 26–42 evens
- **Enriched**
  1, 3–17 odds, 19–25, 27–43 odds

3 Practice and Assess

Check

Answers for Check Your Understanding

1. Compare the lengths represented by the fractions.
2. Divide the numerator of the fraction by the denominator and compare the resulting decimal with the original decimal.

Reteaching

Activity

Materials: Colored pencils, 8 × 8 grids

- Use one color to shade $\frac{9}{16}$ on a grid. Then start at the same place and use another color to shade $\frac{5}{8}$.
  Shade so that all of $\frac{5}{8}$ covers $\frac{9}{16}$ or is covered by $\frac{9}{16}$.
  Which fraction is greater ? $\frac{5}{8}$ How do you know? Part of $\frac{5}{8}$ is outside $\frac{9}{16}$.
- Now use another grid to compare $\frac{3}{8}$ and $\frac{11}{32}$.
  Which fraction is greater? $\frac{3}{8}$
  Use this method to compare fractions less than 1 with denominators of 2, 4, 8, 16, and 32.

Exercise Notes

Exercise 23

Problem-Solving Tip To help students visualize this problem, have them think about cutting a round pizza into 12 equal slices or into 8 equal slices. Which cutting yields the larger pieces? The one with 8 equal slices.

Exercise Answers

21. The latter; $\frac{1}{4}$ off would be $0.25 per dollar.

22. Possible answers: $\frac{3}{50}$; $\frac{4}{10} = \frac{2}{5}$

23. If the numerators are the same, then the fraction with the larger denominator will have the smaller value.

24. Make sure the fractional part of each mixed number is < 1. Compare whole number parts. If they are equal, compare the fractions.

25–26. See page C5.

35. 46,000

36. 836

37. 620,000,000

38. 99,000,000,000

39. 347,000

40. 25,890,000

41. 749,000,000,000,000

42. 5,000,000,000,000,000,000

43. $\frac{25}{51}$

Alternate Assessment

Portfolio Have students pick two exercises from this lesson, one in which they must compare two fractions with the same denominator and one in which they must compare two fractions with different denominators. For each exercise, have them describe the method they use for comparing the fractions.

Quick Quiz

Compare the fractions.

1. $\frac{3}{4}, \frac{5}{6}$ $\frac{3}{4} < \frac{5}{6}$
2. $\frac{5}{8}, \frac{7}{16}$ $\frac{5}{8} > \frac{7}{16}$
3. $\frac{5}{6}, \frac{7}{9}$ $\frac{5}{6} > \frac{7}{9}$
4. $\frac{7}{12}, \frac{9}{16}$ $\frac{7}{12} > \frac{9}{16}$
5. $\frac{1}{4}, \frac{3}{10}$ $\frac{1}{4} < \frac{3}{10}$

Available on Daily Transparency 3-9

---

20. Test Prep Louise has to sort bolts from smallest to largest. In what order should she sort the following bolts: $\frac{3}{4}$ in., $\frac{11}{16}$ in., $\frac{5}{8}$ in., $\frac{23}{32}$ in.? C

Ⓐ $\frac{3}{4}, \frac{23}{32}, \frac{11}{16}, \frac{5}{8}$ Ⓑ $\frac{5}{8}, \frac{11}{16}, \frac{3}{4}, \frac{23}{32}$ Ⓒ $\frac{5}{8}, \frac{11}{16}, \frac{23}{32}, \frac{3}{4}$ Ⓓ $\frac{5}{8}, \frac{23}{32}, \frac{11}{16}, \frac{3}{4}$

Problem Solving and Reasoning

21. Communicate Carly sees the same item advertised in two different stores. One store is advertising $0.20 off per dollar and the other is advertising $\frac{1}{4}$ off. Which store has the better deal? Explain.

23. Communicate Describe a method you could use to quickly compare two fractions with the same numerator and different denominators.

22. Critical Thinking Name a fraction between 0 and $\frac{1}{10}$ whose numerator is not 1. Name a fraction between $\frac{1}{3}$ and $\frac{1}{2}$ whose denominator is 10. Express the fraction in lowest terms.

24. Journal Write an explanation of how you can compare and order mixed numbers such as $2\frac{3}{4}$ and $2\frac{4}{5}$.

Mixed Review

Make a scatterplot for each set of data. *[Lesson 1-6]*

25.

x	2	3	4	5	6	7	8	9
y	8	6	7	5	4	6	4	3

26.

x	2.3	4.6	3.6	6.3	8.2	9.1	5.3	7.1
y	3.7	4.2	5.3	6.1	8.0	8.7	5.8	6.3

Write each number in scientific notation. *[Lesson 3-5]*

27. 475,600 4.756×10^5 **28.** 580,000 5.8×10^5 **29.** 93,000,000 9.3×10^7 **30.** 3,210,000 3.21×10^6

31. 830 8.3×10^2 **32.** 904,000,000 9.04×10^8 **33.** 50 5.0×10 **34.** 6,535,000,000,000 6.535×10^{12}

Write each number in standard form. *[Lesson 3-5]*

35. 4.6×10^4 **36.** 8.36×10^2 **37.** 6.2×10^8 **38.** 9.9×10^{10}

39. 3.47×10^5 **40.** 2.589×10^7 **41.** 7.49×10^{14} **42.** 5×10^{18}

43. In 1996, the Colorado Symphony Orchestra had 1.02×10^2 members. Of these, 5.0×10^1 played stringed instruments. What fraction of the orchestra members played stringed instruments? Write your answer in lowest terms.

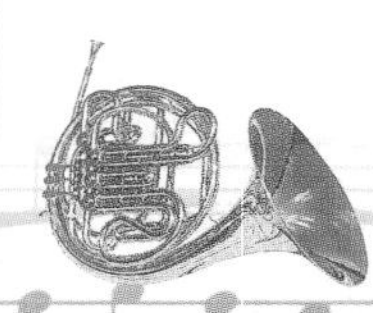

PROBLEM SOLVING 3-9

152 *Chapter 3 • Number Sense: Decimals and Fractions*

PROBLEM SOLVING

Name ____________________

Guided Problem Solving 3-9

GPS PROBLEM 19, STUDENT PAGE 151

Theresa is building a guitar for her daughter. The guitar must be between $\frac{1}{2}$ and $\frac{3}{4}$ of the size of a full-sized guitar. Find and list in order, from least to greatest, four fractions in that range. Express the fractions in lowest terms.

Understand

1. What do you need to find? Four fractions between $\frac{1}{2}$ and $\frac{3}{4}$.

Plan

2. Why do you need to find a common denominator? Possible answer: To make it easier to find many fractions between $\frac{1}{2}$ and $\frac{3}{4}$.
3. Use Guess and Check to determine which common denominator to choose that will allow you to write four fractions in between. d

   a. 4 b. 8 c. 16 d. 20

Solve

4. Write $\frac{1}{2}$ and $\frac{3}{4}$ using the chosen denominator. $\frac{10}{20}, \frac{15}{20}$
5. Find four fractions between $\frac{1}{2}$ and $\frac{3}{4}$ using the common denominator. List in order from least to greatest. $\frac{11}{20}, \frac{12}{20}, \frac{13}{20}, \frac{14}{20}$
6. Write the fractions in lowest terms. Possible answers: $\frac{11}{20}, \frac{3}{5}, \frac{13}{20}, \frac{7}{10}$

Look Back

7. Write $\frac{1}{2}$ amd $\frac{3}{4}$ using a larger common denominator. List four fractions in order from least to greatest between the given fractions. Why may your answers in lowest terms be different than the ones in Item 6? Possible answer: $\frac{13}{24}, \frac{7}{12}, \frac{5}{8}, \frac{2}{3}$; More fraction choices available using a larger denominator; different fractions chosen.

SOLVE ANOTHER PROBLEM

Find four fractions between $\frac{1}{2}$ and $\frac{1}{3}$. List them in order from least to greatest in lowest terms.

Possible answers: $\frac{11}{30}, \frac{2}{5}, \frac{13}{30}, \frac{7}{15}$

ENRICHMENT

Name ____________________

Extend Your Thinking 3-9

Critical Thinking

You can compare fractions using the cross-product method.

Compare $\frac{3}{7}$ and $\frac{4}{9}$. $\frac{3}{7} \circ \frac{4}{9}$

Write the cross-products. $27 = \frac{3}{7} \times \frac{4}{9} = 28$

Compare the cross-products. $27 < 28$

Compare the fractions.   so $\frac{3}{7} < \frac{4}{9}$

Use the cross-product method to order the five fractions below from least to greatest.

$\frac{7}{9}, \quad \frac{8}{11}, \quad \frac{4}{7}, \quad \frac{13}{19}, \quad \frac{3}{4}$

1. Compare the first two fractions. List them in order with the smaller fraction first. $\frac{8}{11}, \frac{7}{9}$
2. Compare the third fraction with the smaller fraction you found in Question 1. Is it smaller or larger? Smaller
3. List the first three fractions in order. $\frac{4}{7}, \frac{8}{11}, \frac{7}{9}$
4. How will you determine the position of the fourth fraction? Show your work. Possible answer: $\frac{13}{19} > \frac{4}{7}$; $\frac{13}{19} < \frac{8}{11}$. So $\frac{13}{19}$ falls between these two fractions.
5. List the fractions in order from least to greatest. $\frac{4}{7}, \frac{13}{19}, \frac{8}{11}, \frac{3}{4}, \frac{7}{9}$
6. When would it be easier to use cross-products to compare fractions than to find equivalent fractions with a common denominator? Possible answer: If two fractions have large unlike denominators, use cross-products.
7. Would you ever use both methods to order a list of fractions? Explain. Possible answer: Yes. List common denominators for some common fractions. Cross-products can be used to determine the rest.

Converting Between Fractions and Decimals

3-10

▶ Lesson Link You've worked with both fractions and decimals. Now you'll learn to convert from one to the other. ◀

Explore Converting Fractions to Decimals

Repeat After Me

Materials: Calculator

1. Write $\frac{1}{9}$, $\frac{4}{9}$, and $\frac{7}{9}$ as decimals by dividing the numerator by the denominator. Describe the pattern in your results.
2. Predict the decimal for $\frac{5}{9}$. Check your prediction on your calculator.
3. Write $\frac{13}{99}$, $\frac{41}{99}$, and $\frac{67}{99}$ as decimals. What patterns do you find?
4. Predict the decimal for $\frac{83}{99}$.
5. Write $\frac{157}{999}$ and $\frac{632}{999}$ as decimals.
6. Predict a fraction that has 0.418418418... for its decimal. Then check your prediction.

You'll Learn ...

- to convert fractions to decimals
- to convert decimals to fractions

... How It's Used

Counter clerks in the deli department need to be able to read $\frac{1}{4}$ lb on a scale that has a decimal readout.

Vocabulary

terminating decimal

repeating decimal

Learn Converting Between Fractions and Decimals

Fractions and decimals are different ways of writing the same quantity. Sometimes one way is better than the other, so you should know how to convert from one to the other.

To convert from a decimal to a fraction, think of the fractional equivalents of place values. You may even want to *read* the decimal.

one tenth $= \frac{1}{10}$

one hundredth $= \frac{1}{100}$

one thousandth $= \frac{1}{1000}$

To write 0.7 as a decimal, think: seven *tenths*.

$$0.7 = \frac{7}{10}$$ (7 ← seven; 10 ← tenths)

After converting a decimal to a fraction, you may need to rewrite the fraction in lowest terms.

MEETING INDIVIDUAL NEEDS

Resources

- 3-10 Practice
- 3-10 Reteaching
- 3-10 Problem Solving
- 3-10 Enrichment
- 3-10 Daily Transparency
  - Problem of the Day
  - Review
  - Quick Quiz
- Technology Master 13

Learning Modalities

Logical It is important that students understand basic fraction concepts before they compute with fractions. By learning the relationships among fractions and decimals, the students will be better able to decide if their computation answers are reasonable.

Visual Students might find that using 10 × 10 grids is helpful for relating fractions and decimals.

Challenge

Have students find the decimals for the fractions $\frac{1}{7}$, $\frac{2}{7}$, and $\frac{3}{7}$. 0.142857, 0.285714, 0.428571

3-10 Lesson Organizer

Objectives

- Convert fractions to decimals.
- Convert decimals to fractions.

Vocabulary

- Terminating decimal, repeating decimal

Materials

- Explore: Calculator

NCTM Standards

- 1–5, 8

▶ Review

Write the fraction for each word name.

1. Fourteen hundredths $\frac{14}{100}$
2. Seven tenths $\frac{7}{10}$
3. Two thousandths $\frac{2}{1000}$
4. Seventy-five hundredths $\frac{75}{100}$

Available on Daily Transparency 3-10

1 Introduce

Explore

The Point

Students use calculators to convert fractions to decimals. From the patterns they find, they predict the value of certain decimals.

Ongoing Assessment

Have students predict the decimals for $\frac{2}{9}$ and $\frac{8}{9}$. 0.222..., 0.888...

For Groups That Finish Early

Use calculators to find the decimal equivalents for $\frac{1}{11}$, $\frac{3}{11}$, and $\frac{5}{11}$. 0.0909..., 0.2727..., 0.4545...

Predict the decimals for $\frac{2}{11}$, $\frac{7}{11}$, and $\frac{10}{11}$. 0.1818..., 0.6363..., 0.9090...

Answers for Explore on next page.

Answers for Explore

1. 0.111111111, 0.444444444, 0.777777777; The decimal is the numerator repeated many times.
2. 0.555555555
3. 0.131313131, 0.414141414, 0.676767676; The decimal is the numerator repeated many times.
4. 0.838383838
5. 0.157157157, 0.632632632
6. $\frac{418}{999}$

2 Teach

Learn

Alternate Examples

1. The interest rate for a certificate of deposit (CD) is given as 0.055. Write this decimal as a fraction in lowest terms.

   $0.055 = \frac{55}{1000} = \frac{11}{200}$

   The rate as a fraction is $\frac{11}{200}$.

2. Convert $\frac{7}{8}$ to a decimal. Tell whether the decimal terminates or repeats.

   7 [÷] 8 [=] 0.875; The decimal terminates.

3. Convert $\frac{5}{6}$ to a decimal. Tell whether the decimal terminates or repeats.

   5 [÷] 6 [=] 0.833333...

   $\frac{5}{6} = 0.8\overline{3}$; The decimal repeats.

Example 1

A sound meter recorded the *piano* (soft) section of a symphony at 0.24 times the loudness of the *forte* (loud) section. Write 0.24 as a fraction in lowest terms.

$0.24 = \frac{24}{100} = \frac{24 \div 4}{100 \div 4} = \frac{6}{25}$

The orchestra played $\frac{6}{25}$ as loud during the *piano* section.

Try It

Convert to a fraction in lowest terms. **a.** 0.3 $\frac{3}{10}$ **b.** 0.75 $\frac{3}{4}$ **c.** 0.368 $\frac{46}{125}$

To convert from a fraction to a decimal, divide the numerator by the denominator. The decimal you obtain will terminate or repeat.

A **terminating decimal** ends. $8\overline{)3.000}$ = 0.375 $\rightarrow \frac{3}{8} = 0.375$

A **repeating decimal** repeats a pattern of digits.

29 [÷] 111 [=] 0.261261261... $\rightarrow \frac{29}{111} = 0.\overline{261}$ ← Use a bar to indicate the repeating pattern.

Examples

Convert to a decimal. Tell whether the decimal terminates or repeats.

2 $\frac{5}{33}$

5 [÷] 33 [=] 0.151515...

$0.\overline{15}$; the decimal repeats

3 $\frac{13}{16}$

13 [÷] 16 [=] 0.8125

0.8125; the decimal terminates

Test Prep

You may see *terminating* and *repeating decimals* referred to as *rational numbers.*

Try It

Convert to a decimal. Tell if the decimal terminates or repeats.

a. $\frac{17}{20}$ 0.85; terminating **b.** $\frac{2}{3}$ $0.\overline{6}$ repeating **c.** $\frac{9}{32}$ 0.28125; terminating

Check Your Understanding

1. When might 0.5 be preferred over $\frac{1}{2}$? When might $\frac{1}{2}$ be preferred?
2. Can 0.23 and 0.230 be expressed as the same fraction? Explain.

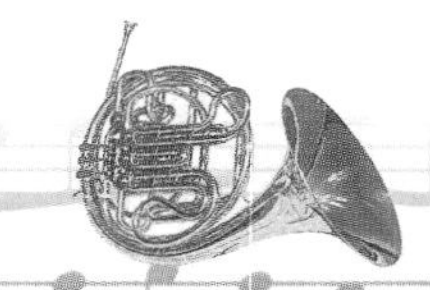

3 Practice and Assess

Check

Be sure that students understand how to express repeating decimals with a bar over *only* the part that repeats. You might tell the class that the part that repeats is called the *repetend*.

Answers for Check Your Understanding

1. 0.5 is preferable when working in centimeters; $\frac{1}{2}$ when working in inches.
2. Yes; $0.23 = \frac{23}{100}$; $0.230 = \frac{230}{1000} = \frac{23}{100}$ in lowest terms.

MATH EVERY DAY

Problem of the Day

A secretary completes 4 letters and types addresses on 4 envelopes. An assistant places the letters in the envelopes at random. What are the chances that only three letters are in their correct envelope? No chance, because all letters must be in their correct envelopes if three of them are.

Available on Daily Transparency 3-10

An Extension is provided in the transparency package.

Fact of the Day

The intensity of sound is measured in decibels, each of which is one tenth of a bel. The bel is named after the famous inventor Alexander Graham Bell.

Mental Math

Give each decimal as a fraction in lowest terms.

1. 0.5 $\frac{1}{2}$
2. 0.25 $\frac{1}{4}$
3. 0.75 $\frac{3}{4}$
4. $.\overline{3}$ $\frac{1}{3}$

3-10 Exercises and Applications

Practice and Apply

1. **Getting Started** Convert 0.025 to a fraction and rewrite it in lowest terms.

a. Write 0.025 as a fraction with a power of 10 as the denominator. $\frac{25}{1000}$

b. Rewrite the resulting fraction in lowest terms. $\frac{1}{40}$

Convert to a fraction in lowest terms.

2. 0.75 $\frac{3}{4}$ **3.** 0.12 $\frac{3}{25}$ **4.** 0.325 $\frac{13}{40}$ **5.** 0.040 $\frac{1}{25}$

6. 0.179 $\frac{179}{1000}$ **7.** 0.108 $\frac{27}{250}$ **8.** 0.555 $\frac{111}{200}$ **9.** 0.812 $\frac{203}{250}$

Convert to a decimal. Tell if the decimal terminates or repeats.

10. $\frac{4}{9}$ **11.** $\frac{4}{7}$ **12.** $\frac{11}{16}$ **13.** $\frac{14}{21}$

14. $\frac{12}{15}$ **15.** $\frac{16}{20}$ **16.** $\frac{10}{18}$ **17.** $\frac{26}{50}$

18. **Science** The masses of the moon and planets differ from Earth's mass. Each planet's pull of gravity also differs from Earth's. The following decimals represent the pull of gravity on the moon and planets compared to the pull of gravity on Earth. Convert to fractions and rewrite in lowest terms.

a. Moon: 0.16 $\frac{4}{25}$ **b.** Mercury: 0.37 $\frac{37}{100}$

c. Mars: 0.38 $\frac{19}{50}$ **d.** Venus: 0.88 $\frac{22}{25}$

Surface of Venus

19. **Test Prep** Which fraction forms a terminating decimal? C

Ⓐ $\frac{8}{9}$ Ⓑ $\frac{5}{6}$ Ⓒ $\frac{7}{8}$ Ⓓ $\frac{10}{11}$

20. **Music** To use a computer to write music, you need to write notes as decimals. What decimals are entered for a half note, quarter note, eighth note, and sixteenth note? 0.5, 0.25, 0.125, 0.0625

Number Sense **Use a calculator to convert each repeating decimal to a fraction.**

21. $0.8\overline{3}$ $\frac{5}{6}$ **22.** $0.\overline{1}$ $\frac{1}{9}$ **23.** $0.\overline{18}$ $\frac{2}{11}$ **24.** $0.\overline{5}$ $\frac{5}{9}$

PRACTICE 3-10

PRACTICE

Name ______________________

Practice 3-10

Converting Between Fractions and Decimals

Convert to a fraction in lowest terms.

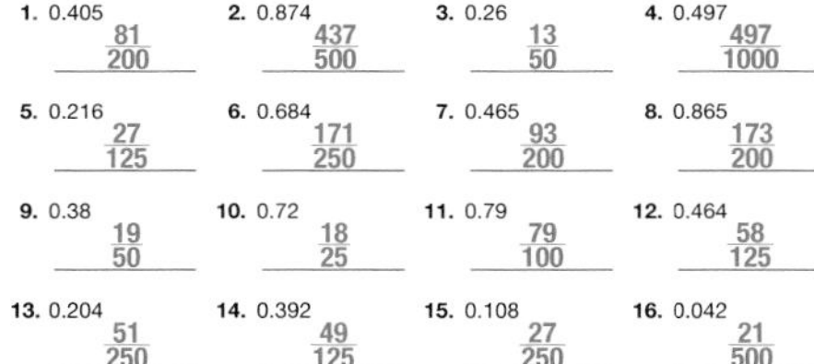

1. 0.405 $\frac{81}{200}$ 2. 0.874 $\frac{437}{500}$ 3. 0.26 $\frac{13}{50}$ 4. 0.497 $\frac{497}{1000}$

5. 0.216 $\frac{27}{125}$ 6. 0.684 $\frac{171}{250}$ 7. 0.465 $\frac{93}{200}$ 8. 0.865 $\frac{173}{200}$

9. 0.38 $\frac{19}{50}$ 10. 0.72 $\frac{18}{25}$ 11. 0.79 $\frac{79}{100}$ 12. 0.464 $\frac{58}{125}$

13. 0.204 $\frac{51}{250}$ 14. 0.392 $\frac{49}{125}$ 15. 0.108 $\frac{27}{250}$ 16. 0.042 $\frac{21}{500}$

Convert to a decimal. Tell if the decimal terminates or repeats.

17. $\frac{3}{5}$ 0.6; terminates 18. $\frac{8}{9}$ $0.\overline{8}$; repeats 19. $\frac{7}{8}$ 0.875; terminates

20. $\frac{5}{11}$ $0.\overline{45}$; repeats 21. $\frac{37}{50}$ 0.74; terminates 22. $\frac{3}{16}$ 0.1875; terminates

23. $\frac{22}{55}$ 0.4; terminates 24. $\frac{4}{12}$ $0.\overline{3}$; repeats 25. $\frac{17}{34}$ 0.5; terminates

Use a calculator to convert each repeating decimal to a fraction.

26. $0.\overline{6}$ $\frac{2}{3}$ 27. $0.\overline{7}$ $\frac{7}{9}$ 28. $0.\overline{27}$ $\frac{3}{11}$ 29. $0.02\overline{27}$ $\frac{1}{44}$

30. $0.1\overline{6}$ $\frac{1}{6}$ 31. $0.\overline{15}$ $\frac{5}{33}$ 32. $0.\overline{47}$ $\frac{47}{99}$ 33. $0.\overline{90}$ $\frac{10}{11}$

34. About $\frac{7}{25}$ of the residents of Seattle, Washington, have attended 16 or more years of school. Convert $\frac{7}{25}$ to a decimal. 0.28

35. **Geography** The area of Brazil is about 0.908 of the area of the United States. Convert 0.908 to a fraction in lowest terms. $\frac{227}{250}$

RETEACHING

Name ______________________

Alternative Lesson 3-10

Converting Between Fractions and Decimals

Fractions and decimals are different ways of writing the same quantity. Therefore, you can convert one to the other whenever necessary.

Example 1

Convert 0.35 to a fraction in lowest terms.

Write the decimal in words.	Write as a fraction.	Write in lowest terms.
0.35 → 35 hundredths →	$\frac{35}{100}$ →	$\frac{7}{20}$

So $0.35 = \frac{7}{20}$.

Try It Convert 0.24 to a fraction in lowest terms.

a. Write the decimal in words. Twenty-four hundredths.

b. Write as a fraction. $\frac{24}{100}$

c. Write in lowest terms. $\frac{6}{25}$

Convert to a fraction in lowest terms.

d. 0.9 $\frac{9}{10}$ **e.** 0.64 $\frac{16}{25}$ **f.** 0.75 $\frac{3}{4}$ **g.** 0.625 $\frac{5}{8}$

Example 2

Use your calculator to convert $\frac{3}{5}$ and $\frac{5}{9}$ to decimals by dividing the numerator by the denominator. Tell if each decimal is a **terminating** or a **repeating decimal.**

Divide 3 by 5 to find a decimal for $\frac{3}{5}$.

Enter	Display
3 [÷] 5 [=]	0.6

Terminating–does not repeat

Divide 5 by 9 to find a decimal for $\frac{5}{9}$.

Enter	Display
5 [÷] 9 [=]	0.555… or $0.\overline{5}$

Repeating–repeats pattern of digits

So, $\frac{3}{5}$ is a terminating decimal and $\frac{5}{9}$ is a repeating decimal.

Try It Convert to a decimal. Tell if the decimal terminates or repeats.

h. $\frac{3}{8}$ 0.375; terminates. **i.** $\frac{7}{12}$ $0.58\overline{3}$; repeats.

j. $\frac{2}{3}$ $0.\overline{6}$; repeats. **k.** $\frac{1}{4}$ 0.25; terminates.

l. $\frac{11}{16}$ 0.6875; terminates. **m.** $\frac{5}{11}$ $0.\overline{45}$; repeats.

n. $\frac{5}{6}$ $0.8\overline{3}$; repeats. **o.** $\frac{9}{25}$ 0.36; terminates.

3-10 Exercises and Applications

Assignment Guide

- **Basic** 1–17 odds, 18–22, 25–27, 31
- **Average** 1, 2–18 evens, 19, 23–28, 32
- **Enriched** 1–17 odds, 19, 21–26, 29–32

Exercise Notes

■ Exercises 10–17

Error Prevention Be sure students know how to identify repeating decimals on their calculators, as some calculators round and some truncate, or cut off at a certain decimal place.

■ Exercises 10–17

Extension Have students look for a pattern in the denominators that might determine whether a decimal representation terminates or repeats. They might discover that the denominators of fractions with terminating decimals contain only factors of 2 and/or 5.

■ Exercises 21–24

Students will need calculators that deal with fractions for these exercises.

Exercise Answers

10. $0.\overline{4}$, repeating
11. $0.\overline{571428}$, repeating
12. 0.6875, terminating
13. $0.\overline{6}$, repeating
14. 0.8, terminating
15. 0.8, terminating
16. $0.\overline{5}$, repeating
17. 0.52, terminating

Reteaching

Activity

Materials: 10 × 10 grids

- Shade $\frac{1}{2}$ of a grid. How many hundredths are shaded? 50 Write this as a decimal. 0.50 How many tenths are shaded? 5 Write this as a decimal. 0.5 On another grid, shade $\frac{3}{5}$. Write this as a decimal. 0.6
- On another grid, shade $\frac{1}{4}$. Write this as a decimal. 0.25 Using the same grid, shade $\frac{3}{4}$. Write this as a decimal. 0.75

Exercise Notes

■ Exercise 26

Extension Have students check their calculators to see whether they round or truncate by finding the decimal value of $\frac{2}{3}$. If a calculator rounds, the last digit will be a 7. If a calculator truncates, the last digit will be a 6.

Exercise Answers

25. a. A decimal; money is calculated with decimals.
   b. A fraction; it is easier to measure cups using fractions.
   c. Either; the answer is $333.\overline{3}$ or $333\frac{1}{3}$ or $\approx$ 333 pairs of binoculars.

26. a. $0.\overline{18}$, 0.181; 2.240418; 2.240
   b. $0.\overline{18}$, 0.182; 2.252796; 2.253
   c. 2.250
   d. 2.251
   e. Result d is the most accurate since it was rounded after all the calculations were done.

31.

Gallons	1	2	3	4	5
Miles	36	72	108	144	180

32.

Hours	1	2	3	4	5
Widgets	532	1064	1596	2128	2660

Alternate Assessment

You may want to use the *Interactive CD-ROM Journal* with this assessment.

Journal Have students write a paragraph about some of the patterns they have encountered when converting fractions to decimals. Students might refer to patterns in the exercises as well as to those in **Explore**; or they may have discovered others.

► Quick Quiz

Write each fraction as a decimal.

1. $\frac{3}{8}$ 0.375
2. $\frac{5}{12}$ $0.41\overline{6}$

Write each decimal as a reduced fraction.

3. 0.56 $\frac{14}{25}$
4. 0.98 $\frac{49}{50}$

Available on Daily Transparency 3-10

Problem Solving and Reasoning

25. Critical Thinking For each problem, is it better to use a fraction or a decimal to solve the problem? Explain.

GPS

a. Sam, Dean, and Matt agree to evenly split the cost of dinner, which totals \$100.00. How much does each owe?

b. Miriam has a recipe that serves 12 and she wants to serve 4. The recipe calls for 2 cups of sugar. How much sugar should she use?

c. Every third seat in a music hall has a pair of rental binoculars attached to the seat back. There are 1000 seats in the music hall. How many pairs of binoculars are there?

26. Journal Calculators and computers either round or truncate numbers after a certain number of digits. To *truncate* means to cut off a number at a certain decimal place. To see what effect this has on accuracy, perform the following calculations to find $\frac{2}{11} \times 12.378$.

a. First, find the decimal equivalent of $\frac{2}{11}$. Truncate the decimal to the thousandths place. Then multiply the answer by 12.378 and write the result. Truncate the result to the thousandths place.

b. Solve the problem as in **a**, but round the decimals to the thousandths place rather than truncating.

c. Multiply 12.378 by 2 first, and then divide the answer by 11. Truncate the result to the thousandths place.

d. Solve the problem as in **c**, but round the decimals to the thousandths place rather than truncating them.

e. Which result is the most accurate? Describe the results in your journal.

Mixed Review

Find the mean of each set of data. *[Lesson 1-4]*

27. 34, 64, 55, 72, 61, 73, 84, 63 **63.25** **28.** 86, 97, 103, 136, 70, 157, 324 **139**

29. 11, 20, 25, 61, 62, 84, 93, 97 **56.625** **30.** 3, 4, 7, 10, 12, 14, 15, 17 **10.25**

31. Julie's car gets 36 miles per gallon. Use the formula $m = 36g$ to make a table showing how many miles (m) Julie can travel on 1, 2, 3, 4, and 5 gallons (g) of gas. *[Lesson 2-3]*

32. WidgetWorx makes 532 widgets per hour. Use the formula $w = 532t$ to make a table showing how many widgets (w) are made in 1, 2, 3, 4, and 5 hours (t). *[Lesson 2-3]*

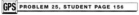

PROBLEM SOLVING 3-10

PROBLEM SOLVING

Name ______ **Guided Problem Solving 3-10**

GPS **PROBLEM 25, STUDENT PAGE 156**

For each problem, is it better to use a fraction or a decimal to solve the problem? Explain.

a. Sam, Dean, and Matt agree to evenly split the cost of dinner, which totaled \$100.00. How much does each owe?

b. Miriam has a recipe that serves 12 and she wants to serve 4. The recipe calls for 2 cups of sugar. How much sugar should she use?

c. Every third seat in a music hall has a pair of rental binoculars attached to the seat back. There are 1000 seats in the music hall. How many pairs of binoculars are there?

— Understand —

1. Underline what you are asked to find.

— Plan —

2. Is money usually written as a fraction or as a decimal? **Decimal.**
3. Is part of a cup usually written as a fraction or as a decimal in a recipe? **Fraction.**
4. Would some seats out of many be written as a fraction or a decimal? **Either.**

— Solve —

5. Would you rather solve using a fraction or a decimal? Explain.

Part a: **Decimal, since the money answer is a decimal.**

Part b: **Fraction, because it is customary measurement.**

Part c: **Fraction, $\frac{1}{3} \times 1000$ is easier than $0.\overline{3} \times 1000$.**

— Look Back —

6. Calculate the answer to each problem to see if you agree with your choices. **\$33.34; $\frac{2}{3}$ cup; 333 pairs of binoculars.**

SOLVE ANOTHER PROBLEM

Is it better to use fractions or decimals to solve a problem involving how much you pay for gas at a service station? Explain.

Decimals. Gallons and price per gallon are in decimal form.

ENRICHMENT

Name ______ **Extend Your Thinking 3-10**

Patterns in Numbers

Use your calculator to find a decimal for each fraction.

1. $\frac{3}{8}$ **0.375**
2. $\frac{5}{6}$ **$0.8\overline{3}$**
3. $\frac{7}{12}$ **$0.58\overline{3}$**
4. $\frac{4}{5}$ **0.8**
5. $\frac{8}{9}$ **$0.\overline{8}$**
6. $\frac{3}{10}$ **0.3**
7. $\frac{4}{15}$ **$0.2\overline{6}$**
8. $\frac{11}{16}$ **0.6875**
9. $\frac{6}{11}$ **$0.\overline{54}$**
10. $\frac{13}{25}$ **0.52**
11. List the denominators for the fractions that produced terminating decimals. **5, 8, 10, 16, 25**
12. Find the prime factors of the denominators in Question 11. **2s and 5s.**
13. List the denominators for the fractions that produced repeating decimals. **6, 9, 11, 12, 15**
14. Find the prime factors of the denominators in Question 13. **2, 3, 5, 11**
15. What pattern do you notice? **Possible answer: Denominators for terminating decimals have only 2s, only 5s, or 2s and 5s as prime factors.**
16. Without dividing, tell whether each of the following fractions will produce a terminating or a repeating decimal.
   a. $\frac{7}{24}$ **Repeating.**
   b. $\frac{35}{64}$ **Terminating.**
   c. $\frac{14}{125}$ **Terminating.**
   d. $\frac{1}{20}$ **Terminating.**
   e. $\frac{17}{111}$ **Repeating.**
   f. $\frac{14}{148}$ **Repeating.**
17. Write a fraction that, as a decimal, will terminate. Use a 2-digit or a 3-digit number as the denominator. **Possible answer: $\frac{102}{160}$**
18. Write a fraction that, as a decimal, will repeat. Use a 2-digit or a 3-digit number as the denominator. **Possible answer: $\frac{36}{101}$**

Section 3B Connect

You've learned about some of the connections between music and fractions. Now you'll use what you've learned to identify notes in one of America's most beloved songs.

One, Two, Three ... Play!

A violin string is 360 mm long. To produce a musical note, a violinist draws the bow across the string while touching the string d mm from the nut. You can use the fraction $\frac{d}{360}$ to find the note produced.

nut

1. There are seven different notes in the first line of the song "Home on the Range." The music below names the seven notes and gives the distance (d) that will produce each note.

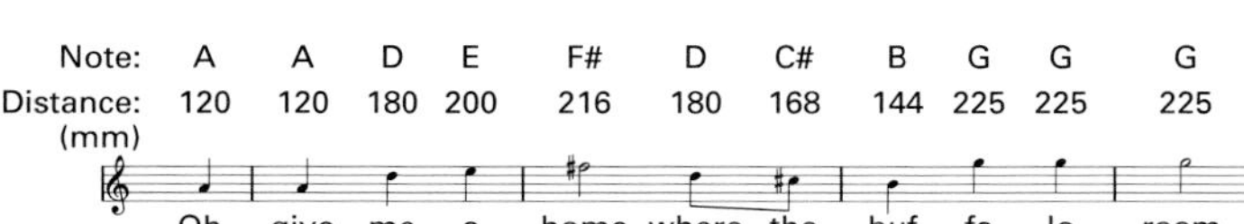

Complete the table, writing $\frac{d}{360}$ in lowest terms.

	A	B	C#	D	E	F#	G
d	120	144					
$\frac{d}{360}$							

2. Write each fraction as a decimal rounded to the nearest thousandth. State whether the decimal terminates or repeats.

3. The violinist hit a sour note given by the fraction $\frac{5}{12}$. How far from the nut did the violinist touch the string? Between what two notes was the sour note?

157

3B Connect

One, Two, Three ... Play!

The Point

In *One, Two, Three ... Play!* on page 133, students discussed the relationship of music and mathematics. Now they will use fractions and decimals to analyze notes in a song.

Resources

Lesson Enhancement Transparency 12

About the Page

- If you have a violin or other string instrument, show students the different sounds produced as you move your finger up and down the string.
- If an instrument is not available, pull a thick rubber band out to different lengths of tautness and "play" across it with your fingers. The "notes" you produce will change as you change the length of the rubber band.
- Explain that the strings are strung tightly on the violin. When violinists press on strings they are really shortening the length of the strings, thus creating different sounds.

Ongoing Assessment

Check that students have written the fractions as equivalent decimals and rounded correctly.

Extension

Music is written in a picture language with "directions" given in symbols at the beginning of the piece. Ask students who are involved in music to explain time signatures, such as $\frac{4}{4}$ and $\frac{6}{8}$.

Possible answer: The denominator shows what kind of note, half, quarter, or eighth, is the unit of measure and receives one beat. The numerator shows how many beats to a measure.

Answers for Connect

1. Possible answers:

1.	Note	A	B	C#	D	E	F#	G
	d	120	144	168	180	200	216	225
	$\frac{d}{360}$	$\frac{1}{3}$	$\frac{2}{5}$	$\frac{7}{15}$	$\frac{1}{2}$	$\frac{5}{9}$	$\frac{3}{5}$	$\frac{5}{8}$

2. A: $\frac{1}{3} \approx 0.333$; Repeats.
   B: $\frac{2}{5} = 0.400$; Terminates.
   C#: $\frac{7}{15} \approx 0.467$; Repeats.
   D: $\frac{1}{2} = 0.500$; Terminates.
   E: $\frac{5}{9} \approx 0.556$; Repeats.
   F#: $\frac{3}{5} = 0.600$; Terminates.
   G: $\frac{5}{8} = 0.625$; Terminates.
3. 150 mm; Between B and C#.

3B Review

Review Correlation

Item(s)	Lesson(s)
1–8	3-1, 3-9
9–12	3-3, 3-4
13–17	3-6
18–21	3-7
22	3-6, 3-7
23–27	3-10
28	3-6

Test Prep

Test-Taking Tip

Tell students to read each question carefully before answering it. Here, students may not read the word "both" and thus select an incorrect answer.

Answers for Review

18. GCF: 8; LCM: 120
19. GCF: 9; LCM: 810
20. GCF: 20; LCM: 300
21. GCF: 27; LCM: 810
22. Possible answer: Factorization can help you decide how many objects to put in a row or stack. A factor will always give you a whole number of rows.

Section 3B Review

REVIEW 3B

Compare using $<$, $>$, or $=$.

1. 0.059 $\boxed{<}$ 0.590 **2.** 2.67 $\boxed{<}$ 2.671 **3.** 412.437 $\boxed{>}$ 412.347 **4.** 4.5 $\boxed{=}$ 4.50

5. $\frac{19}{23}\boxed{>}\frac{27}{35}$ **6.** $\frac{12}{27}\boxed{=}\frac{4}{9}$ **7.** $\frac{13}{15}\boxed{>}\frac{25}{29}$ **8.** $\frac{11}{18}\boxed{>}\frac{14}{23}$

Solve.

9. $0.17w = 1.445$ $w = 8.5$ **10.** $\frac{x}{28.5} = 16$ $x = 456$ **11.** $c - 3.25 = 23.47$ $c = 26.72$ **12.** $81.212 = 3.16n$ $n = 25.7$

Find the prime factorization of each number.

13. 54 2×3^3 **14.** 275 $5^2 \times 11$ **15.** 175 $5^2 \times 7$ **16.** 288 $2^5 \times 3^2$ **17.** 144 $2^4 \times 3^2$

Find the GCF and the LCM.

18. 24, 40 **19.** 81, 90 **20.** 60, 100 **21.** 135, 162

22. 

Many industries are concerned with fitting many objects or containers inside a larger object or container. Describe how factors and factorization can be used to solve these problems.

23. Music Find the fraction you could use to describe a note with duration 0.03125. What is a good name for the note? $\frac{1}{32}$; one thirty-second

Convert each fraction to a decimal.

24. $\frac{7}{9}$ $0.\overline{7}$ **25.** $\frac{3}{7}$ $0.\overline{428571}$ **26.** $\frac{13}{16}$ 0.8125 **27.** $\frac{12}{18}$ $0.\overline{6}$

Test Prep

On a multiple-choice test, you may need to rewrite fractions in lowest terms. Recognizing that there is an even number in the numerator and the denominator, so they are both divisible by 2, can help you work more quickly.

28. In which of the following fractions are both the numerator and the denominator divisible by 2? C

Ⓐ $\frac{9}{16}$ Ⓑ $\frac{8}{15}$ Ⓒ $\frac{16}{22}$ Ⓓ $\frac{15}{26}$

Resources

Practice Masters
Section 3B Review

Assessment Sourcebook
Quiz 3B

TestWorks
Test and Practice Software

PRACTICE

Name ______________________

Practice

Section 3B Review

Compare.

1. $\frac{11}{28} \bigcirc\!\!\!< \frac{18}{44}$ 2. $\frac{6}{8} \bigcirc\!\!\!> \frac{7}{10}$ 3. $\frac{4}{6} \bigcirc\!\!\!= \frac{14}{21}$ 4. $\frac{7}{12} \bigcirc\!\!\!> \frac{14}{25}$

5. $\frac{4}{7} \bigcirc\!\!\!> \frac{28}{50}$ 6. $\frac{9}{22} \bigcirc\!\!\!> \frac{13}{33}$ 7. $\frac{4}{7} \bigcirc\!\!\!< \frac{29}{49}$ 8. $\frac{5}{7} \bigcirc\!\!\!< \frac{36}{50}$

Find the prime factorization of each number.

9. 36 $2^2 \times 3^2$ 10. 945 $3^3 \times 5 \times 7$ 11. 693 $3^2 \times 7 \times 11$

12. 100 $2^2 \times 5^2$ 13. 539 $7^2 \times 11$ 14. 117 $3^2 \times 13$

Find the GCF and LCM.

15. 45, 36 GCF: 9 LCM: 180
16. 140, 28 GCF: 28 LCM: 140
17. 44, 55 GCF: 11 LCM: 220
18. 25, 30 GCF: 5 LCM: 150

19. A bottle contains 0.296 L of teriyaki sauce. Write 0.296 as a fraction in lowest terms. $\frac{37}{125}$

Convert each fraction to a decimal.

20. $\frac{3}{4}$ 0.75 21. $\frac{18}{25}$ 0.72 22. $\frac{5}{9}$ $0.\overline{5}$ 23. $\frac{8}{24}$ $0.\overline{3}$

24. $\frac{6}{11}$ $0.\overline{54}$ 25. $\frac{21}{80}$ 0.2625 26. $\frac{4}{7}$ $0.\overline{571428}$ 27. $\frac{13}{250}$ 0.052

28. Life expectancies for people in eastern and southeastern Asian and African nations are 71, 78, 79, 71, 71, 64, 51, 63, 51, 71, 58, 65, 64, 69, and 64 years. Make a stem-and-leaf diagram to display the data. *[Lesson 1-3]*

stem	leaf
5	1 1 8
6	3 4 4 4 5 9
7	1 1 1 1 8 9

29. The table relates the number m of miles to the number k of kilometers. Write a formula relating these values. *[Lesson 2-3]* $k = 1.61m$

m	1	2	3	4	5
k	1.61	3.22	4.83	6.44	8.05

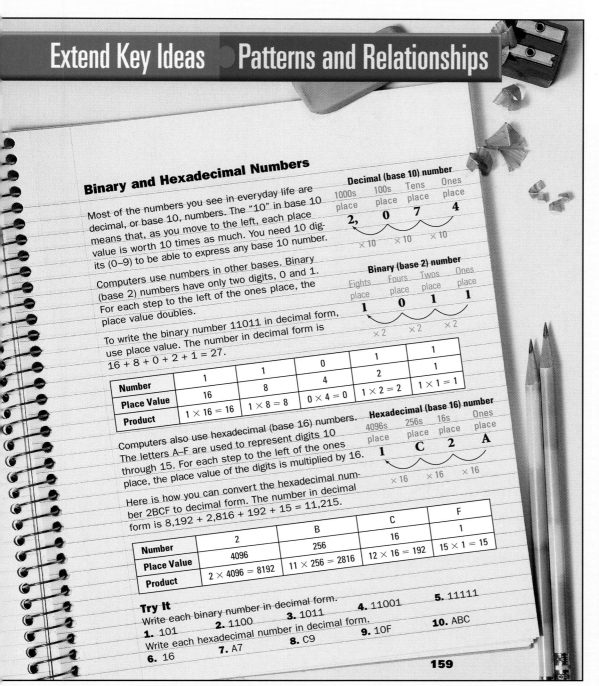

Extend Key Ideas · Patterns and Relationships

Binary and Hexadecimal Numbers

Most of the numbers you see in everyday life are decimal, or base 10, numbers. The "10" in base 10 means that, as you move to the left, each place value is worth 10 times as much. You need 10 digits (0–9) to be able to express any base 10 number.

Decimal (base 10) number

1000s place · 100s place · Tens place · Ones place

2, 0 7 4

× 10 × 10 × 10

Computers use numbers in other bases. Binary (base 2) numbers have only two digits, 0 and 1. For each step to the left of the ones place, the place value doubles.

Binary (base 2) number

Eights place · Fours place · Twos place · Ones place

1 0 1 1

× 2 × 2 × 2

To write the binary number 11011 in decimal form, use place value. The number in decimal form is 16 + 8 + 0 + 2 + 1 = 27.

Number	1	1	0	1	1
Place Value	16	8	4	2	1
Product	1 × 16 = 16	1 × 8 = 8	0 × 4 = 0	1 × 2 = 2	1 × 1 = 1

Computers also use hexadecimal (base 16) numbers. The letters A–F are used to represent digits 10 through 15. For each step to the left of the ones place, the place value of the digits is multiplied by 16.

Hexadecimal (base 16) number

4096s place · 256s place · 16s place · Ones place

1 C 2 A

× 16 × 16 × 16

Here is how you can convert the hexadecimal number 2BCF to decimal form. The number in decimal form is 8,192 + 2,816 + 192 + 15 = 11,215.

Number	2	B	C	F
Place Value	4096	256	16	1
Product	2 × 4096 = 8192	11 × 256 = 2816	12 × 16 = 192	15 × 1 = 15

Try It

Write each binary number in decimal form.

1. 101 **2.** 1100 **3.** 1011 **4.** 11001 **5.** 11111

Write each hexadecimal number in decimal form.

6. 16 **7.** A7 **8.** C9 **9.** 10F **10.** ABC

159

Binary and Hexadecimal Numbers

The Point

Students convert binary and hexadecimal numbers into base 10 numbers.

About the Page

Binary numbers have widespread applications in computers and switching networks. For example, a switch is either open or closed, which can be represented by using 0 and 1. This allows for an entire circuit to be represented by a binary number.

Ask ...

- How is a place value chart constructed? Starting with the ones place, multiply the previous place value by the appropriate power of the base.
- How is a binary or hexadecimal number converted to a number in base 10? Multiply each digit by its binary or hexadecimal place value and add the products.

Extension

Write the numbers 24 and 54 as binary numbers. Write the numbers 200 and 2773 as hexadecimal numbers. 11000; 110110; C8; AD5

Answers for Try It

1. 5
2. 12
3. 11
4. 25
5. 31
6. 22
7. 167
8. 201
9. 271
10. 2,748

Chapter 3 Summary and Review

Review Correlation

Item(s)	Lesson(s)
1, 2	3-1
3–5	3-2
6, 7	3-3
8–10	3-4
11, 12	3-5
13, 14	3-6
15, 16	3-7
17–19	3-8
20, 21	3-9
22–24	3-10

For additional review, see page 674.

Chapter 3 Summary and Review

Graphic Organizer

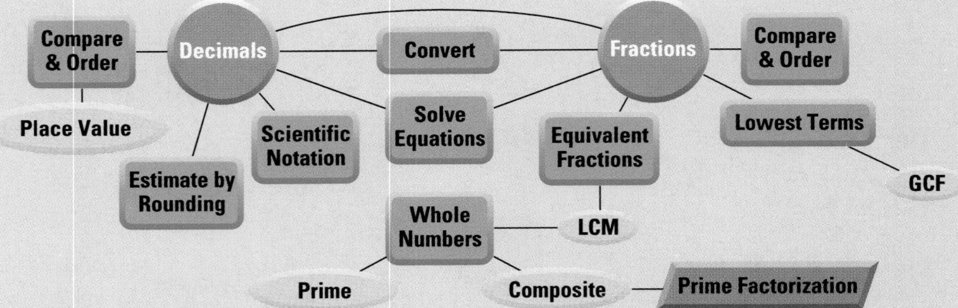

Section 3A Decimal Concepts: Estimating and Solving Equations

Summary

- Decimals can be compared by writing the numbers with their decimal points lined up and comparing digits in each place, from left to right.
- To add or subtract decimals, write the numbers with their decimal points lined up, then add or subtract the digits as usual.
- When you multiply decimals, the decimal in the product has the same number of decimal places as the sum of the decimal places in the factors.
- To divide decimals, move the decimal point the same number of places to the right in both the divisor and dividend until the divisor is a whole number. Then divide the same way as you divide by a whole number.
- **Scientific notation** can be used to express large numbers.

Review

1. Give the value of each 4 in 3428.6341. **400, $\frac{4}{1000}$**
2. Compare 8.041 and 8.04. **8.041 > 8.04**
3. Round 18.6359 to the nearest hundredth. **18.64**
4. Estimate: 602.34 + 239.28 **≈ 840**
5. Estimate: $\frac{319.28}{54.71}$ **≈ 6**
6. Find the sum: 326.78 + 16.835 **343.615**
7. Solve: $12.34 + y = 56.123$ **$y = 43.783$**
8. Find the product: 12.85×2.3 **29.555**
9. Solve: $\frac{e}{4.56} = 12.9$ **$e = 58.824$**
10. Solve: $3.2p = 144.96$ **$p = 45.3$**
11. Write 7.234×10^5 in standard form. **723,400**
12. Write 1,739,000 in scientific notation. **1.739×10^6**

Resources

Practice Masters
Cumulative Review Chapters 1–3

Assessment Sourcebook
Quarterly Test Chapters 1–3

PRACTICE

Name ________________

Practice

Cumulative Review Chapters 1–3

The bar graph shows how many American homes had access to electronic media in 1990. Use the graph for Exercises 1–2. *[Lesson 1-1]*

Electronic Media in U.S. Homes, 1990

Number of every 100 homes: 0, 20, 40, 60, 80, 100

Telephone, Radio, Cable TV, VCR

1. About how many of every 100 homes had a videocassette recorder (VCR)? **72**
2. Which item was in the most homes? **Radio**
   The fewest homes? **Cable TV**

Find the value of each expression. *[Lesson 2-2]*

3. $18 + 21 \div 3$ **25**
4. $7 \times 2 + 5 \times 3$ **29**
5. $3(8 - 2) + 4$ **22**
6. $2 + \frac{10 - 2}{1 + 3}$ **4**
7. $\frac{12}{3} - \frac{24}{6 + 2}$ **1**
8. $30 - (10 - 7) \times 2$ **24**

Use the given formula to complete each table. *[Lesson 2-3]*

9. $y = 2x - 5$

x	5	6	7	8
y	5	7	9	11

10. $D = 25t$

t	3	4	5	6
D	75	100	125	150

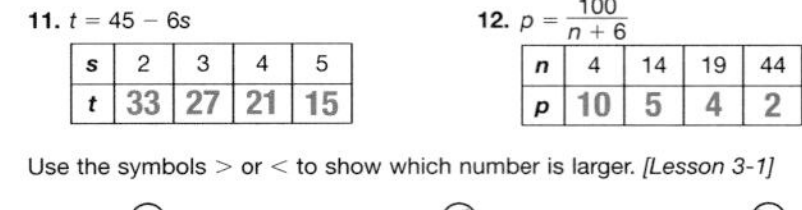

11. $t = 45 - 6s$

s	2	3	4	5
t	33	27	21	15

12. $p = \frac{100}{n + 6}$

n	4	14	19	44
p	10	5	4	2

Use the symbols > or < to show which number is larger. *[Lesson 3-1]*

13. 8.631 (>) 8.63
14. 4.354 (<) 4.356
15. 18.73 (>) 17.83
16. 2.070 (>) 2.007
17. 5.386 (>) 5.376
18. 12.39 (>) 12.3899

Solve each equation. *[Lessons 3-3, 3-4]*

19. $x + 1.7 = 8.63$ $x =$ **6.93**
20. $y - 5.83 = 12.3$ $y =$ **18.13**
21. $6.54 = j + 2.87$ $j =$ **3.67**
22. $8.273 = q - 4.13$ $q =$ **12.403**
23. $2.3x = 20.93$ $x =$ **9.1**
24. $\frac{u}{1.49} = 3.65$ $u =$ **5.4385**
25. $18 = 4.8k$ $k =$ **3.75**
26. $9.03 = \frac{c}{17.8}$ $c =$ **160.734**

Chapter 3 Summary and Review

Section 3B Fraction Concepts

Summary

- One number is **divisible** by another if the first can be divided by the second with no remainder. In this case, the second number is a **factor** of the first. Divisibility tests can be used to tell if one number is a factor of another.
- A whole number greater than 1 is a **prime number** if it has exactly two factors, 1 and itself. If it has more than two factors, it is a **composite number.**
- When you write a composite number as a product of prime numbers, the product is the **prime factorization** of the composite number. You can use a **factor tree** to find a prime factorization.
- The **greatest common factor** (GCF) of two whole numbers is the greatest whole number that is a factor of both numbers.
- The **least common multiple** (LCM) of two whole numbers is the smallest whole number (other than 0) that is a multiple of both numbers.
- A fraction is a number written in the form $\frac{a}{b}$, which means $a \div b$. The top number is the **numerator**. The bottom number is the **denominator.** Fractions are **equivalent** if they represent the same quantity.
- A fraction is in **lowest terms** if 1 is the only common factor of the numerator and the denominator. You can rewrite a fraction in lowest terms by dividing the numerator and denominator by common factors.
- To convert from a decimal to a fraction, think of the fractional equivalents of place values. To convert from a fraction to a decimal, divide the numerator by the denominator.
- A **terminating decimal** ends. A **repeating decimal** repeats a pattern of digits.

Review

13. Test the number 330 for divisibility by 2, 3, 4, 5, 6, 8, 9, and 10. **2, 3, 5, 6, and 10**

14. Use a factor tree to find the prime factorization of 276. $2^2 \times 3 \times 23$

15. Find the GCF of 45 and 65. **5**

16. Find the LCM of 12 and 15. **60**

17. Give two fractions that are equivalent to $\frac{15}{18}$. **Possible answer:** $\frac{5}{6}, \frac{30}{36}$

18. Rewrite $\frac{28}{112}$ in lowest terms. $\frac{1}{4}$

19. Rewrite $\frac{75}{165}$ in lowest terms. $\frac{5}{11}$

20. Compare $\frac{24}{31}$ and $\frac{23}{31}$. $\frac{24}{31} > \frac{23}{31}$

21. Compare $\frac{9}{16}$ and $\frac{5}{9}$. $\frac{9}{16} > \frac{5}{9}$

22. Convert 0.24 to a fraction in lowest terms. $\frac{6}{25}$

23. Convert 0.528 to a fraction in lowest terms. $\frac{66}{125}$

24. Convert $\frac{9}{11}$ to a decimal. Tell if the decimal terminates or repeats. $0.\overline{81}$**; the decimal repeats**

Chapter 3 Assessment

Assessment Correlation

Item(s)	Lesson(s)
1, 2	3-1
3, 4	3-2
5, 6	3-3
7, 8	3-4
9, 10	3-5
11, 12	3-6
13, 14	3-7
15, 16	3-8
17	3-9
18, 19	3-10

Answers for Performance Task
It would take 120 more days; 120 is the LCM of 8 and 30; This makes sense because 120 is divisible by 8-day weeks and 30-day months.

Chapter 3 Assessment

1. Give the value of each 7 in 71,267.073. 70,000, 7, $\frac{7}{100}$
2. Compare 5.6999 and 5.07. 5.6999 > 5.07
3. Round 63.849 to the nearest tenth. 63.8
4. Estimate: 1512.7 ÷ 301.6 ≈ 5
5. Find the difference: 37.65 − 4.238 33.412
6. Solve: $k - 82.37 = 731.2$ $k = 813.57$
7. Solve: $297.57 = 6.5x$ $x = 45.78$
8. An Earth year is 365.3 days. A year on Jupiter is 11.86 times as long as a year on Earth. Find the length of a year on Jupiter (in Earth days). 4332.458 Earth days
9. Write 8.37×10^7 in standard form. 83,700,000
10. Write 87,560,000,000 in scientific notation. 8.756×10^{10}
11. Test the number 672 for divisibility by 2, 3, 4, 5, 6, 8, 9, and 10. 2, 3, 4, 6, and 8
12. Use a factor tree to find the prime factorization of 600. $2^3 \times 3 \times 5^2$
13. Find the GCF of 84 and 108. 12
14. Find the LCM of 10 and 25. 50
15. Give two fractions that are equivalent to $\frac{42}{64}$. Possible answer: $\frac{21}{32}$, $\frac{84}{128}$
16. Of the 78 students in Mr. Takagi's classes, 18 earned a grade of A last semester. What fraction of the students earned A's? Express your answer in lowest terms. $\frac{3}{13}$
17. Compare $\frac{19}{35}$ and $\frac{8}{15}$. $\frac{19}{35} > \frac{8}{15}$
18. Convert 0.35 to a fraction in lowest terms. $\frac{7}{20}$
19. Convert $\frac{13}{16}$ to a decimal. Tell if the decimal terminates or repeats. 0.8125; terminates

Performance Task

Suppose a Martian calendar used 8-day weeks and 30-day months. If the first day of a month fell on a Monday, how many more days would it take before another first day fell on a Monday? How does your answer relate to the numbers 8 and 30? Explain why this relationship makes sense.

Resources

Assessment Sourcebook
Chapter 3 Tests
- Forms A and B (free response)
- Form C (multiple choice)
- Form D (performance assessment)
- Form E (mixed response)
- Form F (cumulative chapter test)

TestWorks
Test and Practice Software

Home and Community Connections
Letter Home for Chapter 3 in English and Spanish

Answers for Assessment (page 163)
• Keeping Gizmos in Stock
Student report should show that the store would sell 1050 Gizmos in a 30-day month and Mr. Garcia would purchase 34 Gizmos in a 4-week month for total sales of 1084 Gizmos a month. The report should also show the equation $12x = 1084$, for x = number of crates. The employer would need 91 packaging crates a month.

Cumulative Review

Cumulative Review Chapters 1–3 — Test Prep

Performance Assessment

Choose one problem.

Going by the Book

Choose a page in each of two different kinds of books. Count how many one-syllable, two-syllable, three-syllable (and so on) words are on each page. Make two line plots, one for each book, to display your results. Do you notice any patterns in the line plots? Which book seems to be intended for more advanced readers? Explain how you reached your conclusion.

Monkeys and Strawberries

Write four different problems that can be solved using the equation $6x + 5 = 47$. You must include at least one of these words or phrases in each problem: more than, product, pickles, dollars, increased by, strawberries, less than, sum, monkeys, times. Pick one of the problems and show how to solve it. Explain each step.

Keeping Gizmos in Stock

Gizmos are packed in crates of 12. You manage a store that normally sells 35 Gizmos per day. In addition, Mr. Garcia comes in every two weeks to purchase 17 Gizmos. Your employer has asked you to determine how many crates of Gizmos need to be ordered from the manufacturer every month. Write a report to your employer, explaining how you solved an equation to answer his question.

Drawing the Solar System

The table shows how far each planet is from the sun, in astronomical units. Make a poster which shows the orbits of all the planets as accurately as possible. (Hint: Start with Pluto so that you'll be sure that you have enough space!)

Planet	Distance from Sun (AU)
Mercury	0.39
Venus	0.72
Earth	1.00
Mars	1.53
Jupiter	5.21
Saturn	9.55
Uranus	19.20
Neptune	30.10
Pluto	39.46

About Performance Assessment

The Performance Assessment options …

- provide teachers with an alternate means of assessing students.
- address different learning modalities.

Teachers may encourage students to choose the most challenging problem.

Learning Modalities
Going by the Book **Individual** Students analyze words to compare the reading levels of books.
Monkeys and Strawberries **Logical** Students write word problems for an equation, then explain how to solve a problem.
Keeping Gizmos in Stock **Verbal** Students explain how to place an order based on given information.
Drawing the Solar System **Visual** Students make a scale model of the solar system.

Suggested Scoring Rubric

See key on page 103.

Going by the Book

4
- Data is well organized, with two accurate line plots.
- Patterns and conclusions are clear.

3
- Data is organized and two line plots are drawn.
- Student indicates patterns found and writes a conclusion.

2
- Data is somewhat organized; two line plots are attempted.
- Student tries to describe patterns and draw a conclusion.

1
- Data is poorly organized; no line plots are attempted.
- No patterns or conclusions.

Answers for Assessment

• Drawing the Solar System

Student's poster should show locations of the planets based on a scale with Pluto located almost 40 times as far from the sun as the Earth, Neptune almost 30 times as far, Uranus almost 20 times as far, Saturn almost 10 times as far, Jupiter about 5 times as far, and Mars about $1\frac{1}{2}$ times as far. Then Venus should be about $\frac{3}{4}$ as far from the sun as the earth and Mercury about $\frac{2}{5}$ as far.

Answer for Keeping Gizmos in Stock on page 162.

Monkeys and Strawberries

4
- Writes four different problems following the guidelines.
- Solves one problem, clearly explaining each step.

3
- Writes four different problems following some guidelines.
- Solves one problem with an explanation of most steps.

2
- Writes at least three problems following some guidelines.
- Cannot solve or explain steps for solving a selected problem.

1
- Cannot write at least three problems following guidelines.
- Cannot solve or explain the solution to a selected problem.

Operations with $\frac{1}{2} \div \frac{1}{3}$ Fractions

Section 4A

Sums and Differences of Fractions: Students learn to estimate solutions to problems containing fractions, to find sums and differences of fractions and mixed numbers, and to solve equations involving fractions and mixed numbers.

4-1 Estimating: Fractions and Mixed Numbers

4-2 Adding and Subtracting Fractions

4-3 Adding and Subtracting Mixed Numbers

Section 4B

Products and Quotients of Fractions: Students learn to multiply and divide fractions and mixed numbers.

4-4 Multiplying Fractions

4-5 Multiplying Mixed Numbers

4-6 Dividing Fractions and Mixed Numbers

Meeting NCTM Standards

Curriculum Standards

STANDARD

			pages
1	**Problem Solving**	Skills and Strategies	165, 166, 177, 182, 190, 194, 195
		Applications	171–172, 176–177, 181–182, 183, 189–190, 194–195, 199–200, 201, 206
		Exploration	168, 173, 178, 186, 191, 197
2	**Communication**	Oral	167, 170, 172, 176, 180, 185, 188, *190*, 193, 199
		Written	172, *177*, 182, 190, 195, 200
		Cooperative Learning	*168, 170, 173, 178, 180, 182, 186, 188, 191, 193, 197, 200*
3	**Reasoning**	Critical Thinking	172, 177, 182, 190, 200
4	**Connections**	Mathematical	See Standards 5–7, 9, 10, 12, 13 below.
		Interdisciplinary	Science 164, *171,* 177, 181, 182, 184, 190, *193,* 194, 198, 202; Arts & Literature 164; Entertainment 165; Social Studies 165, 167, 182, 194; Language 170; History *170*, 175, 181, 187, 189, 195, 197; Music *175;* Consumer 176, *177, 188, 194*; Career 189; Industry *167, 185*
		Technology	166, 188, *195,* 196
		Cultural	164, *175*
5	**Number and Number Relationships**		168–172, 194
6	**Number Systems and Number Theory**		168–206
7	**Computation and Estimation**		168–206
8	**Patterns and Functions**		*200*
9	**Algebra**		176, 177, 179, 181, 182, 184, 200
10	**Statistics**		172, 177, 182, 196
12	**Geometry**		181, 187, 189, 191, 201
13	**Measurement**		172, 189, 191–192, 195, 197–203

Italic type indicates Teacher Edition reference.

Teaching Standards

Focus on Diversity

Sensitivity to the diversity of students' backgrounds and experiences is crucial in selecting worthwhile tasks. Teachers should

- consider gender issues in selecting tasks.
- acknowledge that students have a variety of psychological, cultural, sociological, and political perspectives.

Assessment Standards

Focus on Learning

Interviews One focus of the Learning Standard is the use of assessment to help teachers make informed decisions about subsequent instruction. Interviews, whether informal or formal, give teachers the opportunity to probe a student's understanding and to determine appropriate pace and content of future lessons. Interviews in Chapter 4 have students explain

- rounding, mental math, and estimation procedures.
- operations with fractions.

TECHNOLOGY

For the Teacher

- **Teacher Resource Planner CD-ROM**
  Use the teacher planning CD-ROM to view resources available for Chapter 4. You can prepare custom lesson plans or use the default lesson plans provided.

- **World Wide Web**
  Visit **www.teacher.mathsurf.com** for links to lesson plans from teachers and other professionals, NCTM information, and other sites.

- **TestWorks**
  TestWorks provides ready-made tests and can create custom tests and practice worksheets.

For the Parent

- **World Wide Web**
  Parents can use the Web site at **www.parent.mathsurf.com.**

For the Student

- **Interactive CD-ROM**
  Lesson 4-3 has an *Interactive CD-ROM Lesson*. The *Interactive CD-ROM Journal* and *Interactive CD-ROM Spreadsheet/Grapher Tool* are also used in Chapter 4.

- **Wide World of Mathematics**
  Lesson 4-1 Middle School: Hurricane Prediction
  Lesson 4-1 Middle School: Two-Sport Athlete

- **World Wide Web**
  Use with Chapter and Section Openers; Students can go online to the Scott Foresman-Addison Wesley Web site at **www.mathsurf.com/7/ch4** to collect information about chapter themes.

STANDARDIZED - TEST CORRELATION

SECTION 4A

LESSON	OBJECTIVE	ITBS Form M	CTBS 4th Ed.	CAT 5th Ed.	SAT 9th Ed.	MAT 7th Ed.	Your Form
4-1	• Estimate solutions to problems involving fractions.			✘	✘	✘	
4-2	• Find sums and differences of fractions.	✘	✘	✘	✘	✘	
	• Solve equations involving fractions.			✘		✘	
4-3	• Find sums and differences of mixed numbers.			✘	✘	✘	
	• Solve equations involving mixed numbers.					✘	

SECTION 4B

LESSON	OBJECTIVE	ITBS Form M	CTBS 4th Ed.	CAT 5th Ed.	SAT 9th Ed.	MAT 7th Ed.	Your Form
4-4	• Multiply fractions.	✘	✘	✘	✘	✘	
4-5	• Multiply mixed numbers.	✘		✘	✘		
4-6	• Divide fractions and mixed numbers.	✘	✘	✘	✘	✘	

Key: ITBS - Iowa Test of Basic Skills; CTBS - Comprehensive Test of Basic Skills; CAT - California Achievement Test; SAT - Stanford Achievement Test; MAT - Metropolitan Achievement Test

ASSESSMENT PROGRAM

Traditional Assessment

QUICK QUIZZES	SECTION REVIEW	CHAPTER REVIEW	CHAPTER ASSESSMENT FREE RESPONSE	CHAPTER ASSESSMENT MULTIPLE CHOICE	CUMULATIVE REVIEW
TE: pp. 172, 177, 182, 190, 195, 200	SE: pp. 184, 202 *Quiz 4A, 4B	SE: pp. 204–205	SE: p. 206 *Ch. 4 Tests Forms A, B, E	*Ch. 4 Tests Forms C, E	SE: p. 207 *Ch. 4 Test Form F

Alternate Assessment

INTERVIEW	JOURNAL	ONGOING	PERFORMANCE	PORTFOLIO	PROJECT	SELF
TE: p. 190	SE: pp. 172, 184, 190, 195 200 TE: pp. 166, 172, 195	TE: pp. 168, 173, 178, 186, 191, 197	SE: p. 206 TE: p. 182 *Ch. 4 Tests Forms D, E	TE: p. 177	SE: pp. 182, 200 TE: p. 165	TE: p. 200

*Tests and quizzes are in *Assessment Sourcebook*. Test Form E is a mixed response test.
Forms for Alternate Assessment are also available in *Assessment Sourcebook*.

TestWorks: Test and Practice Software

MIDDLE SCHOOL PACING CHART

REGULAR PACING

Day	5 classes per week
1	Chapter 4 Opener; Problem Solving Focus
2	Section **4A** Opener; Lesson **4-1**
3	Lesson **4-2**
4	Lesson **4-3**
5	**4A** Connect; **4A** Review
6	Section **4B** Opener; Lesson **4-4**
7	Lesson **4-5**; Technology
8	Lesson **4-6**
9	**4B** Connect; 4B Review; Extend Key Ideas
10	Chapter 4 Summary and Review
11	Chapter 4 Assessment Cumulative Review, Chapters 1–4

BLOCK SCHEDULING OPTIONS

Block Scheduling for Complete Course

Chapter 4 may be presented in

- six 90-minute blocks
- nine 75-minute blocks

Each block consists of a combination of

- Chapter and Section Openers
- Explores
- Lesson Development
- Problem Solving Focus
- Technology
- Extend Key Ideas
- Connect
- Review
- Assessment

For details, see *Block Scheduling Handbook.*

Block Scheduling for Interdisciplinary Course

Each block integrates math with another subject area.

In Chapter 4, interdisciplinary topics include

- The Stock Market
- Construction

Themes for Interdisciplinary Team Teaching 4A and 4B are

- The Stock Market
- Greek Temple Designs

For details, see *Block Scheduling Handbook.*

Block Scheduling for Lab-Based Course

In each block, 30–40 minutes is devoted to lab activities including

- Explores in the Student Edition
- Connect pages in the Student Edition
- Technology options in the Student Edition
- Reteaching Activities in the Teacher Edition

For details, see *Block Scheduling Handbook.*

Block Scheduling for Course with *Connected Mathematics*

In each block, investigations from **Connected Mathematics** replace or enhance the lessons in Chapter 4.

Connected Mathematics topics for Chapter 4 can be found in

- *Comparing and Scaling*

For details, see *Block Scheduling Handbook.*

INTERDISCIPLINARY BULLETIN BOARD

Set Up

On a bulletin board, provide a table for recording daily data about stocks of companies listed on the New York Stock Exchange. Allow enough space at the left for drawings representing the companies. Have columns for five business days.

Procedure

Show students where information about the New York Stock Exchange can be found in their local newspaper, on television, or on computer communications.

- Have small groups of students choose a company's stock to follow. They should track prices, gains, and losses during the business week.
- Groups should draw a symbol for their company. For each business day, students should record the closing price of their company's stock, and note what gains or losses occurred over the previous day.

What's Up? What's Down?

Stock Exchange Closing Prices for One Week

	Monday	Tuesday	Wednesday	Thursday	Friday
	$39\frac{3}{8}$ $+\frac{5}{8}$	$39\frac{1}{8}$ $-\frac{1}{4}$	$40\frac{1}{8}$ $+1$	41 $+\frac{7}{8}$	$40\frac{1}{2}$ $-\frac{1}{2}$
	$46\frac{1}{2}$ $-\frac{1}{8}$	$46\frac{5}{8}$ $+\frac{1}{8}$	47 $+\frac{3}{8}$	$45\frac{1}{2}$ $-\frac{1}{2}$	46 $+\frac{1}{2}$
	79 $+1\frac{1}{8}$	$79\frac{1}{8}$ $+\frac{1}{8}$	$80\frac{1}{2}$ $+1\frac{3}{8}$	80 $-\frac{1}{2}$	$80\frac{5}{8}$ $+\frac{5}{8}$
	$52\frac{1}{8}$ $+\frac{1}{4}$	$48\frac{7}{8}$ $+\frac{1}{8}$	$51\frac{3}{4}$ $-\frac{1}{2}$	$52\frac{1}{2}$ $+\frac{3}{4}$	53 $+\frac{1}{2}$
	$48\frac{3}{4}$ $-\frac{5}{8}$	$52\frac{1}{4}$ $+\frac{1}{8}$	49 $+\frac{1}{8}$	$49\frac{5}{8}$ $+\frac{5}{8}$	$49\frac{1}{2}$ $-\frac{1}{8}$

Chapter 4

The information on these pages shows how fractions are used in real-life situations.

World Wide Web

If your class has access to the World Wide Web, you might want to use the information found at the Web site addresses given.

Extensions

The following activities do not require access to the World Wide Web.

Science
Ask students if they feel the breakfast described here has more or less than the recommended allowance of fat. Ask how they can decide. More; Compare the fractions.

People of the World
Have students prepare a report about the ancient Babylonians that describes some aspect of their culture. Some students might want to research the Babylonian number system.

Arts & Literature
Have students work with partners to find music for a favorite song. Ask them to report on the time signature for the piece and to show that each measure has the proper number of beats.

Entertainment
Have students investigate the impact videos have had on movie attendance. Suggest they talk to their parents and other adults about their preferences in regard to going to movies as opposed to renting videos.

Social Studies
Have students locate Aswan, Egypt, and Yuma, Arizona, on a map. Talk about why these areas get so little rain and identify other areas in the world that might also get very little rain.

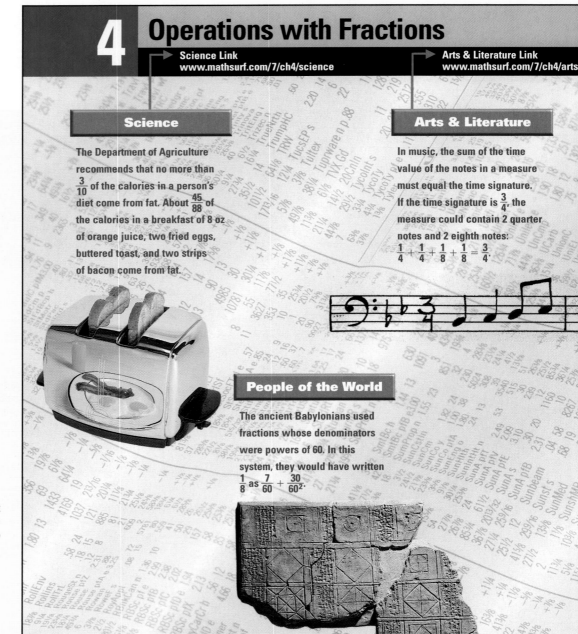

4 Operations with Fractions

Science Link
www.mathsurf.com/7/ch4/science

Arts & Literature Link
www.mathsurf.com/7/ch4/arts

Science

The Department of Agriculture recommends that no more than $\frac{3}{10}$ of the calories in a person's diet come from fat. About $\frac{45}{88}$ of the calories in a breakfast of 8 oz of orange juice, two fried eggs, buttered toast, and two strips of bacon come from fat.

Arts & Literature

In music, the sum of the time value of the notes in a measure must equal the time signature. If the time signature is $\frac{3}{4}$, the measure could contain 2 quarter notes and 2 eighth notes: $\frac{1}{4}+\frac{1}{4}+\frac{1}{8}+\frac{1}{8}=\frac{3}{4}$.

People of the World

The ancient Babylonians used fractions whose denominators were powers of 60. In this system, they would have written $\frac{1}{8}$ as $\frac{7}{60}+\frac{30}{60^2}$.

164

TEACHER TALK

Meet Alma Ramírez

Oakland Charter Academy
Oakland, California

Sometimes, when teaching multiplication of mixed numbers, I find students get "stuck," or they forget steps. Also, after giving an answer, many of them don't check to see if their answer makes sense. For these students, I have found it useful to present a problem and an answer, and ask them to work backwards to figure out why the procedure works. For example, for $1\frac{1}{2} \times 4\frac{1}{2}$, I give $\frac{3}{2} \times \frac{9}{2} = \frac{27}{4} = 6\frac{3}{4}$. Then I have students work backwards, drawing arrows at each step, to show that $6\frac{3}{4} = \frac{27}{4}$, and $\frac{27}{4} = \frac{3}{2} \times \frac{9}{2}$. Finally I have them express $\frac{3}{2}$ and $\frac{9}{2}$ as mixed numbers.

Once students go through this process several times, the computational procedure seems to "click."

Entertainment Link
www.mathsurf.com/7/ch4/ent

Entertainment

According to Motion Picture Association of America estimates, about $\frac{1}{7}$ of the people attending movies are younger than age 16.

Social Studies

People living in Aswan, Egypt, get about $\frac{1}{50}$ of an inch of rain each year. Yuma, Arizona, the driest city in the United States, gets $2\frac{13}{20}$ inches of rain, which is $132\frac{1}{2}$ times more rain than Aswan.

KEY MATH IDEAS

Before adding or subtracting fractions, write them with a common denominator. Then find the sum or difference of the numerators.

You can express a fractional number greater than one as an improper fraction or a mixed number.

Two numbers are **reciprocals** if their product is 1. To divide by a fraction, multiply by its reciprocal.

Most lengths are not whole numbers. You often need to multiply and divide fractions when you solve area problems.

CHAPTER PROJECT

Problem Solving
Understand
Plan
Solve
Look Back

In this project, you will use fractions to describe and graph the populations of the world's nations. To begin this project, find current population figures for the world and the five most populous countries.

165

PROJECT ASSESSMENT

You may choose to use this project as a performance assessment for the chapter.

Performance Assessment Key

Level 4 Full Accomplishment

Level 3 Substantial Accomplishment

Level 2 Partial Accomplishment

Level 1 Little Accomplishment

Suggested Scoring Rubric

Level	Criteria
4	•Five countries are identified and each fraction of the world's total population is reasonable. •Bar graph is accurate.
3	•Five countries are identified but students have some difficulty expressing the populations as a fraction of the total. •Graph and fractions of the total population are acceptable.
2	•Students have difficulty identifying the countries and expressing their populations as fractions of the total. •An attempt is made to make a graph and give fractions of the total population.
1	•Little attempt is made to identify the countries and give fractions. •Bar graph is not correct and fractions of the total are not given.

Chapter Project

Students will investigate the five most populous countries of the world and use fractions and a graph to show each population in terms of the total population of the world.

Resources
Chapter 4 Project Master

Introduce the Project
Talk about where students might find information about current population figures, such as in encyclopedias, almanacs, and the Internet.

Project Progress
Section A, p. 182 Students find the fraction of the world's population that live in each of the five most populous countries and show the data in a bar graph.

Section B, p. 200 Students draw a world map and locate the five most populous countries. They find what fraction of the world's population lives in these five countries and what fraction lives elsewhere.

Community Project

A community project for Chapter 4 is available in *Home and Community Connections.*

Cooperative Learning

You may want to use Teaching Tool Transparency 1: Cooperative Learning Checklist with **Explore** and other group activities in this chapter.

Problem Solving Focus

Finding Unnecessary Information

The Point

Students focus on determining whether a problem has unnecessary information and, if so, which information is not needed to solve the problem.

Resources

Teaching Tool Tranparency 16: Problem-Solving Guidelines

 *Interactive CD-ROM Journal*

About the Page

Using the Problem-Solving Process

In order to solve a problem, students must be able to eliminate the extraneous information and focus on the information needed to solve the problem. Discuss these suggestions for evaluating the given information:

- Read the problem two or three times before beginning.
- Decide what kind of information is needed to solve the problem.
- Analyze all the information given and eliminate any information that is not needed.

Ask ...

- In Problem 1, how can you decide what information is not needed? Answers may vary.
- What additional information do you need in Problem 2? Where can you find it? The number of friends; In Problem 1.

Answers for Problems

1. Senior citizen prices are $2.00 less.
2. No unnecessary numerical information. It is not necessary to know that Damien bought popcorn and trail mix.
3. The trail mix costs $4.60.
4. She sold 2,500,000 CDs in 7 months.

Journal

Have students write an explanation telling how they determine what information in a problem is necessary and what information is not needed.

Problem Solving
Understand
Plan
Solve
Look Back

Finding Unnecessary Information

It is important to analyze the information in a problem carefully. You need to understand which information will help you solve the problem, and which information is unnecessary and can be ignored.

Problem Solving Focus

For each problem, identify the unnecessary numerical information. Some problems may not have unnecessary information. (You do *not* need to solve the problem.)

1. The Strand Movie Theater charges $7.50 per ticket. Senior citizen prices are $2.00 less. For his thirteenth birthday, Damien takes 4 of his school friends to the movies. How much money does he need for the tickets?

2. At the theater, Damien buys popcorn and trail mix for himself and his friends. He gives the cashier a ten dollar bill and gets $1.20 in change. What is the average amount of money Damien spent on each friend?

3. Damien asked for $\frac{3}{4}$ of a pound of trail mix. The scale read 0.80 and the trail mix cost $4.60. Did Damien receive the correct amount of trail mix?

4. The movie was about a young woman who tried to sail around the world. Her planned route was 28,000 miles long. Unfortunately, her boat capsized, and she barely made it to shore in Australia, 7,500 miles from her starting point. Fortunately, she became a famous pop music star there, selling 2,500,000 CDs in 7 months. What fraction of her planned route did she complete?

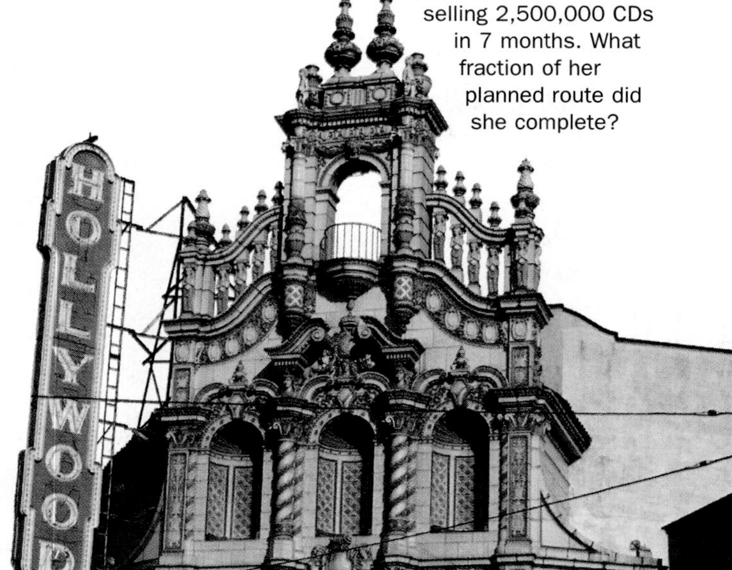

166

Additional Problem

Kareem is planning a birthday party for 12 friends. The party will be from 4 P.M. to 6:15 P.M. He plans to serve cake and ice cream and to play four games. The cake will cost $8.95 and the ice cream will cost $4.98. Kareem is also purchasing party favors and prizes that cost $22.50. About how much is he spending per person for the party?

1. What is the problem asking you to find? The cost per person.
2. How many people are involved? 13, counting Kareem.
3. What information is unnecessary? The time the party will be held and the number of games to be played.
4. What information will you use? How will you use it? The costs and the number of people; Add the costs and divide by the number of people; ($8.95 + $4.98 + $22.50) ÷ 13 = $2.80 per person.

Sums and Differences of Fractions

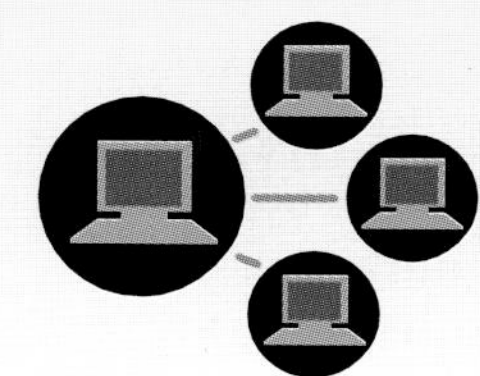

Visit www.teacher.mathsurf.com for links to lesson plans from teachers and other professionals, NCTM information, and other sites.

LESSON PLANNING GUIDE

Student Edition / Ancillaries*

LESSON		MATERIALS	VOCABULARY	DAILY	OTHER
	Chapter 4 Opener				Ch. 4 Project Master Ch. 4 Community Project Teaching Tool Trans. 1
	Problem Solving Focus				Teaching Tool Trans. 16 *Interactive CD-ROM Journal*
	Section 4A Opener				
4-1	**Estimating: Fractions and Mixed Numbers**		mixed number	4–1	*WW Math*—Middle School
4-2	**Adding and Subtracting Fractions**	graph paper, colored pencils	least common denominator (LCD)	4–2	Teaching Tool Trans. 2, 3, 7 Lesson Enhancement Trans. 13 Technology Master 14
4-3	**Adding and Subtracting Mixed Numbers**	graph paper, colored pencils	improper fraction	4–3	Teaching Tool Trans. 7 Lesson Enhancement Trans. 14 Ch. 4 Project Master *Interactive CD-ROM Lesson*
	Connect				Interdisc. Team Teaching 4A
	Review				Practice 4A; Quiz 4A; *TestWorks*

* Daily Ancillaries include Practice, Reteaching, Problem Solving, Enrichment, and Daily Transparency. Teaching Tool Transparencies are in *Teacher's Toolkits*. Lesson Enhancement Transparencies are in *Overhead Transparency Package*.

SKILLS TRACE

LESSON	SKILL	FIRST INTRODUCED GR. 5	GR. 6	GR. 7	DEVELOP	PRACTICE/ APPLY	REVIEW
4-1	**Estimating solutions to problems involving fractions and mixed numbers.**		✘		pp. 168–170	pp. 171–172	pp. 205, 236, 327, 393
4-2	**Adding and subtracting fractions.**	✘			pp. 173–175	pp. 176–177	pp. 205, 243, 332, 398
4-3	**Adding and subtracting mixed numbers.**	✘			pp. 178–180	pp. 181–182	pp. 205, 247, 336

CONNECTED MATHEMATICS

The unit *Comparing and Scaling (Ratio Proportion and Percent),* from the **Connected Mathematics** series, can be used with Section 4A.

INTERDISCIPLINARY TEAM TEACHING

Math and Social Studies

(Worksheet pages 13–14: Teacher pages T13–T14)

In this lesson, students use fractions with stock market data.

Name ______________________ ***Math and Social Studies***

Pick a Winner

Use fractions with stock market data.

The performance of stocks on the stock market is an important indicator of the economic health of the United States, as well as that of the world. A person can get the current price of a stock by calling a broker, checking the stock's performance on the Internet, or watching certain cable channels on TV.

A stock market analyst can get the "big picture" of how a stock is doing by calling up on a computer screen the values of a share of a company's stock over a number of years. By getting a long-term view of a stock, the analyst can tell whether the company is growing, holding steady, or shrinking. This helps analysts rate stocks and pick those likely to increase in value.

The table shows the value of one share of stock of Bethlehem Steel, Coca Cola, and General Motors over a 14-year period.

	Jan. '83	Amt. Change	Oct. '87	Amt. Change	Jan. '94	Amt. Change	Dec. '96
BethStl	$\$19\frac{3}{4}$	$-\$13\frac{1}{2}$	$\$6\frac{1}{4}$	$+\$18$	$\$24\frac{1}{4}$	$-\$15\frac{1}{8}$	$\$9\frac{1}{8}$
CocaCl	$2	$+\$3\frac{1}{8}$	$\$5\frac{1}{8}$	$+\$17\frac{1}{4}$	$\$22\frac{3}{8}$	$+\$25\frac{3}{4}$	$\$48\frac{1}{8}$
GnMotr	$\$31\frac{5}{8}$	$-\$6\frac{5}{8}$	$25	$+\$37\frac{1}{4}$	$\$62\frac{1}{4}$	$-\$6\frac{3}{4}$	$\$55\frac{1}{2}$

1. Identify something in your everyday life that each company in the table might produce.

   See below.

2. Most stocks increase and decrease in value each day they are traded. Many investors, however, do not trade stocks daily. They are interested in a stock's growth over a longer period of time. For the big picture, fill in the amount of change in dollars between the dates in the columns of the table. Use a "+" or "–" to indicate the direction of the change.

3. a. From January 1983 to December 1996, which stock of the three companies increased most in value? Use estimating to find the answer.

   Coca-Cola

   b. In December 1996, a government banking official commented that stock prices were artificially high because of over-enthusiastic buying. This comment caused many investors to sell their stocks. Prices fell "across the board" (though most stocks later recovered). Coca-Cola traded at $49\frac{1}{4}$ one day, dropped $2\frac{1}{4}$ the second day, gained $3\frac{1}{8}$ the third day, and gained another $\frac{5}{8}$ the fourth day. What was the closing price on the fourth day?

   $50\frac{3}{4}$

Name ______________________ ***Math and Social Studies***

   c. Coca-Cola has been experiencing dramatic sales growth outside the United States, which has been reflected in the value of its stock. If someone purchased 100 shares of Coca-Cola in January 1983 and sold them in December 1996, how much money would he or she have made?

   about 46×100 or $4600

4. In October 1987, the stock market experienced a dramatic downturn. General Motors (GM) fell to a low of 25 but managed to rally $4\frac{1}{4}$ points before the stock market closed. What was the closing price of GM?

   $29\frac{1}{4}$

5. In recent years, American automobile companies have improved their profitability. In part, this is a result of more favorable car trading agreements being negotiated between our government and that of Japan. GM had a very profitable last three months in 1996. In one four-day period GM stock prices were $47\frac{1}{8}$ one day, $47\frac{3}{4}$ the second day, $48\frac{1}{2}$ the next, and $49\frac{3}{8}$ the fourth day. Show the day-to-day gain in the stock price in fractions from the first day to the fourth. What was the overall gain in stock price?

   $\frac{5}{8} + \frac{3}{4} + \frac{7}{8}$ = an overall gain of $2\frac{1}{4}$

6. Open a current newspaper to the section where stock prices on the New York Stock Exchange are listed. Find these same three stocks: BethStl, GnMotr, and CocaCl. Write down their value per share. Have they gone up or down since December 1996? Calculate the amount of change. Look at these same stocks in the next business day's newspaper. Have these stocks gone up or down? Your answer may be a fraction, whole number, or mixed number. Indicate the direction of the change by using a plus or minus sign.

   Answers will vary. The stock prices since December 1996 will be up or down according to economic trends, but will probably not show such dramatic changes as seen in the table.

At the New York Stock Exchange, the world's largest, more than one hundred million shares of stocks are traded daily.

Answers

1. Bethlehem Steel: metal for appliances, machinery, buildings, bridges; Coca-Cola: soft drinks; General Motors: cars and trucks

BIBLIOGRAPHY

FOR TEACHERS

Bailey, Jill. *Encyclopedia of the Animal World.* New York, NY: Facts on File, 1989.

Cribb, Joe. *Money.* New York, NY: Knopf, 1990.

Spangler, David. *Math for Real Kids.* Glenview, IL: Good Year Books, 1997.

Parker, Steve. *Electricity.* London, England: Dorling Kindersley, 1992.

FOR STUDENTS

Dunnan, Nancy. *The Stock Market.* Morristown, NJ: Silver Burdett Press, 1990.

McMillan, Bruce. *Penguins at Home.* Burlington, MA: Houghton Mifflin, 1993.

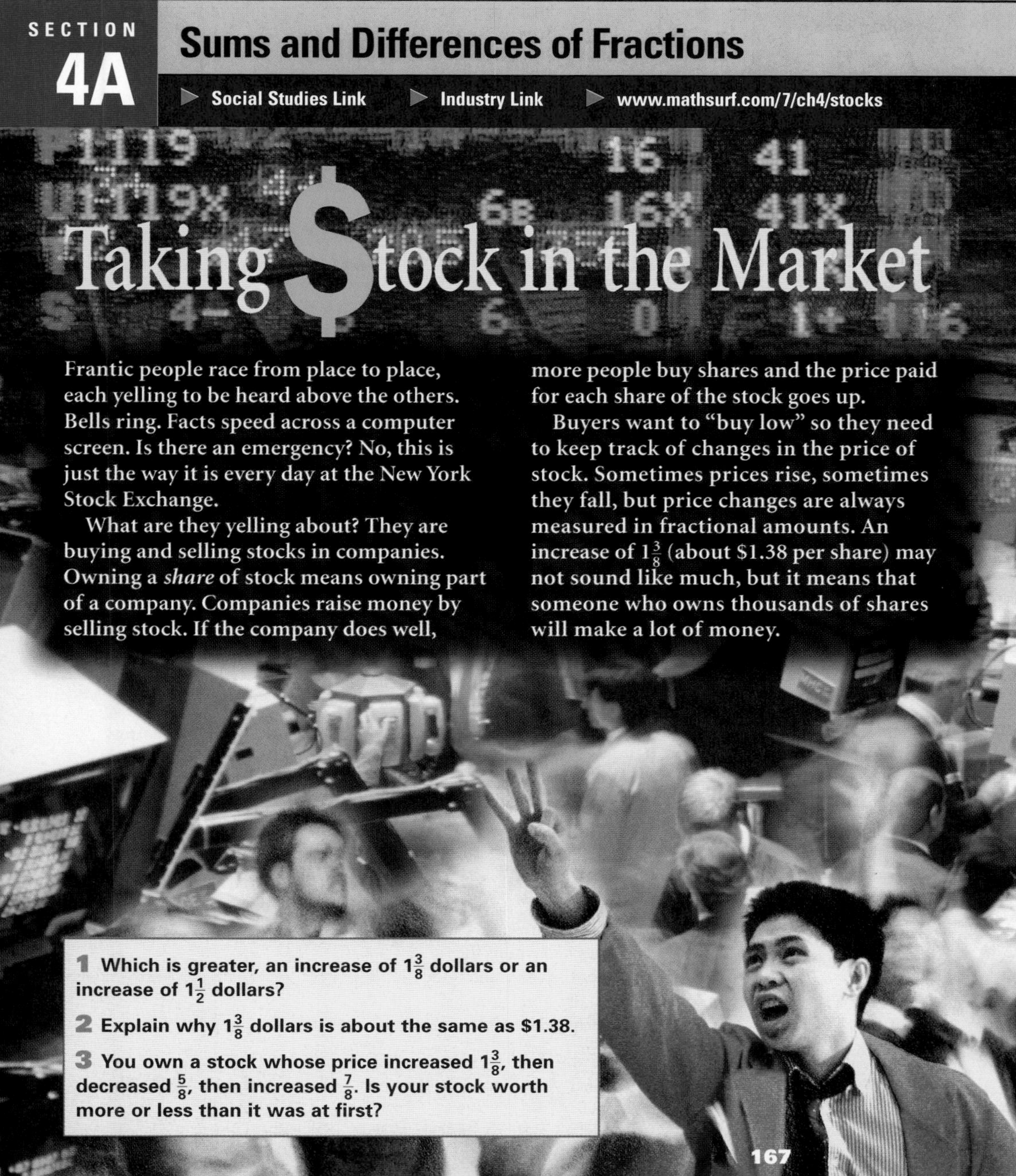

SECTION **4A**

Sums and Differences of Fractions

▶ Social Studies Link ▶ Industry Link ▶ www.mathsurf.com/7/ch4/stocks

Taking $tock in the Market

Frantic people race from place to place, each yelling to be heard above the others. Bells ring. Facts speed across a computer screen. Is there an emergency? No, this is just the way it is every day at the New York Stock Exchange.

What are they yelling about? They are buying and selling stocks in companies. Owning a *share* of stock means owning part of a company. Companies raise money by selling stock. If the company does well, more people buy shares and the price paid for each share of the stock goes up.

Buyers want to "buy low" so they need to keep track of changes in the price of stock. Sometimes prices rise, sometimes they fall, but price changes are always measured in fractional amounts. An increase of $1\frac{3}{8}$ (about \$1.38 per share) may not sound like much, but it means that someone who owns thousands of shares will make a lot of money.

1 Which is greater, an increase of $1\frac{3}{8}$ dollars or an increase of $1\frac{1}{2}$ dollars?

2 Explain why $1\frac{3}{8}$ dollars is about the same as \$1.38.

3 You own a stock whose price increased $1\frac{3}{8}$, then decreased $\frac{5}{8}$, then increased $\frac{7}{8}$. Is your stock worth more or less than it was at first?

167

You may choose to use this project as a performance assessment for the chapter.

Performance Assessment Key

Level 4 Full Accomplishment

Level 3 Substantial Accomplishment

Level 2 Partial Accomplishment

Level 1 Little Accomplishment

Suggested Scoring Rubric

- Five countries are identified and each fraction of the world's total population is reasonable.
- Bar graph is accurate.

- Five countries are identified but students have some difficulty expressing the populations as a fraction of the total.
- Graph and fractions of the total population are acceptable.

- Students have difficulty identifying the countries and expressing their populations as fractions of the total.
- An attempt is made to make a graph and give fractions of the total population.

- Little attempt is made to identify the countries and give fractions.
- Bar graph is not correct and fractions of the total are not given.

Section 4A

Theme: The Stock Market

World Wide Web

If your class has access to the World Wide Web, you might want to use the information found at the Web site address given. The interdisciplinary links relate to the topics discussed in this section.

About the Page

This page introduces the theme of this section, the stock market, and discusses how stocks are bought and sold.

Ask ...

- Do you know anyone who owns shares of stock in a company? If so, has the stock increased or decreased in value?
- How would you find out the price of a share of stock in a company? What would you have to do to buy shares of stock?

Extensions

The following activities do not require access to the World Wide Web.

Social Studies
Have interested students investigate the stock market. Have them find information on its history and on the impact the market has on the country's economy.

Industry
Ask students to investigate the securities industry and how stocks are bought and sold.

Answers for Questions

1. An increase of $1\frac{3}{8}$ dollars.
2. $3 \div 8 = 0.375$, which rounds to 0.38. So, $1\frac{3}{8} \approx 1.38$.
3. More; $1\frac{3}{8} - \frac{5}{8} + \frac{7}{8} = 1\frac{5}{8}$

Connect

On page 183, students will add and subtract fractions and mixed numbers to compare stock prices.

4-1 Lesson Organizer

Objective

- Estimate solutions to problems involving fractions.

Vocabulary

- Mixed number

NCTM Standards

- 1–7, 10, 13

Review

Find each product.

1. $\frac{1}{3}$ of 18 6 2. $\frac{1}{4}$ of 20 5

Estimate each quotient.

3. 58 ÷ 8 7 4. 83 ÷ 9 9

Available on Daily Transparency 4-1

Lesson Link

Have students discuss examples of situations in which they have estimated solutions to decimal problems. Discuss the techniques used in the estimations.

1 Introduce

Explore

The Point
Students explore estimating with fractions by deciding whether fractions are closer to 0, $\frac{1}{2}$, or 1.

Ongoing Assessment
If students are having difficulty deciding into which category each stock should be placed, suggest that they draw a number line from 0 to 1 with $\frac{1}{2}$ marked also, and then write $\frac{1}{2}$ as $\frac{4}{8}$, $\frac{8}{16}$, $\frac{16}{32}$, and $\frac{32}{64}$. Then have them place the amounts the stocks rose on the number line.

4-1 Estimating: Fractions and Mixed Numbers

You'll Learn ...

- to estimate solutions to problems involving fractions

... How It's Used

Investment managers must be able to check the progress of stocks and bonds as prices rise and fall by fractional amounts.

Vocabulary

mixed number

Lesson Link You have estimated solutions to decimal problems. Now you'll see how you can estimate solutions to problems involving fractions. ◄

Explore Estimating with Fractions

Super Stocks

Mary, an investor on the American Stock Exchange, found that eight of her stocks rose in price yesterday. She decided to sell the stocks that were up by an amount close to 0, to hold on to the stocks that were up by close to $\frac{1}{2}$, and to buy more of the stocks that were up by an amount close to 1. Here are the stocks and the amounts the stocks rose.

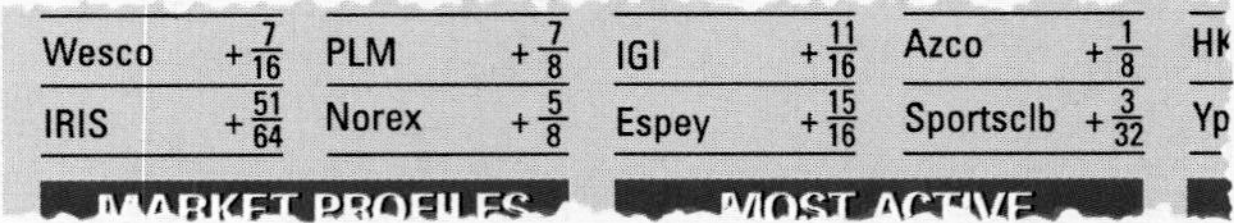

Wesco	$+\frac{7}{16}$	PLM	$+\frac{7}{8}$	IGI	$+\frac{11}{16}$	Azco	$+\frac{1}{8}$	HK
IRIS	$+\frac{51}{64}$	Norex	$+\frac{5}{8}$	Espey	$+\frac{15}{16}$	Sportsclb	$+\frac{3}{32}$	Yp

1. Into which category should Mary put each of the eight stocks? Explain your reasoning.
2. Mary has another stock that was up $\frac{1}{4}$. What category should it go into? Is there only one answer? Explain.
3. Suppose a stock is up by an amount with a denominator of 16. How can you use the numerator to tell what category it is in?

Learn Estimating: Fractions and Mixed Numbers

One way to estimate sums and differences of fractions is to round the fractions to either 0, $\frac{1}{2}$, or 1 and add or subtract mentally. You can use a number line to help decide if a fraction is closer to 0, $\frac{1}{2}$, or 1.

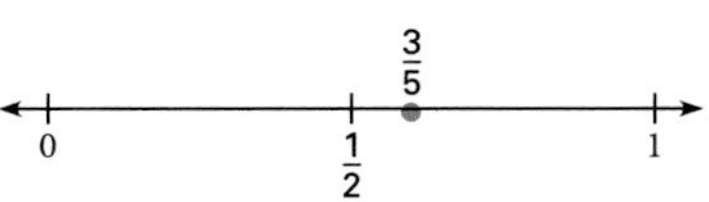

MEETING INDIVIDUAL NEEDS

Resources

4-1 Practice
4-1 Reteaching
4-1 Problem Solving
4-1 Enrichment
4-1 Daily Transparency
  Problem of the Day
  Review
  Quick Quiz

Wide World of Mathematics Middle School: Hurricane Prediction

Learning Modalities

Visual Have students use a number line to estimate sums of fractions. Have a student locate the first addend on the number line and estimate the location of the sum.

Social Have students work together in groups to decide on one way that estimation with fractions is like estimation with whole numbers. Have each group report its decision to the class.

Inclusion

Have students use Fraction Bars or other fraction models to represent each fraction in addition problems. By comparing these representations they can see fractions that are close to 1 or to $\frac{1}{2}$ before estimating answers. Have students add new vocabulary to reference book.

Example 1

A recording company whose stock trades on the New York Stock Exchange was up $\frac{3}{8}$ on Monday and up $\frac{15}{16}$ on Tuesday. Estimate the total amount the stock was up at the end of the two days.

Use a number line to round each fraction to 0, $\frac{1}{2}$, or 1.

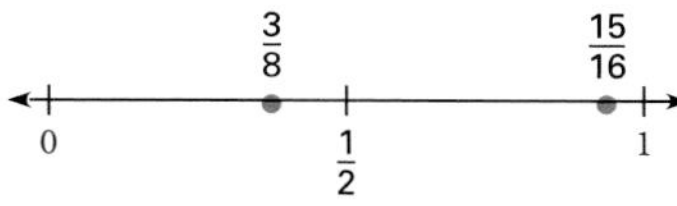

Since $\frac{3}{8}$ is close to $\frac{1}{2}$, it rounds to $\frac{1}{2}$. Since $\frac{15}{16}$ is close to 1, it rounds to 1.

$\frac{3}{8} + \frac{15}{16}$ is about $\frac{1}{2} + 1 = 1\frac{1}{2}$.

The stock was up about $1\frac{1}{2}$.

Try It

Estimate.

a. $\frac{4}{9} + \frac{2}{11} \approx \frac{1}{2}$ **b.** $\frac{8}{10} - \frac{3}{14} \approx 1$ **c.** $\frac{7}{9} + \frac{12}{15} \approx 2$

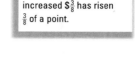

Brokers say a stock whose price has increased $\$\frac{3}{8}$ has risen $\frac{3}{8}$ of a point.

ESTIMATION

When the numerator and denominator are close in value, the fraction is close to 1. When the numerator is about half the denominator, the fraction is close to $\frac{1}{2}$. When the numerator is much smaller than the denominator, the fraction is close to 0.

Recall that a **mixed number** is made up of a whole number and a fraction. $4\frac{1}{2}$ and $2\frac{2}{7}$ are mixed numbers. You can estimate sums, differences, and products of mixed numbers by rounding to the nearest whole number.

Example 2

Estimate: $4\frac{3}{16} + 7\frac{6}{10}$

$4\frac{3}{16}$ rounds to 4. $7\frac{6}{10}$ rounds to 8.

$4\frac{3}{16} + 7\frac{6}{10} \approx 4 + 8 = 12$

Try It

Estimate.

a. $3\frac{5}{12} + 5\frac{9}{11} \approx 9$ **b.** $9\frac{2}{15} - 4\frac{7}{11} \approx 4$ **c.** $7\frac{3}{21} \cdot 2\frac{9}{14} \approx 21$

For Groups That Finish Early

Write the eight factors all with a common denominator and order from least to greatest.

$\frac{6}{64}, \frac{8}{64}, \frac{28}{64}, \frac{40}{64}, \frac{44}{64}, \frac{51}{64}, \frac{56}{64}, \frac{60}{64}$

Follow Up

Have students discuss how they decided which category to put each stock into for Step 1. Have volunteers discuss their answers to Steps 2 and 3.

Answers for Explore

1. Sell: Azco, Sportsclb; Rise was close to 0.

   Hold: Wesco, IGI, Norex; Rise is close to $\frac{1}{2}$.

   Buy: PLM, IRIS, and Espey; Rise is close to 1.
2. Either sell or hold. $\frac{1}{4}$ is exactly halfway between 0 and $\frac{1}{2}$.
3. Sell if numerator is 1, 2, or 3; hold if numerator is 5 through 11; Buy if numerator is 13 or greater. Either sell or hold if numerator is 4, and either hold or buy if numerator is 12.

2 Teach

Learn

Alternate Examples

1. A stock was up $\frac{5}{8}$ on Wednesday and up $\frac{7}{16}$ on Thursday.

   Estimate the total amount the stock was up at the end of the two days.

   Use a number line to round each fraction to 0, $\frac{1}{2}$, or 1.

   Since $\frac{5}{8}$ and $\frac{7}{16}$ are both close to $\frac{1}{2}$, they both round to $\frac{1}{2}$.

   $\frac{5}{8} + \frac{7}{16}$ is about $\frac{1}{2} + \frac{1}{2} = 1$.

   The stock was up about 1.
2. Estimate $3\frac{5}{8} + 6\frac{3}{10}$.

   $3\frac{5}{8}$ rounds to 4.

   $6\frac{3}{10}$ rounds to 6.

   $3\frac{5}{8} + 6\frac{3}{10} \approx 4 + 6 = 10$

MATH EVERY DAY

Problem of the Day

Draw a picture that shows how you can separate this wheel of cheese into 8 equal pieces by making only 3 cuts.

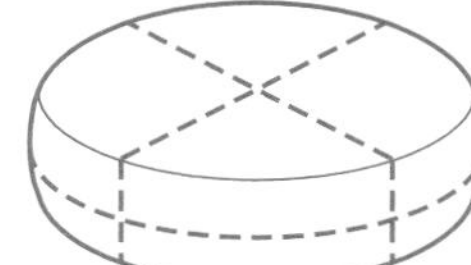

Available on Daily Transparency 4-1

An Extension is provided in the transparency package.

Fact of the Day

Before stock exchanges were formed in the United States, stocks and bonds were auctioned or were sold by brokers who often worked in coffeehouses.

Mental Math

Do these mentally.

1. 200 ÷ 40 5
2. 2000 ÷ 400 5
3. 20,000 ÷ 4,000 5
4. 2 ÷ 0.4 5

Alternate Examples

3. Estimate $40\frac{3}{4} \div 5\frac{7}{8}$.

   First round $5\frac{7}{8}$ to 6.
   Both 36 and 42 are compatible with 6, so round $40\frac{3}{4}$ to 42, which is closer.
   $40\frac{3}{4} \div 5\frac{7}{8} \approx 42 \div 6 = 7$

4. If gold sells for $425.40 per ounce, estimate the value of $\frac{1}{2}$ ounce of gold. Determine if the estimate is too high or too low.
   $\$425.40 \times \frac{1}{2} \approx \$400 \times \frac{1}{2} = \$200$
   The value of the gold is about $200. The estimate is too low because $425.40 was rounded to $400, a smaller number.

3 Practice and Assess

Check

Be sure students realize that when the dividend remains the same and the divisor increases, the quotient decreases. Have students consider examples such as $12 \div 2 = 6$, $12 \div 3 = 4$, and $12 \div 4 = 3$ to help understand this.

Answers for Check Your Understanding

1. Round $3\frac{7}{9}$ to 4 and $1\frac{3}{4}$ to 2, then subtract. Your estimate is 2.
2. Low. By rounding up to 2 you have increased the divisor so the quotient will decrease.
3. A number line can show you whether a fraction is closer to 0, $\frac{1}{2}$, or 1.
4. $\frac{1}{2}$; Round $9\frac{3}{8}$ to 9; When working with fractions, round to 0, $\frac{1}{2}$, or 1. When working with mixed numbers, round to the nearest whole number.

▶ Language Link

Many words start with the prefix *com-*. It comes from the Latin word *cum,* which means "with" or "together." *Compatible* means "going together well."

You can use compatible numbers to estimate quotients of mixed numbers. Round the divisor first, then replace the dividend with the nearest compatible number. You can also use compatible numbers to estimate products of fractions and whole numbers.

Examples

3 Estimate: $43\frac{2}{3} \div 8\frac{2}{15}$

First round $8\frac{2}{15}$ to 8.

Both 40 and 48 are compatible with 8, so replace $43\frac{2}{3}$ with 40, which is closer.

$43\frac{2}{3} \div 8\frac{2}{15} \approx 40 \div 8 = 5$

4 Precious metals like gold, silver, and platinum sell on the options market. If gold sells for $392.50 an ounce, estimate the value of $\frac{1}{4}$ ounce of gold. Determine if the estimate is too high or too low.

$\$392.50 \times \frac{1}{4} \approx \$400 \times \frac{1}{4} = \$100$

The value of the gold is about $100. The estimate is high because $392.50 was rounded to $400, a greater number.

Gold ingot

Try It

Estimate.

a. $23\frac{4}{9} \div 5\frac{3}{13} \approx 5$ **b.** $32\frac{4}{5} \div 6\frac{3}{4} \approx 5$ **c.** $21\frac{7}{8} \times 8\frac{1}{6} \approx 176$

Check

1. Explain how you would use rounding to estimate $3\frac{7}{9} - 1\frac{3}{4}$.
2. $20 \div 1\frac{3}{4}$ is about $20 \div 2 = 10$. Is the estimate of 10 for the quotient high or low? Explain.
3. How can you use a number line to help round a fraction?
4. To what number would you round $\frac{3}{8}$ if you were adding $\frac{13}{14}$ and $\frac{3}{8}$? To what number would you round $\frac{3}{8}$ if you were adding $4\frac{13}{14}$ and $9\frac{3}{8}$? If your answers to these questions are different, explain why.

MEETING MIDDLE SCHOOL CLASSROOM NEEDS

Tips from Middle School Teachers

I try to stress reasonable answers to problems involving fractions and mixed numbers. It is a good idea to have students give a range for the answer before actually computing. For example, the answer to $5\frac{6}{15} + 7\frac{9}{15}$ is between 12 and 14.

Cooperative Learning

Have pairs of students write fraction exercises and estimate the results. Then have them exchange problems, make estimates, and compare their answers.

History Connection

Philadelphia was the nation's capital when the first U.S. stock exchange was opened there in 1790.

Practice and Apply

Getting Started Round each fraction to 0, $\frac{1}{2}$, or 1.

1. $\frac{3}{8}$ $\frac{1}{2}$ **2.** $\frac{7}{8}$ 1 **3.** $\frac{1}{5}$ 0 **4.** $\frac{3}{5}$ $\frac{1}{2}$ **5.** $\frac{1}{8}$ 0

Estimate each sum or difference.

6. $\frac{1}{8} + \frac{2}{5} \approx \frac{1}{2}$ **7.** $\frac{6}{7} - \frac{3}{8} \approx \frac{1}{2}$ **8.** $\frac{2}{3} + \frac{1}{9} \approx 1$ **9.** $\frac{9}{10} - \frac{7}{8} \approx 0$ **10.** $\frac{3}{16} - \frac{1}{8} \approx 0$

11. $\frac{3}{8} + \frac{3}{7} \approx 1$ **12.** $\frac{7}{8} + \frac{12}{13} \approx 2$ **13.** $\frac{3}{4} - \frac{3}{8} \approx \frac{1}{2}$ **14.** $\frac{5}{6} + \frac{1}{4} \approx 1$ **15.** $\frac{4}{5} - \frac{1}{8} \approx 1$

Round each mixed number to the nearest whole number, then estimate each sum or difference.

16. $3\frac{3}{4} + 2\frac{1}{9} \approx 6$ **17.** $5\frac{4}{10} + 6\frac{5}{7} \approx 12$ **18.** $12\frac{4}{5} - 7\frac{2}{3} \approx 5$ **19.** $11\frac{2}{5} - 9\frac{9}{10} \approx 1$

20. $6\frac{1}{4} + 1\frac{5}{9} \approx 8$ **21.** $10\frac{3}{4} + 3\frac{1}{6} \approx 14$ **22.** $5\frac{3}{5} - 4\frac{1}{3} \approx 2$ **23.** $15\frac{4}{5} - 11\frac{7}{8} \approx 4$

Use compatible numbers to estimate each product or quotient.

24. $17 \times \frac{1}{3} \approx 6$ **25.** $18\frac{7}{8} \div 5\frac{1}{6} \approx 4$ **26.** $\frac{1}{5} \times 31 \approx 6$ **27.** $52\frac{4}{11} \div 6\frac{1}{2} \approx 9$

28. $23 \times \frac{1}{2} \approx 11$ or 12 **29.** $13\frac{3}{4} \div 2\frac{1}{3} \approx 7$ **30.** $\frac{1}{3} \times 11 \approx 4$ **31.** $61\frac{4}{5} \div 7\frac{1}{5} \approx 9$

32. The length of a chicken egg can be $1\frac{15}{16}$ in. The length of an ostrich egg can be $6\frac{3}{8}$ in. Use rounding to estimate the difference between the lengths of these eggs. ≈ 4 in.

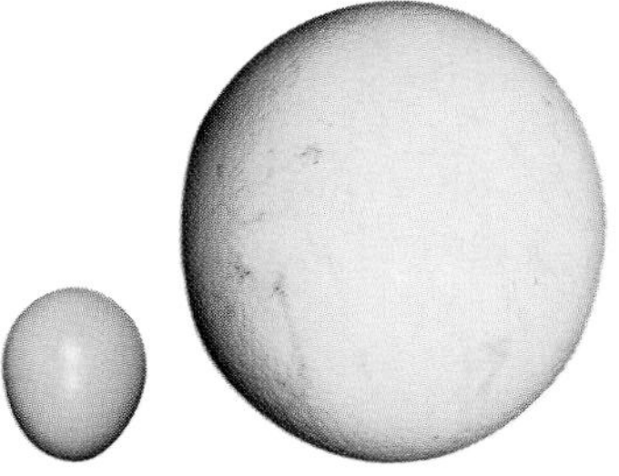

33. An ostrich can weigh up to 280 lb. If a chicken weighs $8\frac{1}{2}$ lb, use rounding to estimate how many times heavier the ostrich is than the chicken.
≈ 30 times

PRACTICE 4-1

4-1 Exercises and Applications

Assignment Guide

- **Basic**
  1–10, 20–27, 32, 34–36, 39–46
- **Average**
  3–10, 12–26 evens, 32–36, 39–46
- **Enriched**
  4–9, 11–23 odds, 28–44

Exercise Notes

Exercise 27

Extension Have students discuss why 48 ÷ 6 is a closer estimate than 49 ÷ 7. For 48 ÷ 6, both numbers have been rounded to smaller numbers, keeping the estimated quotient close to the exact answer.

For 49 ÷ 7, rounding $52\frac{4}{11}$ to a smaller number and $6\frac{1}{2}$ to a larger number produces a smaller estimated quotient.

Exercise 33

Science Although the ostrich is the largest of existing birds, it cannot fly. It is now found in the wild only in East Africa.

PRACTICE

Name ______________________

Practice 4-1

Estimating: Fractions and Mixed Numbers

Estimate each sum or difference.

1. $\frac{3}{8} + \frac{2}{3}$ 1 2. $\frac{7}{8} - \frac{1}{2}$ $\frac{1}{2}$ 3. $\frac{3}{16} + \frac{11}{12}$ 1 4. $\frac{9}{10} - \frac{3}{8}$ $\frac{1}{2}$

5. $\frac{2}{3} - \frac{3}{8}$ 0 6. $\frac{5}{6} + \frac{1}{3}$ $1\frac{1}{2}$ 7. $\frac{4}{5} - \frac{1}{7}$ 1 8. $\frac{1}{5} + \frac{7}{15}$ $\frac{1}{2}$

Round each mixed number to the nearest whole number, then estimate each sum or difference.

9. $2\frac{7}{8} + 3\frac{1}{4}$ 6 10. $12\frac{5}{8} - 3\frac{4}{5}$ 9 11. $7\frac{5}{6} + 4\frac{1}{3}$ 12 12. $12\frac{2}{5} - 8\frac{3}{7}$ 4

13. $15\frac{2}{3} - 7\frac{1}{6}$ 9 14. $11\frac{1}{2} + 9\frac{3}{5}$ 22 15. $10\frac{1}{4} - 5\frac{1}{2}$ 4 16. $8\frac{1}{5} + 6\frac{5}{7}$ 15

17. $12\frac{7}{8} + 6\frac{4}{5}$ 20 18. $14\frac{1}{8} - 2\frac{3}{4}$ 11 19. $13\frac{3}{8} + 2\frac{1}{3}$ 15 20. $14\frac{2}{9} - 9\frac{9}{10}$ 4

Use compatible numbers to estimate each product or quotient.

21. $8\frac{1}{3} \times \frac{1}{2}$ 4 22. $23\frac{1}{6} \div 7\frac{1}{2}$ 3 23. $\frac{1}{6} \times 40\frac{2}{3}$ 7 24. $35\frac{2}{3} \div 4\frac{7}{8}$ 7

25. $43\frac{1}{2} \div 4\frac{1}{2}$ 11 26. $\frac{1}{3} \times 32\frac{1}{4}$ 11 27. $73\frac{4}{11} \div 6\frac{1}{4}$ 12 28. $62\frac{1}{2} \times \frac{1}{8}$ 8

29. $\frac{1}{4} \times 35\frac{1}{7}$ 9 30. $28\frac{6}{7} \div 5\frac{2}{3}$ 5 31. $41\frac{1}{7} \times \frac{1}{5}$ 8 32. $83\frac{3}{8} \div 11\frac{9}{16}$ 7

33. The hypsilophodon was about $2\frac{1}{3}$ m long, and the geranosaurus was about $1\frac{1}{5}$ m long. Use rounding to estimate the difference between the length of these dinosaurs. About 1 m

34. Tim's bucket can hold up to $12\frac{1}{3}$ quarts of liquid. If it is $\frac{1}{3}$ full of water, estimate the number of quarts of water in the bucket. 4 quarts

RETEACHING

Name ______________________

Alternative Lesson 4-1

Estimating: Fractions and Mixed Numbers

One way to estimate sums and differences of fractions is to round the fractions to either 0, $\frac{1}{2}$, or 1 and add or subtract mentally. A **mixed number** is made up of a whole number and a fraction. You can estimate sums, differences, and products of mixed numbers by rounding to the nearest whole number.

Example 1

Estimate $\frac{5}{6} + \frac{3}{8}$ by rounding each fraction to 0, $\frac{1}{2}$, or 1.

Draw a line to divide each grid in half. Use the shaded portions of the grids to estimate each fraction.

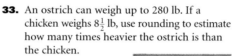

$\frac{5}{6}$ is about 1. $\frac{3}{8}$ is about $\frac{1}{2}$.

Then add your estimates. $1 + \frac{1}{2} = 1\frac{1}{2}$

Since $1 + \frac{1}{2} = 1\frac{1}{2}$, $\frac{5}{6} + \frac{3}{8}$ is about $1\frac{1}{2}$.

Try It Estimate each sum or difference. You may draw grids to help.

a. $\frac{9}{10} - \frac{1}{6}$ $\frac{9}{10}$ is about 1. $\frac{1}{6}$ is about 0.

Since 1 − 0 = 1, $\frac{9}{10} - \frac{1}{6}$ is about 1.

b. $\frac{3}{4} + \frac{5}{8}$ $1\frac{1}{2}$ c. $\frac{5}{6} - \frac{3}{5}$ $\frac{1}{2}$

Example 2

Estimate $6\frac{9}{10} - 4\frac{1}{8}$ by rounding each mixed number to the nearest whole number.

If the fraction part is $\frac{1}{2}$ or greater, round to the next whole number. Since $\frac{9}{10}$ is more than $\frac{1}{2}$, round $6\frac{9}{10}$ to 7.

If the fraction part is less than $\frac{1}{2}$, round to the given whole number. Since $\frac{1}{8}$ is less than $\frac{1}{2}$, round $4\frac{1}{8}$ to 4.

Then subtract your estimates. $7 - 4 = 3$

Since $7 - 4 = 3$, $6\frac{9}{10} - 4\frac{1}{8}$ is about 3.

Try It Estimate each sum or difference.

d. $5\frac{1}{4} + 2\frac{7}{8}$ $5\frac{1}{4}$ is about 5. $2\frac{7}{8}$ is about 3.

Since 5 + 3 = 8, $5\frac{1}{4} + 2\frac{7}{8}$ is about 8.

e. $9\frac{1}{3} - 3\frac{7}{8}$ 5 f. $7\frac{4}{5} + 3\frac{2}{3}$ 12

g. $4\frac{9}{10} + 9\frac{3}{8}$ 14 h. $14\frac{7}{8} - 13\frac{3}{7}$ 2

Reteaching

Activity

Materials: Fraction Bars or other fraction models.

Use fraction models to decide whether each fraction is closer to 0, $\frac{1}{2}$, or 1.

1. $\frac{1}{3}$ $\frac{1}{2}$ 2. $\frac{3}{5}$ $\frac{1}{2}$

3. $\frac{7}{8}$ 1 4. $\frac{2}{3}$ $\frac{1}{2}$

5. $\frac{1}{6}$ 0 6. $\frac{3}{8}$ $\frac{1}{2}$

Exercise Notes

■ Exercises 39–40

Geography In the decade of the 1980s, the combined population increases in California, Florida, and Texas totaled 54% of the total increase in national population. This was the first time in census history that only 3 states accounted for more than half of the growth in the national population.

Exercise Answers

36. Possible answer: High. When you decrease the divisor, you increase the quotient.

37. Possible answer: Yes; $\approx (5 \times 10) + (5 \times 10) = \$100$. Since you rounded up $\frac{1}{4}$ and down $\frac{1}{8}$, the estimate is an overestimate, so the stock will cost less than \$100.

38. Possible answer: Judging how much gas will be needed to fill your tank.

Alternate Assessment

Interview Have students tell you orally how to do one of the following:

- round a fraction to 0, $\frac{1}{2}$, or 1.
- estimate the sum or difference of two mixed numbers.
- estimate the quotient of two mixed numbers.

➤ Quick Quiz

Estimate each result.

1. $\frac{1}{6} + \frac{3}{4}$ 1
2. $7\frac{2}{3} - 3\frac{1}{4}$ 5
3. $14 \cdot \frac{1}{5}$ 3
4. $25\frac{1}{5} \div 5\frac{9}{10}$ 4

Available on Daily Transparency 4-1

PROBLEM SOLVING 4-1

34. **Test Prep** Use compatible numbers to find the best estimate for the following product, then tell whether the estimate is high or low: $\frac{1}{7} \times 40$. **D**

Ⓐ 5; low Ⓑ 5; high Ⓒ 6; low Ⓓ 6; high

35. **Measurement** About how many $6\frac{3}{4}$-inch pieces can be cut from a board measuring $37\frac{1}{5}$ inches? Estimate to find your answer. GPS **≈ 5 pieces**

Problem Solving and Reasoning

36. **Communicate** $45 \div 9\frac{1}{3}$ is about $45 \div 9 = 5$. Is the estimate of 5 for the quotient high or low? Explain.

37. **Critical Thinking** A share of Stock A is selling for $5\frac{1}{8}$. A share of Stock B is selling for $4\frac{3}{4}$. Suppose you have \$100. Can you buy 10 shares of Stock A and 10 shares of Stock B? Estimate to find your answer. Explain how you know your answer is correct.

38. Journal Write about a situation in which an estimated sum or an estimated difference might be more useful than an exact calculation.

Prices on Tokyo Stock Exchange

Mixed Review

Use the bar graph to answer each question. *[Lesson 1-1]*

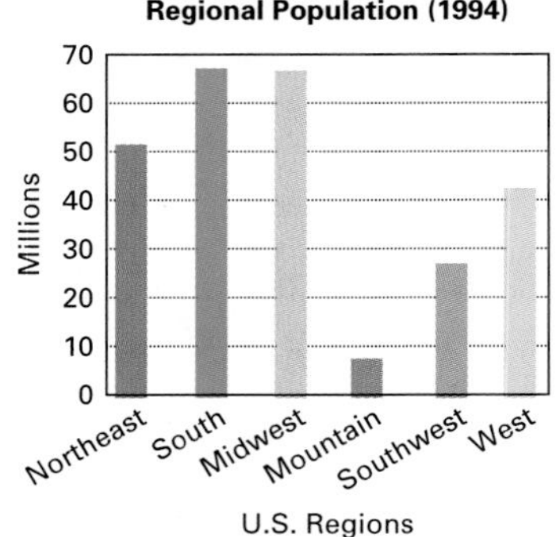

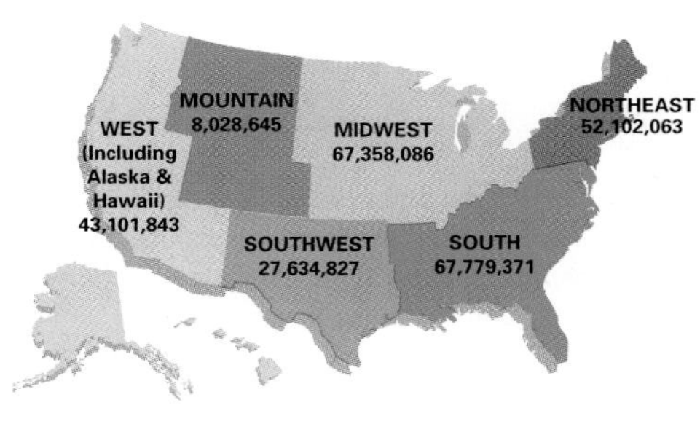

39. Which region has the highest population? The lowest? **South; Mountain**

40. Which two regions are closest in population? **South and MIdwest**

Use < or > to compare the numbers. *[Lesson 3-1]*

41. 8.30 ☐> 8.299 **42.** 15.40 ☐< 16.39 **43.** 6.825 ☐> 6.725

44. 8.638 ☐< 8.647 **45.** 0.078 ☐< 0.780 **46.** 18.05 ☐< 18.051

172 *Chapter 4 • Operations with Fractions*

PROBLEM SOLVING

Name ______________

Guided Problem Solving 4-1

GPS PROBLEM 35, STUDENT PAGE 172

About how many $6\frac{3}{4}$-inch pieces can be cut from a board measuring $37\frac{1}{5}$ inches? Estimate to find your answer.

Possible answers: Items 6–9.

— Understand —

1. What are you asked to do? Find how many $6\frac{3}{4}$-inch pieces can be cut from a $37\frac{1}{5}$-inch board.
2. What is the length of the board? $37\frac{1}{5}$ inches.
3. What is the length of each piece that will be cut from the board? $6\frac{3}{4}$ inches.

— Plan —

4. What operation will you use to find the answer? Division.
5. Will you estimate using rounded or compatible numbers? Compatible.

— Solve —

6. What number will you use for $6\frac{3}{4}$? 7 For $37\frac{1}{5}$? 35
7. Write a number sentence to find the answer $35 \div 7 = 5$
8. Write a sentence to tell about how many pieces can be cut. About five $6\frac{3}{4}$-inch pieces can be cut from a $37\frac{1}{5}$-inch board.

— Look Back —

9. Explain how you can draw a diagram to check your answer. Draw a number line divided into $\frac{1}{4}$ sections. Count off as many $6\frac{3}{4}$ pieces as possible in $37\frac{1}{5}$.

SOLVE ANOTHER PROBLEM

About how many $8\frac{1}{8}$-inch pieces can be cut from a board measuring $67\frac{1}{2}$ inches? Estimate to find your answer. About 8 pieces.

ENRICHMENT

Name ______________

Extend Your Thinking 4-1

Decision Making Poss. answers: Items 2-6

Mr. Jones wants to arrange 24 desks into groups so that students can work together. He wants each group to be the same size.

1. What are the different sized groups Mr. Jones can use? 2 groups of 12, 3 of 8, 4 of 6, 6 of 4, 8 of 3, 12 of 2.
2. What does Mr. Jones need to consider when he moves the desks into the groups? Whether or not all students can see the chalkboard, all group members can communicate, if there is enough aisle space.
3. The current project is a class debate. There will be four teams. Show two ways that Mr. Jones can arrange the desks so that students on each team will be sitting together.

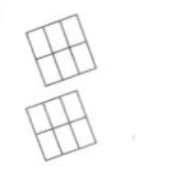

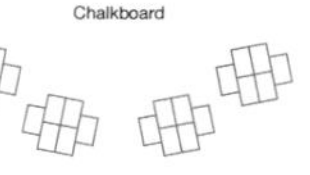

4. Which of the ways you found in Question 3 is the best? Why? The second way because students can talk among themselves and plan better.
5. For the next project, each group will perform a skit showing a typical day in the life of a teenager in another country. What would be the best size groups for this project? Explain. Groups of eight, so that there will be sufficient people to research the topic, and write and act in the skit.
6. How can Mr. Jones arrange the desks for students to work on the skit? Why is this the best seating arrangement?

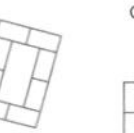
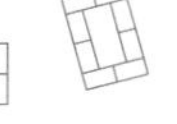

It keeps the groups far enough apart. However, some students will have to move to see the chalkboard.

Adding and Subtracting Fractions

4-2

▶ Lesson Link You've estimated sums and differences of fractions. Now you'll find exact sums and differences of fractions and solve equations that contain fractions. ◀

Explore Adding Fractions

Fraction Action

Materials: Graph paper, Colored pencils

Adding Two Fractions

- Draw three rectangles on graph paper. Use the denominators to determine the length and width of the rectangles.
- In the first rectangle, color the number of squares equal to the first fraction.
- In the second rectangle, color the number of squares equal to the second fraction.
- In the third rectangle, color one square for each colored square in the first two rectangles. Describe the result.

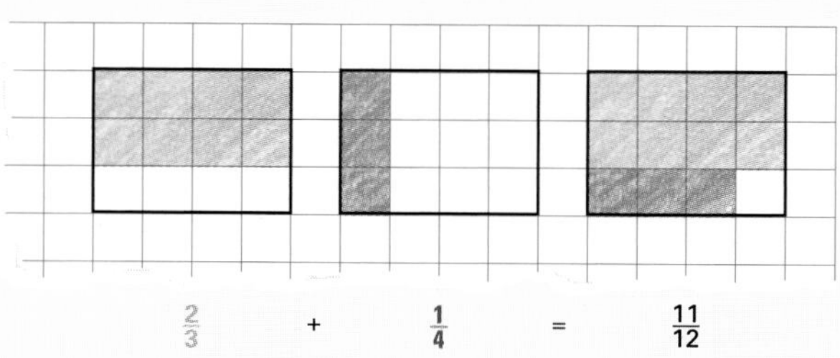

$\frac{2}{3} + \frac{1}{4} = \frac{11}{12}$

1. Model each sum.

a. $\frac{1}{2}+\frac{2}{5}$ **b.** $\frac{2}{5}+\frac{1}{3}$ **c.** $\frac{1}{4}+\frac{3}{5}$ **d.** $\frac{1}{2}+\frac{1}{3}$

2. How are the denominators of the fractions that are added related to the denominators of your answers?

3. Does $\frac{1}{4}+\frac{1}{5}$ have the same answer as $\frac{1}{5}+\frac{1}{4}$? Explain.

4. How is adding two fractions similar to adding two decimals?

You'll Learn ...

- to find sums and differences of fractions
- to solve equations involving fractions

... How It's Used

Fragrance manufacturers have to add fractional amounts of different flower essences when developing new perfumes.

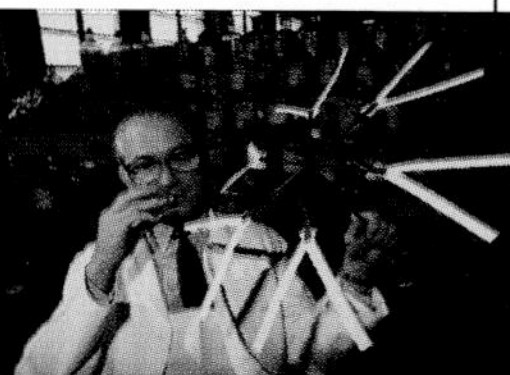

Vocabulary

least common denominator (LCD)

MEETING INDIVIDUAL NEEDS

Resources

- 4-2 Practice
- 4-2 Reteaching
- 4-2 Problem Solving
- 4-2 Enrichment
- 4-2 Daily Transparency
  - Problem of the Day
  - Review
  - Quick Quiz
- Teaching Tool Transparencies 2, 3, 7
- Lesson Enhancement Transparency 13
- Technology Master 14

Learning Modalities

Verbal Have students write several different word problems that would be solved by finding $\frac{1}{2}+\frac{1}{4}$.

Kinesthetic Have a group of 6 students sit at the front of the class. Have parts of the group stand to show $\frac{1}{2}$ of the group and $\frac{1}{6}$ of the group. Have the class discuss what part of the group is $\frac{1}{2}+\frac{1}{6}$.

Challenge

Find three unit fractions (fractions with numerator of 1) whose sum is 1. Find four unit fractions whose sum is 1. Possible answers: $\frac{1}{2}+\frac{1}{3}+\frac{1}{6}=1$; $\frac{1}{2}+\frac{1}{4}+\frac{1}{6}+\frac{1}{12}=1$

4-2 Lesson Organizer

Objectives

- Find sums and differences of fractions.
- Solve equations involving fractions.

Vocabulary

- Least common denominator (LCD)

Materials

- Explore: Graph paper, colored pencils

NCTM Standards

- 1–4, 6, 7, 9, 10

► Review

Find the LCM of each pair of numbers.

1. 4, 8 8
2. 6, 9 18
3. 8, 9 72
3. 12,16 48

Available on Daily Transparency 4-2

1 Introduce

Explore

You may wish to use Lesson Enhancement Transparency 13 and Teaching Tool Transparency 7: $\frac{1}{4}$-Inch Graph Paper with **Explore.**

The Point

Students explore adding fractions by modeling sums on graph paper. Students will discover that they can generate a common denominator by multiplying the denominators of the fractions in a sum.

Ongoing Assessment

Check to see that students are drawing rectangles with the correct dimensions.

For Groups That Finish Early

Use rectangles to find $\frac{1}{2}+\frac{1}{4}$ in two different ways. Students might use rectangles with 24 squares or 48 squares.

Answers for Explore on next page.

Answers for Explore

1. See page C6.
2. The denominator of the answer is the product of the two denominators of the addends.
3. Yes. Addition is commutative.
4. When adding fractions, you must have the same denominator. When adding decimals, you add tenths to tenths, hundredths to hundredths, and so on.

2 Teach

Learn

Discuss examples of everyday uses for addition of fractions, such as stock reports, cooking, sewing, or weighing items when shopping.

Alternate Examples

1. Add. Rewrite in lowest terms.

$\frac{2}{9} + \frac{4}{9}$

The denominators are the same, so add the numerators.

$\frac{2}{9} + \frac{4}{9} = \frac{2+4}{9}$

$= \frac{6}{9}$

Rewrite in lowest terms by dividing the numerator and denominator by 3.

$= \frac{6 \div 3}{9 \div 3}$

$= \frac{2}{3}$

Learn Adding and Subtracting Fractions

To add or subtract fractions, think of each fraction as a portion of a whole.

In the model, each fraction gives the portion of a whole circle that is shaded. Each denominator gives the number of equal parts into which the circle is divided.

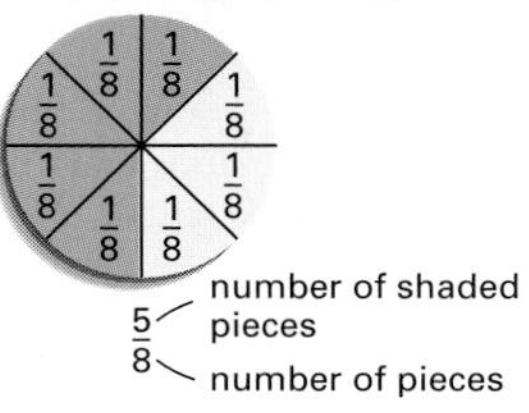

Each numerator gives the number of equal parts that are shaded.

ADDING OR SUBTRACTING FRACTIONS WITH THE SAME DENOMINATOR

- Add or subtract their numerators.
- Write the sum or difference over the denominator.
- Rewrite in lowest terms.

Remember

You can find the LCM by listing both sets of multiples until you find the first match.

[Page 141]

If the denominators are different, the fractions need to be rewritten so that they have a common denominator. The **least common denominator (LCD)** is the least common multiple (LCM) of the denominators.

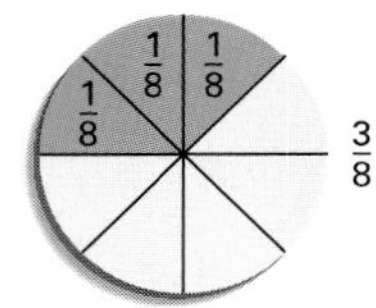

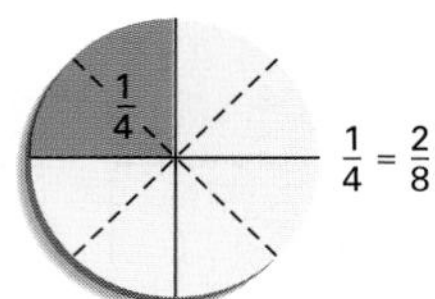

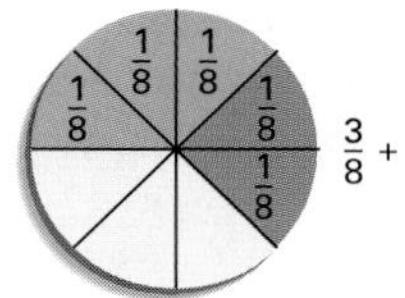

ADDING OR SUBTRACTING FRACTIONS WITH DIFFERENT DENOMINATORS

- Rewrite the fractions using the LCD.
- Add or subtract.
- Rewrite in lowest terms.

Example 1

Add. Rewrite in lowest terms. $\frac{1}{10} + \frac{3}{10}$

$\frac{1}{10} + \frac{3}{10} = \frac{1+3}{10}$ The denominators are the same, so add the numerators.

$= \frac{4 \div 2}{10 \div 2} = \frac{2}{5}$ Rewrite in lowest terms by dividing the numerator and denominator by 2.

MATH EVERY DAY

Problem of the Day

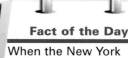

At Jan's birthday party, the celebrants ate half the slices of the huge birthday cake. After playing party games for an hour, they ate 6 more slices of cake. One-eighth of the cake was left. Into how many slices was the birthday cake cut? 16 slices

Available on Daily Transparency 4-2

An Extension is provided in the transparency package.

Fact of the Day

When the New York Stock Exchange was founded, fewer than 100 stocks were traded each day. Most of the trading was in bonds.

Mental Math

Do these mentally.

1. $\frac{2}{5} + \frac{2}{5}$ $\frac{4}{5}$
2. $\frac{2}{7} + \frac{3}{7}$ $\frac{5}{7}$
3. $\frac{1}{9} + \frac{5}{9}$ $\frac{6}{9}$ or $\frac{2}{3}$

Example 2

Subtract. $\frac{1}{4} - \frac{1}{6}$

$\frac{1}{4} - \frac{1}{6} = \frac{1 \cdot 3}{4 \cdot 3} - \frac{1 \cdot 2}{6 \cdot 2}$ — Find the LCD. Multiples of 4 are 4, 8, [12], 16, ... Multiples of 6 are 6, [12], 18, ... Use 12 as the LCD.

$= \frac{3}{12} - \frac{2}{12}$ — Rewrite the fractions using the common denominator.

$= \frac{1}{12}$ — Subtract.

You can solve equations that contain fractions the same way as you solve equations that contain whole numbers and decimals.

Example 3

Lucia bought the stock *MorganF* on the American Stock Exchange yesterday. Today the stock closed at a price of $\frac{5}{8}$, which was down $\frac{1}{16}$. Down $\frac{1}{16}$ represents the loss of $\frac{1}{16}$ of a dollar. At what price did Lucia buy the stock?

Let b = the buying price. — Choose a variable.

$b - \frac{1}{16} = \frac{5}{8}$ — Write an equation.

$b - \frac{1}{16} + \frac{1}{16} = \frac{5}{8} + \frac{1}{16}$ — To undo subtracting $\frac{1}{16}$, add $\frac{1}{16}$ to both sides.

$b = \frac{5 \cdot 2}{8 \cdot 2} + \frac{1}{16}$ — Find the LCD. Multiples of 8: 8, [16], 24, ... Multiples of 16: [16], 32, 48, ... Use 16 as the LCD.

$= \frac{10}{16} + \frac{1}{16}$ — Rewrite with the LCD.

$= \frac{11}{16}$ — Add.

Lucia bought the stock for a price of $\frac{11}{16}$.

Try It

Solve. **a.** $d + \frac{1}{4} = \frac{5}{6}$ $d = \frac{7}{12}$ **b.** $w - \frac{3}{5} = \frac{1}{3}$ $w = \frac{14}{15}$ **c.** $h + \frac{1}{2} = \frac{5}{6}$ $h = \frac{1}{3}$

▶ History Link

The American Stock Exchange was founded in 1921, 129 years later than the New York Stock Exchange, which was founded in 1792. The Philadelphia Stock Exchange is even older; it was founded in 1790.

Study TIP

You can always find a common denominator by multiplying the numerator and denominator of each fraction by the denominator of the other.

MEETING MIDDLE SCHOOL CLASSROOM NEEDS

Tips from Middle School Teachers

Sometimes it is helpful to write fractions using word names. For example: $\frac{3}{\;}$ is *three fourths* and $\frac{1}{\;}$ is *one third.* Relate three fourths + one third to problems like 14 inches + 1 foot. The units are different, making addition difficult unless you can rename using the common unit.

Team Teaching

Work with a music teacher to connect addition of fractions and the sum of note values in a measure.

Cultural Connection

The first European stock exchange was established in Antwerp, Belgium, in 1531. Today there are stock exchanges all over the world. Exchanges exist in Amsterdam, the Netherlands; Frankfurt, Germany; Hong Kong; Johannesburg, South Africa; London; Paris; Sydney, Australia; Tokyo; Toronto, Canada; and Zurich, Switzerland.

2. Subtract. $\frac{2}{\;} - \frac{1}{\;}$

   Find the LCD. Multiples of 3 are 3, 6, 9, ... and multiples of 2 are 2, 4, 6, ... Use 6 as the LCD. Rewrite the fractions using the LCD.

   $\frac{2}{\;} - \frac{1}{\;} = \frac{2 \cdot 2}{\;} - \frac{1 \cdot 3}{\;}$

   $= \frac{4}{\;} - \frac{3}{\;}$

   $= \frac{1}{\;}$

3. A recipe for oatmeal cookies includes $\frac{1}{\;}$ cup of chopped walnuts. This is $\frac{1}{\;}$ cup less than the amount needed for brownies. How many cups of chopped walnuts are needed to make the brownies?

   Let w = the amount of walnuts needed for the brownie recipe.

   $w - \frac{1}{\;} = \frac{1}{\;}$

   $w - \frac{1}{\;} + \frac{1}{\;} = \frac{1}{\;} + \frac{1}{\;}$

   $w = \frac{1}{\;} + \frac{1}{\;}$

   $w = \frac{1 \cdot 2}{\;} + \frac{1}{\;}$

   $= \frac{2}{\;} + \frac{1}{\;}$

   $= \frac{3}{\;}$

   The brownie recipe requires $\frac{3}{\;}$ cup of chopped walnuts.

4-2 Exercises and Applications

Assignment Guide

- Basic
  1–22, 23–31 odds, 32, 33–47 odds
- Average
  1–21 odds, 23–32, 34–56 evens
- Enriched
  1–27 odds, 28–40, 41–55 odds

3 Practice and Assess

Check

Answers for Check Your Understanding

1. Because you can only add like quantities.
2. No; Any common multiple of the 2 denominators will do. Using the LCD keeps the numbers as small as possible and makes calculating easier.

Exercise Notes

Exercise 28

Error Prevention You may want to have students write the equation $\frac{1}{2} + n = 1$ to help them determine the value of n in Part a. This may also help students see that n must be greater than $\frac{1}{2}$ in order for $\frac{1}{2} + n$ to be greater than 1.

Exercise Answers

1. As written 2. Rewritten
3. Rewritten 4. Rewritten
5. As written 6. Rewritten

Reteaching

Activity

Materials: Fraction models

Use fraction models to find each sum.

1. $\frac{1}{2} + \frac{1}{6}$ $\frac{2}{3}$
2. $\frac{3}{8} + \frac{1}{2}$ $\frac{7}{8}$
3. $\frac{1}{4} + \frac{5}{8}$ $\frac{7}{8}$
4. $\frac{1}{2} + \frac{1}{3}$ $\frac{5}{6}$

Check Your Understanding

1. Why do you need common denominators to add or subtract fractions?
2. Is the least common denominator always the only possible denominator to use when you add or subtract fractions? Explain.

PRACTICE 4-2

4-2 Exercises and Applications

Practice and Apply

Getting Started Can each pair of fractions be added or subtracted as written or does it need to be rewritten with a common denominator?

1. $\frac{3}{4}, \frac{1}{4}$ **2.** $\frac{1}{3}, \frac{1}{4}$ **3.** $\frac{2}{3}, \frac{3}{8}$ **4.** $\frac{2}{5}, \frac{2}{7}$ **5.** $\frac{7}{8}, \frac{3}{8}$ **6.** $\frac{3}{4}, \frac{3}{5}$

Find the least common denominator for each pair of fractions.

7. $\frac{2}{3}, \frac{1}{4}$ 12 **8.** $\frac{3}{8}, \frac{3}{4}$ 8 **9.** $\frac{7}{8}, \frac{1}{6}$ 24 **10.** $\frac{1}{3}, \frac{2}{5}$ 15 **11.** $\frac{3}{5}, \frac{1}{4}$ 20 **12.** $\frac{1}{3}, \frac{1}{4}$ 12

Find each sum or difference. Rewrite in lowest terms.

13. $\frac{3}{10} + \frac{5}{10}$ $\frac{4}{5}$ **14.** $\frac{11}{12} - \frac{7}{12}$ $\frac{1}{3}$ **15.** $\frac{3}{16} + \frac{11}{16}$ $\frac{7}{8}$ **16.** $\frac{13}{24} - \frac{5}{24}$ $\frac{1}{3}$ **17.** $\frac{3}{4} - \frac{1}{3}$ $\frac{5}{12}$

18. $\frac{4}{5} - \frac{1}{3}$ $\frac{7}{15}$ **19.** $\frac{1}{6} + \frac{5}{9}$ $\frac{13}{18}$ **20.** $\frac{5}{8} - \frac{1}{6}$ $\frac{11}{24}$ **21.** $\frac{2}{5} + \frac{1}{10}$ $\frac{1}{2}$ **22.** $\frac{4}{21} + \frac{5}{7}$ $\frac{19}{21}$

Solve each equation.

23. $y + \frac{2}{3} = \frac{8}{9}$ $y = \frac{2}{9}$ **24.** $t - \frac{2}{5} = \frac{1}{3}$ $t = \frac{11}{15}$ **25.** $\frac{3}{7} + n = \frac{3}{4}$ $n = \frac{9}{28}$ **26.** $r - \frac{3}{8} = \frac{1}{6}$ $r = \frac{13}{24}$

27. Consumer The price of Mary's stock went up $\frac{5}{8}$ the day she bought it. The next day the price went up $\frac{1}{4}$. What was the total increase over the 2 days? $\frac{7}{8}$

Madrid Stock Exchange

28. Algebra What do you know about n if the sum $\frac{1}{2} + n$ is:

a. Equal to 1? $n = \frac{1}{2}$ **b.** Greater than 1? $n > \frac{1}{2}$

29. Test Prep Which fraction, when added to $\frac{1}{6}$, results in a sum of $\frac{2}{3}$? A

Ⓐ $\frac{1}{2}$ Ⓑ $\frac{1}{3}$ Ⓒ $\frac{1}{4}$ Ⓓ $\frac{1}{5}$

PRACTICE

Name ________________

Practice 4-2

Adding and Subtracting Fractions

Find the least common denominator for each pair of fractions.

1. $\frac{2}{5}, \frac{3}{8}$ 40
2. $\frac{3}{4}, \frac{5}{8}$ 8
3. $\frac{2}{3}, \frac{1}{7}$ 21
4. $\frac{3}{5}, \frac{7}{10}$ 10
5. $\frac{5}{6}, \frac{1}{14}$ 42
6. $\frac{3}{8}, \frac{3}{10}$ 40
7. $\frac{5}{7}, \frac{1}{4}$ 28
8. $\frac{7}{8}, \frac{5}{12}$ 24

Find each sum or difference. Rewrite in lowest terms.

9. $\frac{9}{11} - \frac{5}{11}$ $\frac{4}{11}$
10. $\frac{3}{4} + \frac{1}{14}$ $\frac{23}{28}$
11. $\frac{19}{60} - \frac{1}{4}$ $\frac{1}{15}$
12. $\frac{1}{2} + \frac{1}{3}$ $\frac{5}{6}$
13. $\frac{7}{15} - \frac{1}{5}$ $\frac{4}{15}$
14. $\frac{1}{3} + \frac{1}{25}$ $\frac{28}{75}$
15. $\frac{7}{9} - \frac{1}{9}$ $\frac{2}{3}$
16. $\frac{11}{25} - \frac{1}{5}$ $\frac{6}{25}$

Solve each equation.

17. $m - \frac{4}{15} = \frac{3}{5}$ $m = \frac{13}{15}$
18. $q - \frac{1}{2} = \frac{1}{8}$ $q = \frac{5}{8}$
19. $h - \frac{1}{9} = \frac{1}{2}$ $h = \frac{11}{18}$
20. $z + \frac{3}{11} = \frac{10}{11}$ $z = \frac{7}{11}$
21. $s - \frac{2}{25} = \frac{2}{3}$ $s = \frac{56}{75}$
22. $s - \frac{1}{4} = \frac{4}{7}$ $s = \frac{23}{28}$
23. $g + \frac{1}{3} = \frac{8}{9}$ $g = \frac{5}{9}$
24. $s + \frac{2}{5} = \frac{9}{10}$ $s = \frac{1}{2}$
25. $a - \frac{14}{25} = \frac{1}{5}$ $a = \frac{19}{25}$
26. $j + \frac{1}{9} = \frac{34}{63}$ $j = \frac{3}{7}$
27. $q - \frac{5}{11} = \frac{1}{4}$ $q = \frac{31}{44}$
28. $y + \frac{11}{15} = \frac{14}{15}$ $y = \frac{1}{5}$

29. The price of Rolando's stock went up $\frac{7}{8}$ the day he bought it, but the next day it went down $\frac{3}{16}$. What was the total increase over the two days? $\frac{11}{16}$

30. In 1994, about $\frac{3}{5}$ of the federal budget was spent on human resources, and $\frac{1}{20}$ of the federal budget was spent on physical resources. About what fraction of the federal budget was spent on human and physical resources combined? $\frac{13}{20}$

RETEACHING

Name ________________

Alternative Lesson 4-2

Adding and Subtracting Fractions

To add or subtract fractions, think of each fraction as a portion of the whole. Each denominator gives the number of equal parts into which the whole is divided. Each numerator gives the number of equal parts that are being considered. The **least common denominator (LCD)** is the least common multiple (LCM) of the denominators.

To add or subtract fractions:
1. If the denominators are not the same, rewrite using the LCD.
2. Add or subtract their numerators.
3. Write the sum or difference over the denominator.
4. Rewrite in lowest terms.

Example

Subtract. Rewrite in lowest terms. $\frac{3}{4} - \frac{2}{3}$

Step 1: The denominators are not the same. Rewrite using the LCD. Find the LCM for 3 and 4.

List the multiples 3: 3 6 9 [12]
4: 4 8 [12] 16

The LCD is 12.

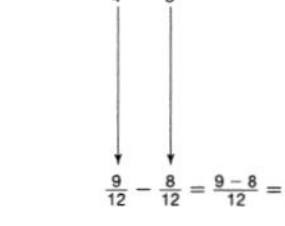

$\frac{3}{4} - \frac{2}{3}$

$\frac{9}{12} - \frac{8}{12} = \frac{9-8}{12} = \frac{1}{12}$

Step 2: Subtract the numerators.

Step 3: Write the difference over the denominator.

Step 4: The difference is in lowest terms.

So $\frac{3}{4} - \frac{2}{3} = \frac{1}{12}$.

Try It Subtract. Rewrite in lowest terms. $\frac{7}{10} - \frac{3}{10}$

a. The denominators are the same. Subtract the numerators and write over the denominator. $\frac{7-3}{10} = \frac{4}{10}$

b. Rewrite in lowest terms. $\frac{2}{5}$

Add or subtract. Rewrite in lowest terms.

c. $\frac{2}{16} + \frac{4}{16}$ $\frac{6}{16} = \frac{3}{8}$
d. $\frac{8}{12} - \frac{5}{12}$ $\frac{3}{12} = \frac{1}{4}$
e. $\frac{1}{4} + \frac{1}{4}$ $\frac{2}{4} = \frac{1}{2}$
f. $\frac{2}{3} - \frac{1}{2}$ $\frac{1}{6}$
g. $\frac{3}{10} - \frac{1}{5}$ $\frac{1}{10}$
h. $\frac{7}{8} - \frac{4}{8}$ $\frac{3}{8}$
i. $\frac{6}{10} + \frac{3}{10}$ $\frac{9}{10}$
j. $\frac{1}{6} + \frac{3}{8}$ $\frac{13}{24}$

30. Science The circle graph shows the different ways electrical energy is produced in the United States.

a. How much of the total energy is produced by gas and hydroelectric generators? $\frac{1}{5}$

b. How much more of the total energy is produced by coal than by oil? $\frac{13}{25}$

c. How much more of the total energy is produced by nuclear generators than hydroelectric generators? $\frac{1}{10}$

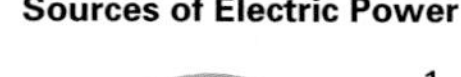

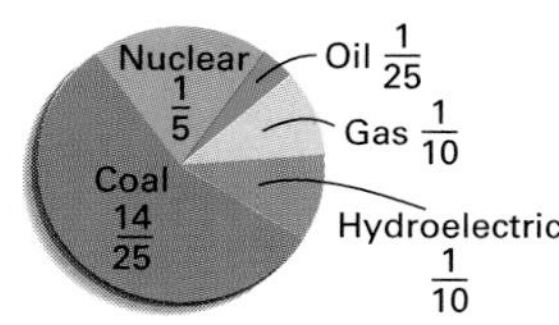

Problem Solving and Reasoning

31. Choose a Strategy Andrea watched the prices of two stocks for a week. Which stock had the greatest gain? Stock A

	Monday	Tuesday	Wednesday	Thursday	Friday
Stock A	$+\frac{1}{4}$	$+\frac{1}{8}$	$-\frac{5}{8}$	$+\frac{1}{2}$	$-\frac{1}{8}$
Stock B	$+\frac{1}{8}$	$-\frac{7}{8}$	$+\frac{1}{8}$	$+\frac{1}{4}$	$+\frac{3}{8}$

Problem Solving STRATEGIES
- Look for a Pattern
- Make an Organized List
- Make a Table
- Guess and Check
- Work Backward
- Use Logical Reasoning
- Draw a Diagram
- Solve a Simpler Problem

32. Critical Thinking Using each number only once, use the numbers 2, 4, 6, and 8 to write an expression with two proper fractions that have:

GPS

a. The largest possible sum $\frac{2}{4}+\frac{6}{8}$

b. The largest possible difference $\frac{4}{6}-\frac{2}{8}$

c. The smallest possible sum $\frac{2}{6}+\frac{4}{8}$

d. The smallest possible difference $\frac{4}{8}-\frac{2}{6}$

Mixed Review

Solve each equation. Check your answer. *[Lesson 2-8]*

33. $5p + 2 = 37$ $p = 7$ **34.** $21k - 18 = 273$ $k = 13\frac{6}{7}$ **35.** $11u - 31 = 47$ $u = 8$ **36.** $97 = 9d + 7$ $d = 10$

37. $\frac{a}{12} + 31 = 114$ $a = 996$ **38.** $67 = \frac{w}{3} - 36$ $w = 309$ **39.** $\frac{x}{31} - 3 = 93$ $x = 2976$ **40.** $\frac{c}{17} + 52 = 209$ $c = 2669$

Estimate. *[Lesson 3-2]*

41. $86.342 - 37.5 \approx 48$ **42.** $\frac{361.2}{118.7} \approx 3$ **43.** $62.7 \times 20.19 \approx 1260$ **44.** $32.78 + 117.32 \approx 150$

45. $72.01 + 39.25 \approx 111$ **46.** $269.03 - 41.7 \approx 227$ **47.** $31.2 \times 48.7 \approx 1500$ **48.** $248.6 \div 51.03 \approx 5$

49. $92.1 - 36.7 \approx 55$ **50.** $\frac{108.5}{53.1} \approx 2$ **51.** $47.2 \times 9.87 \approx 470$ **52.** $31.42 + 31.98 \approx 63$

53. $213.9 - 84.7 \approx 130$ **54.** $\frac{5{,}280}{10.2} \approx 528$ **55.** $104.16 \times 51.97 \approx 5{,}000$ **56.** $247.54 + 598.217 \approx 850$

Exercise Notes

Exercise 30

Consumer Since 1958 the United States has consumed more energy than it produces. The difference has been met with energy imports.

Exercise 31

Problem-Solving Tip You may want to use Teaching Tool Transparencies 2 and 3: Guided Problem Solving, pages 1–2.

Exercise 32

Extension Have volunteers discuss how they solved this problem. Have students discuss how they decided which expressions to try in order to get the largest and smallest results.

Alternate Assessment

Portfolio Have students select work that they have completed which shows how the addition of fractions can be modeled. Have students add comments about how the written steps for adding fractions relate to the models.

Quick Quiz

Find each sum or difference. Rewrite in lowest terms.

1. $\frac{1}{4}+\frac{5}{8}$ $\frac{7}{8}$
2. $\frac{7}{9}-\frac{1}{6}$ $\frac{11}{18}$

Solve the following equation.

3. $s+\frac{1}{2}=\frac{2}{3}$ $s=\frac{1}{6}$

Available on Daily Transparency 4-2

PROBLEM SOLVING

Name ______________________

Guided Problem Solving 4-2

GPS PROBLEM 32, STUDENT PAGE 177

Using each number only once, use the numbers 2, 4, 6, and 8 to write an expression with two proper fractions that have:

a. The largest possible sum b. The largest possible difference
c. The smallest possible sum d. The smallest possible difference

— Understand —

1. What is a proper fraction? A fraction with the numerator less than the denominator.
2. How many proper fractions will you write in each expression? 2 fractions.
3. How many different digits are in each pair of fractions? 4 digits.

— Plan —

4. List all the proper fractions you can make using the numbers 2, 4, 6, and 8. $\frac{2}{4}, \frac{2}{6}, \frac{2}{8}, \frac{4}{6}, \frac{4}{8}, \frac{6}{8}$
5. What are the pairs of fractions you can use when writing the expressions? $\frac{2}{4}, \frac{6}{8}$; $\frac{2}{6}, \frac{4}{8}$; $\frac{2}{8}, \frac{4}{6}$

— Solve —

6. For each pair of fractions, find the sum and the difference.

Fraction Pairs	Sum	Difference
$\frac{2}{4}, \frac{6}{8}$	$1\frac{1}{4}$	$\frac{1}{4}$
$\frac{2}{6}, \frac{4}{8}$	$\frac{5}{6}$	$\frac{1}{6}$
$\frac{2}{8}, \frac{4}{6}$	$\frac{11}{12}$	$\frac{5}{12}$

7. Write an expression for each part of the problem.

Part a. $\frac{2}{4}+\frac{6}{8}$ Part b. $\frac{4}{6}-\frac{2}{8}$
Part c. $\frac{2}{6}+\frac{4}{8}$ Part d. $\frac{4}{8}-\frac{2}{6}$

— Look Back —

8. How can you tell that your answers are reasonable without calculating? Estimate the sums and differences. Use compensation to adjust for the values of the fractions.

SOLVE ANOTHER PROBLEM

Use the numbers 2, 3, 6, and 8 to answer the question above.

a. $\frac{2}{3}+\frac{6}{8}$ b. $\frac{3}{6}-\frac{2}{8}$ c. $\frac{2}{6}+\frac{3}{8}$ d. $\frac{3}{8}-\frac{2}{6}$

ENRICHMENT

Name ______________________

Extend Your Thinking 4-2

Visual Thinking

For each row, circle the letter of the figure on the right that would go with the three figures on the left.

1. 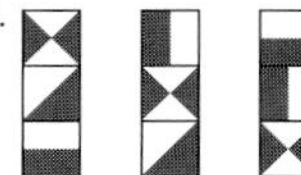 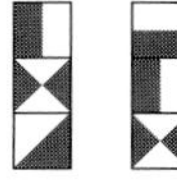 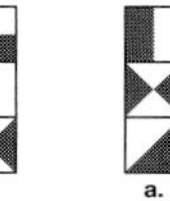 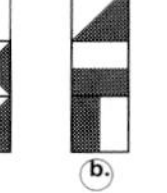 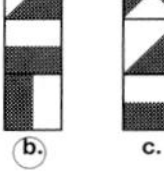

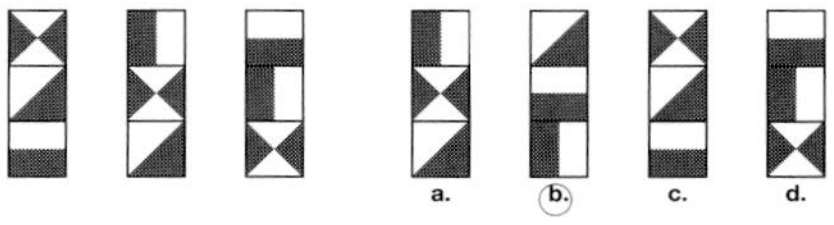

a. (b.) c. d.

2. 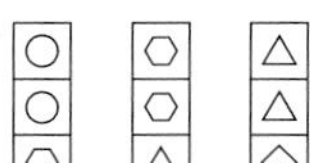  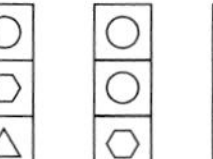

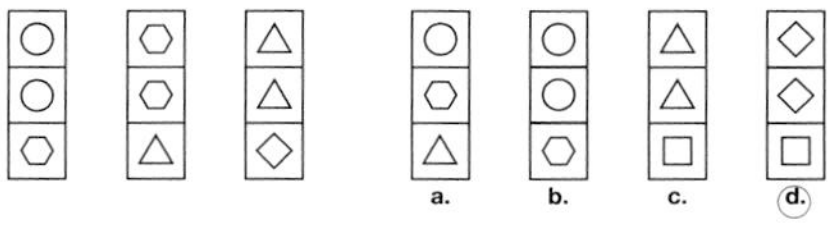

a. b. c. (d.)

3. 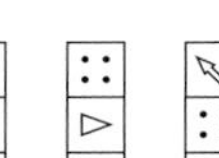 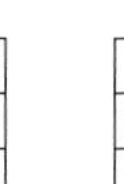 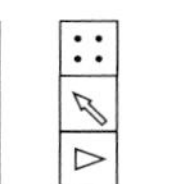 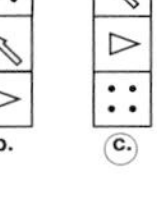

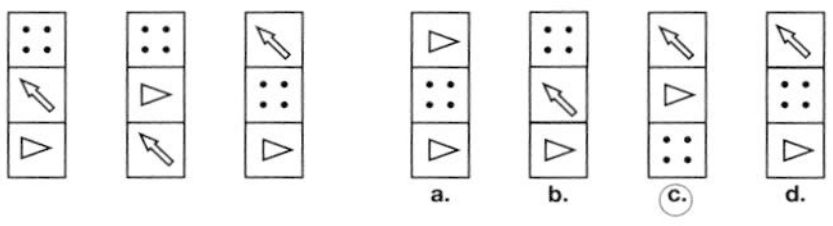

a. b. (c.) d.

4. 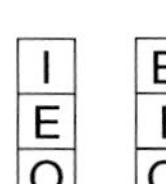 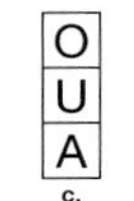

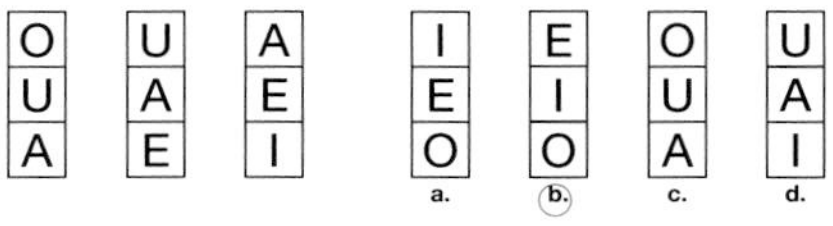

O	U	A		I	E	O	U
U	A	E		E	I	U	A
A	E	I		O	O	A	I

a. (b.) c. d.

INTERACTIVE LESSON

4-3 Lesson Organizer

Objectives

- Find sums and differences of mixed numbers.
- Solve equations involving mixed numbers.

Vocabulary

- Improper fraction

Materials

- Explore: Graph paper, colored pencils

NCTM Standards

- 1–4, 6, 7, 9, 10, 12

► Review

Find each missing numerator.

1. $3 = \frac{?}{5}$ 15
2. $6 = \frac{?}{4}$ 24
3. $5 = \frac{?}{7}$ 35

Available on Daily Transparency 4-3

1 Introduce

Explore

You may wish to use Lesson Enhancement Transparency 14 and Teaching Tool Transparency 7: $\frac{1}{4}$-Inch Graph Paper with **Explore**.

The Point
Students explore adding mixed numbers by modeling addends and sums on graph paper.

Ongoing Assessment
Check student work to make sure that students are drawing squares of the same size and that each part is shown by nonoverlapping vertical bars of the same size.

For Groups That Finish Early
How could you draw squares and vertical bars to solve subtraction problems? Answers may vary. Use your method to find:

1. $2\frac{4}{5} - \frac{3}{5}$ $2\frac{1}{5}$
2. $4\frac{3}{4} - 1\frac{1}{4}$ $3\frac{1}{2}$

4-3 Adding and Subtracting Mixed Numbers

You'll Learn ...

- to find sums and differences of mixed numbers
- to solve equations involving mixed numbers

... How It's Used

Plumbers have to deal with fractional lengths when they work with water pipes.

Vocabulary

improper fraction

► Lesson Link You've seen how to add and subtract fractions. Now you'll add and subtract mixed numbers. ◄

Explore Adding Mixed Numbers

Mixed Results

Materials: Graph paper, Colored pencils

Adding Two Mixed Numbers

- Model each mixed number using squares. Make the side lengths of the squares equal to the denominators of the fractions.
- To find the sum, first copy the filled squares. Then combine the fractionally-filled squares. When you combine these fractions, make as many complete squares as you can.

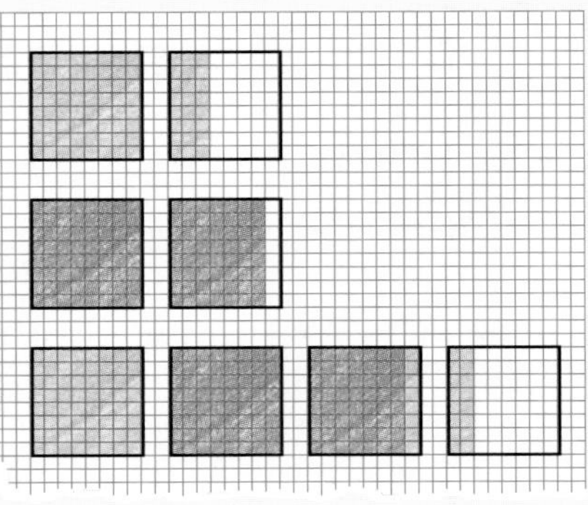

$1\frac{3}{8} + 1\frac{7}{8} = 3\frac{2}{8}$

1. Model each sum.
   a. $1\frac{3}{5} + 2\frac{1}{5}$ b. $1\frac{3}{4} + 2\frac{1}{4}$ c. $1\frac{2}{5} + 1\frac{4}{5}$
2. When adding mixed numbers, how do you find the two parts of the sum?
3. How is adding two mixed numbers like adding two fractions?

DID YOU KNOW?

Mixed numbers are called *mixed* because they are written in two kinds of math notation.

Learn Adding and Subtracting Mixed Numbers

When you add mixed numbers, you add the whole numbers and fractions separately. Sometimes you get a fraction such as $\frac{9}{4}$.

A fraction that is greater than 1, such as $\frac{9}{4}$, is called an **improper fraction**. You can use division to rewrite an improper fraction as a mixed number.

MEETING INDIVIDUAL NEEDS

Resources

4-3 Practice
4-3 Reteaching
4-3 Problem Solving
4-3 Enrichment
4-3 Daily Transparency
Problem of the Day
Review
Quick Quiz
Teaching Tool Transparency 7
Lesson Enhancement Transparency 14
Chapter 4 Project Master
Technology Master 15

Interactive CD-ROM Lesson

Learning Modalities

Verbal Have students write a description of procedures used to add or subtract mixed numbers.

Kinesthetic Have students cut out circles and parts of circles to represent mixed numbers. Then have them combine all the circles and parts of circles to show addition of mixed numbers.

English Language Development

Have students work in groups to create word problems involving addition and subtraction of fractions and mixed numbers. One student in each group could then read the problems to other groups who must take notes as they listen and solve the problems.

To rename $\frac{9}{4}$ as a mixed number, think: $9 \div 4 = 2$ with remainder **1**, so $\frac{9}{4} = 2\frac{1}{4}$.

To write a mixed number such as $3\frac{4}{5}$ as an improper fraction:

$3\frac{4}{5} = \frac{15}{5} + \frac{4}{5}$ — Rewrite the whole number. Use the same denominator as the fraction.

$= \frac{19}{5}$ — Add.

> **Remember**
>
> 3 means *3 wholes.* Any whole number can be written as a fraction with a denominator of 1.
> **[Previous course]**

Examples

1 Last year, Margot bought stock in a medical equipment company at $6\frac{7}{8}$. Since then, the price has gone up $4\frac{3}{8}$. Find the current price.

Estimate: $7 + 4 = 11$

$6\frac{7}{8} + 4\frac{3}{8} = 10 + \frac{10}{8}$ — Add the whole numbers and add the fractions.

$= 10 + 1\frac{2}{8}$ — Rewrite the improper fraction as a mixed number.

$= 11\frac{2}{8} = 11\frac{1}{4}$ — Add and rewrite in lowest terms.

The current price of the stock is $11\frac{1}{4}$.

2 Solve. $w + 3\frac{3}{4} = 5\frac{1}{5}$

$w + 3\frac{3}{4} - 3\frac{3}{4} = 5\frac{1}{5} - 3\frac{3}{4}$ — To undo adding $3\frac{3}{4}$, subtract $3\frac{3}{4}$ from both sides.

$w = 5\frac{4}{20} - 3\frac{15}{20}$ — Rewrite fractions using the LCD.

$w = 4 + \frac{20}{20} + \frac{4}{20} - 3\frac{15}{20}$ — Rewrite 5 as $4 + \frac{20}{20}$.

$w = 4\frac{24}{20} - 3\frac{15}{20}$ — Combine the whole numbers and fractions.

$w = 1\frac{9}{20}$ — Subtract whole numbers and fractions.

Try It

Add or subtract.

a. $4\frac{1}{2} + 3\frac{5}{8}$ $8\frac{1}{8}$ **b.** $3 - 1\frac{1}{3}$ $1\frac{2}{3}$ **c.** $6\frac{2}{5} - 2\frac{1}{2}$ $3\frac{9}{10}$

MATH EVERY DAY

Problem of the Day

On a map, Brownstown is 6 cm west of Seymour. Harrisburg is 13 cm east of Seymour and 8 cm west of Mayville. If 1 cm represents 10 mi, how many miles is Mayville from Brownstown? How many miles is Harrisburg from Brownstown? 270 mi, 190 mi

Available on Daily Transparency 4-3

An Extension is provided in the transparency package.

Fact of the Day

In 1991, a worldwide list of the 100 best stocks to own included Nintendo. It was the first time that the electronic toy industry was on the list.

Estimation

Estimate.

1. $\frac{1}{3} + \frac{1}{4}$ $\frac{1}{2}$
2. $\frac{4}{5} + \frac{1}{6}$ 1
3. $\frac{2}{3} + \frac{3}{4}$ $1\frac{1}{2}$
4. $\frac{7}{10} + \frac{1}{5}$ 1

Follow Up

Have students show the models that they drew in Step 1 and discuss their answers to Steps 2–4.

Answers for Explore

1. a–c. See page C6.
2. Add the whole numbers together and add the fractional parts together.
3. It is the same, except that there are whole numbers to add and that any portion of the fractional sum equal to 1 is added to the whole number part of the sum.

2 Teach

Learn

Alternate Examples

1. George needs $2\frac{3}{4}$ cups of flour to make a cake and $1\frac{3}{4}$ cups of flour to make pancakes. Find the total amount of flour needed.

   Estimate: $3 + 2 = 5$

   $2\frac{3}{4} + 1\frac{3}{4} = 3 + \frac{6}{4}$

   $= 3 + 1\frac{2}{4}$

   $= 4\frac{2}{4}$

   $= 4\frac{1}{2}$

   The total amount of flour is $4\frac{1}{2}$ cups.

2. Solve $s + 4\frac{2}{3} = 7\frac{1}{4}$.

   $s + 4\frac{2}{3} - 4\frac{2}{3} = 7\frac{1}{4} - 4\frac{2}{3}$

   $s = 7\frac{3}{12} - 4\frac{8}{12}$

   $s = 6 + \frac{12}{12} + \frac{3}{12} - 4\frac{8}{12}$

   $s = 6\frac{15}{12} - 4\frac{8}{12}$

   $s = 2\frac{7}{12}$

Students see two methods of subtracting mixed numbers. One method uses renaming one mixed number, and the other uses rewriting both mixed numbers as improper fractions.

Answers for What Do You Think?

1. Ramon worked the problem using mixed numbers; Melissa rewrote the mixed numbers as improper fractions.
2. Melissa knew that $5 = \frac{40}{8}$ and that $\frac{40}{8} + \frac{1}{8} = \frac{41}{8}$, so $5\frac{1}{8} = \frac{41}{8}$.

3 Practice and Assess

Check

Answers for Check Your Understanding

1. Possible answer: $11 \div 3 = 3$ with remainder 2, so $\frac{11}{3} = 3\frac{2}{3}$.
2. When the fraction in the second mixed number is greater than the fraction in the first mixed number.

Ramon and Melissa own stock in the MATHtoys Company. One week the price went from $2\frac{5}{8}$ to $5\frac{1}{8}$ per share. They want to know the price increase.

Ramon thinks ...

I'll subtract the whole number parts and the fraction parts.

$$5\frac{1}{8} - 2\frac{5}{8} = 4\frac{9}{8} - 2\frac{5}{8} = 2\frac{4}{8} = 2\frac{1}{2}$$

The price went up $2.50 per share.

Melissa thinks ...

I'll write as improper fractions and then subtract.

$$5\frac{1}{8} - 2\frac{5}{8} = \frac{41}{8} - \frac{21}{8} = \frac{20}{8} = 2\frac{4}{8} = 2\frac{1}{2}$$

The price went up $2.50 per share.

What do you think?

1. How did Ramon's method differ from Melissa's?
2. How did Melissa know that $5\frac{1}{8}$ is equal to $\frac{41}{8}$?

Check Your Understanding

1. Explain how to write $\frac{11}{3}$ as a mixed number.
2. When you subtract mixed numbers, when do you need to rewrite a whole number as a whole number plus a fraction?

MEETING MIDDLE SCHOOL CLASSROOM NEEDS

Tips from Middle School Teachers

When my students need to rename mixed numbers so that they have common denominators, I always have them rewrite the entire mixed number, using the common denominator. They are not as likely to forget the whole numbers when they add or subtract. For example: $4\frac{1}{5} + 3\frac{2}{3} = 4\frac{3}{15} + 3\frac{10}{15} = 7\frac{13}{15}$.

Team Teaching

Work with a home economics teacher to demonstrate addition and subtraction of mixed numbers in cooking.

Cooperative Learning

Have students work in small groups. Each person in the group should pick a stock and record its price at the beginning of the week and at the end of the week. Have students work together to determine the amount each stock has increased or decreased during the week.

4-3 Exercises and Applications

Practice and Apply

Getting Started Rewrite each improper fraction as a mixed number.

1. $\frac{24}{7}$ $3\frac{3}{7}$ **2.** $\frac{16}{3}$ $5\frac{1}{3}$ **3.** $\frac{34}{9}$ $3\frac{7}{9}$ **4.** $\frac{61}{5}$ $12\frac{1}{5}$ **5.** $\frac{39}{8}$ $4\frac{7}{8}$ **6.** $\frac{49}{4}$ $12\frac{1}{4}$

Rewrite each mixed number as an improper fraction.

7. $3\frac{1}{8}$ $\frac{25}{8}$ **8.** $5\frac{4}{5}$ $\frac{29}{5}$ **9.** $7\frac{3}{4}$ $\frac{31}{4}$ **10.** $4\frac{7}{9}$ $\frac{43}{9}$ **11.** $6\frac{7}{8}$ $\frac{55}{8}$ **12.** $8\frac{5}{11}$ $\frac{93}{11}$

Find each sum or difference.

13. $7\frac{7}{8} - 3\frac{5}{8}$ $4\frac{1}{4}$ **14.** $5\frac{2}{9} + 2\frac{4}{9}$ $7\frac{2}{3}$ **15.** $4\frac{1}{7} - 1\frac{6}{7}$ $2\frac{2}{7}$ **16.** $6\frac{8}{9} + 8\frac{4}{9}$ $15\frac{1}{3}$

17. $9 - 2\frac{1}{5}$ $6\frac{4}{5}$ **18.** $10\frac{1}{2} + 5\frac{2}{3}$ $16\frac{1}{6}$ **19.** $6\frac{3}{8} - 3\frac{1}{2}$ $2\frac{7}{8}$ **20.** $25\frac{7}{9} + 18\frac{2}{3}$ $44\frac{4}{9}$

Solve each equation.

21. $n + 3\frac{3}{7} = 6\frac{2}{3}$ $n = 3\frac{5}{21}$ **22.** $11\frac{7}{9} + x = 26\frac{1}{10}$ $x = 14\frac{29}{90}$ **23.** $y - 4\frac{2}{5} = 2\frac{1}{4}$ $y = 6\frac{13}{20}$ **24.** $z - 8\frac{5}{6} = 9\frac{7}{8}$ $z = 18\frac{17}{24}$

25. Geometry Find the perimeter of each figure.

a.

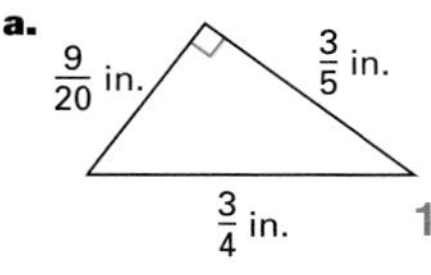

$1\frac{4}{5}$ in.

b.

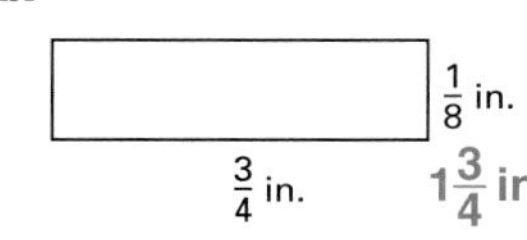

$1\frac{3}{4}$ in.

26. History On October 29, 1929, known as Black Tuesday, the stock market crashed. The Dow Jones average, which measures stock prices, started that day at $298\frac{97}{100}$, and finished $38\frac{33}{100}$ points lower. What was the Dow Jones average at the end of the day? $260\frac{16}{25}$

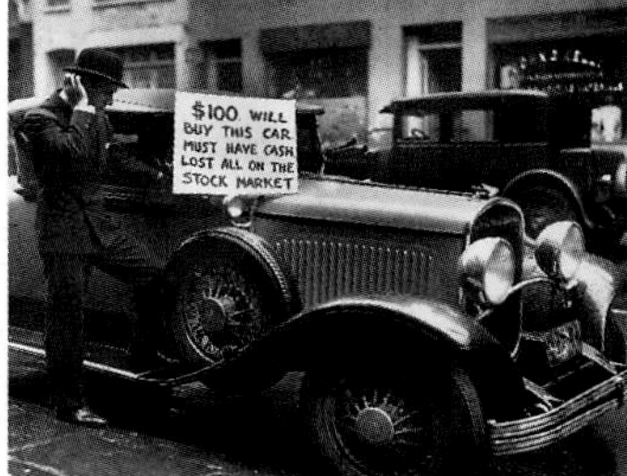

27. Science One *Astronomical Unit* (AU) is the average distance from Earth to the sun. If, when they are lined up, Mars is about $1\frac{1}{2}$ AU from the sun and Jupiter is about $3\frac{7}{10}$ AU from Mars, how far is Jupiter from the sun? $5\frac{1}{5}$ AU

28. Test Prep Find the sum expressed in lowest terms: $3\frac{5}{6} + 7\frac{3}{4} = 10\frac{38}{24}$ D

Ⓐ $5\frac{19}{12}$ Ⓑ $10\frac{19}{12}$ Ⓒ $11\frac{14}{24}$ Ⓓ $11\frac{7}{12}$

PRACTICE 4-3

4-3 Exercises and Applications

Assignment Guide

- **Basic** 1–24, 26–30 evens, 36–44 evens
- **Average** 1–25 odds, 26–44
- **Enriched** 1–25 odds, 26–38, 39–43 odds

Exercise Notes

Exercises 13–20

Error Prevention Some students may forget to add or subtract the whole numbers. Encourage students to estimate the sum or difference and then check their answers with the estimates.

Exercise 26

History The stock market crash in 1929 ushered in the Great Depression of the 1930s. During this period there was high unemployment and many businesses and banks failed.

PRACTICE

Name ______________________

Practice 4-3

Adding and Subtracting Mixed Numbers

Rewrite each mixed number as an improper fraction.

1. $4\frac{3}{8}$ $\frac{35}{8}$ 2. $7\frac{1}{9}$ $\frac{64}{9}$ 3. $2\frac{3}{5}$ $\frac{13}{5}$ 4. $3\frac{5}{6}$ $\frac{23}{6}$

Find each sum or difference.

5. $27\frac{7}{10} - 15\frac{7}{10}$ 12 6. $29\frac{8}{15} - 20\frac{1}{3}$ $9\frac{1}{5}$ 7. $7\frac{3}{10} + 23\frac{8}{25}$ $30\frac{31}{50}$ 8. $3\frac{1}{6} + 8\frac{5}{8}$ $11\frac{19}{24}$

9. $8\frac{13}{18} + 11\frac{11}{18}$ $20\frac{1}{3}$ 10. $24\frac{5}{7} + 23\frac{1}{8}$ $47\frac{47}{56}$ 11. $3\frac{4}{25} + 3\frac{4}{5}$ $6\frac{24}{25}$ 12. $32\frac{24}{25} - 14\frac{19}{25}$ $18\frac{1}{5}$

Solve each equation.

13. $k - 7\frac{1}{10} = 4\frac{5}{18}$ $k = 11\frac{17}{45}$ 14. $q + 1\frac{1}{2} = 23\frac{2}{3}$ $q = 22\frac{1}{6}$ 15. $f + 13\frac{1}{6} = 20\frac{17}{30}$ $f = 7\frac{2}{5}$

16. $r - \frac{1}{5} = 7\frac{3}{7}$ $r = 7\frac{22}{35}$ 17. $z - 17\frac{17}{20} = 11\frac{2}{15}$ $z = 28\frac{59}{60}$ 18. $m - 19\frac{5}{9} = 4\frac{4}{7}$ $m = 24\frac{8}{63}$

Geometry Find the perimeter of each figure.

19. $12\frac{1}{5}$ cm

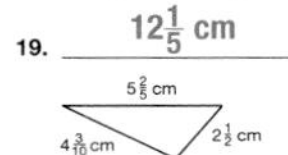

20. $5\frac{5}{8}$ in.

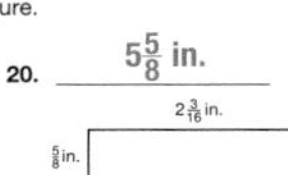

21. On May 21, 1996, Iomega stock was priced at $43\frac{3}{8}$. On May 22, it was priced at 54.

a. How much did the price go up on May 22? $10\frac{5}{8}$

b. On May 23, the price went down $2\frac{3}{4}$. What was the closing price on May 23? $51\frac{1}{4}$

RETEACHING

Name ______________________

Alternative Lesson 4-3

Adding and Subtracting Mixed Numbers

Improper fractions are greater than 1 and have numerators that are greater than their denominators. $\frac{9}{7}$ is an improper fraction. You can use division to rewrite an improper fraction as a mixed number.

Example 1

a. Write $\frac{9}{7}$ as a mixed number.

Divide 9 by 7.

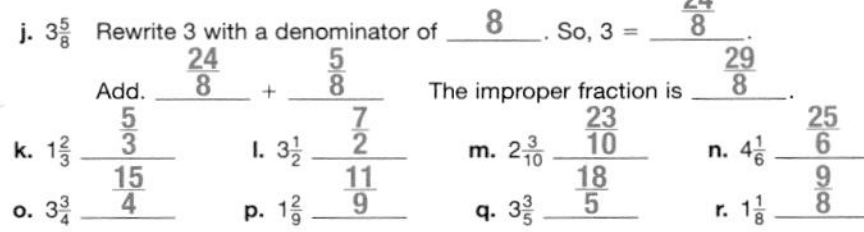

So $\frac{9}{7}$ can be written as $1\frac{2}{7}$.

b. Write $2\frac{4}{5}$ as an improper fraction.

Rewrite the whole number using the same denominator as the fraction. Add the two fractions.

$2\frac{4}{5} = \frac{10}{5} + \frac{4}{5} = \frac{10+4}{5} = \frac{14}{5}$

So $2\frac{4}{5}$ can be written as $\frac{14}{5}$.

Try It Write each improper fraction as a mixed number.

a. $\frac{8}{5}$ Divide 8 by 5. The quotient is 1. The remainder is 3. The mixed number is $1\frac{3}{8}$.

b. $\frac{21}{4}$ $5\frac{1}{4}$ c. $\frac{17}{9}$ $1\frac{8}{9}$ d. $\frac{13}{3}$ $4\frac{1}{3}$ e. $\frac{27}{8}$ $3\frac{3}{8}$

f. $\frac{22}{5}$ $4\frac{2}{5}$ g. $\frac{17}{6}$ $2\frac{5}{6}$ h. $\frac{11}{2}$ $5\frac{1}{2}$ i. $\frac{45}{8}$ $5\frac{5}{8}$

Write each mixed number as an improper fraction.

j. $3\frac{5}{8}$ Rewrite 3 with a denominator of 8. So, 3 = $\frac{24}{8}$.

Add. $\frac{24}{8}$ + $\frac{5}{8}$ The improper fraction is $\frac{29}{8}$.

k. $1\frac{2}{3}$ $\frac{5}{3}$ l. $3\frac{1}{2}$ $\frac{7}{2}$ m. $2\frac{3}{10}$ $\frac{23}{10}$ n. $4\frac{1}{6}$ $\frac{25}{6}$

o. $3\frac{3}{4}$ $\frac{15}{4}$ p. $1\frac{2}{9}$ $\frac{11}{9}$ q. $3\frac{3}{5}$ $\frac{18}{5}$ r. $1\frac{1}{8}$ $\frac{9}{8}$

Add or subtract.

s. $2\frac{2}{3} + 3\frac{2}{3}$ $6\frac{1}{3}$ t. $7\frac{7}{8} - 2\frac{5}{8}$ $5\frac{1}{4}$ u. $9 - 7\frac{2}{3}$ $1\frac{1}{3}$

v. $9\frac{1}{5} + 8\frac{2}{3}$ $17\frac{13}{15}$ w. $2\frac{6}{7} + 1\frac{1}{5}$ $4\frac{2}{35}$ x. $5\frac{1}{4} - 4\frac{5}{6}$ $\frac{5}{12}$

Reteaching

Activity

Materials: Fraction models

Use fraction circles, Fraction Bars, or other materials to model each problem. For subtraction, model the first mixed number, then take away an amount equal to the second mixed number.

1. $2\frac{1}{2} + 3\frac{1}{4}$ $5\frac{3}{4}$
2. $3\frac{2}{3} + 2\frac{1}{2}$ $6\frac{1}{6}$
3. $4\frac{1}{2} - 1\frac{1}{4}$ $3\frac{1}{4}$
4. $3\frac{2}{3} - 1\frac{1}{2}$ $2\frac{1}{6}$

Project Progress

You may want to have students use Chapter 4 Project Master.

Exercise Answers

30. Possible answer: $5\frac{1}{2} + 3\frac{5}{8} + 1\frac{10}{16} = 10\frac{3}{4}$

31. Possible answer: Rename $4\frac{3}{5}$ as $3\frac{8}{5}$, then subtract $2\frac{4}{5}$. The difference is $1\frac{4}{5}$.

Alternate Assessment

Performance Have students work together in pairs. Each student should write two word problems, one involving addition of mixed numbers and one involving subtraction of mixed numbers. Have each student solve the problems written by his or her partner.

Quick Quiz

Find each sum or difference.

1. $4\frac{2}{3} + 2\frac{1}{2}$ $7\frac{1}{6}$
2. $5\frac{3}{4} - 2\frac{1}{3}$ $3\frac{5}{12}$
3. $6\frac{2}{5} - 1\frac{1}{2}$ $4\frac{9}{10}$

Solve for *m*.

4. $m - 2\frac{5}{6} = 3\frac{1}{3}$ $6\frac{1}{6}$

Available on Daily Transparency 4-3

PROBLEM SOLVING 4-3

29. Social Studies Many newspapers publish daily stock market reports. The reports usually include the high and the low price for that day as well as the last, or closing, price for the day.

a. What was the difference in cost between the high and the low for a share of Dig Video? $\frac{1}{8}$

b. For Dig Video, how much higher than the low was the last price of the day? $\frac{1}{16}$

STOCK	HIGH	LOW	LAST
DigiLink	$17\frac{1}{2}$	$16\frac{3}{16}$	$16\frac{3}{16}$
Dig Mic	$17\frac{3}{4}$	$15\frac{5}{8}$	$17\frac{1}{2}$
Dig Video	$9\frac{1}{2}$	$9\frac{3}{8}$	$9\frac{7}{16}$
Dionex	35	$32\frac{1}{4}$	35

Problem Solving and Reasoning

30. Choose a Strategy Find three mixed numbers with different denominators that have a sum of $10\frac{3}{4}$. GPS

31. Communicate Write an explanation of the method you would use to subtract $2\frac{4}{5}$ from $4\frac{3}{5}$.

32. Critical Thinking Kara's bedroom is $15\frac{1}{4}$ feet long and $10\frac{1}{6}$ feet wide. She is getting a new carpet that is sold in rolls that are 12 feet wide. How much excess width will there be when the carpet is installed? $1\frac{5}{6}$ feet

Problem Solving STRATEGIES

- Look for a Pattern
- Make an Organized List
- Make a Table
- Guess and Check
- Work Backward
- Use Logical Reasoning
- Draw a Diagram
- Solve a Simpler Problem

Mixed Review

Science You can use the formula $d = r \cdot t$ to find the distance (d) traveled when you know the rate (r) and the amount of time (t). Substitute the given values into the formula. Then use the formula to find d. *[Lesson 2-1]*

33. $r = 25$ mi/hr, $t = 2$ hr $d = 50$ mi
34. $r = 16$ ft/sec, $t = 42$ sec $d = 672$ ft
35. $r = 75$ km/hr, $t = 5$ hr $d = 375$ km
36. $r = 82$ m/sec, $t = 40$ sec $d = 3280$ m
37. $r = 55$ mi/hr, $t = 4$ hr $d = 220$ mi
38. $r = 120$ ft/sec, $t = 90$ sec $d = 10{,}800$ ft

Solve each equation. *[Lesson 3-3]*

39. $132.63 + x = 201.49$ $x = 68.86$
40. $x - 62.75 = 31.87$ $x = 94.62$
41. $69.31 = x + 23.75$ $x = 45.56$
42. $6.234 = y - 15.7$ $y = 21.934$
43. $p + 0.093 = 0.142$ $p = 0.049$
44. $g - 0.072 = 6.39$ $g = 6.462$

Project Progress

Using the population data you have collected, find the fraction of the world's population that lives in each of the 5 most populous countries. Round numbers to the nearest ten million when you make your fractions, and write them in lowest terms. Make a bar graph showing the populations of these countries.

Problem Solving: Understand, Plan, Solve, Look Back

PROBLEM SOLVING

Name ______

Guided Problem Solving 4-3

GPS PROBLEM 30, STUDENT PAGE 182

Find three mixed numbers with different denominators that have a sum of $10\frac{3}{4}$.

Possible answers: Items 5a, 7, 8, 9

— Understand —

1. How many numbers are you asked to find? 3 numbers.
2. What kind of numbers are they? Mixed numbers.
3. What do you know about the sum of the numbers? It is $10\frac{3}{4}$.
4. Will the denominators be the same or different? Different.

— Plan —

5. Solve this simpler related problem.
   a. Find three different whole numbers that have a sum of 11. 1, 3, 7
   b. How could you use the sum of two of the numbers and 11 to find the third? Subtract the sum from 11 to find the third number.
6. Tell how you could use the same strategy to solve your problem. Find 2 mixed numbers that have a sum less than $10\frac{3}{4}$. Subtract the sum from $10\frac{3}{4}$ to find the third number.

— Solve —

7. What denominators will you choose? 2, 8, 16
8. What are your three mixed numbers? $5\frac{1}{2}, 3\frac{5}{8}, 1\frac{10}{16}$

— Look Back —

9. What other strategies could you use to solve the problem? Guess and Check, Work Backward.

SOLVE ANOTHER PROBLEM

Find three mixed numbers with different denominators that have a sum of $7\frac{4}{5}$. Possible answer: $1\frac{1}{10}, 1\frac{1}{2}, 5\frac{1}{5}$

ENRICHMENT

Name ______

Extend Your Thinking 4-3

Visual Thinking

Find the number of cubes in each shape. Each cube rests on another cube unless shown otherwise.

1. 14 cubes
2. 26 cubes

3. 37 cubes
4. 24 cubes

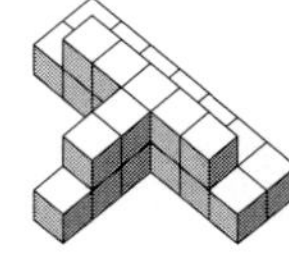

5. 16 cubes
6. 30 cubes

Section 4A Connect

You saw at the beginning of this section that investors need to understand fractions well if they are to succeed in the stock market. Now you will have an opportunity to follow the fortunes of one young investor.

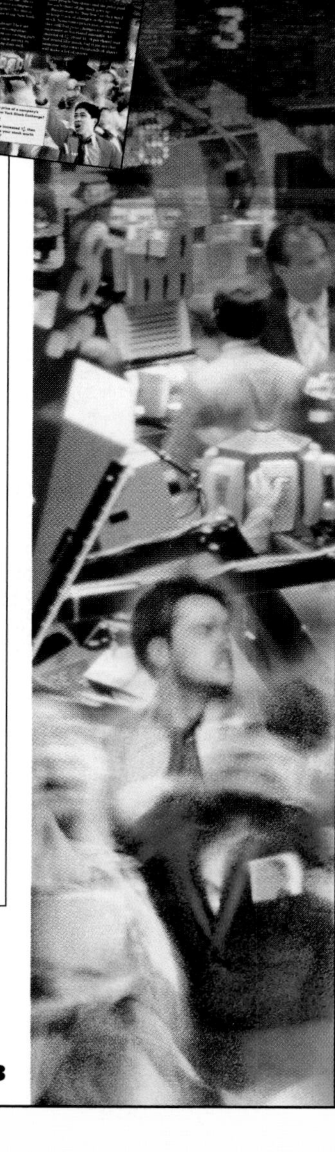

Taking Stock in the Market

Felipe saved $55 from his paper route. He decided to buy one share of stock in the newspaper he delivered.

1. Felipe bought his share of stock on Monday, July 1. The price was $52\frac{3}{4}$. How much money did he have left?
2. During July, the stock reached a high of $56\frac{7}{16}$, then fell $1\frac{1}{8}$. Find the price at the end of the month.
3. On August 1, the stock rose $5\frac{3}{4}$. On August 2, it rose another $2\frac{7}{8}$. Find how much it rose during the first 2 days of August.
4. On August 3, the stock fell $3\frac{1}{2}$. Find the price at the close of trading on August 3.
5. By August 31, the stock had gained $2\frac{5}{8}$ from its August 3 price. How does the price compare with the price on August 1?
6. Felipe sold his stock on August 31. Find how much money he gained or lost. Write a paragraph that describes the performance of Felipe's stock.

183

Answers for Connect

1. $2.25
2. $55\frac{5}{16}$
3. $8\frac{5}{8}$
4. $60\frac{7}{16}$
5. Up 2
6. Gained $10\frac{5}{16}$. Felipe's stock performed well over 3 months.

   Gains exceeded losses by $10\frac{5}{16}$.

Taking Stock in the Market

The Point

In *Taking Stock in the Market* on page 167, students discussed how stocks are bought and sold. Now they add and subtract fractions to track the fluctuations in stock prices.

About the Page

- Explain that there are usually fees charged when stock is bought or sold. For this problem, the fees are being ignored. Also, people usually buy more than one share of stock at a time because of such fees.
- Remind students that when comparing prices, regardless of whether they are going up or going down, they subtract to find the difference.
- You may want to explain to students that they can use the solution for Step 2 to find the answer for Step 3. Likewise, they can use the solution for Step 3 to find the answer for Step 4.

Ongoing Assessment

Check that students have answered Question 2 correctly before they continue.

Extension

- Stock prices are listed daily in most newspapers. Show students how to determine the closing price of a stock on the stock table.
- Ask students to select a stock that they might like to own and graph the changes in the closing price each day for a month. Students can then determine whether they would have made or lost money if they had purchased this stock, and the amount of money they would have made or lost.

4A Review

Review Correlation

Item(s)	Lesson(s)
1–9	4-1
10–14	4-2
15–27	4-3

Test Prep

Test-Taking Tip

Tell students that on some multiple-choice tests they can evaluate the choices and eliminate any that are not sensible. Then they can check the remaining choices to find the correct answer.

Exercise Notes

■ Exercise 25

Literature This contest was inspired by a fictional story called *The Celebrated Jumping Frog of Calaveras County*. The story was written by Mark Twain.

Section 4A Review

REVIEW 4A

Round each addend to 0, $\frac{1}{2}$, or 1, then estimate each sum or difference.

1. $\frac{4}{5} - \frac{1}{6}$ ≈ 1 **2.** $\frac{2}{7} + \frac{7}{8}$ ≈ $1\frac{1}{2}$ **3.** $\frac{1}{3} + \frac{8}{9}$ ≈ $1\frac{1}{2}$ **4.** $\frac{6}{7} + \frac{1}{8}$ ≈ 1 **5.** $\frac{7}{8} - \frac{2}{3}$ ≈ 0

Round each mixed number to the nearest whole number, then estimate each sum or difference.

6. $8\frac{3}{4} - 6\frac{1}{3}$ ≈ 3 **7.** $4\frac{5}{7} + 3\frac{2}{9}$ ≈ 8 **8.** $11\frac{5}{6} - 7\frac{7}{9}$ ≈ 4 **9.** $14\frac{1}{2} + 5\frac{9}{10}$ ≈ 21

Find each sum or difference.

10. $\frac{4}{5} - \frac{1}{2}$ $\frac{3}{10}$ **11.** $\frac{2}{3} + \frac{1}{8}$ $\frac{19}{24}$ **12.** $\frac{6}{7} - \frac{1}{4}$ $\frac{17}{28}$ **13.** $\frac{5}{9} + \frac{2}{5}$ $\frac{43}{45}$ **14.** $\frac{2}{9} + \frac{5}{8}$ $\frac{61}{72}$

15. $4\frac{2}{5} + 3\frac{4}{5}$ $8\frac{1}{5}$ **16.** $8\frac{1}{2} - 4\frac{3}{8}$ $4\frac{1}{8}$ **17.** $10\frac{1}{2} - 5\frac{7}{10}$ $4\frac{4}{5}$ **18.** $9\frac{2}{7} + 6\frac{3}{4}$ $16\frac{1}{28}$ **19.** $2\frac{7}{8} + 3\frac{3}{4}$ $6\frac{5}{8}$

20.  Describe several ways you might express 4 as an improper fraction.

Possible answer: $\frac{4}{1}, \frac{8}{2}, \frac{12}{3}, \frac{16}{4}$ and so on.

Solve each equation.

21. $z + 2\frac{2}{5} = 5\frac{3}{4}$ $z = 3\frac{7}{20}$ **22.** $m - 6\frac{2}{3} = 3\frac{2}{7}$ $m = 9\frac{20}{21}$ **23.** $x - 4\frac{3}{8} = 5\frac{1}{2}$ $x = 9\frac{7}{8}$ **24.** $a + 1\frac{3}{4} = 8\frac{7}{8}$ $a = 7\frac{1}{8}$

25. Science Every year, the World Frog Jump Championships are held in Angels Camp, California. One year, the frog Free Willy won the contest by jumping 19 feet, $\frac{1}{2}$ inch, in 3 hops. The world record is 21 feet, $5\frac{3}{4}$ inches, held by Rosie the Ribeter. How much farther than Free Willy did Rosie the Ribeter jump?

2 ft $5\frac{1}{4}$ in.

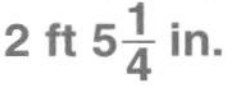

Test Prep

On a multiple choice test, recognizing that the best answer choice is usually in lowest terms can help you work more quickly.

26. Find the sum: $3\frac{5}{8} + 5\frac{7}{40}$ D

Ⓐ $8\frac{32}{40}$ Ⓑ $8\frac{16}{20}$ Ⓒ $8\frac{8}{10}$ Ⓓ $8\frac{4}{5}$

27. Find the difference: $9\frac{1}{3} - 1\frac{5}{6}$ D

Ⓐ $6\frac{3}{6}$ Ⓑ $6\frac{1}{2}$ Ⓒ $7\frac{3}{6}$ Ⓓ $7\frac{1}{2}$

Resources

Practice Masters
Section 4A Review

Assessment Sourcebook
Quiz 4A

TestWorks
Test and Practice Software

PRACTICE

Name ______________________ **Practice**

Section 4A Review

Round each addend to 0, $\frac{1}{2}$, or 1, then estimate each sum or difference.

1. $\frac{4}{5} - \frac{3}{8}$ $\frac{1}{2}$ 2. $\frac{1}{3} + \frac{9}{16}$ 1 3. $\frac{1}{7} + \frac{4}{9}$ $\frac{1}{2}$ 4. $\frac{8}{9} - \frac{3}{7}$ $\frac{1}{2}$

Round each mixed number to the nearest whole number, then estimate each sum or difference.

5. $4\frac{1}{5} + 9\frac{7}{8}$ 14 6. $8\frac{3}{8} - 2\frac{3}{4}$ 5 7. $11\frac{4}{5} + 7\frac{2}{7}$ 19 8. $12\frac{4}{9} - 5\frac{1}{3}$ 7

Find each sum or difference.

9. $\frac{37}{40} - \frac{3}{10}$ $\frac{5}{8}$ 10. $\frac{23}{65} - \frac{1}{5}$ $\frac{2}{13}$ 11. $\frac{1}{24} + \frac{1}{16}$ $\frac{5}{48}$ 12. $\frac{13}{25} + \frac{1}{5}$ $\frac{18}{25}$

Solve each equation.

13. $j + \frac{5}{8} = \frac{65}{72}$ $j = \frac{5}{18}$ 14. $n - \frac{1}{10} = \frac{3}{8}$ $n = \frac{19}{40}$ 15. $h + \frac{3}{4} = \frac{11}{12}$ $h = \frac{1}{6}$ 16. $q - \frac{3}{16} = \frac{1}{3}$ $q = \frac{25}{48}$

17. $k + 2\frac{7}{20} = 8\frac{2}{5}$ $k = 6\frac{1}{20}$ 18. $d - 9\frac{1}{12} = 10\frac{1}{4}$ $d = 19\frac{1}{3}$ 19. $c - 17\frac{5}{7} = 5\frac{4}{21}$ $c = 22\frac{19}{21}$ 20. $p + 11\frac{1}{2} = 20\frac{7}{10}$ $p = 9\frac{1}{5}$

21. A cake recipe calls for $\frac{3}{4}$ cup cocoa plus enough flour to make a total of $3\frac{1}{3}$ cups. How much flour is in the recipe? $2\frac{7}{12}$ cups

22. A computer printer can print 8 pages per minute. *[Lesson 2-5]*

a. Write an expression for the number of pages that can be printed in t minutes. $8t$

b. How many pages can be printed in 9 minutes? 72

23. **Science** A male American toad can reach a length of 13.97 cm, which is 5.08 cm longer than the length of a female American toad. Write and solve an equation to find the length of a female American toad.

$13.97 = x + 5.08$; 8.89 cm

Visit **www.teacher.mathsurf.com** for links to lesson plans from teachers and other professionals, NCTM information, and other sites.

Products and Quotients of Fractions

LESSON PLANNING GUIDE

Student Edition				Ancillaries*	
LESSON		MATERIALS	VOCABULARY	DAILY	OTHER
	Section 4B Opener				
4-4	**Multiplying Fractions**	graph paper, colored pencils		4-4	Teaching Tool Trans. 2, 3, 7 Lesson Enhancement Trans. 15 *WW Math*—Middle School
4-5	**Multiplying Mixed Numbers**			4-5	Lesson Enhancement Trans. 16 Technology Master 16
	Technology	spreadsheet software			*Interactive CD-ROM Spreadsheet/Grapher Tool*
4-6	**Dividing Fractions and Mixed Numbers**		reciprocal	4-6	Lesson Enhancement Trans. 17 Technology Master 17
	Connect				Lesson Enhancement Trans. 18 Interdisc. Team Teaching 4B Ch. 4 Project Master
	Review				Practice 4B; Quiz 4B; *TestWorks*
	Extend Key ideas				
	Chapter 4 Summary and Review				
	Chapter 4 Assessment				Ch. 4 Tests Forms A–F *TestWorks*; Ch. 4 Letter Home
	Cumulative Review Chapters 1–4				Cumulative Review Ch. 1–4

* Daily Ancillaries include Practice, Reteaching, Problem Solving, Enrichment, and Daily Transparency. Teaching Tool Transparencies are in *Teacher's Toolkits*. Lesson Enhancement Transparencies are in *Overhead Transparency Package*.

SKILLS TRACE

LESSON	SKILL	FIRST INTRODUCED GR. 5	GR. 6	GR. 7	DEVELOP	PRACTICE/ APPLY	REVIEW
4-4	**Multiplying fractions.**	✗			pp. 186–188	pp. 189–190	pp. 205, 252, 364
4-5	**Multiplying mixed numbers.**	✗			pp. 191–193	pp. 194–195	pp. 205, 257, 370
4-6	**Dividing fractions and mixed numbers.**	✗			pp. 197–198	pp. 199–200	pp. 205, 262, 374

CONNECTED MATHEMATICS

The unit *Comparing and Scaling (Ratio Proportion and Percent),* from the **Connected Mathematics** series, can be used with Section 4B.

INTERDISCIPLINARY TEAM TEACHING

Math and Social Studies

(Worksheet pages 15–16: Teacher pages T15–T16)

In this lesson, students use fractions with Greek temple designs.

Name ______________________ ***Math and Social Studies***

BUILDING THE PARTHENON

Use fractions with Greek temple designs.

The highest point in the ancient city of Athens was the Acropolis (in Greek *akros* means "highest"; *polis* means "city"). Among all the temples within the Acropolis, the Parthenon was the largest and the most grand. This magnificent temple was built to honor the goddess Athena, for whom the city was named. Today, approximately 2500 years after it was built, the Parthenon still stands. Although many of its marble columns and statues have been destroyed by war and the ravages of time, its stately design and perfect proportions make it a symbol of great architecture.

The Parthenon was built of white marble taken from a quarry about 10 miles away. Large slabs of the marble were hauled by oxen up the steep hill, and stonecutters cut it to make steps, flooring, walls, roof, sculptures, and columns. The basic shape of the Parthenon is a rectangle, with its length being a little over twice as long as its width. Inside the temple were two rooms. In one room there was a statue of Athena; the other room was the city's treasury. Surrounding the rooms was an outer porch supported by outside columns, forming a colonnade. Above the columns, on the ends of the building, are long triangular sections called pediments. The pediments contained marble figures of ancient Greek gods and mortals who played roles in myths about Athena. Pediments and columns are two of the basic features of the classical style. New buildings built in this style are said to be neoclassical ("neo" means "new").

1. Looking at the pictures of the Parthenon, what do you observe about the lines of the building?

Answers will vary but might include that the building consists mainly of vertical columns, a horizontal roof, and a triangular pediment.

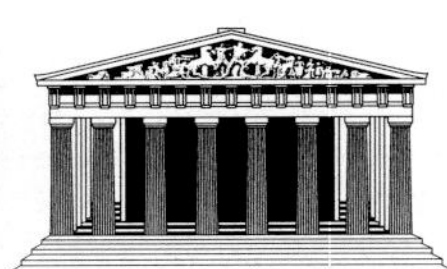

Left: The Parthenon as it looks today. Right: The Parthenon as it was when built, some 2500 years ago.

Name ______________________ ***Math and Social Studies***

2. Each end of the Parthenon is 160 feet wide, with 8 columns set apart at equal distances. Each side is 340 feet long. How many columns were built along each side, if they were the same distance apart as at the ends?

8 columns per 160 ft is one column for each 20-ft section. 340 ÷ 20 = 17 columns

3. Each marble column was made of several sections. Stonecutters cut each section into the shape of a drum with a hole in the center. With the help of pulleys, the marble "drums" were stacked on top of one another. Metal rods were then inserted into the holes to keep the sections together. If each marble drum was approximately $3\frac{2}{5}$ feet high, how tall a column would be made by stacking 11 marble drums?

See below.

4. Even though all the columns appear straight, they actually are thicker at the bottom. Also, the columns at the very ends are thicker than the columns in the center. This was done because the end columns were to be viewed against a background of blue sky and would have appeared too thin if they were identical to the other columns. The Greeks spaced the columns in a very precise, pleasing manner. They used a formula similar to this: the distance from the center of one column to the center of the next column is approximately 5 times the radius of the column.

If the radius of the columns is $4\frac{2}{5}$ feet, how far apart should the centers of the columns be?

See below.

5. Near the Parthenon is the small but elegant Temple of Athena Nike. (That means "Victorious Athena," not Athena in athletic shoes.) The centers of its columns are spaced $12\frac{1}{3}$ feet apart. If the Greeks used the same formula as they did for the columns of the Parthenon, what is the radius of the columns used in this temple?

See below.

6. Museum restoration workers have reconstructed the pediment of the west end of the Parthenon. The pediment itself is a long, low triangle whose base was $6\frac{2}{3}$ times its height. The base is the same as the length of the end of the Parthenon (160 feet). What was the height of the original pediment?

See below.

7. Take a look at some of the large buildings near where you live, such as your school or large office buildings. Notice any repeated design elements such as windows or columns. Use a tape measure to measure the distance between these elements, or use a ruler and measure them on a photograph. Do the elements seem to be the "right size" for the building? Are they spaced as consistently as the columns on a Greek temple?

See below.

Answers

3. Write $3\frac{2}{5}$ as an improper fraction, $\frac{17}{5}$, multiply by 11 drums: $\frac{17}{5} \times 11 = \frac{187}{5}$

   Change to a mixed number: $37\frac{2}{5}$ feet high.

4. Change $4\frac{2}{5}$ to an improper fraction: $\frac{22}{5}$.

   $\frac{22}{5} \times 5 = 22$ feet apart.

5. Since the distance from center to center of adjacent columns is $5 \times$ the radius, if we divide $12\frac{1}{3}$ (the distance) by 5, we can find the radius.

   Change $12\frac{1}{3}$ to an improper fraction, $\frac{37}{3}$, and multiply by the reciprocal of 5 which is $\frac{1}{5}$: $\frac{37}{3} \times \frac{1}{5} = \frac{37}{15}$.

   Change to a mixed number: $2\frac{7}{15}$ feet is the radius of the columns.

6. height = length divided by $6\frac{2}{3}$.

   Change $6\frac{2}{3}$ to an improper fraction: $\frac{20}{3}$.

   $h = 160 \times \frac{3}{20}$ (reciprocal of $\frac{20}{3}$).

   Reduce by factoring by 20 and reduce to $h = 8 \times 3 = 24$ *feet.*

7. Answers will vary. You may be able to furnish students with photographs or other information about their school building that will allow them to make measurements and comparisons of design elements.

BIBLIOGRAPHY

FOR TEACHERS

Bailey, Jill. *Encyclopedia of the Animal World*. New York, NY: Facts on File, 1989.

Cribb, Joe. *Money*. New York, NY: Knopf, 1990.

Spangler, David. *Math for Real Kids*. Glenview, IL: Good Year Books, 1997.

Parker, Steve. *Electricity*. London, England: Dorling Kindersley, 1992.

FOR STUDENTS

Brown, David. *The Random House Book of How Things Were Built*. New York, NY: Random House, 1992.

Ganeri, Anita. *The Oceans Atlas*. London, England: Dorling Kindersley, 1994.

Krause, Chester L. and Clifford Mishler. *Standard Catalog of Coins*. San Diego, CA: Ponterio & Assoc., 1997.

SECTION 4B

Products and Quotients of Fractions

▶ Industry Link ▶ www.mathsurf.com/7/ch4/construction

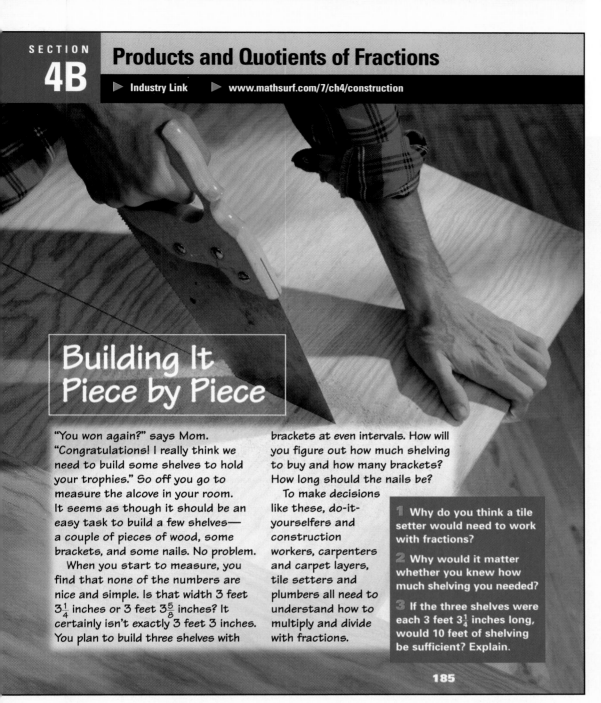

Building It Piece by Piece

"You won again?" says Mom. "Congratulations! I really think we need to build some shelves to hold your trophies." So off you go to measure the alcove in your room. It seems as though it should be an easy task to build a few shelves—a couple of pieces of wood, some brackets, and some nails. No problem.

When you start to measure, you find that none of the numbers are nice and simple. Is that width 3 feet $3\frac{1}{4}$ inches or 3 feet $3\frac{5}{8}$ inches? It certainly isn't exactly 3 feet 3 inches. You plan to build three shelves with brackets at even intervals. How will you figure out how much shelving to buy and how many brackets? How long should the nails be?

To make decisions like these, do-it-yourselfers and construction workers, carpenters and carpet layers, tile setters and plumbers all need to understand how to multiply and divide with fractions.

1 Why do you think a tile setter would need to work with fractions?

2 Why would it matter whether you knew how much shelving you needed?

3 If the three shelves were each 3 feet $3\frac{1}{4}$ inches long, would 10 feet of shelving be sufficient? Explain.

185

Where are we now?

In Section 4A, students learned to compute with and solve equations using addition and subtraction of fractions and mixed numbers.

They learned how to

- estimate solutions to problems containing fractions.
- add and subtract fractions and mixed numbers.
- solve equations using fractions and mixed numbers.

Where are we going?

In Section 4B, students will

- multiply fractions and mixed numbers.
- divide fractions and mixed numbers.

Theme: Construction and Building

World Wide Web

If your class has access to the World Wide Web, you might want to use the information found at the Web site address given. The interdisciplinary link relates to topics discussed in this section.

About the Page

This page introduces the theme of this section, construction and building, and discusses how fractions are used in these fields.

Ask …

- When building shelves or doing repairs or remodeling, why do measurements have to be exact? Possible answer: So the pieces will fit together.
- What is probably the first thing that carpenters, tile setters, and carpet layers do when they begin a project? Measure

Extension

The following activity does not require access to the World Wide Web.

Industry

Have students investigate the kinds of contractors that are involved in the construction industry, such as carpenters, electricians, plumbers, and so on.

Answers for Questions

1. Dimensions of the tiles and the floor might not be whole units.
2. So that you buy enough but not have too much left over.
3. Yes, 3×3 ft $= 9$ ft, $3\frac{1}{4}$ in. < 4 in., and 3×4 in. $= 1$ foot, so 3×3 ft $3\frac{1}{4}$ in. < 10 feet.

Connect

On page 201, students will determine quantities of products needed for remodeling by multiplying and dividing measurements on a blueprint.

4-4 Lesson Organizer

Objective

- Multiply fractions.

Materials

- Explore: Graph paper, colored pencils

NCTM Standards

- 1–4, 6, 7, 12, 13

Review

Find the GCF of each pair of numbers.

1. 4, 8 4
2. 9, 15 3
3. 12, 30 6
4. 21, 56 7

Available on Daily Transparency 4-4

1 Introduce

Explore

You may wish to use Lesson Enhancement Transparency 15 and Teaching Tool Transparency 7: $\frac{1}{4}$-Inch Graph Paper with **Explore**.

The Point

Students explore multiplying fractions by shading regions of rectangles. For example, $\frac{2}{3}$ is modeled by shading 2 of the 3 horizontal bars and $\frac{3}{4}$ is modeled by shading 3 of the 4 vertical bars. The overlap shows $\frac{2}{3}$ of $\frac{3}{4}$ or $\frac{2}{3} \cdot \frac{3}{4}$.

Ongoing Assessment

Check student work to make sure that students are shading horizontal and vertical bars to represent the two factors. It is helpful if students use different colors for the horizontal and vertical bars.

For Groups That Finish Early

Write a paragraph describing how you can multiply fractions without drawing rectangles. Answers may vary.

4-4 Multiplying Fractions

You'll Learn ...

- to multiply fractions

... How It's Used

Costume designers often have to make several identical outfits for a show. They will need to multiply fractions to order the right amounts of fabric.

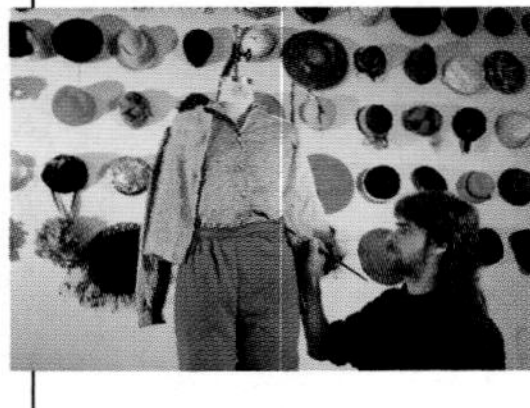

Lesson Link You've added and subtracted fractions and solved equations involving addition and subtraction of fractions. Now you'll multiply fractions. ◄

Explore Multiplying Fractions

A Model for Our Times

Materials: Graph paper, Colored pencils

Multiplying a Fraction by a Fraction

$\frac{2}{3} \times \frac{3}{4} = \frac{6}{12}$

- Draw a rectangle on graph paper. Use the denominators of the fractions you are multiplying to determine the length and width of the rectangle.
- Color a rectangle to represent the first fraction.
- Color a rectangle to represent the second fraction. Describe the section in the model where the two fractions overlap.

1. Model each product. **a.** $\frac{1}{2} \cdot \frac{2}{3}$ **b.** $\frac{1}{4} \cdot \frac{4}{5}$ **c.** $\frac{2}{5} \cdot \frac{3}{7}$ **d.** $\frac{3}{4} \cdot \frac{5}{6}$
2. How do the denominators of the fractions that are multiplied relate to the denominators of your answers? How are the numerators related?
3. Does $\frac{1}{2} \cdot \frac{1}{3}$ have the same answer as $\frac{1}{3} \cdot \frac{1}{2}$? Explain.
4. When you multiply two fractions that are between 0 and 1, is the product less than or greater than the original fractions?

Learn Multiplying Fractions

You can use a rectangle to model the product of two fractions. Recall that the formula for the area (A) of a rectangle with length l and width w is $A = lw$.

The first rectangle shows that $2 \cdot 3 = 6$.

The second rectangle shows that $\frac{1}{2} \cdot \frac{1}{3} = \frac{1}{6}$.

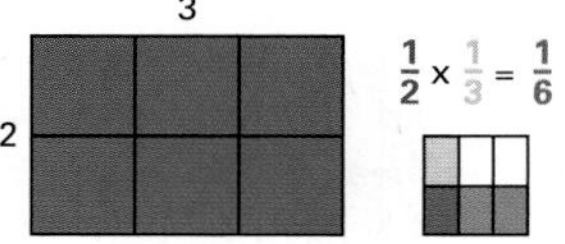

MEETING INDIVIDUAL NEEDS

Resources

- 4-4 Practice
- 4-4 Reteaching
- 4-4 Problem Solving
- 4-4 Enrichment
- 4-4 Daily Transparency
  - Problem of the Day
  - Review
  - Quick Quiz
- Teaching Tool Transparencies 2, 3, 7
- Lesson Enhancement Transparency 15

Wide World of Mathematics Middle School: Two-Sport Athlete

Learning Modalities

Verbal Have students describe the process used in **Explore** to find products using rectangles drawn on graph paper.

Social Have students work in groups and take turns explaining how a multiplication of fractions problem was solved.

English Language Development

Have students compare phrases such as *3 groups of 6* and *$\frac{1}{2}$ of 6* to help them see that both are multiplication situations. Provide additional examples and call on students to explain why each is a multiplication situation. Help students use appropriate math terms and expressions.

MULTIPLYING FRACTIONS

- Multiply the numerators and multiply the denominators.
- Simplify the product if possible.

Examples

1 Most nails are round. A *spike*, the longest and strongest type of nail, has a square cross section. The greater the area of the cross section, the harder a spike is to remove. A $\frac{3}{8}$ in. square spike requires 6000 lb of force to remove it from a piece of locust wood. Find the cross-sectional area of the spike.

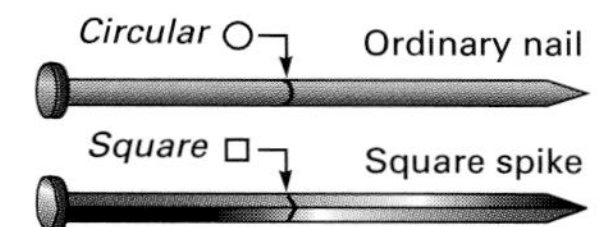

$A = lw = \frac{3}{8} \cdot \frac{3}{8}$ — Substitute $\frac{3}{8}$ for both l and w.

$= \frac{3 \cdot 3}{8 \cdot 8}$ — Multiply the numerators and denominators.

$= \frac{9}{64}$ — Simplify.

The cross-sectional area is $\frac{9}{64}$ square inches.

2 Multiply. Rewrite in lowest terms. $\frac{2}{5} \cdot \frac{7}{8}$

$\frac{2}{5} \cdot \frac{7}{8} = \frac{2 \cdot 7}{5 \cdot 8}$ — Multiply the numerators and the denominators.

$= \frac{14}{40}$ — Simplify.

$= \frac{14 \div 2}{40 \div 2}$ — Divide the numerator and denominator by 2 to rewrite in lowest terms.

$= \frac{7}{20}$ — Simplify.

Try It

Multiply. Rewrite in lowest terms.

a. $\frac{3}{7} \cdot \frac{5}{8}$ $\frac{15}{56}$ **b.** $\frac{8}{9} \cdot \frac{3}{4}$ $\frac{2}{3}$ **c.** $\frac{3}{10} \cdot \frac{5}{6}$ $\frac{1}{4}$ **d.** $\frac{2}{3} \cdot \frac{1}{4}$ $\frac{1}{6}$ **e.** $\frac{3}{5} \cdot \frac{1}{6}$ $\frac{1}{10}$

Remember

The formula for the area of a rectangle is $A = lw$. **[Page 58]**

History Link

The most famous *spike* is probably the Golden Spike, which completed the Central Pacific Railroad tracks at Promontory Point, Utah, in 1869.

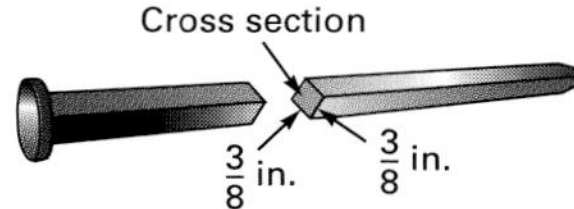

MATH EVERY DAY

Problem of the Day

Jeremy has ostriches and dogs on his farm. His son tallied 35 heads and 78 legs for the ostriches and dogs combined. How many dogs and ostriches does Jeremy have? 4 dogs and 31 ostriches

Available on Daily Transparency 4-4

An Extension is provided in the transparency package.

Fact of the Day

Because of its shape, a young mackerel (a type of saltwater fish) that is 6 inches or less in length is called a *spike*.

Estimation

Estimate.

1. $17 \times \frac{1}{4}$ 4
2. $\frac{1}{3} \times 25$ 8
3. $19 \times \frac{1}{6}$ 3
4. $\frac{1}{5} \times 49$ 10

Answers for Explore

1. See page C6 for drawings.
   a. $\frac{1}{2} \bullet \frac{2}{3} = \frac{2}{6} = \frac{1}{3}$
   b. $\frac{1}{4} \bullet \frac{4}{5} = \frac{4}{20} = \frac{1}{5}$
   c. $\frac{2}{5} \bullet \frac{3}{7} = \frac{6}{35}$
   d. $\frac{3}{4} \bullet \frac{5}{6} = \frac{15}{24} = \frac{5}{8}$
2. In each case, the denominator of the product is the product of the first 2 denominators. The numerator of the product is the product of the first 2 numerators.
3. Yes. Multiplication is commutative.
4. The product will be less than the original fractions.

2 Teach

Learn

Alternate Examples

1. A square stamp measures $\frac{5}{8}$ in. on each side. Find the area of the stamp.

   $A = lw = \frac{5}{8} \bullet \frac{5}{8}$
   $= \frac{5 \bullet 5}{8 \bullet 8}$
   $= \frac{25}{64}$

   The area is $\frac{25}{64}$ square inches.

2. Multiply. Rewrite in lowest terms.
   $\frac{3}{4} \bullet \frac{2}{7}$

   $\frac{3}{4} \bullet \frac{2}{7} = \frac{3 \bullet 2}{4 \bullet 7}$
   $= \frac{6}{28}$
   $= \frac{6 \div 2}{28 \div 2}$
   $= \frac{3}{14}$

Alternate Examples

3. Multiply. Rewrite in lowest terms. $\frac{3}{4} \bullet \frac{5}{6}$

$\frac{3}{4} \bullet \frac{5}{6} = \frac{\cancel{3}^{1}}{4} \bullet \frac{5}{\cancel{6}_{2}}$

$= \frac{5}{8}$

4. Multiply. Rewrite in lowest terms. $\frac{63}{64} \bullet \frac{56}{81}$

$\frac{63}{64} \bullet \frac{56}{81} = \frac{63}{\cancel{64}_{8}} \bullet \frac{\cancel{56}^{7}}{81}$

$= \frac{\cancel{63}^{7}}{\cancel{64}_{8}} \bullet \frac{\cancel{56}^{7}}{\cancel{81}_{9}}$

$= \frac{49}{72}$

3 Practice and Assess

Check

Answers for Check Your Understanding

1. Possible answer: You can use the GCF to divide the numerator and denominator to make the numbers easier to work with.
2. Possible answer: Yes; When you multiply any number by a fraction less than one, the answer is always less than the original number.
3. Erica is correct; Since multiplying a number by $\frac{1}{4}$ means multiplying its numerator by 1 and its denominator by 4, you're actually dividing the number by 4. This is the same as finding $\frac{1}{4}$ of the number.

Remember

The GCF is the largest factor that divides evenly into two numbers.
[Page 139]

You can save yourself work by dividing the numerator and the denominator by common factors *before* you multiply.

$\frac{\cancel{4}^{1}}{10} \cdot \frac{15}{\cancel{8}_{2}}$ Divide 4 and 8 by 4, a common factor.

$= \frac{\cancel{4}^{1}}{\cancel{10}_{2}} \cdot \frac{\cancel{15}^{3}}{\cancel{8}_{2}}$ Divide 15 and 10 by 5, a common factor.

$= \frac{3}{4}$ Multiply the factors that remain.

Examples

3 Multiply. Rewrite in lowest terms. $\frac{5}{8} \cdot \frac{4}{7}$

$\frac{5}{8} \cdot \frac{4}{7} = \frac{5}{\cancel{8}_{2}} \cdot \frac{\cancel{4}^{1}}{7}$ Divide 8 and 4 by 4, a common factor.

$= \frac{5}{14}$ Multiply the fractions that remain.

4 Multiply. Rewrite in lowest terms. $\frac{49}{50} \cdot \frac{25}{28}$

$\frac{49}{50} \cdot \frac{25}{28} = \frac{49}{\cancel{50}_{2}} \cdot \frac{\cancel{25}^{1}}{28}$ Divide 25 and 50 by 25, a common factor.

$= \frac{\cancel{49}^{7}}{\cancel{50}_{2}} \cdot \frac{\cancel{25}^{1}}{\cancel{28}_{4}}$ Divide 49 and 28 by 7, a common factor.

$= \frac{7}{8}$ Multiply the fractions that remain.

Try It

Multiply. Rewrite in lowest terms.

a. $\frac{14}{15} \cdot \frac{20}{21}$ $\frac{8}{9}$ **b.** $\frac{12}{27} \cdot \frac{18}{24}$ $\frac{1}{3}$ **c.** $\frac{18}{35} \cdot \frac{21}{50}$ $\frac{27}{125}$ **d.** $\frac{3}{5} \cdot \frac{5}{6}$ $\frac{1}{2}$ **e.** $\frac{16}{34} \cdot \frac{17}{32}$ $\frac{1}{4}$

HINT

If your calculator has a fraction key, you can use it to multiply fractions. To multiply $\frac{7}{12} \cdot \frac{5}{9}$, enter 7 [/] 12 [×] 5 [/] 9 [=]. The product is $\frac{35}{108}$.

Check Your Understanding

1. How can the greatest common factor be used to help multiply fractions?
2. Two fractions are each less than 1. Is their product less than 1? Explain.
3. Erica said, "When I multiply $\frac{1}{4}$ times a number, I'm really finding $\frac{1}{4}$ of the number." Is she correct? Explain.

MEETING MIDDLE SCHOOL CLASSROOM NEEDS

Tips from Middle School Teachers

I encourage my students to divide a numerator and denominator by the largest common factor that they find, even if they aren't sure of the GCF. The answer will be easier to rewrite in lowest terms.

Consumer Connection

Common wire spikes vary from 3 inches to 6 inches in length. However, some wire spikes can be as long as 12 inches.

Cooperative Learning

Have students work in pairs using grids to find products of fractions. For example, while one student shades $\frac{1}{2} \bullet \frac{2}{3}$, the other shades $\frac{2}{3} \bullet \frac{1}{2}$. Have them compare their results.

Give students the opportunity to make up several products similar to the one above and have them compare results.

4-4 Exercises and Applications

Practice and Apply

Getting Started **Multiply the numerators and the denominators to find each product.**

1. $\frac{1}{2} \cdot \frac{2}{3}$ $\frac{1}{3}$
2. $\frac{2}{5} \cdot \frac{3}{7}$ $\frac{6}{35}$
3. $\frac{4}{5} \cdot \frac{2}{9}$ $\frac{8}{45}$
4. $\frac{1}{10} \cdot \frac{1}{3}$ $\frac{1}{30}$
5. $\frac{1}{4} \cdot \frac{3}{5}$ $\frac{3}{20}$

Find each product. Rewrite in lowest terms.

6. $\frac{1}{2} \cdot \frac{2}{9}$ $\frac{1}{9}$
7. $\frac{3}{5} \cdot \frac{2}{3}$ $\frac{2}{5}$
8. $\frac{3}{4} \cdot \frac{6}{7}$ $\frac{9}{14}$
9. $\frac{4}{9} \cdot \frac{3}{4}$ $\frac{1}{3}$
10. $\frac{1}{3} \cdot \frac{3}{8}$ $\frac{1}{8}$
11. $\frac{4}{5} \cdot \frac{3}{8}$ $\frac{3}{10}$
12. $\frac{3}{4} \cdot \frac{5}{9}$ $\frac{5}{12}$
13. $\frac{5}{7} \cdot \frac{1}{5}$ $\frac{1}{7}$
14. $\frac{6}{11} \cdot \frac{5}{6}$ $\frac{5}{11}$
15. $\frac{2}{9} \cdot \frac{3}{4}$ $\frac{1}{6}$

Divide the numerator and the denominator of the following fractions by common factors *before* you multiply. Then multiply the fractions that remain.

16. $\frac{8}{15} \cdot \frac{5}{16}$ $\frac{1}{6}$
17. $\frac{9}{14} \cdot \frac{7}{18}$ $\frac{1}{4}$
18. $\frac{15}{27} \cdot \frac{18}{25}$ $\frac{2}{5}$
19. $\frac{8}{21} \cdot \frac{15}{16}$ $\frac{5}{14}$
20. $\frac{4}{35} \cdot \frac{7}{24}$ $\frac{1}{30}$
21. $\frac{18}{35} \cdot \frac{14}{45}$ $\frac{4}{25}$
22. $\frac{24}{49} \cdot \frac{35}{48}$ $\frac{5}{14}$
23. $\frac{20}{49} \cdot \frac{21}{40}$ $\frac{3}{14}$
24. $\frac{27}{56} \cdot \frac{35}{36}$ $\frac{15}{32}$
25. $\frac{14}{36} \cdot \frac{18}{35}$ $\frac{1}{5}$

26. **Measurement** Find the area of each rectangle.

 a. $\frac{7}{8}$ in. by $\frac{7}{16}$ in. $\frac{49}{128}$ in^2

 b. $\frac{3}{4}$ in. by $\frac{3}{8}$ in. $\frac{9}{32}$ in^2

27. **Test Prep** What will the denominator be when the product $\frac{27}{48} \cdot \frac{24}{45}$ is expressed in lowest terms? B

 Ⓐ 3 Ⓑ 10 Ⓒ 45 Ⓓ 2160

28. **Career** A tile setter is tiling a floor with tiles that measure $\frac{3}{4}$ ft on each side. If he uses 17 tiles along a wall, how long is the wall? $\frac{51}{4}$ ft $= 12\frac{3}{4}$ ft

29. **History** From 1892 until 1954, New York's Ellis Island was the entry point to the United States for most immigrants coming over the Atlantic Ocean. In 1911, 650,000 people arrived at Ellis Island. About $\frac{1}{50}$ of those were turned away for economic or health reasons. How many people were turned away? 13,000

PRACTICE

Name ______________________

Practice 4-4

Multiplying Fractions

Find each product. Rewrite in lowest terms.

1. $\frac{1}{8} \cdot \frac{2}{3}$ $\frac{1}{12}$
2. $\frac{5}{9} \cdot \frac{3}{5}$ $\frac{1}{3}$
3. $\frac{1}{2} \cdot \frac{4}{5}$ $\frac{2}{5}$
4. $\frac{8}{9} \cdot \frac{5}{6}$ $\frac{20}{27}$
5. $\frac{2}{9} \cdot \frac{3}{5}$ $\frac{2}{15}$
6. $\frac{7}{9} \cdot \frac{9}{10}$ $\frac{7}{10}$
7. $\frac{5}{6} \cdot \frac{4}{9}$ $\frac{10}{27}$
8. $\frac{5}{8} \cdot \frac{4}{9}$ $\frac{5}{18}$
9. $\frac{1}{8} \cdot \frac{6}{7}$ $\frac{3}{28}$
10. $\frac{1}{2} \cdot \frac{4}{5}$ $\frac{2}{5}$
11. $\frac{3}{4} \cdot \frac{5}{6}$ $\frac{5}{8}$
12. $\frac{2}{5} \cdot \frac{3}{10}$ $\frac{3}{25}$
13. $\frac{2}{7} \cdot \frac{3}{4}$ $\frac{3}{14}$
14. $\frac{3}{10} \cdot \frac{1}{9}$ $\frac{1}{30}$
15. $\frac{8}{9} \cdot \frac{3}{7}$ $\frac{8}{21}$

Divide the numerator and the denominator of the following fractions by common factors *before* you multiply. Then multiply the fractions that remain.

16. $\frac{10}{17} \cdot \frac{7}{16}$ $\frac{35}{136}$
17. $\frac{3}{40} \cdot \frac{5}{21}$ $\frac{1}{56}$
18. $\frac{12}{35} \cdot \frac{10}{21}$ $\frac{8}{49}$
19. $\frac{19}{36} \cdot \frac{9}{13}$ $\frac{19}{52}$
20. $\frac{11}{32} \cdot \frac{9}{11}$ $\frac{9}{32}$
21. $\frac{35}{72} \cdot \frac{36}{43}$ $\frac{35}{86}$
22. $\frac{9}{28} \cdot \frac{8}{15}$ $\frac{6}{35}$
23. $\frac{9}{11} \cdot \frac{25}{27}$ $\frac{25}{33}$
24. $\frac{6}{19} \cdot \frac{19}{50}$ $\frac{3}{25}$
25. $\frac{5}{36} \cdot \frac{16}{45}$ $\frac{4}{81}$
26. $\frac{45}{91} \cdot \frac{13}{33}$ $\frac{15}{77}$
27. $\frac{16}{51} \cdot \frac{63}{80}$ $\frac{21}{85}$

Measurement Find the area of each rectangle.

28. $\frac{9}{25}$ cm^2 — $\frac{2}{5}$ cm by $\frac{9}{10}$ cm

29. $\frac{7}{24}$ in^2 — $\frac{3}{8}$ in. by $\frac{7}{9}$ in.

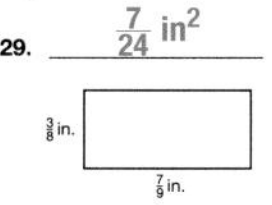

30. A sheet of plywood is $\frac{5}{8}$ in. thick. How tall is a stack of 21 sheets of plywood? $13\frac{1}{8}$ in.

31. A poster measures 38 cm across. If a photocopy machine is used to make a copy that is $\frac{3}{5}$ of the original size, what is the width of the copy? $22\frac{4}{5}$ cm

RETEACHING

Name ______________________

Alternative Lesson 4-4

Multiplying Fractions

You can use models to multiply fractions. You can also multiply the numerators and multiply the denominators.

Example 1

Multiply. Rewrite in lowest terms. $\frac{1}{4} \cdot \frac{2}{3}$

Use the rectangles to model the product.

Show $\frac{1}{4}$. Show $\frac{2}{3}$.

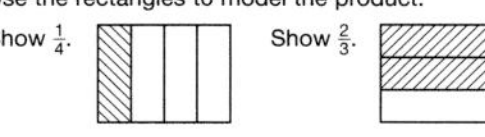

Combine the rectangles. The product is the area that is shaded twice. Two twelfths are shaded.

$\frac{1}{4} \cdot \frac{2}{3} = \frac{2}{12} = \frac{1}{6}$

Try It Complete the models to find each product.

a. $\frac{3}{4} \cdot \frac{1}{3}$ $\frac{3}{12} = \frac{1}{4}$

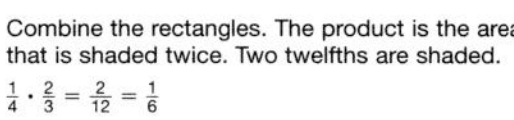

b. $\frac{3}{8} \cdot \frac{1}{2}$ $\frac{3}{16}$

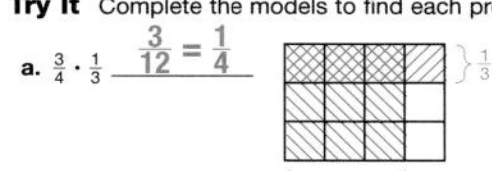

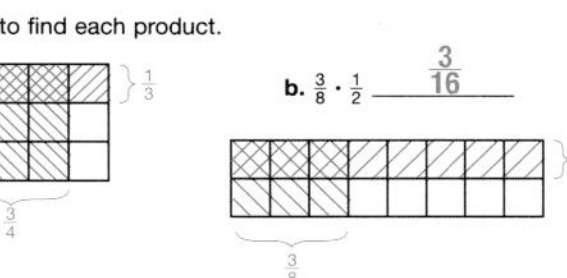

Example 2

Multiply. Rewrite in lowest terms. $\frac{3}{4} \cdot \frac{1}{6}$

Step 1: Multiply the numerators and the denominators. $\frac{3 \times 1}{4 \times 6} = \frac{3}{24}$

Step 2: Divide the numerator and denominator by a common factor to rewrite in lowest terms. A common factor of 3 and 24 is 3. $\frac{3 \div 3}{24 \div 3} = \frac{1}{8}$

$\frac{3}{4} \cdot \frac{1}{6} = \frac{3}{24} = \frac{1}{8}$

Try It Multiply. Rewrite in lowest terms. $\frac{7}{8} \cdot \frac{4}{5}$

c. Multiply the numerators. 28

d. Multiply the denominators. 40

e. Find a common factor. 4

f. Rewrite in lowest terms. $\frac{7}{10}$

Find each product. Rewrite in lowest terms.

g. $\frac{2}{3} \cdot \frac{9}{10}$ $\frac{3}{5}$

h. $\frac{5}{9} \cdot \frac{6}{10}$ $\frac{1}{3}$

i. $\frac{3}{4} \cdot \frac{5}{6}$ $\frac{5}{8}$

4-4 Exercises and Applications

Assignment Guide

- Basic
 1–20, 26–28, 31–39 odds
- Average
 1–25 odds, 26–32, 34–40
- Enriched
 6–24 evens, 26–34, 36–44

Exercise Notes

Exercise 27

Test Prep If students choose Answer D, they multiplied correctiy, but did not first divide by common factors or rewrite the product in lowest terms.

Exercise 29

History About 12 million immigrants entered the United States through Ellis Island during the time it was an entry point.

Exercise 31

Error Prevention Students may need to determine first that 1 square yard = 9 square feet.

Reteaching

Activity

Materials: Paper squares

- Since $\frac{1}{4}$ of $\frac{1}{2}$ means $\frac{1}{4} \cdot \frac{1}{2}$, you can cut a paper square and fold it to show $\frac{1}{4} \cdot \frac{1}{2}$. First, fold it into 4 equal strips. Then, fold the square in half across the other folds to form 8 rectangles. Shade 1 of the rectangles. The area of the shaded portion is $\frac{1}{8}$, showing that $\frac{1}{4} \cdot \frac{1}{2} = \frac{1}{8}$.

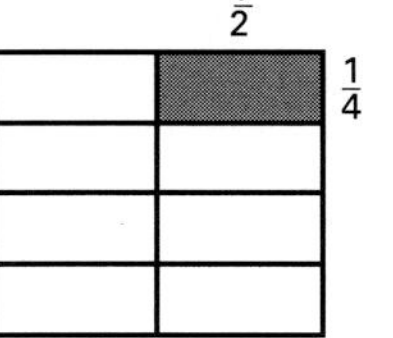

- Fold another square to show $\frac{1}{3} \cdot \frac{1}{3}$. Find the answer. $\frac{1}{9}$

Exercise Notes

■ Exercise 32

Problem-Solving Tip You may want to use Teaching Tool Transparencies 2 and 3: Guided Problem Solving, pages 1–2.

Exercise Answers

32. 2, 3, and 6

33. Possible answer: Multiplying a whole number by a whole number is the same as adding the number a whole number of times, so your answer is at least as big as the original number. When you multiply a whole number by a fraction, you are not adding the number even one time, so your answer will be smaller.

34. Possible answer: 9 is $\frac{3}{4}$ of 12, so you multiply the quantities in the recipe by $\frac{3}{4}$ to get the right amount for 9 people.

35. **Students per Grade**

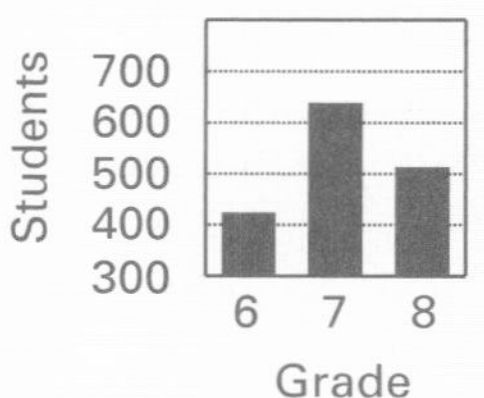

36. **Weights of Dogs**

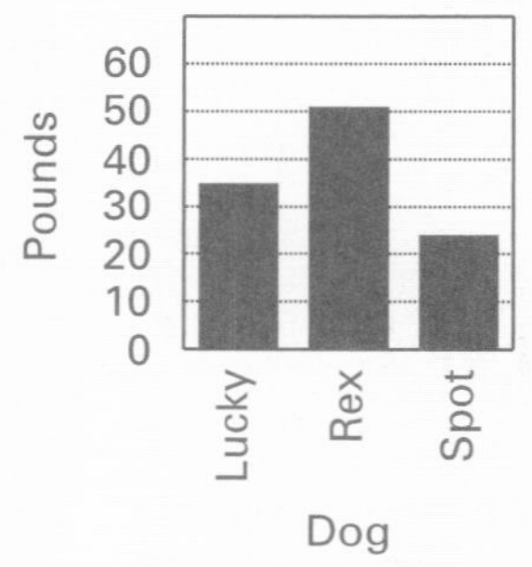

Alternate Assessment

Interview Have students find the following products and describe how they found the results.

1. $\frac{2}{5} \cdot \frac{3}{4}$ $\frac{3}{10}$ 2. $\frac{4}{9} \cdot \frac{3}{7}$ $\frac{4}{21}$

▶ Quick Quiz

Find each product.

1. $\frac{8}{9} \times \frac{3}{8}$ $\frac{1}{3}$
2. $\frac{4}{5} \times \frac{3}{16}$ $\frac{3}{20}$
3. $\frac{2}{3} \times \frac{9}{10}$ $\frac{3}{5}$

Available on Daily Transparency 4-4

PROBLEM SOLVING 4-4

30. **Science** Gravitational attraction on the moon isn't as strong as gravity on Earth because of the moon's smaller mass. The weight of an object on the moon is about $\frac{1}{6}$ of what it would weigh on Earth. What would be the weight of each animal if it were on the moon?
    a. Otter: 13 lb $\frac{13}{6}$ lb $= 2\frac{1}{6}$ lb
    b. Raccoon: 21 lb $\frac{7}{2}$ lb $= 3\frac{1}{2}$ lb
    c. Coyote: 75 lb $\frac{25}{2}$ lb $= 12\frac{1}{2}$ lb
    d. Alligator: 150 lb 25 lb

Problem Solving and Reasoning

31. **Critical Thinking** A square yard measures 3 ft by 3 ft. GPS How many square yards of floor space are in a 2 ft by 6 ft closet? $1\frac{1}{3}$

32. **Choose a Strategy** Find three different common factors you could use to divide the numerator and denominator of each fraction in the following problem: $\frac{12}{30} \cdot \frac{24}{60}$.

33. **Communicate** Explain why the answer is larger than the number you start with when you multiply a whole number by a whole number and smaller when you multiply a whole number by a proper fraction.

34. Journal You have a recipe that makes enough punch for twelve people. Explain how multiplication of fractions can help you adjust the recipe for nine people.

Problem Solving STRATEGIES
- Look for a Pattern
- Make an Organized List
- Make a Table
- Guess and Check
- Work Backward
- Use Logical Reasoning
- Draw a Diagram
- Solve a Simpler Problem

Mixed Review

Make a bar graph for each set of data. *[Lesson 1-2]*

35.

Grade	6	7	8
No. of Students	421	635	507

36.

Dog	Lucky	Rex	Spot
Weight (lb)	35	51	23

Solve each equation. *[Lesson 3-4]*

37. $8.26p = 9.499$ $p = 1.15$
38. $0.64 = \frac{s}{5.23}$ $s = 3.3472$
39. $39.52 = 10.4u$ $u = 3.8$
40. $\frac{z}{1.873} = 5.01$ $z = 9.38373$
41. $0.73x = 1.9345$ $x = 2.65$
42. $\frac{g}{38.42} = 21.75$ $g = 835.635$
43. $76.858 = 8.3y$ $y = 9.26$
44. $3.72 = \frac{k}{0.057}$ $y = 0.21204$

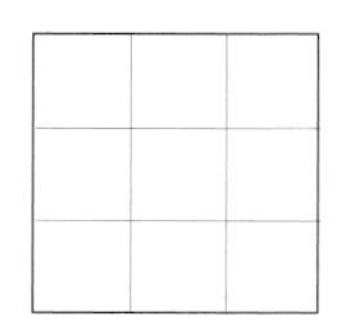

PROBLEM SOLVING

Name ______________ **Guided Problem Solving 4-4**

GPS **PROBLEM 31, STUDENT PAGE 190**

A square yard measures 3 ft by 3 ft. How many square yards of floor space are in a 2 ft by 6 ft closet?

Understand

1. What are you asked to find? The number of square yards of floor space in a 2 ft by 6 ft closet.
2. Circle the information that you need.

Plan

At the right is a diagram of 1 square yard. Divide the diagram to show square feet.

4. How many square feet are equal to 1 square yard? 9 square feet.
5. How many square yards are equal to 18 square feet? 2 square yards.
6. How many square yards are equal to 27 square feet? 3 square yards.
7. Analyze your answers to Items 5 and 6. Write an expression to show the number of square yards in x square feet. $x \div 9$

Solve

8. How many square feet of floor space are in a 2 ft by 6 ft closet? $12\ ft^2$
9. How many square yards of floor space are in the closet? $1\frac{1}{3}\ yd^2$

Look Back

10. How can you check your answer? Possible answer: Draw a diagram and divide it into 9 square feet sections.

SOLVE ANOTHER PROBLEM

A square foot measures 12 in. by 12 in. How many square feet of shelf paper is needed to line the bottom of a 10 in. by 18 in. drawer? $1\frac{1}{4}\ ft^2$

ENRICHMENT

Name ______________ **Extend Your Thinking 4-4**

Critical Thinking

Find the area of each shaded part.

1. $\frac{11}{48}\ yd^2$

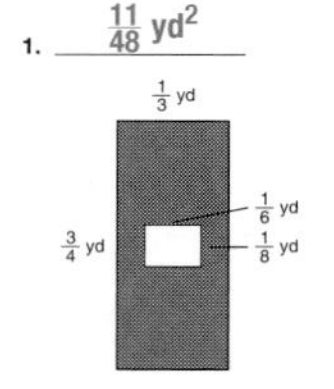

2. $\frac{1}{16}\ in^2$

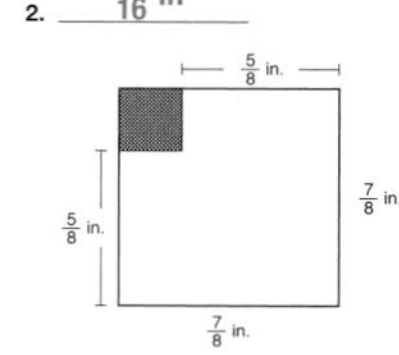

3. $\frac{1}{6}\ ft^2$

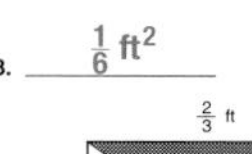
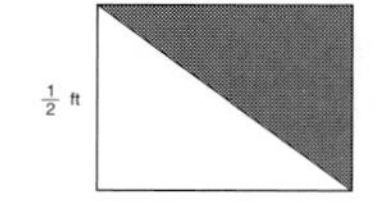

4. $\frac{3}{32}\ mi^2$

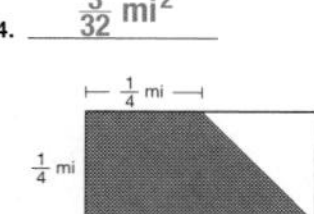
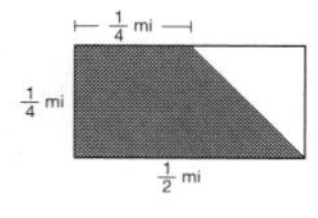

5. $\frac{5}{18}\ yd^2$

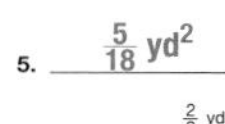

6. $\frac{1}{6}\ in^2$

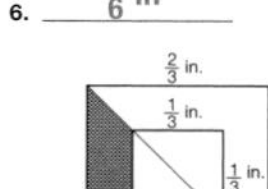

Multiplying Mixed Numbers

4-5

▶ Lesson Link You have found products of fractions. Now you'll find products of mixed numbers. ◀

You'll Learn ...

■ to multiply mixed numbers

... How It's Used

Gardeners need to multiply mixed numbers when they mix fertilizers.

Explore Multiplying Mixed Numbers

The Math Writing on the Wall

Your kitchen has a length of 18 ft and a width of 9 ft. You've hired a contractor to knock down a wall and build an addition that will increase the width by 7 ft.

9 ft | 7 ft | 18 ft | Old | Addition

1. Find the area of the "old" kitchen, the addition, and the "new" kitchen.
2. Explain how your results show that $18(9 + 7) = (18 \cdot 9) + (18 \cdot 7)$.
3. Draw a sketch that models each equation.
   a. $24(11 + 7) = (24 \cdot 11) + (24 \cdot 7)$ b. $6\left(2 + \frac{1}{3}\right) = (6 \cdot 2) + \left(6 \cdot \frac{1}{3}\right)$
4. Describe two ways you can find the product $4 \cdot 8\frac{1}{2}$.

Learn Multiplying Mixed Numbers

Remember

The Distributive Property states that $a(b + c) = ab + ac$.

[Page 62]

Jenny wanted to find the area of the large rectangle. She knew that she could use the formula $A = lw$. She decided that she would add the areas of the two smaller rectangles.

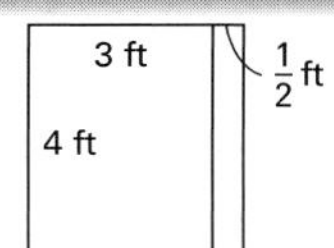

area of large rectangle = area of left rectangle + area of right rectangle

$$\begin{aligned} l \cdot w \quad &\quad\; l \cdot w \quad\quad\quad l \cdot w \\ 4 \cdot 3\tfrac{1}{2} &= (4 \cdot 3) + \left(4 \cdot \tfrac{1}{2}\right) \\ &= 12 + 2 \\ &= 14 \text{ ft}^2 \end{aligned}$$

MEETING INDIVIDUAL NEEDS

Resources

- 4-5 Practice
- 4-5 Reteaching
- 4-5 Problem Solving
- 4-5 Enrichment
- 4-5 Daily Transparency
  - Problem of the Day
  - Review
  - Quick Quiz
- Lesson Enhancement Transparency 16
- Technology Master 16

Learning Modalities

Verbal Have students describe how they can multiply any two mixed numbers.

Visual Draw a rectangle with dimensions $1\frac{1}{2}$ and $2\frac{1}{3}$. Have students subdivide it into smaller rectangles with known areas in order to determine the area of the large rectangle.

Challenge

Write examples of multiplication problems, involving mixed numbers, that can be solved mentally. How are these problems different from ones that would be difficult to solve mentally?

4-5 Lesson Organizer

Objective

■ Multiply mixed numbers.

NCTM Standards

■ 1–2, 4–7, 12

▶ Review

Write each mixed number as an improper fraction.

1. $3\frac{1}{2}$ $\frac{7}{2}$ 2. $5\frac{1}{3}$ $\frac{16}{3}$
3. $2\frac{2}{9}$ $\frac{20}{9}$ 4. $6\frac{3}{4}$ $\frac{27}{4}$

Available on Daily Transparency 4-5

▶ Lesson Link

Discuss situations from the previous lesson which involved multiplying fractions. Discuss whether or not these situations might also involve mixed numbers.

1 Introduce

Explore

You may wish to use Lesson Enhancement Transparency 16 with **Explore**.

The Point

Students explore multiplying mixed numbers by drawing models illustrating the distributive property for whole numbers and extending it to mixed numbers.

Ongoing Assessment

Check students' work to make sure that they are drawing rectangles with appropriate dimensions.

For Groups That Finish Early

Explain how your sketches in Step 3 relate to the equations.

Answers for Explore

1. "Old": area = 162 ft². Addition: area = 126 ft². "New": area = 288 ft².
2. Area of "new" = Area of "old" + Area of addition. Area of "new" = 18 • 16 = 18(9 + 7). Area of "old" = 18 • 9. Area of addition = 18 • 7. So, 18 (9 + 7) = 18 • 9 + 18 • 7.
3. See next page.

Answers for Explore

3. a.

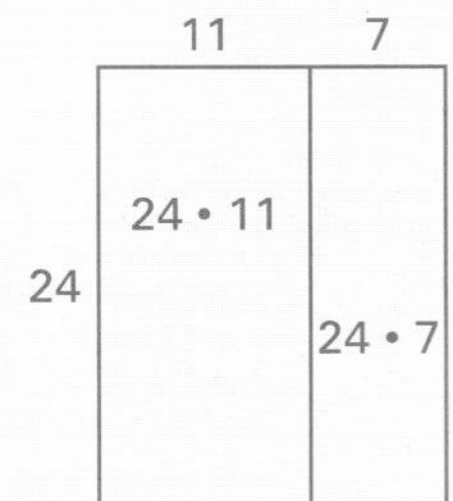

b.

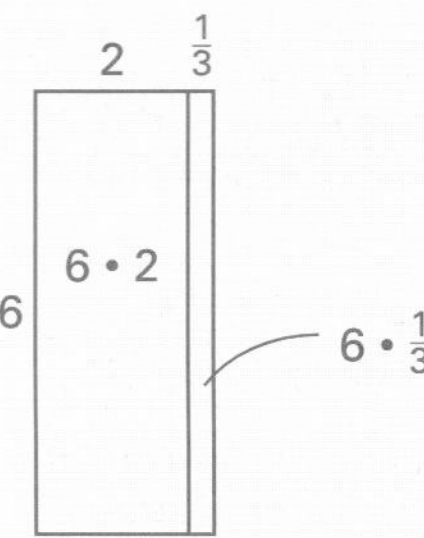

4. $4 \cdot 8\frac{1}{2} = 4 \cdot 8 + 4 \cdot \frac{1}{2}$ or $8\frac{1}{2} + 8\frac{1}{2} + 8\frac{1}{2} + 8\frac{1}{2}$

2 Teach

Learn

Alternate Examples

1. Multiply $10 \cdot 3\frac{1}{5}$.

$$10 \times 3\frac{1}{5} = \frac{10}{1} \cdot \frac{16}{5} = \frac{\overset{2}{\cancel{10}}}{1} \cdot \frac{16}{\underset{1}{\cancel{5}}} = 32$$

2. Find the number of board feet in a plank that is $2\frac{1}{6}$ ft long, $4\frac{1}{2}$ ft wide, and 2 in. thick.

$$2\frac{1}{6} \cdot 4\frac{1}{2} \cdot 2 = \frac{13}{6} \cdot \frac{9}{2} \cdot \frac{2}{1} = \frac{13}{\underset{2}{\cancel{6}}} \cdot \frac{\overset{3}{\cancel{9}}}{\underset{1}{\cancel{2}}} \cdot \frac{\overset{1}{\cancel{2}}}{1} = \frac{39}{2} = 19\frac{1}{2}$$

The plank measures $19\frac{1}{2}$ board feet.

Jenny's method shows that the distributive property can be used to multiply a whole number by a mixed number. Using the distributive property, you may be able to find the product mentally.

You can also multiply mixed numbers by rewriting them as improper fractions. Then multiply the numerators and multiply the denominators.

Study TIP

Although it is quicker to divide by the GCF, any common factor will do. Sometimes it is easier to divide by a smaller factor several times.

Examples

1 Multiply: $12 \times 4\frac{2}{3}$

$= \frac{\overset{4}{\cancel{12}}}{1} \times \frac{14}{\underset{1}{\cancel{3}}}$ Divide 12 and 3 by 3, a common factor.

$= \frac{4 \times 14}{1 \times 1}$ Multiply numerators and denominators.

$= 56$ Multiply.

2 The measure of a piece of lumber in *board feet* equals $l \cdot w \cdot t$. Length (l) and width (w) are measured in feet and thickness (t) is measured in inches. Find the number of board feet in the plank.

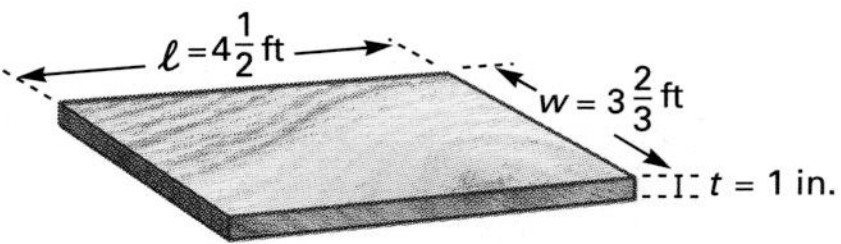

$4\frac{1}{2} \cdot 3\frac{2}{3} \cdot 1 = \frac{9}{2} \cdot \frac{11}{3} \cdot \frac{1}{1}$ Write mixed numbers as improper fractions.

$= \frac{9 \cdot 11 \cdot 1}{2 \cdot 3 \cdot 1}$ Multiply numerators and denominators.

$= \frac{\overset{3}{\cancel{9}} \cdot 11 \cdot 1}{2 \cdot \underset{1}{\cancel{3}} \cdot 1}$ Divide 9 and 3 by 3, a common factor.

$= \frac{33}{2}$ Multiply.

$= 16\frac{1}{2}$ Change to a mixed number.

The plank measures $16\frac{1}{2}$ board feet.

Try It

Multiply. Rewrite in lowest terms.

a. $8 \cdot 2\frac{1}{4}$ 18 **b.** $4\frac{2}{7} \cdot 1\frac{2}{5}$ 6 **c.** $2\frac{1}{10} \cdot 2\frac{1}{7}$ $4\frac{1}{2}$ **d.** $3\frac{3}{10} \cdot 5$ $16\frac{1}{2}$ **e.** $6\frac{1}{2} \cdot 2\frac{2}{3}$ $17\frac{1}{3}$

MATH EVERY DAY

Problem of the Day

There are 12 animals used in the Chinese Zodiac Calendar. In order, they are: Monkey, Rooster, Dog, Pig, Rat, Chicken, Tiger, Rabbit, Dragon, Snake, Horse, Ram. If you were born in the year of the Pig, how old will you be when you celebrate the year of the Snake for the fourth time? What year will it be when you are 40 years old? 42 years old; the year of the Rabbit

Available on Daily Transparency 4-5

An Extension is provided in the transparency package.

Fact of the Day

A board foot is equal to the volume of a board that measures 12 inches by 12 inches by 1 inch. This unit of measure came into existence about 100 years ago.

Mental Math

Do these mentally.

1. 198 + 144 342
2. 149 + 33 182
3. 297 + 103 400

Andy and Paula are helping their parents build a storage shed. They need to know the area of the 6 ft by $5\frac{1}{3}$ ft space where the shed will go.

Andy thinks . . .

I'll use the distributive property to multiply.

$6 \cdot 5\frac{1}{3} = 6(5 + \frac{1}{3})$ Rewrite $5\frac{1}{3}$ as a sum.

$= (6 \cdot 5) + (6 \cdot \frac{1}{3})$ Use the distributive property.

$= 30 + 2$ Multiply.

$= 32$ Add.

The area is 32 square feet.

Paula thinks . . .

I'll rewrite the mixed number as an improper fraction and then multiply.

$6 \cdot 5\frac{1}{3} = 6 \cdot \frac{16}{3}$ Rewrite $5\frac{1}{3}$ as an improper fraction.

$= \frac{\cancel{6}^{2}}{1} \cdot \frac{16}{\cancel{3}_{1}}$ Divide 6 and 3 by 3, a common factor.

$= 32$ Multiply.

The area is 32 square feet.

What do you think?

1. Whose method would you use to multiply $90 \times 100\frac{1}{3}$?
2. Can both methods be used for the product $4\frac{2}{3} \times 2$?

Remember

An improper fraction is always greater than 1, so the numerator is always greater than the denominator.

[Page 178]

Check Your Understanding

1. How can you find $3\frac{1}{2} \cdot 4$ using addition? Using the distributive property?
2. How can you find the product of a mixed number and a fraction less than 1?

What Do You Think?

Students see two methods of multiplying a mixed number by a whole number. One method uses the distributive property, and the other method uses improper fractions. Students can decide when each method might be easier.

Answers for What Do You Think?

1. Andy's. The numbers are compatible, so they are easy to multiply directly.
2. Yes

3 Practice and Assess

Check

Answers for Check Your Understanding

1. Addition: $3\frac{1}{2} + 3\frac{1}{2} + 3\frac{1}{2} + 3\frac{1}{2}$. Distributive property: $3\frac{1}{2} \cdot 4 = 3 \cdot 4 + \frac{1}{2} \cdot 4$
2. Rewrite the mixed number as an improper fraction and multiply as usual.

MEETING MIDDLE SCHOOL CLASSROOM NEEDS

Tips from Middle School Teachers

I like to give my students a copy of a sale flier advertising discounts of $\frac{1}{3}$ off or $\frac{1}{2}$ off. I ask them to determine the amount saved if they buy the item on sale.

Cooperative Learning

Give students exercises with multiplication of fractions and mixed numbers. Have them work together in groups to decide which exercises have a product greater than 1.

Science Connection

In the United States, between two and three billion trees are planted each year, and millions of acres of other forest areas are left to reproduce naturally. As a result, more wood is grown each year than is harvested or destroyed by insects and diseases.

4-5 Exercises and Applications

Assignment Guide

- **Basic**
  2–24 evens, 27–30, 32, 36–50 evens
- **Average**
  1–25 odds, 26–32, 35–49 odds
- **Enriched**
  1–25 odds, 26–34, 35–49 odds

Exercise Notes

Exercise 29

Consumer There are seven major groups of dogs. They are (1) sporting dogs, (2) hounds, (3) working dogs, (4) terriers, (5) toy dogs, (6) nonsporting dogs, and (7) herding dogs.

Exercise Answers

27. Possible answer: Greater; Part of the multiplier is a whole number and multiplying by a value at least as great as the whole number 1 always results in a larger number.

Reteaching

Activity

- Use several small paper squares to represent whole numbers. Tear some of the squares in half to model $3 \cdot 2\frac{1}{2}$.
- What addition problem does this model show? $2\frac{1}{2} + 2\frac{1}{2} + 2\frac{1}{2}$
- Group the whole squares together and group the half squares together. How does this show how the distributive property could be used to find the product? It shows $3 \cdot 2 + 3 \cdot \frac{1}{2}$.
- What could you do to the model to show how improper fractions could be used to find the product? Regroup to show $2\frac{1}{2} + 2\frac{1}{2} + 2\frac{1}{2}$ again. Then tear or fold the whole squares in half to show $3 \times \frac{5}{2}$.
- What is the result? $7\frac{1}{2}$

PRACTICE 4-5

4-5 Exercises and Applications

Practice and Apply

Getting Started **Rewrite each mixed number as an improper fraction.**

1. $3\frac{3}{8}$ $\frac{27}{8}$ **2.** $5\frac{4}{5}$ $\frac{29}{5}$ **3.** $8\frac{7}{8}$ $\frac{71}{8}$ **4.** $6\frac{5}{7}$ $\frac{47}{7}$ **5.** $2\frac{1}{6}$ $\frac{13}{6}$

Use the distributive property to find each product mentally.

6. $5 \cdot 1\frac{1}{3}$ $6\frac{2}{3}$ **7.** $4 \cdot 3\frac{1}{2}$ 14 **8.** $7 \cdot 2\frac{1}{5}$ $15\frac{2}{5}$ **9.** $5\frac{1}{3} \cdot 3$ 16 **10.** $1\frac{3}{4} \cdot 12$ 21

Find each product.

11. $5\frac{3}{5} \cdot 2\frac{6}{7}$ 16 **12.** $7\frac{1}{5} \cdot 3\frac{8}{9}$ 28 **13.** $6\frac{2}{3} \cdot 8\frac{2}{5}$ 56 **14.** $10\frac{4}{5} \cdot 4\frac{4}{9}$ 48 **15.** $3\frac{1}{3} \cdot 2\frac{7}{10}$ 9

16. $2\frac{4}{5} \cdot 3\frac{1}{3}$ $9\frac{1}{3}$ **17.** $4\frac{1}{6} \cdot 1\frac{3}{5}$ $6\frac{2}{3}$ **18.** $5\frac{1}{3} \cdot 2\frac{3}{5}$ $13\frac{13}{15}$ **19.** $9\frac{3}{4} \cdot 7\frac{1}{2}$ $73\frac{1}{8}$ **20.** $6\frac{2}{5} \cdot 4\frac{3}{4}$ $30\frac{2}{5}$

21. $1\frac{4}{9} \cdot 2\frac{2}{3}$ $3\frac{23}{27}$ **22.** $6\frac{1}{3} \cdot 3\frac{1}{6}$ $20\frac{1}{18}$ **23.** $7\frac{1}{2} \cdot 5\frac{4}{5}$ $43\frac{1}{2}$ **24.** $2\frac{3}{8} \cdot 6\frac{1}{4}$ $14\frac{27}{32}$ **25.** $7\frac{3}{7} \cdot 1\frac{1}{4}$ $9\frac{2}{7}$

26. Science As a roller-coaster car reaches the bottom of a slope and begins to go up the next slope, its acceleration, combined with the downward pull of gravity, can make you feel $3\frac{1}{2}$ times your weight—a sensation called supergravity, or *super-g's*. Calculate how heavy a 120 lb person would feel in a speeding roller coaster experiencing super-g's. 420 lb

27. Number Sense Is the product of two mixed numbers less than or greater than each factor? Explain your answer.

GPS

28. Social Studies The area of the Pacific Ocean is about $12\frac{1}{2}$ times greater than the area of the Arctic Ocean. If the area of the Arctic Ocean is about 5,105,000 mi², about what is the area of the Pacific Ocean? 63,812,500 mi²

29. Problem Solving In a dog show, breeds are divided into *groups*. The terrier group, which includes the Airedale, has $1\frac{3}{10}$ times as many breeds as the working group, which includes the Great Dane. If there are 20 breeds in the working group, how many are there in the terrier group? 26

PRACTICE

Name ______________________

Practice 4-5

Multiplying Mixed Numbers

Use the distributive property to find each product mentally.

1. $6 \cdot 7\frac{3}{5}$ $45\frac{3}{5}$
2. $7 \cdot 2\frac{9}{10}$ $20\frac{3}{10}$
3. $3 \cdot 6\frac{3}{5}$ $19\frac{4}{5}$
4. $4\frac{1}{8} \cdot 7$ $28\frac{7}{8}$
5. $1\frac{2}{7} \cdot 7$ 9
6. $5 \cdot 5\frac{1}{6}$ $25\frac{5}{6}$
7. $6 \cdot 2\frac{4}{9}$ $14\frac{2}{3}$
8. $8 \cdot 3\frac{3}{4}$ 30
9. $6\frac{3}{5} \cdot 4$ $26\frac{2}{5}$
10. $4\frac{7}{9} \cdot 4$ $19\frac{1}{9}$
11. $4\frac{1}{6} \cdot 9$ $37\frac{1}{2}$
12. $2 \cdot 5\frac{6}{7}$ $11\frac{5}{7}$

Find each product.

13. $9\frac{1}{2} \cdot 1\frac{1}{2}$ $14\frac{1}{4}$
14. $8\frac{5}{8} \cdot 3\frac{3}{5}$ $31\frac{1}{20}$
15. $1\frac{5}{7} \cdot 4\frac{2}{3}$ 8
16. $7\frac{6}{7} \cdot 8\frac{1}{3}$ $65\frac{10}{21}$
17. $6\frac{1}{2} \cdot 5\frac{3}{4}$ $37\frac{3}{8}$
18. $9\frac{1}{3} \cdot 4\frac{3}{7}$ $41\frac{1}{3}$
19. $4\frac{9}{10} \cdot \frac{1}{2}$ $2\frac{9}{20}$
20. $4\frac{3}{5} \cdot 6\frac{1}{9}$ $28\frac{1}{9}$
21. $2\frac{1}{2} \cdot 6\frac{1}{3}$ $15\frac{5}{6}$
22. $6\frac{3}{4} \cdot 1\frac{2}{3}$ $11\frac{1}{4}$
23. $8\frac{1}{2} \cdot 3\frac{3}{4}$ $31\frac{7}{8}$
24. $6\frac{2}{3} \cdot 3\frac{2}{3}$ $24\frac{4}{9}$
25. $5\frac{5}{6} \cdot 3\frac{7}{10}$ $21\frac{7}{12}$
26. $8\frac{6}{7} \cdot 3\frac{1}{4}$ $28\frac{11}{14}$
27. $8\frac{2}{3} \cdot 7\frac{1}{3}$ $63\frac{5}{9}$
28. $2\frac{1}{7} \cdot 5\frac{5}{8}$ $12\frac{3}{56}$
29. $7\frac{2}{7} \cdot 2\frac{1}{7}$ $15\frac{30}{49}$
30. $7\frac{3}{4} \cdot 5\frac{2}{3}$ $43\frac{11}{12}$
31. $3\frac{1}{3} \cdot 2\frac{1}{10}$ 7
32. $5\frac{1}{2} \cdot 1\frac{3}{4}$ $9\frac{5}{8}$
33. $6\frac{5}{8} \cdot 4\frac{3}{5}$ $30\frac{19}{40}$
34. $2\frac{1}{2} \cdot 4\frac{2}{5}$ 11
35. $8\frac{1}{3} \cdot 5\frac{8}{9}$ $49\frac{2}{27}$
36. $7\frac{1}{8} \cdot 7\frac{1}{3}$ $52\frac{1}{4}$

37. **Measurement** A one-kilogram object weighs about $2\frac{1}{5}$ pounds. Find the weight, in pounds, of a computer monitor with mass $7\frac{3}{8}$ kilograms. $16\frac{9}{40}$ lb

38. **Social Science** The population of Sweden is about $1\frac{11}{16}$ times as great as the population of Denmark. Find the population of Sweden if the population of Denmark is about 5,190,000. About 8,760,000

RETEACHING

Name ______________________

Alternative Lesson 4-5

Multiplying Mixed Numbers

You can multiply mixed numbers by rewriting them as improper fractions. Then multiply the numerators and multiply the denominators.

Example

Multiply $2\frac{2}{5} \cdot 1\frac{1}{9}$.

Step 1: Write mixed numbers as improper fractions. $2\frac{2}{5} = \frac{12}{5}$ $1\frac{1}{9} = \frac{10}{9}$

Step 2: Multiply numerators and denominators. $\frac{12}{5} \cdot \frac{10}{9} = \frac{12 \cdot 10}{5 \cdot 9} = \frac{120}{45}$

Step 3: Write as a fraction in lowest terms. $\frac{120 \div 15}{45 \div 15} = \frac{8}{3}$

Step 4: Write as a mixed number. $\frac{8}{3} = 2\frac{2}{3}$

So $2\frac{2}{5} \cdot 1\frac{1}{9} = 2\frac{2}{3}$.

Try It Multiply $1\frac{3}{4} \cdot 2\frac{2}{3}$.

a. Write as improper fractions. $1\frac{3}{4} =$ $\frac{7}{4}$ $2\frac{2}{3} =$ $\frac{8}{3}$

b. Multiply numerators. $7 \cdot 8 = 56$

c. Multiply denominators. $4 \cdot 3 = 12$

d. Write numerator over denominator. $\frac{56}{12}$

e. Write in lowest terms. $\frac{14}{3}$

f. Write as a mixed number. $4\frac{2}{3}$

Find each product.

g. $1\frac{1}{3} \cdot 2\frac{2}{5}$ $3\frac{1}{5}$
h. $1\frac{7}{8} \cdot 2\frac{1}{3}$ $4\frac{3}{8}$
i. $3\frac{1}{6} \cdot 2\frac{2}{3}$ $8\frac{4}{9}$
j. $1\frac{1}{2} \cdot 1\frac{1}{2}$ $2\frac{1}{4}$
k. $1\frac{1}{5} \cdot 2\frac{1}{7}$ $2\frac{4}{7}$
l. $3\frac{1}{3} \cdot 2\frac{1}{4}$ $7\frac{1}{2}$
m. $1\frac{5}{6} \cdot 1\frac{3}{6}$ $2\frac{3}{4}$
n. $2\frac{1}{2} \cdot 1\frac{1}{3}$ $3\frac{1}{3}$
o. $2\frac{1}{2} \cdot 2\frac{1}{5}$ $5\frac{1}{2}$
p. $2\frac{1}{2} \cdot 2\frac{4}{5}$ 7
q. $3\frac{2}{3} \cdot 1\frac{1}{2}$ $5\frac{1}{2}$
r. $1\frac{5}{6} \cdot 1\frac{1}{2}$ $2\frac{3}{4}$

30. **Test Prep** Choose the best estimate for the product of the expression $4\frac{6}{7} \cdot 5\frac{1}{8}$. B

Ⓐ 20 Ⓑ 25 Ⓒ 30 Ⓓ 35

31. **History** Susan B. Anthony was a leader in the women's suffrage movement. A special $1.00 coin was minted in 1979 to honor her. The coin is $\frac{3}{4}$ copper and $\frac{1}{4}$ nickel. It weighs $8\frac{1}{2}$ grams. How many grams of copper are in the coin? $6\frac{3}{8}$ grams

Problem Solving and Reasoning

32. **Choose a Strategy** Find the areas of the rooms diagrammed. How much larger than the dining room is the area of the family room? $135\frac{1}{12}$ ft²

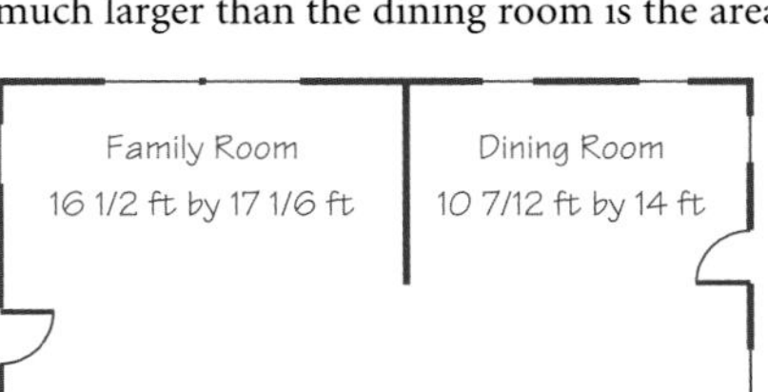

Problem Solving STRATEGIES

- Look for a Pattern
- Make an Organized List
- Make a Table
- Guess and Check
- Work Backward
- Use Logical Reasoning
- Draw a Diagram
- Solve a Simpler Problem

33. **Communicate** Write a step-by-step description of the method you would use to multiply 8 and $4\frac{3}{4}$.

34. **Journal** Draw a diagram to illustrate the product $2\frac{1}{2} \cdot 1\frac{3}{4}$.

Mixed Review

Make a line plot for each set of data and name any outliers. *[Lesson 1-3]*

35. 23, 25, 22, 26, 35, 24, 23, 23, 26
36. 3, 5, 8, 4, 7, 3, 7, 6, 4, 3, 7, 2, 4, 1
37. 7, 9, 12, 13, 8, 9, 13, 10, 6, 9, 9, 7
38. 42, 44, 43, 45, 33, 44, 46, 41, 43

Write each number in scientific notation. *[Lesson 3-5]*

39. 18 1.8×10^1
40. 625,000 6.25×10^5
41. 42,100,000 4.21×10^7
42. 867,530,900 8.675309×10^8
43. 127,000,000 1.27×10^8
44. 2,600 2.6×10^3
45. 19,330 1.933×10^4
46. 2,700,000,000,000 2.7×10^{12}
47. 270 2.7×10^2
48. 186,000 1.86×10^5
49. 93,000,000 9.3×10^7
50. 5,555,230,000,000 5.55523×10^{12}

PROBLEM SOLVING 4-5

Exercise Answers

33. Possible answer: First change $4\frac{3}{4}$ to the improper fraction $\frac{19}{4}$. Divide 8 and 4 by 4, then multiply. $2 \times 19 = 38$

34.

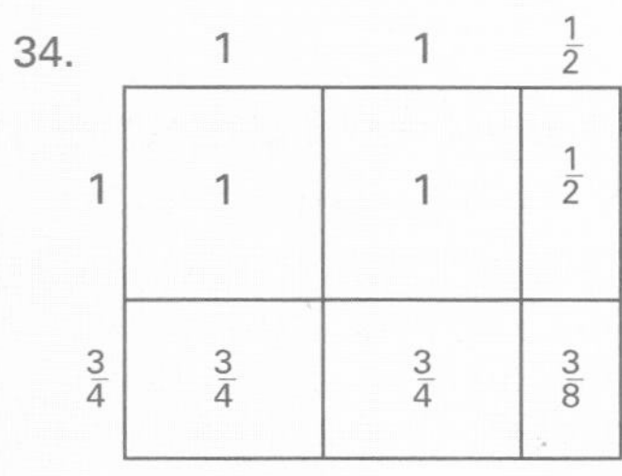

$1 + 1 + \frac{1}{2} + \frac{3}{4} + \frac{3}{4} + \frac{3}{8} = 4\frac{3}{8}$

35.

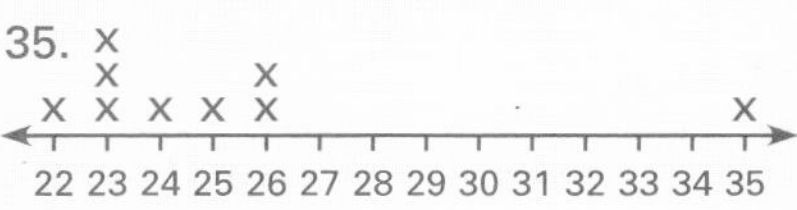

Outlier: 35

36.

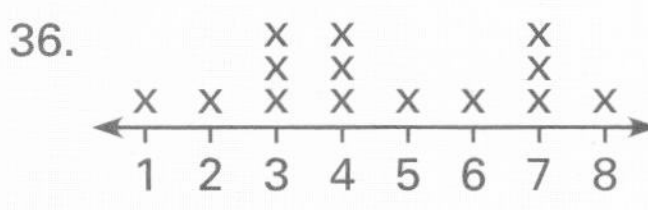

37.

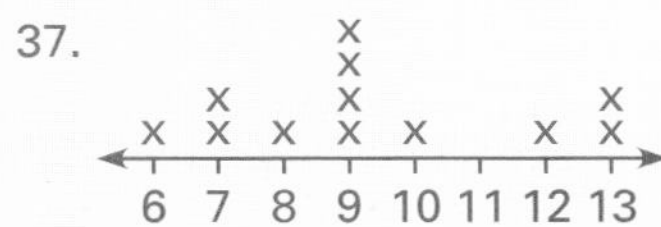

38.

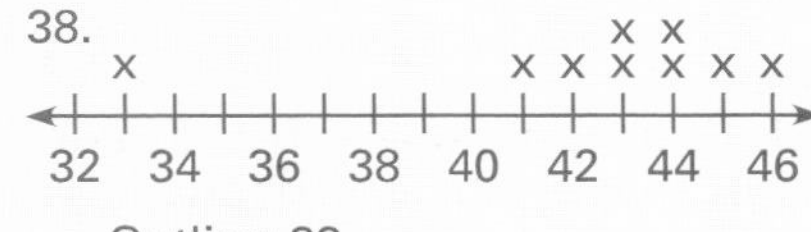

Outlier: 33

Alternate Assessment

You may want to use the *Interactive CD-ROM Journal* with this assessment.

Journal Have students write a paragraph describing different methods of multiplying a mixed number by a whole number.

PROBLEM SOLVING

Name ______

Guided Problem Solving 4-5

GPS PROBLEM 32, STUDENT PAGE 195

Find the areas of the rooms diagrammed. How much larger than the dining room is the area of the family room?

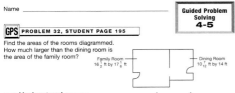

Family Room $16\frac{1}{2}$ ft by $17\frac{1}{6}$ ft — Dining Room $10\frac{7}{12}$ ft by 14 ft

Understand

1. What are the dimensions of the family room? $16\frac{1}{2}$ ft by $17\frac{1}{6}$ ft
2. What are the dimensions of the dining room? $10\frac{7}{12}$ ft by 14 ft

Plan

3. How will you find the area of each room? Multiply length by width.
4. Use improper fractions to show how to find the area of the family room. $\frac{33}{2} \cdot \frac{103}{6}$
5. Use the Distributive Property to show how to find the area of the dining room. $(14 \cdot 10) + (14 \cdot \frac{7}{12})$
6. Which operation will you use to find how much larger the family room is than the dining room? Subtraction.

Solve

7. Find the area of the family room. $283\frac{1}{4}$ ft² Of the dining room. $148\frac{1}{6}$ ft²
8. How much larger is the family room than the dining room? $135\frac{1}{12}$ ft²

Look Back

9. Would it be easier to find the answer by converting the measures to inches? Explain. Possible answer: Yes, once converted to inches, you would not need to calculate using fractions.

SOLVE ANOTHER PROBLEM

Find the areas of the rooms diagrammed. How much larger than the bathroom is the area of the bedroom?

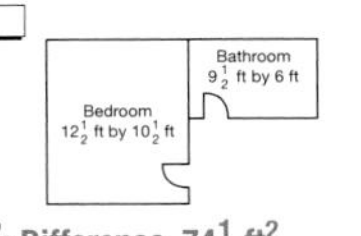

Bedroom, $131\frac{1}{4}$ ft²; Bathroom, 57 ft²; Difference, $74\frac{1}{4}$ ft²

ENRICHMENT

Name ______

Extend Your Thinking 4-5

Decision Making

A grab bag at a school rummage sale costs $15.00. Only the packers know what is inside each bag. Ferdinand and Rachel want to buy one grab bag. Ferdinand has $10.50 and Rachel has $6.75. Possible answers given.

1. How much should each person contribute to the purchase? Why? Ferdinand $9 and Rachel $6 so that each contributes as much as possible, but still has a little left over.
2. Based on how much each person contributed, what fraction of the surprises in the grab bag should each person receive? Why? Ferdinand would get $\frac{3}{5}$ of the grab bag and Rachel would get $\frac{2}{5}$; $\frac{9}{15} = \frac{3}{5}$ and $\frac{6}{15} = \frac{2}{5}$.
3. The grab bag contents are listed below.
   1 wallet-size calculator; 2 tickets to a matinee; 3 school pencils; 4 pocket combs; 5 bus tokens; 2 school sports buttons
   What would be a fair way for Ferdinand and Rachel to divide the contents so that each gets their fair share? Assign a value to each item and divide them with Ferdinand receiving about $\frac{3}{5}$ of the value and Rachel receiving about $\frac{2}{5}$.
4. Using the way you decided, who gets which items? Explain why you chose the items for each to receive. Ferdinand: $12 of $20 value—2 tickets ($7), 2 combs ($1), 5 tokens ($3), and 1 button ($1); Rachel: $8 of $20 value—calculator ($5), 2 combs ($1), 3 pencils ($1), and 1 button ($1)
5. How would your answer change if each person was entitled to one half of the contents? Each would receive items worth about $10. Ferdinand would get the tickets and tokens. Rachel would get everything else.

Quick Quiz

Find each product.

1. $2\frac{1}{2} \times 1\frac{1}{5}$ 3
2. $3\frac{1}{3} \times 4\frac{1}{2}$ 15
3. $2\frac{2}{3} \times 3$ 8

Available on Daily Transparency 4-5

Technology

Using a Spreadsheet • Writing Formulas

The Point
Students use a spreadsheet formula to calculate a basketball player's total points scored.

Materials
Spreadsheet software

Resources

Interactive CD-ROM Spreadsheet/Grapher Tool

About the Page

- Some spreadsheet programs may use a "+" at the beginning of each formula rather than "=."
- The parentheses in the formula are there for emphasis rather than necessity. The spreadsheet will calculate according to order of operations.

Ask ...
- How does spreadsheet software represent multipication and division? Possible answer: * for multiplication; / for division.

Answers for Try It
a. 53

b. $18

On Your Own
These questions emphasize to students the main advantages of using a spreadsheet: instantaneous recalculations when data is changed or updated, and the ease of duplicating formulas so that information for many players may be obtained.

Answers for On Your Own
- If you use a spreadsheet and save it, you can go back and add or change data without redoing everything. Spreadsheets also let you do many computations more quickly.
- Make 10 columns like column B, one for every player.

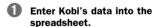

TECHNOLOGY

Using a Spreadsheet • Writing Formulas

Problem: You are the statistician for the school's basketball team. So far this season, Kobi has scored 7 3-point baskets, 37 2-point baskets, and 15 1-point free throws. How many points did she score?

You can use the capabilities of a spreadsheet to answer this question quickly.

1 Enter Kobi's data into the spreadsheet.

	A	B
1	3-point baskets	7
2	2-point baskets	37
3	1-point free throws	15

2 To calculate Kobi's total number of points, multiply the number in B1 by 3, add this to 2 times the number in B2, and add the number in B3. As a spreadsheet formula, this is:
=(3*B1)+(2*B2)+B3

	A	B
1	3-point baskets	7
2	2-point baskets	37
3	1-point free throws	15
4	Total points	=(3*B1)+(2*B2)+B3

3 If you type this formula into cell B4 and press enter**, the spreadsheet calculates Kobi's point total.**

	A	B
1	3-point baskets	7
2	2-point baskets	37
3	1-point free throws	15
4	Total points	110

Solution: Kobi has scored 110 points so far this season.

Notice that, in spreadsheet formulas, multiplication is usually shown by *. In spreadsheets, division is usually shown by /.

TRY IT

a. So far this season, Audrey has scored four 3-point baskets, sixteen 2-point baskets, and nine 1-point free throws. Use a spreadsheet to find how many points she has scored.

b. A family of four is charged $7.00 each for movie tickets, and they have a $10 gift certificate. Use a spreadsheet to find how much they pay.

ON YOUR OWN

- Why might you want to use a spreadsheet to find Kobi's point total instead of calculating it yourself? (*Hint:* The season isn't over yet.)
- Explain how you would set up a spreadsheet to find the point totals for every player on a 10-player team.

Dividing Fractions and Mixed Numbers

4-6

▶ Lesson Link You've seen how to add, subtract, and multiply fractions and mixed numbers. Now you'll divide fractions and mixed numbers. ◀

You'll Learn ...

■ to divide fractions and mixed numbers

... How It's Used

Graphic artists often need to divide fractions to see how many times a pattern will be repeated in a given space.

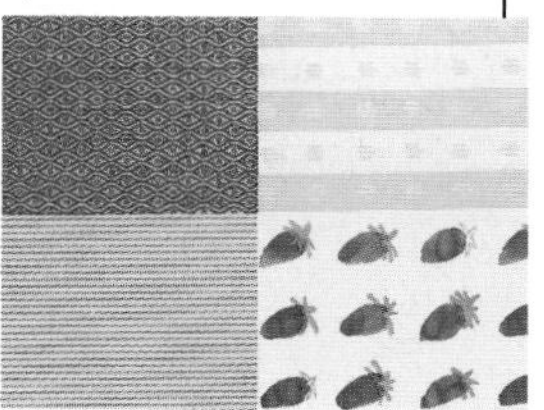

Vocabulary

reciprocal

Explore Dividing Fractions

You Can Rule the World!

A building inspector carries a 6-ft measuring tape. To measure a 12-ft room, the inspector used 2 lengths of the tape. That's because $12 \div 6 = 2$.

1. Suppose the inspector forgot the tape and had only a $\frac{1}{2}$-ft ruler. How many lengths of the ruler would be needed to measure a 12-ft room? What is $12 \div \frac{1}{2}$? Explain.
2. Copy and complete the table for measuring rooms with rulers of the given lengths.

Length of Room	Length of Ruler	Number of Lengths of Ruler
12 ft	$\frac{1}{2}$ ft	24
12 ft	$\frac{1}{4}$ ft	
18 ft	$\frac{1}{2}$ ft	
18 ft	$\frac{1}{4}$ ft	

3. How could you find $18 \div \frac{1}{2}$ by multiplying instead of dividing? How could you find $12 \div \frac{1}{3}$ by multiplying instead of dividing?

▶ History Link

The *foot* was given its name because it was the length of the average man's foot. It was standardized as the length of the English King Henry I's foot. Henry I ruled from 1100 to 1135.

Learn Dividing Fractions and Mixed Numbers

When you divide, you find out how many times the divisor is contained in a number.

$14 \div 2$ means "How many 2's are there in 14?"

$3 \div \frac{1}{4}$ means "How many $\frac{1}{4}$'s are in 3?"

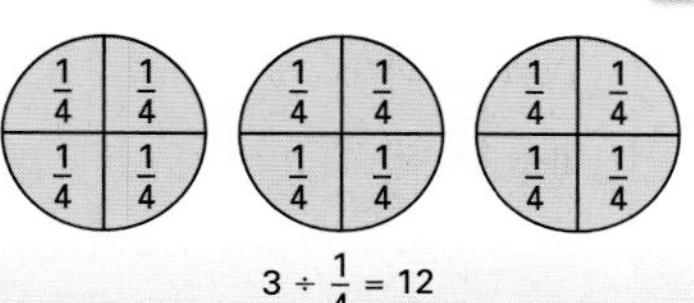

$3 \div \frac{1}{4} = 12$

MEETING INDIVIDUAL NEEDS

Resources

4-6 Practice
4-6 Reteaching
4-6 Problem Solving
4-6 Enrichment
4-6 Daily Transparency
  Problem of the Day
  Review
  Quick Quiz
Lesson Enhancement Transparency 17
Technology Master 17
Chapter 4 Project Master

Learning Modalities

Visual Have students draw rectangles and subdivide them to find quotients. For example, to find $\frac{3}{\ } \div \frac{3}{\ }$, shade $\frac{3}{\ }$ of a rectangle, divide the same rectangle into 8 equal parts, and count the groups of $\frac{3}{\ }$ that are shaded.

Kinesthetic Have students use fraction models to solve division of fraction problems.

Inclusion

For students having difficulty dividing fractions, write some fractions, mixed numbers, and whole numbers on the board and ask them to write the reciprocal for each. For whole numbers and mixed numbers, have them write the improper fraction first. Then give them several division problems, using the original numbers as divisors, and ask them to rewrite each as a multiplication expression, using the reciprocal of the divisor. Have students add new vocabulary to reference book.

4-6 Lesson Organizer

Objective

■ Divide fractions and mixed numbers.

Vocabulary

■ Reciprocal

NCTM Standards

■ 1–4, 6, 7, 9, 13

▶ Review

Write each mixed number as an improper fraction.

1. $1\frac{4}{\ }$ $\frac{9}{\ }$
2. $3\frac{1}{\ }$ $\frac{7}{\ }$
3. $4\frac{2}{\ }$ $\frac{14}{\ }$
4. $9\frac{3}{\ }$ $\frac{39}{\ }$

Available on Daily Transparency 4-6

1 Introduce

Explore

You may wish to use Lesson Enhancement Transparency 17 with **Explore**.

The Point
Students explore dividing fractions by determining how many fractional lengths are needed to measure a given length.

Ongoing Assessment
As students work, ask if their answers are reasonable. Suggest that students check their work visually by using a number line.

For Groups That Finish Early
Write a paragraph to describe how you would find $25 \div 2\frac{1}{\ }$ by multiplying.

Answers for Explore

1. 24 lengths. 24. Each whole is made up of 2 halves, so 12 wholes would be 12 • 2 or 24 halves.
2. 24, 48, 36, 72
3. Multiply 18 by 2; Multiply 12 by 3.

2 Teach

Learn

Alternate Examples

1. Divide. Rewrite in lowest terms. $\frac{3}{8} \div \frac{1}{4}$

$\frac{3}{8} \div \frac{1}{4} = \frac{3}{8} \bullet \frac{4}{1}$

$= \frac{3}{\cancel{8}_2} \bullet \frac{\cancel{4}^1}{1}$

$= \frac{3}{2} = 1\frac{1}{2}$

2. Jake has 40 feet of rope. He needs pieces of rope $2\frac{1}{2}$ feet long to practice knot tying. How many pieces of rope can he cut?

$40 \div 2\frac{1}{2} = \frac{40}{1} \div \frac{5}{2}$

$= \frac{40}{1} \bullet \frac{2}{5}$

$= \frac{\cancel{40}^8}{1} \bullet \frac{2}{\cancel{5}_1}$

$= 16$

Jake can cut 16 pieces of rope.

3 Practice and Assess

Check

Answers for Check Your Understanding

1. $3\frac{3}{8} \div 1\frac{1}{8} = 3\frac{3}{8} \div \frac{9}{8}$

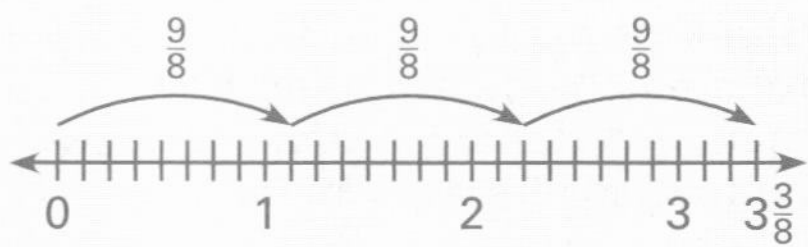

There are 3 groups of $1\frac{1}{8}$ in $3\frac{3}{8}$, so $3\frac{3}{8} \div 1\frac{1}{8} = 3$.

2. $20 \div 5 = 20 \bullet \frac{1}{5}$

You can use **reciprocals** when you divide by a fraction or a mixed number. Two numbers are reciprocals if their product is 1.

The reciprocal of $\frac{4}{11}$ is $\frac{11}{4}$ because $\frac{4}{11} \cdot \frac{11}{4} = \frac{44}{44} = 1$.

To divide by a fraction, multiply by the reciprocal of the fraction. Simplify if possible.

MENTAL MATH

To find the reciprocal of a fraction, simply interchange the numerator and denominator. The reciprocal of a whole number is 1 over that number.

Example 1

Divide. Rewrite in lowest terms. $\frac{5}{6} \div \frac{2}{3}$

$\frac{5}{6} \div \frac{2}{3} = \frac{5}{6} \cdot \frac{3}{2}$ — Multiply by the reciprocal of $\frac{2}{3}$.

$= \frac{5 \cdot \cancel{3}^1}{_2\cancel{6} \cdot 2}$ — Divide 3 and 6 by 3, a common factor.

$= \frac{5}{4} = 1\frac{1}{4}$ — Multiply.

To divide with mixed numbers, rewrite the mixed numbers as improper fractions. Then multiply by the reciprocal of the divisor.

Science Link

A knot in a piece of wood is a lump where a branch grows out. When cut across, knots provide attractive designs in the grain of wood.

Example 2

Mary needs to cover her $112\frac{1}{2}$-in.-long wall with $9\frac{3}{8}$-in.-wide knotty pine paneling. How many panels does she need?

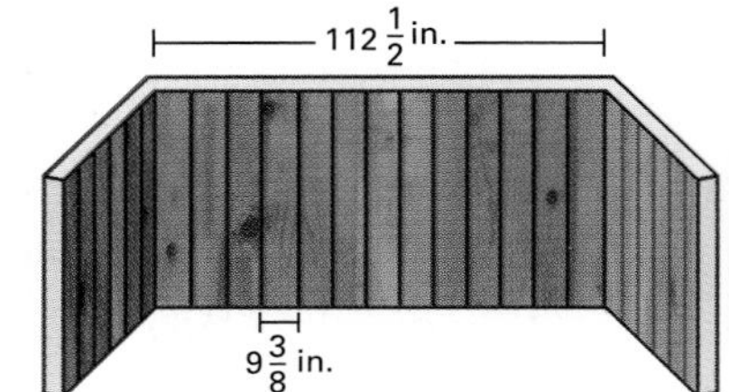

$112\frac{1}{2} \div 9\frac{3}{8} = \frac{225}{2} \div \frac{75}{8}$ — Rewrite the mixed numbers as improper fractions.

$= \frac{225}{2} \cdot \frac{8}{75}$ — Multiply by the reciprocal of $\frac{75}{8}$.

$= \frac{\cancel{225}^3 \cdot \cancel{8}^4}{_1\cancel{2} \cdot \cancel{75}_1}$ — Divide 225 and 75 by 75. Divide 8 and 2 by 2.

$= 12$ — Multiply.

Twelve panels are needed.

Try It

Divide. Rewrite in lowest terms. **a.** $5 \div \frac{1}{7}$ 35 **b.** $\frac{3}{7} \div \frac{12}{21}$ $\frac{3}{4}$ **c.** $3\frac{7}{9} \div 2\frac{5}{6}$ $1\frac{1}{3}$

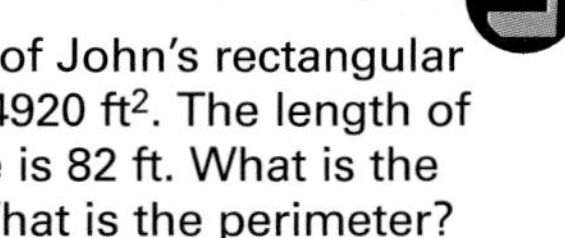

MATH EVERY DAY

Problem of the Day

The area of John's rectangular home is 4920 ft². The length of the home is 82 ft. What is the width? What is the perimeter? 60 ft; 284 ft

Available on Daily Transparency 4-6

An Extension is provided in the transparency package.

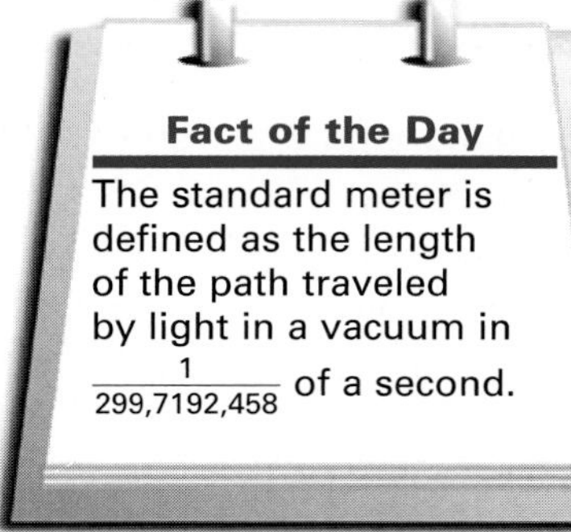

Fact of the Day

The standard meter is defined as the length of the path traveled by light in a vacuum in $\frac{1}{299{,}7192{,}458}$ of a second.

Estimation

Estimate.

1. $14\frac{1}{2} \div 2\frac{2}{3}$ 5
2. $23\frac{1}{6} \div 7\frac{1}{4}$ 3
3. $34\frac{1}{2} \div 4\frac{3}{4}$ 7

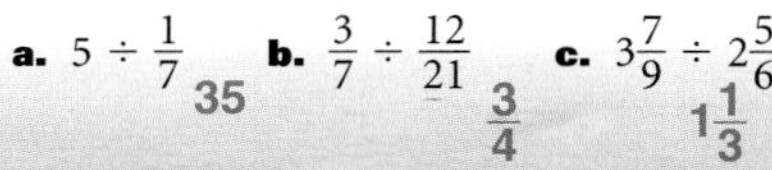

Check Your Understanding

1. Make a model to show that $3\frac{3}{8} \div 1\frac{1}{8} = 3$.
2. How can you use the rule for multiplying by the reciprocal to find $20 \div 5$?

4-6 Exercises and Applications

PRACTICE 4-6

Practice and Apply

Getting Started **Find the reciprocal of each fraction.**

1. $\frac{1}{2}$ 2 **2.** $\frac{3}{8}$ $\frac{8}{3}$ **3.** $\frac{3}{10}$ $\frac{10}{3}$ **4.** $\frac{2}{5}$ $\frac{5}{2}$ **5.** $\frac{1}{4}$ 4

Change each mixed number to an improper fraction and write its reciprocal.

6. $1\frac{1}{8}$ $\frac{9}{8}; \frac{8}{9}$ **7.** $3\frac{1}{2}$ $\frac{7}{2}; \frac{2}{7}$ **8.** $2\frac{3}{5}$ $\frac{13}{5}; \frac{5}{13}$ **9.** $4\frac{3}{4}$ $\frac{19}{4}; \frac{4}{19}$ **10.** $3\frac{2}{3}$ $\frac{11}{3}; \frac{3}{11}$

Rewrite each division expression as a multiplication expression to find the quotient.

11. $\frac{3}{8} \div \frac{1}{4}$ $\frac{3}{8} \times 4 = 1\frac{1}{2}$ **12.** $\frac{1}{2} \div \frac{2}{7}$ $\frac{1}{2} \times \frac{7}{2} = 1\frac{3}{4}$ **13.** $\frac{3}{5} \div \frac{1}{3}$ $\frac{3}{5} \times 3 = 1\frac{4}{5}$ **14.** $\frac{3}{4} \div \frac{2}{3}$ $\frac{3}{4} \times \frac{3}{2} = 1\frac{1}{8}$

15. $\frac{5}{8} \div 3\frac{1}{2}$ $\frac{5}{8} \times \frac{2}{7} = \frac{5}{28}$ **16.** $1\frac{1}{2} \div 2\frac{2}{3}$ $\frac{3}{2} \times \frac{3}{8} = \frac{9}{16}$ **17.** $2\frac{2}{5} \div \frac{5}{6}$ $\frac{12}{5} \times \frac{6}{5} = 2\frac{22}{25}$ **18.** $4\frac{5}{8} \div 3\frac{1}{3}$ $\frac{37}{8} \times \frac{3}{10} = 1\frac{31}{80}$

Find each quotient. Rewrite in lowest terms.

19. $\frac{3}{7} \div \frac{3}{5}$ $\frac{5}{7}$ **20.** $\frac{7}{8} \div \frac{1}{6}$ $5\frac{1}{4}$ **21.** $\frac{5}{8} \div \frac{1}{4}$ $2\frac{1}{2}$ **22.** $\frac{2}{3} \div \frac{1}{4}$ $2\frac{2}{3}$

23. $5\frac{3}{4} \div 3\frac{2}{3}$ $1\frac{25}{44}$ **24.** $2 \div \frac{2}{3}$ 3 **25.** $7\frac{3}{4} \div 1\frac{2}{3}$ $4\frac{13}{20}$ **26.** $4\frac{3}{4} \div 2\frac{2}{3}$ $1\frac{25}{32}$

27. **Test Prep** Choose the correct operation to complete the sentence. The reciprocal of a number is the number that when ______ the original number results in the answer 1. C

Ⓐ added to Ⓑ subtracted from Ⓒ multiplied by Ⓓ divided by

28. **Measurement** A nail weighs about $\frac{1}{10}$ oz. How many nails are in a 5-lb box? 800

4-6 Exercises and Applications

Assignment Guide

- Basic
  1–10, 11–31 odds, 32, 35–39 odds
- Average
  2–26 evens, 27–30, 32–40 evens
- Enriched
  1–25 odds, 27–32, 33–39 odds

Exercise Notes

Exercise 27

Test Prep Students who choose Answer D probably have not read the question carefully and simply related the term *reciprocal* with division.

Exercise 28

Error Prevention Be sure students notice that the total weight of the box is given in pounds, while the weight of each nail is given as a fraction of an ounce. Some might need to be reminded that 1 pound = 16 ounces.

Project Progress

You may want to have students use Chapter 4 Project Master.

PRACTICE

Name ______________________

Practice 4-6

Dividing Fractions and Mixed Numbers

Change each mixed number to an improper fraction and write its reciprocal.

1. $1\frac{1}{5}$ $\frac{6}{5}; \frac{5}{6}$ **2.** $4\frac{5}{6}$ $\frac{29}{6}; \frac{6}{29}$ **3.** $3\frac{1}{4}$ $\frac{13}{4}; \frac{4}{13}$

4. $5\frac{7}{9}$ $\frac{52}{9}; \frac{9}{52}$ **5.** $7\frac{3}{5}$ $\frac{38}{5}; \frac{5}{38}$ **6.** $2\frac{5}{7}$ $\frac{19}{7}; \frac{7}{19}$

7. $6\frac{7}{8}$ $\frac{55}{8}; \frac{8}{55}$ **8.** $9\frac{3}{10}$ $\frac{93}{10}; \frac{10}{93}$ **9.** $3\frac{6}{7}$ $\frac{27}{7}; \frac{7}{27}$

Rewrite each division expression as a multiplication expression to find the quotient.

10. $\frac{1}{9} \div \frac{5}{6}$ $\frac{1}{9} \cdot \frac{6}{5} = \frac{2}{15}$ **11.** $\frac{1}{2} \div \frac{4}{5}$ $\frac{1}{2} \cdot \frac{5}{4} = \frac{5}{8}$ **12.** $\frac{1}{2} \div \frac{2}{3}$ $\frac{1}{2} \cdot \frac{3}{2} = \frac{3}{4}$ **13.** $\frac{3}{5} \div \frac{4}{9}$ $\frac{3}{5} \cdot \frac{9}{4} = 1\frac{7}{20}$

14. $\frac{2}{3} \div \frac{5}{6}$ $\frac{2}{3} \cdot \frac{6}{5} = \frac{4}{5}$ **15.** $\frac{1}{2} \div 3\frac{1}{4}$ $\frac{1}{2} \cdot \frac{4}{13} = \frac{2}{13}$ **16.** $4\frac{2}{5} \div \frac{4}{5}$ $\frac{22}{5} \cdot \frac{5}{4} = 5\frac{1}{2}$ **17.** $6\frac{2}{3} \div \frac{3}{4}$ $\frac{20}{3} \cdot \frac{4}{3} = 8\frac{8}{9}$

18. $1\frac{3}{8} \div \frac{2}{3}$ $\frac{11}{8} \cdot \frac{3}{2} = 2\frac{1}{16}$ **19.** $3\frac{2}{9} \div 2\frac{1}{3}$ $\frac{29}{9} \cdot \frac{3}{7} = 1\frac{8}{21}$ **20.** $5\frac{1}{2} \div 1\frac{1}{2}$ $\frac{11}{2} \cdot \frac{2}{3} = 3\frac{2}{3}$ **21.** $11\frac{1}{2} \div 3\frac{1}{2}$ $\frac{23}{2} \cdot \frac{2}{7} = 3\frac{2}{7}$

Find each quotient. Rewrite in lowest terms.

22. $\frac{1}{2} \div \frac{6}{7}$ $\frac{7}{12}$ **23.** $\frac{1}{10} \div \frac{8}{9}$ $\frac{9}{80}$ **24.** $\frac{2}{7} \div \frac{3}{4}$ $\frac{8}{21}$

25. $\frac{3}{4} \div \frac{3}{5}$ $1\frac{1}{4}$ **26.** $5\frac{1}{3} \div \frac{5}{7}$ $7\frac{7}{15}$ **27.** $2\frac{4}{5} \div \frac{1}{3}$ $8\frac{2}{5}$

28. $2\frac{1}{2} \div \frac{1}{10}$ 25 **29.** $\frac{4}{5} \div 4\frac{2}{3}$ $\frac{6}{35}$ **30.** $1\frac{1}{8} \div 1\frac{4}{5}$ $\frac{5}{8}$

31. $2\frac{1}{3} \div 1\frac{3}{4}$ $1\frac{1}{3}$ **32.** $3\frac{3}{4} \div 4\frac{1}{2}$ $\frac{5}{6}$ **33.** $2\frac{5}{8} \div 2\frac{4}{5}$ $\frac{15}{16}$

34. Measurement A mile is about $1\frac{3}{5}$ km. How many miles are in $6\frac{4}{5}$ km? $4\frac{1}{4}$ mi

35. Measurement A 10-oz drinking glass holds $1\frac{1}{4}$ cups of liquid. How many drinking glasses are needed for 5 gallons (80 cups) of lemonade? 64 glasses

RETEACHING

Name ______________________

Alternative Lesson 4-6

Dividing Fractions and Mixed Numbers

You can use **reciprocals** when you divide by a fraction or mixed number. Two numbers are reciprocals if their product is 1. To divide by a fraction, multiply by the reciprocal of the fraction. Convert mixed numbers to improper fractions before multiplying.

Example 1

Find the reciprocal of $1\frac{3}{4}$.

Write $1\frac{3}{4}$ as a fraction. $1\frac{3}{4} = \frac{7}{4}$

The numerator of the fraction becomes the denominator of the reciprocal. The denominator of the fraction becomes the numerator of the reciprocal.

Fraction $\frac{7}{4}$ → Reciprocal $\frac{4}{7}$

Check to see that the product of the fraction and its reciprocal is 1. $\frac{7}{4} \cdot \frac{4}{7} = \frac{28}{28} = 1$

So $\frac{4}{7}$ is the reciprocal of $\frac{7}{4}$ and $1\frac{3}{4}$.

Try It Write the reciprocal of each fraction.

a. $\frac{4}{5}$ $\frac{5}{4}$ **b.** $\frac{8}{3}$ $\frac{3}{8}$ **c.** $\frac{10}{12}$ $\frac{12}{10}$ **d.** $\frac{5}{9}$ $\frac{9}{5}$

e. $1\frac{5}{6}$ $\frac{6}{11}$ **f.** $2\frac{3}{5}$ $\frac{5}{13}$ **g.** $1\frac{1}{2}$ $\frac{2}{3}$ **h.** $4\frac{1}{6}$ $\frac{6}{25}$

Example 2

Divide. $2\frac{2}{3} \div 1\frac{1}{2}$

Step 1: Rewrite the mixed numbers as improper fractions. $2\frac{2}{3} \div 1\frac{1}{2} = \frac{8}{3} \div \frac{3}{2}$

Step 2: Multiply by the reciprocal of the divisor. $\frac{2}{3}$ is the reciprocal of $\frac{3}{2}$. $\frac{8}{3} \div \frac{3}{2} = \frac{8}{3} \times \frac{2}{3}$

Step 3: Multiply. $\frac{8 \times 2}{3 \times 3} = \frac{16}{9}$

Step 4: Rewrite as a mixed number. $\frac{16}{9} = 1\frac{7}{9}$

So $2\frac{2}{3} \div 1\frac{1}{2} = 1\frac{7}{9}$.

Try It Find each quotient. Rewrite in lowest terms.

i. $\frac{3}{4} \div \frac{6}{7}$ $\frac{7}{8}$ **j.** $\frac{5}{9} \div \frac{1}{6}$ $3\frac{1}{3}$ **k.** $\frac{1}{3} \div \frac{1}{3}$ 1

l. $1\frac{1}{2} \div 2\frac{1}{4}$ $\frac{2}{3}$ **m.** $3\frac{3}{5} \div 2\frac{1}{4}$ $1\frac{3}{5}$ **n.** $2\frac{3}{8} \div 1\frac{1}{8}$ $2\frac{1}{9}$

o. $\frac{1}{2} \div \frac{3}{4}$ $\frac{2}{3}$ **p.** $\frac{5}{6} \div \frac{2}{3}$ $1\frac{1}{4}$ **q.** $3\frac{1}{3} \div 2\frac{1}{2}$ $1\frac{1}{3}$

Reteaching

Activity

- Fold a sheet of paper into 4 equal parts. Shade $\frac{1}{2}$ of the paper. How many $\frac{1}{4}$s are shaded? 2 What is $\frac{1}{2} \div \frac{1}{4}$? 2
- Fold the paper so that there are now 8 equal parts. How many $\frac{1}{8}$s are shaded? 4 What is $\frac{1}{2} \div \frac{1}{8}$? 4
- Shade more of the sheet of paper so that $\frac{3}{4}$ of it is shaded. How many $\frac{3}{8}$s are shaded? 2 What is $\frac{3}{4} \div \frac{3}{8}$? 2

Project Progress

You may want to have students use Chapter 4 Project Master.

Exercise Answers

31. Possible answer: A whole number is the sum of that many ones. A proper fraction is less than one so there must be more of them contained in the whole number.

34.

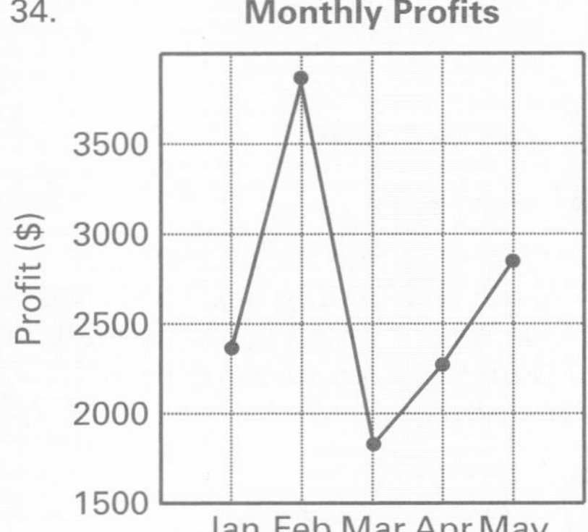

35.

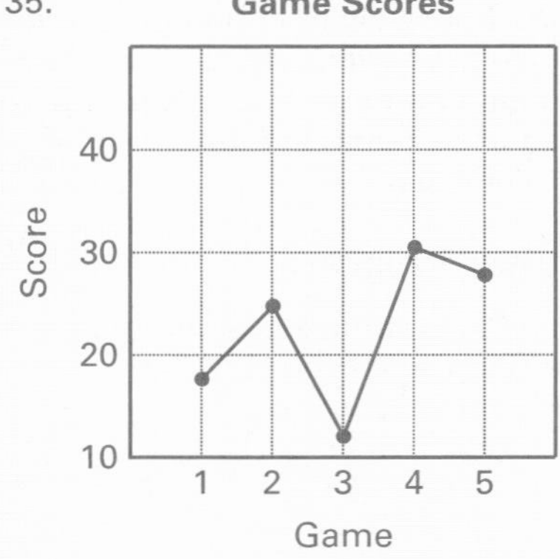

Alternate Assessment

Self Assessment Have students determine the part of dividing fractions that they find most difficult to do or to remember. Some might have difficulty finding reciprocals, while others might forget to write the problem as a multiplication expression.

➤ Quick Quiz

Find each quotient. Rewrite in lowest terms.

1. $\frac{4}{5} \div \frac{2}{3}$ $1\frac{1}{5}$
2. $2\frac{1}{4} \div \frac{3}{8}$ 6
3. $3\frac{1}{3} \div \frac{1}{4}$ $13\frac{1}{3}$

Available on Daily Transparency 4-6

PROBLEM SOLVING 4-6

29. Ranchers in the American West often wear what is called a ten-gallon hat. However, a ten-gallon hat actually holds only $\frac{3}{4}$ of a gallon. How many ten-gallon hats would be needed to hold ten gallons? $13\frac{1}{3}$ or 14 hats

30. Measurement A developer plans to subdivide 12 acres of land into $\frac{3}{4}$-acre building sites. How many building sites will there be? 16

Problem Solving and Reasoning

31. 

Explain why, when you divide a whole number other than zero by a proper fraction, the quotient is always greater than the whole number.

32. Critical Thinking GPS A border design measures $4\frac{3}{8}$ inches. How many times does a single row repeat around the top of the walls of a room that measures $12\frac{1}{2}$ ft by $10\frac{1}{4}$ ft? $124\frac{4}{5}$ times

33. Critical Thinking Write an equation to solve for *x*. Then solve the equation.

a. 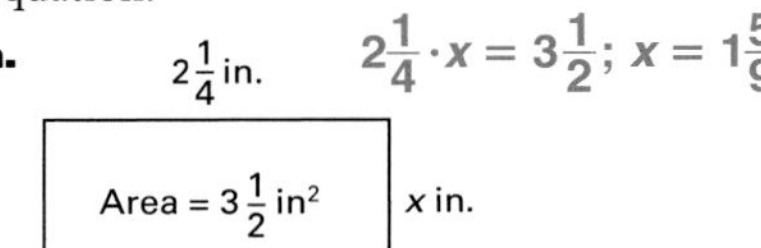

$2\frac{1}{4} \cdot x = 3\frac{1}{2};\ x = 1\frac{5}{9}$

b. 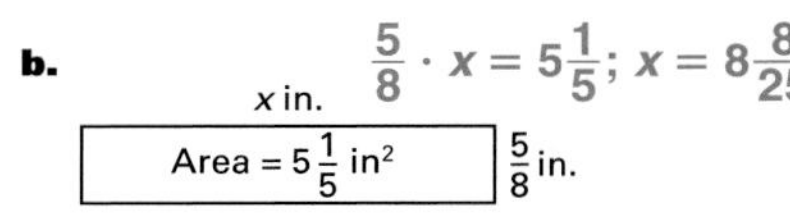

$\frac{5}{8} \cdot x = 5\frac{1}{5};\ x = 8\frac{8}{25}$

Mixed Review

Make a line graph for each set of data. *[Lesson 1-5]*

34.

Month	Jan.	Feb.	Mar.	Apr.	May
Profit ($)	2460	3820	1760	2340	2900

35.

Game	1	2	3	4	5
Score	18	25	12	31	28

Test each number for divisibility by 2, 3, 4, 5, 6, 8, 9, and 10. *[Lesson 3-6]*

36. 385 5 **37.** 642 2, 3, 6 **38.** 94 2 **39.** 6230 2, 5, 10 **40.** 1028 2, 4

Project Progress

Draw or trace a world map, and show the 5 most populous countries. Find the *total* fraction of the world's population that lives in these countries, and find the fraction of the population that does not live in these countries.

Problem Solving: Understand, Plan, Solve, Look Back

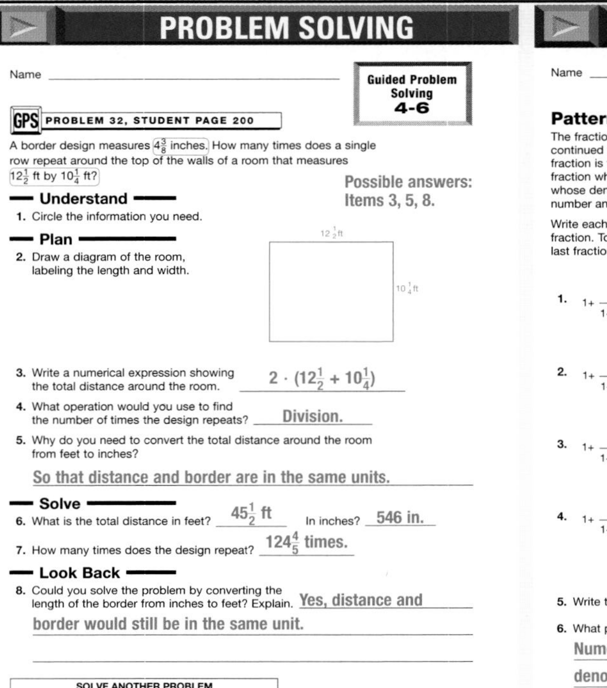

PROBLEM SOLVING

Name ____________ Guided Problem Solving 4-6

GPS PROBLEM 32, STUDENT PAGE 200

A border design measures $4\frac{3}{8}$ inches. How many times does a single row repeat around the top of the walls of a room that measures $12\frac{1}{2}$ ft by $10\frac{1}{4}$ ft?

Possible answers: Items 3, 5, 8.

— Understand —

1. Circle the information you need.

— Plan —

2. Draw a diagram of the room, labeling the length and width. ($12\frac{1}{2}$ ft, $10\frac{1}{4}$ ft)

3. Write a numerical expression showing the total distance around the room. $2 \cdot (12\frac{1}{2} + 10\frac{1}{4})$

4. What operation would you use to find the number of times the design repeats? Division.

5. Why do you need to convert the total distance around the room from feet to inches? So that distance and border are in the same units.

— Solve —

6. What is the total distance in feet? $45\frac{1}{2}$ ft In inches? 546 in.

7. How many times does the design repeat? $124\frac{4}{5}$ times.

— Look Back —

8. Could you solve the problem by converting the length of the border from inches to feet? Explain. Yes, distance and border would still be in the same unit.

SOLVE ANOTHER PROBLEM

A border design measures $3\frac{1}{2}$ inches. How many times does a single row repeat around the top of the walls of a room that measures $10\frac{3}{4}$ ft by $13\frac{3}{4}$ ft? 168 times.

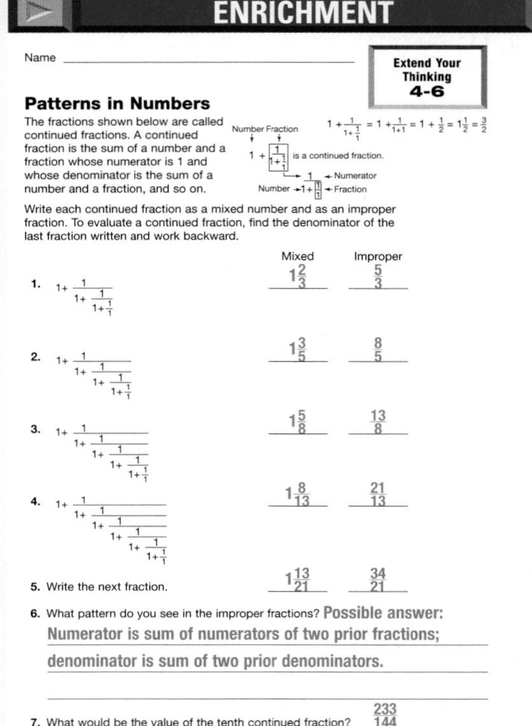

ENRICHMENT

Name ____________ Extend Your Thinking 4-6

Patterns in Numbers

The fractions shown below are called continued fractions. A continued fraction is the sum of a number and a fraction whose numerator is 1 and whose denominator is the sum of a number and a fraction, and so on.

$1 + \frac{1}{1+\frac{1}{1}} = 1 + \frac{1}{1+1} = 1 + \frac{1}{2} = 1\frac{1}{2} = \frac{3}{2}$

Write each continued fraction as a mixed number and as an improper fraction. To evaluate a continued fraction, find the denominator of the last fraction written and work backward.

		Mixed	Improper
1.	$1+\frac{1}{1+\frac{1}{1+\frac{1}{1}}}$	$1\frac{2}{3}$	$\frac{5}{3}$
2.	$1+\frac{1}{1+\frac{1}{1+\frac{1}{1+\frac{1}{1}}}}$	$1\frac{3}{5}$	$\frac{8}{5}$
3.	$1+\frac{1}{1+\frac{1}{1+\frac{1}{1+\frac{1}{1+\frac{1}{1}}}}}$	$1\frac{5}{8}$	$\frac{13}{8}$
4.	$1+\frac{1}{1+\frac{1}{1+\frac{1}{1+\frac{1}{1+\frac{1}{1+\frac{1}{1}}}}}}$	$1\frac{8}{13}$	$\frac{21}{13}$
5.	Write the next fraction.	$1\frac{13}{21}$	$\frac{34}{21}$

6. What pattern do you see in the improper fractions? Possible answer: Numerator is sum of numerators of two prior fractions; denominator is sum of two prior denominators.

7. What would be the value of the tenth continued fraction? $\frac{233}{144}$

You've learned about the importance of fractions in architecture and building. Now you will have an opportunity to apply what you've learned to the remodeling of a home. This home is in the Greek revival style. To be historically accurate, it has no closets or kitchen.

Building It Piece by Piece

Below is a blueprint for the first floor of a Greek revival–style home.

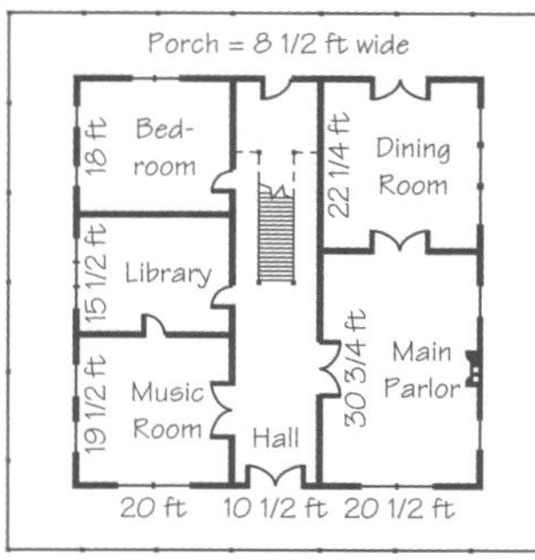

1. Find the length and width of the house, not including the porch.
2. Estimate the area of each room and the hall.
3. The dining room carpet comes on 12-foot-wide rolls. How many feet of carpet must be ordered?
4. The porch must be painted with a special paint that costs $17.85 per gallon. If a gallon covers 200 square feet, how many gallons must be purchased for the porch floors? What will the cost be?
5. Wood for the library floor costs $6 per square foot. How much will the floor cost?
6. Sections of crown molding, each $2\frac{9}{16}$ ft in length, will circle the main parlor at the tops of the walls. How many sections will be needed?
7. The kitchen is to be built as a separate rectangular building. It is to be bigger than the library but smaller than the dining room. Neither the length nor the width will have whole-number measurements. Draw a possible floor plan. Show the measurements on your diagram.

Answers for Connect

1. Length: 53 ft; Width: 51 ft.
2. Estimated areas: Bedroom 360 ft^2; Library 320 ft^2; Music Room: 400 ft^2; Dining Room: 440 ft^2; Main Parlor: 620 ft^2; Hall: 530 ft^2.
3. 41 ft
4. 11 gallons; $196.35
5. $1860
6. 40
7. Student diagram should be a rectangle with given dimensions that produce an area greater than 310 square feet but less than $456\frac{1}{8}$ square feet. Both dimensions should be mixed numbers.

Building It Piece by Piece

The Point

In *Building It Piece by Piece* on page 185, students discussed home building projects. Now they will compute with fractions to determine carpet, paint, and flooring needs for remodeling a home.

Resources

Lesson Enhancement Transparency 18

About the Page

- Assist students in reading the blueprint. Explain that a blueprint is a "top down" view of the floor plan of a house that shows the placement of the walls, windows, and doors.
- Help students determine in which direction the carpet will be installed in Question 3.
- Note that the outer rectangle of the blueprint identifies a porch that goes all of the way around the home. Students will need this information for Question 4.
- Remind students that when calculating how much material to buy, it is wise to round up rather than round down.

Ongoing Assessment

Check that students have determined the correct area of each room concerned before they begin finding the amount of carpeting, wood flooring, or floor paint.

Extension

Ask students to measure their own bedroom, determine the area, and compute the cost of purchasing new carpeting at $22.50 per square yard. Students may need to be reminded that 9 square feet = 1 square yard. Suggest that students carpet the closet and include those measurements in the area and the cost.

4B Review

Review Correlation

Item(s)	Lesson(s)
1–4	4-2, 4-3
5, 6, 8, 9	4-4
7, 10–14	4-5
15–24	4-6
25	4-5
26	4-6
27–28	4-4

Test Prep

Test-Taking Tip

When students encounter computation on multiple-choice tests, they should always estimate before they compute. This is especially helpful when computing with fractions and decimals.

Section 4B Review

REVIEW 4B

Find each sum or difference.

1. $\frac{4}{7} - \frac{1}{3}$ $\frac{5}{21}$ **2.** $\frac{4}{9} + \frac{1}{2}$ $\frac{17}{18}$ **3.** $9\frac{1}{4} - 5\frac{3}{8}$ $3\frac{7}{8}$ **4.** $7\frac{3}{5} + \frac{5}{6}$ $8\frac{13}{30}$

Find each product. Rewrite in lowest terms.

5. $\frac{1}{3} \cdot \frac{3}{8}$ $\frac{1}{8}$ **6.** $\frac{2}{7} \cdot \frac{3}{4}$ $\frac{3}{14}$ **7.** $\frac{3}{5} \cdot 2\frac{5}{6}$ $1\frac{7}{10}$ **8.** $\frac{3}{8} \cdot \frac{5}{9}$ $\frac{5}{24}$ **9.** $\frac{7}{8} \cdot \frac{2}{3}$ $\frac{7}{12}$

10. $3\frac{4}{7} \cdot \frac{7}{8}$ $3\frac{1}{8}$ **11.** $\frac{2}{5} \cdot 2\frac{7}{10}$ $1\frac{2}{25}$ **12.** $5 \cdot \frac{3}{8}$ $1\frac{7}{8}$ **13.** $\frac{7}{9} \cdot 7$ $5\frac{4}{9}$ **14.** $2\frac{1}{4} \cdot \frac{3}{4}$ $1\frac{11}{16}$

Find each quotient. Rewrite in lowest terms.

15. $\frac{1}{2} \div \frac{1}{4}$ 2 **16.** $\frac{5}{7} \div \frac{1}{4}$ $2\frac{6}{7}$ **17.** $\frac{3}{4} \div 6$ $\frac{1}{8}$ **18.** $\frac{1}{4} \div \frac{1}{2}$ $\frac{1}{2}$ **19.** $\frac{2}{5} \div 1\frac{1}{4}$ $\frac{8}{25}$

20. $\frac{4}{5} \div 3\frac{1}{3}$ $\frac{6}{25}$ **21.** $5\frac{4}{5} \div 9\frac{2}{7}$ $\frac{203}{325}$ **22.** $10\frac{3}{4} \div 4$ $2\frac{11}{16}$ **23.** $8\frac{1}{8} \div 12$ $\frac{65}{96}$ **24.** $3\frac{1}{4} \div 5\frac{1}{12}$ $\frac{39}{61}$

25. **Science** The length of a kangaroo's leap can be up to $6\frac{1}{2}$ times its height. If a kangaroo is $6\frac{3}{4}$ feet tall, about how far can it jump? ≈ 42 ft

26. DeWayne is building a 72-ft-long dock. If each plank is $\frac{3}{4}$ of a foot wide, how many planks does he need? 96 planks

Test Prep

On a multiple choice test in which you are asked to multiply fractions, recognizing that common factors can be used to divide the numerators and denominators of fractions before multiplying will help you work more quickly.

27. Multiply. $\frac{27}{56} \cdot \frac{42}{81}$ A

Ⓐ $\frac{1}{4}$ Ⓑ $\frac{1}{3}$ Ⓒ $\frac{2}{3}$ Ⓓ $\frac{3}{4}$

28. Multiply. $\frac{10}{33} \cdot \frac{11}{20}$ B

Ⓐ $\frac{1}{12}$ Ⓑ $\frac{1}{6}$ Ⓒ $\frac{5}{12}$ Ⓓ $\frac{3}{4}$

Resources

Practice Masters
Section 4B Review

Assessment Sourcebook
Quiz 4B

TestWorks
Test and Practice Software

PRACTICE

Name ______________________

Practice

Section 4B Review

Find each product. Rewrite in lowest terms.

1. $\frac{1}{3} \cdot \frac{1}{5}$ $\frac{1}{15}$ 2. $\frac{6}{7} \cdot \frac{1}{5}$ $\frac{6}{35}$ 3. $\frac{7}{10} \cdot \frac{2}{5}$ $\frac{7}{25}$

4. $\frac{1}{8} \cdot \frac{3}{5}$ $\frac{3}{40}$ 5. $\frac{11}{14} \cdot \frac{7}{22}$ $\frac{1}{4}$ 6. $\frac{2}{45} \cdot \frac{9}{10}$ $\frac{1}{25}$

7. $\frac{11}{26} \cdot \frac{8}{11}$ $\frac{4}{13}$ 8. $\frac{20}{21} \cdot \frac{15}{22}$ $\frac{50}{77}$ 9. $\frac{3}{4} \cdot 2\frac{6}{7}$ $2\frac{1}{7}$

10. $\frac{1}{2} \cdot 3\frac{5}{7}$ $1\frac{6}{7}$ 11. $\frac{8}{9} \cdot 6\frac{1}{5}$ $5\frac{23}{45}$ 12. $\frac{2}{5} \cdot 6\frac{2}{7}$ $2\frac{18}{35}$

13. $1\frac{1}{3} \cdot 3\frac{1}{2}$ $4\frac{2}{3}$ 14. $6\frac{2}{3} \cdot 2\frac{3}{7}$ $16\frac{4}{21}$ 15. $7\frac{2}{3} \cdot 9\frac{3}{4}$ $74\frac{3}{4}$

16. $4\frac{1}{5} \cdot 3\frac{2}{3}$ $15\frac{2}{5}$ 17. $2\frac{2}{7} \cdot 1\frac{1}{5}$ $2\frac{26}{35}$ 18. $\frac{7}{11} \cdot \frac{5}{13}$ $\frac{35}{143}$

Find each quotient. Rewrite in lowest terms.

19. $\frac{1}{5} \div \frac{1}{3}$ $\frac{3}{5}$ 20. $\frac{7}{10} \div \frac{3}{4}$ $\frac{14}{15}$ 21. $\frac{1}{2} \div \frac{8}{9}$ $\frac{9}{16}$

22. $\frac{1}{2} \div \frac{8}{9}$ $\frac{9}{16}$ 23. $2\frac{2}{3} \div 3$ $\frac{8}{9}$ 24. $11\frac{1}{2} \div \frac{1}{5}$ $57\frac{1}{2}$

25. $2 \div 3\frac{1}{3}$ $\frac{3}{5}$ 26. $1\frac{7}{9} \div 2\frac{2}{5}$ $\frac{20}{27}$ 27. $2\frac{4}{5} \div 1\frac{1}{2}$ $1\frac{13}{15}$

28. $5\frac{1}{3} \div 2\frac{4}{5}$ $1\frac{19}{21}$ 29. $\frac{1}{4} \div \frac{9}{10}$ $\frac{5}{18}$ 30. $2\frac{1}{5} \div 5\frac{4}{5}$ $\frac{11}{29}$

31. A recipe calls for $1\frac{2}{3}$ cups of flour. If Ron is making $1\frac{1}{2}$ times the recipe, how much flour should he use? $2\frac{1}{2}$ cups

32. **Geometry** The table shows the relationship between the side length x, and the perimeter P, of a square. Find a formula relating the variables. *[Lesson 2-3]* $P = 4x$

x	2	4	6	8
P	8	16	24	32

33. **Science** The spider *tegenaria atrica* can travel at speeds up to 1.17 mi/hr. How long will this spider take to travel 1.638 miles at that speed? *[Lesson 3-4]* 1.4 hr

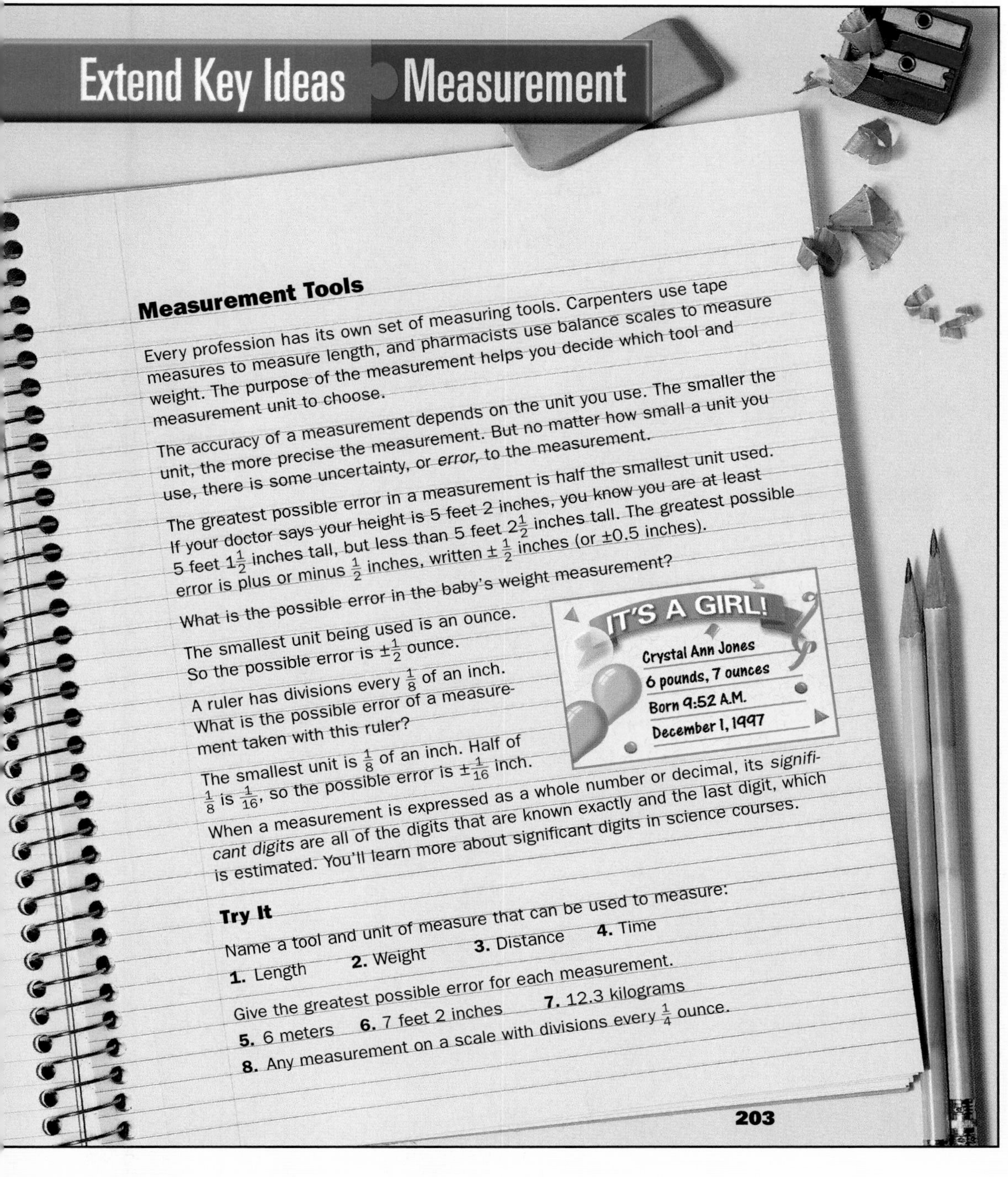

Extend Key Ideas Measurement

Measurement Tools

Every profession has its own set of measuring tools. Carpenters use tape measures to measure length, and pharmacists use balance scales to measure weight. The purpose of the measurement helps you decide which tool and measurement unit to choose.

The accuracy of a measurement depends on the unit you use. The smaller the unit, the more precise the measurement. But no matter how small a unit you use, there is some uncertainty, or *error*, to the measurement.

The greatest possible error in a measurement is half the smallest unit used. If your doctor says your height is 5 feet 2 inches, you know you are at least 5 feet $1\frac{1}{2}$ inches tall, but less than 5 feet $2\frac{1}{2}$ inches tall. The greatest possible error is plus or minus $\frac{1}{2}$ inches, written $\pm\frac{1}{2}$ inches (or ±0.5 inches).

What is the possible error in the baby's weight measurement?

The smallest unit being used is an ounce. So the possible error is $\pm\frac{1}{2}$ ounce.

IT'S A GIRL!
Crystal Ann Jones
6 pounds, 7 ounces
Born 9:52 A.M.
December 1, 1997

A ruler has divisions every $\frac{1}{8}$ of an inch. What is the possible error of a measurement taken with this ruler?

The smallest unit is $\frac{1}{8}$ of an inch. Half of $\frac{1}{8}$ is $\frac{1}{16}$, so the possible error is $\pm\frac{1}{16}$ inch.

When a measurement is expressed as a whole number or decimal, its *significant digits* are all of the digits that are known exactly and the last digit, which is estimated. You'll learn more about significant digits in science courses.

Try It

Name a tool and unit of measure that can be used to measure:

1. Length **2.** Weight **3.** Distance **4.** Time

Give the greatest possible error for each measurement.

5. 6 meters **6.** 7 feet 2 inches **7.** 12.3 kilograms

8. Any measurement on a scale with divisions every $\frac{1}{4}$ ounce.

203

Answers for Try It

1. Possible answers: Ruler, inches
2. Possible answers: Scale, kilograms
3. Possible answers: Odometer, miles
4. Possible answers: Stopwatch, seconds
5. ±1/2 m = ±0.5 m
6. ±1/2 in. = ±0.5 in.
7. ±0.5 kg
8. ±1/8 oz = ±0.125 oz

Extend Key Ideas

Measurement Tools

The Point

Students choose appropriate measurement tools and determine the greatest error possible for given measurements.

About the Page

- It may be difficult for students to accept the fact that measurements are not exact. Even an Olympic swimming event which is timed to a hundredth of a second, has a possible error of ±5 thousandth of a second.
- A measurement, however, is not incorrect by half the smallest unit of measure used; it is correct within that range.
- Students might recall reading scientific data in which the writer indicated the precision of some data in terms of significant digits.

Ask ...

- Suppose you used a centimeter ruler to measure the length of a piece of paper, and you read 28 cm from the ruler. Is the paper exactly 28 cm long? How long is the paper? No; Between 27.5 and 28.5 cm.
- This measurement wasn't close enough for you, so you found a millimeter ruler, and measured the paper to be 279 mm. Is this measurement exact? How long is the paper? No; Between 278.5 and 279.5 mm.

Extension

Have students measure several objects in the classroom, using different tools, such as an inch ruler, a centimeter ruler, or a meter stick. Have them record their measurements, and also give the greatest possible error.

Chapter 4 Summary and Review

Review Correlation

Item(s)	Lesson(s)
1–4	4-1
5–7	4-2
8–10	4-3
11–13	4-4
14–16	4-5
17–20	4-6

For additional review, see page 675.

Chapter 4 Summary and Review

Graphic Organizer

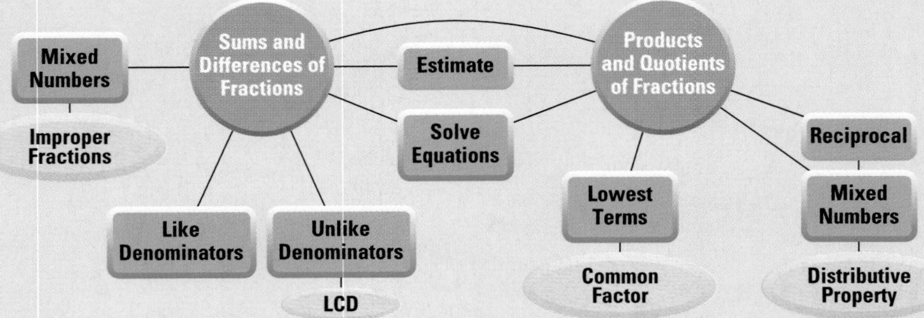

Section 4A Sums and Differences of Fractions

Summary

- To estimate sums and differences of fractions, round the fractions to 0, $\frac{1}{2}$, or 1, then add or subtract mentally.
- A **mixed number** is made up of a whole number and a fraction.
- To estimate sums, differences, and products of mixed numbers, round to the nearest whole.
- Use compatible numbers to estimate quotients of mixed numbers and products of fractions and whole numbers.
- To add or subtract fractions with the same denominator, add or subtract the numerators. Write the result over the denominator and rewrite in lowest terms.
- The **least common denominator (LCD)** of two fractions is the LCM of the denominators. To add or subtract fractions with different denominators, rewrite the fractions using the LCD.
- Equations containing fractions can be solved using inverse operations.
- An **improper fraction** is a fraction that is greater than one.
- Add mixed numbers by adding the whole numbers and the fractions separately. You may have to change the resulting fraction to a mixed number and add it to the whole number.

Resources

Practice Masters
Cumulative Review Chapters 1–4

PRACTICE

Name ______________________

Practice

Cumulative Review Chapters 1–4

The circle graph shows sources of funding for American public elementary and secondary schools. Use the graph to answer Exercises 1–3. *[Lesson 1-1]*

Public School Funding, 1992 (State 46.4%; Local 47%; Federal 6.6%)

1. List the sources of funding in order of size from largest to smallest. **Local, State, Federal**
2. Which two sources provide about the same amount of funding? **Local, State**
3. Which source provides about 6.6% of public school funding? **Federal**

Write an algebraic expression for each phrase. *[Lesson 2-5]*

4. one-fifth of a number (w) $\frac{w}{5}$
5. seven more than a number (k) $k + 7$
6. three times the difference of a number (g) and 8 $3(g - 8)$

Solve each equation. *[Lessons 3-3, 3-4]*

7. $3.16 = x - 5.23$ $x =$ **8.39**
8. $n + 8.3 = 12.147$ $n =$ **3.847**
9. $7.1 = j + 1.85$ $j =$ **5.25**
10. $p - 2.1 = 8.99$ $p =$ **11.09**
11. $3.21s = 17.013$ $s =$ **5.3**
12. $0.9s = 13.86$ $s =$ **15.4**
13. $\frac{m}{2.36} = 5.9$ $m =$ **13.924**
14. $\frac{z}{3.72} = 1.54$ $z =$ **5.7288**

Find each sum or difference. *[Lesson 4-3]*

15. $15\frac{10}{11} + 14\frac{2}{3}$ $30\frac{19}{33}$
16. $15\frac{20}{21} - 2\frac{2}{7}$ $13\frac{2}{3}$
17. $37\frac{68}{75} - 22\frac{21}{25}$ $15\frac{1}{15}$
18. $13\frac{3}{35} - \frac{4}{5}$ $12\frac{2}{7}$
19. $19\frac{1}{3} + 11\frac{9}{20}$ $30\frac{47}{60}$
20. $28\frac{9}{10} - 16\frac{2}{5}$ $12\frac{1}{2}$

Find each product. *[Lesson 4-5]*

21. $3\frac{1}{2} \cdot 7\frac{7}{8}$ $27\frac{9}{16}$
22. $3\frac{7}{10} \cdot 5\frac{3}{4}$ $21\frac{11}{40}$
23. $7\frac{2}{5} \cdot 4\frac{1}{2}$ $33\frac{3}{10}$
24. $7\frac{1}{6} \cdot 6\frac{4}{5}$ $48\frac{11}{15}$
25. $4\frac{4}{9} \cdot 7\frac{5}{8}$ $33\frac{8}{9}$
26. $5\frac{1}{2} \cdot 2\frac{4}{9}$ $13\frac{4}{9}$

Chapter 4 Summary and Review

Section 4A Sums and Differences of Fractions *continued*

- Subtract mixed numbers by subtracting the whole numbers and subtracting the fractions. Sometimes you need to rewrite the whole-number part of the first number to subtract the fractions.
- Another way to add and subtract mixed numbers is to rewrite both numbers as improper fractions, then add or subtract.

Review

1. Estimate the sum $\frac{5}{8} + \frac{15}{16}$. $\approx 1\frac{1}{2}$

2. Estimate the difference $\frac{10}{11} - \frac{8}{9}$. ≈ 0

3. Use compatible numbers to estimate the quotient $24\frac{3}{4} \div 5\frac{1}{3}$. ≈ 5

4. Paul bought a stock at $32\frac{11}{16}$. Estimate the price after it went down $3\frac{3}{4}$. ≈ 29

5. Find the sum $\frac{13}{15} + \frac{7}{10}$. $1\frac{17}{30}$

6. Solve the equation $x + \frac{1}{6} = \frac{8}{9}$. $\frac{13}{18}$

7. Find the difference $\frac{11}{12} - \frac{3}{5}$. $\frac{19}{60}$

8. Write $3\frac{7}{8}$ as an improper fraction. $\frac{31}{8}$

9. Find the sum $2\frac{3}{4} + 6\frac{5}{8}$. $9\frac{3}{8}$

10. Find the difference $13\frac{2}{3} - 7\frac{4}{5}$. $5\frac{13}{15}$

Section 4B Products and Quotients of Fractions

Summary

- To multiply fractions, multiply the numerators and multiply the denominators. Simplify the product if possible.
- You can multiply mixed numbers by using the distributive property or by rewriting them as improper fractions.
- Two numbers are **reciprocals** if their product is 1.
- To divide by a fraction, multiply by its reciprocal.
- To divide mixed numbers, first rewrite them as improper fractions.

Review

11. Find the product $\frac{2}{3} \cdot \frac{9}{11}$. $\frac{6}{11}$

12. Find the product $\frac{16}{21} \cdot \frac{15}{8}$. $1\frac{3}{7}$

13. Find the area of a rectangular piece of wood with dimensions $\frac{3}{8}$ ft by $\frac{5}{6}$ ft. $\frac{5}{16}$ ft^2

14. Susan is $2\frac{1}{4}$ times as old as Hal. Hal is 16. How old is Susan? 36 yr

15. Find the product $3\frac{1}{7} \cdot 5\frac{8}{11}$. 18

16. Find the product $8\frac{3}{8} \cdot 7\frac{2}{5}$. $61\frac{39}{40}$

17. Find the quotient $\frac{7}{8} \div \frac{14}{9}$. $\frac{9}{16}$

18. Find the quotient $2\frac{4}{15} \div 1\frac{5}{6}$. $1\frac{13}{55}$

19. A floppy disk holds $1\frac{11}{25}$ megabytes. How many disks are needed for 60 megabytes? $41\frac{2}{3}$ or 42 disks

20. A cupcake weighs $3\frac{1}{2}$ ounces. How many cupcakes are there in a 28-ounce package? 8

Chapter 4 Assessment

Assessment Correlation

Item(s)	Lesson(s)
1–4	4-1
5–7	4-2
8–10	4-3
11	4-2
12, 13	4-3
14, 15	4-4
16, 17	4-5
18, 19	4-6
20	4-5
21	4-6

Answers for Performance Task

a.

	Men	Women
Sales Agents	$\frac{1}{4}$	$\frac{5}{12}$
Clerical Employees	$\frac{4}{21}$	$\frac{1}{7}$

b. There are 35 female sales agents, 16 male and 12 female clerical employees. Total: 84 workers.

Chapter 4 Assessment

Estimate each sum, difference, or quotient.

1. $\frac{1}{15} + \frac{5}{11}$ $\approx \frac{1}{2}$ **2.** $\frac{7}{13} - \frac{11}{23}$ ≈ 0 **3.** $20\frac{5}{8} \div 7\frac{1}{3}$ ≈ 3

4. Karen bought a stock at $41\frac{3}{8}$. Her stock went up $6\frac{3}{4}$ points. Estimate the new price. $\approx 48\frac{1}{2}$

Find each sum or difference.

5. $\frac{7}{16} + \frac{3}{10}$ $\frac{59}{80}$ **6.** $\frac{9}{14} - \frac{2}{7}$ $\frac{5}{14}$ **7.** $\frac{13}{16} + \frac{7}{12}$ $1\frac{19}{48}$

8. $32\frac{6}{7} - 14\frac{1}{4}$ $18\frac{17}{28}$ **9.** $6\frac{8}{15} + 17\frac{7}{20}$ $23\frac{53}{60}$ **10.** $63\frac{1}{5} - 39\frac{2}{3}$ $23\frac{8}{15}$

11. Solve the equation $y - \frac{3}{8} = \frac{1}{6}$. $\frac{13}{24}$

12. Write $\frac{53}{11}$ as a mixed number. $4\frac{9}{11}$

13. In a 3-day hike, Ka-fei walked $7\frac{3}{4}$ miles the first day, $12\frac{4}{5}$ miles the second day, and $9\frac{5}{8}$ miles the third day. How far did he walk altogether? $30\frac{7}{40}$

Find each product or quotient.

14. $\frac{4}{5} \cdot \frac{3}{10}$ $\frac{6}{25}$ **15.** $\frac{7}{30} \cdot \frac{50}{21}$ $\frac{5}{9}$ **16.** $5\frac{3}{8} \cdot 12\frac{2}{3}$ $68\frac{1}{12}$

17. $\frac{1}{4} \cdot 10\frac{7}{8}$ $2\frac{23}{32}$ **18.** $\frac{6}{19} \div \frac{12}{13}$ $\frac{13}{38}$ **19.** $8\frac{2}{5} \div 3\frac{5}{9}$ $2\frac{29}{80}$

20. Rodney has $4200 in his bank account. If Esmeralda's account balance is $2\frac{5}{7}$ times Rodney's balance, how much money does she have in her account? $11,400

21. A plank is $6\frac{3}{4}$ in. wide. How many planks need to be laid side by side to form a walkway that is 54 in. wide? 8

Performance Task

Two-thirds of the people working at Happy Homes Realty are sales agents and the rest are clerical employees. If five-eighths of the agents are women and four-sevenths of the clerical employees are men, find the fraction of the people in the office who are male agents, female agents, male clerical employees, and female clerical employees.

a. Make a chart to show your results.

b. If there are 21 male sales agents, find how many people are employed all together and how many people are in each category.

Performance Assessment Key

See Performance Assessment Key on page 165.

Resources

Assessment Sourcebook

Chapter 4 Tests
- Forms A and B (free response)
- Form C (multiple choice)
- Form D (performance)
- Form E (mixed response)
- Form F (cumulative chapter test)

TestWorks
Tests and Practice Software

Home and Community Connections
- Letter Home for Chapter 4 in English and Spanish

Suggested Scoring Rubric

4
- Calculates fractions correctly and clearly displays them on chart.
- Finds the actual number of employees in the company and by category.

3
- Uses correct method to calculate fractions and adequately displays them on a chart.
- Demonstrates understanding of the method which should be used to find the actual number of employees in the company and in each category.

2
- Attempts to calculate fractions. Chart is incomplete or not clear.
- Attempts to find the actual number of employees in the company and/or each category with some success.

1
- Minimal success at calculating fractions. No display of results on chart.
- Makes little or no attempt to find the actual number of employees.

Cumulative Review Test Prep

Cumulative Review Chapters 1–4 — Test Prep

Multiple Choice

Choose the best answer.

1. Find the mean of 41, 31, 36, 31, 27, 38, 41, 31, 47, and 29. *[Lesson 1-4]* C

Ⓐ 31 Ⓑ 33.5 Ⓒ 35.2 Ⓓ 41

2. Which formula was used to create the table below? *[Lesson 2-3]* C

x	2	3	4	5	6
y	7	10	13	16	19

Ⓐ $y = 2x + 3$ Ⓑ $y = 4x - 5$

Ⓒ $y = 3x + 1$ Ⓓ $y = 4x - 1$

3. A music club advertises, "Buy a CD for $15, then take as many as you want for $8 each." Fran ordered five CDs from the club. How much will she pay? *[Lesson 2-8]* B

Ⓐ $40 Ⓑ $47 Ⓒ $55 Ⓓ $75

4. Estimate the product 12.8×19.7. *[Lesson 3-4]* C

Ⓐ 200 Ⓑ 230 Ⓒ 260 Ⓓ 300

5. Express the number 64,000,000 in scientific notation. *[Lesson 3-5]* B

Ⓐ 6.4×10^6 Ⓑ 6.4×10^7

Ⓒ 64×10^6 Ⓓ 0.64×10^8

6. Find the GCF of 96 and 72. *[Lesson 3-7]* C

Ⓐ 12 Ⓑ 16 Ⓒ 24 Ⓓ 288

7. Which is the solution to the equation $6.523 = u - 3.45$? *[Lesson 3-3]* B

Ⓐ 3.073 Ⓑ 9.973

Ⓒ 9.568 Ⓓ 22.50435

8. Which one of the following fractions is not equivalent to the others? *[Lesson 3-8]* C

Ⓐ $\frac{12}{15}$ Ⓑ $\frac{20}{25}$ Ⓒ $\frac{25}{30}$ Ⓓ $\frac{28}{35}$

9. Which fraction forms a repeating decimal? *[Lesson 3-10]* C

Ⓐ $\frac{11}{50}$ Ⓑ $\frac{32}{125}$ Ⓒ $\frac{10}{13}$ Ⓓ $\frac{39}{256}$

10. Estimate the sum $\frac{1}{11} + \frac{5}{12}$. *[Lesson 4-1]* B

Ⓐ 0 Ⓑ $\frac{1}{2}$ Ⓒ 1 Ⓓ $\frac{3}{2}$

11. Which is the solution to the equation $y + \frac{3}{20} = \frac{5}{8}$? *[Lesson 4-2]* A

Ⓐ $\frac{19}{40}$ Ⓑ $\frac{1}{8}$ Ⓒ $\frac{31}{40}$ Ⓓ $\frac{2}{7}$

12. Find the sum $8\frac{21}{22} + 12\frac{25}{33}$. *[Lesson 4-3]* D

Ⓐ $20\frac{113}{66}$ Ⓑ $20\frac{46}{55}$

Ⓒ $114\frac{173}{726}$ Ⓓ $21\frac{47}{66}$

13. Find the product $\frac{9}{22} \cdot \frac{55}{12}$. Reduce to lowest terms. *[Lesson 4-4]* C

Ⓐ $\frac{54}{605}$ Ⓑ $\frac{45}{24}$ Ⓒ $\frac{15}{8}$ Ⓓ $\frac{659}{132}$

14. A record on a turntable rotates every $1\frac{4}{5}$ seconds. How many times does it rotate in 45 seconds? *[Lesson 4-6]* C

Ⓐ 15 times Ⓑ 20 times

Ⓒ 25 times Ⓓ 30 times

About Multiple-Choice Tests

The Cumulative Review found at the end of Chapters 2, 4, 6, 8, 10, and 12 can be used to prepare students for standardized tests.

Students sometimes do not perform as well on standardized tests as they do on other tests. There may be several reasons for this related to the format and content of the test.

- **Format**
  Students may have limited experience with multiple-choice tests. For some questions, such tests are harder because having options may confuse the student.
- **Content**
  A standardized test may cover a broader range of content than normally covered on a test, and the relative emphasis given to various strands may be different than given in class. Also, some questions may assess general aptitude or thinking skills and not include specific pieces of mathematical content.

It is important not to let the differences between standardized tests and other tests shake your students' confidence.

Chapter 5 ▶ OVERVIEW

Geometry and Measurement

Section 5A

Geometric Figures: Students study lines, angles, and their relationships. They name and measure angles, and name and classify polygons. Students examine the relationship between the areas and perimeters of squares and rectangles.

5-1 Angles

5-2 Parallel and Perpendicular Lines

5-3 Triangles and Quadrilaterals

5-4 Polygons

5-5 Perimeter and Area

Section 5B

Geometric Formulas: Students use the area to find the length of a side of a square, study the relationships among the lengths of the sides of a right triangle, and find the areas of triangles, parallelograms, trapezoids, and irregular shapes.

5-6 Squares and Square Roots

5-7 The Pythagorean Theorem

5-8 Areas of Triangles

5-9 Areas of Parallelograms and Trapezoids

5-10 Problem Solving: Areas of Irregular Figures

Meeting NCTM Standards

Curriculum Standards

Standard			pages
1	**Problem Solving**	Skills and Strategies	209, 210, 226, 231, 236, 247, 252, 262
		Applications	215–216, 220–221, 225–226, 230–231, 235–236, 237, 242–243, 246–247, 251–252, 256–257, 261–262, 263
		Exploration	212, 217, 222, 227, 233, 240, 244, 248, 253, 258
2	**Communication**	Oral	211, 214, 219, 221, 224, 229, 234, 239, 241, 243, 246, 250, *252*, 255, 260, *262*
		Written	210, 216, 221, 226, 231, 236, 237, 243, 247, 252, 257, 262
		Cooperative Learning	*208, 211, 212, 214, 227, 233, 240, 244, 250, 253, 258, 260*
3	**Reasoning**	Critical Thinking	216, 221, 226, 231, 243, 247, 257, 262, 265
4	**Connections**	Mathematical	See Standards 5, 12, 13, below.
		Interdisciplinary	Sports 242, *247;* Arts & Literature 208, *211, 229, 242*; Language *212*, 223, 234, 241, 245; Science 209, 216, 223, 226, 228, 230, 235, 247; History 219, *224*, 236, 251, 257; Geography 220, 235, 257, *260;* Photography *220*; Consumer *226, 235*; Social Studies 209, 228, 238, 252, 255, 261; Architecture 237, 242; Industry *211, 235, 239*; Music 208
		Technology	210, 211, 216, 232, 242
		Cultural	208, *219*, 234, 243, *250, 255*
5	**Number and Number Relationships**		240–243
7	**Computation and Estimation**		*218, 223, 241,* 249
8	**Patterns and Functions**		*231, 252*
9	**Algebra**		244–246
12	**Geometry**		211–263
13	**Measurement**		212–216, 220, 233–236, 242, 247, 248–263

Italic type indicates Teacher-Edition reference.

Teaching Standards

Focus on Mathematical Tasks

It is the teacher's responsibility to select, adapt, and generate mathematical tasks. In choosing mathematical tasks, teachers should consider

- the mathematical content.
- the students themselves.
- the ways students learn math.

Assessment Standards

Focus on Coherence

Self Assessment As assessment, curriculum and instruction become more explicitly connected through a coherent assessment system, students will see how each is related and contributes to their learning. Self-assessment can provide a framework by which students measure their mathematical growth. Self-assessment in Chapter 5 has students

- justify classifications.
- identify difficult concepts.

TECHNOLOGY

For the Teacher

- **Teacher Resource Planner CD-ROM**
  Use the teacher planning CD-ROM to view resources available for Chapter 5. You can prepare custom lesson plans or use the default lesson plans provided.

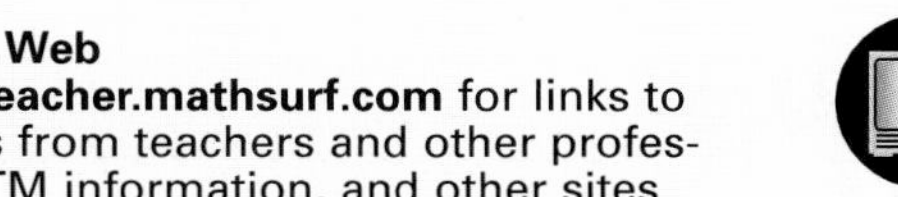

- **World Wide Web**
  Visit **www.teacher.mathsurf.com** for links to lesson plans from teachers and other professionals, NCTM information, and other sites.

- **TestWorks**
  TestWorks provides ready-made tests and can create custom tests and practice worksheets.

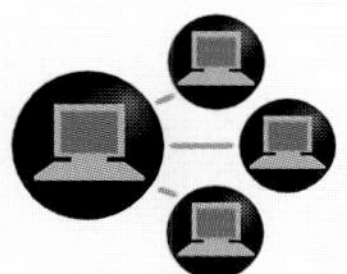

For the Parent

- **World Wide Web**
  Parents can use the Web site at **www.parent.mathsurf.com**.

For the Student

- **Interactive CD-ROM**
  Lesson 5-7 has an *Interactive CD-ROM Lesson*. The *Interactive CD-ROM Journal* and *Interactive CD-ROM Geometry Tool* are also used in Chapter 5.

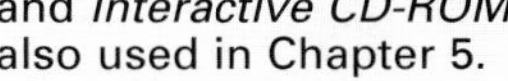

- **Wide World of Mathematics**
  Lesson 5-3 Geometry: A Bridge up for Grabs
  Lesson 5-5 Middle School: Huge Mall Opens
  Lesson 5-7 Middle School: Youthbuild

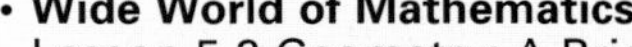

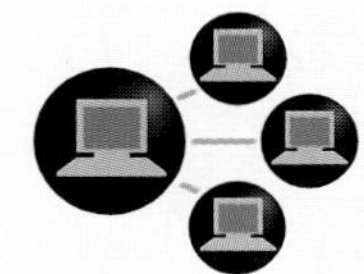

- **World Wide Web**
  Use with Chapter and Section Openers; Students can go online to the Scott Foresman-Addison Wesley Web site at **www.mathsurf.com/7/ch5** to collect information about chapter themes.

- **Jasper Woodbury Videodisc**
  Lesson 5-5: *Blueprint for Success*

STANDARDIZED - TEST CORRELATION

SECTION 5A

LESSON	OBJECTIVE	ITBS Form M	CTBS 4th Ed.	CAT 5th Ed.	SAT 9th Ed.	MAT 7th Ed.	Your Form
5-1	• Name angles.		✗	✗	✗	✗	
	• Measure angles.		✗		✗		
5-2	• Recognize parallel lines and their properties.			✗	✗		
	• Recognize perpendicular lines and their properties.			✗	✗		
5-3	• Name and classify triangles.	✗	✗				
	• Name and classify quadrilaterals.	✗	✗				
	• Find the measures of angles in these figures.		✗				
5-4	• Classify polygons.	✗	✗	✗			
	• Find the angle sum of polygons.						
5-5	• Examine the relationship between perimeter and area.	✗	✗	✗	✗	✗	

SECTION 5B

LESSON	OBJECTIVE	ITBS Form M	CTBS 4th Ed.	CAT 5th Ed.	SAT 9th Ed.	MAT 7th Ed.	Your Form
5-6	• Find the side of a square when you know its area.				✗		
	• Find a square root.				✗		
5-7	• Use the special relationship among the sides of a right triangle.						
	• Learn the Pythagorean Theorem.						
5-8	• Find the area of a triangle.	✗	✗		✗		
5-9	• Find the area of a parallelogram.	✗	✗		✗		
	• Find the area of a trapezoid.						
5-10	• Find the areas of irregular shapes.	✗	✗		✗		

Key: ITBS - Iowa Test of Basic Skills; CTBS - Comprehensive Test of Basic Skills; CAT - California Achievement Test; SAT - Stanford Achievement Test; MAT - Metropolitan Achievement Test

ASSESSMENT PROGRAM

Traditional Assessment

QUICK QUIZZES	SECTION REVIEW	CHAPTER REVIEW	CHAPTER ASSESSMENT FREE RESPONSE	CHAPTER ASSESSMENT MULTIPLE CHOICE	CUMULATIVE REVIEW
TE: pp. 216, 221, 226, 231, 236, 243, 247, 252, 257, 262	SE: pp. 238, 264 *Quiz 5A, 5B	SE: pp. 266–267	SE: p. 268 *Ch. 5 Tests Forms A, B, E	*Ch. 5 Tests Forms C, E	SE: p. 269 *Ch. 5 Test Form F

Alternate Assessment

INTERVIEW	JOURNAL	ONGOING	PERFORMANCE	PORTFOLIO	PROJECT	SELF
TE: pp. 252, 262	SE: pp. 216, 221, 226, 231, 236, 238, 252, 257, 264 TE: pp. 210, 216, 221, 231, 243, 252	TE: pp. 212, 218, 223, 227, 233, 240, 244, 248, 253, 258	SE: p. 268 *Ch. 5 Tests Forms D, E	TE: pp. 236, 247	SE: pp. 226, 243, 262 TE: p. 209	TE: pp. 226, 257

*Tests and quizzes are in *Assessment Sourcebook*. Test Form E is a mixed response test.
Forms for Alternate Assessment are also available in *Assessment Sourcebook*.

TestWorks: Test and Practice Software

MIDDLE SCHOOL PACING CHART

REGULAR PACING

Day	5 classes per week
1	Chapter 5 Opener; Problem Solving Focus
2	Section **5A** Opener; Lesson **5-1**
3	Lesson **5-2**
4	Lesson **5-3**
5	Lesson **5-4**; Technology
6	Lesson **5-5**
7	**5A** Connect; **5A** Review
8	Section **5B** Opener; Lesson **5-6**
9	Lesson **5-7**
10	Lesson **5-8**
11	Lesson **5-9**
12	Lesson **5-10**
13	**5B** Connect; **5B** Review; Extend Key Ideas
14	Chapter 5 Summary and Review
15	Chapter 5 Assessment, Cumulative Review, Chapters 1–5

BLOCK SCHEDULING OPTIONS

Block Scheduling for
Complete Course

Chapter 5 may be presented in

- nine 90-minute blocks
- twelve 75-minute blocks

Each block consists of a combination of

- Chapter and Section Openers
- Explores
- Lesson Development
- Problem Solving Focus
- Technology
- Extend Key Ideas
- Connect
- Review
- Assessment

For details, see *Block Scheduling Handbook*.

Block Scheduling for
Interdisciplinary Course

Each block integrates math with another subject area.

In Chapter 5, interdisciplinary topics include

- Buildings
- Play Surfaces

Themes for Interdisciplinary Team Teaching 5A and 5B are

- Structures Made of Polygons
- Area and Distance

For details, see *Block Scheduling Handbook*.

Block Scheduling for
Lab-Based Course

In each block, 30–40 minutes is devoted to lab activities including

- Explores in the Student Edition
- Connect pages in the Student Edition
- Technology options in the Student Edition
- Reteaching Activities in the Teacher Edition

For details, see *Block Scheduling Handbook*.

Block Scheduling for
Course with *Connected Mathematics*

In each block, investigations from **Connected Mathematics** replace or enhance the lessons in Chapter 5.

Connected Mathematics topics for Chapter 5 can be found in

- *Stretching and Shrinking*

For details, see *Block Scheduling Handbook*.

INTERDISCIPLINARY BULLETIN BOARD

Set Up

Have resource materials available for researching sizes of playing fields.

Procedure

- Have small groups of students research the dimensions of playing fields of sports such as football, baseball, soccer, basketball, rugby, and field hockey.
- Students should determine the area of the largest field, and one group should draw its size using an appropriate scale. Students should indicate length, width, and area measurements of the field. Attach the drawing to the bulletin board.
- Other groups should draw and attach increasingly smaller fields inside the larger ones.

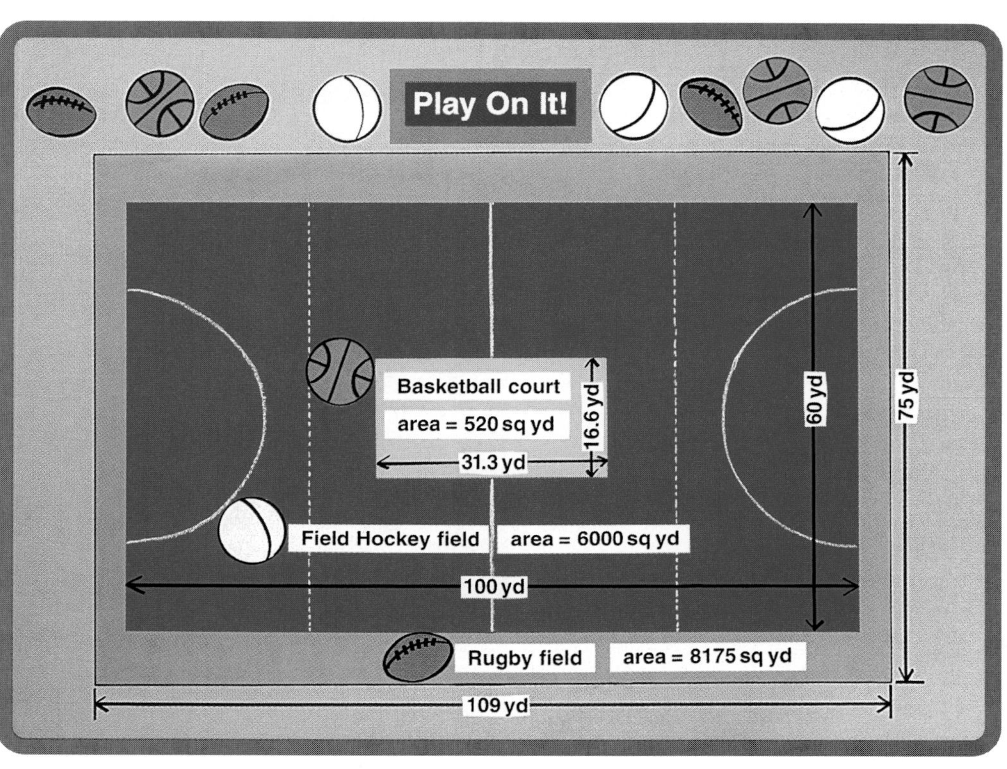

Chapter 5

The information on these pages shows how geometry and measurement are used in real-life situations.

World Wide Web

If your class has access to the World Wide Web, you might want to use the information found at the Web site addresses given.

Extensions

The following activities do not require access to the World Wide Web.

People of the World
Tatamis are thick mats traditionally made of woven straw. Each is about 3 ft × 6 ft. Have students estimate the size of their bedroom based on the size of a tatami (small single bed).

Entertainment
Ask students to describe different ways they listen to music. Ask why they think CDs have changed the music business.

Arts & Literature
Have students find examples of sonnets written in iambic pentameter, and illustrate for the class how those sonnets follow the guidelines given here.

Science
Have students work in groups to find information about other crystals. Ask them to present their findings to the class.

Social Studies
Have students locate the Nile River on a map. Suggest that they find out how the Nile has affected the lives of the people who live near it.

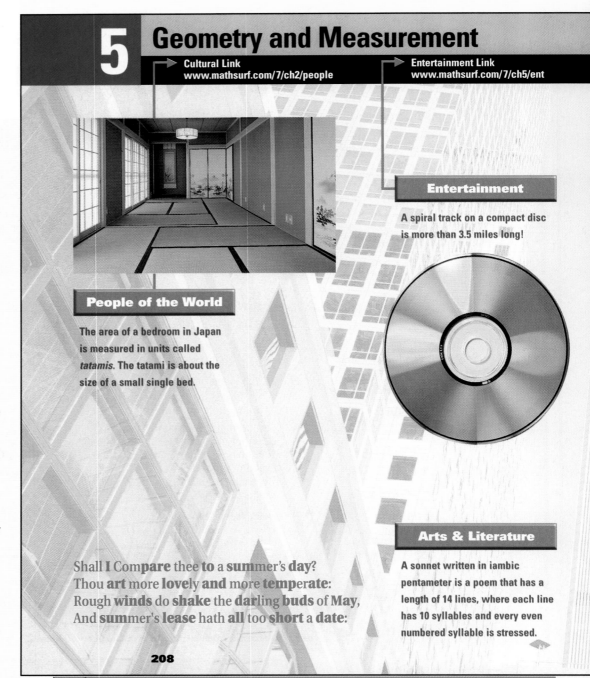

5 Geometry and Measurement

Cultural Link
www.mathsurf.com/7/ch2/people

Entertainment Link
www.mathsurf.com/7/ch5/ent

Entertainment

A spiral track on a compact disc is more than 3.5 miles long!

People of the World

The area of a bedroom in Japan is measured in units called *tatamis.* The tatami is about the size of a small single bed.

Shall I Compare thee to a summer's day?
Thou art more lovely and more temperate:
Rough winds do shake the darling buds of May,
And summer's lease hath all too short a date:

Arts & Literature

A sonnet written in iambic pentameter is a poem that has a length of 14 lines, where each line has 10 syllables and every even numbered syllable is stressed.

208

TEACHER TALK

Meet Robert and Mary Margaret Capraro

Morningside Elementary School
Miami, Florida
North Twin Lakes Elementary School
Hialeah, Florida

"Activity-oriented" characterizes the way we introduce geometry and measurement. For the following activity, we use spice drops and toothpicks or wooden skewers.

As we begin the unit, we have students use spice drops and toothpicks to create segments, rays, and angles. Students use the corner of a piece of paper as a right angle and classify their spice-drop angles, thus learning the important similarities and differences between acute, right, and obtuse angles.

During our study of polygons, we continue to have students use spice drops and skewers to make both regular and nonregular polygons. We have students name each polygon and list its attributes. We also have students classify the polygons according to the number of sides. They further classify the triangles and quadrilaterals according to lengths of sides and measures of angles.

Science Link
www.mathsurf.com/7/ch5/science

Science

A crystal's shape can help classify it. A cross section of an emerald is a hexagon. The cross section of a salt crystal is a square.

Social Studies

The Nile is the world's longest river. It flows through four countries (Egypt, Sudan, Tanzania, and Uganda) and measures 6670 km.

KEY MATH IDEAS

A straight line extends forever in two directions. Rays and segments are parts of lines.

Angles are made of rays. They are measured in degrees.

A polygon is a figure whose sides are straight. The number of sides of a polygon tells you the sum of its angle measures.

The distance around a figure is its perimeter. The space it encloses is its area. You can use formulas to calculate the areas of many types of polygons.

You can use the Pythagorean Theorem to find the length of a side in a right triangle. Solving for the side length involves squaring numbers and finding their square roots.

CHAPTER PROJECT

Problem Solving

Understand
Plan
Solve
Look Back

In this project, you will calculate the area of your school's ground floor. Begin the project by sketching the floor plan of your school building or buildings.

209

PROJECT ASSESSMENT

You may choose to use this project as a performance assessment for the chapter.

Performance Assessment Key

Level 4 Full Accomplishment

Level 3 Substantial Accomplishment

Level 2 Partial Accomplishment

Level 1 Little Accomplishment

Suggested Scoring Rubric

4	•All necessary dimensions are measured or estimated correctly. •Gives a reasonable estimate of the total area and satisfactorily justifies how the measurements were obtained.
3	•Most dimensions are measured or estimated correctly. •Gives a reasonable estimate of the total area, but not all measurements are satisfactorily justified.
2	•Some measurements are measured or estimated incorrectly. •Attempts to give a total area, but justifications are not satisfactory.
1	•Does not attempt to accurately measure or estimate necessary dimensions. •A total area, if given, is inaccurate.

Chapter Project

Students will find the appropriate measures and calculate the area of the ground floor of their school.

Materials
Tape measure

Resources
Chapter 5 Project Master

Introduce the Project

- Begin by talking about what is meant by the area of the ground floor of the school.
- Ask students how they might go about finding the necessary dimensions.
- Suggest that students draw a floor plan of the ground floor of their school to scale to help them determine the total area.
- Suggest how students might estimate the dimensions of rooms in the school to which they do not have access.

Project Progress

Section A, page 226 Students measure and estimate dimensions they will need to find the area of the ground floor of their school.

Section B, page 262 Students calculate the area of their school's ground floor. Then they prepare a report explaining how they found the measurements and how they calculated the area.

Community Project

A community project for Chapter 5 is available in *Home and Community Connections.*

Cooperative Learning

You may want to use Teaching Tool Transparency 1: Cooperative Learning Checklist with **Explore** and other group activities in this chapter.

Problem Solving Focus

Identifying Missing Information

The Point
Students focus on determining if all the information they need to solve a problem is given.

Resources
Teaching Tool Transparency 16: Problem-Solving Guidelines

 *Interactive CD-ROM Journal*

About the Page

Using the Problem-Solving Process
Tell students that in solving real-world problems, people often need to find missing information. Discuss the following suggestions for getting started:

- Determine what the problem is asking and what information is needed to find the answer.
- Determine if all the necessary information is given, and if not, where the missing information can be found.

Ask ...

- What information do you need to solve Problem 1? Is all the information given? How much money Lou has, and the cost of both the frame and mat; No, the amount of money Lou has is not given.
- Is there a problem that gives enough information so you can solve it? Yes, Problem 2.
- How would you solve Problem 4 if all the necessary facts were given? Add the number of inches of mat to the length of each side of the photo.

Answers for Problems

1. Need to know how much money Lou has.
2. 2.25 in.
3. Need to know the size of this photograph.
4. Need to know how wide the mat should be.

Journal

Have students write about a problem they have had to solve for which they did not have enough information. Have them explain how they found the missing information.

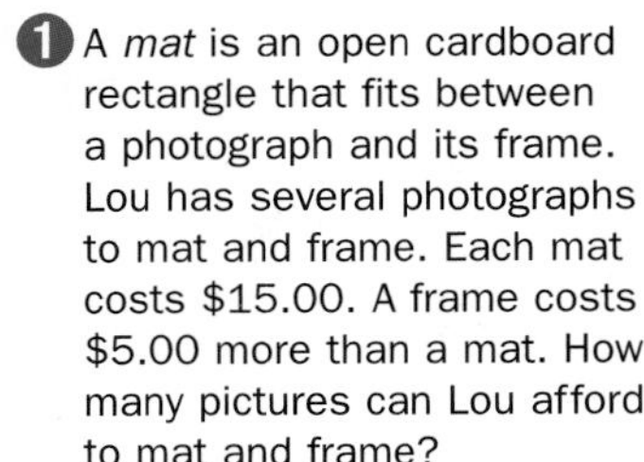

Identifying Missing Information

As you plan how you are going to solve a problem, you need to be sure you have all the necessary information. Sometimes you will encounter a problem that is missing important information.

Problem Solving Focus

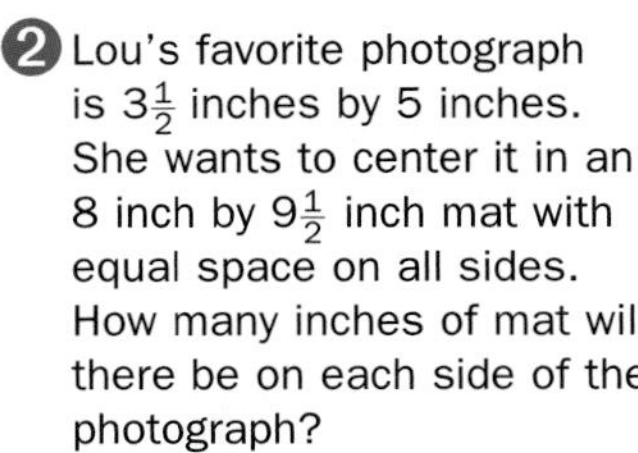

Identify any additional information needed to solve each problem. If a problem is not missing any information, give its solution.

1. A *mat* is an open cardboard rectangle that fits between a photograph and its frame. Lou has several photographs to mat and frame. Each mat costs $15.00. A frame costs $5.00 more than a mat. How many pictures can Lou afford to mat and frame?
2. Lou's favorite photograph is $3\frac{1}{2}$ inches by 5 inches. She wants to center it in an 8 inch by $9\frac{1}{2}$ inch mat with equal space on all sides. How many inches of mat will there be on each side of the photograph?
3. For the next photograph, Lou wants 2 inches of mat on all sides. How large should the mat be?
4. One of Lou's photos is 4 inches by 6 inches. What size frame should Lou buy for this photo?

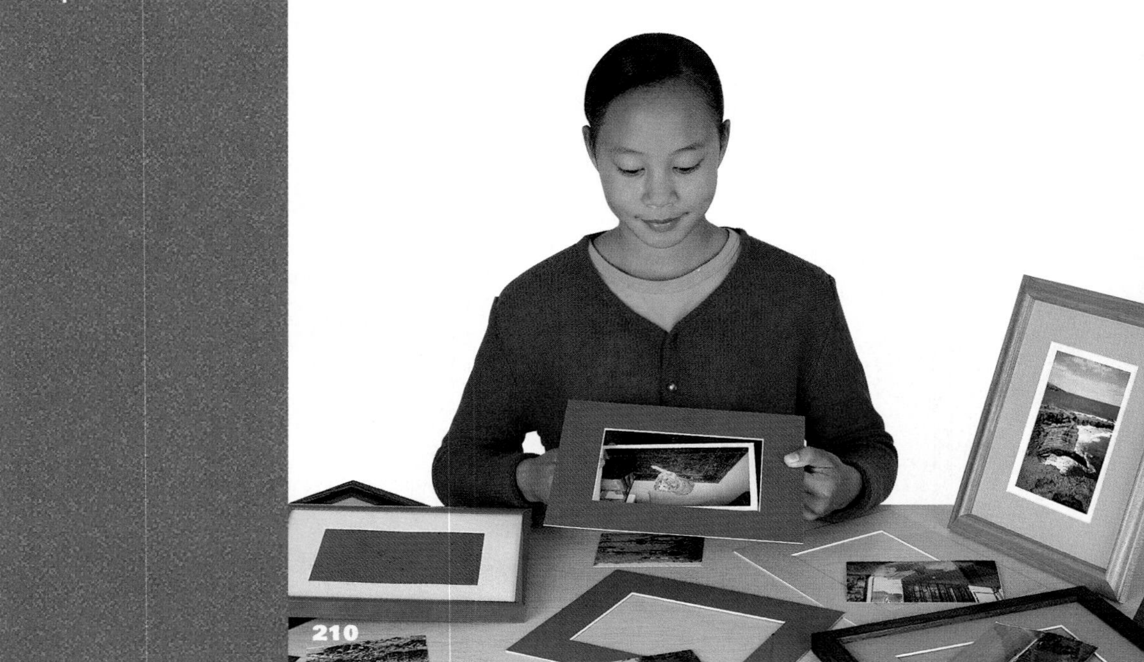

210

Additional Problem

Caleb wants to paint a design on one of the longer walls of his room, so he decided to paint the wall white before he started. His room is 10 ft by 12 ft and 7 ft high. He found that a quart of white paint costs $5.99. How much will he have to pay for the paint?

1. What is the problem about? Buying paint for a wall.
2. What does the problem ask you to find? The cost of the paint.
3. How would you find the amount of paint Caleb needs? Multiply length of the longer wall (12 ft) by the height (7 ft) to find the area of the wall. Divide this product by the number of square feet a quart of paint covers.
4. Is all the information you need to solve the problem given? If not, what is missing? No; You need to know how many square feet a quart of paint covers.
5. Where could you find the information needed? Possible answers: A paint store; The label on a quart can of paint.

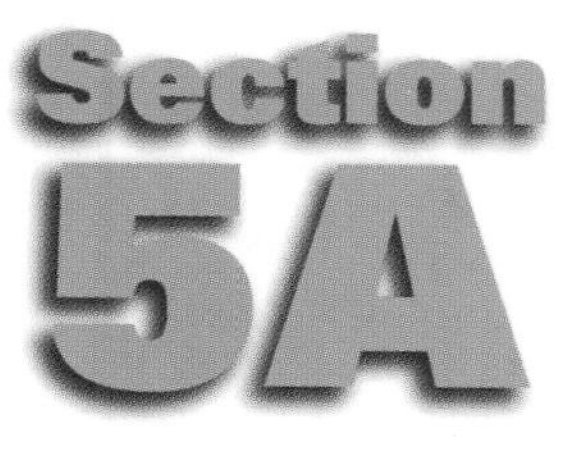

Section 5A Geometric Figures

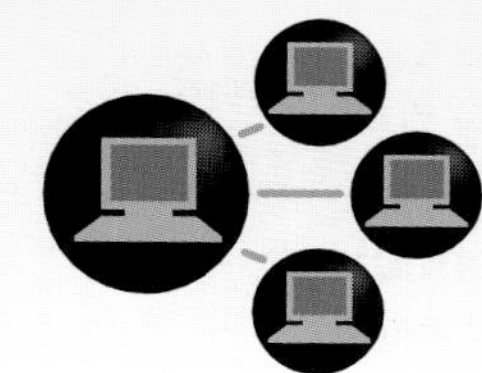

Visit **www.teacher.mathsurf.com** for links to lesson plans from teachers and other professionals, NCTM information, and other sites.

LESSON PLANNING GUIDE

Student Edition				Ancillaries	
LESSON		MATERIALS	VOCABULARY	DAILY	OTHER
	Chapter 5 Opener				Ch. 5 Project Master Ch. 5 Community Project Teaching Tool Trans. 1
	Problem Solving Focus				Teaching Tool Trans. 16 *Interactive CD-ROM Journal*
	Section 5A Opener				
5-1	**Angles**	protractor, transparent paper	ray, angle, vertex, acute angle, right angle, obtuse angle, straight angle, complementary, supplementary, congruent, bisect, angle bisector	5-1	Teaching Tool Trans. 6, 15 Lesson Enhancement Trans. 19 Technology Master 18
5-2	**Parallel and Perpendicular Lines**	lined paper, straightedge, protractor	plane, parallel, transversal, alternate interior angles, corresponding angles, vertical angles, midpoint, congruent segments, segment bisector, perpendicular, perpendicular bisector	5-2	Teaching Tool Trans. 15 Lesson Enhancement Trans. 20 Technology Master 19
5-3	**Triangles and Quadrilaterals**	ruler, protractor	quadrilateral, parallelogram, rhombus, trapezoid	5-3	Teaching Tool Trans. 14, 15 Lesson Enhance. Trans. 21, 22 Technology Master 20 *WW Math*—Geometry Ch. 5 Project Master
5-4	**Polygons**	pattern blocks	polygon, pentagon, hexagon, octagon, regular polygon	5-4	Teaching Tool Trans. 18 Lesson Enhancement Trans. 23
	Technology	Dynamic geometry software			*Interactive CD-ROM Geometry Tool*
5-5	**Perimeter and Area**	graph paper, scissors		5-5	Teaching Tool Trans. 7 Technology Master 21 *WW Math*—Middle School
	Connect	inch or metric ruler, protractor, paper			Teaching Tool Trans. 14, 15 Interdisc. Team Teaching 5A
	Review				Practice 5A; Quiz 5A; *TestWorks*

SKILLS TRACE

LESSON	SKILL	FIRST INTRODUCED GR. 5	GR. 6	GR. 7	DEVELOP	PRACTICE/ APPLY	REVIEW
5-1	**Naming and measuring angles.**	✘			pp. 212–214	pp. 215–216	pp. 267, 277, 557
5-2	**Recognizing properties of parallel and perpendicular lines.**			✘ p. 217	pp. 217–219	pp. 220–221	pp. 267, 281, 562
5-3	**Classifying triangles, quadrilaterals, and measuring their angles.**		✘	✘	pp. 222–224	pp. 225–226	pp. 267, 285, 566
5-4	**Classifying polygons and finding their angle sums.**		✘		pp. 227–229	pp. 230–231	pp. 267, 290, 570
5-5	**Relating perimeter and area.**			✘ p. 233	pp. 233–234	pp. 235–236	pp. 267, 297, 577

INTERDISCIPLINARY TEAM TEACHING

Math and Science/Technology

(Worksheet pages 17–18: Teacher pages T17–T18)

In this lesson, students design a structure made of polygons.

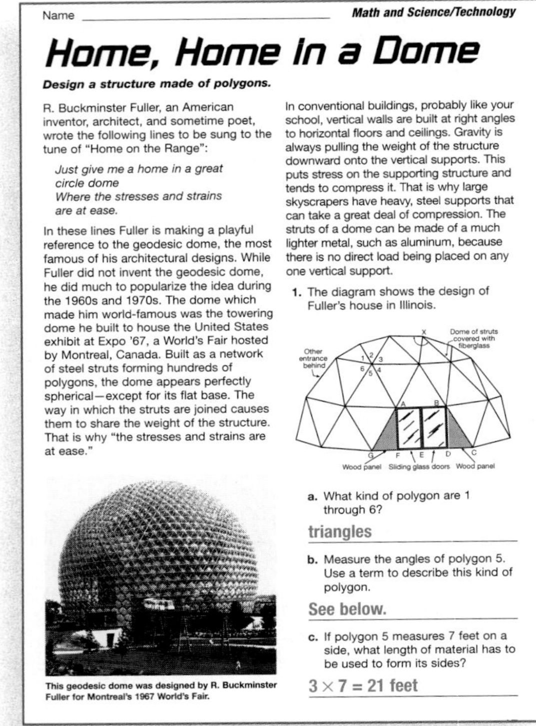

Name ______________________ *Math and Science/Technology*

Home, Home In a Dome

Design a structure made of polygons.

R. Buckminster Fuller, an American inventor, architect, and sometime poet, wrote the following lines to be sung to the tune of "Home on the Range":

Just give me a home in a great circle dome
Where the stresses and strains are at ease.

In these lines Fuller is making a playful reference to the geodesic dome, the most famous of his architectural designs. While Fuller did not invent the geodesic dome, he did much to popularize the idea during the 1960s and 1970s. The dome which made him world-famous was the towering dome he built to house the United States exhibit at Expo '67, a World's Fair hosted by Montreal, Canada. Built as a network of steel struts forming hundreds of polygons, the dome appears perfectly spherical—except for its flat base. The way in which the struts are joined causes them to share the weight of the structure. That is why "the stresses and strains are at ease."

This geodesic dome was designed by R. Buckminster Fuller for Montreal's 1967 World's Fair.

In conventional buildings, probably like your school, vertical walls are built at right angles to horizontal floors and ceilings. Gravity is always pulling the weight of the structure downward onto the vertical supports. This puts stress on the supporting structure and tends to compress it. That is why large skyscrapers have heavy, steel supports that can take a great deal of compression. The struts of a dome can be made of a much lighter metal, such as aluminum, because there is no direct load being placed on any one vertical support.

1. The diagram shows the design of Fuller's house in Illinois.

a. What kind of polygon are 1 through 6?
triangles

b. Measure the angles of polygon 5. Use a term to describe this kind of polygon.
See below.

c. If polygon 5 measures 7 feet on a side, what length of material has to be used to form its sides?
$3 \times 7 = 21$ feet

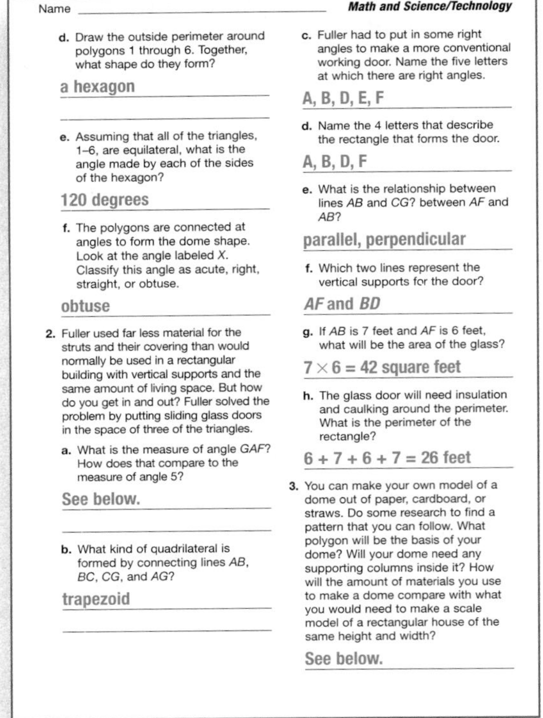

Name ______________________ *Math and Science/Technology*

d. Draw the outside perimeter around polygons 1 through 6. Together, what shape do they form?
a hexagon

e. Assuming that all of the triangles, 1–6, are equilateral, what is the angle made by each of the sides of the hexagon?
120 degrees

f. The polygons are connected at angles to form the dome shape. Look at the angle labeled *X*. Classify this angle as acute, right, straight, or obtuse.
obtuse

2. Fuller used far less material for the struts and their covering than would normally be used in a rectangular building with vertical supports and the same amount of living space. But how do you get in and out? Fuller solved the problem by putting sliding glass doors in the space of three of the triangles.

a. What is the measure of angle *GAF*? How does that compare to the measure of angle 5?
See below.

b. What kind of quadrilateral is formed by connecting lines *AB*, *BC*, *CG*, and *AG*?
trapezoid

c. Fuller had to put in some right angles to make a more conventional working door. Name the five letters at which there are right angles.
A, B, D, E, F

d. Name the 4 letters that describe the rectangle that forms the door.
A, B, D, F

e. What is the relationship between lines *AB* and *CG*? between *AF* and *AB*?
parallel, perpendicular

f. Which two lines represent the vertical supports for the door?
AF and *BD*

g. If *AB* is 7 feet and *AF* is 6 feet, what will be the area of the glass?
$7 \times 6 = 42$ square feet

h. The glass door will need insulation and caulking around the perimeter. What is the perimeter of the rectangle?
$6 + 7 + 6 + 7 = 26$ feet

3. You can make your own model of a dome out of paper, cardboard, or straws. Do some research to find a pattern that you can follow. What polygon will be the basis of your dome? Will your dome need any supporting columns inside it? How will the amount of materials you use to make a dome compare with what you would need to make a scale model of a rectangular house of the same height and width?
See below.

Answers

1. b. Polygon 5 has three angles of 60 degrees; an equilateral triangle.
2. a. 30 degrees; half of 60 degrees at 5.
3. Dome models use triangles, have no internal supports, and use less material than models of comparable rectangular houses.

BIBLIOGRAPHY

FOR TEACHERS

Diagram Group. *Rules of the Game*. New York, NY: St. Martin's Press, 1990.

Glickman, A. M. *Metric Conversion Tables*. Woodbury, NY: Barron's Educational Series, Inc., 1990.

Heafford, Philip Ernest. *Great Book of Math Puzzles*. New York, NY: Sterling, 1993.

Spangler, David. *Math for Real Kids*. Glenview, IL: Good Year Books, 1997.

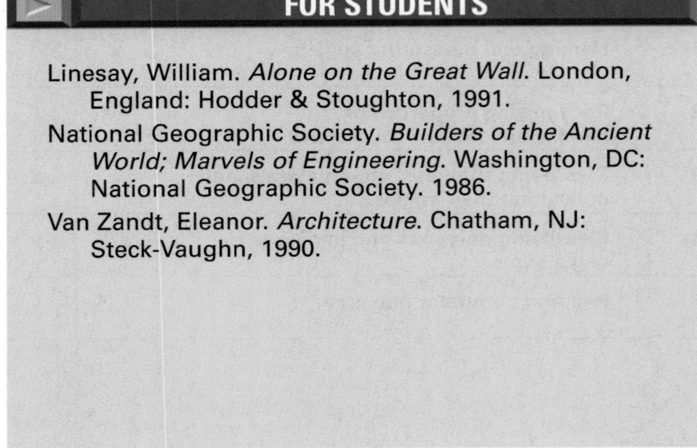

FOR STUDENTS

Linesay, William. *Alone on the Great Wall*. London, England: Hodder & Stoughton, 1991.

National Geographic Society. *Builders of the Ancient World; Marvels of Engineering*. Washington, DC: National Geographic Society. 1986.

Van Zandt, Eleanor. *Architecture*. Chatham, NJ: Steck-Vaughn, 1990.

SECTION 5A

Geometric Figures

▶ Fine Arts Link ▶ Industry Link ▶ www.mathsurf.com/7/ch5/buildings

FROM THE DOME *to Your Home...*

What's more than two football fields wide, can withstand 200-mile-per-hour winds, protects 75,000 people from the weather, and looks like a hemisphere but isn't?

Answer: ***The dome on the Louisiana Superdome, the world's largest indoor stadium. Covering almost 10 acres, the dome is the crown on one of the world's most unusual buildings.***

The dome isn't really a hemisphere. Instead, it's constructed of lines and angles that form simple geometric figures. Other unusual buildings, such as the Transamerica Pyramid in San Francisco, are also based on geometric figures.

From the pyramids of ancient Egypt to today's most modern buildings, architectural design has used the simple figures of geometry. Now you'll also learn to spot geometric figures in the buildings around you—in your school, your home or apartment, and in the office buildings in your town.

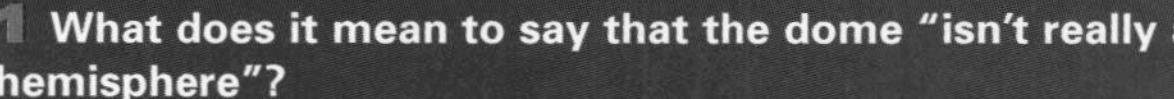

1 What does it mean to say that the dome "isn't really a hemisphere"?

2 Describe some of the shapes you see in the dome. Name any figures you recognize.

3 Name an unusual building that you're familiar with. How is geometry used in the design of the building?

211

Where are we now?

In Grade 6, students studied the geometry of polygons. They learned to calculate the distance around the outside of a polygon and the amount of surface it covers.

They learned how to

- classify lines.
- construct and measure angles.
- find the perimeter of polygons.
- find the area of squares, rectangles, triangles, and parallelograms.

Where are we going?

In Grade 7, Section 5A, students will

- name and measure angles.
- learn the properties of parallel and perpendicular lines.
- name and classify triangles and quadrilaterals.
- find measures of angles in triangles and quadrilaterals.
- classify and find the angle sum of polygons.
- examine the relationship between perimeter and area.

Section 5A

Theme: Unusual Buildings

World Wide Web

If your class has access to the World Wide Web, you might want to use the information found at the Web site address given. The interdisciplinary links relate to the topics discussed in this section.

About the Page

This page introduces the theme of the section, unusual buildings, and discusses the geometry used in architectural design.

Ask ...

- What geometric shapes do you see in your classroom?
- Have you seen any unusual buildings? Where? Can you describe what they looked like?

Extensions

The following activities do not require access to the World Wide Web.

Fine Arts

Have groups of students select a famous architect and research some of the buildings he or she has designed.

Industry

Interested students might investigate the cost of building structures such as the Louisiana Superdome or the Transamerica Building.

Answers for Questions

1. The shape of the dome is not exactly half of a sphere.
2. Possible answers: rectangles, half sphere.
3. Possible answer: The Pentagon on the outskirts of Washington, D.C.; It is built in the shape of a pentagon around a pentagonal courtyard.

Connect

On page 237, students use their understanding of geometry to design a building.

Lesson Organizer

Objectives

- Name angles.
- Measure angles.

Vocabulary

- Ray, angle, vertex, acute angle, right angle, obtuse angle, straight angle, complementary, supplementary, congruent, bisect, angle bisector

Materials

- Explore: Protractor, transparent paper

NCTM Standards

- 1–4, 12, 13

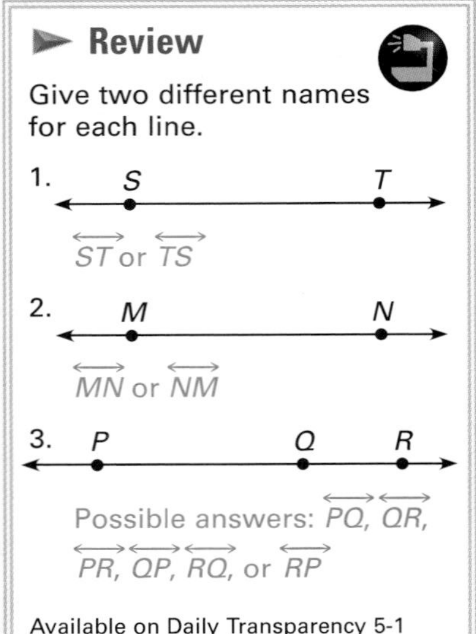

Review

Give two different names for each line.

1. S, T — $\overleftrightarrow{ST}$ or $\overleftrightarrow{TS}$

2. M, N — $\overleftrightarrow{MN}$ or $\overleftrightarrow{NM}$

3. P, Q, R — Possible answers: $\overleftrightarrow{PQ}$, $\overleftrightarrow{QR}$, $\overleftrightarrow{PR}$, $\overleftrightarrow{QP}$, $\overleftrightarrow{RQ}$, or $\overleftrightarrow{RP}$

Available on Daily Transparency 5-1

1 Introduce

Explore

You may want to use Teaching Tool Transparencies 6: Cuisenaire Angle Ruler and 15: Protractor with this lesson.

The Point
Students review measuring angles with a protractor.

Ongoing Assessment
Watch for students who use the wrong scale when measuring or drawing angles with a protractor.

5-1 Angles

You'll Learn ...

- to name angles
- to measure angles

... How It's Used

Airplane navigators must measure angles very accurately to keep their planes on course.

Vocabulary

ray
angle
vertex
acute angle
right angle
obtuse angle
straight angle
complementary
supplementary
congruent
bisect
angle bisector

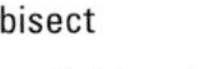

▶ **Lesson Link** You've seen angles in circle graphs. Now you'll look more closely at angles to see how they are named, drawn, and measured. ◀

Explore Angles

What's Your Angle?

Materials: Protractor, Transparent paper

The 1815-foot-tall CN Tower in Toronto, Ontario, Canada, is the world's tallest unsupported building. It contains the 7-story Skypod, the tower's revolving restaurant and office complex.

1. Copy the four labeled angles shown on the Skypod.
2. The measure of the angle labeled with a 4 is 45 degrees. Use your protractor to determine how the measurement is made. Extend the sides of the angle if necessary.
3. Find the measures of angles 1, 2, and 3.
4. Explain how to measure an angle with a protractor. Be sure to include different types of angles in your explanation.

Learn Angles

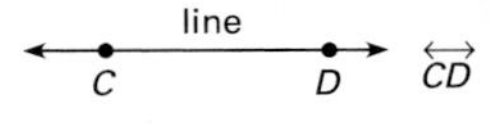

Recall that a *line* extends without end in both directions. You can think of a **ray** as part of a line. A ray has one endpoint and extends without end in *one* direction.

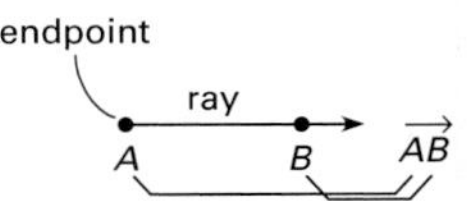

A ray is named by its endpoint and one other point on the ray. The figure shows ray AB, written $\overrightarrow{AB}$. Notice that the arrow points from the endpoint through another point on the ray.

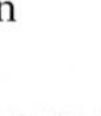
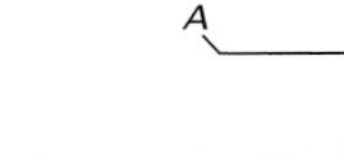

MEETING INDIVIDUAL NEEDS

Resources

5-1 Practice
5-1 Reteaching
5-1 Problem Solving
5-1 Enrichment
5-1 Daily Transparency
Problem of the Day
Review
Quick Quiz
Teaching Tool Transparencies 6, 15
Lesson Enhancement Transparency 19
Technology Master 18

Learning Modalities

Visual Have students use a marking pen to label angles in magazine or newspaper photos as acute, right, or obtuse.

Kinesthetic Have students use the corner of a sheet of paper to determine if an angle is a right angle.

English Language Development

Be sure students understand the difference between *complementary* and *complimentary*. Point out that the words sound alike but have different meanings and are spelled differently, even though they differ by only one letter.

Have students work in pairs to define in their own words and draw examples of the vocabulary list for this lesson.

Two rays with a common endpoint form an **angle**. The two rays are the sides of the angle. The common endpoint is the **vertex**.

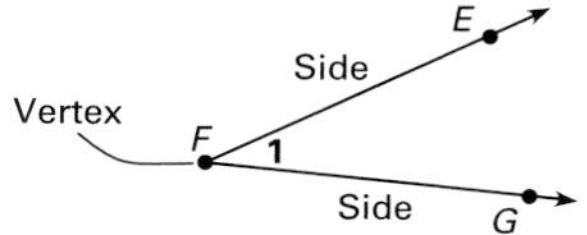

∠EFG or ∠GFE or ∠F or ∠1
Always write the vertex letter in the middle.

You can use the angle symbol (∠), the vertex, and a point on each side to name an angle. You can use the vertex alone, or a number, to name the angle if there is no chance of confusion.

Angles are measured in degrees (°). They can be classified according to their measures.

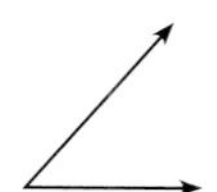

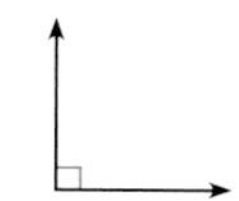

An **acute angle** has a measure less than 90°.

A **right angle** has a measure of exactly 90°.

An **obtuse angle** has a measure greater than 90° and less than 180°.

A **straight angle** has a measure of exactly 180°.

You can use a protractor to find the measure of an angle.

▶ Language Link

When the word *right* refers to an angle, it has nothing to do with left and right or wrong and right. This usage is like *upright,* meaning "standing up straight."

Example 1

Name the angle and find its measure.

The angle is $\angle LTK$, $\angle KTL$, or $\angle T$.

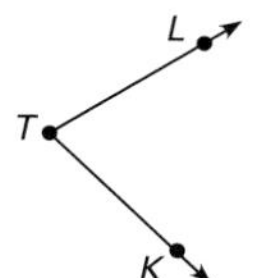

To find the measure, place a protractor on the angle so that the center mark is on the vertex and the 0° lines match one side of the angle.

Find the point where the other side of the angle meets the degree scale on the protractor. Read the measure: 76°. Use the letter m to write the measure: $m\angle T = 76°$.

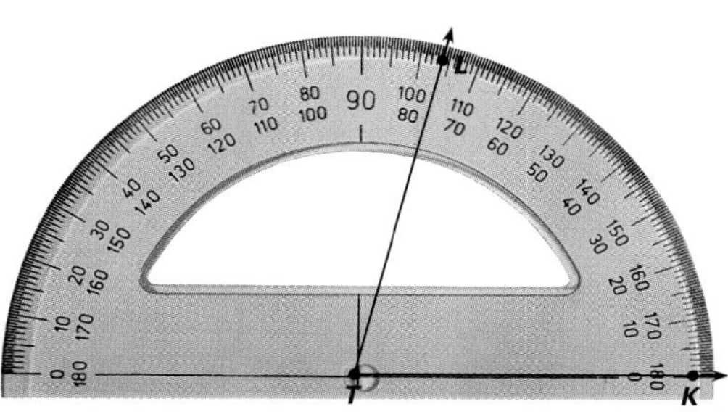

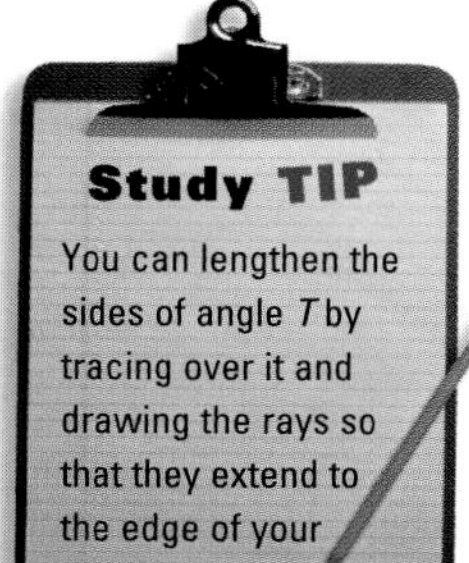

Study TIP
You can lengthen the sides of angle T by tracing over it and drawing the rays so that they extend to the edge of your protractor.

For Groups That Finish Early

Find a pair of angles having a sum of 180°. Then find a pair of angles having a sum of 90°. $m\angle 1 + m\angle 2 = 180°$; $m\angle 3 + m\angle 4 = 90°$

Follow Up

Have students look around the classroom to find angles that seem to have the same measure as ∠1 and ∠2, or ∠3 and ∠4.

Answers for Explore

3. $m\angle 1 = 90°$; $m\angle 2 = 90°$; $m\angle 3 = 45°$
4. Possible answer: Place the center mark of the protractor at the point where the two sides of the angle meet, and have the 0° mark on one side. Read the measure where the other side meets the degree scale.

2 Teach

Learn

You may want to use Lesson Enhancement Transparency 19 with **Learn.**

Be sure students understand how naming a line is different from naming a ray. Emphasize that any two points (in either order) can be used to name a line, but when we name a ray, the endpoint is *always* named first.

Alternate Examples

1. Name the angle and find its measure.

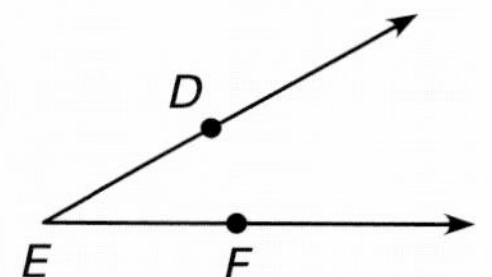

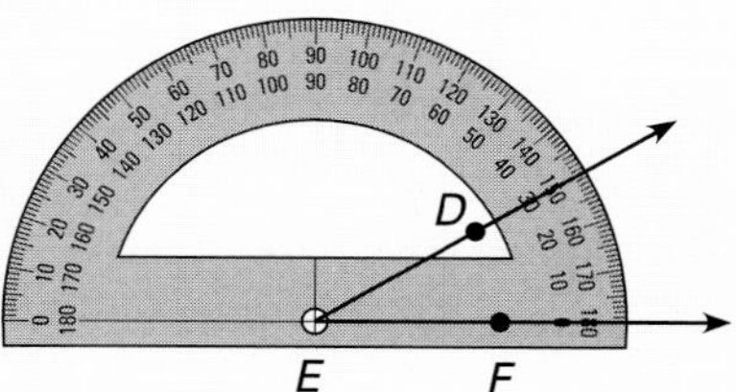

The angle is ∠DEF, ∠FED, or ∠E.

Use the letter m to write the measure: $m\angle E = 30°$.

MATH EVERY DAY

▶ Problem of the Day

Choose any three-digit number, such as 342. Write a six-digit number, repeating the digits of the chosen number—342,342. Divide the six-digit number by 7. Divide that quotient by 11. Divide that quotient by 13. What is the final quotient? Try this with another three-digit number. Describe the results. Every number of the form *xyz,xyz* is equal to 1,001 times *xyz*. The product of 7, 11, and 13 is 1001. So, when *xyz,xyz* is divided by 7, 11, and 13, the result will always be *xyz*, the chosen number.

Available on Daily Transparency 5-1

An Extension is provided in the transparency package.

Fact of the Day
The CN Tower in downtown Toronto was built in 1976.

Mental Math

Do these mentally.

1. 40 × 30 1200
2. 80 × 700 56,000
3. 700 × 600 420,000
4. 9000 × 7000 63,000,000

Alternate Examples

2. Find the measures of a complement and a supplement of $\angle S$.

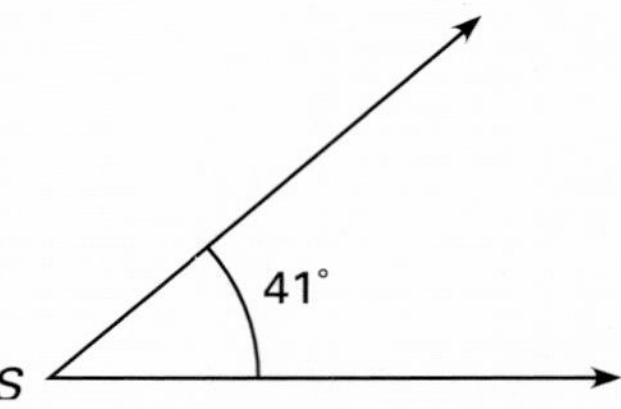

The complement of $\angle S$ measures $90° - 41° = 49°$.

The supplement of $\angle S$ measures $180° - 41° = 139°$.

3. Two angles lie along a line and share a side. If the measure of the acute angle is 32°, what is the measure of the other angle?

The angles are supplementary, so the sum of their measures is 180°. If the acute angle measures 32°, the other angle measures $180° - 32° = 148°$.

3 Practice and Assess

Check

Be sure students realize that complementary angles, as well as supplementary angles, may or may not have the same vertex. You might want to draw a diagram like the following to illustrate both cases for complementary angles.

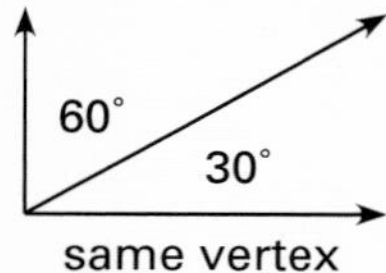

same vertex

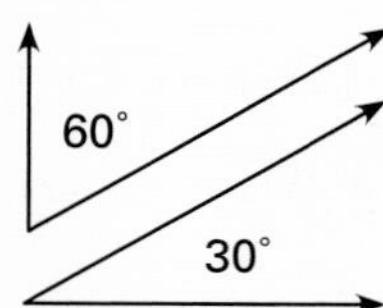

different vertices

Answers for Check Your Understanding

1. Agree; The measures of complementary angles add to 90°, so the complement must measure less than 90°.
2. 45°; 90°

Two angles are **complementary** if the sum of their measures is 90°. Two angles are **supplementary** if the sum of their measures is 180°.

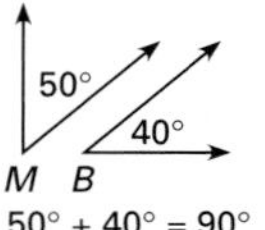

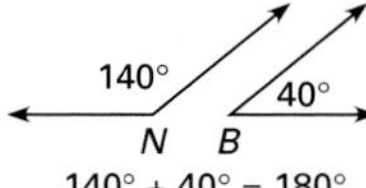

Study TIP

Notice that **C** comes before **S**, and 90° is less than 180°, so **C**omplementary refers to 90° and **S**upplementary to 180°.

Examples

2 Find the measures of a complement and a supplement of $\angle N$.

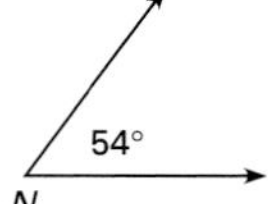

The sum of the measures of $\angle N$ and an angle complementary to it is 90°.

A complement of $\angle N$ measures $90° - 54° = 36°$.

The sum of the measures of $\angle N$ and an angle supplementary to it is 180°.

A supplement of $\angle N$ measures $180° - 54° = 126°$.

3 Identify a pair of supplementary angles in the supports of the bridge. If the measure of the acute angle is 60°, what is the measure of the other angle?

Since a straight angle measures 180°, any pair of angles that share a side and lie along a line is supplementary. If the acute angle measures 60°, the other angle measures $180° - 60° = 120°$.

Try It

Find the measures of a complement and a supplement of a 43° angle.

Complement: 47°; Supplement: 137°.

If two angles have the same measure, they are **congruent**. The symbol ≅ means "is congruent to." A ray that divides an angle into two congruent angles **bisects** the angle. The ray is the **angle bisector**. In this figure, $\overrightarrow{GM}$ bisects $\angle FGH$, so $\angle FGM \cong \angle MGH$.

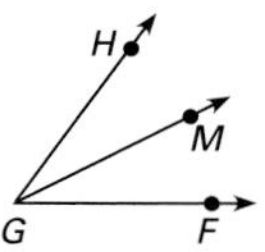

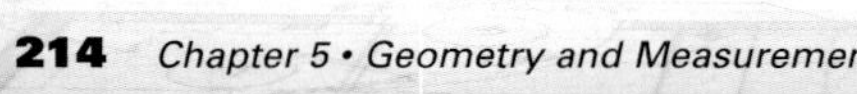

Check Your Understanding

1. Tell whether you agree or disagree with this statement: The complement of an acute angle must be an acute angle. Explain.
2. What are the measures of the angles formed by the bisector of a right angle? A straight angle?

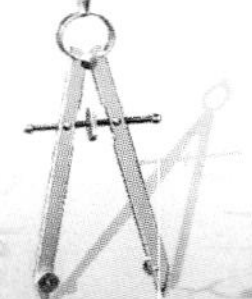

MEETING MIDDLE SCHOOL CLASSROOM NEEDS

Tips from Middle School Teachers

I like to have my students look around the classroom and find as many angles as possible. This is a good time to point out that angles viewed in a three-dimensional setting may not look the same as they do when viewed on a book page. For example, when you view a right angle from certain vantage points, the angle might not *look* like a right angle.

Team Teaching

Work with an art teacher to introduce the concept of geometry in art. Students can work with perspective drawing or string art.

Cooperative Learning

Some students may still have trouble measuring with a protractor. It might be helpful to have them work in pairs to draw angles and then exchange and measure the angles.

5-1 Exercises and Applications

Practice and Apply

1. **Getting Started** Follow these steps to measure an angle using a protractor.

   a. Draw two intersecting rays that form an angle.

   b. Place the protractor on the angle so that the center mark is on the vertex and the 0° line matches one side of the angle.

   c. Find the point where the other side of the angle meets the degree scale on the protractor. Read the measure.

Name each angle and give its measure.

2. 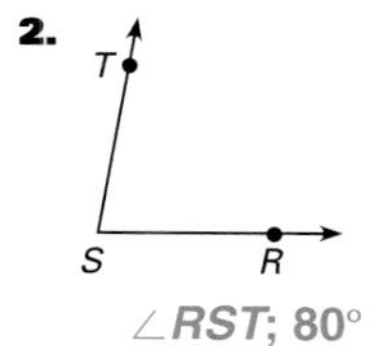
∠RST; 80°

3. 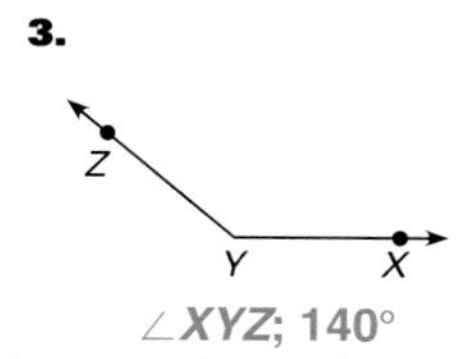
∠XYZ; 140°

4. 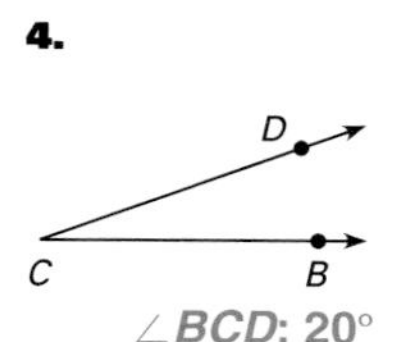
∠BCD; 20°

5. 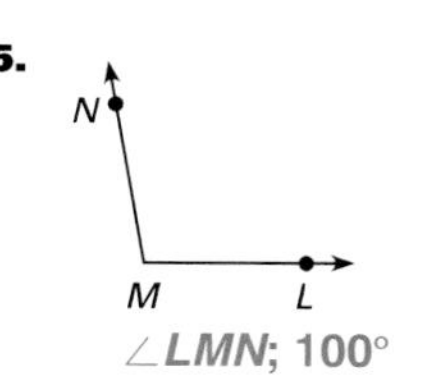
∠LMN; 100°

Find the measures of a complement and a supplement of ∠N.

6. 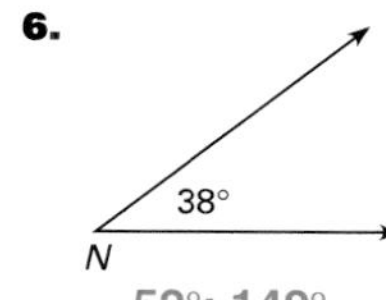
52°; 142°

7. 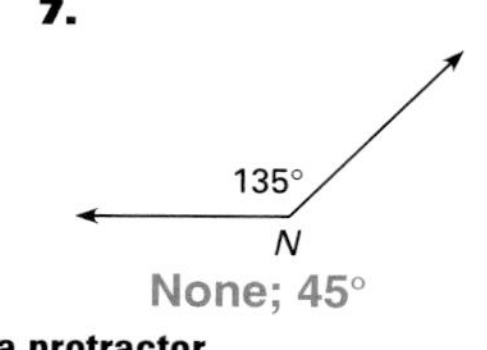
None; 45°

8. 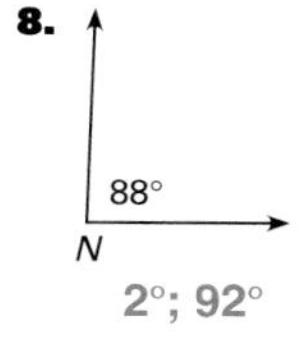
2°; 92°

9. 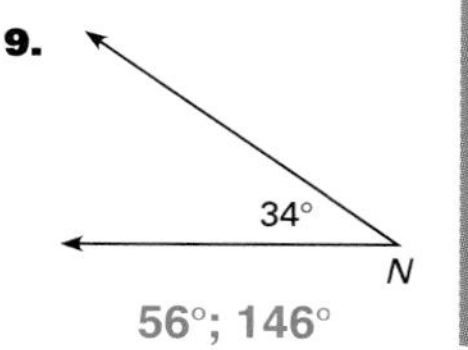
56°; 146°

Measure each angle using a protractor.

10. 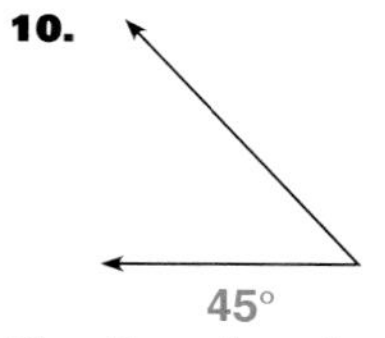
45°

11. 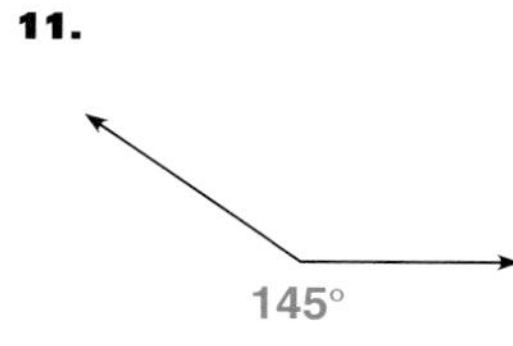
145°

12. 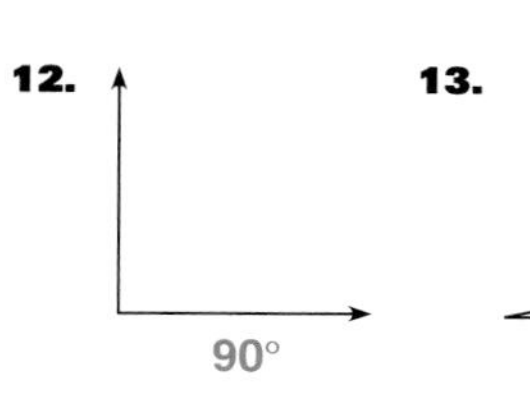
90°

13. 13°

Classify each angle.

14. Straight

15. 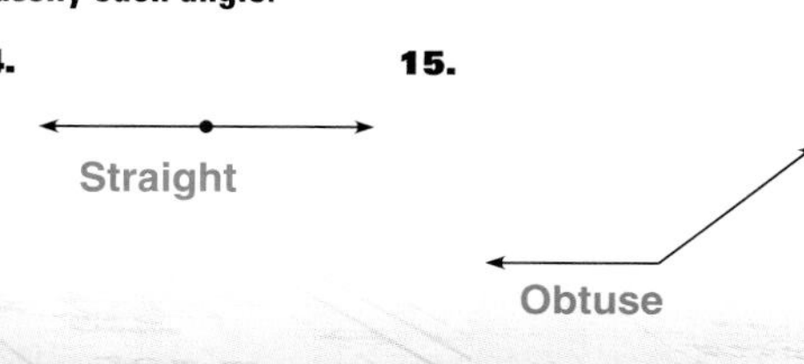
Obtuse

16. 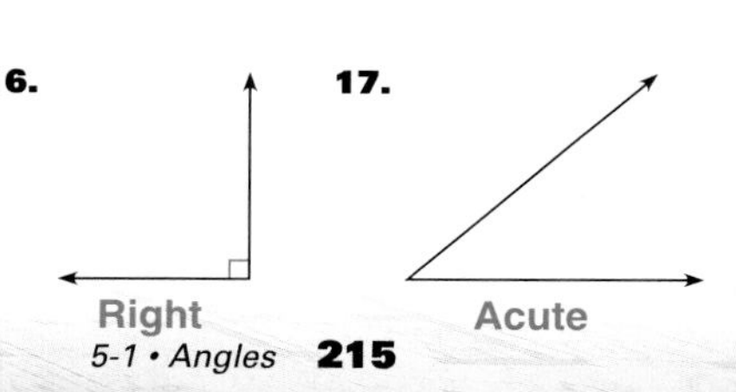
Right

17. Acute

PRACTICE

Name ______

Practice 5-1

Angles

Name each angle and give its measure.

1. ∠ABC; 65° 2. ∠TUV; 125° 3. ∠PQR; 40°

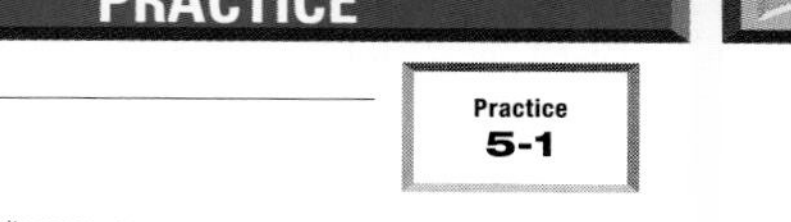

Find the complement and the supplement of ∠P.

4. complement: 37° supplement: 127°
5. complement: 12° supplement: 102°
6. complement: None supplement: 62°

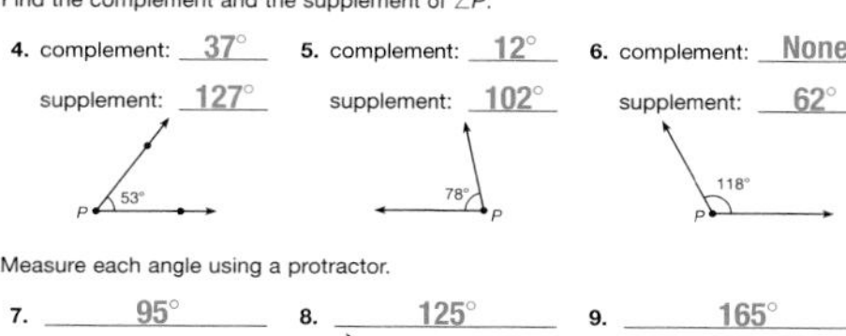

Measure each angle using a protractor.

7. 95° 8. 125° 9. 165°

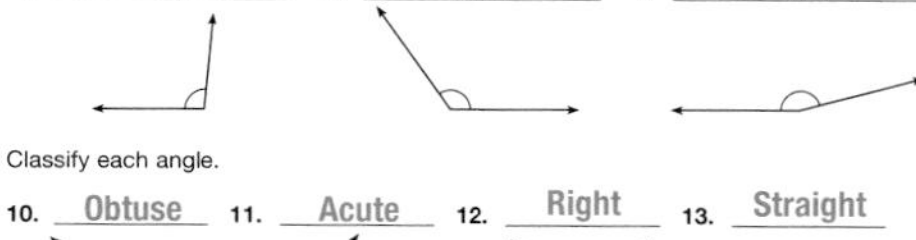

Classify each angle.

10. Obtuse 11. Acute 12. Right 13. Straight

14. **Science** When a beam of light strikes a flat mirror, the light reflects at the same angle at which it hit the mirror's surface.

   a. If light strikes a mirror at 63°, at what angle will the light reflect? 63°

   b. What is the measure of the angle between the angle at which the light strikes the mirror (63°), and the angle at which the light reflects? 54°

RETEACHING

Name ______

Alternative Lesson 5-1

Angles

A **ray** is a part of a line. It has one endpoint and extends without end in one direction. A ray is named by its endpoint and one other point on the ray. The diagram on the right shows $\overrightarrow{XY}$ (ray $\overrightarrow{XY}$). This ray has endpoint *X* and extends in the direction of *Y*.

Two rays with a common endpoint form an **angle.** The rays are the sides of the angle. The common endpoint is the **vertex.** You can use the angle symbol (∠), the vertex, and a point on each side to name an angle. This angle could be named ∠*MNP* or ∠*PNM*. You could also call this ∠*N* or ∠1.

Example

Name the angle and give its measure.

The vertex of the angle is *B*, so it will be the middle letter of the angle name. A point from each ray makes up the rest of the angle name, so the angle can be named ∠*ABC*, ∠*CBA* or ∠*B*.

Use a protractor to measure the angle. Place the center mark of the protractor on the vertex and the 0° line on one side of the angle.

Beginning with 0°, follow the increasing degree numbers until you find the point where the other side of the angle meets the degree scale on the protractor. You may need to extend the sides of the angle to help you read the protractor.

The measure of ∠*ABC* (*m*∠*ABC*) is 60°.

Try It Name each angle and give its measure.

a. What is the vertex of the angle at the right? E

b. What is the name of the angle at the right? ∠DEF or ∠FED

c. What is the measure of the angle at the right? 35°

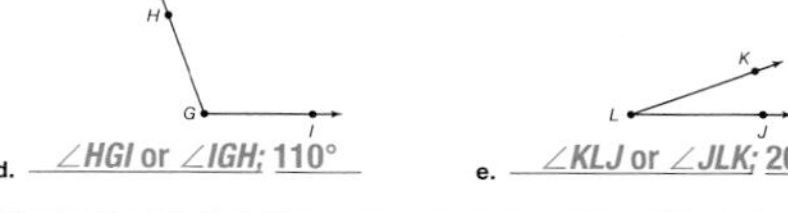

d. ∠HGI or ∠IGH; 110° e. ∠KLJ or ∠JLK; 20°

5-1 Exercises and Applications

Assignment Guide

- Basic
  1–13 odds, 14–19, 21–37 odds
- Average
  1–17 odds, 18–21, 23–37 odds
- Enriched
  2–16 evens, 18–21, 22–36 evens

Exercise Notes

Exercise 7

Error Prevention Watch for students who think that the complement is 45° since 45° + 90° = 135°. Point out that any angle larger than 90° does not have a complement.

Exercises 10–13

Extension You may want to trace these angles on a transparency and have student volunteers use Teaching Tool Transparency 6: Cuisenaire Angle Ruler, to measure the angles.

Exercise Answers

1.a–c. Answers may vary.

Reteaching

Activity

Materials: Index card

- Draw several angles and use an index card to classify each as acute, right, or obtuse. Place a corner of the index card at the vertex of the angle with an edge of the card along one side of the angle.
- Use the pictures below to help you decide if each angle is acute, right, or obtuse.

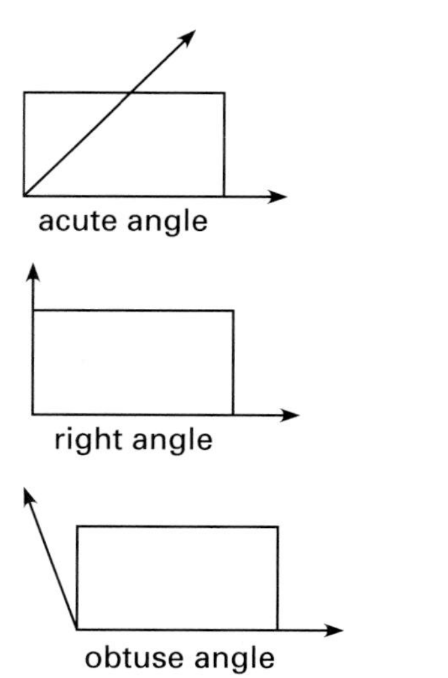

Exercise Notes

■ Exercise 18

Science A periscope is an instrument that allows the viewer to see an object from a concealed or submerged position. It involves the use of two parallel mirrors.

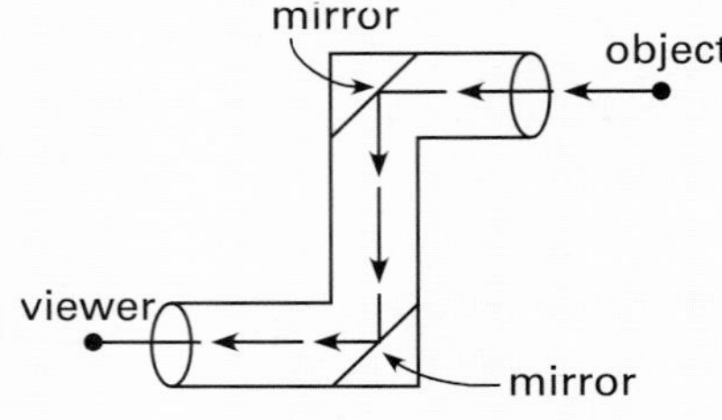

Exercise Answers

21. Check students' drawings

30. GCF = 2; LCM = 714

31. GCF = 5; LCM = 2805

32. GCF = 21; LCM = 126

33. GCF = 12; LCM = 672

34. GCF = 105; LCM = 3150

35. GCF = 33; LCM = 2178

36. GCF = 1; LCM = 1,276,275

37. GCF = 4; LCM = 504

Alternate Assessment

You may want to use the *Interactive CD-ROM Journal* with this assessment.

Journal Have students make a list of the new terms appearing in this lesson and write a description for each term. If helpful, the descriptions might include pictures that illustrate the terms.

► Quick Quiz

Measure each angle, classify the angle, and then find the complement and supplement of the angle.

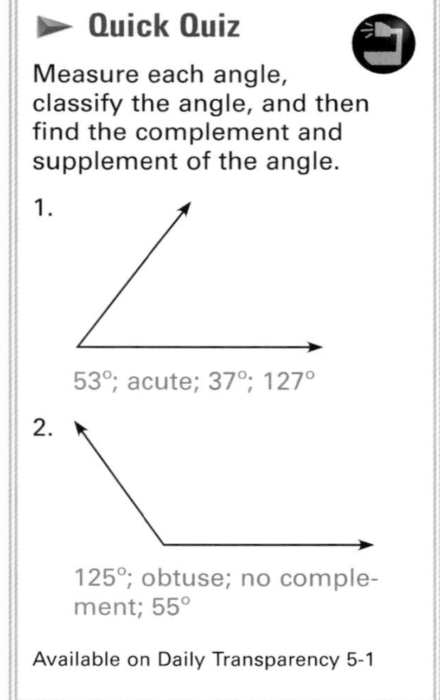

1. 53°; acute; 37°; 127°

2. 125°; obtuse; no complement; 55°

Available on Daily Transparency 5-1

---

18. Science When a beam of light strikes a flat mirror, the light reflects at the same angle at which it hit the mirror's surface. GPS

a. If light strikes a mirror at a 50° angle, at what angle will the light reflect? 50°

b. What is the measure of the angle *between* the angle at which light strikes the mirror (50°), and the angle at which the light reflects? 80°

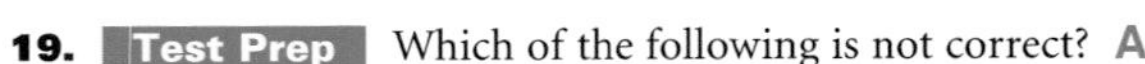

19. Test Prep Which of the following is not correct? A

Ⓐ Obtuse angle: 37° Ⓑ Acute angle: 79° Ⓒ Right angle: 90° Ⓓ Straight angle: 180°

Problem Solving and Reasoning

20. Critical Thinking Tell what type of angles are formed when each angle is bisected. Make a sketch to help show your answers. Check students' sketches

a. An obtuse angle Acute angles **b.** A right angle Acute angles

c. A straight angle Right angles **d.** An acute angle Acute angles

21.  Journal Draw an angle. Use the method shown below to bisect the angle with a compass and straightedge.

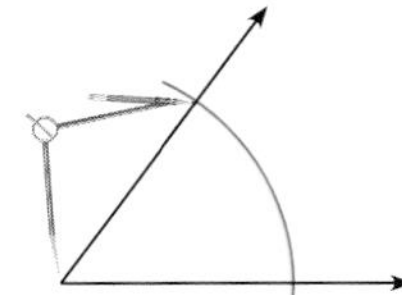

1. Place the compass tip at the vertex of the angle. Make an arc that intersects both sides of the angle.

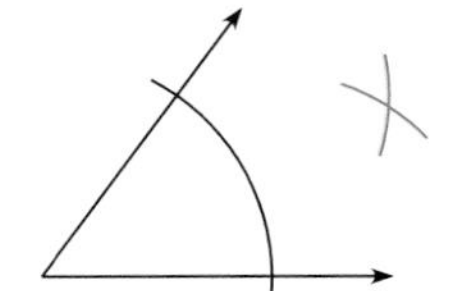

2. Place the compass tip at a point where the arc intersects the angle. Make an arc. Make another arc with the tip at the other intersection point.

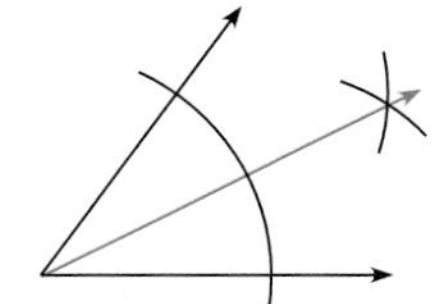

3. Draw a ray from the vertex of the angle through the point where the arcs you made in Step 2 cross. This ray bisects the angle.

Mixed Review

Use > or < to compare each pair of numbers. *[Lesson 3-1]*

22. 8.40 [>] 7.41 **23.** 6.423 [<] 64.23 **24.** 2.875 [>] 2.758 **25.** 5.246 [>] 5.245

26. 3.899 [<] 3.9 **27.** 23.74 [>] 23.477 **28.** 9.127 [<] 9.217 **29.** 0.8 [>] 0.0999

Find the GCF and the LCM of each pair of numbers. *[Lesson 3-7]*

30. 34, 42 **31.** 165, 85 **32.** 42, 63 **33.** 84, 96

34. 525, 630 **35.** 198, 363 **36.** 1001, 1275 **37.** 36, 56

PROBLEM SOLVING 5-1

PROBLEM SOLVING

Name ______________________ Guided Problem Solving 5-1

GPS PROBLEM 18, STUDENT PAGE 216

When a beam of light strikes a flat mirror, the light reflects at the same angle at which it hit the mirror's surface.

a. If light strikes a mirror at a 50° angle, at what angle will the light reflect?

b. What is the measure of the angle *between* the angle at which light strikes the mirror (50°), and the angle at which the light reflects?

Light beam 1 2 3

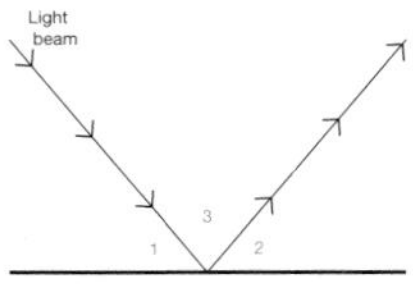

— Understand —

1. In the diagram, label the angle formed when the light
 a. strikes the mirror as ∠1. b. reflects from the mirror as ∠2.
2. Label the angle between ∠1 and ∠2 as ∠3.
3. What is the measure of ∠1? 50°

— Plan —

4. Which two angles will be congruent? ∠1 and ∠2
5. What is the sum of the three angles shown in the diagram? 180°
6. Write an expression showing how to find the measure of the noncongruent angle. ∠3 = 180° − (∠1 − ∠2)

— Solve —

7. What is the measure of ∠2? 50° Of ∠3? 80°

— Look Back —

8. How can you check your answer? Possible answer: Measure the angles with a protractor. The total measures must equal 180°.

SOLVE ANOTHER PROBLEM

a. If light strikes a mirror at a 65° angle, at what angle will the light reflect? 65°
b. What is the measure of the angle *between* the angle at which light strikes the mirror (65°), and the angle at which the light reflects? 50°

ENRICHMENT

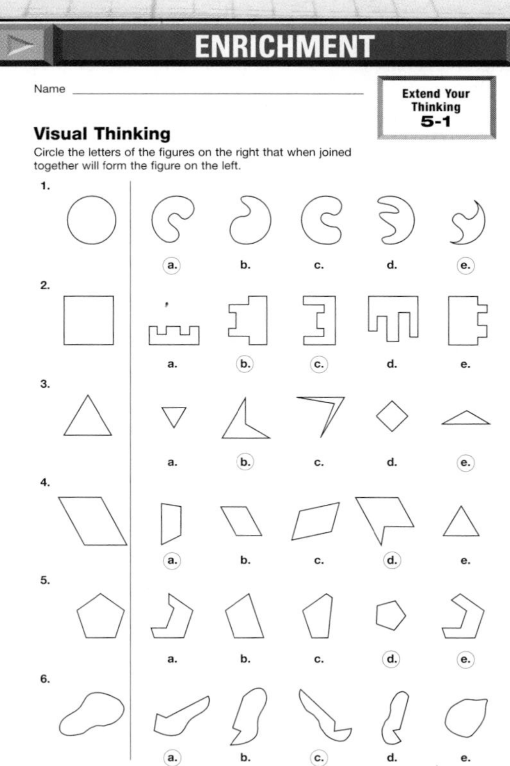
Name ______________________ Extend Your Thinking 5-1

Visual Thinking

Circle the letters of the figures on the right that when joined together will form the figure on the left.

1. a. b. c. d. e.
2. a. b. c. d. e.
3. a. b. c. d. e.
4. a. b. c. d. e.
5. a. b. c. d. e.
6. a. b. c. d. e.

Parallel and Perpendicular Lines

5-2

▶ Lesson Link You have seen that rays are related to lines. Now you'll look more closely at lines, especially those that never meet and those that meet to form right angles. ◀

Explore Parallel and Perpendicular Lines

The Game Is on the Line!

Materials: Lined paper, Straightedge, Protractor

Select two lines on your paper that are more than one space apart.

1. Describe the lines on your paper. What's special about them?
2. Draw a slanted line through these lines and label the angles as shown. Measure angles 1–8 and record your measurements.
3. Did you find any congruent angles? If so, name them.
4. Did you find any supplementary angles? If so, name them.
5. Redraw the figure. This time, use a straightedge to draw a vertical line. What is the measure of each angle now?

Learn Parallel and Perpendicular Lines

A **plane** is an infinite, flat surface. Lines in a plane that never meet are called **parallel** lines. The figure shows parallel ribs (red) near the base of Paris's famous Eiffel Tower. To strengthen the tower, designer Gustave Eiffel constructed slanted struts (blue) across the parallel ribs. Lines that intersect two or more parallel lines in this way are called **transversals** .

You'll Learn ...

- to recognize parallel lines and their properties
- to recognize perpendicular lines and their properties

... How It's Used

Railroad construction engineers need to build tracks that are exactly parallel. The ties that hold the track in place must be perpendicular to the tracks.

Vocabulary

plane
parallel
transversal
alternate interior angles
corresponding angles
vertical angles
midpoint
congruent segments
segment bisector
perpendicular
perpendicular bisector

Lesson Organizer

Objectives

- Recognize parallel lines and their properties.
- Recognize perpendicular lines and their properties.

Vocabulary

- Plane, parallel, transversal, alternate interior angles, corresponding angles, vertical angles, midpoint, congruent segments, segment bisector, perpendicular, perpendicular bisector

Materials

- Explore: Lined paper, straightedge, protractor

NCTM Standards

- 1–4, 12, 13

▶ Review

1. Describe some lines in your classroom that would never meet. Answers may vary.
2. Describe some lines in your classroom that seem to meet at a right angle. Answers may vary.
3. When are two angles supplementary? If the sum of their measures is 180°.

Available on Daily Transparency 5-2

MEETING INDIVIDUAL NEEDS

Resources

- **5-2** Practice
- **5-2** Reteaching
- **5-2** Problem Solving
- **5-2** Enrichment
- **5-2** Daily Transparency
  - Problem of the Day
  - Review
  - Quick Quiz
- Teaching Tool Transparency 15
- Lesson Enhancement Transparency 20
- Technology Master 19

Learning Modalities

Visual Have students collect pictures from magazines or newspapers that illustrate parallel and/or perpendicular lines.

Social Students can work with a partner to draw diagrams that illustrate parallel and perpendicular lines, as well as the relationships between angles formed by these lines.

English Language Development

Be sure students understand that vertical angles are different from vertical lines. Emphasize that *any* two intersecting lines form two pairs of vertical angles, whether or not either of the lines is vertical.

Have students write definitions for the vocabulary words in this lesson, then read each definition to other students who must identify the term and draw an example.

1 Introduce

Explore

You may want to use Teaching Tool Transparency 15: Protractor with **Explore**.

The Point
Students discover that when two parallel lines are cut by a transversal, some angles formed are congruent and some are supplementary.

Answers for Explore on next page.

Ongoing Assessment
Watch for students who have trouble when measuring angles because the diagrams in which the angles appear are small. Remind them that the sides of the angle can always be extended if necessary.

For Groups That Finish Early
Use a sheet of unlined paper instead of lined paper. First draw two lines that would eventually meet, that is, two nonparallel lines. Then repeat Steps 2–4. How do the results compare? Now there are no pairs of congruent angles, but there are still several pairs of supplementary angles.

Follow Up
Have students discuss whether their answers for Steps 3 or 4 would ever change if they picked a different slanted line in Step 2.

Answers for Explore
Answers may vary.

2 Teach

Learn

You may want to use Lesson Enhancement Transparency 20 with **Learn**.

Be sure students understand that parallel lines are in the same plane. A special name (skew lines) is given to lines that do not meet and that are not in the same plane. (See Exercise 22.)

Alternate Examples

1. A street intersects two parallel streets so that $m\angle 2 = 72^{\circ}$. Find $m\angle 3$, $m\angle 8$, $m\angle 6$, and $m\angle 4$.

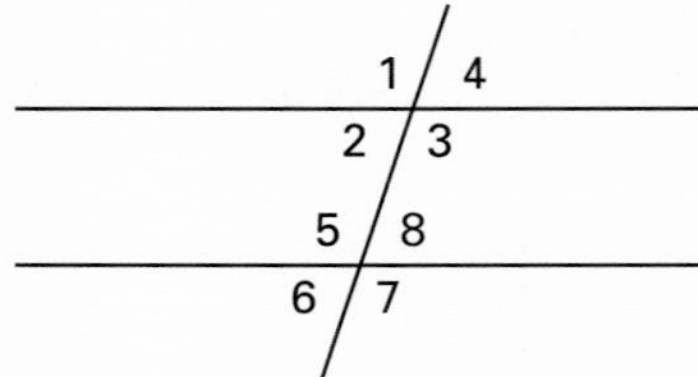

$\angle 2$ and $\angle 4$ are vertical angles, so they are congruent. $m\angle 4 = 72^{\circ}$.

$\angle 2$ and $\angle 8$ are alternate interior angles, so they are congruent. $m\angle 8 = 72^{\circ}$.

$\angle 2$ and $\angle 6$ are corresponding angles, so they are congruent. $m\angle 6 = 72^{\circ}$.

$\angle 2$ and $\angle 3$ are supplementary, so $m\angle 2 + m\angle 3 = 180^{\circ}$. Then $72^{\circ} + m\angle 3 = 180^{\circ}$. $m\angle 3 = 108^{\circ}$.

When a transversal intersects two parallel lines, pairs of congruent angles are formed. Here are some of the congruent angles:

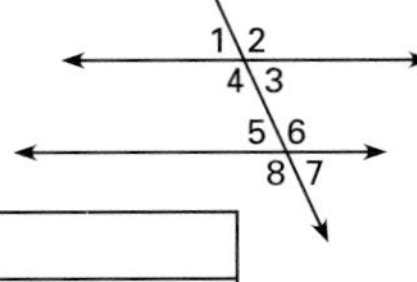

Alternate Interior Angles	$\angle 3 \cong \angle 5$, $\angle 4 \cong \angle 6$
Corresponding Angles	$\angle 1 \cong \angle 5$, $\angle 2 \cong \angle 6$, $\angle 3 \cong \angle 7$, $\angle 4 \cong \angle 8$
Vertical Angles	$\angle 1 \cong \angle 3$, $\angle 2 \cong \angle 4$, $\angle 5 \cong \angle 7$, $\angle 6 \cong \angle 8$

DID YOU KNOW?
Studs are always 16 inches apart in the walls of a house. When you hang a picture you can lightly tap on the wall to find a stud.

Example 1

A carpenter has framed a wall with six parallel studs crossed by a transversal brace. If $m\angle 2 = 62^{\circ}$, what are $m\angle 3$, $m\angle 8$, $m\angle 6$, and $m\angle 4$?

Framed Wall with Transversal

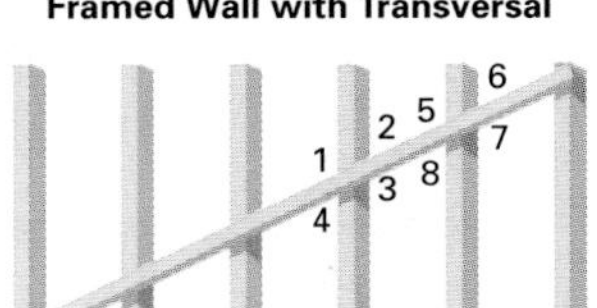

Vertical angles $\angle 2$ and $\angle 4$ are congruent, so $m\angle 4 = 62^{\circ}$.

Alternate interior angles $\angle 2$ and $\angle 8$ are congruent, so $m\angle 8 = 62^{\circ}$.

Corresponding angles $\angle 2$ and $\angle 6$ are congruent, so $m\angle 6 = 62^{\circ}$.

$\angle 2$ and $\angle 3$ form a straight angle, so they are supplementary.

$m\angle 3 + m\angle 2 = 180^{\circ}$	$\angle 2$ and $\angle 3$ are supplementary.
$m\angle 3 + 62^{\circ} = 180^{\circ}$	Substitute 62° for $m\angle 2$.
$m\angle 3 + 62^{\circ} - 62^{\circ} = 180^{\circ} - 62^{\circ}$	To undo adding 62°, subtract 62° from both sides.
$m\angle 3 = 118^{\circ}$	Subtract.

Try It

Name each angle pair. a. Corresponding b. Vertical c. Alternate Interior

a. $\angle 2$, $\angle 6$ **b.** $\angle 5$, $\angle 7$ **c.** $\angle 4$, $\angle 6$

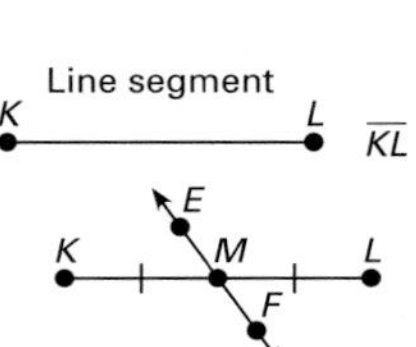

$m\angle 3 = 121^{\circ}$. Find the measure of each angle.

d. $\angle 4$ 59° **e.** $\angle 5$ 121° **f.** $\angle 7$ 121° **g.** $\angle 2$ 59°

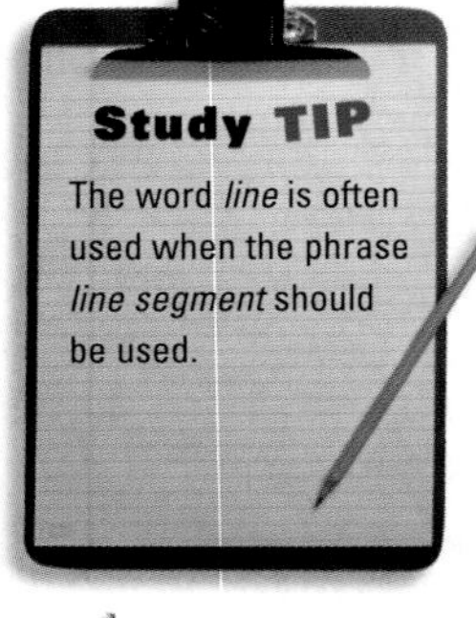

Study TIP
The word *line* is often used when the phrase *line segment* should be used.

A line segment is formed by two endpoints and all the points between them. Line $\overleftrightarrow{EF}$ intersects line segment $\overline{KL}$ at its **midpoint** M, the point that divides it into two **congruent segments**. Congruent segments have equal lengths.

Line segment K L $\overline{KL}$

E K M L F

$\overleftrightarrow{EF}$ is the **segment bisector** of $\overline{KL}$ because it passes through the midpoint M. The two marks on $\overline{KL}$ show the equal parts.

MATH EVERY DAY

Problem of the Day

Rearrange these pieces of a tangram puzzle to make a rectangle that is not a square. Be sure to use all pieces.

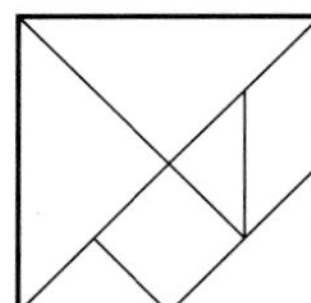

Possible answer:

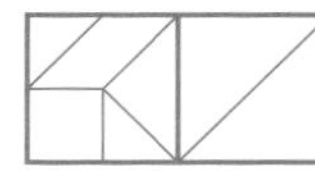

Available on Daily Transparency 5-2

An Extension is provided in the transparency package.

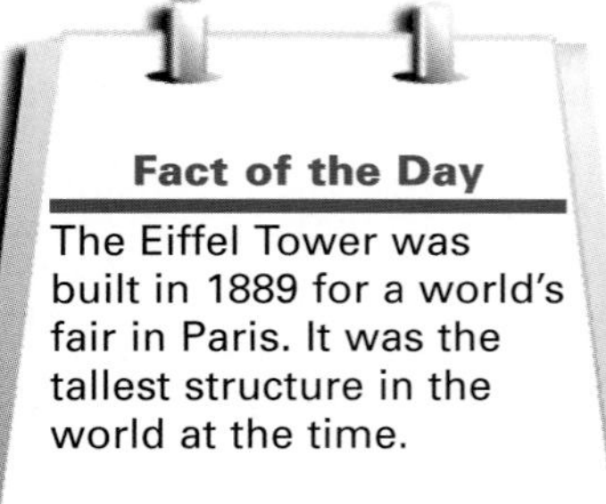

Fact of the Day

The Eiffel Tower was built in 1889 for a world's fair in Paris. It was the tallest structure in the world at the time.

Estimation

Estimate.

1. 39×31 1200
2. 81×689 56,000
3. 703×602 420,000
4. 8999×6999 63,000,000

Now imagine that $m\angle EMK$ is increased to 90°. **Perpendicular** lines, rays, and line segments form right angles. The symbol ⊥ means "is perpendicular to." $\overleftrightarrow{EF} \perp \overline{KL}$, so $\overleftrightarrow{EF}$ is the **perpendicular bisector** of $\overline{KL}$.

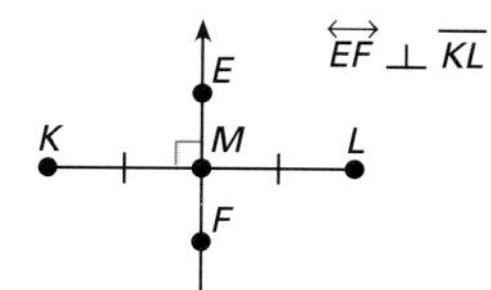

Example 2

An archer places an arrow 16 in. from each end of the bowstring. The arrow makes a 90° angle to the string. Why is the arrow the perpendicular bisector of the bowstring?

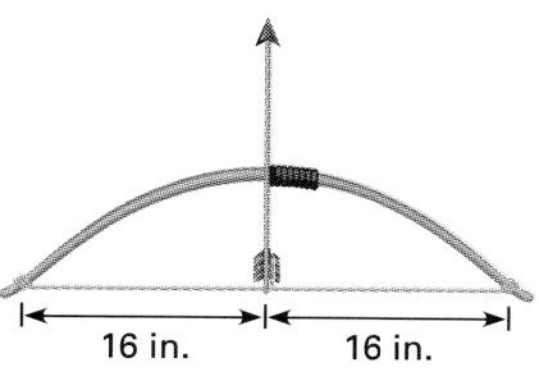

The arrow forms a right angle with the bowstring, so the arrow is perpendicular to the string.

The arrow also intersects the string at its midpoint, 16 in. from each end.

Since the arrow is perpendicular to the segment at its midpoint, the arrow is the perpendicular bisector of the segment.

Try It

a. Identify any midpoint on the kite and tell why it is a midpoint.

b. Identify any perpendicular bisector on the kite and tell why it is a perpendicular bisector.

A
C
D
E
$\overline{CE} \cong \overline{ED}$
B

> **History Link**
>
> From the 1300s to the 1500s, the Perpendicular Style of Gothic architecture developed in England. Westminster Abbey is an example of this style of building.

Check Your Understanding

1. Point out a pair of parallel lines and a pair of perpendicular lines in your classroom.

2. Explain how you could determine if two lines are parallel; if two lines are perpendicular.

3. Suppose a transversal intersects two parallel lines. If it is perpendicular to one of the parallel lines, is it perpendicular to the other? Explain.

4. Is it possible for two nonintersecting lines *not* to be parallel? If so, describe or give an example of such lines. If not, explain why not.

MEETING MIDDLE SCHOOL CLASSROOM NEEDS

Tips from Middle School Teachers

I like to have students find various examples of parallel lines and perpendicular lines in the classroom. For the parallel lines, I have them point out transversals and then name corresponding angles, vertical angles, and alternate interior angles.

Team Teaching

Work with a drafting teacher or an art teacher to demonstrate tools, such as a T-square, that are used to draw parallel and/or perpendicular lines.

Cultural Connection

Benjamin Banneker was a noted African inventor, mathematician, and astronomer, who helped survey and lay out the plan for Washington, D.C.

Alternate Examples

2. A light post is inserted on a street so that it is on a painted segment 16 feet from each end. The post is perpendicular to the ground. Why is the post the perpendicular bisector of the segment?

   Since the post is perpendicular to the ground at its midpoint, the post is the perpendicular bisector of the segment.

Answers for Try It

a. The midpoint of the shorter "stick" is at the point where it is intersected by the longer one.

b. The longer stick is the perpendicular bisector of the shorter; The longer intersects the shorter at its midpoint and forms a right angle.

3 Practice and Assess

Check

Have students discuss what happens if a line is perpendicular to one of two parallel lines. Lead them to see that the line is perpendicular to the other line as well.

Answers for Check Your Understanding

1. Answers may vary.
2. Measure the perpendicular distance between them at different points; Measure an angle they make with each other.
3. Yes; Because the transversal is a straight line, if it is perpendicular to one line, it is perpendicular to the other.
4. Yes; Any two lines that cannot fit in the same plane are neither intersecting nor parallel.

5-2 Exercises and Applications

Assignment Guide

- **Basic**
  1–15, 19–39 odds
- **Average**
  5–23, 25–39 odds
- **Enriched**
  6–23, 24–38 evens

Exercise Notes

Exercises 16–18

Geography The city of Washington, D.C., is laid out in four quadrants labeled NE, NW, SE, and SW. Every street address is followed by one of those designations.

Exercise Answers

16. Possible answer: M Street and N Street.
17. Possible answer: New Hampshire Ave. and Massachusetts Ave.
18. Possible answer: 19th Street and M Street.

Reteaching

Activity

Materials: Heavy paper or cardboard, wire brads, protractor

- Use three strips of heavy paper or cardboard. Make each strip at least 10 in. long. Connect the strips as shown by using wire brads.

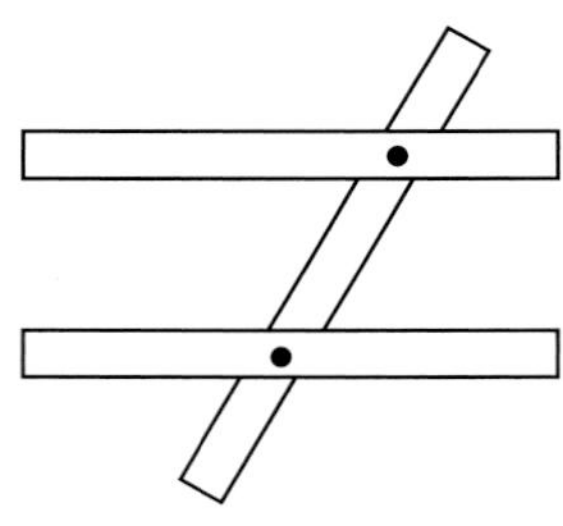

- Use the resulting object as a model of two lines intersected by a transversal. Position the lines in various locations and take turns pointing out pairs of corresponding angles, alternate interior angles, and vertical angles.
- Use a protractor to measure the angles and demonstrate how the measurements compare when the lines are parallel versus nonparallel.

PRACTICE 5-2

5-2 Exercises and Applications

Practice and Apply

Getting Started **Determine if each pair of lines is parallel, perpendicular, or neither.**

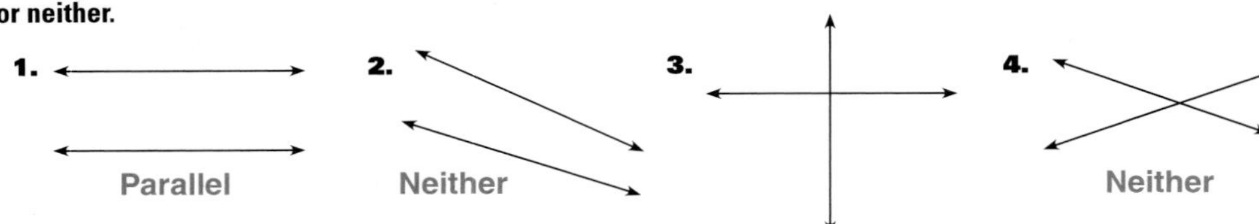

1. Parallel **2.** Neither **3.** Perpendicular **4.** Neither

Write the word that describes the lines or line segments.

5. Two rails of a railroad track Parallel
6. Adjacent edges of a square floor tile Perpendicular
7. Top and side of a door Perpendicular
8. Opposite sides of a basketball court Parallel
9. Telephone pole and the street Perpendicular
10. Shelves of a bookcase Parallel

Use the figure to name each set of angles or lines. Possible answers for 11–14.

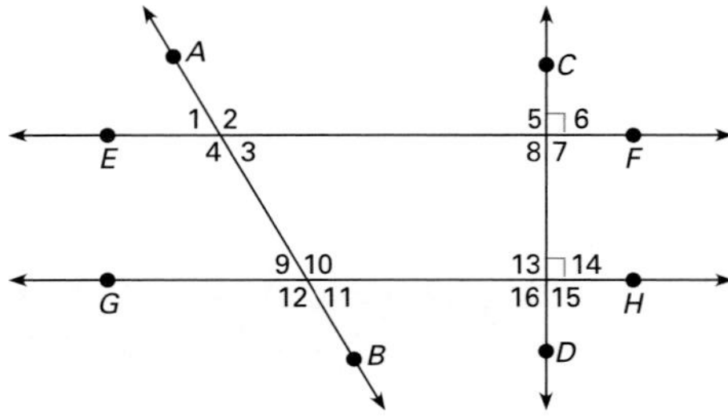

11. A pair of parallel lines $\overleftrightarrow{EF}$ and $\overleftrightarrow{GH}$

12. A pair of perpendicular lines $\overleftrightarrow{CD}$ and $\overleftrightarrow{EF}$

13. A pair of supplementary angles ∠1 and ∠2

14. Two pairs of congruent angles ∠5 and ∠6; ∠9 and ∠11

15. Measurement Draw a line segment, then measure it and identify its midpoint. Use the midpoint and your protractor to draw a perpendicular bisector. Answers may vary.

GPS

Geography **Use the street map of downtown Washington, DC, for Exercises 16–18.**

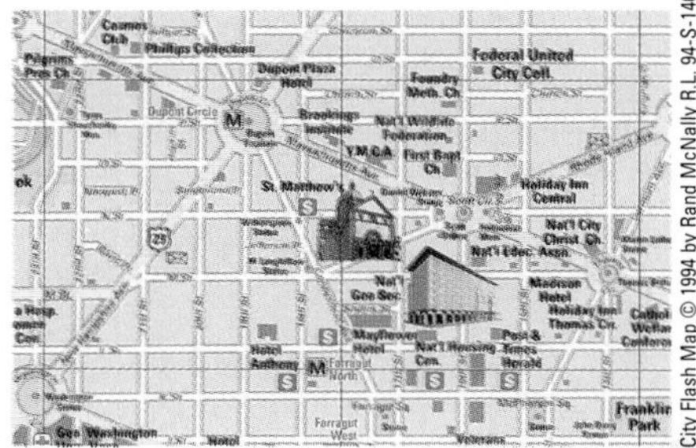

City Flash Map © 1994 by Rand McNally R.L. 94-S-140

16. Name two streets that are parallel.

17. Name two streets that are transversals of the parallel streets you identified.

18. Name two streets that are perpendicular.

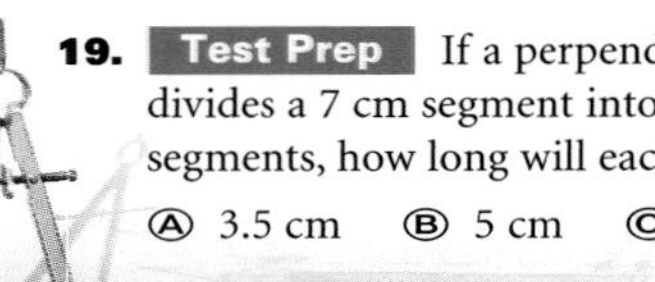

19. **Test Prep** If a perpendicular bisector divides a 7 cm segment into two congruent segments, how long will each one be? A

Ⓐ 3.5 cm Ⓑ 5 cm Ⓒ 9 cm Ⓓ 14 cm

PRACTICE

Name ____________

Practice 5-2

Parallel and Perpendicular Lines

Write the word that describes the lines or line segments.

1. the strings on a guitar Parallel
2. the marks left by a skidding car Parallel
3. sidewalks on opposite sides a street Parallel
4. the segments that make up a + sign Perpendicular
5. the wires suspended between telephone poles Parallel
6. the hands of a clock at 9:00 P.M. Perpendicular
7. two palm trees in Los Angeles Parallel

Use the figure to name each pair of angles or lines.

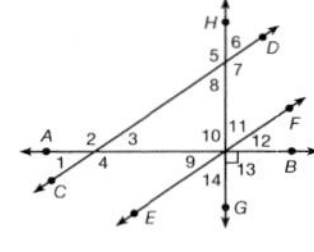

8. a pair of parallel lines $\overleftrightarrow{CD}$ and $\overleftrightarrow{EF}$
9. a pair of perpendicular lines $\overleftrightarrow{AB}$ and $\overleftrightarrow{GH}$
10. a pair of supplementary angles ∠5 and ∠6
11. a pair of corresponding angles ∠3 and ∠12
12. a pair of alternate interior angles ∠8 and ∠11
13. a pair of complementary angles ∠11 and ∠12
14. a pair of vertical angles ∠9 and ∠12

Possible answers: Exercises 10–14

15. In the figure above, name three angles that are congruent to ∠6.
∠8, ∠11, and ∠14

16. Use a ruler to draw a segment bisector of $\overline{UV}$.

17. Use a ruler and a protractor to draw a perpendicular bisector of $\overline{XY}$.

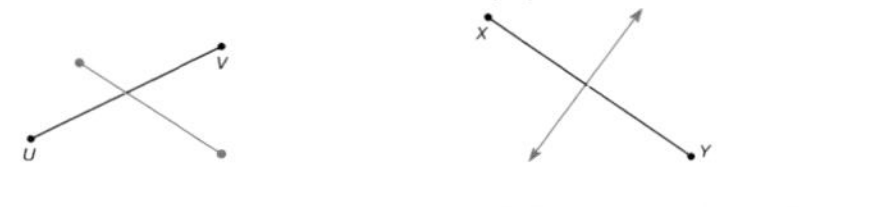

RETEACHING

Name ____________

Alternative Lesson 5-2

Parallel and Perpendicular Lines

A plane is an infinite flat surface. Lines in a plane that never meet are called **parallel** lines. Lines that intersect to form a right angle (90°) are called **perpendicular** lines. Lines that intersect two or more lines are **transversals.**

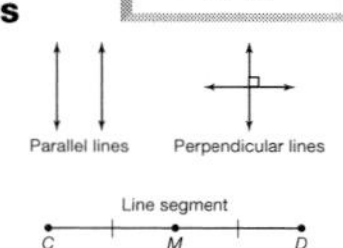

A line segment is formed by two endpoints and all the points between them. A **midpoint** divides a line segment into two **congruent segments.** Congruent segments have equal lengths.

Line segment
C M D
Midpoint of $\overline{CD}$

Example 1

Write *parallel* or *perpendicular* to describe the lines formed by the left and right sides of a bulletin board.

Sketch a rectangle to represent a bulletin board. If the left and right sides were extended, they would never meet.

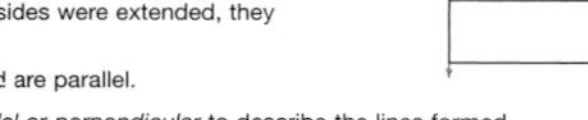

So, the lines formed are parallel.

Try It Write *parallel* or *perpendicular* to describe the lines formed by this book.

a. Top and bottom sides Parallel b. Top and left sides Perpendicular

Example 2

Use the figure to name a line segment, a midpoint, two congruent segments, and a transversal.

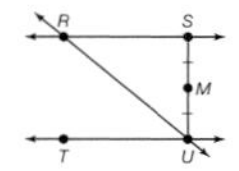

Two endpoints are *S* and *U*, so they form a line segment, $\overline{SU}$.

The midpoint of $\overline{SU}$ is *M*.

The midpoint divides a line segment into two congruent segments, so $\overline{MS}$ and $\overline{MU}$ are congruent.

Line $\overleftrightarrow{RU}$ intersects lines $\overleftrightarrow{RS}$ and $\overleftrightarrow{TU}$, so $\overleftrightarrow{RU}$ is a transversal.

Try It Use the figure to name each of the following. Possible answers given.

c. A line segment $\overline{XZ}$, $\overline{WZ}$, $\overline{WX}$, $\overline{XY}$, $\overline{YZ}$, $\overline{ZM}$, or $\overline{MX}$
d. A midpoint *M*
e. Two congruent segments $\overline{ZM}$ and $\overline{MX}$
f. A transversal $\overleftrightarrow{WX}$, $\overleftrightarrow{ZY}$, $\overleftrightarrow{WZ}$, or $\overleftrightarrow{XY}$

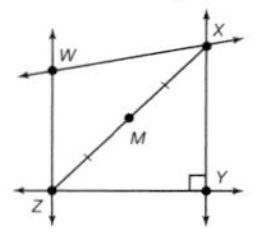

Problem Solving and Reasoning

Critical Thinking Identify parallel and perpendicular lines on the buildings in the photos.

20. 

21. 

Neue Staatsgalerie Museum, Munich, Germany

22. Communicate Two lines that do not intersect and are not parallel are *skew*. Describe to a friend two pairs of skew lines that you observe in your classroom.

23. Journal Draw a line segment. Use the method shown below to construct its perpendicular bisector with a compass and straightedge.

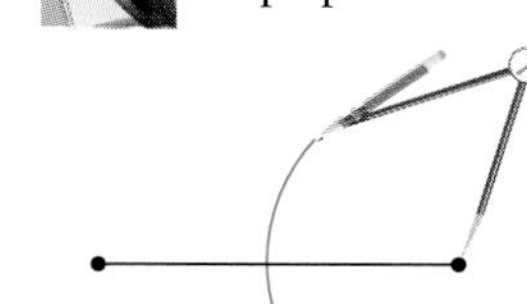

1. Open your compass to more than half of the segment's length. Place the point of your compass on one endpoint and make an arc.

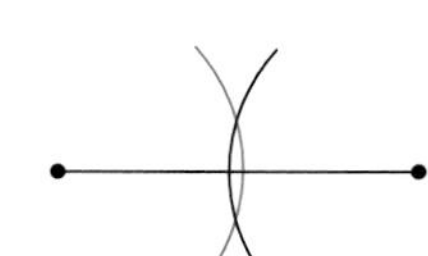

2. Using the same compass setting, make an arc from the other endpoint. It should intersect your first arc in two places.

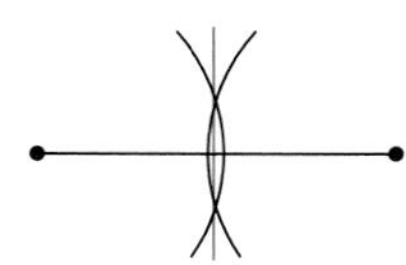

3. Draw the line joining these points. This line is the perpendicular bisector of the segment.

PROBLEM SOLVING 5-2

Mixed Review

Estimate. *[Lesson 3-2]*

24. 12.95 + 26.34 ≈ 39 **25.** 184.3 − 98.6 ≈ 85 **26.** 7.86 × 9.23 ≈ 72 **27.** 373.28 ÷ 24.78 ≈ 15

28. 63.21 − 19.42 ≈ 44 **29.** $\frac{842.7}{23.75}$ ≈ 40 **30.** 39.67 × 17.3 ≈ 800 **31.** 931.5 + 68.3 ≈ 1000

Express each fraction in lowest terms. *[Lesson 3-8]*

32. $\frac{24}{36}$ $\frac{2}{3}$ **33.** $\frac{18}{54}$ $\frac{1}{3}$ **34.** $\frac{44}{121}$ $\frac{4}{11}$ **35.** $\frac{42}{91}$ $\frac{6}{13}$

36. $\frac{38}{95}$ $\frac{2}{5}$ **37.** $\frac{72}{105}$ $\frac{24}{35}$ **38.** $\frac{81}{192}$ $\frac{27}{64}$ **39.** $\frac{45}{80}$ $\frac{9}{16}$

PROBLEM SOLVING

Name ______________________

Guided Problem Solving 5-2

GPS PROBLEM 15, STUDENT PAGE 220

Draw a line segment, then measure it and identify its midpoint. Use the midpoint and your protractor to draw a perpendicular bisector.

Understand

1. Underline the two things you are asked to draw.
2. What is a perpendicular bisector? A line through the midpoint that is perpendicular to the line segment.

Plan

3. How will you find the midpoint? Measure the segment and mark a point that is halfway between the two endpoints.
4. What will be the measure of the angle formed by the line segment and the perpendicular bisector? 90°

Solve

5. Draw your line segment. Measure it and identify its midpoint. Then use your protractor to draw a perpendicular bisector.
Possible answer:

Look Back

6. Does it matter which of the two congruent segments you use when you measure the angle needed to draw the perpendicular bisector? Explain. Possible answer: No, both segments form complementary 90° angles.

SOLVE ANOTHER PROBLEM

Draw a line segment. Use your protractor and ruler to draw another line segment that has one of the endpoints of the first segment as its midpoint.

Possible answer:

ENRICHMENT

Name ______________________

Extend Your Thinking 5-2

Critical Thinking

There is a relationship between the angles formed when a line crosses one pair of parallel lines. Possible answers: Items 1–4

1. Draw two parallel lines. Then draw a transversal through them. Label the angles 1, 2, 3, ..., 8. Measure one of the angles inside the two parallel lines with your protractor and write its measure on your diagram.

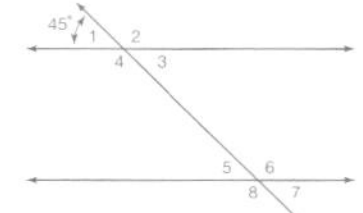

2. List all pairs of alternate interior angles and their measures. ∠3 and ∠5, measure 45°; ∠4 and ∠6, measure 135°.
3. List all pairs of corresponding angles and their measures. ∠1 and ∠5, ∠3 and ∠7, 45°; ∠2 and ∠6, ∠4 and ∠8, 135°.
4. List all pairs of vertical angles and their measures. ∠1 and ∠3, ∠5 and ∠7, 45°; ∠2 and ∠4, ∠6 and ∠8, 135°.

For a rose garden, different colored roses are planted in rows. Rows of the same color are parallel. You may want to use colored pencils to highlight the rows.

Use what you know about angles to find the measure of

5. the acute angle made by the red and white roses? 20°
6. the obtuse angle between the red and white roses? 160°
7. the acute angle between the white and yellow roses? 70°
8. the angle between the red and yellow roses? 90°

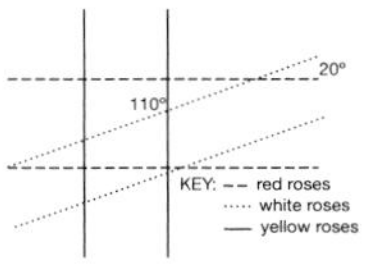

Exercise Notes

■ Exercises 20–21

Photography Remind students that parallel and perpendicular lines may not look parallel or perpendicular in a photo because of the perspective from which the photo was taken.

Exercise Answers

20. Perpendicular: The lines that meet at the corners of the door; Parallel: Opposite sides of the door.
21. Perpendicular: Vertical and horizontal lines on the building; Parallel: Opposite sides on the "stripes" of the building.
22. Possible answer: The corner of a wall and the ceiling is skew to the corner of an adjacent wall and the floor.
23. Check students' drawings.

Alternate Assessment

You may want to use the *Interactive CD-ROM Journal* with this assessment.

Journal For each type of angle presented in this lesson, have students draw a diagram to illustrate the angle or angles. They can keep these diagrams in their journals.

Quick Quiz

In the following figure $\overleftrightarrow{AB}$ and $\overleftrightarrow{CD}$ are parallel lines, and m∠1 = 28°.

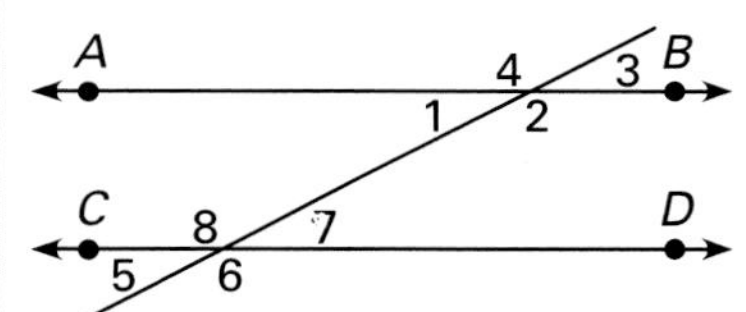

Find the measure of each angle.

1. ∠2 152° 2. ∠3 28°
3. ∠4 152° 4. ∠5 28°

Available on Daily Transparency 5-2

5-3 Lesson Organizer

Objectives

- Name and classify triangles.
- Name and classify quadrilaterals.
- Find the measures of angles in these figures.

Vocabulary

- Quadrilateral, parallelogram, rhombus, trapezoid

Materials

- Explore: Ruler, protractor

NCTM Standards

- 1–4, 12

Review

Classify each angle.

1. obtuse
2. right
3. acute

Solve each equation.

4. $x + 70 + 30 = 180$ $x = 80$
5. $x + 75 + 89 + 110 = 360$ $x = 86$

Available on Daily Transparency 5-3

Lesson Link

Discuss how often triangles and quadrilaterals occur. For example, triangles appear in bridges and frameworks for skyscrapers. Quadrilaterals occur so frequently in tile patterns, window frames, and so on, that we often overlook them.

1 Introduce

Explore

You may wish to use Teaching Tool Transparencies 14: Rulers and 15: Protractors with **Explore**.

The Point
Students discover the relationship between the number of congruent sides and congruent angles in a triangle.

5-3 Triangles and Quadrilaterals

You'll Learn ...

- to name and classify triangles
- to name and classify quadrilaterals
- to find the measures of angles in these figures

... How It's Used

Interior designers use triangles and quadrilaterals to help create patterns.

Vocabulary

equilateral triangle
isosceles triangle
scalene triangle
acute triangle
right triangle
obtuse triangle
quadrilateral
parallelogram
rhombus
trapezoid

Lesson Link You've looked at some important angle properties. Now you'll investigate commonly seen figures that have three or four angles.

Explore Triangles

Sides and Angles

Materials: Ruler, Protractor

1. Draw a triangle with three congruent sides. Measure the angles and describe your results.
2. Draw a triangle with two congruent sides; make the third side a different length. Measure the angles and describe your results.
3. Draw a triangle with three sides of unequal lengths. Measure the angles and describe your results.
4. Repeat Steps 1–3, changing the lengths of the sides you use.
5. Describe the relationship between the number of congruent sides and the number of congruent angles that a triangle has.

Learn Triangles and Quadrilaterals

Architects use triangles in their buildings for strength as well as for their visual appeal. You can classify triangles by the number of congruent sides they have.

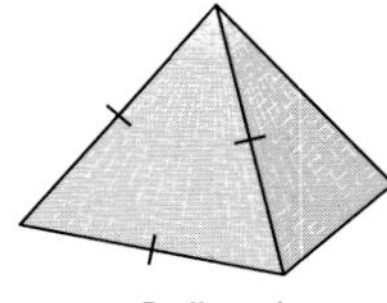
Equilateral

Isosceles

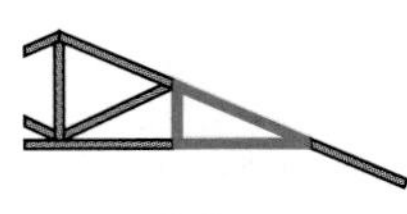
Scalene

MEETING INDIVIDUAL NEEDS

Resources

5-3 Practice
5-3 Reteaching
5-3 Problem Solving
5-3 Enrichment
5-3 Daily Transparency
Problem of the Day
Review
Quick Quiz
Teaching Tool Transparencies 14, 15
Lesson Enhancement Transparencies 21, 22
Technology Master 20
Chapter 5 Project Master

Wide World of Mathematics
Geometry: A Bridge up for Grabs

Learning Modalities

Kinesthetic Have students cut out paper triangles and then cut off the corners and rearrange them to form a straight angle.

Verbal Hold up a picture of a geometric figure, either a triangle or a quadrilateral. Then have students give as many names as possible to classify the figure.

Inclusion

Some students who have trouble in other areas of mathematics excel in geometry. Be sure to give these students a chance to demonstrate their skills in geometry. Have students add new vocabulary words to their reference books with an example of each.

You can also classify triangles by their angle measures.

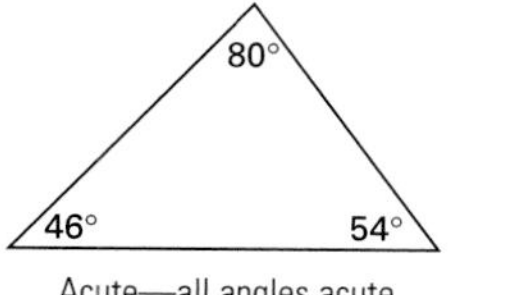

Acute—all angles acute

Right—one right angle

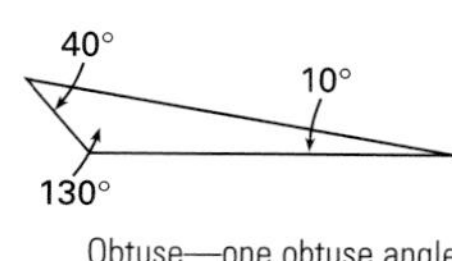

Obtuse—one obtuse angle

> **Science Link**
> Classification, or grouping things by their properties, is a very important part of scientific study.

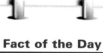

A **quadrilateral** is a four-sided figure. You have already learned to identify rectangles and squares. The chart gives three new types of quadrilaterals, **parallelograms**, **rhombuses**, and **trapezoids**, and relates all the types of quadrilaterals according to their properties.

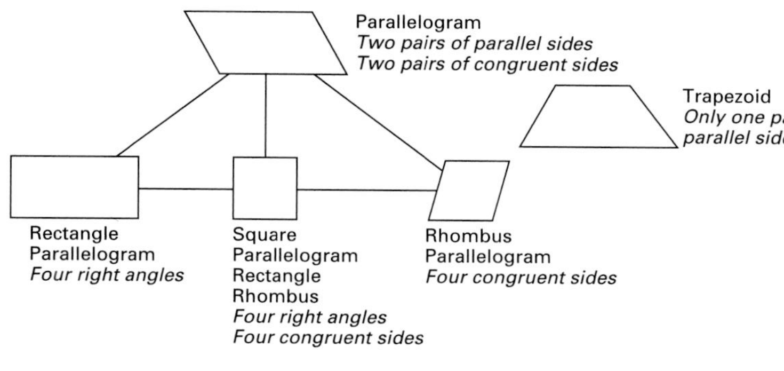

> **Language Link**
> *Quadri-* means "four." It comes from the Latin word *quattuor*. *Quattuor* is also the root word for "quarter," which means "one fourth."

Examples

Classify each figure in as many ways as you can.

1

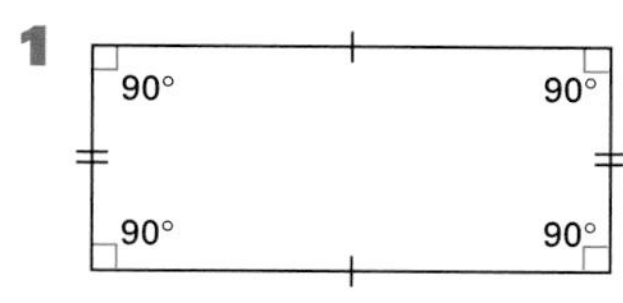

The figure is a quadrilateral, a parallelogram, and a rectangle.

2

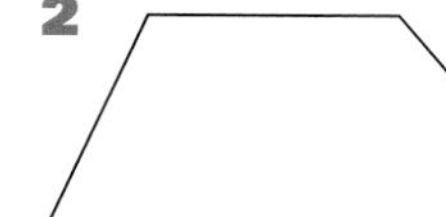

The figure is a quadrilateral and a trapezoid.

The figure illustrates a special property of triangles. The three angles of any triangle can be rearranged to form a straight angle. Recall that the measure of a straight angle is 180°. This means that the sum of the measures of the angles of any triangle is 180°.

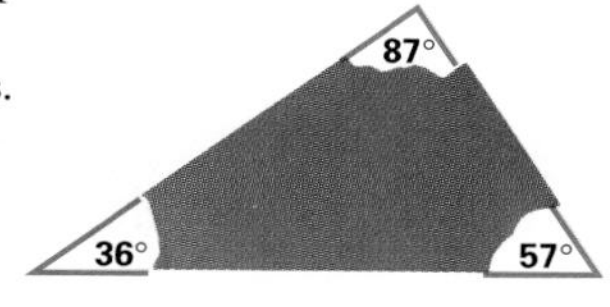

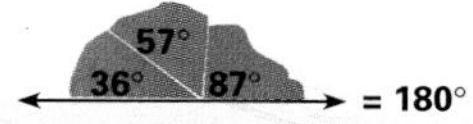

MATH EVERY DAY

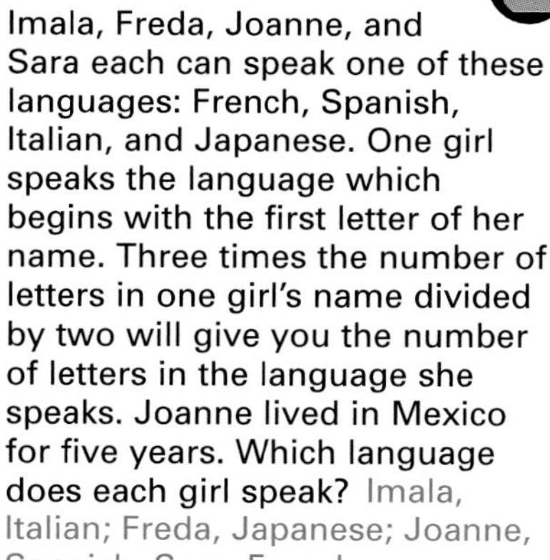

Problem of the Day

Imala, Freda, Joanne, and Sara each can speak one of these languages: French, Spanish, Italian, and Japanese. One girl speaks the language which begins with the first letter of her name. Three times the number of letters in one girl's name divided by two will give you the number of letters in the language she speaks. Joanne lived in Mexico for five years. Which language does each girl speak? Imala, Italian; Freda, Japanese; Joanne, Spanish; Sara, French.

Available on Daily Transparency 5-3

An Extension is provided in the transparency package.

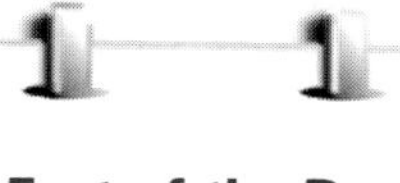

Fact of the Day

Egyptian pyramids, built before 1000 B.C., have sides that meet at a point at the top. New World pyramids have flat tops.

Estimation

Estimate.

1. 8.9 × 4.7 45
2. 49.5 × 102.3 5000
3. 0.97 × 1.04 1
4. 1.38 × 7.99 8

Ongoing Assessment

Watch for students who do not measure angles and segments accurately. Some may need reminders about determining both types of measurements.

For Groups That Finish Early

Which of Steps 1–4 will always yield the same angle measurements, no matter what lengths are used? Step 1, since it yields an equilateral triangle and the angles will always be 60°.

Follow Up

Have students discuss why there are only three possible cases for the answer to Step 5.

Answers for Explore

1–5. Answers may vary.

2 Teach

Learn

You may wish to use Lesson Enhancement Transparencies 21 and 22 with **Learn**.

Emphasize to students that when they are asked to classify a triangle, they must decide whether to classify by angles, sides, or both.

Alternate Examples

Classify each figure in as many ways as you can.

1.

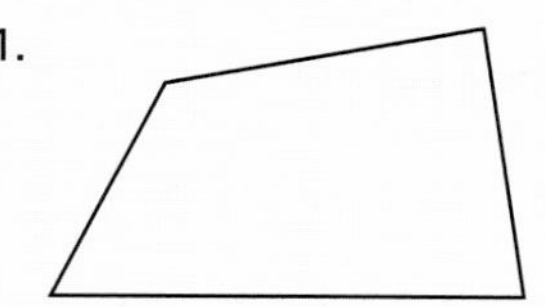

The figure is a quadrilateral.

2.

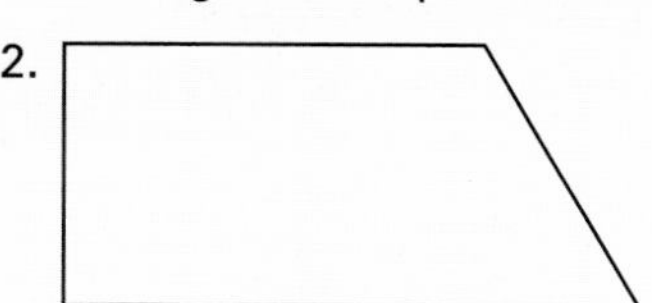

The figure is a quadrilateral and a trapezoid.

Alternate Examples

3. Find the measure of the unknown angle.

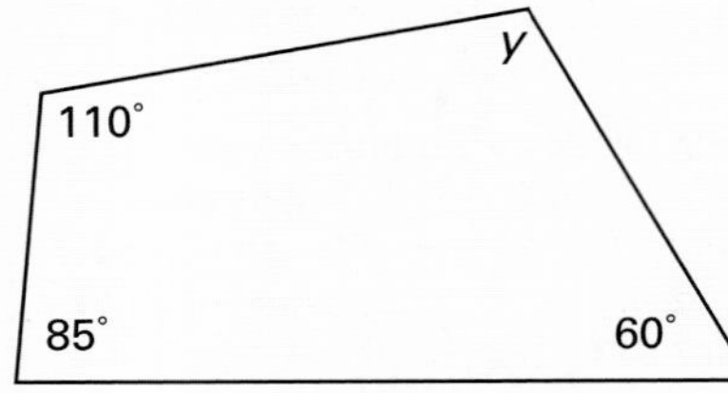

$y + 110 + 85 + 60 = 360$

$y + 255 = 360$

$y = 105°$

4. Find the measure of the unknown angle.

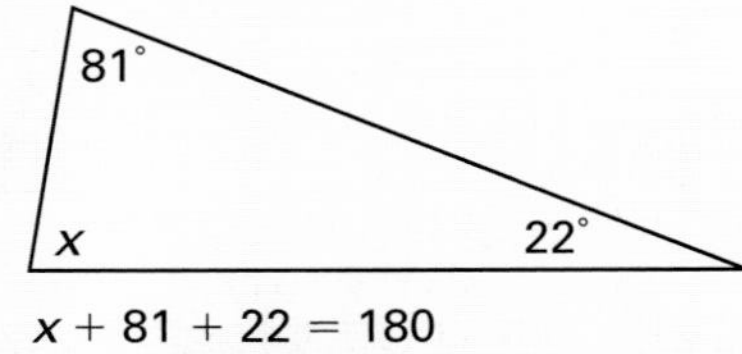

$x + 81 + 22 = 180$

$x + 103 = 180$

$x = 77°$

3 Practice and Assess

Check

Be sure that students understand how to interpret the quadrilateral chart on page 223.

Answers for Check Your Understanding

1. Yes; A square has opposite sides parallel and all sides congruent, so it is a rhombus. A square has opposite sides parallel and all angles are right angles, so it is a rectangle. Consequently, a square is a quadrilateral that is both a rhombus and a rectangle.
2. No, the angles of an equilateral triangle must be 60°; Yes, an isosceles triangle can have an obtuse angle.

Study TIP

There are many new vocabulary words in this section. It will help you to keep a small notebook with a list that you can add to as you learn new words.

Notice that any quadrilateral can be divided into two triangles. The sum of the measures of the angles of any quadrilateral is 180° + 180°, or 360°.

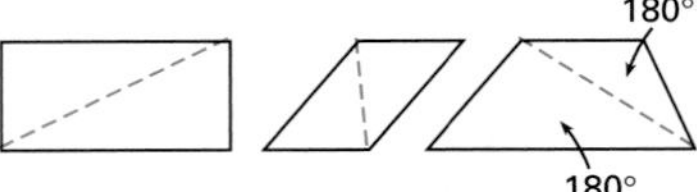

Examples

3 An ancient building in Tulum, Mexico, had the quadrilateral foundation shown. If its angle measures are 98°, 82°, 98°, and $x°$, find the measure of the unknown angle.

$x + 98 + 82 + 98 = 360$	The sum of the angles of a quadrilateral is 360°.
$x + 278 = 360$	Add 98, 82, and 98.
$x + 278 - 278 = 360 - 278$	To undo adding 278, subtract 278 from both sides.
$x = 82°$	Simplify.

4 Find the measure of the unknown angle.

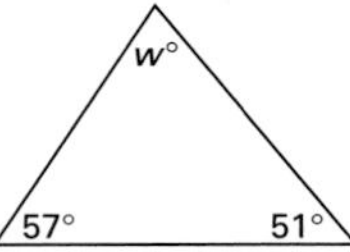

$w + 57 + 51 = 180$	The sum of the angles of a triangle is 180°.
$w + 108 = 180$	Add 57 and 51.
$w + 108 - 108 = 180 - 108$	To undo adding 108, subtract 108 from both sides.
$w = 72°$	Simplify.

Try It

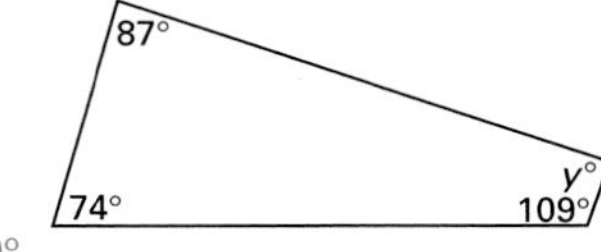

a. Find the measure of the unknown angle. 90°

Check Your Understanding

1. Can a quadrilateral be both a rhombus and a rectangle? Explain.
2. Can a triangle be both equilateral and right? Isosceles and obtuse? Explain.

MEETING MIDDLE SCHOOL CLASSROOM NEEDS

Tips from Middle School Teachers

I like to have students cut out paper models of various types of quadrilaterals, including rectangles, rhombuses, and trapezoids. Then I have them cut off the corners and rearrange them to show that the sum of the angles is always 360°. Even if they have been told this earlier, they usually are surprised.

History Connection

Pyramids were built in the Americas at about 1200 B.C. They were used for military defense and also for platforms of temples and palaces. Archaeologists have called the American pyramids temple mounds or platform mounds, although excavations reveal that tombs also might have been a part of these pyramids. The oldest American pyramids were built around a ceremonial plaza at the Olmec site of La Venta in southeastern Mexico.

Team Teaching

Work with an industrial arts teacher. Use wood models to demonstrate the fact that a triangle is a rigid figure, but a quadrilateral is not. Point out that a brace can be inserted into a wooden quadrilateral (such as a gate frame), so that the figure becomes two rigid triangles.

5-3 Exercises and Applications

Practice and Apply

1. **Getting Started** Follow these steps to find the measure of an unknown angle in a quadrilateral.
   a. Identify the known and unknown angle measures.
   b. Write an equation using the known and unknown angle measures and 360.
   c. Add the known angle measures together. Subtract the sum from each side of the equation.
   d. Write the difference.

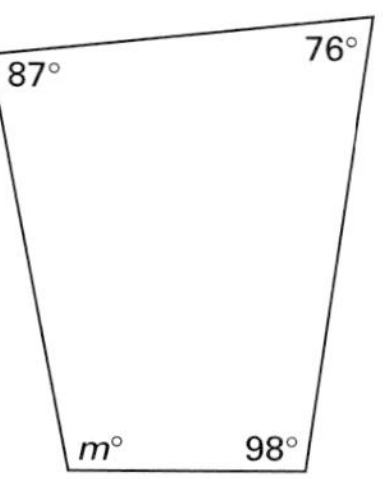

Classify each triangle by its sides and by its angles.

2. Obtuse isosceles (35°, 110°, 35°)

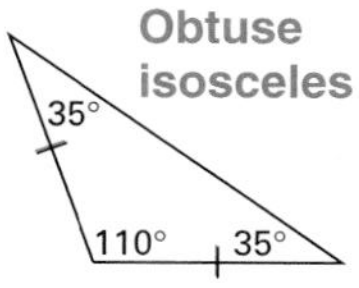

3. Right scalene (60°, 30°)

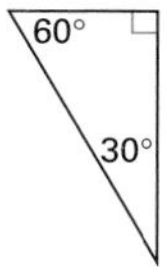

4. Acute equilateral (60°, 60°, 60°)

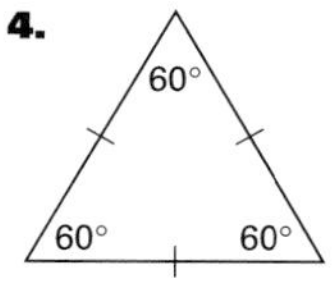

5. Right isosceles

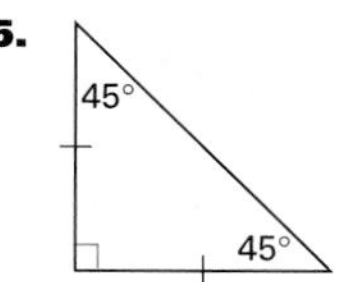

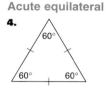

Classify each quadrilateral in as many ways as you can.

6. 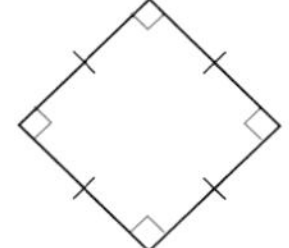

7. 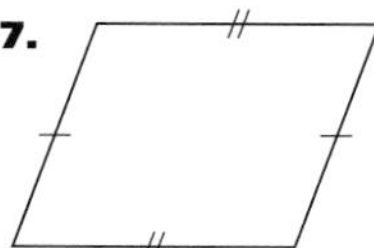

8. 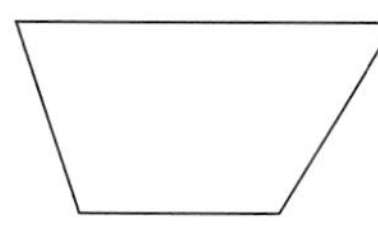

9.

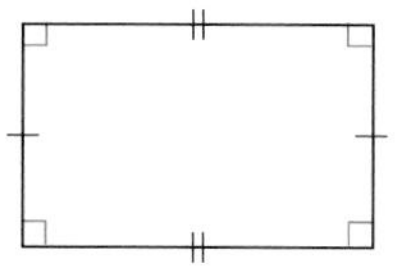

10. 

11. 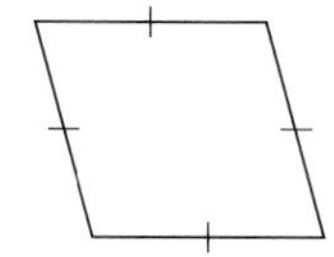

Find the measure of each unknown angle.

12. In triangle ABC, $m\angle A = 50°$, $m\angle B = 22°$, $m\angle C = x$. $x = 108°$

13. In triangle XYZ, $m\angle X = 104°$, $m\angle Y = 38°$, $m\angle Z = t$. $t = 38°$

14. In quadrilateral $DEFG$, $m\angle D = 88°$, $m\angle E = 93°$, $m\angle F = 74°$, $m\angle G = x$. $x = 105°$

15. In quadrilateral $MNOP$, $m\angle M = 107°$, $m\angle N = 44°$, $m\angle O = 32°$, $m\angle P = x$. $x = 177°$

PRACTICE 5-3

PRACTICE

Name ______

Practice 5-3

Triangles and Quadrilaterals

Classify each triangle by its sides and by its angles.

1. Isosceles, acute (55°, 55°, 70°) 2. Scalene, obtuse (95°, 40°, 45°) 3. Scalene, right (55°, 35°, 90°)

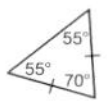

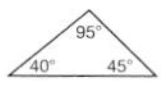

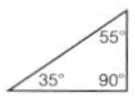

Classify each quadrilateral in as many ways as you can.

4. Quadrilateral, parallelogram, rectangle
5. Quadrilateral, trapezoid
6. Quadrilateral, parallelogram, rhombus

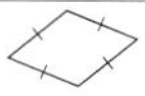

Find the missing angle in each triangle or quadrilateral.

7. $x =$ 75° (108°, 99°, 78°) 8. $n =$ 97° (48°, 35°) 9. $u =$ 95° (123°, 70°, 72°)

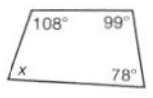

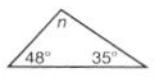

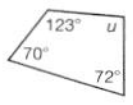

Fill in each blank with *always, sometimes,* or *never.*

10. A trapezoid is never a parallelogram.

11. A rectangle is sometimes a rhombus.

12. **Social Science** The flag of the Congo is shown at the right. (Green, Yellow, Red)

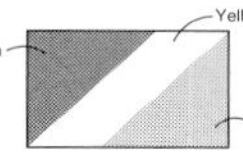

a. Classify the red and green portions of the flag in as many ways as you can. (Hint: The top edge of the green region is slightly longer than the height of the flag.)
Right triangles, scalene triangles

b. Classify the yellow portion of the flag in as many ways as you can. Quadrilateral, parallelogram

RETEACHING

Name ______

Alternative Lesson 5-3

Triangles and Quadrilaterals

Triangles are three-sided figures. You can classify triangles by the number of congruent sides they have.

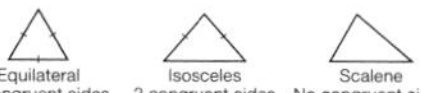

Equilateral: 3 congruent sides — Isosceles: 2 congruent sides — Scalene: No congruent sides

Quadrilaterals are four-sided figures. Quadrilaterals can be classified by their properties.

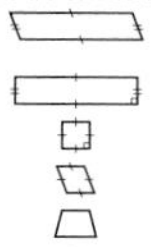

Parallelogram	Two pairs of parallel sides; two pairs of congruent sides
Rectangle	Parallelogram with four right angles
Square	Rectangle with four congruent sides
Rhombus	Parallelogram with four congruent sides
Trapezoid	Only one pair of parallel sides

Example 1

Classify this triangle by its sides.

The triangle has two congruent sides.

So, the figure is an isosceles triangle.

Try It Classify each triangle by its sides.

a. Scalene b. Equilateral c. Scalene

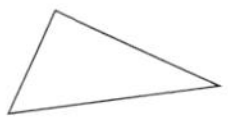

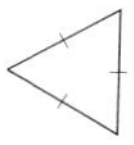

Example 2

Classify this quadrilateral in as many ways as you can.

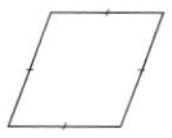

The quadrilateral has two pairs of parallel sides, four congruent sides, and no right angles.

The quadrilateral is a rhombus and a parallelogram.

Try It Classify each quadrilateral in as many ways as you can.

d. Rectangle, Parallelogram e. Trapezoid

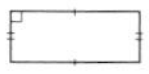

5-3 Exercises and Applications

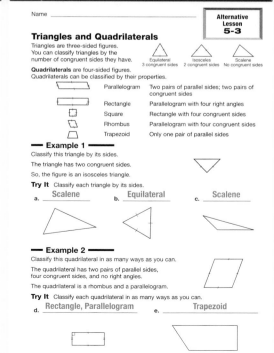

Assignment Guide

- **Basic** 1–17, 22–34 evens
- **Average** 2–19, 21–33 odds
- **Enriched** 2–20, 22–34 evens

Exercise Notes

Exercise 6

Error Prevention Watch for students who are confused by the fact that the square is oriented at an angle. Stress that the angle measures and the side lengths are not affected by the position of the figure. If necessary, have students rotate the page so that the base of the square is horizontal.

Exercise 10

Error Prevention Watch for students who say that the figure is a parallelogram since it has two pairs of congruent sides. Point out that the congruent sides are not opposite each other.

Exercise Answers

1. a. Known: 87°, 76°, 98°; Unknown: m
   b. $87 + 76 + 98 + m = 360$
   c. $261 - 261 + m = 360 - 261$
   d. 99
6. Quadrilateral, square, parallelogram, rectangle, rhombus.
7. Quadrilateral, parallelogram.
8. Quadrilateral, trapezoid.
9. Quadrilateral, rectangle, parallelogram.
10. Quadrilateral.
11. Quadrilateral, rhombus, parallelogram.

Reteaching

Activity

Materials: Magazines, newspapers, or catalogs

Cut out pictures and make a collage to show examples of the various types of triangles and quadrilaterals presented in this lesson.

Exercise Notes

■ Exercise 17

Consumer Point out that gym shoes have a pattern on the sole to increase traction. With a slick sole like ordinary shoes, gym shoes would be dangerous.

Project Progress

You may want to have students use Chapter 5 Project Master.

Exercise Answers

18. Rectangles and squares.
19. Parallelograms, rectangles, scalene triangles, right triangles.
20. Rectangles, isosceles triangles.

Alternate Assessment

Self Assessment Have students write a paragraph explaining how it is possible for a quadrilateral to be classified in more than one way. Have them include examples and diagrams.

▶ Quick Quiz

Classify each triangle by its angles and by its sides.

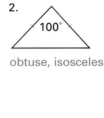

1. 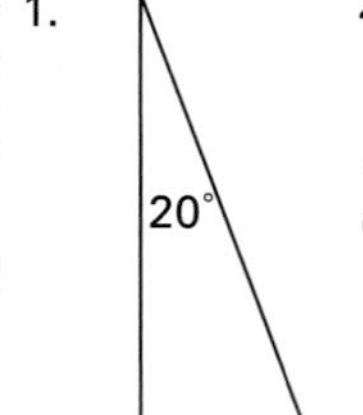

right, scalene

2. 100°
obtuse, isosceles

Classify each quadrilateral in as many ways as you can.

3. 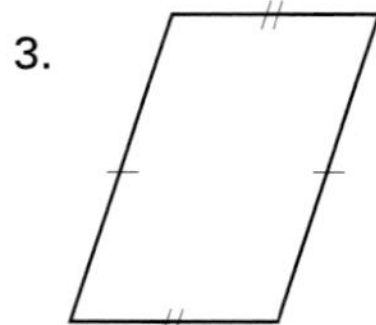
quadrilateral parallelogram

4. quadrilateral trapezoid

Available on Daily Transparency 5-3

---

16. Science A molecule of boron fluoride forms a molecular arrangement, as shown. An atom of boron is bonded to three atoms of fluorine. The angle between each bond measures 120°. Find the total measure of all the angles formed between the bonds. **360°**

GPS

F B F F

Problem Solving and Reasoning

17. 

Place a piece of paper over the bottom of a gym shoe and make a crayon rubbing of the tread print. Identify different geometric shapes in the tread rubbing. **Answers may vary.**

Critical Thinking Identify the types of triangles or quadrilaterals in the buildings.

18. 
The Legal Center, Newark, NJ

19. 
National Gallery, Washington, DC

20. 
Los Angeles Museum of Contemporary Art

PROBLEM SOLVING 5-3

Mixed Review

Solve each equation. *[Lesson 3-3]*

21. $23.64 = y - 8.31$ **$y = 31.95$**
22. $u + 0.643 = 1.86$ **$u = 1.217$**
23. $x - 12.73 = 0.05$ **$x = 12.78$**
24. $364.21 + c = 584.17$ **$c = 219.96$**
25. $k - 38.2 = 68.375$ **$k = 106.575$**
26. $129.6 = d + 18.31$ **$d = 111.29$**

Use >, <, or = to compare each pair of numbers. *[Lesson 3-9]*

27. $\frac{6}{7} > \frac{5}{6}$
28. $\frac{16}{20} > \frac{19}{25}$
29. $\frac{22}{42} < \frac{17}{32}$
30. $\frac{45}{63} = \frac{40}{56}$
31. $\frac{3}{14} < \frac{6}{27}$
32. $\frac{18}{25} < \frac{23}{30}$
33. $\frac{3}{11} < \frac{5}{13}$
34. $\frac{19}{49} > \frac{24}{63}$

Project Progress

Measure the dimensions of the building(s) in the floor plan you sketched for your school. You may need to estimate some lengths that you cannot measure directly.

Problem Solving
Understand
Plan
Solve
Look Back

PROBLEM SOLVING

Name ______________________

Guided Problem Solving 5-3

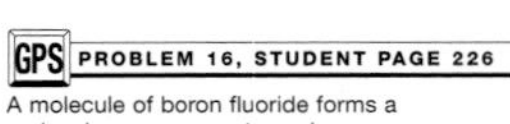

A molecule of boron fluoride forms a molecular arrangement, as shown. An atom of boron is bonded to three atoms of fluorine. The angle between each bond measures 120°. Find the total measure of all the angles formed between the bonds.

— Understand —

1. Underline what you are asked to find.
2. How many angles are represented in the diagram? **3**
3. What is the measure of the angle formed by each bond? **120°**

— Plan —

4. Which letter represents the vertex of the angles formed? **B**
5. Write the angle measure for each angle in the diagram. **120°**
6. Which operation can you use to find the total measures of all the angles formed? **Multiplication or Addition.**

— Solve —

7. What is the total measure of all the angles between the bonds? **360°**

— Look Back —

8. The outer edges of the model of the fluorine atom are curved. Use these edges to connect the three atoms. What figure is formed? How can you use this to support your answer to Item 7? **Possible answer: Circle; A circle consists of 360°, which is also the sum of the angle measures.**

SOLVE ANOTHER PROBLEM

Curtis drew this diagram. The angle between each "spoke" measures 90°. Find the total measure of all the angles formed between the spokes.

360°

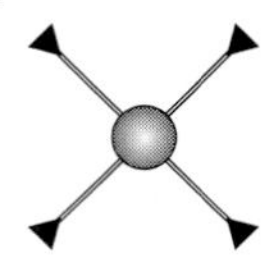

ENRICHMENT

Name ______________________

Extend Your Thinking 5-3

Decision Making

Jeremy was planning a treat for Jamie's birthday. He wanted to take Jamie to an event and have something to eat. He listed the possibilities and his estimated costs for the two boys. **Possible answers: Items 3–5**

Activities		Food	
Movie	$12	Pizza	$15
Football game at the high school	$ 7	Vendor food at the event	$10
Concert	$35	Hamburgers	$ 8
Street fair	$10	Burritos	$11

1. Which combination is the most expensive? What is its cost? **Concert and pizza; $50**
2. Which combination is the least expensive? What is its cost? **Football game and hamburgers; $15**
3. What other things, in addition to cost, might influence Jeremy's decision? Why should he consider these things? **Transportation, Jamie's interests, curfews, whether or not other friends will want to participate, time of event; He wants the treat to be enjoyable for Jamie.**
4. If you were Jeremy, which combination would you select? Why? **Movie and hamburgers; An afternoon matinee is less expensive, shown at times when buses might run, and should not conflict with curfews.**
5. Suppose you are going to treat a friend to a movie and pizza. What would you consider in planning the event? How much would it cost? **Answers will vary.**

Polygons

5-4

▶ Lesson Link In the last lesson, you learned about geometric figures with three or four sides. Now you'll investigate figures that have more than four sides. ◀

You'll Learn ...

- to classify polygons
- to find the angle sum of polygons

... How It's Used

Structural engineers use many different shapes in the design of bridges and railroad trestles.

Vocabulary

polygon
pentagon
hexagon
octagon
regular polygon

Explore Many-Sided Figures

Getting in Shape

Materials: Pattern blocks

1. Name the pattern block shapes.
2. Use combinations of pattern blocks to create as many different five-sided figures as you can. Trace each figure on your paper.
3. Use combinations of pattern blocks to create as many different six-sided figures as you can. Trace each figure on your paper.
4. Look at the figures you traced. Find a way to classify the figures into different groups, other than by the number of sides.

Learn Polygons

Many of the shapes that you see in the design of buildings are **polygons**. A polygon is a geometric figure with at least three sides.

In the last lesson, you worked with two types of polygons—triangles and quadrilaterals. The sides meet at vertices, with exactly two at each vertex.

A polygon is classified by the number of sides it has.

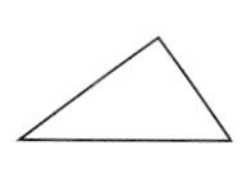

3 sides
triangle

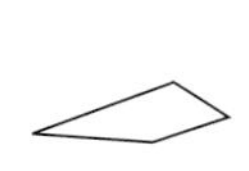

4 sides
quadrilateral

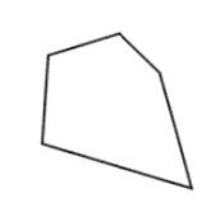

5 sides
pentagon

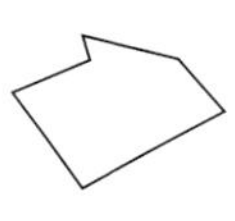

6 sides
hexagon

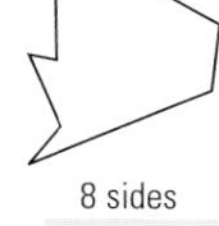

8 sides
octagon

5-4 Lesson Organizer

Objectives

- Classify polygons.
- Find the angle sums of polygons.

Vocabulary

- Polygon, pentagon, hexagon, octagon, regular polygon

Materials

- Explore: Pattern blocks

NCTM Standards

- 1–4, 12

▶ Review

1. Name a quadrilateral with 4 congruent sides. Square or rhombus
2. Name a quadrilateral with 4 congruent angles. Rectangle or square
3. If all sides of a quadrilateral are congruent, must all angles be congruent? Explain. No; A rhombus has 4 congruent sides, but the angles are not always congruent.

Available on Daily Transparency 5-4

MEETING INDIVIDUAL NEEDS

Resources

- 5-4 Practice
- 5-4 Reteaching
- 5-4 Problem Solving
- 5-4 Enrichment
- 5-4 Daily Transparency
  - Problem of the Day
  - Review
  - Quick Quiz
- Teaching Tool Transparency 18
- Lesson Enhancement Transparency 23

Learning Modalities

Visual Have students sketch examples of regular and nonregular polygons as they are found in the real world.

Verbal Hold up pictures of various types of polygons and have students discuss why the polygons are regular or not.

Challenge

Have students divide the following trapezoid into four congruent trapezoids having the same shape as the original figure.

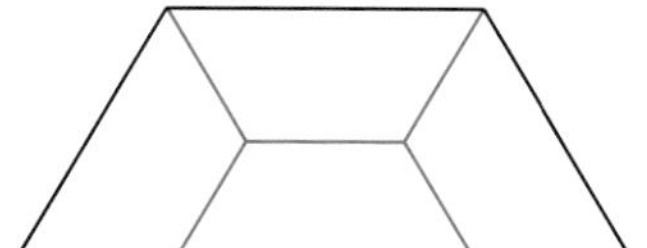

1 Introduce

Explore

You may wish to use Teaching Tool Transparency 18: Power Polygons with **Explore**.

The Point
Students investigate different ways to classify polygons.

Ongoing Assessment
Watch for students who have trouble creating figures from pattern blocks. Remind them that the blocks can be turned and flipped.

For Groups That Finish Early
Compare your results with those of other groups and see if any of your answers are the same.

Answers for Explore on next page.

Answers for Explore

1. A trapezoid, a rhombus (parallelogram), a hexagon, a triangle, and a square.

2–4. Answers may vary.

2 Teach

Learn

You may wish to use Lesson Enhancement Transparency 23 with **Learn.**

Point out that the least number of sides possible for a polygon is three, but there is no greatest possible number.

Alternate Examples

Classify each polygon and determine if it is regular.

1.

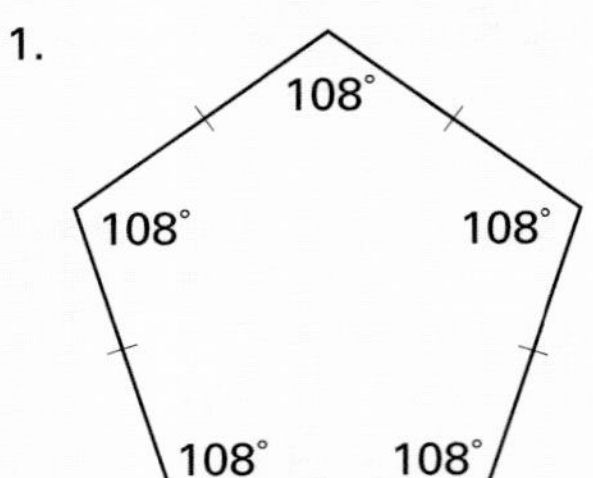

It has 5 sides. The sides and angles are congruent.

Regular pentagon

2.

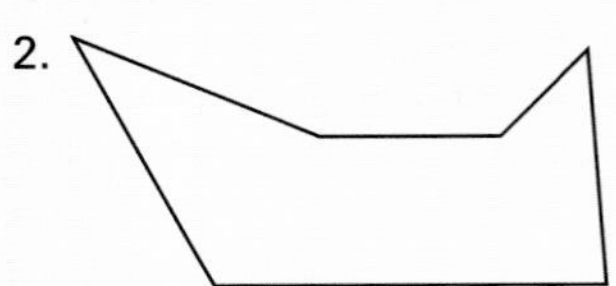

It has 6 sides. The sides and angles are not congruent.

Nonregular hexagon

3. Find the sum of the measures of the angles of a 9-sided polygon.

Sketch a 9-sided polygon. Choose one vertex and draw segments to as many other vertices as possible.

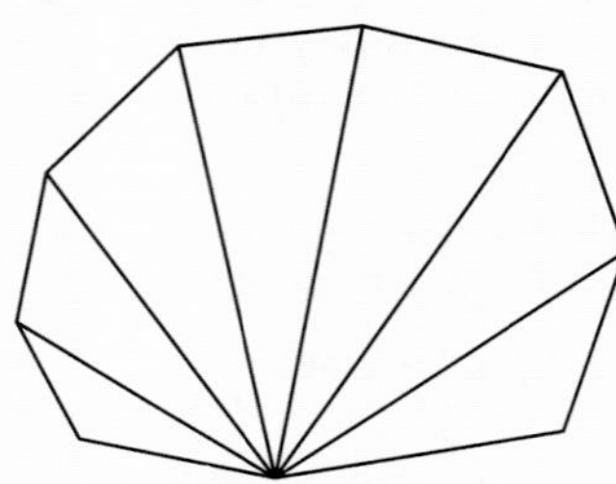

There are 7 triangles.
$7 \times 180 = 1260°$
The sum of the measures of the angles of a 9-sided polygon is 1260°.

Social Studies Link

The Pentagon, in Washington, DC, is the headquarters of the United States Department of Defense. It is one of the world's largest office buildings. It houses more than 23,000 employees in 3,707,745 square feet of office space.

In a **regular polygon**, all of the sides and all of the angles are congruent. An equilateral triangle and a square are examples of regular polygons.

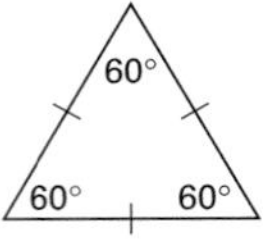

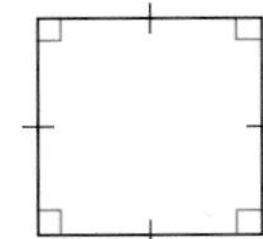

Examples

Classify each polygon and determine if it is regular.

1

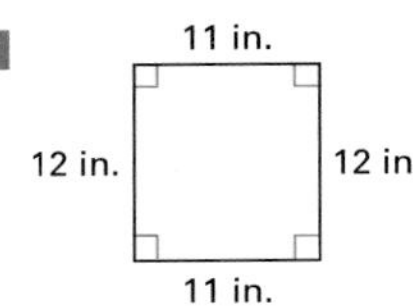

It has four sides. The angles are congruent. The sides are not congruent.

Nonregular quadrilateral.

2

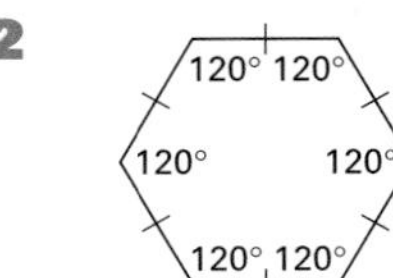

It has six sides. The angles are congruent. The marks show that the sides are congruent.

Regular hexagon.

Science Link

Honeybees are very good at geometry! They build their honeycombs with perfect hexagonal cells.

In the last lesson, you saw that a quadrilateral could be divided into two triangles to find the sum of the measures of the angles. You can divide any polygon into triangles to find the sum of the measures of the angles.

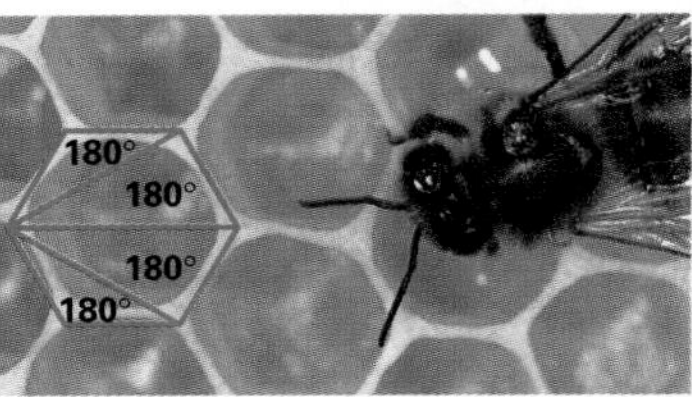

$180° + 180° + 180° + 180° = 720°$

Example 3

Find the sum of the measures of the angles of a hexagon.

- Sketch a hexagon.
- Choose one vertex and draw segments to as many other vertices as possible.
- There are four triangles, so $4 \cdot 180° = 720°$.

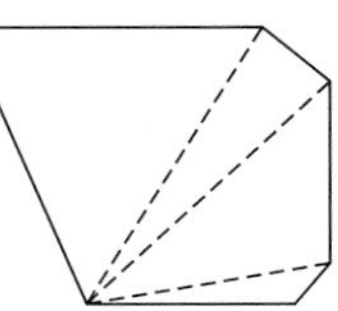

The sum of the measures of the angles of a hexagon is 720°.

Try It

a. Find the sum of the measures of the angles of an octagon. 1080°

b. Find the sum of the measures of the angles of a 12-sided polygon. 1800°

MATH EVERY DAY

Problem of the Day

Use the clues to help you arrange these figures in order.

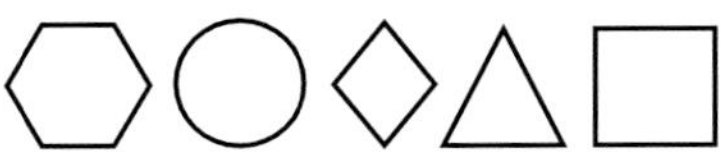

A. The triangle is just to the right of the square.
B. Neither the diamond nor the circle is next to the square.
C. Neither the hexagon nor the circle is next to the diamond.
D. Neither the circle nor the hexagon is next to the triangle.

Circle, hexagon, square, triangle, diamond

Available on Daily Transparency 5-4

An Extension is provided in the transparency package.

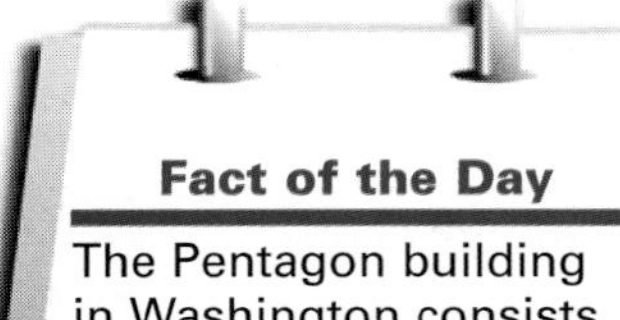

Fact of the Day

The Pentagon building in Washington consists of 5 pentagons in ring formation connected by 10 corridors.

Mental Math

Use mental math.

1. $80\overline{)72,000}$ 900
2. $900\overline{)810,000}$ 900
3. $4000\overline{)1,600,000}$ 400
4. $50,000\overline{)350,000,000}$ 7000

The number of triangles you can divide a polygon into is 2 less than the number of sides it has. You can find the sum of the angle measures by subtracting 2 from the number of sides, then multiplying by 180°.

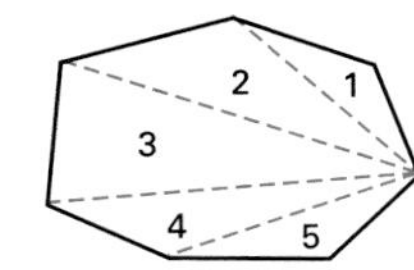

7 sides, 5 triangles

You can use the formula $S = (n - 2)180°$ to find the sum (S) of the measures of the angles of a polygon with n sides.

Find the sum of the measures of the angles of a stop sign.

Winona thinks ...

I'll use the formula.

$S = (n - 2)180°$	Use the formula for the sum of the measures of the angles.
$= (8 - 2)180°$	Substitute 8 for n.
$= 1080°$	Simplify.

The sum is 1080°.

Ramon thinks ...

I'll sketch a stop sign and draw triangles from a vertex. There are six triangles. I'll multiply 6 by 180°.

The sum is 1080°.

What do you think?

1. Explain Ramon's method. Could he draw the triangles another way?

2. Give another way to find the answer.

Check Your Understanding

1. Is a rectangle a regular polygon? Is a rhombus? Explain.

2. Name a regular polygon with three sides; with four sides.

WHAT DO YOU THINK?

Students see two methods of solving a problem. One method uses a formula and the other involves drawing a diagram. Students can decide which of the two correct methods is easier for them.

Answers for What Do You Think?

1. Ramon divided the polygon into triangles to find the sum of the measures of the angles; He could have drawn the triangles from any vertex.
2. Use a protractor to measure the angles.

3 Practice and Assess

Check

Remind students that *two* conditions must be met before a polygon is said to be regular. That is, all sides must be congruent *and* all angles must be congruent.

Answers for Check Your Understanding

1. Sometimes; A rectangle with congruent sides and a rhombus with right angles are regular polygons.
2. Equilateral triangle; Square.

MEETING MIDDLE SCHOOL CLASSROOM NEEDS

Tips from Middle School Teachers

I like to have students work in small groups. I give each group a polygon drawn on a large sheet of paper. Then I have them trace the figure several times. Next they must find as many ways as possible to divide the figure into triangles by drawing segments from one vertex. Of course, the number of ways increases as the number of sides increases.

Fine Arts Connection

During the late 19th century, a group of young architects—Louis Sullivan, Daniel Burnham, William Holabird, and Martin Roach—who worked in William Le Baron Jenney's Chicago office became leaders of the Chicago School of American architecture. One of Sullivan's most famous pupils was Frank Lloyd Wright, who was one of the greatest architects of the 20th century.

Team Teaching

Work with an art teacher to show students several different drawings by the Dutch artist Maurits Escher. Point out that Escher made wide use of geometry in his drawings.

Assignment Guide

- **Basic**
  1–8, 17–18, 26–42 evens
- **Average**
  1–23, 26–42 evens
- **Enriched**
  5–26, 27–41 odds

Exercise Answers

1. Regular hexagon
2. Nonregular polygon
3. Nonregular quadrilateral
4. Regular triangle
5. Sides are not congruent.
6. Sides and angles are not congruent.
7. Sides and angles are not congruent.
8. Sides and angles are not congruent.
9. Possible answer: Rectangles, squares, parallelograms.
10. Possible answer: Squares, rectangles, right triangles.

15. See page C6.

Reteaching

Activity

Materials: Scissors

- Work in pairs. Draw a large polygon on a sheet of paper. Exchange papers with your partner.
- Choose one vertex and draw segments to as many other vertices as possible. Cut on the segments to form triangles.
- Determine the number of degrees in the angles of the original polygon.

5-4 Exercises and Applications

PRACTICE 5-4

Practice and Apply

Getting Started Classify each polygon and determine if it is regular.

1. 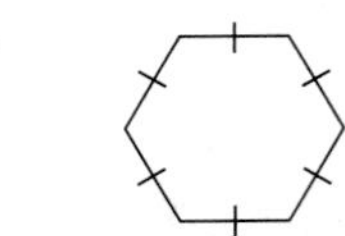
Each angle measures 120°.

2. 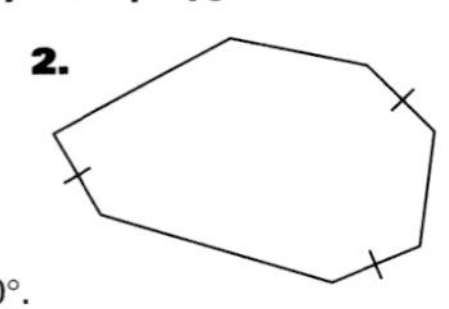

3. 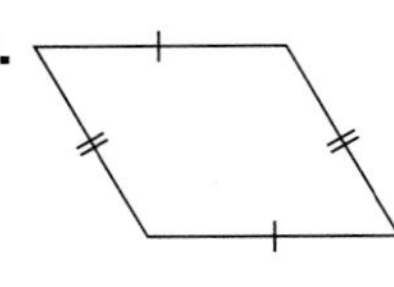

4. 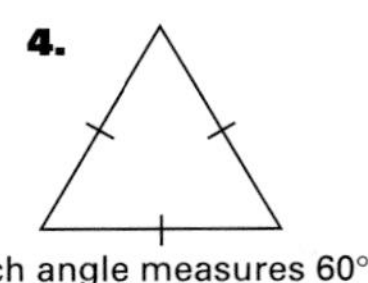
Each angle measures 60°.

Tell why each polygon is not a regular polygon.

5. 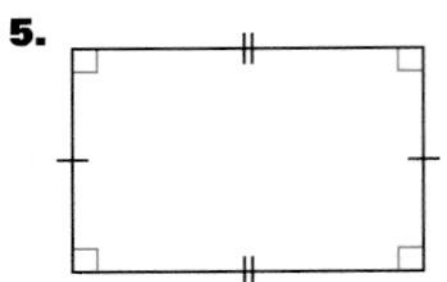

6. 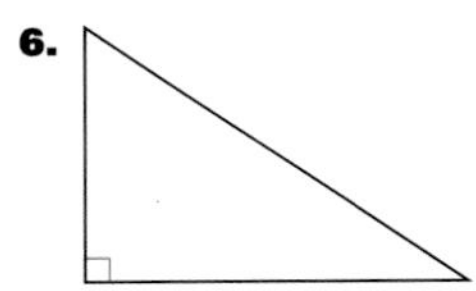

7. 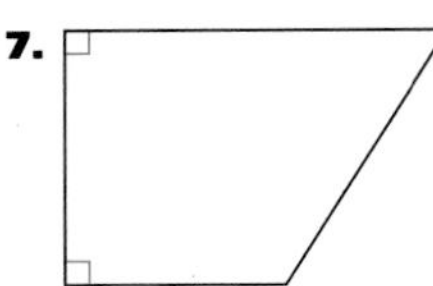

8. 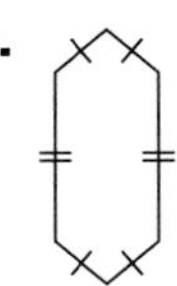

Use the picture of each building to identify as many polygons as you can.

9. 

10. 

Find the sum of the measures of the angles of each polygon.

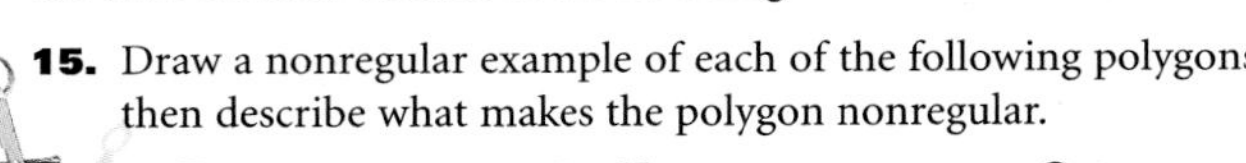

11. 7-sided polygon 900° **12.** 15-sided polygon 2340° **13.** 20-sided polygon 3240°

14. Science Mica is a type of mineral that can be split into flexible sheets that are thinner than paper. These sheets are often hexagon-shaped. If a piece of mica can be split into 142 hexagon-shaped sheets, what is the total number of sides of all the hexagons that are formed? 852

15. Draw a nonregular example of each of the following polygons, then describe what makes the polygon nonregular.

a. Pentagon **b.** Hexagon **c.** Octagon

PRACTICE

Name ______________________

Practice 5-4

Polygons

Tell why each polygon is not a regular polygon.

1. Angles are not all congruent.
2. Sides are not all congruent.
3. Angles are not all congruent.

In each design, identify as many polygons as you can. Possible answers:

4. Trapezoids, rectangles
5. Regular hexagons
6. Right triangles, squares
7. Equilateral triangle, trapezoid, hexagons
8. Triangles, pentagons, square
9. Trapezoids, regular pentagons

Find the sum of the measures of the angles of each polygon.

10. pentagon 540°
11. 10-sided polygon 1440°
12. 32-sided polygon 5400°

13. Recall that an equilateral polygon has all sides congruent, and an equiangular polygon has all angles congruent. Draw each of the following, if possible.

a. equiangular hexagon that is not regular — Possible answer:
b. equilateral quadrilateral that is not regular — Possible answer:
c. equiangular triangle that is not equilateral — Not possible

RETEACHING

Name ______________________

Alternative Lesson 5-4

Polygons

A **polygon** is a geometric figure with at least three sides. A polygon is classified by the number of sides it has. In a **regular** polygon, all of the sides and all of the angles are congruent.

3 sides triangle | 4 sides quadrilateral | 5 sides pentagon | 6 sides hexagon | 8 sides octagon

You can find the sum of the measures of the angles of a polygon by dividing it into triangles.

Example 1

Name the polygon and determine if it is regular.

Count the sides.
There are six sides, so the polygon is a hexagon.

Are the sides and angles congruent?
Yes, so the hexagon is regular.

The polygon is a regular hexagon.

120° 120° 120° 120° 120° 120°

Try It Name each polygon and determine if it is regular.

a. Regular quadrilateral
b. Nonregular octagon

Example 2

Find the sum of the measures of a 5-sided polygon, called a pentagon.

Choose a vertex and divide the figure into triangles.
There are three triangles.

Multiply the number of triangles by 180°: 3 × 180 = 540.

The sum of the measures of the angles of a pentagon is 540°.

Try It Find the sum of the measures of the angles of each polygon.

c. 360° d. 900° e. 180° f. 720°

16. Regular polygons are both equilateral, which means having congruent sides, and equiangular, which means having congruent angles. Non-regular polygons sometimes have one of these characteristics but not the other.

a. Sketch an equilateral polygon that is not equiangular.

b. Sketch an equiangular polygon that is not equilateral.

17. **Test Prep** How many triangles will be formed if you sketch an octagon, choose one vertex, and draw diagonals to as many other vertices as possible? C

Ⓐ 8 Ⓑ 7 Ⓒ 6 Ⓓ 5

Problem Solving and Reasoning

Choose a Strategy **The sum of the measures of the angles of a polygon is given. How many sides does each polygon have?**

18. 1620° 11 **19.** 1980° 13 **20.** 2520° 16

Problem Solving STRATEGIES

- Look for a Pattern
- Make an Organized List
- Make a Table
- Guess and Check
- Work Backward
- Use Logical Reasoning
- Draw a Diagram
- Solve a Simpler Problem

Critical Thinking **Find the measure of each angle in the polygon.**

21. Regular pentagon 108° **22.** Regular hexagon 120°

23. Regular octagon 135° **24.** Regular decagon 144°

25.  A friend was out ill during this lesson. Write a paragraph to him or her explaining what a polygon and a regular polygon are. Use your own words.

26. **Communicate** The polygons you have worked with in this section are called *convex* polygons. Two examples of *concave* polygons are shown at the right. Describe the difference between the two types of polygons.

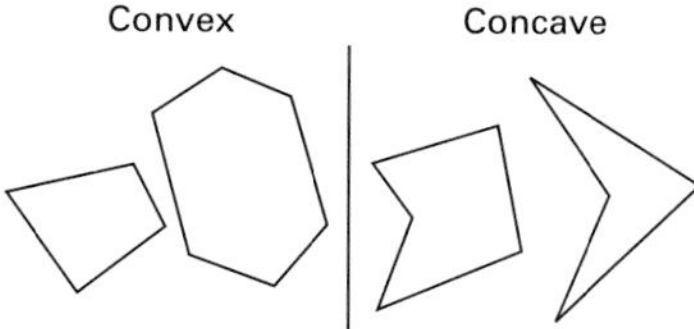

PROBLEM SOLVING 5-4

Mixed Review

Solve each equation. *[Lesson 3-4]*

27. $1.82m = 6.552$ $m = 3.6$

28. $\frac{s}{81.45} = 7.89$ $s = 642.6405$

29. $8.468 = 5.8y$ $y = 1.46$

30. $3.72 = \frac{k}{0.057}$ $k = 0.21204$

31. $3.75x = 36.9$ $x = 9.84$

32. $130.5 = \frac{a}{7.43}$ $a = 969.615$

33. $79.744 = 6.23b$ $b = 12.8$

34. $\frac{x}{4.7531} = 4.6$ $x = 21.86426$

Convert to a decimal. Tell if the decimal terminates or repeats. *[Lesson 3-10]*

35. $\frac{7}{16}$ **36.** $\frac{8}{15}$ **37.** $\frac{3}{7}$ **38.** $\frac{5}{6}$

39. $\frac{21}{160}$ **40.** $\frac{16}{21}$ **41.** $\frac{7}{8}$ **42.** $\frac{11}{18}$

Exercise Notes

■ Exercise 26

Science The terms convex and concave are also used to describe lenses. Note that a concave lens or a concave polygon curves inward or "caves in."

Exercise Answers

16. a. Possible answer:

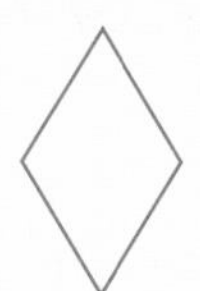

b. Possible answer:

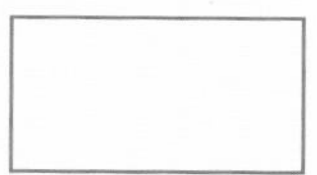

25. Answers may vary.

26. Concave polygons have "dents."

35. 0.4375; Terminates.

36. $0.5\overline{3}$; Repeats.

37. $0.\overline{428571}$; Repeats.

38. $0.8\overline{3}$; Repeats.

39. 0.13125; Terminates.

40. $0.\overline{761904}$; Repeats.

41. 0.875; Terminates.

42. $0.6\overline{1}$; Repeats.

Alternate Assessment

You may want to use the *Interactive CD-ROM Journal* with this assessment.

Journal Write a paragraph describing how you find the sum of the measures of the angles of a polygon.

▶ Quick Quiz

1. Tell why the polygon is not a regular polygon.

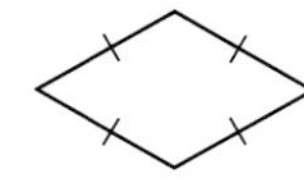

Angles are not congruent.

Find the sum of the measures of the angles of each polygon.

2. 11-sided polygon 1620°

3. 12-sided polygon 1800°

Available on Daily Transparency 5-4

PROBLEM SOLVING

Name ______

Guided Problem Solving 5-4

GPS PROBLEM 18, STUDENT PAGE 231

The sum of the measures of the angles of a polygon is 1620°. How many sides does the polygon have?

— Understand —

1. What are you asked to find? The number of sides in a polygon whose sum of the measures of the angles is 1620°.

— Plan —

2. Choose the expression that shows how to find the number of triangles in a figure with n sides. d

a. $\frac{n}{2}$ b. $n + 2$ c. $2n$ d. $n - 2$

3. What formula relates the number of sides and the sum of the angle measures of a polygon? $S = (n - 2)\,180°$

4. Use the formula to complete the table.

Sides	3	4	5	6
Number of triangles	1	2	3	4
Sum of the angles	180°	360°	540°	720°

5. What do you need to do to find the number of triangles in a polygon when you know the sum of the measures of the angles? Divide by 180.

6. What do you need to do to find the number of sides when you know the number of triangles in the polygon? Add 2.

— Solve —

7. Find the number of triangles in a polygon whose sum of the angles is 1620°. 9 triangles.

8. Find the number of sides in a polygon that has the same number of triangles as the polygon in Item 7. 11 sides.

— Look Back —

9. What other strategies could you use to solve the problem? Possible answer: Draw a Diagram, Look for a Pattern.

SOLVE ANOTHER PROBLEM

The sum of the measures of the angles of a polygon is 2160°. How many sides does the polygon have? 14 sides.

ENRICHMENT

Name ______

Extend Your Thinking 5-4

Patterns in Geometry

An exterior angle is the angle formed by one side of the triangle and the extension of the adjacent side. The exterior angles are marked in the triangle.

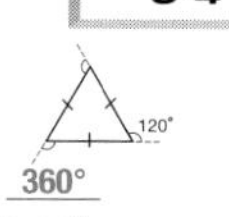

1. What is the sum of the exterior angles in the triangle? 360°

2. For each vertex of the regular polygons below, extend one side and write the measure of the exterior angle. Then find the sum of all the exterior angles.

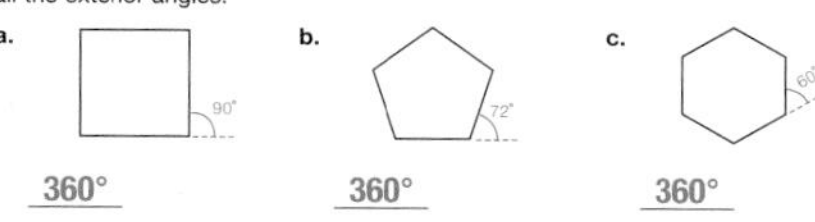

a. 360° b. 360° c. 360°

3. What pattern did you discover? Possible answer: The sum of the exterior angles is always 360°.

4. Find the sum of the exterior angles for these nonregular polygons.

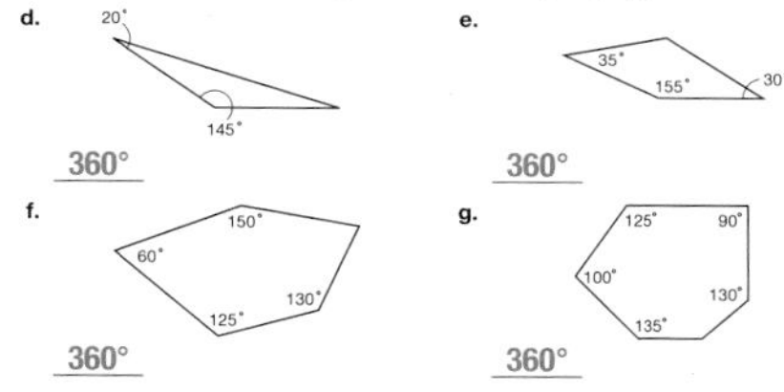

d. 360° e. 360° f. 360° g. 360°

5. Is the pattern the same or different? Why do you think this is true? Possible answer: The same, since the sum of angle measures is the same for all polygons with the same number of sides, the sum of their supplementary angles would also be the same.

Technology

Using Dynamic Geometry Software • Investigating Polygons

The Point
Students use geometry software to discover that regardless of how a triangle's shape is altered, the sum of the angle measures will be 180º.

Materials
Dynamic geometry software

Resources

Interactive CD-ROM Geometry Tool

About the Page

If students are not familiar with the software, you may want to include a brief demonstration of some of the features.

Ask ...

- How do you indicate to the software which angle you are intending? Identify the vertex as the middle letter.
- How is it possible that the sum remains constant at 180º? The amount of increase in one or two angles must equal the amount of decrease in the other one or two angles.

Answers for Try It

a. Sum of the angle measures is always 360º.

b. Sum of the angle measures is always 540º.

Answers for On Your Own

- Advantage: Gives precise measurements quickly. Disadvantage: Can only be used to measure angles drawn by the program.
- Since there are three angles that contain the points, the computer must use the order to tell which angle you want. It assumes that the second point you select is the vertex of the angle.

TECHNOLOGY

Using Dynamic Geometry Software • Investigating Polygons

Problem: What happens to the sum of the angle measures of a triangle when its shape and size are changed?

You can use dynamic geometry software to explore this problem.

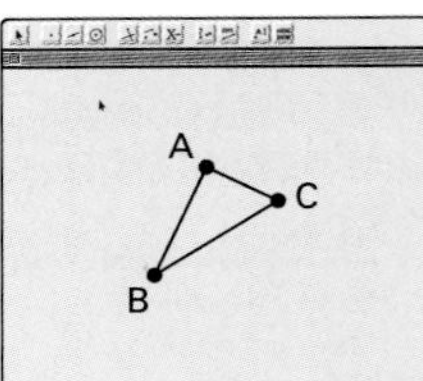

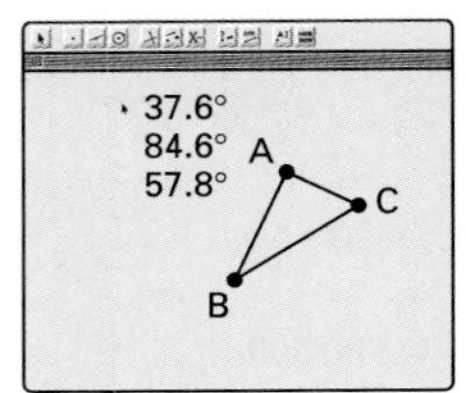

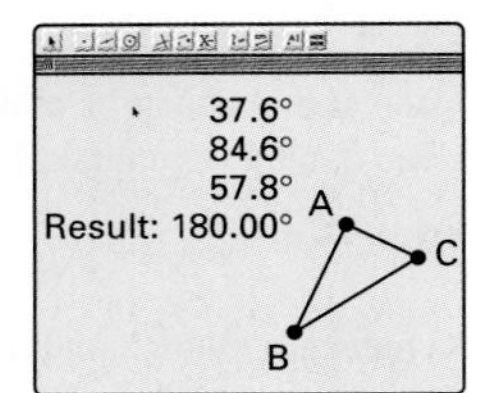

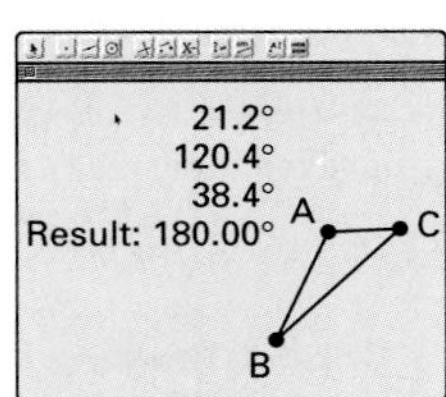

1. **Use your software to make a triangle. Label its vertices *A, B,* and *C.***
2. **Use the angle measurement tool to find $m\angle BAC$. (You will probably need to click on points *B, A,* and *C* in that order.) Then, find $m\angle ABC$ and $m\angle BCA$. Drag the measures to the upper left corner of your screen.**
3. **Use the software's calculator to find the sum of the three angle measures.**
4. **Click on a vertex and hold down the mouse button. Drag the vertex around the screen.**

Solution: The measures of the individual angles change, but the sum of the angle measures stays the same at 180°.

TRY IT

a. What happens to the sum of the angle measures of a convex quadrilateral when you change its shape and size?

b. What happens to the sum of the angle measures of a convex pentagon when you change its shape and size?

ON YOUR OWN

- What are some advantages and disadvantages of using geometry software to measure an angle instead of using a protractor?
- Why do you think you have to select three vertices in the proper order when you measure an angle with geometry software?

232

Perimeter and Area

5-5

► Lesson Link You've seen formulas for the areas and perimeters of squares and rectangles. Now you'll look more closely at the relationships between the areas and perimeters of those quadrilaterals. ◄

You'll Learn ...

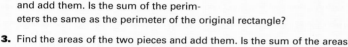

- to examine the relationship between perimeter and area

... How It's Used

City planners use the relationship between perimeter and area to make sure they use land in the most efficient way.

Explore Perimeter and Area

Cut and Compare

Materials: Graph paper, Scissors

1. Draw a 4 by 6 rectangle on graph paper. Find its area and perimeter.
2. Cut out the rectangle. Then cut it in half. Find the perimeters of the two pieces and add them. Is the sum of the perimeters the same as the perimeter of the original rectangle?
3. Find the areas of the two pieces and add them. Is the sum of the areas the same as the area of the original rectangle?
4. Rearrange the pieces to form a different rectangle. How do its perimeter and area compare with those of the rectangle you drew in Step 1?

Learn Perimeter and Area

The area of a geometric figure is the number of square units needed to cover the figure. Recall that the formula $A = lw$ gives the area (A) of a rectangle with length l and width w.

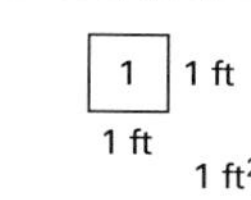

The words *base* and *height* are often used instead of *length* and *width*. The formula $A = bh$ can be used to find the area (A) of a rectangle with base b and height h. The perimeter, or distance around, any polygon can be found by adding the lengths of the sides.

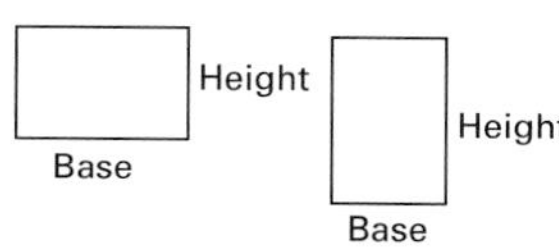

Perimeter is a distance, so it is measured in units of length.

MEETING INDIVIDUAL NEEDS

Resources

5-5 Practice
5-5 Reteaching
5-5 Problem Solving
5-5 Enrichment
5-5 Daily Transparency
Problem of the Day
Review
Quick Quiz
Teaching Tool Transparency 7
Technology Master 21

Wide World of Mathematics Middle School: Huge Mall Opens

Learning Modalities

Kinesthetic To differentiate between perimeter and area, have students outline any 2-D geometric figure on the floor with masking tape or string. Have the students walk around the figure to "experience" perimeter. Then have students cover the interior of the figure with newspaper to emphasize the difference between area and perimeter.

Social Have students work together to find areas and perimeters of various rectangles in the classroom.

Challenge

Only two rectangles with sides that are whole numbers have a perimeter and an area with the same number of units. Have students find at least one of them. 4×4 or 6×3

5-5 Lesson Organizer

Objective

- Examine the relationship between perimeter and area.

Materials

- Explore: Graph paper, scissors

NCTM Standards

- 1, 2, 4, 12, 13

► Review

Use $A = bh$ to find A.

1. $b = 42$, $h = 50$ 2100
2. $b = 105$, $h = 81$ 8505
3. $b = 500$, $h = 450$ 225,000

Available on Daily Transparency 5-5

1 Introduce

Explore

You may wish to use Teaching Tool Transparency 7: $\frac{1}{4}$-Inch Graph Paper with **Explore**.

The Point
Students discover that figures with the same area might not have the same perimeter.

Ongoing Assessment
Watch for students who may cut along the diagonal to cut the rectangle in half.

For Groups That Finish Early
Start with the same 4 by 6 rectangle, but cut it in half in a different way and then repeat Steps 2–4.

Follow Up
Have students discuss what they discovered by doing **Explore**.

Answers for Explore

1. Area: 24; Perimeter: 20
2. 4 by 3 rectangles: 28; 2 by 6 rectangles: 32; No
3. 24; Yes.
4. Area is the same; Perimeter may be different.

2 Teach

Learn

Point out that other units besides squares could be used to find areas, but in most cases this would be inconvenient.

Alternate Examples

A rectangular lawn is 55 feet long by 48 feet wide.

1. Find the perimeter of the lawn.

   $p = 55 + 48 + 55 + 48$

   $p = 206$

   The perimeter is 206 feet.

2. Find the area of the lawn.

   $A = bh$

   $= 55 \cdot 48$

   $= 2640$

   The area is 2640 ft^2.

3 Practice and Assess

Check

Some students may at first think that rectangles with the same area also have the same perimeter. If students have trouble finding an example in Question 3, you might have them start with a 5×4 and a 10×2 rectangle, both of which have an area of 20. But the first has a perimeter of 18 and the second has a perimeter of 24.

Answers for Check Your Understanding

1. Measurement in feet could be perimeter; In ft^2 could be area.
2. Substitute side length for both length and width; Squares are rectangles with equal sides.
3. They might not have the same perimeter. Possible answer:

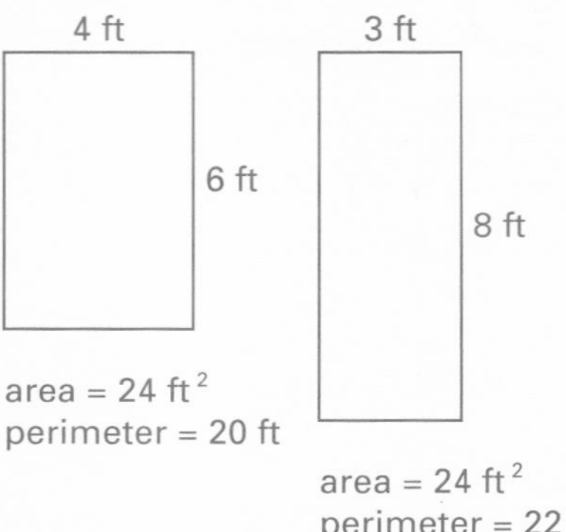

DID YOU KNOW?

The Great Wall, a fortification along the northern border of China, was begun in 221 B.C. when Emperor Shi Huangdi of the Qin dynasty ordered the unification of several existing walls. It stretches 1500 miles!

Examples

The Palace Museum, in Beijing, China, is the world's largest palace. It contains more than 75 buildings and over 9000 rooms. The palace grounds are rectangular, with a length of 3150 ft and a width of 2460 ft.

1 A moat surrounds the palace grounds. Find the length of the moat.

The length of the moat is the perimeter of the palace grounds.

$p = 3150 + 2460 + 3150 + 2460$ Add the length of each side.

$= 11{,}220$ Add.

The moat is 11,220 ft ($2\frac{1}{8}$ miles!) long.

2 Find the area of the palace grounds.

$A = bh$ Use the formula for the area of a rectangle.

$= 3{,}150 \cdot 2{,}460$ Substitute 3,150 for b and 2,460 for h.

$= 7{,}749{,}000$ Multiply.

The area is about 7.75 million ft^2. Note that ft^2 means "square feet."

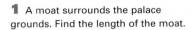

Language Link

Whenever you see *meter* in a word, you know the word has something to do with measurement. The Greek word meaning "to measure" was *metrein,* pronounced "met-ray-in."

Try It

The maintenance supervisor of Logan Middle School is planning to refinish the basketball court.

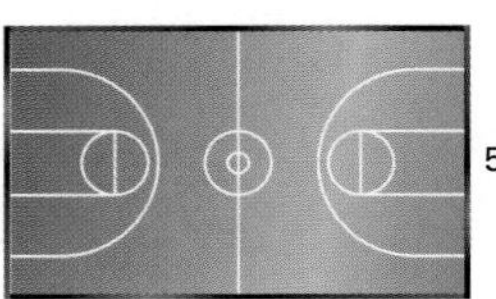

a. What is the perimeter of the court? 268 ft

b. Find the area to be refinished. 4200 ft^2

Check Your Understanding

1. Explain the difference between measurements made in ft and in ft^2.
2. How can you use the rectangle formulas to find the perimeter and area of a square? Why does it make sense to do so?
3. Two rectangles have the same area. Do they have the same perimeter? Use an example to explain.

MATH EVERY DAY

Problem of the Day

The distance around the Earth at its equator is about 41,000 kilometers. The diameter of a nickel is about 2 cm. About how many nickels placed side-by-side would it take to encircle the Earth at the equator? What is the value of the coins?
2,050,000,000 nickels (Since 41,000 km = 4,100,000,000 cm, 4,100,000,000 ÷ 2 = 2,050,000,000); $102,500,000 (2,050,000,000 × 0.05)

Available on Daily Transparency 5-5

An Extension is provided in the transparency package.

Fact of the Day

Besides the moat, the Imperial Palace in Beijing is surrounded by a 35-foot-high wall.

Mental Math

Do these mentally.

1. 148 − 99 49
2. 314 − 298 16
3. 478 − 197 281

5-5 Exercises and Applications

Practice and Apply

1. **Getting Started** Follow these steps to determine the perimeter and the area of a rectangle with a base of 14 ft and a height of 10 ft.

   a. Add the lengths of the sides to find the perimeter. **48 ft**

   b. Use the formula $A = bh$ to find the area of the rectangle. Substitute 14 for b and 10 for h. $A = 14 \text{ ft} \times 10 \text{ ft}$

   c. Simplify the equation. $A = 140 \text{ ft}^2$

Find the perimeter and area of each rectangular playing area.

	Game	Base (length)	Height (width)	Perimeter	Area
2.	Table tennis	9 ft	5 ft	28 ft	45 ft^2
3.	Basketball	26 m	14 m	80 m	364 m^2
4.	Soccer	100 m	73 m	346 m	7300 m^2
5.	Football	120 yd	53 yd	346 yd	6360 yd^2

Find the perimeter and area of the base of each rectangular building.

6. Largest multilevel industrial building: Kwai Chung container port, Hong Kong, China—906 ft by 958 ft **P: 3,728 ft; A: 867,948 ft^2**

7. Largest ground area, commercial building: flower auction building, Aalsmeer, Netherlands—2546 ft by 2070 ft **P: 9,232 ft; A: 5,270,220 ft^2**

8. **Geography** The state of Colorado is shaped like a rectangle, with a base measuring about 385 miles and a height of about 275 miles. Find the approximate perimeter and area of Colorado. **P: 1,320 mi; A: 105,875 mi^2**

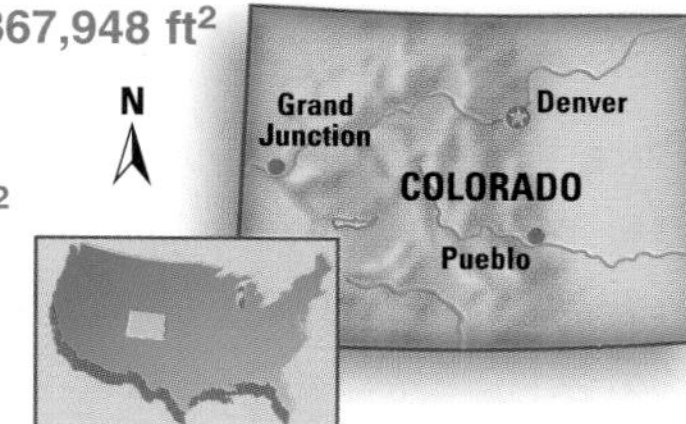

Science The National Air and Space Museum in Washington, DC, held a contest in which students attempted to land their paper and balsa wood airplanes inside a rectangle 35 feet away.

9. The rectangle inside which students must land their planes measures 12 ft by 9 ft. Find the perimeter and the area of the rectangle. **P: 42 ft; A: 108 ft^2**

10. In the final portion of the contest, students must land their planes on a tiny "runway" measuring 1 ft by 5 ft. Find the perimeter and the area of the runway. **P: 12 ft; A: 5 ft^2**

PRACTICE 5-5

5-5 Exercises and Applications

Assignment Guide

- Basic
  1–12, 13–27 odds
- Average
  2–13, 14–26 evens
- Enriched
  2–18, 20–26 evens

Exercise Notes

Exercise 7

Industry A large part of the flowers sold in the United States are grown in other countries. Most of them are flown in on cargo planes. The Netherlands provides a large quantity of flowers for the rest of the world.

Exercise 8

Geography Colorado and Wyoming both appear rectangular on a map. Some other states have two or three linear borders but many states have water boundaries which are not straight.

Exercises 9–10

Consumer The National Air and Space Museum in Washington, D.C., holds the record for the highest museum attendance on a single day. On April 14, 1984, a total of 118,437 people attended.

PRACTICE

Name ______________________ **Practice 5-5**

Perimeter and Area

Find the perimeter and area of each playing area.

Game	Base (length)	Height (width)	Perimeter	Area
1. tennis, singles	26 yd	9 yd	70 yd	234 yd^2
2. volleyball	60 ft	30 ft	180 ft	1,800 ft^2
3. badminton, singles	44 ft	17 ft	122 ft	748 ft^2
4. cricket	170 m	160 m	660 m	27,200 m^2
5. racquetball	40 ft	20 ft	120 ft	800 ft^2
6. ice hockey	61 m	30 m	182 m	1,830 m^2

Find the area and the perimeter of each bridge or canal. Assume that each has the shape of a rectangle.

7. Busiest bridge: Howrah Bridge, Calcutta, India—1500 ft by 72 ft
   area: 108,000 ft^2 perimeter: 3144 ft
8. Widest bridge: Sydney Harbor Bridge, Australia—49 m by 503 m
   area: 24,647 m^2 perimeter: 1,104 m
9. Longest canal: Erie Barge Canal, New York—0.028 mi by 365 mi
   area: 10.22 mi^2 perimeter: 730.056 mi
10. Largest lock: Berendrecht lock, Antwerp, Belgium—1640 ft by 223 ft
   area: 365,720 ft^2 perimeter: 3726 ft
11. Largest cut: Corinth Canal, Greece—6917 yd by 27 yd
   area: 186,759 yd^2 perimeter: 13,888 yd
12. **Geography** The state of Wyoming is shaped like a rectangle, with a base measuring about 350 miles and a height of about 280 miles. Find the approximate area and perimeter of Wyoming.
   area: 98,000 mi^2 perimeter: 1,260 mi
13. Orlando painted a mural measuring 3.7 m by 4.6 m. Find the area and perimeter of the mural.
   area: 17.02 m^2 perimeter: 16.6 m

RETEACHING

Name ______________________ **Alternative Lesson 5-5**

Perimeter and Area

Two measurements of quadrilaterals are perimeter and area. The perimeter, or distance around, any polygon can be found by adding the lengths of the sides. It is measured in units of length.

The area of a geometric figure is the number of square units needed to cover the figure. The area of a rectangle can be found using the formula $A = bh$, where A is the area, b is the base, and h is the height of the rectangle. Area is measured in square units.

Example 1

Find the perimeter of the rectangle.

To find the perimeter of the rectangle, add the lengths of its sides.

$P = 3 + 5 + 3 + 5 = 16$

The perimeter of the rectangle is 16 cm.

(5 cm by 3 cm rectangle)

Try It Find the perimeter of each rectangle.

a. 38 in. b. 32 cm c. 120 in.

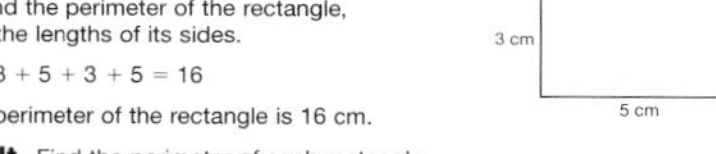

Example 2

Find the area of the rectangle.

To find the area of the rectangle, multiply its base and height.

$A = 3 \times 5 = 15$

The area is 15 cm^2.

(5 cm by 3 cm rectangle)

Try It Find the area of each rectangle.

d. 49 in^2 e. 162 cm^2 f. 432 cm^2

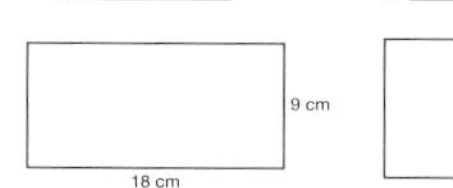

Reteaching

Activity

Materials: Graph paper

- Work in groups of three. One person should draw a rectangle on the grid. The next person should find the area. The third person should find the perimeter.
- Take turns so that each person performs all three roles.

Exercise Notes

■ Exercise 12

Test Prep Some students might give B as their answer. Remind them that square units are used to measure area, but the side lengths of the squares are used to measure perimeter.

Exercise Answers

13. Yes; If width is very small, area will be small even though perimeter is large; For example, a rectangle with length 54 cm and width 1 cm has a perimeter of 110 cm and an area of 54 cm². A rectangle with length 25 cm and width 20 cm has a smaller perimeter of 90 cm and a much larger area of 500 cm².

15. Possible answers: Perimeter: How far it is to run around a field, how much ribbon to go around a box; Area: How much carpet to lay in a room, how many chairs can be set up in a room.

Alternate Assessment

Portfolio Have students choose one exercise that they think best illustrates the concepts of this lesson. Have them include this exercise in their portfolios.

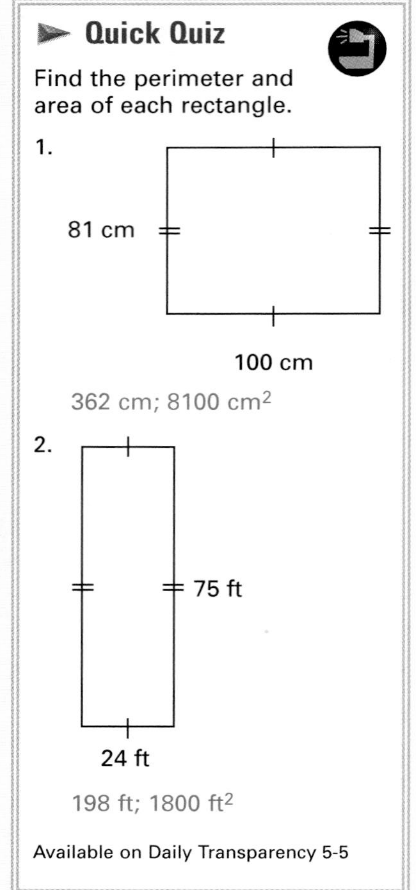

Quick Quiz

Find the perimeter and area of each rectangle.

1.

362 cm; 8100 cm²

2.

198 ft; 1800 ft²

Available on Daily Transparency 5-5

11. History The Woolworth Building in New York City was once the tallest in the world. It is 241 m tall. Its base is nearly rectangular, with a length of about 60 m and a width of about 46 m. Find the approximate area of the base of the Woolworth Building. 2760 m²

12. Test Prep If the length of the side of a square is given in centimeters, the perimeter would be given in which units? A

Ⓐ cm Ⓑ cm² Ⓒ m Ⓓ m²

Problem Solving and Reasoning

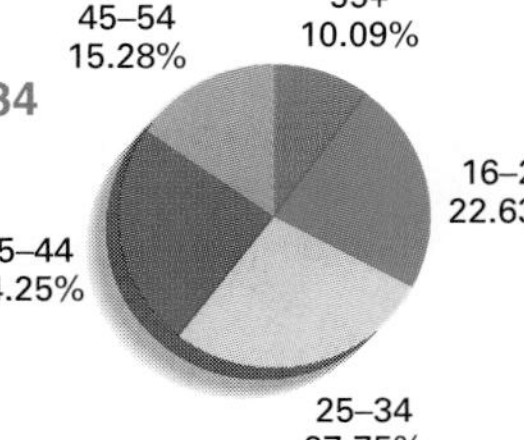

Problem Solving
STRATEGIES
• Look for a Pattern
• Make an Organized List
• Make a Table
• Guess and Check
• Work Backward
• Use Logical Reasoning
• Draw a Diagram
• Solve a Simpler Problem

13. Choose a Strategy GPS Is it possible for one rectangle to have a greater area than another but a smaller perimeter? If so, give an example. If not, explain why not.

14. Communicate Use addition to find the perimeter of a rectangle that measures 14 m by 9 m. Then find the perimeter using the following formula: $P = 2b + 2h$. Substitute 14 for b and 9 for h. Explain which method you prefer for finding perimeter. 46 m; Explanations may vary.

15. Journal Make a list of times when you would need to know the perimeter of something. Do the same for area. Are there any times when you would need to know both?

Mixed Review

U.S. Workers by Age, 1993

Age group	Percent
16–24	22.63%
25–34	27.75%
35–44	24.25%
45–54	15.28%
55+	10.09%

Use the circle graph for Exercises 16–18. *[Lesson 1-1]*

16. Which age group has the largest number of workers? 25–34

17. About what percent of workers are 55 or older? 10%

18. Which age group has about $\frac{1}{4}$ of the workers? 35–44

Round each mixed number to the nearest whole number, then estimate each sum or difference. *[Lesson 4-1]*

19. $3\frac{2}{3} + 7\frac{5}{8} \approx 12$ **20.** $12\frac{2}{7} - 2\frac{3}{8} \approx 10$ **21.** $9\frac{3}{4} + 6\frac{1}{3} \approx 16$

22. $4\frac{13}{16} - 1\frac{1}{8} \approx 4$ **23.** $18\frac{4}{5} - 7\frac{3}{16} \approx 12$ **24.** $6\frac{8}{9} + 7\frac{2}{5} \approx 14$

25. $67\frac{2}{11} - 32\frac{6}{7} \approx 34$ **26.** $45\frac{4}{9} + 52\frac{7}{10} \approx 98$ **27.** $18\frac{3}{10} + 16\frac{5}{8} \approx 35$

PROBLEM SOLVING

Name ____________ **Guided Problem Solving 5-5**

Is it possible for one rectangle to have a greater area than another but a smaller perimeter? If so, give an example. If not, explain why not.

Possible answers: Items 4–7

— Understand —

1. What are you asked to decide? If a rectangle can have a greater area and smaller perimeter than another rectangle.

— Plan —

2. Draw a 1-cm × 6-cm rectangle. Label the sides. Possible answer: (6 cm, 1 cm, 1 cm, 6 cm)

3. Find the perimeter and the area of the rectangle. 14 cm; 6 cm²

4. Choose an area that is greater than, but *not* more than double the area of the rectangle. Then find the factors for that area. Possible answer: 8; 1 × 8; 2 × 4

— Solve —

5. Find the perimeter for each pair of factors. 1 × 8, 18 cm; 2 × 4, 12 cm

6. Continue trying different areas. Did you find an example of a rectangle with a greater area and smaller perimeter? Explain. Yes, 2 × 4 rectangle has area of 8 cm² and perimeter of 12 cm, 1 × 6 has area of 6 cm² and perimeter of 14 cm.

— Look Back —

7. What other strategy could you use to find the answer? Make a Table.

SOLVE ANOTHER PROBLEM

Is it possible for one square to have a greater area than another but a smaller perimeter? If so, give an example. If not, explain why not. No. For every one unit increase in side length, perimeter increases by 4 and area increases by 2 units more than previous increase.

ENRICHMENT

Name ____________ **Extend Your Thinking 5-5**

Critical Thinking

Figures with the same perimeter can have different areas. Likewise, figures with the same area can have different perimeters. For all the questions below, use only whole numbers to complete the tables.

1. Complete the table to show all possible dimensions for a rectangle with a perimeter of 36 inches. Then find each area.

Dimensions	Area	Dimensions	Area	Dimensions	Area
1 × 17	17 in²	4 × 14	56 in²	7 × 11	77 in²
2 × 16	32 in²	5 × 13	65 in²	8 × 10	80 in²
3 × 15	45 in²	6 × 12	72 in²	9 × 9	81 in²

2. What are the dimensions of the figure with the largest area? 9 × 9

3. What is the name of the figure with the largest area? Square.

4. Complete the table to show all possible dimensions for a rectangle with an area of 36 in². Then find each perimeter.

Dimensions	Perimeter	Dimensions	Perimeter	Dimensions	Perimeter
1 × 36	74 in.	3 × 12	30 in.	6 × 6	24 in.
2 × 18	40 in.	4 × 9	26 in.		

5. What are the dimensions of the figure with the shortest perimeter? 6 × 6

6. What is the name of the figure with the shortest perimeter? Square.

7. Make a conjecture about the relationship between perimeter and area. Possible answer: For a given area, a square has the least perimeter of all rectangles. For a given perimeter, a square has the greatest area of all rectangles.

8. How could you test to see that your conjecture is correct? Possible answer: Test by comparing perimeters of several rectangles with the same area. Also, test by comparing areas of several rectangles with the same perimeter.

You've learned about some of the world's most unusual buildings. You've seen how architects use angles, parallel and perpendicular lines, and polygons in the design of their buildings. Now you'll have a chance to design a building of your own.

From the Dome to Your Home ...

Materials: Inch or metric ruler, Protractor, Drawing paper

You've been chosen to design the headquarters of a company that produces a familiar product.

1. Decide on the product the company produces. It could be a well-known food product, a brand of clothing, an entertainment device, an item of sporting equipment, or any other product that you enjoy. Choose a product with features that you can somehow show in your building design.

Gas station, Zillah, WA

2. Draw the floor plan and one outside view of company headquarters. Use one sheet of paper for each. Include as many of the following as possible in your design:

a. Different types of angles.

b. Parallel lines and perpendicular lines.

c. Different types of triangles and quadrilaterals.

d. Different types of polygons with more than 4 sides.

e. Creative ideas that reflect some of the characteristics of the product you chose in Step 1.

3. Explain how you used the items listed in Step 2 in your design.

From the Dome to Your Home ...

The Point

In *From the Dome to Your Home ...* on page 211, students saw how geometry is used in building construction. Now they will use geometry to design their own building.

Materials

Inch or metric ruler, protractor, drawing paper

Resources

Teaching Tool Transparencies 14: Rulers and 15: Protractors

About the Page

- Brainstorm product ideas with the class to stimulate student thinking.
- Suggest that students select a product with which they are familiar so they can describe it accurately.
- Ask students if they have ever seen a building that "looks like" the product that was produced or sold inside the building, such as a drive-in restaurant that looked like a hot dog or a root beer mug.
- Remind students that a floor plan is a top view of the layout of the inside of a building. It would be helpful if students could look at a real blueprint or floor plan, if one is available.

Ongoing Assessment

Check that students have drawn reasonable designs that include angles, parallel and perpendicular lines, and polygons.

Extension

When students have completed their designs, have them create a logo or sign for the building that reflects the characteristics of the product produced in the building.

Answers for Connect

1–3. Answers may vary.

5A Review

Review Correlation

Item(s)	Lesson(s)
1–3	5-3
4–9	5-3, 5-4
10	5-1, 5-2
11	5-5
12	5-3

Test Prep

Test-Taking Tip
Tell students that they can check some answers by using the inverse operation. Here the hint says to add to find the sum of the angle measures. To check, students can start with 180, subtract 62 and then subtract 83.

Answers for Review

4. Square, regular polygon, quadrilateral, rectangle, parallelogram, rhombus.
5. Convex polygon, nonregular hexagon.
6. Right triangle, nonregular polygon.
10. Answers may vary.

Section 5A Review

REVIEW 5A

Find the missing angle in each quadrilateral.

1. 143°

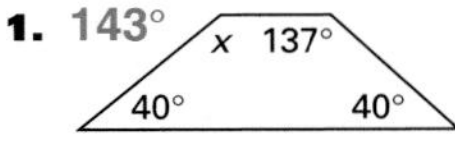

2. 127°

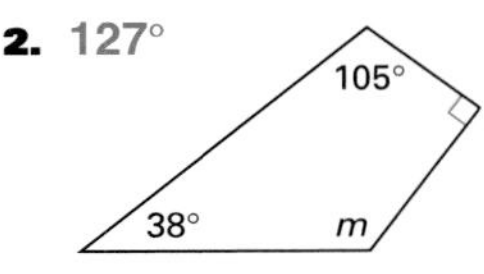

3. 13°

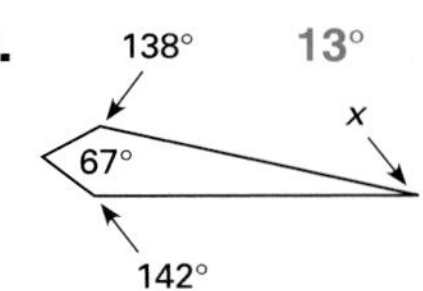

Classify each figure in as many ways as you can.

4.

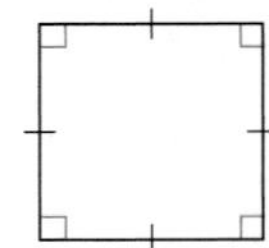

5.

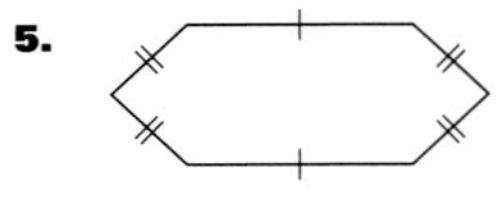

6.

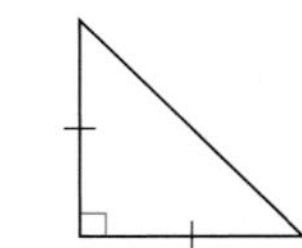

Find the sum of the measures of the angles of each polygon.

7. Nine-sided polygon 1260° **8.** Eleven-sided polygon 1620° **9.** Sixteen-sided polygon 2520°

10. 

Draw any angle and label the vertex A. Use a protractor to draw its bisector. Draw any segment $\overline{AB}$. Use a protractor to draw its perpendicular bisector. Explain the methods you have used.

11. Social Studies The National Portrait Gallery in Washington, DC, houses portraits of all the presidents of the United States, as well as portraits of other famous Americans. What are the perimeter and the area of the courtyard of the gallery? P: 800 ft; A: 33,600 ft²

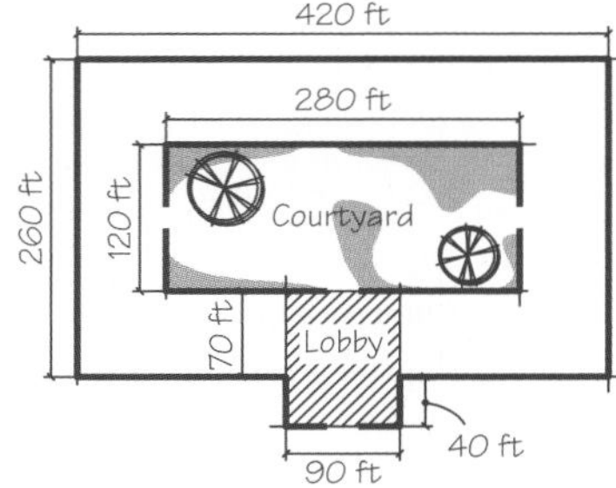

Test Prep

On a multiple choice test where you are asked to find an unknown angle measure in a triangle that has two of its angles given, you can add each possible angle to the two that are given. When you get a sum of 180°, you have the correct answer.

12. Find the measure of the unknown angle. C

Ⓐ 10° Ⓑ 31° Ⓒ 35° Ⓓ 45°

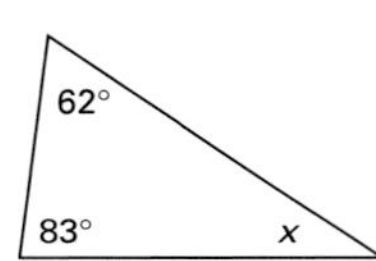

Resources

Practice Masters
Section 5A Review

Assessment Sourcebook
Quiz 5A

TestWorks
Test and Practice Software

PRACTICE

Name ______________________ Practice

Section 5A Review

Name each angle and find its measure. Classify it as acute, right, or obtuse.

1. ∠DEF; 55°; Acute
2. ∠UVW; 135°; Obtuse
3. ∠LMN; 90°; Right

Find the missing angle in each quadrilateral.

4. k = 142°
5. x = 57°
6. c = 95°

Classify each figure in as many ways as you can.

7. Trapezoid, quadrilateral
8. Rhombus, parallelogram, quadrilateral

Find the sum of the measures of the angles of each polygon.

9. octagon 1080°
10. 14-sided polygon 2160°

11. A door measures 30 in. by 96 in. Find the perimeter and the area of the door.
perimeter: 252 in. area: 2880 in²

12. Heather and Denise are running laps. They start together at the same starting point. Heather completes a lap every 120 sec, and Denise completes a lap every 96 sec. In how many seconds will they again meet at the starting point? *[Lesson 3-7]* After 480 sec

13. On October 15, 1996, shares of Chips and Technologies stock increased $\$4\frac{7}{8}$ to $\$19\frac{3}{4}$. What was the original price? *[Lesson 4-3]* $\$14\frac{7}{8}$

Section 5B

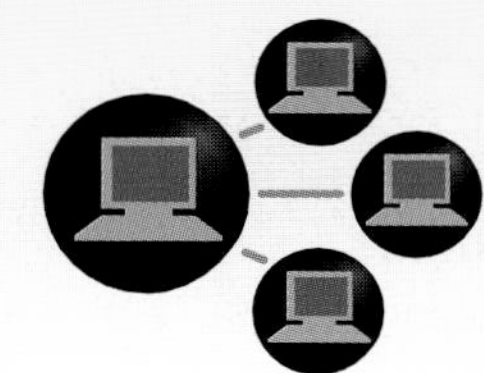

Visit **www.teacher.mathsurf.com** for links to lesson plans from teachers and other professionals, NCTM information, and other sites.

Geometric Formulas

LESSON PLANNING GUIDE

Student Edition			Ancillaries	
LESSON	MATERIALS	VOCABULARY	DAILY	OTHER
Section 5B Opener				
5-6 Squares and Square Roots	geoboard, rubber bands	perfect square, square root, radical sign	5–6	Teaching Tool Trans. 9, 22 Technology Master 22
5-7 The Pythagorean Theorem	metric ruler, graph paper, calculator	hypotenuse, leg	5–7	Teaching Tool Trans. 7, 14 Technology Master 23 *Interactive CD-ROM Lesson* *WW Math*—Middle School
5-8 Areas of Triangles	graph paper, scissors,		5–8	Teaching Tool Trans. 7, 19 Lesson Enhance. Trans. 24, 25 Technology Master 24
5-9 Areas of Parallelograms and Trapezoids	graph paper, scissors, straightedge		5–9	Teaching Tool Trans. 7
5-10 Problem Solving: Areas of Irregular Figures			5–10	Lesson Enhancement Trans. 26 Ch. 5 Project Master
Connect	graph paper			Teaching Tool Trans. 7 Interdisc. Team Teaching 5B
Review				Practice 5B; Quiz 5B; *TestWorks*
Extend Key Ideas				
Chapter 5 Summary and Review				
Chapter 5 Assessment				Ch. 5 Tests Forms A–F *TestWorks*; Ch. 5 Letter Home
Cumulative Review, Chapters 1–5				Cumulative Review Ch. 1–5

SKILLS TRACE

LESSON	SKILL	FIRST INTRODUCED GR. 5	GR. 6	GR. 7	DEVELOP	PRACTICE/ APPLY	REVIEW
5-6	**Finding and applying square roots.**			✘ p. 240	pp. 240–241	pp. 242–243	pp. 264, 267, 302, 402
5-7	**Analyzing and applying the Pythagorean Theorem.**			✘ p. 244	pp. 244–245	pp. 246–247	pp. 264, 267, 307, 409
5-8	**Finding the area of a triangle.**	✘			pp. 248–250	pp. 251–252	pp. 264, 267, 312, 414
5-9	**Finding areas of parallelograms and trapezoids.**	✘			pp. 253–255	pp. 256–257	pp. 264, 267, 327, 419
5-10	**Finding areas of irregular shapes.**	✘			pp. 258–260	pp. 261–262	pp. 264, 267, 332

CONNECTED MATHEMATICS

The unit *Stretching and Shrinking (Similarity)*, from the **Connected Mathematics** series, can be used with Section 5B.

INTERDISCIPLINARY TEAM TEACHING

Math and Social Studies

(Worksheet pages 19–20: Teacher pages T19–T20)

In this lesson, students calculate area and distance in Bern, Switzerland.

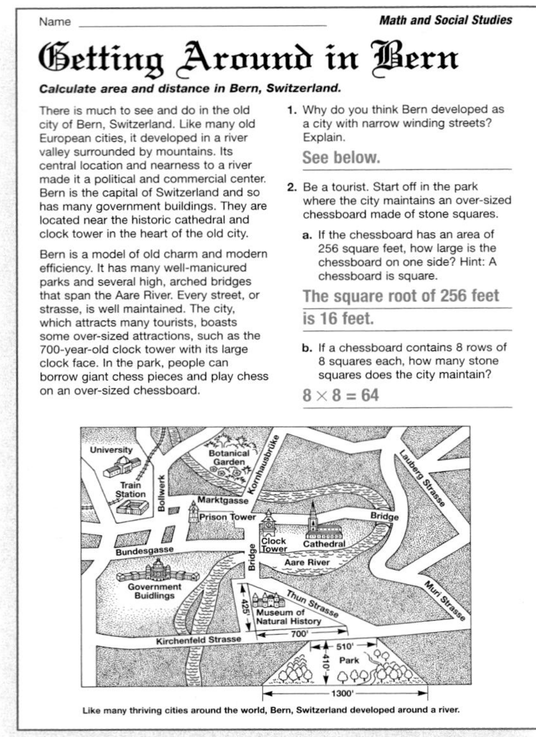

Name ____________ *Math and Social Studies*

Getting Around in Bern

Calculate area and distance in Bern, Switzerland.

There is much to see and do in the old city of Bern, Switzerland. Like many old European cities, it developed in a river valley surrounded by mountains. Its central location and nearness to a river made it a political and commercial center. Bern is the capital of Switzerland and so has many government buildings. They are located near the historic cathedral and clock tower in the heart of the old city.

Bern is a model of old charm and modern efficiency. It has many well-manicured parks and several high, arched bridges that span the Aare River. Every street, or strasse, is well maintained. The city, which attracts many tourists, boasts some over-sized attractions, such as the 700-year-old clock tower with its large clock face. In the park, people can borrow giant chess pieces and play chess on an over-sized chessboard.

1. Why do you think Bern developed as a city with narrow winding streets? Explain.
   See below.
2. Be a tourist. Start off in the park where the city maintains an over-sized chessboard made of stone squares.
   a. If the chessboard has an area of 256 square feet, how large is the chessboard on one side? Hint: A chessboard is square.
   The square root of 256 feet is 16 feet.
   b. If a chessboard contains 8 rows of 8 squares each, how many stone squares does the city maintain?
   $8 \times 8 = 64$

Like many thriving cities around the world, Bern, Switzerland developed around a river.

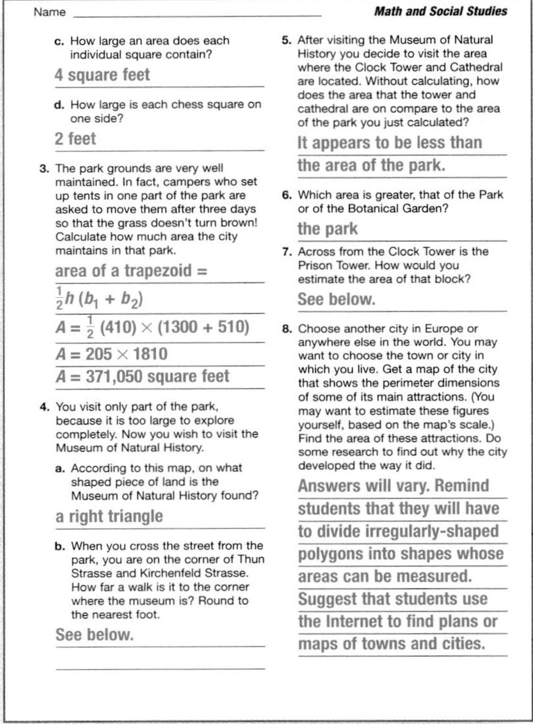

Name ____________ *Math and Social Studies*

c. How large an area does each individual square contain?
4 square feet

d. How large is each chess square on one side?
2 feet

3. The park grounds are very well maintained. In fact, campers who set up tents in one part of the park are asked to move them after three days so that the grass doesn't turn brown! Calculate how much area the city maintains in that park.
   area of a trapezoid =
   $\frac{1}{2}h(b_1 + b_2)$
   $A = \frac{1}{2}(410) \times (1300 + 510)$
   $A = 205 \times 1810$
   $A = 371{,}050$ square feet
4. You visit only part of the park, because it is too large to explore completely. Now you wish to visit the Museum of Natural History.
   a. According to this map, on what shaped piece of land is the Museum of Natural History found?
   a right triangle
   b. When you cross the street from the park, you are on the corner of Thun Strasse and Kirchenfeld Strasse. How far a walk is it to the corner where the museum is? Round to the nearest foot.
   See below.
5. After visiting the Museum of Natural History you decide to visit the area where the Clock Tower and Cathedral are located. Without calculating, how does the area that the tower and cathedral are on compare to the area of the park you just calculated?
   It appears to be less than the area of the park.
6. Which area is greater, that of the Park or of the Botanical Garden?
   the park
7. Across from the Clock Tower is the Prison Tower. How would you estimate the area of that block?
   See below.
8. Choose another city in Europe or anywhere else in the world. You may want to choose the town or city in which you live. Get a map of the city that shows the perimeter dimensions of some of its main attractions. (You may want to estimate these figures yourself, based on the map's scale.) Find the area of these attractions. Do some research to find out why the city developed the way it did.
   Answers will vary. Remind students that they will have to divide irregularly-shaped polygons into shapes whose areas can be measured. Suggest that students use the Internet to find plans or maps of towns and cities.

Answers

1. The winding river runs through the city and the roads must wind with it. Also, older cities tend to have narrow streets because they were built before the automobile was invented.

4. b. To find the hypotenuse, use the Pythagorean Theorem. $a^2 + b^2 = c^2$; $(425)^2 + (700)^2 = c^2 = 180{,}625 + 490{,}000 = 670{,}625$; square root = 818.9; rounds to 819 feet.

7. Divide it into a large and a small rectangle. Get the dimensions needed to calculate the area of each and then add them together.

BIBLIOGRAPHY

FOR TEACHERS

Diagram Group. *Rules of the Game*. New York, NY: St. Martin's Press, 1990.

Glickman, A. M. *Metric Conversion Tables*. Woodbury, NY: Barron's Educational Series, Inc., 1990.

Heafford, Philip Ernest. *Great Book of Math Puzzles*. New York, NY: Sterling, 1993.

Spangler, David. *Math for Real Kids*. Glenview, IL: Good Year Books, 1997.

FOR STUDENTS

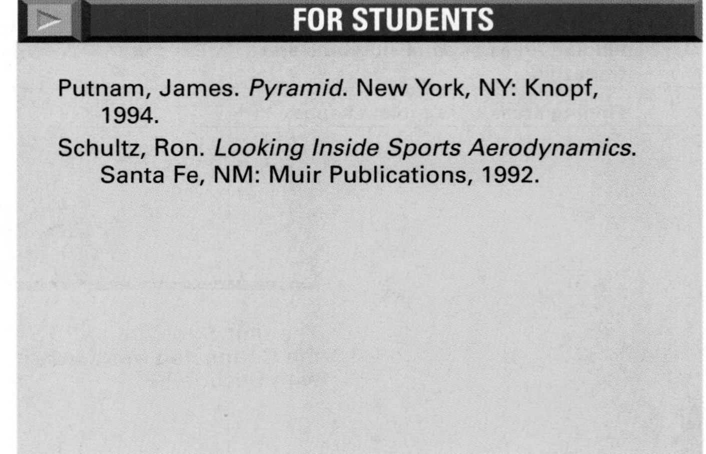

Putnam, James. *Pyramid*. New York, NY: Knopf, 1994.

Schultz, Ron. *Looking Inside Sports Aerodynamics*. Santa Fe, NM: Muir Publications, 1992.

SECTION 5B

Geometric Formulas

▶ Industry Link ▶ www.mathsurf.com/7/ch5/play_surfaces

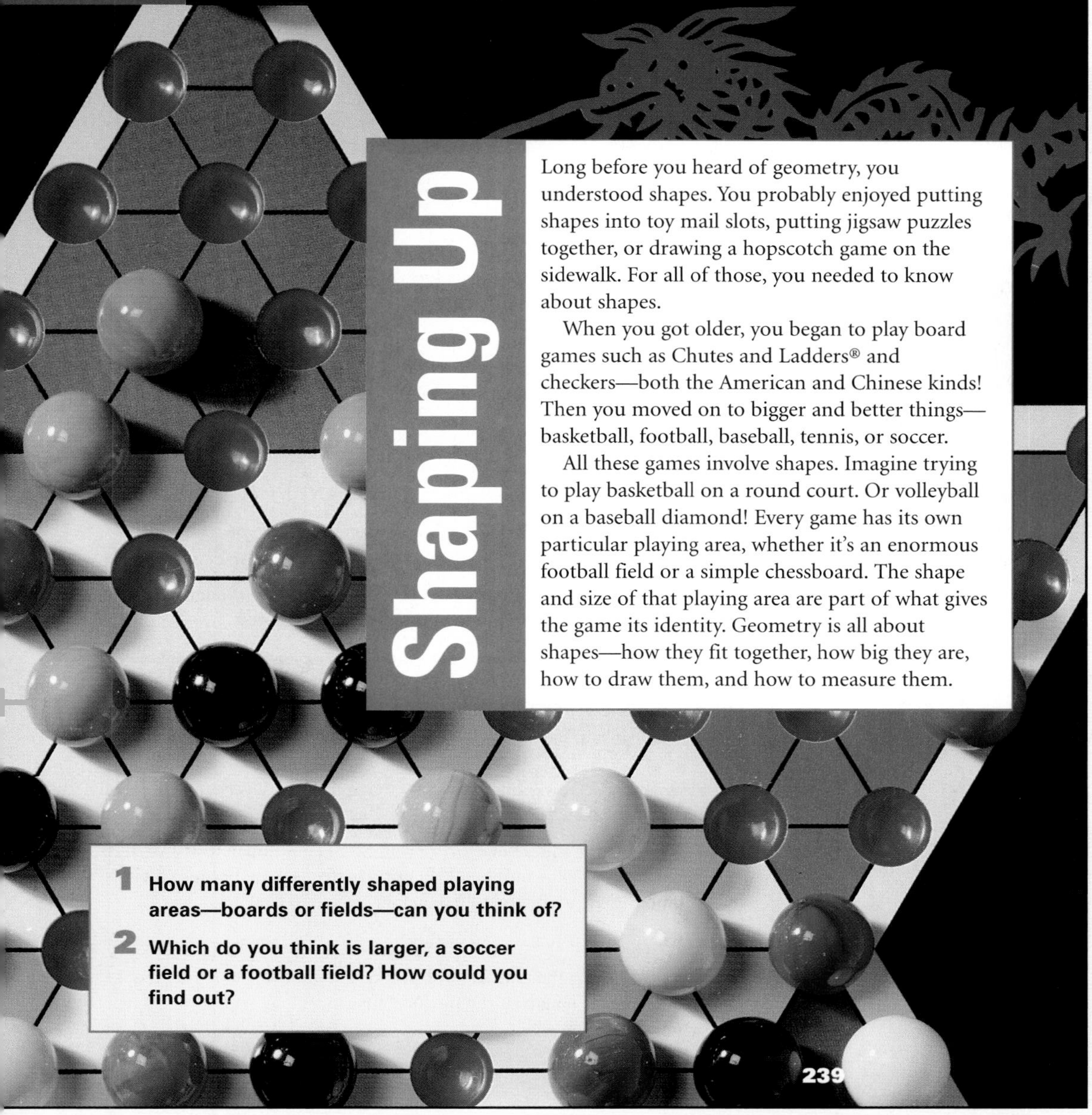

Shaping Up

Long before you heard of geometry, you understood shapes. You probably enjoyed putting shapes into toy mail slots, putting jigsaw puzzles together, or drawing a hopscotch game on the sidewalk. For all of those, you needed to know about shapes.

When you got older, you began to play board games such as Chutes and Ladders® and checkers—both the American and Chinese kinds! Then you moved on to bigger and better things—basketball, football, baseball, tennis, or soccer.

All these games involve shapes. Imagine trying to play basketball on a round court. Or volleyball on a baseball diamond! Every game has its own particular playing area, whether it's an enormous football field or a simple chessboard. The shape and size of that playing area are part of what gives the game its identity. Geometry is all about shapes—how they fit together, how big they are, how to draw them, and how to measure them.

1 How many differently shaped playing areas—boards or fields—can you think of?

2 Which do you think is larger, a soccer field or a football field? How could you find out?

239

Where are we now?

In Section 5A, students studied angles, parallel and perpendicular lines, and polygons.

They learned how to

- name and measure angles.
- identify parallel and perpendicular lines.
- name and classify triangles and quadrilaterals.
- find measures of angles in triangles and quadrilaterals.
- classify and find the angle sum of polygons.
- examine the relationship between perimeter and area.

Where are we going?

In Section 5B, students will

- use area to find the length of a side of a square.
- find square root.
- use the Pythagorean Theorem.
- find the area of triangles, parallelograms, and trapezoids.
- find the area of irregular shapes.

Theme: Playing Surfaces

World Wide Web

If your class has access to the World Wide Web, you might want to use the information found at the Web site address given. The interdisciplinary link relates to topics discussed in this lesson.

About the Page

This page introduces the theme of the section, playing surfaces, and discusses the shapes of board games and sports fields.

Ask ...

- Have you ever played Chinese checkers? What is the shape of that playing area? Star-shaped
- How would you describe the pieces in a jigsaw puzzle? Possible answer: Irregular shapes.

Extensions

The following activity does not require access to the World Wide Web.

Industry

Have students research the company that produces their favorite game. Suggest that they find out how large the company is, where it is located, and how it creates and design new games.

Answers for Questions

1. Possible answers: Rectangular: basketball, soccer, football, rugby, tennis, racquetball, handball, etc. Square: many board games. Oval: Australian rules football, track. Diamond: baseball. Star-shaped: Chinese checkers.
2. Possible answer: Soccer field; Measure it or look up the regulations.

Connect

On page 263, students use geometric shapes to design a multi-game play area.

Lesson Organizer

Objectives

- Find the side of a square when you know its area.
- Find a square root.

Materials

- Explore: Geoboard, rubber bands
- Learn: Calculator

Vocabulary

- Perfect square, square root, radical sign

NCTM Standards

- 1–5, 12, 13

Review

Use an exponent to name each expression.

1. 8×8 8^2
2. $7 \times 7 \times 7$ 7^3
3. $2 \times 2 \times 2 \times 2$ 2^4

Round to the nearest hundredth.

4. 7.5768876 7.58
5. 12.341177 12.34

Available on Daily Transparency 5-6

5-6 Squares and Square Roots

You'll Learn ...

- to find the side of a square when you know its area
- to find a square root

... How It's Used

Surveyors use square roots to calculate distances they can't directly measure.

Vocabulary

perfect square

square root

radical sign

Lesson Link You've learned to use the length of a side of a square to find the area. Now you'll use the area to find the length of a side.

Explore Squares and Square Roots

I'm Board with Squares

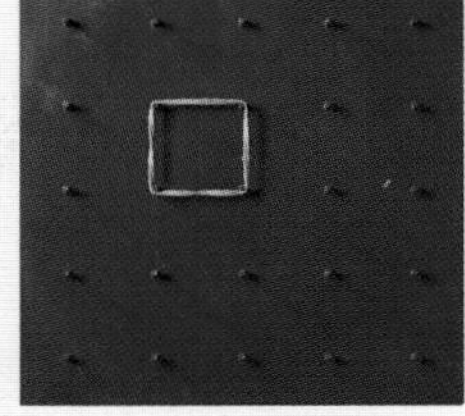

Materials: Geoboard, Rubber bands

The square shown on the geoboard has sides 1 unit long. Its area is 1 square unit.

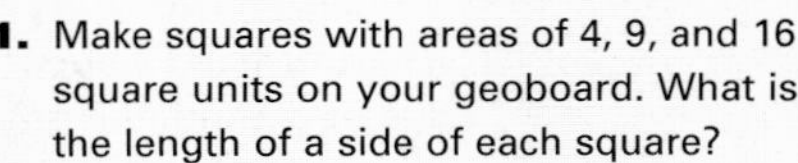

1. Make squares with areas of 4, 9, and 16 square units on your geoboard. What is the length of a side of each square?
2. Make a square with an area of 2 square units. How do you know that the area of your square is 2 square units?
3. How do you know that the figure you made is a square?
4. Estimate the length of a side of your square. How did you decide on your estimate?
5. Make a square with an area of 8 square units. Estimate the length of a side. Compare your estimate to your estimate for Step 4.

Learn Squares and Square Roots

Recall that you can use an exponent to show that a number has been multiplied by itself one or more times. You can write 7×7 as 7^2, or 7 *squared.*

A **perfect square** is the square of a whole number. The number 16 is a perfect square because $16 = 4^2$. The number 29 is not a perfect square because there is no whole number that can be squared to get 29.

You know that 36 is the square of 6 because $6^2 = 36$.

You can also say that 6 is the **square root** of 36. The square root of a number is the length of the side of a square with an area equal to the number.

6 | 36

MEETING INDIVIDUAL NEEDS

Resources

- **5-6** Practice
- **5-6** Reteaching
- **5-6** Problem Solving
- **5-6** Enrichment
- **5-6** Daily Transparency
  - Problem of the Day
  - Review
  - Quick Quiz
- Teaching Tool Transparencies 9, 22
- Technology Master 22

Learning Modalities

Verbal Have students write a paragraph describing the distinction between perfect square numbers and numbers that are not perfect squares. Then have them explain why this distinction is useful in finding square roots.

Visual Have students make a large poster showing the various squares on a grid with the area clearly marked in the center of each square, along with the side length labeled on one side.

English Language Development

Discuss with students that the square of a whole number is called a perfect square. Some students may not understand how a number can be called square. Remind them that squaring a number means the same as multiplying the number by itself, just as we do when we find the area of a square.

1 Introduce

Explore

You may wish to use Teaching Tool Transparency 9: Isometric Dot Paper with **Explore**.

The Point

Students understand the relationship between the area of a square and the length of its side.

Ongoing Assessment

Some students may have trouble with Step 2. Remind them that the base of the square does not have to be horizontal.

For Groups That Finish Early

Make other squares on the geoboard and estimate the side lengths.

Use a **radical sign**, $\sqrt{\ }$, to write a square root.

Example 1

A square chessboard has an area of 144 square inches. How long is each side of the board?

Look for a number that equals 144 when it is squared.

$12^2 = 144$. So $\sqrt{144} = 12$.

Each side of the chessboard is 12 inches long.

▶ **Language Link**

The word *radical* comes from the Latin word *radix*, which means "root." The word *radish* comes from the same Latin word.

Try It

Find each square root.

a. $\sqrt{81}$ 9 **b.** $\sqrt{121}$ 11 **c.** $\sqrt{225}$ 15 **d.** $\sqrt{10{,}000}$ 100 **e.** $\sqrt{64}$ 8

You can use a calculator to find square roots.

Examples

2 Find $\sqrt{1024}$.

Enter 1024 $\boxed{\sqrt{x}}$

$\sqrt{1024} = 32$

3 Find $\sqrt{33}$.

Enter 33 $\boxed{\sqrt{x}}$

$\sqrt{33} \approx 5.7445626$

$\sqrt{33} \approx 5.74$ Round to 2 decimal places.

Try It

Find each square root. Round to 2 decimal places.

a. $\sqrt{85}$ 9.22 **b.** $\sqrt{41}$ 6.40 **c.** $\sqrt{73}$ 8.54 **d.** $\sqrt{90}$ 9.49 **e.** $\sqrt{300}$ 17.32

Study TIP

You will find it very useful to learn the squares of the first 20 whole numbers.

Check Your Understanding

1. If you know the area of a square, how can you find the length of a side?

2. Give two consecutive whole numbers that have $\sqrt{29}$ between them. Explain how you chose the numbers.

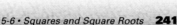

MATH EVERY DAY

▶ **Problem of the Day**

A photo is enlarged so that each side of the new photo doubles that of the original photo. The area of the new photo is how many times as large as the area of the original photo? 4 times as large

Available on Daily Transparency 5-6

An Extension is provided in the transparency package.

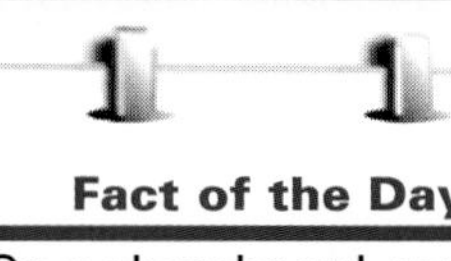

Fact of the Day

On a chessboard, rows of squares running across the board are called *ranks*, and rows running up and down are called *files*.

Estimation

Estimate.

1. 16,789 − 8,588 8000
2. 899 − 312 600
3. 89,115 − 53,025 40,000
4. 234,100 − 109,112 100,000

Follow Up

Have students discuss in their own words how they think they might find the area of a square if the square is too big to fit on a geoboard.

Answers for Explore

1. 2, 3, 4
2. Because it is made up of four half-squares.
3. Because all four sides are the same length and the corners are right angles.
4. $\approx 1\frac{1}{2}$; I compared it with the distance between the pegs.
5. The side is a little bit less than 3.

2 Teach

Learn

You may wish to use Teaching Tool Transparency 22: Scientific Calculator with **Learn**.

Alternate Examples

1. A square pool has an area of 121 square meters. How long is each side of the pool?

   Look for a number that equals 121 when squared. $11^2 = 121$. So $\sqrt{121} = 11$.

   Each side is 11 meters long.

2. Find $\sqrt{1600}$.

   Enter 1600 $\boxed{\sqrt{x}}$.

   $\sqrt{1600} = 40$

3. Find $\sqrt{52}$.

   Enter 52 $\boxed{\sqrt{x}}$.

   $\sqrt{52} \approx 7.2111026$

   Round to 2 decimal places.

   $\sqrt{52} \approx 7.21$

3 Practice and Assess

Check

Allow students to make a table of perfect squares to use until they have memorized the squares of the first 20 numbers.

Answers for Check Your Understanding

1. By finding the square root of the area.
2. 5 and 6; $5^2 = 25$ and $6^2 = 36$ and $25 < 29 < 36$, so $\sqrt{25} < \sqrt{29} < \sqrt{36}$.

Assignment Guide

- **Basic**
  1–39 odds, 40–42, 45–57 odds
- **Average**
  2–38 evens, 40–43, 44–56 evens
- **Enriched**
  6–40 evens, 41–43, 44–56 evens

Exercise Notes

Exercise 36

Sports Point out that, in general, a diamond shape is a rhombus, requiring only that it have 4 congruent sides. However, a softball or baseball diamond also has 4 right angles, making it a square.

Exercise 39

Fine Arts The Louvre Museum is the home of the *Mona Lisa*, probably the most famous painting in the world. Most people are surprised when they see that the painting is fairly small, about 77 cm by 53 cm.

Exercise 41

Test Prep If students selected C, they simply divided 267 by 2 and got 133.5.

5-6 Exercises and Applications

Practice and Apply

Getting Started **Give the value of each expression.**

1. 4^2 16 **2.** 11^2 121 **3.** 25^2 625 **4.** 30^2 900 **5.** 9^2 81

6. $(0.9)^2$ 0.81 **7.** $(0.11)^2$ 0.0121 **8.** $\left(\frac{1}{2}\right)^2$ $\frac{1}{4}$ **9.** $\left(\frac{3}{8}\right)^2$ $\frac{9}{64}$ **10.** $\left(\frac{2}{3}\right)^2$ $\frac{4}{9}$

Determine if each number is a perfect square.

11. 4 Yes **12.** 12 No **13.** 16 Yes **14.** 49 Yes **15.** 164 No

Find each square root.

16. $\sqrt{289}$ 17 **17.** $\sqrt{100}$ 10 **18.** $\sqrt{169}$ 13 **19.** $\sqrt{81}$ 9 **20.** $\sqrt{900}$ 30

21. $\sqrt{225}$ 15 **22.** $\sqrt{121}$ 11 **23.** $\sqrt{10{,}000}$ 100 **24.** $\sqrt{144}$ 12 **25.** $\sqrt{625}$ 25

Use a calculator to find each square root. Round the answer to two decimal places.

26. $\sqrt{175}$ 13.23 **27.** $\sqrt{544}$ 23.32 **28.** $\sqrt{1264}$ 35.55 **29.** $\sqrt{731}$ 27.04 **30.** $\sqrt{125}$ 11.18

31. $\sqrt{98}$ 9.90 **32.** $\sqrt{105}$ 10.25 **33.** $\sqrt{57}$ 7.55 **34.** $\sqrt{1572}$ 39.65 **35.** $\sqrt{12}$ 3.46

36. Measurement A softball diamond has an area of 3600 ft². How long is each side of the diamond? 60 ft

37. Number Sense What counting number is the same as its square root? 1

38. Measurement The area of the four-square court is 100 ft². What is the length of a side of the court? 10 ft

39. Architecture Architect I. M. Pei designed a pyramid-shaped addition for the Louvre museum in Paris. The square base of the structure covers about 13,225 ft². What is the approximate length of each side? ≈ 115 ft

Reteaching

Activity

Materials: Index cards, scientific calculator

- Work with a partner to make a set of cards, each with a perfect square written on the card.
- Take turns showing each other a card. The other person must then name the square root of the number on the card.
- At first, you may use a calculator if necessary, but eventually try to memorize as many square roots as possible. This will make exercises involving square roots easier for you in the future.

PRACTICE

Name ________________

Practice 5-6

Squares and Square Roots

Determine if each number is a perfect square.

1. 90 No 2. 225 Yes 3. 49 Yes 4. 28 No
5. 289 Yes 6. 144 Yes 7. 240 No 8. 1000 No

Find each square root.

9. $\sqrt{196}$ 14 10. $\sqrt{4}$ 2 11. $\sqrt{289}$ 17 12. $\sqrt{16}$ 4
13. $\sqrt{361}$ 19 14. $\sqrt{64}$ 8 15. $\sqrt{1}$ 1 16. $\sqrt{25}$ 5
17. $\sqrt{9}$ 3 18. $\sqrt{484}$ 22 19. $\sqrt{256}$ 16 20. $\sqrt{400}$ 20
21. $\sqrt{324}$ 18 22. $\sqrt{729}$ 27 23. $\sqrt{36}$ 6 24. $\sqrt{1296}$ 36
25. $\sqrt{1600}$ 40 26. $\sqrt{49}$ 7 27. $\sqrt{22{,}500}$ 150 28. $\sqrt{3025}$ 55

Use a calculator to find each square root. Round the answer to two decimal places.

29. $\sqrt{10}$ 3.16 30. $\sqrt{48}$ 6.93 31. $\sqrt{28}$ 5.29 32. $\sqrt{55}$ 7.42
33. $\sqrt{72}$ 8.49 34. $\sqrt{37}$ 6.08 35. $\sqrt{86}$ 9.27 36. $\sqrt{98}$ 9.90
37. $\sqrt{946}$ 30.76 38. $\sqrt{14}$ 3.74 39. $\sqrt{62}$ 7.87 40. $\sqrt{316}$ 17.78
41. $\sqrt{68}$ 8.25 42. $\sqrt{146}$ 12.08 43. $\sqrt{76}$ 8.72 44. $\sqrt{521}$ 22.83
45. $\sqrt{813}$ 28.51 46. $\sqrt{83}$ 9.11 47. $\sqrt{23}$ 4.80 48. $\sqrt{617}$ 24.84
49. $\sqrt{35}$ 5.92 50. $\sqrt{123}$ 11.09 51. $\sqrt{51}$ 7.14 52. $\sqrt{463}$ 21.52
53. $\sqrt{583}$ 24.15 54. $\sqrt{96}$ 9.80 55. $\sqrt{203}$ 14.25 56. $\sqrt{1200}$ 34.64
57. $\sqrt{278}$ 16.67 58. $\sqrt{43}$ 6.56 59. $\sqrt{401}$ 20.02 60. $\sqrt{328}$ 18.11
61. $\sqrt{1365}$ 36.95 62. $\sqrt{785}$ 28.02 63. $\sqrt{635}$ 25.20 64. $\sqrt{2424}$ 49.23

65. The largest pyramid in Egypt, built almost 5000 years ago, covers an area of about 63,300 yd². Find the length of each side of the square base. About 252 yd

66. Square floor tiles frequently have an area of 929 cm². Find the length of a side of one of these tiles. About 30 cm

RETEACHING

Name ________________

Alternative Lesson 5-6

Squares and Square Roots

You know that 9 × 9 = 81. The factors, 9 × 9, can also be written as 9^2, or 9 *squared.*

A **perfect square** is the square of a whole number. The number, 81, is a perfect square because it is the square of 9.

You can also say that 9 is the **square root** of 81. The square root of a number is the length of the side of a square with an area equal to the number.

The area of the square at the right is 81 square units. The length of a side is the square root of 81, or 9 units.

81

9

Use a **radical sign,** $\sqrt{}$, to write a square root: $\sqrt{81} = 9$.

Example 1

Determine if 64 and 75 are perfect squares.

Think: What number times itself equals 64?
8 × 8 = 64
So, 64 is a perfect square.

What number times itself equals 75?
8 × 8 = 64, 9 × 9 = 81. No whole number times itself equals 75.
So, 75 is *not* a perfect square.

Try It Determine if each number is a perfect square.

a. 24 No. b. 36 Yes. c. 49 Yes. d. 121 Yes.

Example 2

Find the square root of 16.

Think: What number times itself equals 16?

$4 \times 4 = 4^2 = 16$

So, $\sqrt{16} = 4$.

Try It Find each square root.

e. 9 = 3 × 3 Therefore $\sqrt{9}$ = 3
f. 25 = 5 × 5 Therefore $\sqrt{25}$ = 5
g. 4 = 2 × 2 Therefore $\sqrt{4}$ = 2
h. 100 = 10 × 10 Therefore $\sqrt{100}$ = 10
i. 400 = 20 × 20 Therefore $\sqrt{400}$ = 20
j. 2500 = 50 × 50 Therefore $\sqrt{2500}$ = 50

40. Schoolchildren in Ghana play the game of Achi on a board like the one shown. If the perimeter of an Achi board is 192 cm, what is its area? **2304 cm²**

GPS

41. **Test Prep** Between which consecutive whole numbers does $\sqrt{267}$ lie? **B**

Ⓐ 6 and 7 Ⓑ 16 and 17

Ⓒ 133 and 134 Ⓓ 265 and 266

Problem Solving and Reasoning

42. Communicate The scatterplot shows the relationship between the whole numbers from 0 to 100 and their square roots.

a. Use the scatterplot to find the square root of 49. Explain how you did this.

b. Use the scatterplot to estimate the square root of 10. Explain how you did this.

c. Use the scatterplot to estimate the square root of 56. Explain how you did this.

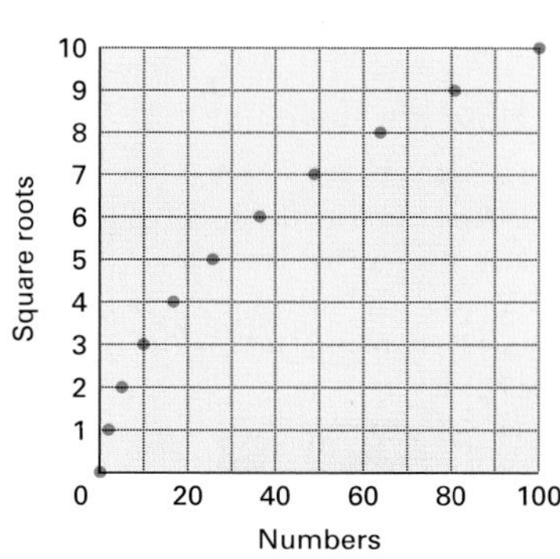

43. Critical Thinking Find two perfect squares that have a sum of 100. **36 and 64**

Mixed Review

Make a scatterplot for each set of data. *[Lesson 1-6]*

44.

x	2	3	4	5	6	7	8	9
y	3	5	4	6	7	5	8	4

45.

x	3.2	4.3	5.1	6.4	7.2	7.8	8.3	9.7
y	7.6	8.2	6.3	4.2	3.1	3.5	4.4	6.6

Find each sum or difference. Rewrite in lowest terms. *[Lesson 4-2]*

46. $\frac{2}{3}+\frac{5}{6}$ $1\frac{1}{2}$ **47.** $\frac{11}{12}-\frac{3}{4}$ $\frac{1}{6}$ **48.** $\frac{3}{5}+\frac{4}{7}$ $1\frac{6}{35}$ **49.** $\frac{21}{25}-\frac{4}{15}$ $\frac{43}{75}$

50. $\frac{5}{12}-\frac{1}{8}$ $\frac{7}{24}$ **51.** $\frac{7}{16}+\frac{23}{40}$ $1\frac{1}{80}$ **52.** $\frac{30}{49}-\frac{11}{28}$ $\frac{43}{196}$ **53.** $\frac{4}{7}+\frac{5}{13}$ $\frac{87}{91}$

54. $\frac{3}{4}+\frac{1}{12}$ $\frac{5}{6}$ **55.** $\frac{9}{20}-\frac{4}{15}$ $\frac{11}{60}$ **56.** $\frac{21}{50}+\frac{11}{18}$ $1\frac{7}{225}$ **57.** $\frac{99}{100}-\frac{9}{11}$ $\frac{189}{1100}$

PROBLEM SOLVING 5-6

PROBLEM SOLVING

Name ______ Guided Problem Solving 5-6

GPS PROBLEM 40, STUDENT PAGE 243

Schoolchildren in Ghana play the game of Achi on a board like the one shown. If the perimeter of an Achi board is 192 cm, what is its area?

Possible answers: Items 3, 4, 5, and 8

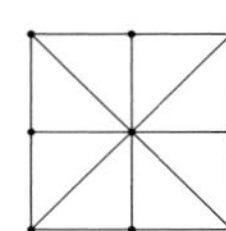

— Understand —

1. Underline the perimeter.
2. What polygon is the Achi board? Square

— Plan —

3. What is the formula to find the perimeter of this figure? $P = 4s$
4. How can you use the formula to find the length of one side? Divide the perimeter by 4.
5. How can you find the area once you know the length of one side? Multiply the length of the side by itself.

— Solve —

6. What is the length of one side? 48 cm
7. What is the area of the Achi board? 2304 cm²

— Look Back —

8. How can you work backward from your answer to find the perimeter? Multiply the square root of the area by 4.

SOLVE ANOTHER PROBLEM

Butch has a square checkerboard. If the perimeter of the checkerboard is 160 cm, what is the area?

1600 cm²

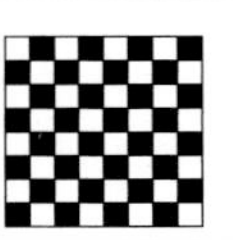

ENRICHMENT

Name ______ Extend Your Thinking 5-6

Visual Thinking

A diagonal connects two non-adjacent vertices of a polygon. Draw only the diagonals needed to divide each figure into the smaller figures given.

Possible answers given.

1. 2 equilateral triangles, 2 quadrilaterals

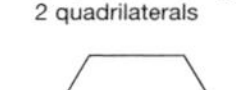

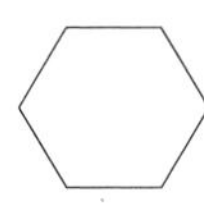

2. 2 right triangles, 2 isosceles triangles

3. 1 trapezoid, 1 isosceles triangle, 1 scalene triangle

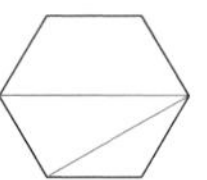

4. 3 isosceles triangles, 1 equilateral triangle

5. 1 pentagon, 1 isosceles triangle

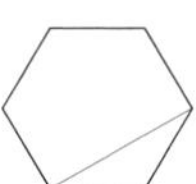

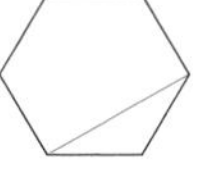

6. 1 quadrilateral, 2 isosceles triangles

7. 4 equilateral triangles, 4 right triangles

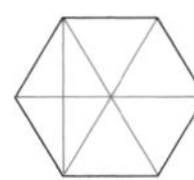

8. 2 squares, 4 right triangles

Exercise Answers

42. a. 7; I estimated the shape of the curve and judged where $\sqrt{49}$ would be.

b. $\sqrt{10}$ is a little bit more than 3. I estimated the shape of the curve and judged where $\sqrt{10}$ would be.

c. $\approx 7\frac{1}{2}$; I estimated the shape of the curve and judged where $\sqrt{56}$ would be.

44.

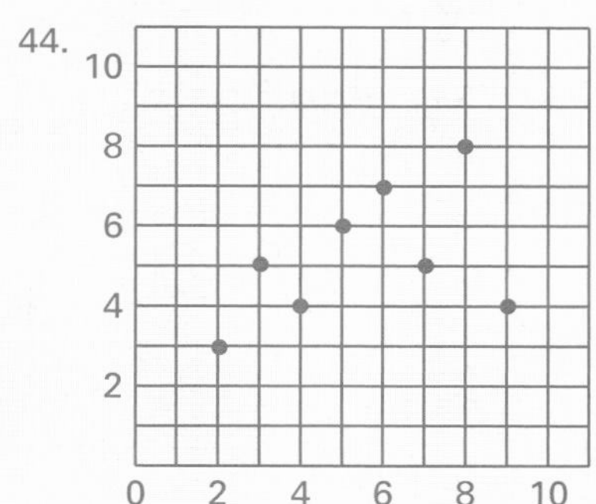

45.

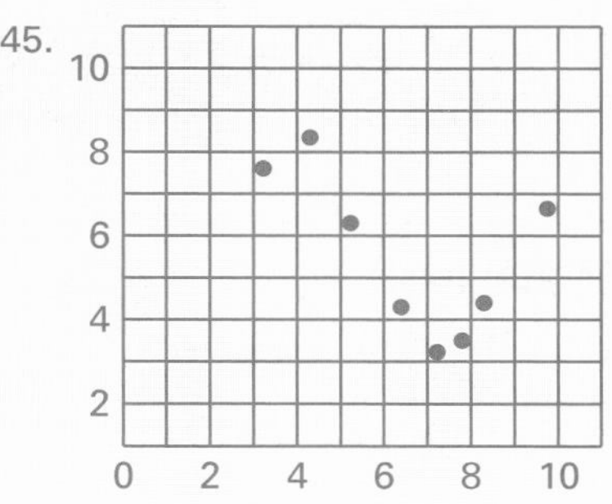

Alternate Assessment

You may want to use the *Interactive CD-ROM Journal* with this assessment.

Journal Have students write a paragraph explaining how to estimate the square root of a number that is not a perfect square, assuming that a calculator is not available. Students recognize that they must locate two perfect squares, one smaller and one larger than the given number. The estimate will be between the square roots of those two numbers.

Quick Quiz

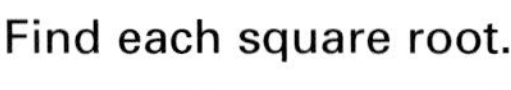

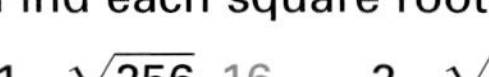

Find each square root.

1. $\sqrt{256}$ 16 2. $\sqrt{324}$ 18

Use a calculator to find each square root. Round the answer to 2 decimal places.

3. $\sqrt{150}$ 12.25 4. $\sqrt{89}$ 9.43

Available on Daily Transparency 5-6

INTERACTIVE LESSON

5-7 Lesson Organizer

Objectives

- Use the special relationship among the sides of a right triangle.
- Use the Pythagorean Theorem.

Materials

- Explore: Metric ruler, graph paper, calculator

Vocabulary

- Hypotenuse, leg

NCTM Standards

- 1–4, 12, 13

Review

Find $a^2 + b^2$ for the given values of a and b.

1. $a = 6$, $b = 8$ 100
2. $a = 5$, $b = 12$ 169
3. $a = 10$, $b = 15$ 325
4. $a = 10$, $b = 20$ 500

Available on Daily Transparency 5-7

1 Introduce

Explore

You may wish to use Teaching Tool Transparencies 7: $\frac{1}{4}$-Inch Graph Paper and 14: Rulers with **Explore**.

The Point
Students discover the Pythagorean relationship by measuring sides of triangles and then using the results to compute values for $a^2 + b^2$ and c^2.

Ongoing Assessment
For Step 3, some students may not get exactly the same values for $a^2 + b^2$ and c^2. Point out that they must be very careful in measuring the sides. Even with careful measurement, they will have to round the lengths to the nearest millimeter. So there may be slight variations between $a^2 + b^2$ and c^2.

5-7 The Pythagorean Theorem

You'll Learn ...

- to use the special relationship among the sides of a right triangle
- the Pythagorean Theorem

... How It's Used

Construction workers from the ancient Egyptians to the workers of today have used the Pythagorean Theorem to make the corners of their buildings square.

Vocabulary

hypotenuse

leg

► Lesson Link You've seen several types of triangles. Now you will see an important relationship among the lengths of the sides of a right triangle. ◄

Explore Side Lengths in Right Triangles

The Rights of Triangles

Materials: Metric ruler, Graph paper, Calculator

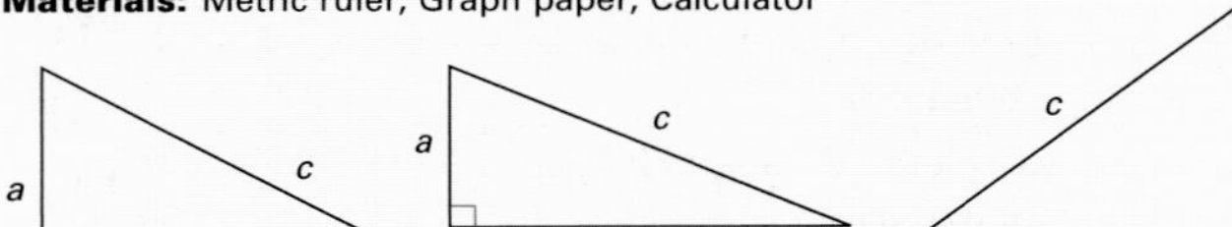

1. Begin a table like the one shown. Measure each triangle in millimeters and fill in the table. The first triangle is started for you.

a	b	c	$a^2 + b^2$	c^2
24	45	51	2601	

2. Describe any patterns you see in your table.
3. On your graph paper, draw a right triangle by using two perpendicular line segments of any length. Then connect the endpoints to form a triangle. Label the sides a, b, and c, using c for the longest side. Measure the sides and add the results to your table. Do your results match the pattern you saw in Step 2?
4. Now draw a triangle that is *not* a right triangle. Add its measurements to your table. Do the results match the pattern you saw in Step 2?

Learn The Pythagorean Theorem

The **hypotenuse** of a right triangle is the side opposite the right angle and is the longest side. The other two sides are called **legs**.

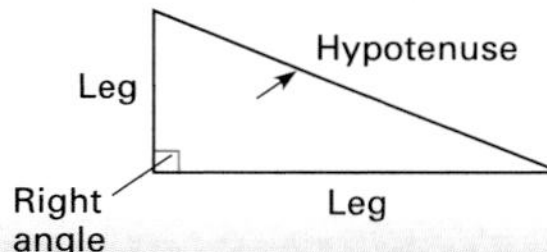

MEETING INDIVIDUAL NEEDS

Resources

5-7 Practice
5-7 Reteaching
5-7 Problem Solving
5-7 Enrichment
5-7 Daily Transparency
Problem of the Day
Review
Quick Quiz

Teaching Tool Transparencies 7, 14

Technology Master 23

Interactive CD-ROM Lesson

Wide World of Mathematics Middle School: Youthbuild

Learning Modalities

Kinesthetic Have students cut out the five pieces from square C and rearrange them to cover squares A and B. Point out that this shows that $a^2 + b^2 = c^2$.

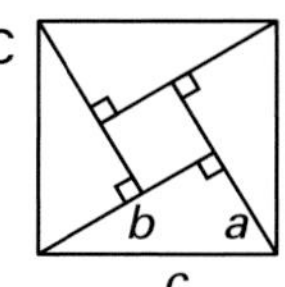

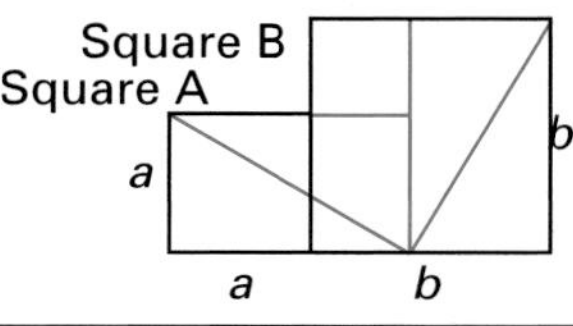

Visual Have students make a diagram showing a right triangle with a square drawn on each of the three sides, each square labeled with its area.

Inclusion

Encourage students to draw diagrams and use manipulatives that will help them apply the Pythagorean Theorem. Have them add new vocabulary to their reference book.

The triangle shown has legs that are 3 units and 4 units long and a hypotenuse 5 units long. Notice that $3^2 + 4^2 = 5^2$.

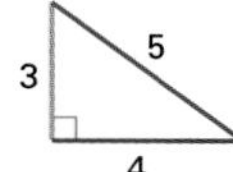

THE PYTHAGOREAN THEOREM

In a right triangle, the sum of the squares of the lengths of the legs is equal to the square of the length of the hypotenuse.

$a^2 + b^2 = c^2$

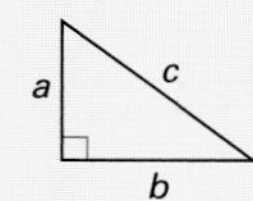

It is also true that if a triangle's side lengths satisfy $a^2 + b^2 = c^2$, then the triangle must be a right triangle.

Examples

1 Find the crosscourt distance on a tennis court.

$a^2 + b^2 = c^2$	Use the Pythagorean Theorem.
$36^2 + 78^2 = c^2$	Substitute 36 for a and 78 for b.
$1296 + 6084 = c^2$	Square 36 and 78.
$7380 = c^2$	Add.
$\sqrt{7380} = c \approx 86$	Find $\sqrt{7380}$ and round to the nearest whole number.

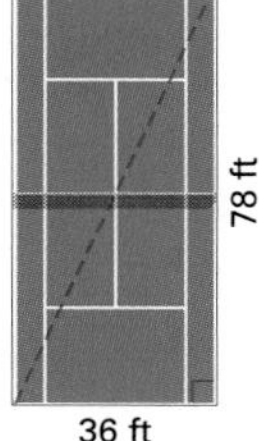

The crosscourt distance is about 86 ft.

2 Find the length of the shorter leg.

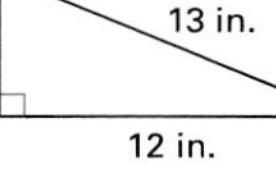

$a^2 + b^2 = c^2$	Use the Pythagorean Theorem.
$a^2 + 12^2 = 13^2$	Substitute 12 for b and 13 for c.
$a^2 + 144 = 169$	Square 12 and 13.
$a^2 + 144 - 144 = 169 - 144$	To undo adding 144, subtract 144 from both sides.
$a^2 = 25$	Subtract.
$a = \sqrt{25} = 5$ in.	Find $\sqrt{25}$.

Try It

Find the missing length in each right triangle.

a. $c = 25$ ft

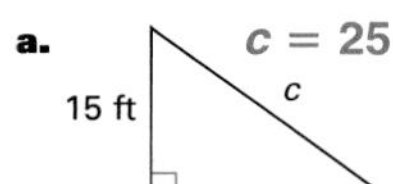

b. $b \approx 10.39$ ft

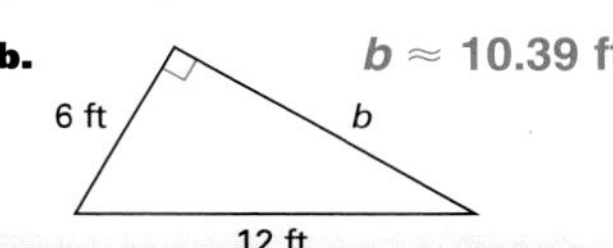

DID YOU KNOW?

Although we call the relationship between the legs and hypotenuse of a right triangle the Pythagorean Theorem, it was being used by builders for many centuries before Pythagoras was born.

Language Link

A set of three whole numbers that can form the sides of a right triangle is called a *Pythagorean triple.*

MATH EVERY DAY

Problem of the Day

Katerina saved \$300 when she bought four identical chairs on sale for \$2000. What was the original price of one chair? \$575

Available on Daily Transparency 5-7

An Extension is provided in the transparency package.

Fact of the Day

The principle behind the Pythagorean Theorem was known to some Chinese, Egyptians, and Babylonians before the Greek Pythagoras stated it.

Mental Math

Do these mentally.

1. 2.2×1000 2200
2. $0.5 \div 10$ 0.05
3. 8.95×100 895
4. $90.5 \div 1000$ 0.0905

For Groups That Finish Early

For the table in Step 1, multiply the values of a, b, and c by 2 and then find the values for $a^2 + b^2$ and c^2. Does the same pattern still hold? Yes

Follow Up

Have students write a paragraph describing what they discovered in **Explore**.

Answers for Explore

1.

a	b	c	$a^2 + b^2$	c^2
24	45	51	2601	2601
15	36	39	1521	1521
36	48	60	3600	3600

2. $a^2 + b^2 = c^2$
3. Yes
4. No

2 Teach

Learn

Alternate Examples

1. A rectangle is 80 feet long by 60 feet wide. What is the length of the diagonal?

   The diagonal and 2 sides of the rectangle form a right triangle with legs of 60 feet and 80 feet.

   Use the Pythagorean Theorem and substitute 80 for a and 60 for b.

   $a^2 + b^2 = c^2$

   $80^2 + 60^2 = c^2$

   $6400 + 3600 = c^2$

   $10{,}000 = c^2$

   $\sqrt{10000} = c = 100$

   The diagonal is 100 ft long.

2. Find the length of the longer leg.

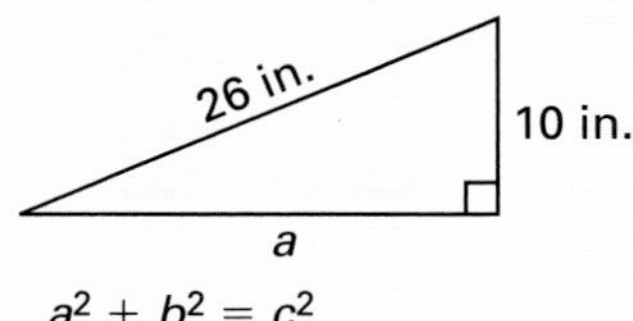

   $a^2 + b^2 = c^2$

   $a^2 + 10^2 = 26^2$

   $a^2 + 100 = 676$

   $a^2 = 576$

   $a = \sqrt{576} = 24$

   The longer leg is 24 in. long.

5-7 Exercises and Applications

Assignment Guide

- Basic
  1–17, 19–20, 23–31 odds
- Average
  3–21, 23–24, 26-32 evens
- Enriched
  5–7, 9–32

3 Practice and Assess

Check

Answers for Check Your Understanding

1. Calculate $a^2 + b^2$ and c^2. If these quantities are equal, the triangle is a right triangle.
2. No; Because the right angle is always the largest angle in a right triangle, so the side opposite it (the hypotenuse) must always be the longest side.

Exercise Answers

1. Hypotenuse *r*; legs *p* and *q*.
2. Hypotenuse *g*; legs *e* and *f*.
3. Hypotenuse *s*; legs *t* and *u*.
4. Hypotenuse *d*; legs *b* and *c*.

Reteaching

Activity

Materials: Graph paper

- Draw a right triangle on a sheet of graph paper. Then draw squares on each leg of the triangle and label the area of each square as shown below.

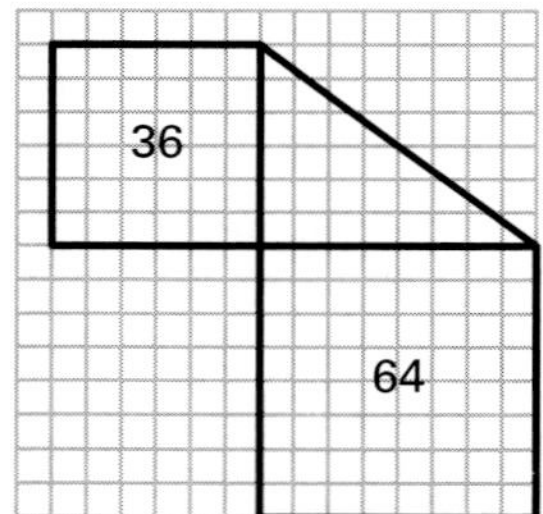

- Add the two areas to find the area of the square that would fit on the hypotenuse. For the figure above, the area would be 100. Make a square of that size and lay it on the hypotenuse to show that it does fit.
- Repeat for two other right triangles.

Check Your Understanding

1. How can you use the side lengths of a triangle to decide if it is a right triangle?
2. Can a leg of a right triangle ever be longer than the hypotenuse? Explain.

5-7 Exercises and Applications

PRACTICE 5-7

Practice and Apply

Getting Started Name the hypotenuse and legs of each triangle.

1. 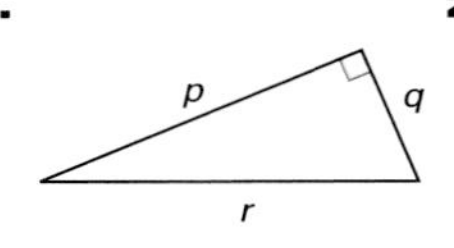

2. 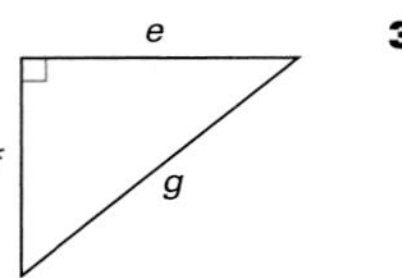

3.

4. 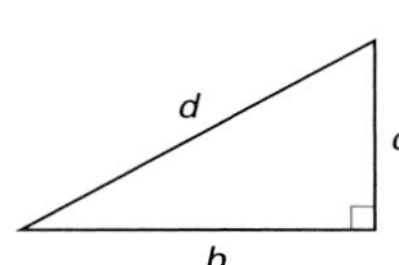

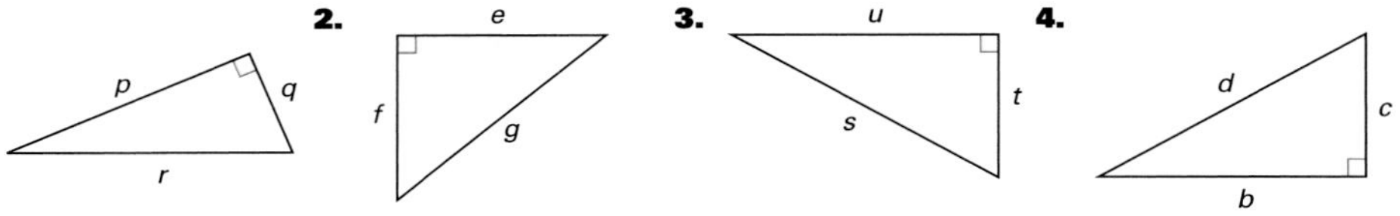

Use the Pythagorean Theorem to write an equation expressing the relationship between the legs and the hypotenuse for each triangle.

5. 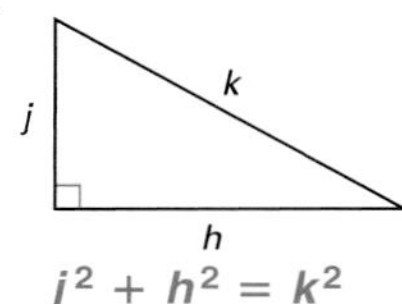

$j^2 + h^2 = k^2$

6. 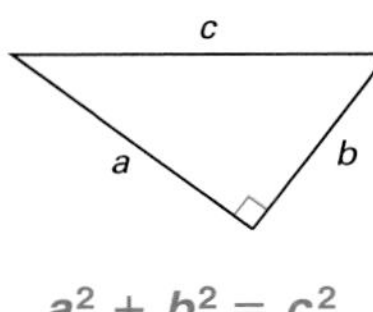

$a^2 + b^2 = c^2$

7. 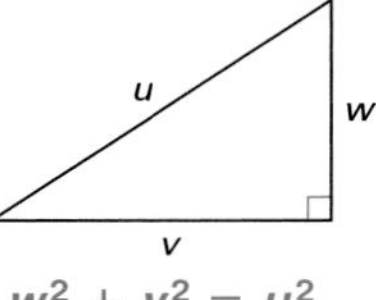

$w^2 + v^2 = u^2$

8. 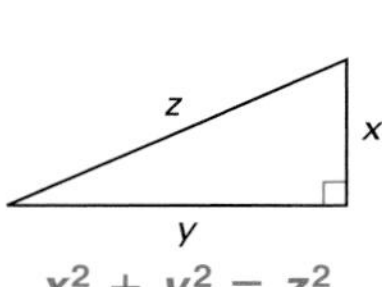

$x^2 + y^2 = z^2$

Determine if each triangle is a right triangle.

9. Yes 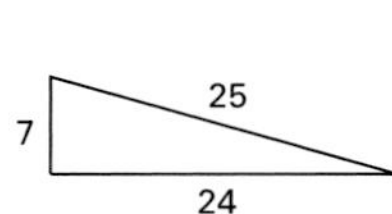

10. No 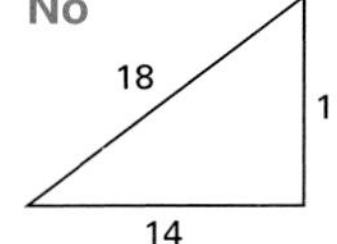

11. No 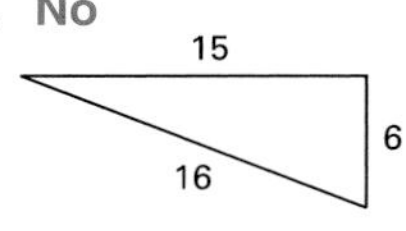

12. Yes 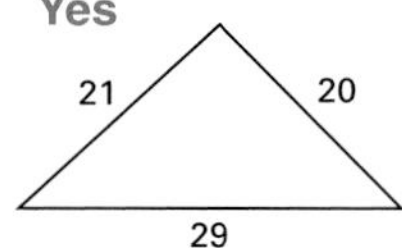

Find the missing length in each right triangle.

13. $a = 9$ in. 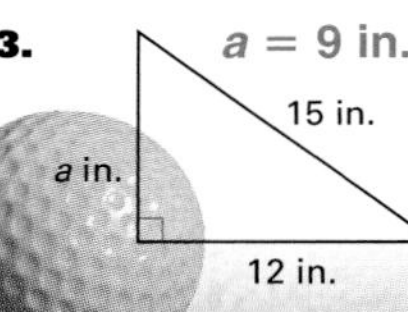

14. $x = 16$ m 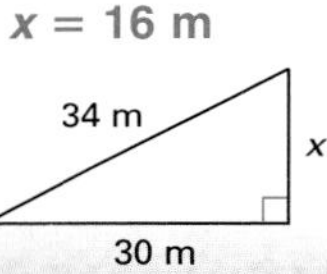

15. $y = 35$ cm 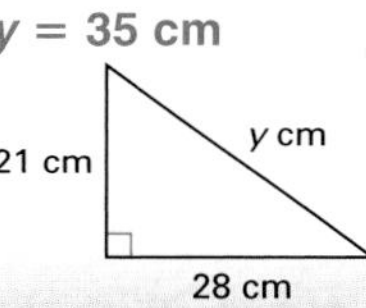

16. $n = 24$ ft 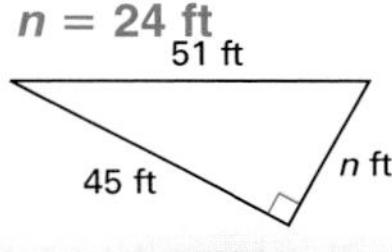

PRACTICE

Name ____________________

Practice 5-7

The Pythagorean Theorem

Use the Pythagorean Theorem to write an equation expressing the relationship between the legs and the hypotenuse for each triangle.

1. $g^2 + h^2 = f^2$ 2. $x^2 + z^2 = y^2$ 3. $u^2 + v^2 = w^2$

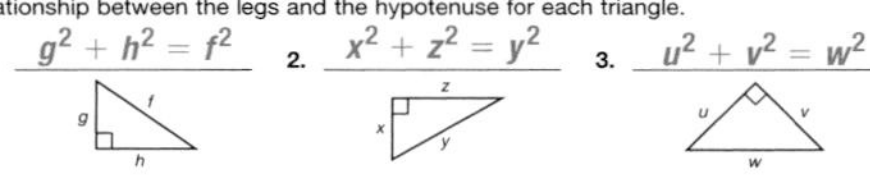

Determine if each triangle is a right triangle.

4. Yes 5. No 6. Yes

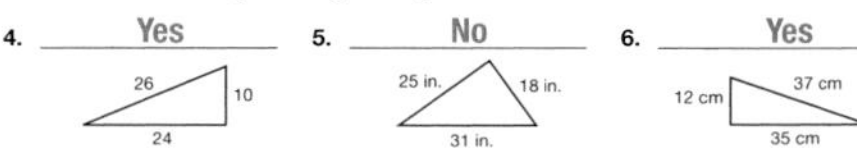

Find the missing length in each right triangle.

7. $t =$ 8 8. $d =$ 53 m 9. $m =$ 56 in.

10. $x =$ 21 yd 11. $u =$ 41 cm 12. $r =$ 55 ft

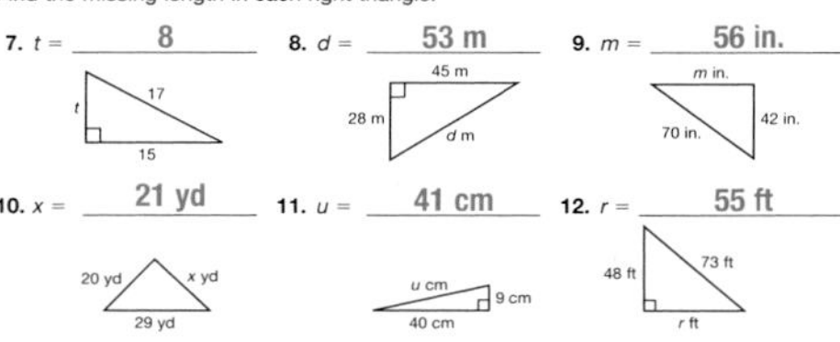

13. **Geography** The state of Colorado is shaped like a rectangle, with a base measuring about 385 mi and a height of about 275 mi. About how far is it from the northwest corner to the southeast corner of Colorado? About 473 mi

14. A drawing tool is shaped like a right triangle. One leg measures about 14.48 cm, and the hypotenuse measures 20.48 cm. What is the length of the other leg? Round your answer to the nearest hundredth of a centimeter. 14.48 cm

15. An 8-foot ladder is leaned against a high wall from 4 feet away. How high up the wall does the ladder reach? Round your answer to the nearest tenth of a foot. 6.9 ft

RETEACHING

Name ____________________

Alternative Lesson 5-7

The Pythagorean Theorem

The **hypotenuse** of a right triangle is the side opposite the right angle and is the longest side. The other two sides are called **legs.** In the triangle at the right, sides *a* and *b* are the legs. Side *c* is the hypotenuse.

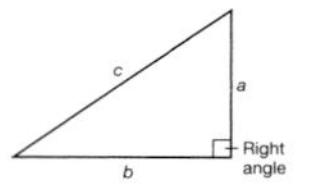

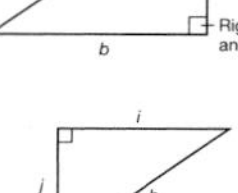

The **Pythagorean Theorem** states that the sum of the squares of the lengths of the legs of a right triangle is equal to the square of the length of the hypotenuse. This can be written algebraically as $a^2 + b^2 = c^2$.

Example 1

Name the hypotenuse and legs of the right triangle.

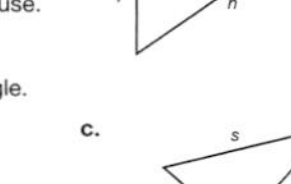

Side *h* is opposite the right angle, so it is the hypotenuse.

Sides *i* and *j* are the legs.

Try It Name the hypotenuse and legs of each triangle.

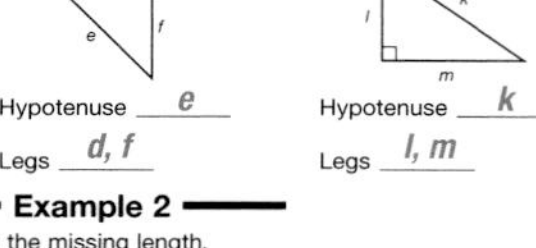

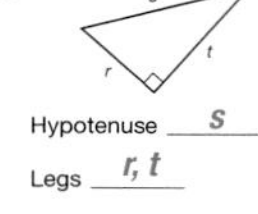

a. Hypotenuse *e*; Legs *d, f*

b. Hypotenuse *k*; Legs *l, m*

c. Hypotenuse *s*; Legs *r, t*

Example 2

Find the missing length.

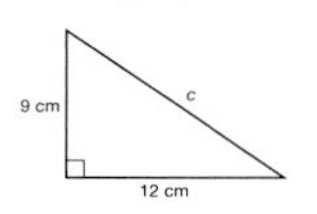

Use the Pythagorean Theorem to find the length of side *c*.	$a^2 + b^2 = c^2$
Substitute 9 for *a* and 12 for *b*.	$9^2 + 12^2 = c^2$
Square 9 and 12.	$81 + 144 = c^2$
Add.	$225 = c^2$
Find $\sqrt{225}$.	$15 = c$

The length of the hypotenuse is 15 cm.

Try It Find the missing length in each right triangle.

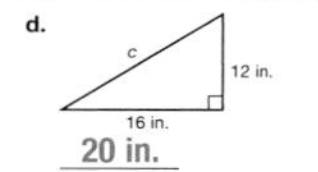

d. 20 in. e. 13 cm f. 10 in.

17. **Measurement** The runner is trying to steal second base. The catcher makes a perfect throw from home plate to second base. The runner is out! How far was the throw from home plate to second base? ≈ 127.3 ft

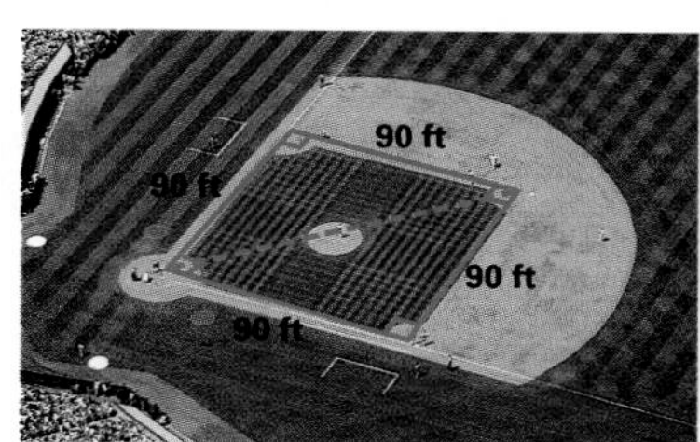

18. **Science** Engineers who build bridges often use truss construction. The basic unit of a truss is a triangle. A king post is often used to strengthen a truss. What is the length of the king post shown in the diagram? ≈ 26 ft

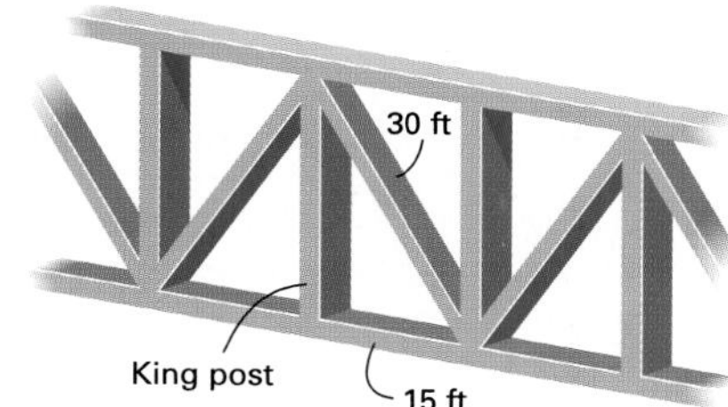

19. **Test Prep** In triangle ABC, $\overline{AB}$ measures 5 cm, $\overline{BC}$ measures 5 cm, and $\overline{CA}$ measures about 7.07 cm. Which of these best describes triangle ABC? C

Ⓐ Right triangle
Ⓑ Scalene triangle
Ⓒ Isosceles right triangle
Ⓓ Scalene right triangle

PROBLEM SOLVING 5-7

Problem Solving and Reasoning

20. **Choose a Strategy** An 8 ft ladder leans against a building with the base of the ladder 3 ft from the building. How high is the point where the ladder touches the building? ≈ 7.42 ft

GPS

Problem Solving STRATEGIES

- Look for a Pattern
- Make an Organized List
- Make a Table
- Guess and Check
- Work Backward
- Use Logical Reasoning
- Draw a Diagram
- Solve a Simpler Problem

21. **Communicate** Would you expect to get another right triangle by adding 1 to the length of each side of a right triangle? By doubling each side? Explain.

22. **Critical Thinking** A square diving pool has sides 30 ft long. Would a 45 ft length of rope be long enough to reach diagonally across the pool? Yes; the diagonal is ≈ 42.43 ft.

Mixed Review

Draw a scatterplot and a trend line for each set of data. *[Lesson 1-7]*

23.

x	8	6	3	8	5	4	3	7
y	3	4	6	4	5	6	5	3

24.

x	7.2	4.7	7.6	3.2	9.3	6.4	2.3	5.8
y	6.5	5.7	5.2	6.3	5.4	6.1	5.7	6.0

Find each sum or difference. *[Lesson 4-3]*

25. $12\frac{7}{12} + 7\frac{9}{16}$ $20\frac{7}{48}$
26. $7\frac{3}{8} - 3\frac{1}{5}$ $4\frac{7}{40}$
27. $8\frac{5}{7} + 13\frac{4}{5}$ $22\frac{18}{35}$
28. $4\frac{7}{18} - 1\frac{41}{66}$ $2\frac{76}{99}$
29. $7\frac{3}{10} - 3\frac{4}{7}$ $3\frac{51}{70}$
30. $18\frac{1}{2} + 31\frac{7}{8}$ $50\frac{3}{8}$
31. $53\frac{5}{7} - 17\frac{2}{3}$ $36\frac{1}{21}$
32. $63\frac{1}{6} + 54\frac{2}{3}$ $117\frac{5}{6}$

PROBLEM SOLVING

Name ______________________

Guided Problem Solving 5-7

GPS PROBLEM 20, STUDENT PAGE 247

An 8 ft ladder leans against a building with the base of the ladder 3 ft from the building. How high is the point where the ladder touches the building?

— Understand —

1. Underline the question.
2. Circle the information you need.

— Plan —

3. Which of the following strategies could you use to find the height? b

a. Make a List b. Draw a Diagram c. Use a Table

4. Use the strategy you chose in Item 3 to show the information in the problem.
Possible answer:

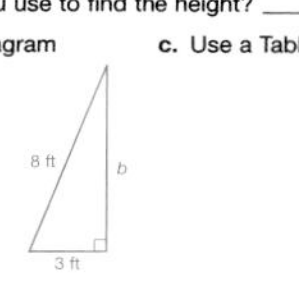

5. What figure is formed by the building, the ladder, and the ground? Right triangle.

6. What formula will you use to find the height?
The Pythagorean Theorem; $a^2 + b^2 = c^2$

7. Rewrite the formula substituting the values you know. $3^2 + b^2 = 8^2$

— Solve —

8. Solve your equation to find the height of the point where the ladder touches the building. Round your answer to the nearest hundredth. 7.42 ft

— Look Back —

9. How could you use the strategy, Solve a Simpler Problem to find the height? Possible answer: Use numbers that are perfect squares.

SOLVE ANOTHER PROBLEM

A 13 ft ladder leans against a building with the base of the ladder 5 ft from the building. How high is the point where the ladder touches the building? 12 ft

ENRICHMENT

Name ______________________

Extend Your Thinking 5-7

Critical Thinking

Some right triangles have special properties. Use the Pythagorean Theorem to find the missing leg in each triangle below. Use your calculator and round all your answers to the nearest tenth.

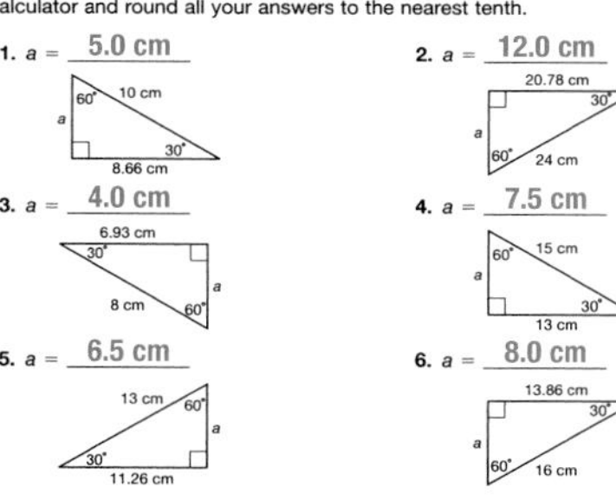

1. $a =$ 5.0 cm
2. $a =$ 12.0 cm
3. $a =$ 4.0 cm
4. $a =$ 7.5 cm
5. $a =$ 6.5 cm
6. $a =$ 8.0 cm

7. What do you notice about the length of the hypotenuse in each triangle above and the length of one of the sides? Possible answer: The side opposite the 30° angle is one half the length of the hypotenuse.

Use your observation to give the length of the side in the triangles below.

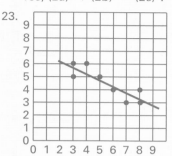

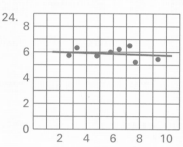

8. $a =$ 2.0 cm
3.46 cm, 30°, a, 4 cm, 60°

9. $a =$ 3.0 cm
60°, 6 cm, a, 30°, 5.2 cm

10. $a =$ 2.5 cm

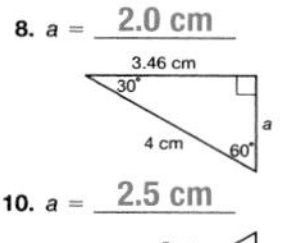

11. $a =$ 4.5 cm

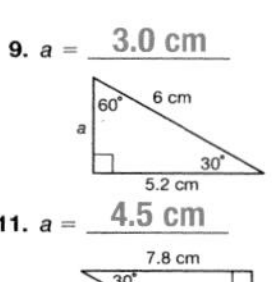

Exercise Notes

Exercise 17

Sports Remind students that a baseball diamond is a square, so when the diagonal is drawn from home plate to second base, the result is two right triangles.

Exercise Answers

21. No; If $a^2 + b^2 = c^2$, then $(a + 1)^2 + (b + 1)^2 \neq (c + 1)^2$; Yes; $(2a)^2 + (2b)^2 = (2c)^2$.

23.

24.

Alternate Assessment

Portfolio Have students pick one of the exercises from this lesson that best illustrates the use of the Pythagorean Theorem and include it in their portfolio.

Quick Quiz

1. Is this a right triangle?

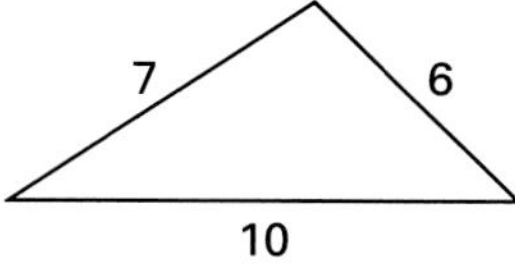

No

2. Find the missing length in this right triangle.

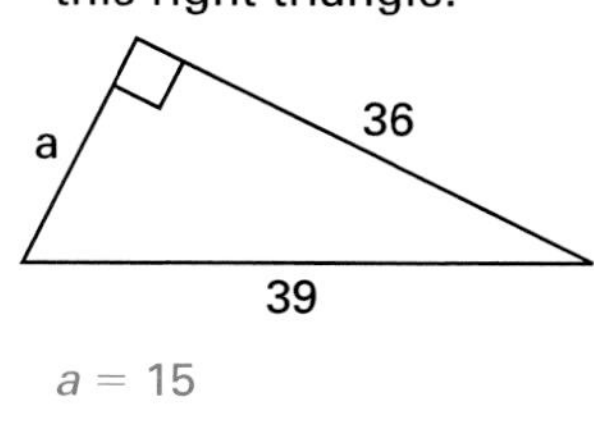

$a = 15$

Available on Daily Transparency 5-7

5-8 Lesson Organizer

Objective

- Find the area of a triangle.

Materials

- Explore: Graph paper, scissors

NCTM Standards

- 1, 2, 4, 12, 13

Review

Evaluate each expression.

1. $\frac{1}{2} \cdot 8 \cdot 10$ 40
2. $\frac{1}{2} \cdot 40 \cdot 50$ 1000
3. $\frac{1}{2} \cdot 25 \cdot 35$ 437.5

Solve each equation.

4. $60 = \frac{1}{2} \cdot b \cdot 20$ $b = 6$
5. $49.5 = \frac{1}{2} \cdot 9 \cdot h$ $h = 11$

Available on Daily Transparency 5-8

Lesson Link

Be sure students know the formula for finding the area of a rectangle. Have them discuss the meaning of the three variables.

1 Introduce

Explore

You may wish to use Teaching Tool Transparency 7: $\frac{1}{4}$-Inch Graph Paper with **Explore**.

The Point

Students understand how the formula for the area of a triangle can be derived from the formula for the area of a rectangle.

Ongoing Assessment

In Step 2, ask students how many smaller rectangles are formed when they draw the perpendicular segment. 2 Then ask them to name the area of each smaller rectangle. Answers will vary. Finally, have them find the area of each smaller triangle that is formed. Answers will vary.

5-8 Areas of Triangles

You'll Learn ...

- to find the area of a triangle

... How It's Used

Installers of siding need to be able to calculate triangular areas to make a reasonable estimate for a job.

Lesson Link You know the formula for the area of a rectangle. Now you'll relate that formula to the formula for the area of a triangle. ◄

Explore Triangles

Wreck a Rectangle

Materials: Graph paper, Scissors

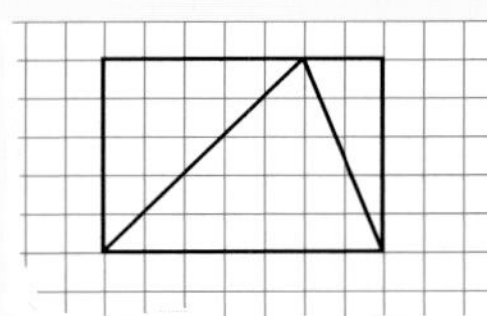

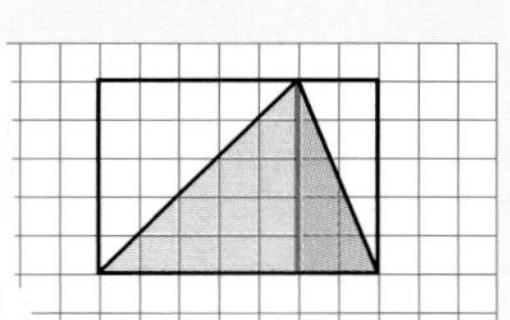

1. Draw a rectangle with any length and width on graph paper. Inside, draw a triangle as shown.
2. Draw a second rectangle and triangle exactly like the first. Draw a perpendicular line from a vertex of the triangle to the opposite base.

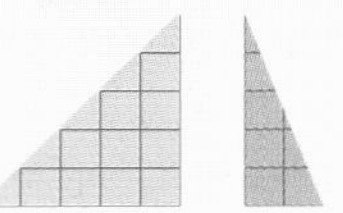

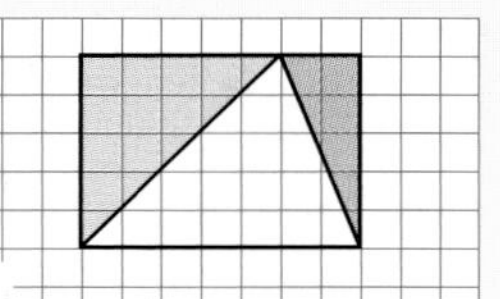

3. Cut out the second triangle. Then cut it into two pieces along the perpendicular line.
4. Return to the first rectangle. Fit the two new triangles onto the parts of the rectangle that are *not* contained in the first triangle.
5. How does the area of the triangle you drew in Step 1 compare with the area of the rectangle? Explain.
6. Draw a different rectangle and repeat Steps 1–5. Describe your results.

MEETING INDIVIDUAL NEEDS

Resources

- **5-8** Practice
- **5-8** Reteaching
- **5-8** Problem Solving
- **5-8** Enrichment
- **5-8** Daily Transparency
  - Problem of the Day
  - Review
  - Quick Quiz
- Teaching Tool Transparencies 7, 19
- Lesson Enhancement Transparencies 24, 25
- Technology Master 24

Learning Modalities

Kinesthetic Have students use index cards to cut out various triangles having the same base and height. Stress that the triangles have the same area even though they have different shapes.

Verbal Have students write a paragraph describing how they would go about finding the area of a triangular lot that needs to be covered with sod.

English Language Development

Point out that in finding area we multiply numbers (lengths), but these lengths are determined by measuring line segments. Frequently, we talk about multiplying the base by the height, but we really mean we are multiplying the lengths of the base and height.

Learn Areas of Triangles

The *height* (h) of a triangle is the line segment drawn perpendicular to the *base* (b) from the vertex opposite the base. The length of that segment is also called the height.

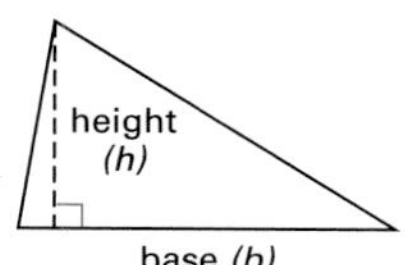

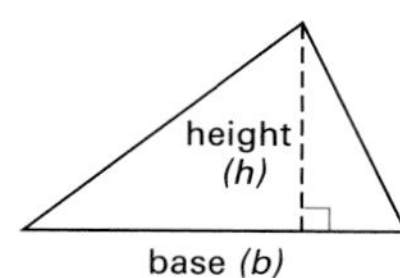

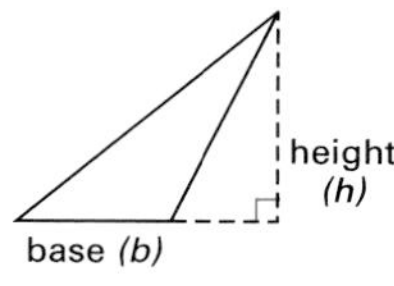

Notice that a height of an obtuse triangle may be outside the triangle.

Remember

An obtuse angle is between 90° and 180°. [Page 213]

AREA OF A TRIANGLE

The area of a triangle is half the product of the lengths of the base and the height.

$A = \frac{1}{2}bh$

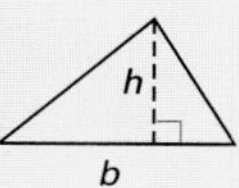

MENTAL MATH

When you calculate the area of a triangle, see if the base or height is an even number. If so, you can save time by first dividing the even number by 2.

Examples

1 Find the area of the shaded portion of the "Sixteen Soldiers" game board shown at right. The base of the shaded triangle is 12 cm and the height is 9 cm.

$A = \frac{1}{2}bh$ Use the formula for area of a triangle.

$= \frac{1}{2} \cdot 12 \cdot 9$ Substitute 12 for b and 9 for h.

$= 54$ Multiply.

The area of the shaded portion is 54 cm^2.

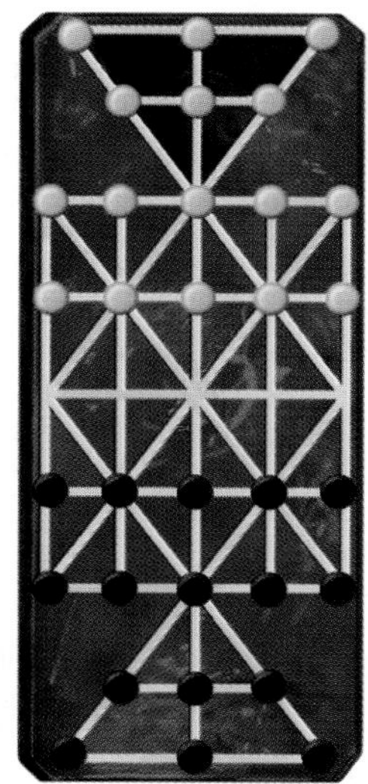

2 Find the area of the triangle.

$A = \frac{1}{2}bh$

$= \frac{1}{2} \cdot 8 \cdot 3$

$= 12$

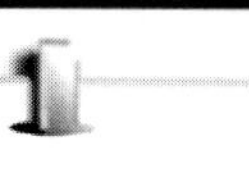

The area is 12 cm^2.

MATH EVERY DAY

Problem of the Day

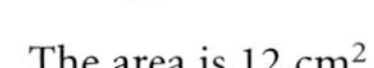

Of the 115 students enrolled in Medora Middle School, three times as many students have brown hair as have blonde hair. The other fifteen students have red hair. Make a bar graph that shows this data.

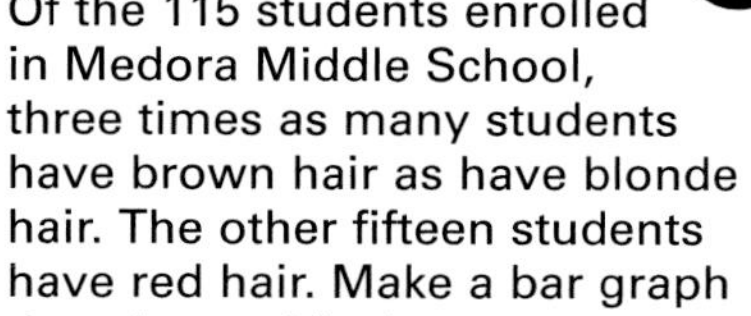

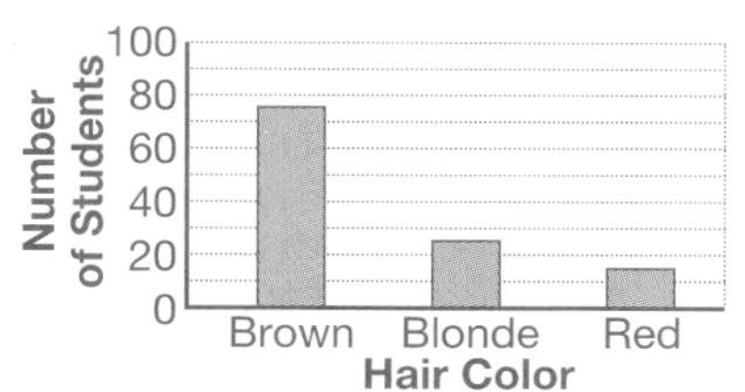

Available on Daily Transparency 5-8

An Extension is provided in the transparency package.

Fact of the Day

The Great Pyramid of Khufu contains more than 2 million stone blocks, with an average weight of 2.3 metric tons each.

Estimation

Estimate.

1. 1.8)29.5 15
2. 3.75)99.2 25
3. 0.98)4.98 5
4. 4.17)48.12 12

For Groups That Finish Early

Repeat Steps 1–5 by using a rectangle in which the height is larger than the base. Does this affect the outcome? No.

Follow Up

Have students discuss how the activity they just completed would be useful in finding the area of a triangle if they know the base and height of the triangle.

Answers for Explore

5. It is half the area; The two triangles exactly cover the rectangle.
6. It doesn't matter what size the triangle and rectangle are, the relationship stays the same.

2 Teach

Learn

You may want to use Lesson Enhancement Transparencies 24 and 25 with **Learn**.

You may want to use Teaching Tool Transparency 19: Tangram with **Example 3**.

Alternate Examples

1. Find the area of the shaded portion of the window.

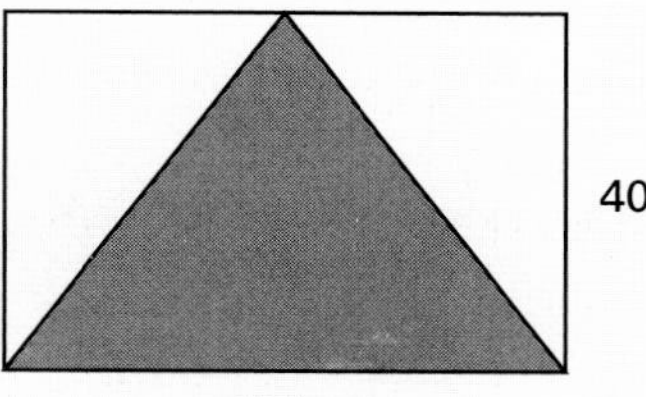

$A = \frac{1}{2}bh$

$= \frac{1}{2} \cdot 60 \cdot 40$

$= 1200$

The area is 1200 in^2.

2. Find the area of the triangle.

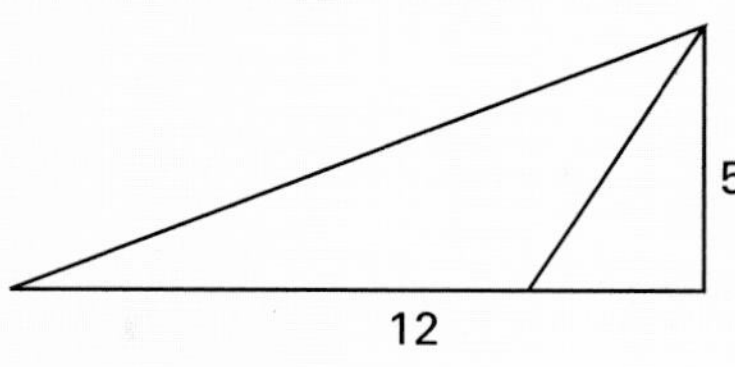

$A = \frac{1}{2}bh$

$= \frac{1}{2} \cdot 12 \cdot 5$

$= 30$

The area is 30 square units.

Alternate Examples

3. Find the area of the triangle.

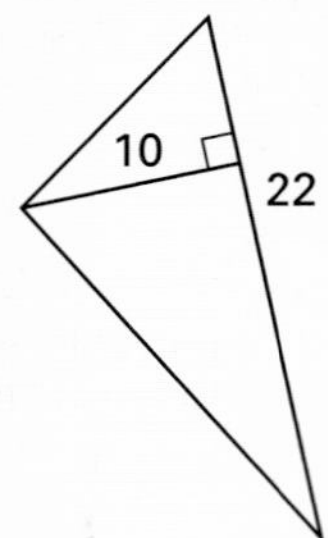

$A = bh$

$A = \frac{1}{2}$

$= \frac{1}{2} \cdot 22 \cdot 10$

$= 110$

The area is 110 square units.

3 Practice and Assess

Check

Remind students that the height of a triangle is the line segment drawn perpendicular to the base from the vertex opposite the base. Also remind them that it is often helpful to draw a diagram when solving a problem.

Answers for Check Your Understanding

1. Each is $\frac{1}{2}$ the area of the rectangle.
2. Yes. The formula is $A = \frac{1}{2}bh$ and the same numbers would be substituted in both cases.

Test Prep

You can find the area of a triangle by using any base with its related height. They will all give the same result.

Every triangle has three bases, and a height can be drawn for each base.

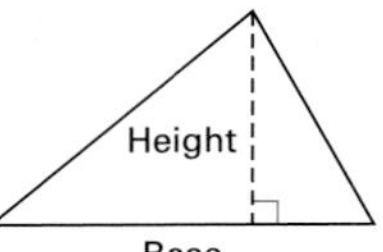

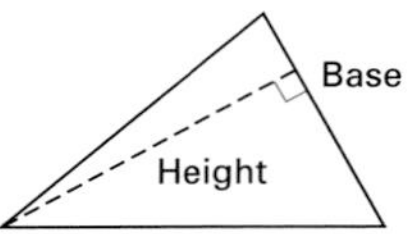

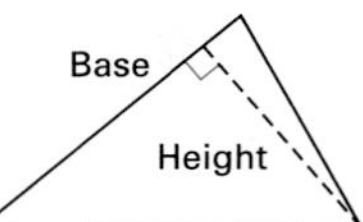

In the game of Tangoes™, players rearrange seven geometric figures into shapes of people, animals, and other figures. Often the pieces are arranged so the bases are not horizontal.

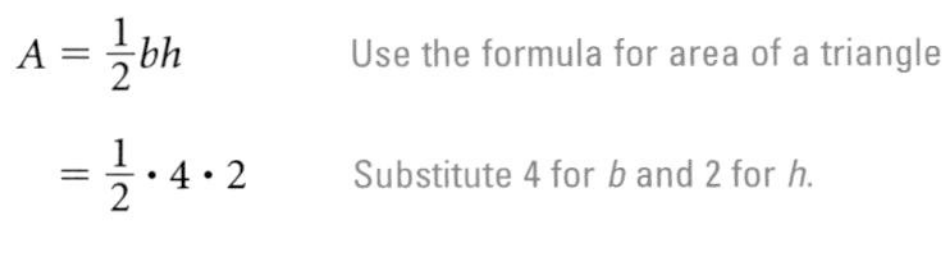

Example 3

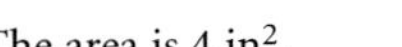

Find the area of the outlined triangle.

$A = \frac{1}{2}bh$ — Use the formula for area of a triangle.

$= \frac{1}{2} \cdot 4 \cdot 2$ — Substitute 4 for b and 2 for h.

$= 4$ — Multiply.

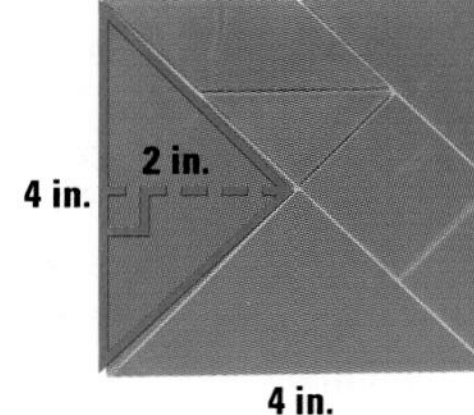

The area is 4 in^2.

Try It

Find the area of each triangle.

a. 42 in^2

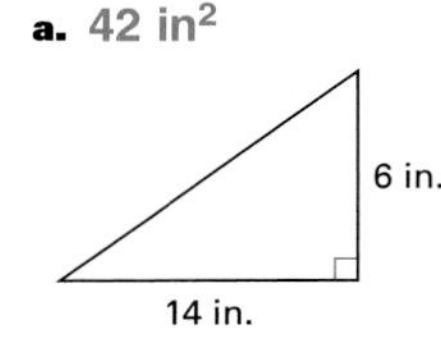

b. 152 in^2

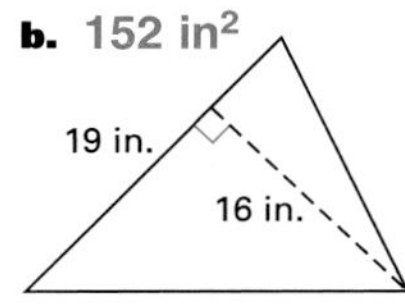

c. 60 ft^2

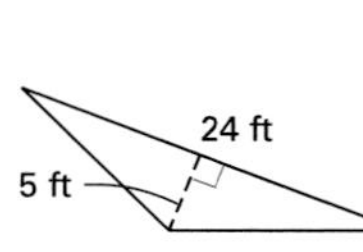

Check Your Understanding

1. Compare the areas of the triangles with the area of the rectangle.
2. Two triangles with different shapes both have bases of 6 cm and heights of 4 cm. Do they have the same areas? Explain.

MEETING MIDDLE SCHOOL CLASSROOM NEEDS

Tips from Middle School Teachers

I like to have students make a poster or bulletin board with a square, one or more rectangles, and one or more triangles, all having the same area, for example, 16 cm^2. This gives students a better appreciation for the concept of area.

Cooperative Learning

Have students work together to make a model using string, thumbtacks, and cardboard to show that many different triangles can have the same area. For example, two thumbtacks could remain fixed to represent the length of the base, while the third thumbtack could move to different locations, all representing equal heights with the same length.

Cultural Connection

Another popular game besides Chinese checkers is mentioned in this lesson. That is the game of Tangoes™ (tangrams). Both games originated in China. The earliest reference to the tangram appears in a Chinese book dated 1813, but the game was probably played long before that. Students might research tangrams and make their own set.

5-8 Exercises and Applications

Practice and Apply

1. **Getting Started** Follow these steps to find the area of the triangle shown.
   a. What is the base? 9
   b. What is the height? 4
   c. Multiply the base by the height. 36
   d. Multiply the product by $\frac{1}{2}$ to determine the area of the triangle. 18 sq. units

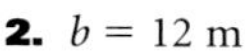

Find the area of each triangle.

2. $b = 12$ m, $h = 20$ m **120 m²**
3. $b = 25$ ft, $h = 5$ ft **$62\frac{1}{2}$ ft²**
4. $b = 3.5$ cm, $h = 1.4$ cm **2.45 cm²**
5. $b = 20$ in., $h = \frac{2}{3}$ in. **$6\frac{2}{3}$ in²**
6. **78.75 cm²** (10.5 cm, 15 cm)
7. (8 ft, 5.5 ft) **22 ft²**

8. ($\frac{3}{5}$ in., $\frac{3}{4}$ in.) **$\frac{9}{40}$ in²**

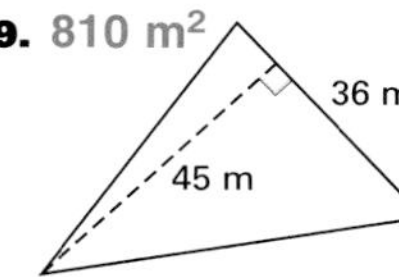

9. **810 m²** (36 m, 45 m)

Find the missing measurement of each triangle.

10. $b = 20$ m, $h = ?$ **15 m**, $A = 150$ m²
11. $b = 18$ ft, $h = ?$ **18 ft**, $A = 162$ ft²
12. $b = ?$ **36 cm**, $h = 44$ cm, $A = 792$ cm²
13. $b = ?$ **90 in.**, $h = 72$ in., $A = 3240$ in²
14. $b = 100$ mm, $h = 0.2$ mm, $A = ?$ **10 mm²**
15. $b = ?$ **18 yd**, $h = 25$ yd, $A = 225$ yd²
16. $b = 54$ cm, $h = ?$ **168 cm**, $A = 4536$ cm²
17. $b = ?$ **26 in.**, $h = 95$ in., $A = 1235$ in²

18. **History** The ancient Egyptians built great pyramids to serve as tombs for their kings. Each face of the largest pyramid has a base about 230 meters long. The height of each face is about 92 meters. What is the area of a face? **10,580 m²**

PRACTICE 5-8

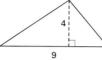

5-8 Exercises and Applications

Assignment Guide

- Basic
  1–19 odds, 20–42 evens
- Average
  1, 2–22 evens, 23–43 odds
- Enriched
  2–20 evens, 21–23, 24–42 evens

Exercise Notes

Exercises 10–17

Error Prevention Some students might consistently find half of the product of the given numbers. Point out that the missing measurement is often the base or the height and that it is important to write the formula and then substitute the given values before computing.

Exercise 18

History The Great Pyramid of Khufu, the largest of the Egyptian pyramids, required the work of 100,000 laborers for 20 to 30 years.

PRACTICE

Name ____________ **Practice 5-8**

Area of Triangles

Find the area of each triangle.

1. $b = 3$ m, $h = 8$ m, $A =$ 12 m²
2. $b = 12$ mi, $h = 5$ mi, $A =$ 30 mi²
3. $b = 7$ in., $h = 14$ in., $A =$ 49 in²
4. $b = 21$ cm, $h = 16$ cm, $A =$ 168 cm²
5. $b = 6.8$ km, $h = 11.0$ km, $A =$ 37.4 km²
6. $b = 3\frac{1}{4}$ yd, $h = 8\frac{1}{2}$ yd, $A =$ $13\frac{13}{16}$ yd²
7. $b = 5.7$ m, $h = 2.4$ m, $A =$ 6.84 m²
8. $b = \frac{1}{4}$ ft, $h = \frac{3}{5}$ ft, $A =$ $\frac{3}{40}$ ft²
9. $A =$ 76.5 km² (9 km, 17 km)
10. $A =$ 3.905 yd² (1.1 yd, 7.1 yd)
11. $A =$ $6\frac{7}{8}$ in² ($5\frac{1}{2}$ in., $2\frac{1}{2}$ in.)
12. $A =$ 11.1 cm² (3.7 cm, 6 cm)

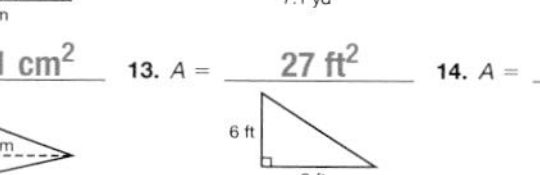

13. $A =$ 27 ft² (6 ft, 9 ft)

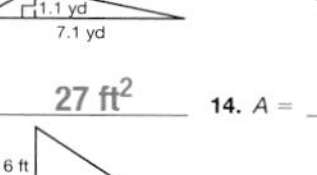

14. $A =$ 8.64 m² (3.6 m, 4.8 m)

Find the missing measurements of the following triangles.

15. $b =$ 64 mi, $h = 81$ mi, $A = 2592$ mi²
16. $b = 46$ cm, $h =$ 16 cm, $A = 368$ cm²
17. $b =$ 40 in., $h = 35$ in., $A = 700$ in²
18. $b = 63$ m, $h =$ 34 m, $A = 1071$ m²
19. $b =$ 39 km, $h = 24$ km, $A = 468$ km²
20. $b = 10$ yd, $h =$ 83 yd, $A = 415$ yd²
21. $b = 68$ cm, $h =$ 22 cm, $A = 748$ cm²
22. $b =$ 74 ft, $h = 25$ ft, $A = 925$ ft²

23. **Social Studies** The flag of Puerto Rico features three red stripes and a blue triangle with a white star inside. Find the area of the triangle (including the star). 270 in²

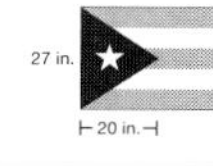

RETEACHING

Name ____________ **Alternative Lesson 5-8**

Area of Triangles

The **height** (*h*) of a triangle is a line segment drawn perpendicular to the **base** (*b*) from the vertex opposite the base.

The area of a triangle is half the product of the lengths of the base and the height. This can be written using the formula $A = \frac{1}{2}bh$ where *A* is area, *b* is base, and *h* is height.

Example

Find the area of the triangle.

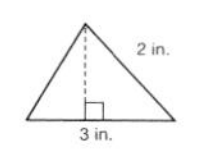

The height is 2 in.
The base is 3 in.

Use the formula for area of a triangle. $A = \frac{1}{2}bh$

Substitute 3 for *b* and 2 for *h*. $= \frac{1}{2} \cdot 3 \cdot 2$

Multiply. $= \frac{1}{2} \cdot 6$

$= 3$

The area is 3 in².

Try It Find the area of each triangle.

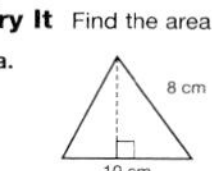

a. Base 10 cm, Height 8 cm, Area 40 cm²
b. Base 5 in., Height 6 in., Area 15 in²
c. Base 7 cm, Height 8 cm, Area 28 cm²

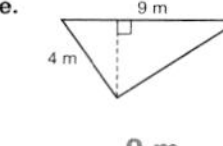

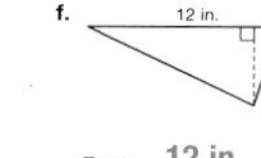

d. Base 20 ft, Height 5 ft, Area 50 ft²
e. Base 9 m, Height 4 m, Area 18 m²
f. Base 12 in., Height 5 in., Area 30 in²

Reteaching

Activity

- Work in groups of three. First, have one person draw a large triangle on a sheet of paper. That person then determines the base and height of the triangle and uses that information to determine the area.
- A second person should determine the area by using a different base and its related height.
- The third person must use the remaining base and its related height. Check to see if each person finds the same area. If not, work together to discover any errors.

Exercise Answers

21. True; the area of each is half the product of the base and the height. Since these quantities are the same for each triangle, the area will be the same also.

22. Possible answers:

a.

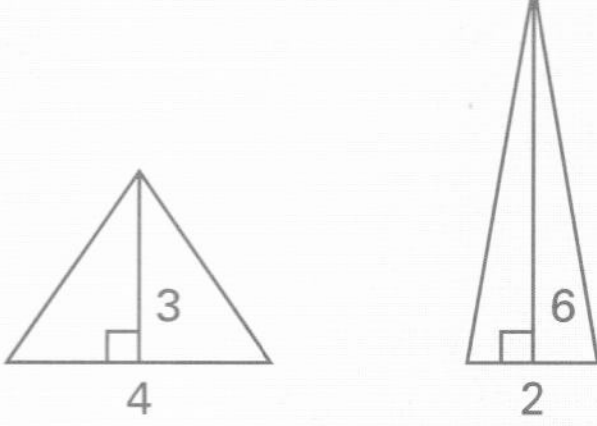

b.

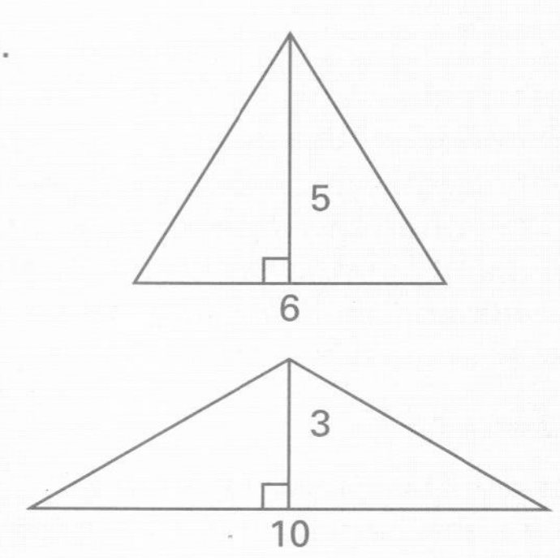

c.

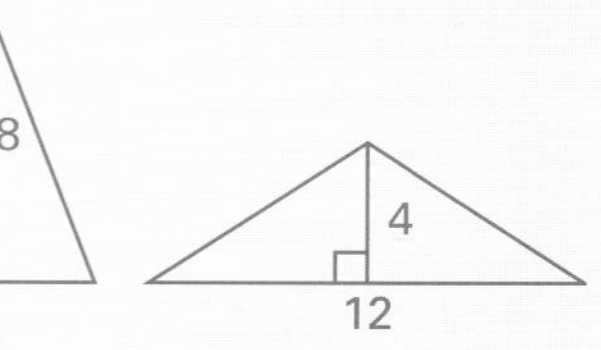

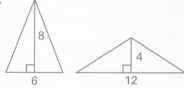

23. Answers may vary.

Alternate Assessment

Interview Have students name at least one situation in daily life where it might be helpful to find the area of a triangle. Then have them describe how they would find the area.

Quick Quiz

Find the area of each triangle.

1. $b = 24$ ft, $h = 40$ ft — 480 ft^2
2. $b = 1.5$ m, $h = 1.2$ m — 0.9 m^2

Find the missing measurements of the following triangles.

3. $b = 50$ cm, $h = ?$, $A = 200$ cm^2 — $h = 8$ cm
4. $b = ?$, $h = 7.6$ cm, $A = 38$ cm — $b = 10$ cm

Available on Daily Transparency 5-8

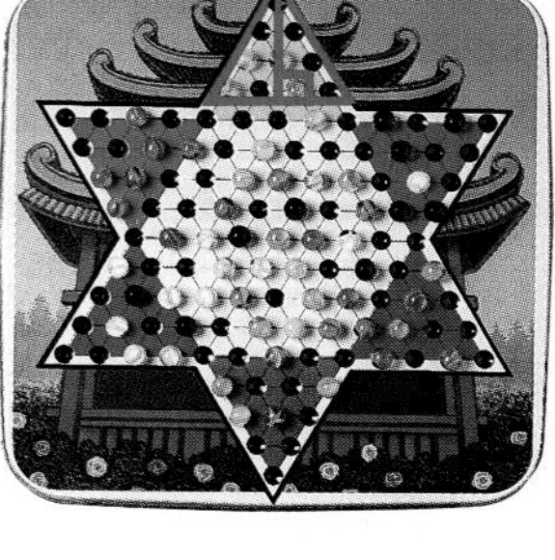

19. Social Studies The game of Chinese checkers is thought to have originated in China and migrated to Europe in the early 1800s. The game is played on a star-shaped board. If the base of the triangle is 4 in. and its height is 3.5 in., what is the area of the triangle-shaped part of the star? 7 in^2

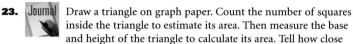

20. **Test Prep** Which triangle has the smallest area? A

Ⓐ $b = \frac{1}{2}, h = 12$ Ⓑ $b = 3, h = 4$

Ⓒ $b = \frac{2}{3}, h = 15$ Ⓓ $b = \frac{3}{4}, h = 16$

Problem Solving and Reasoning

21. Communicate True or false: All triangles with equal bases and heights have equal areas. Explain your answer.

22. Choose a Strategy Draw and label the following triangles. Include labels for both base and height.

a. Two different triangles, each with an area of 6 square units

b. Two different triangles, each with an area of 15 square units

c. Two different triangles, each with an area of 24 square units

23. Journal Draw a triangle on graph paper. Count the number of squares inside the triangle to estimate its area. Then measure the base and height of the triangle to calculate its area. Tell how close your estimate was to your calculation of the triangle's area.

Problem Solving STRATEGIES

- Look for a Pattern
- Make an Organized List
- Make a Table
- Guess and Check
- Work Backward
- Use Logical Reasoning
- Draw a Diagram
- Solve a Simpler Problem

Mixed Review

Test each number for divisibility by 2, 3, 4, 5, 6, 8, 9, and 10. *[Lesson 3-6]*

24. 562 2 **25.** 843 3 **26.** 78 2, 3, 6 **27.** 3125 5

28. 6578 2 **29.** 48,628 2, 4 **30.** 78,376 2, 4, 8 **31.** 364,859 None

Find each product. Rewrite in lowest terms. *[Lesson 4-4]*

32. $\frac{5}{7} \cdot \frac{7}{9}$ $\frac{5}{9}$ **33.** $\frac{13}{16} \cdot \frac{28}{39}$ $\frac{7}{12}$ **34.** $\frac{5}{12} \cdot \frac{6}{35}$ $\frac{1}{14}$ **35.** $\frac{5}{9} \cdot \frac{21}{25}$ $\frac{7}{15}$

36. $\frac{7}{15} \cdot \frac{3}{8}$ $\frac{7}{40}$ **37.** $\frac{5}{11} \cdot \frac{22}{45}$ $\frac{2}{9}$ **38.** $\frac{3}{5} \cdot \frac{7}{13}$ $\frac{21}{65}$ **39.** $\frac{8}{9} \cdot \frac{7}{25}$ $\frac{56}{225}$

40. $\frac{3}{10} \cdot \frac{2}{15}$ $\frac{1}{25}$ **41.** $\frac{5}{8} \cdot \frac{11}{12}$ $\frac{55}{96}$ **42.** $\frac{7}{24} \cdot \frac{12}{14}$ $\frac{1}{4}$ **43.** $\frac{6}{19} \cdot \frac{19}{6}$ 1

PROBLEM SOLVING

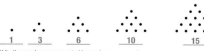

Name ______

Guided Problem Solving 5-8

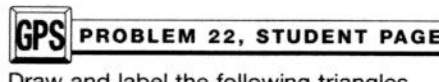

Draw and label the following triangles. Include labels for both base and height.

a. Two different triangles, each with an area of 6 square units
b. Two different triangles, each with an area of 15 square units
c. Two different triangles, each with an area of 24 square units

Understand

1. Circle the area of the triangles you will draw.
2. What is the formula to find the area of a triangle? $A = \frac{1}{2}bh$

Plan

3. What will the product of the base and height have to be for each triangle?
a. 12 b. 30 c. 48
4. Find two factor pairs for each product in Item 3. Possible answers:
a. 2, 6; 3, 4 b. 3, 10; 5, 6 c. 3, 16; 4, 12
5. How can you use factor pairs as dimensions of each triangle? One factor as base, the other as height.

Solve

6. Draw and label *two* triangles for each area.
a. 6 square units b. 15 square units c. 24 square units
Check students' work.

Look Back

7. How can you use the two factor pairs you found in Item 4 to draw and label two more triangles? Possible answer: Trade measures of base and height.

SOLVE ANOTHER PROBLEM

Draw and label two different triangles, each with an area of 40 square units. Check students' work.

ENRICHMENT

Name ______

Extend Your Thinking 5-8

Patterns in Geometry

Triangular numbers can be shown by the arrangements below.

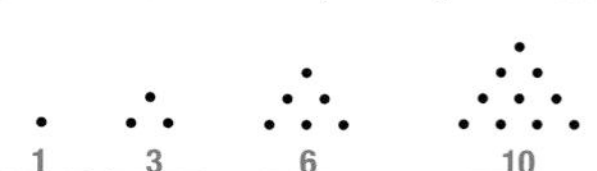
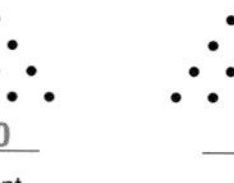

1 3 6 10 15

1. Write the numbers represented by each arrangement.
2. What pattern do you see in the arrangements? Possible answer: Difference between consecutive numbers increases by 1.
3. The pattern is also shown by the expression $\frac{n(n+1)}{2}$, where n is the place in the pattern. Write a number sentence to show the tenth and the fifteenth triangular numbers. $\frac{10(10+1)}{2} = 55$; $\frac{15(15+1)}{2} = 120$

Square numbers can be shown by the arrangements below.

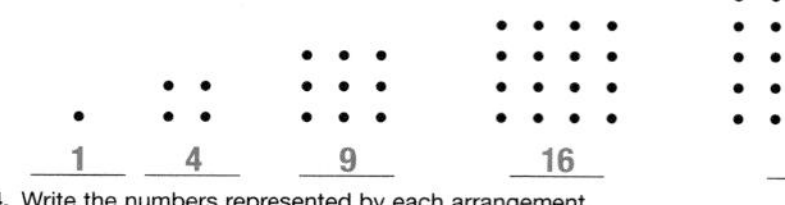

1 4 9 16 25

4. Write the numbers represented by each arrangement.
5. What pattern do you see in the arrangements? Possible answer: Each square number is the place in the pattern squared.
6. Write a number sentence to show the tenth and fifteenth square numbers? $10^2 = 100$; $15^2 = 225$
7. What are the two smallest numbers that can be shown as both a triangular number and as a square number? Explain. 1 and 36 Triangular: 1, 3, 6, 10, 15, 21, 28, 36. Square: 1, 4, 9, 16, 25, 36. 1 and 36 are in both of the patterns.

Areas of Parallelograms and Trapezoids

5-9

▶ Lesson Link You've found the areas of rectangles, squares, and triangles. Now you'll find the areas of parallelograms and trapezoids. ◀

You'll Learn ...

■ to find the area of a parallelogram

■ to find the area of a trapezoid

... How It's Used

Quilters sometimes use parallelogram-shaped pieces of cloth in their designs.

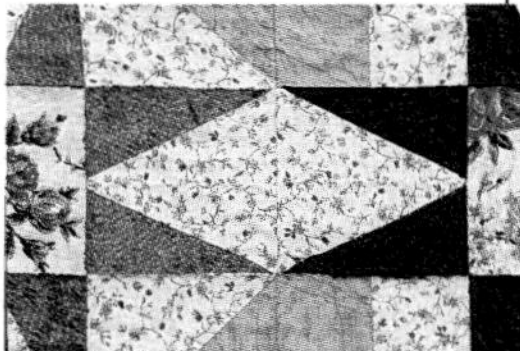

Explore | Areas of Parallelograms

Tangling with Rectangles

Materials: Graph paper, Scissors, Straightedge

1. Draw a parallelogram on graph paper. Draw a perpendicular line from a vertex to the opposite base.

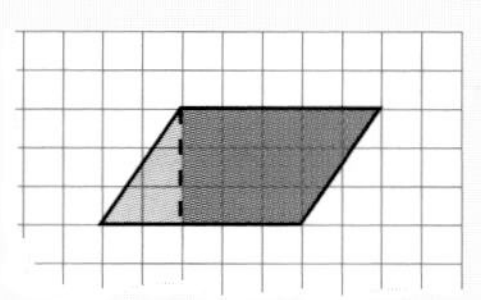

2. Cut out the parallelogram, then cut it into two pieces along the perpendicular line. Arrange the two pieces to form a rectangle. What are the base and the height of the rectangle?

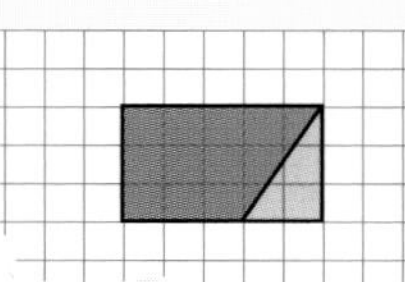

3. Repeat Steps 1–2 with a different parallelogram.
4. Describe a method for finding the area of a parallelogram.

Learn | Areas of Parallelograms and Trapezoids

The *height* of a parallelogram or trapezoid is the length of a segment that connects two parallel bases. It is perpendicular to both bases.

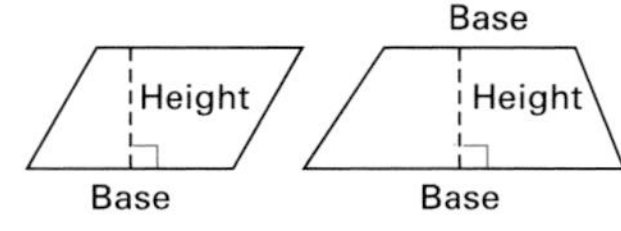

You can use the base and the height of a parallelogram to find its area.

AREA OF A PARALLELOGRAM

The area of a parallelogram is the product of its height and the length of its base.

$A = bh$

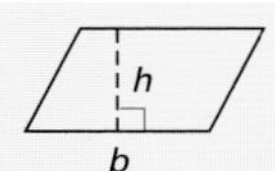

MEETING INDIVIDUAL NEEDS

Resources

5-9 Practice
5-9 Reteaching
5-9 Problem Solving
5-9 Enrichment
5-9 Daily Transparency
- Problem of the Day
- Review
- Quick Quiz

Teaching Tool Transparency 7

Learning Modalities

Visual Have students cut out photos from magazines and newspapers to illustrate parallelograms and trapezoids.

Individual Have students write one or more paragraphs explaining any difficulties they have encountered in this lesson, as well as any hints they might share about overcoming these difficulties.

English Language Development

In both the formulas for this lesson, the word *product* appears. Be sure students understand the mathematical meaning of this word versus its everyday usage. Have them write the two meanings of *product* in their own words.

Lesson Organizer

Objectives

- Find the area of a parallelogram.
- Find the area of a trapezoid.

Materials

- Explore: Graph paper, scissors, straightedge

NCTM Standards

- 1, 2, 4, 12, 13

Review

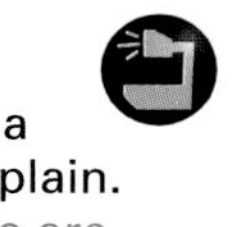

1. Is every rectangle a parallelogram? Explain. Yes; opposite sides are parallel and congruent.
2. Is every parallelogram a rectangle? No; the angles are not always right angles.

Available on Daily Transparency 5-9

▶ Lesson Link

Have students review the quadrilateral chart on page 223.

1 Introduce

Explore

You may wish to use Teaching Tool Transparency 7: $\frac{1}{4}$-Inch Graph Paper with **Explore**.

The Point

Students understand how the formula for the area of a parallelogram can be derived from the formula for the area of a rectangle.

Ongoing Assessment

Watch for students who think the height is the slanted side of the parallelogram rather than the perpendicular distance between the sides.

For Groups That Finish Early

Use the same parallelogram as you did in Step 1, but draw the height in a different location.

Answers for Explore on next page.

Follow Up
Have students discuss if the method in **Explore** would work for any parallelogram.

Answers for Explore
1–3. Answers may vary.
4. Multiply the base by the height.

2 Teach

Learn

Alternate Examples

1. Find the area of the parallelogram-shaped park.

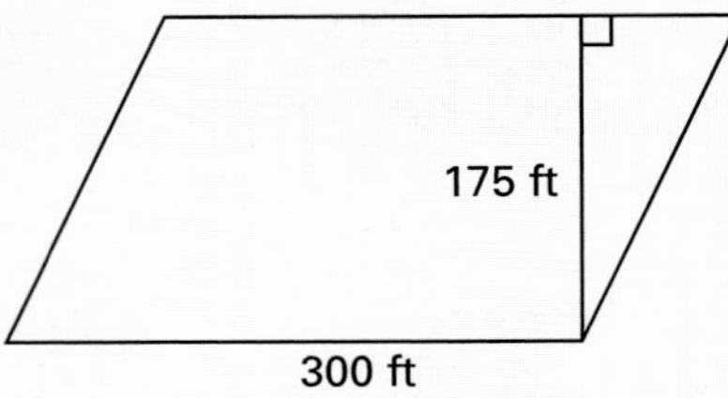

Use the formula for the area of a parallelogram and substitute the known values.

$A = bh$
$= 300 \cdot 175$
$= 52{,}500$

The area is 52,500 ft^2.

2. Find the area of the trapezoid shown in the diagram.

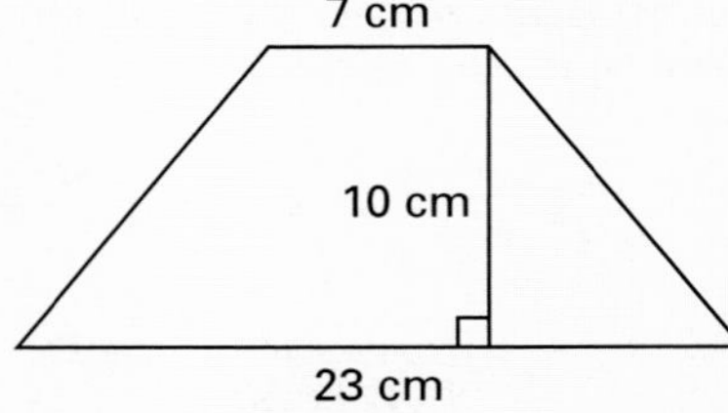

Use the formula for the area of a trapezoid and substitute the known values.

$A = \frac{1}{2}h(b_1 + b_2)$
$= \frac{1}{2} \cdot 10 \cdot (7 + 23)$
$= \frac{1}{2} \cdot 10(30)$
$= 150\ cm^2$

The area is 150 cm^2.

Example 1

This window in Jerusalem, designed by Marc Chagall, is made of small pieces of stained glass. Find the area of the parallelogram-shaped piece of glass.

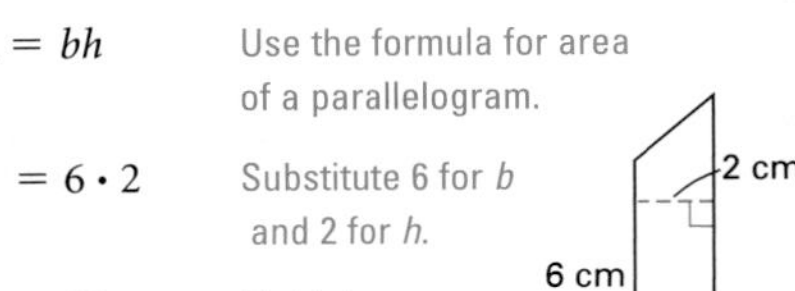

$A = bh$ Use the formula for area of a parallelogram.

$= 6 \cdot 2$ Substitute 6 for b and 2 for h.

$= 12$ Multiply.

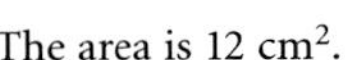

The area is 12 cm^2.

Try It

Find the area of each parallelogram.

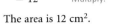

a.
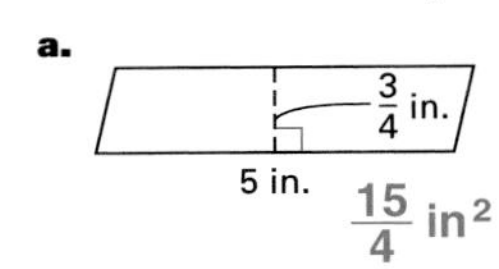

$\frac{15}{4}$ in^2

b.
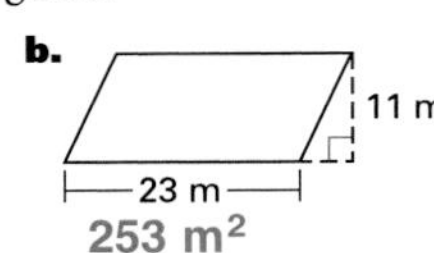

253 m^2

c.
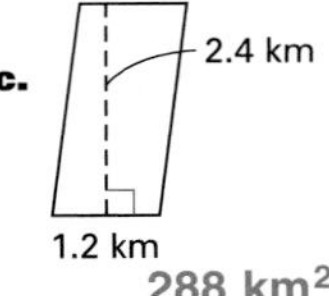

288 km^2

To find the area of a trapezoid, you must know the length of each base and the height. The bases are usually given the labels b_1 and b_2.

AREA OF A TRAPEZOID

The area of a trapezoid is half its height multiplied by the sum of the lengths of its two bases.

$A = \frac{1}{2}h(b_1 + b_2)$

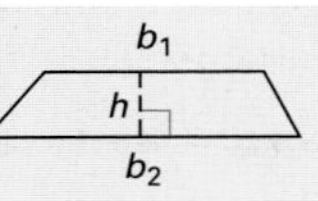

Example 2

Find the area of the trapezoid shown in the diagram at the right.

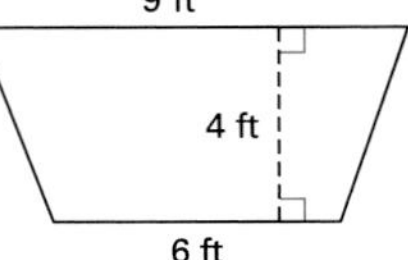

$A = \frac{1}{2}h(b_1 + b_2)$ Use the formula for the area of a trapezoid.

$= \frac{1}{2} \cdot 4(6 + 9)$ Substitute 4 for h, 6 for b_1, and 9 for b_2.

$= \frac{1}{2} \cdot 4(15)$ Add.

$= 30\ ft^2$ Multiply.

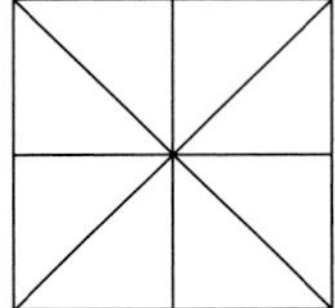

MATH EVERY DAY

Problem of the Day

Tapatan, a Philippine game, is played on a square game board like the one below. If the area of this game board is 110.25 in^2, what is the length of each side?

10.5 in.

Available on Daily Transparency 5-9

An Extension is provided in the transparency package.

Fact of the Day

A bone at the base of the forefinger is shaped like a trapezoid. It is actually called the trapezoid bone.

Mental Math

Do these mentally.

1. 80,000 − 30,000 50,000
2. 1,200,000 − 900,000 300,000
3. 17,000,000 − 11,000,000 6,000,000

Example 3

In international basketball, the free-throw lane is different from the one used in the United States. How much greater is the area of the international lane?

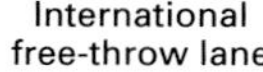

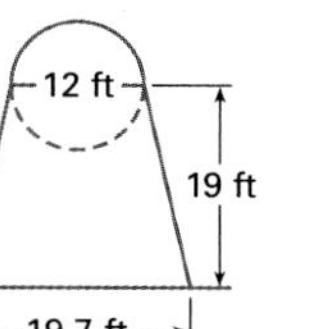

The international free-throw lane is shaped like a trapezoid.

$A = \frac{1}{2}h(b_1 + b_2)$ Use the formula for the area of a trapezoid.

$= \frac{1}{2} \cdot 19(12 + 19.7)$ Substitute 19 for h, 12 for b_1, and 19.7 for b_2.

$= \frac{1}{2} \cdot 19(31.7)$ Add.

$= 301.15 \text{ ft}^2$ Multiply.

The U.S. free-throw lane is shaped like a rectangle.

$A = bh$ Use the formula for the area of a rectangle.

$= 12 \cdot 19$ Substitute 12 for b and 19 for h.

$= 228 \text{ ft}^2$ Multiply.

$301.15 - 228 = 73.15 \text{ ft}^2$

The area of the international free-throw lane is 73.15 ft^2 greater.

Social Studies Link

Women's basketball was first included in the Olympic Games in Montreal, Ontario, in 1976. That year the women's team from the Soviet Union won the gold medal.

Try It

Find the area of each trapezoid.

a. 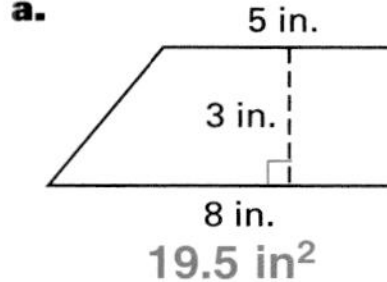

19.5 in^2

b. 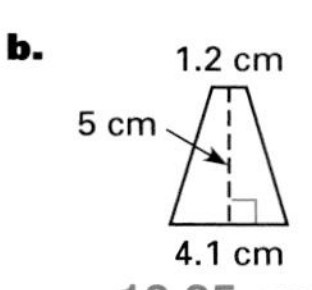

13.25 cm^2

c. 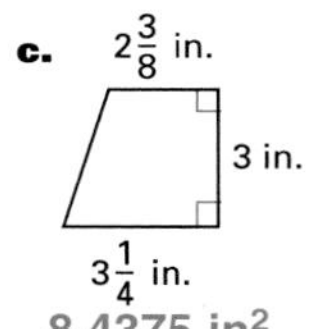

8.4375 in^2

DID YOU KNOW?

A *trapeze* is actually in the shape of a *trapezoid.* The ropes are wider apart at the top than at the bottom, to make the bar safer to perform on.

Check Your Understanding

1. A rectangle and a parallelogram have the same base and height. How are their areas related?

2. How can you use the Distributive Property to write the formula for the area of a trapezoid in a different form?

Alternate Examples

3. A new room being added to a house has two windows, one in the shape of a trapezoid and the other a rectangle. The homeowner must buy shades to cover both the windows. What is the total area?

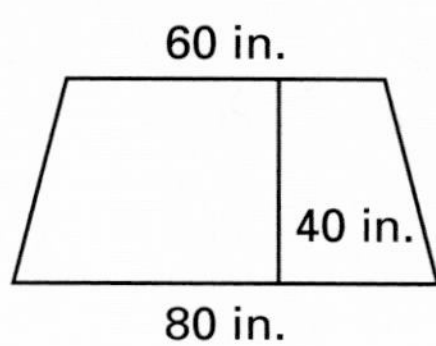

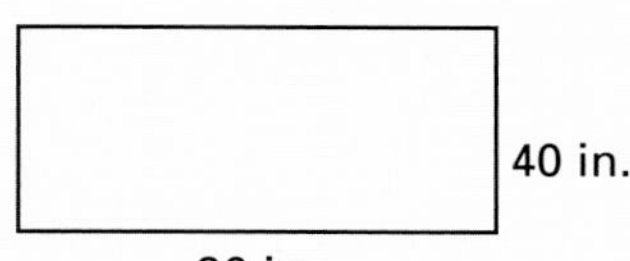

For the first window, use the formula for the area of a trapezoid. Substitute known values.

$A = \frac{1}{2}h(b_1 + b_2)$

$= \frac{1}{2} \cdot 40 \cdot (80 + 60)$

$= \frac{1}{2} \cdot 40(140)$

$= 2800 \text{ in}^2$

For the second window, use the formula for the area of a rectangle. Substitute known values.

$A = bh$

$= 90 \cdot 40$

$= 3600 \text{ in}^2$

$2800 + 3600 = 6400 \text{ in}^2$

MEETING MIDDLE SCHOOL CLASSROOM NEEDS

Tips from Middle School Teachers

I find that students enjoy looking through books of architecture to find various examples of geometric figures. They are frequently surprised at the variety of geometric shapes they find.

Team Teaching

Work with an art teacher to show students paintings and/or graphic designs that employ a variety of geometric figures.

Cultural Connection

Designs appearing on blankets and pottery of Native Americans, such as the Hopi and the Navajo, often use geometric shapes. Have students find photos in books or magazines, and discuss why some of the shapes are used.

Regular geometric shapes are chosen to simplify the weaving process in Navajo blankets. Shapes used on pottery form complex patterns. Most shapes are from nature.

3 Practice and Assess

Check

Remind students that a rectangle is a special kind of parallelogram, one in which all angles are right angles.

Answers for Check Your Understanding

1. They are equal.
2. $A = \frac{1}{2}hb_1 + \frac{1}{2}hb_2$.

5-9 Exercises and Applications

Assignment Guide

- **Basic**
  1–17, 19–20, 22–38 evens
- **Average**
  3–20, 21–39 odds
- **Enriched**
  5–19 odds, 20–23, 24–38 evens

Exercise Notes

Exercises 13–16

Error Prevention When students use $A = \frac{1}{2}hb_1 + \frac{1}{2}hb_2$, some will multiply both the h and the quantity $b_1 + b_2$ by $\frac{1}{2}$. Remind students that each factor in a product is used only once.

Exercise Answers

1. Height n; base m.
2. Height d; bases e and f.
3. Height x; base y.
4. Height t; bases s and u.

Reteaching

Activity

Materials: Graph paper

- On graph paper, draw a trapezoid with bases 6 units and 4 units and height 2 units. Draw a segment connecting two vertices that aren't already connected.
- Notice that there are now two triangles. The triangles completely cover the trapezoid and they do not overlap, so the sum of their areas will be the area of the trapezoid.
- Find the area of each triangle, using 4 units as the base of one triangle and 6 units as the base of the other triangle. For each triangle, the height is 2 units. Triangle 1: A = 4 sq. units; Triangle 2: A = 6 sq. units.
- Add the areas of the triangles to get the area of the trapezoid. 4 sq. units + 6 sq. units = 10 sq. units

PRACTICE 5-9

5-9 Exercises and Applications

Practice and Apply

Getting Started Name the height and base(s) for each figure.

1. 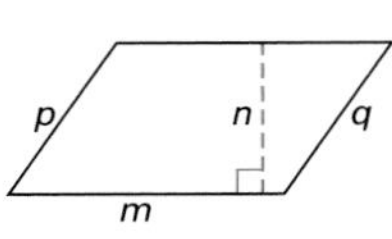

2. 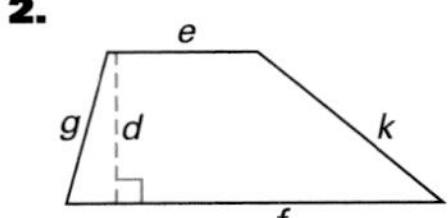

3. 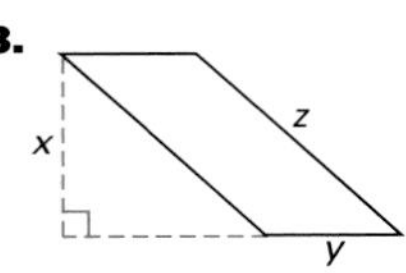

4. 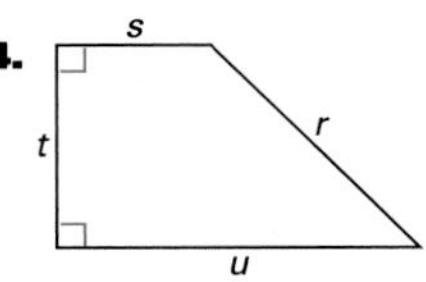

Which formula would you use to find the area of each figure, $A = bh$ or $A = \frac{1}{2}h(b_1 + b_2)$?

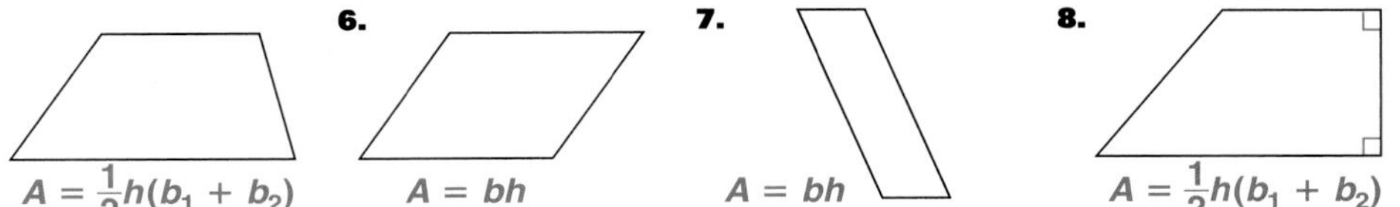

5. 6. 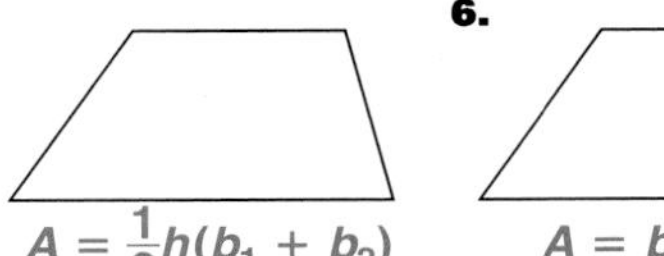
7. 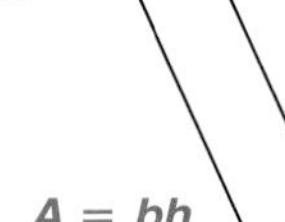
8. 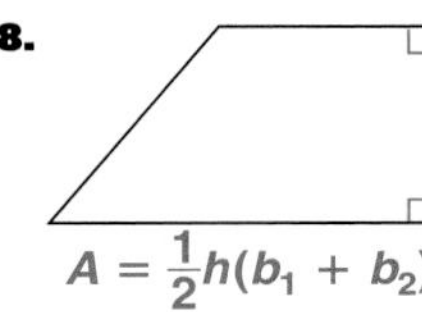

$A = \frac{1}{2}h(b_1 + b_2)$ $A = bh$ $A = bh$ $A = \frac{1}{2}h(b_1 + b_2)$

Find the area of each parallelogram.

9. 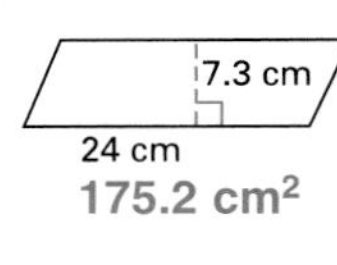

175.2 cm²

10. 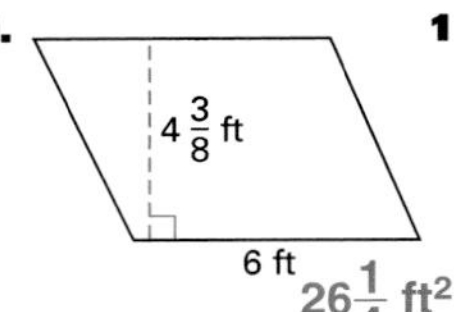

$26\frac{1}{4}$ ft²

11. 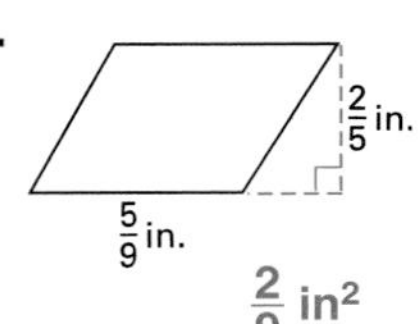

$\frac{2}{9}$ in²

12. 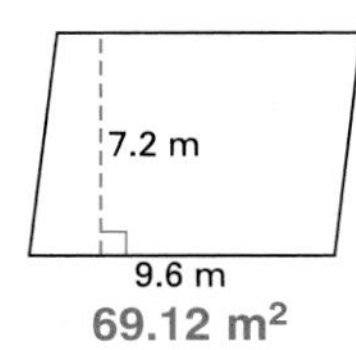

69.12 m²

Find the area of each trapezoid.

13. 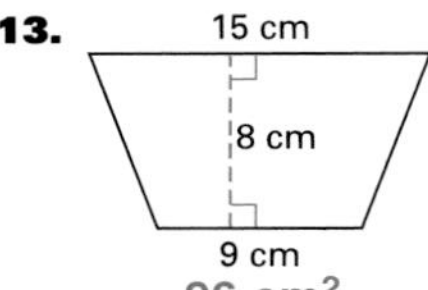

96 cm²

14. 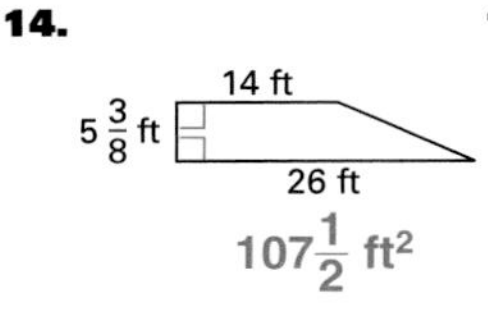

$107\frac{1}{2}$ ft²

15. 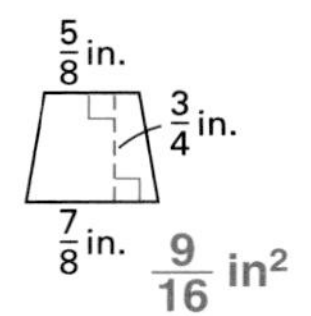

$\frac{9}{16}$ in²

16. 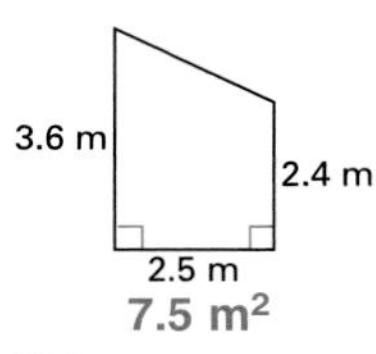

7.5 m²

17. **Measurement** The game of tiddlywinks is thought to have originated in England. Although it is often thought of as a children's game, it is popular on university campuses. How much larger is the area of the 2-point portion of the board than the area of the 10-point portion? 64 cm²

GPS

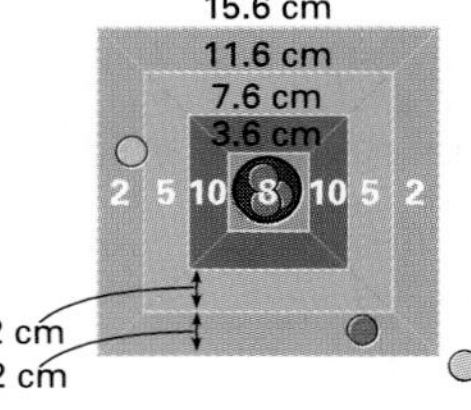

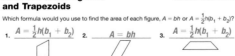

PRACTICE

Name ____________

Practice 5-9

Area of Parallelograms and Trapezoids

Which formula would you use to find the area of each figure, $A = bh$ or $A = \frac{1}{2}h(b_1 + b_2)$?

1. $A = \frac{1}{2}h(b_1 + b_2)$ 2. $A = bh$ 3. $A = \frac{1}{2}h(b_1 + b_2)$

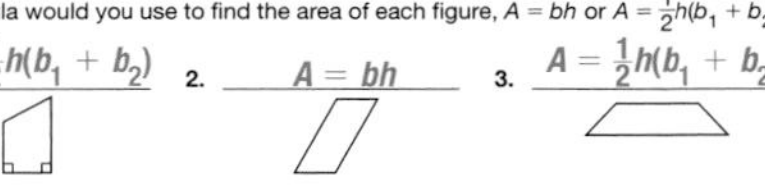

Find the area of each parallelogram.

4. 288 m² 5. 67.41 cm² 6. $1\frac{11}{16}$ in²

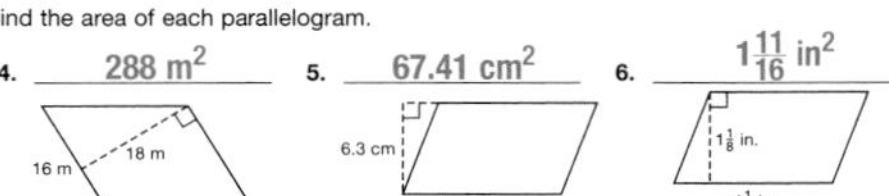

Find the area of each trapezoid.

7. 7.36 cm² 8. 76 ft² 9. $47\frac{1}{4}$ in²

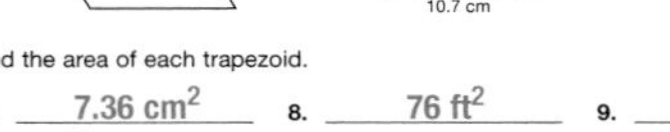
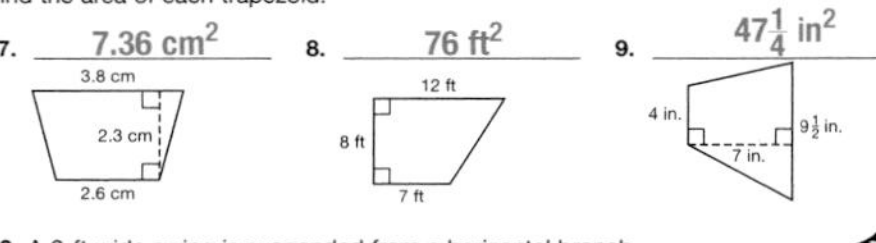

10. A 2-ft wide swing is suspended from a horizontal branch by 8-ft long ropes. Find the area that is formed when the swing is pushed sideways so that it is only $7\frac{1}{2}$ ft below the branch, as shown.

15 ft²

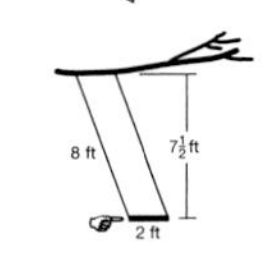
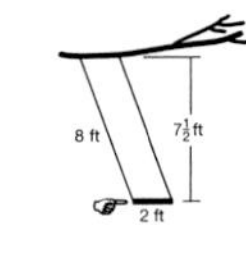

11. **Social Science** The flag of Kuwait is shown at the right. Find each area.

a. Black region 2,560 cm²
b. Green region (top stripe) 5,504 cm²
c. White region 4,864 cm²
d. Red region (bottom stripe) 5,504 cm²

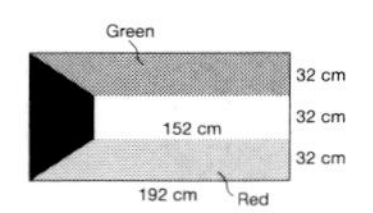

RETEACHING

Name ____________

Alternative Lesson 5-9

Area of Parallelograms and Trapezoids

The *height* of a parallelogram or trapezoid is the length of a perpendicular segment that connects two parallel bases.

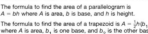

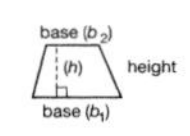

The formula to find the area of a parallelogram is $A = bh$ where A is area, b is base, and h is height.

The formula to find the area of a trapezoid is $A = \frac{1}{2}h(b_1 + b_2)$ where A is area, b_1 is one base, and b_2 is the other base.

Example 1

Find the area of the parallelogram.

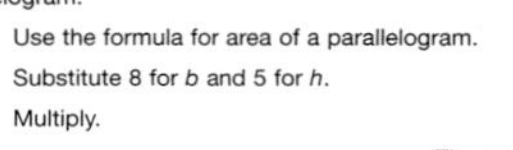

Use the formula for area of a parallelogram.	$A = bh$
Substitute 8 for b and 5 for h.	$= 8 \cdot 5$
Multiply.	$= 40$

The area is 40 cm².

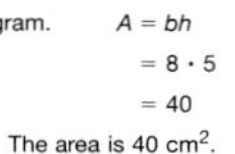

Try It Find the area of each parallelogram.

a. Base 9 in.
Height 12 in.
Area 108 in²

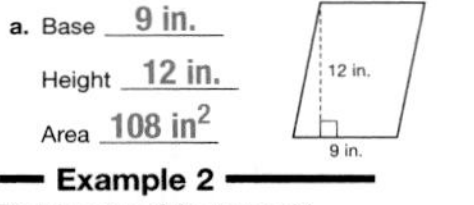

b. Base 9 cm
Height 15 cm
Area 135 cm²

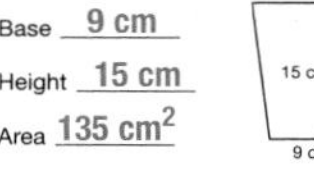
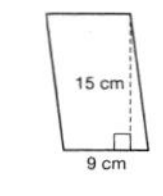

Example 2

Find the area of the trapezoid.

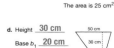

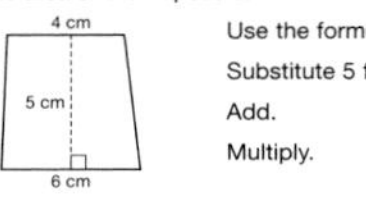

Use the formula for area of a trapezoid.	$A = \frac{1}{2}h(b_1 + b_2)$
Substitute 5 for h, 6 for b_1, and 4 for b_2.	$= \frac{1}{2} \cdot 5(6 + 4)$
Add.	$= \frac{1}{2} \cdot 5(10)$
Multiply.	$= 25$

The area is 25 cm².

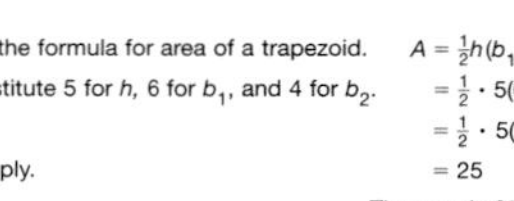

Try It Find the area of each trapezoid.

c. Height 10 in.
Base b_1 6 in.
Base b_2 8 in.
$b_1 + b_2$ 14 in. Area 70 in²

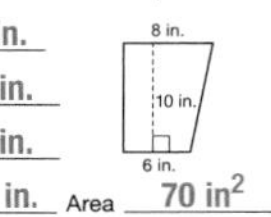

d. Height 30 cm
Base b_1 20 cm
Base b_2 50 cm
$b_1 + b_2$ 70 cm Area 1050 cm²

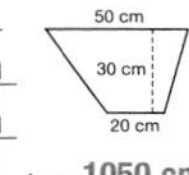

18. Geography The state of Nevada is shaped like a trapezoid. Calculate the approximate area of Nevada using the formula for area of a trapezoid. ≈ 108,000 mi²

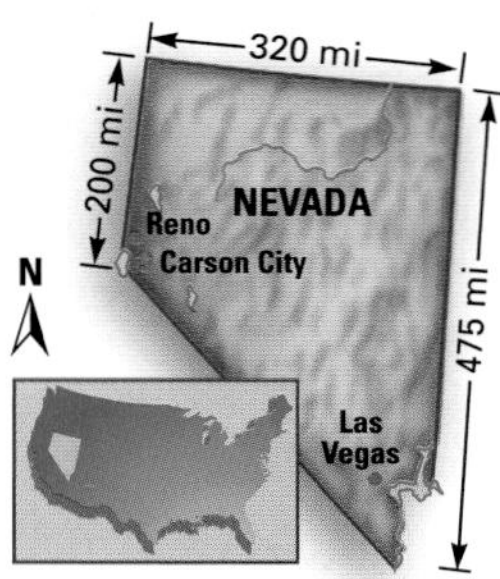

19. **Test Prep** Which trapezoid has the greatest area? A

Ⓐ $b_1 = 10, b_2 = 6, h = 3.1$

Ⓑ $b_1 = 8, b_2 = 7, h = 3.2$

Ⓒ $b_1 = 10, b_2 = 4, h = 3.4$

Ⓓ $b_1 = 9, b_2 = 4, h = 3.5$

20. History "Morris" games, where you need to get three pieces in a row, have been popular around the world for centuries. Versions of these games have been found in a 4400-year-old Egyptian temple and a 2900-year-old Viking ship. A game board for Twelve Men's Morris is shown. Find the areas of the highlighted trapezoids. 10 in², 16 in²

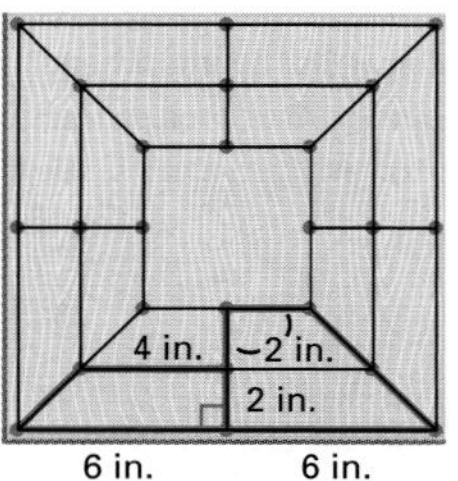

Problem Solving and Reasoning

21. Communicate Explain how the area of a parallelogram is related to the area of a triangle with the same base and height.

22. Communicate One problem at sporting events is the availability of parking. A standard slant parking spot is 9 ft by 24 ft. What is the area of one parking space? 216 ft²

9 ft

24 ft

23. Journal Using the two small triangles and the square from a set of Tangoes™, make a rectangle, a trapezoid, and a parallelogram. Make drawings of the figures you form or trace around the figures. If the area of a small triangle is 1 square unit, what are the areas of your figures?

Mixed Review

Find the GCF and the LCM of each pair of numbers. *[Lesson 3-7]*

24. 336, 210 **25.** 54, 88 **26.** 81, 126 **27.** 210, 168

28. 165, 195 **29.** 780, 510 **30.** 385, 390 **31.** 420, 270

Find each product. *[Lesson 4-5]*

32. $4\frac{3}{5} \cdot 7\frac{2}{3}$ $35\frac{4}{15}$ **33.** $4\frac{8}{9} \cdot 3\frac{6}{7}$ $18\frac{6}{7}$ **34.** $9\frac{4}{5} \cdot 5\frac{2}{3}$ $55\frac{8}{15}$ **35.** $6\frac{1}{2} \cdot 8\frac{1}{2}$ $55\frac{1}{4}$

36. $3\frac{2}{3} \cdot 1\frac{1}{3}$ $4\frac{8}{9}$ **37.** $2\frac{1}{6} \cdot 7\frac{2}{3}$ $16\frac{11}{18}$ **38.** $8\frac{1}{4} \cdot 10\frac{7}{10}$ $88\frac{11}{40}$ **39.** $4\frac{3}{8} \cdot 3\frac{1}{3}$ $14\frac{7}{12}$

PROBLEM SOLVING

Name ______________

Guided Problem Solving 5-9

GPS PROBLEM 17, STUDENT PAGE 256

The game of tiddlywinks is thought to have originated in England. Although it is often thought of as a children's game, it is popular on university campuses. How much larger is the area of the 2-point portion of the board than the area of the 10-point portion?

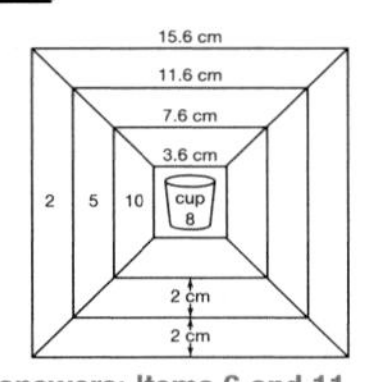

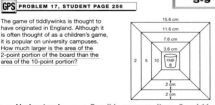

— Understand — Possible answers: Items 6 and 11

1. Underline what you are asked to find.

— Plan —

2. What is the area of the entire gameboard? 243.36 cm²
3. If the gameboard did not have the 2-point strip, what would its area be? 134.56 cm²
4. Which operation would you use to find the area of the 2-point section? Subtraction.
5. Which two areas would you use to find the area of the 10-point section? Area of 7.6 cm-square and area of 3.6 cm-square.

— Solve —

6. What is the area of the 2-point section? 108.8 cm²
7. What is the area of the 10-point section? 44.8 cm²
8. How much larger is the area of the 2-point portion of the board than the area of the 10-point portion? 64 cm²

— Look Back —

9. Write an equation using a different operation to find the area of the 2-point portion. $4 \times \frac{1}{2}h(b_1 + b_2) =$ $4 \times \frac{1}{2} \times 2(11.6 + 15.6) = 108.8$

SOLVE ANOTHER PROBLEM

How much smaller is the area of the 10-point portion than the area of the 5-point portion? 32 cm²

ENRICHMENT

Name ______________

Extend Your Thinking 5-9

Critical Thinking

Find the areas of the parallelograms below.

Parallelogram *X*

6 cm²

Parallelogram *Y*

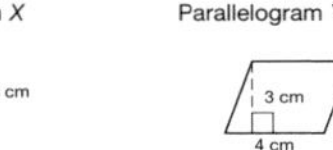

12 cm²

Parallelogram *Z*

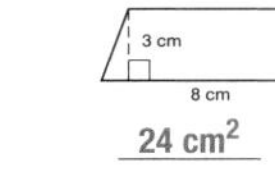

24 cm²

1. What happens to the area of a parallelogram when the length of one dimension is doubled? The area doubles.
2. Write an equation to show the area of each parallelogram when both dimensions are doubled.
   a. Parallelogram *X* $4 \cdot 6 = 24$ b. Parallelogram *Y* $8 \cdot 6 = 48$
   c. Parallelogram *Z* $16 \cdot 6 = 96$
3. What happens to the area of a parallelogram when the length of both dimensions is doubled? The area quadruples.
4. Write an equation to show the area of each parallelogram when both dimensions are tripled.
   a. Parallelogram *X* $6 \cdot 9 = 54$ b. Parallelogram *Y* $12 \cdot 9 = 108$
   c. Parallelogram *Z* $24 \cdot 9 = 216$
5. What happens to the area of a parallelogram when the length of both dimensions is tripled? The area increases by a factor of 9.
6. What pattern do you see in how the area of a parallelogram changes when the both dimensions are multiplied by the same factor? The area increases by the square of the factor.

Exercise Answers

21. Area of parallelogram is twice the area of a triangle with the same base and height.

23. Possible answer: Each area is 4 square units.

24. GCF = 42; LCM = 1,680.
25. GCF = 2; LCM = 2,376.
26. GCF = 9; LCM = 1,134.
27. GCF = 42; LCM = 840.
28. GCF = 15; LCM = 2,145.
29. GCF = 30; LCM = 13,260.
30. GCF = 5; LCM = 30,030.
31. GCF = 30; LCM = 3780.

Alternate Assessment

Self Assessment Have students assess their ability to find the areas of parallelograms and trapezoids. Ask them to explain what they found most difficult about this lesson.

Quick Quiz

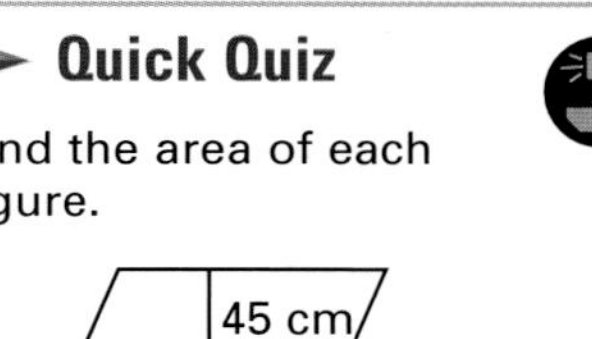

Find the area of each figure.

1.

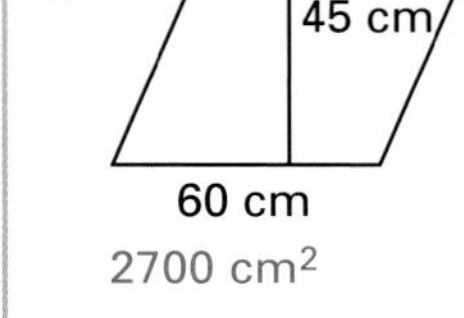

2700 cm²

2.

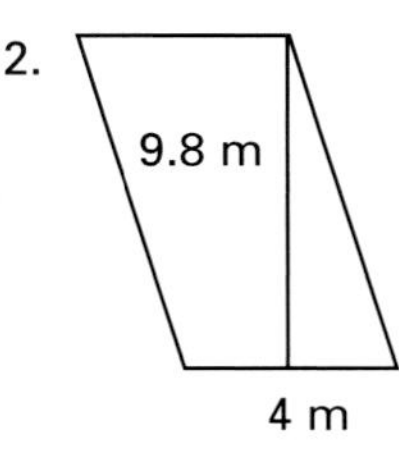

39.2 m²

3.

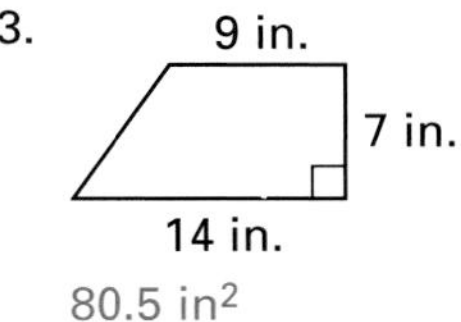

80.5 in²

4.

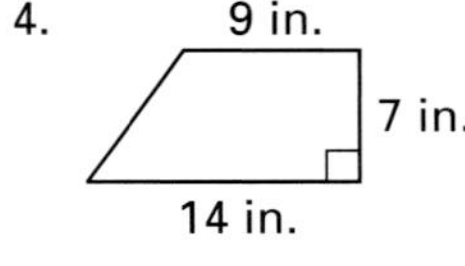

41.82 cm²

Available on Daily Transparency 5-9

5-10 Lesson Organizer

Objective

- Find the areas of irregular shapes.

NCTM Standards

- 1–4, 12, 13

Review

1. Name as many shapes as you can that you have studied in this chapter. Possible answers: squares, rhombuses, parallelograms, rectangles, triangles, trapezoids.
2. Name as many formulas as you can that you have used for finding the areas of geometric shapes. Possible answers: $A = bh$, $A = \frac{1}{2}bh$, $A = \frac{1}{2}h(b_1 + b_2)$

Available on Daily Transparency 5-10

Lesson Link

Point out that one way of dividing a figure may be more advantageous than others. For example, in covering an irregular shape with carpet, one way might involve fewer cuts.

1 Introduce

Explore

You may wish to use Lesson Enhancement Transparency 26 with **Explore**.

The Point
Students recognize that an irregular shape can be divided into familiar shapes, usually in several ways. They use this technique to find the area of an irregular figure.

Ongoing Assessment
Watch for students who find only two ways of dividing the figure. It is likely that they assume that both segments they draw must be vertical or both must be horizontal.

For Groups That Finish Early
Divide the figure in a way that involves trapezoids and/or parallelograms instead of rectangles.

Answers for Explore on page C7.

5-10 Problem Solving: Areas of Irregular Figures

You'll Learn ...

- to find the areas of irregular shapes

... How It's Used

Developers work with areas of irregular figures when planning new housing tracts.

Lesson Link You've found the areas of several common geometric figures. Now you'll see how you can find areas of *composite,* or *irregular,* figures.

Explore Irregular Figures

Par for the Course

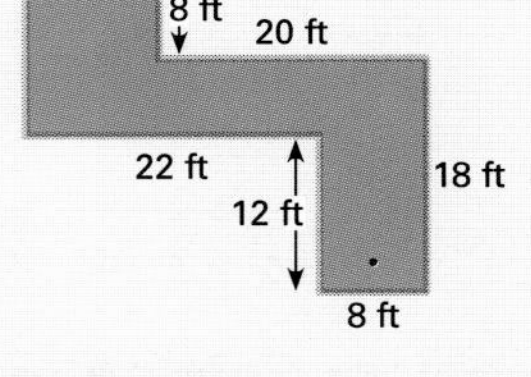

The seventh hole at Marty's Miniature Golf is shown. Marty needs to order new carpet to cover the entire hole.

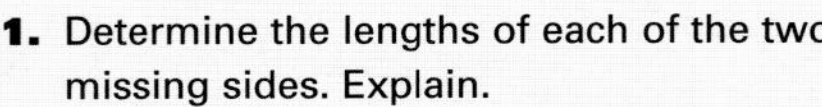

1. Determine the lengths of each of the two missing sides. Explain.

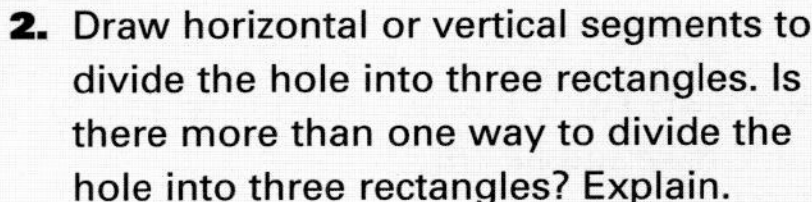

2. Draw horizontal or vertical segments to divide the hole into three rectangles. Is there more than one way to divide the hole into three rectangles? Explain.

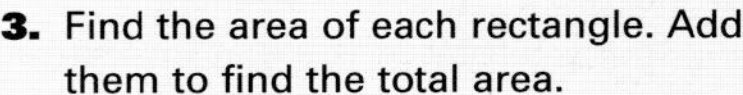

3. Find the area of each rectangle. Add them to find the total area.

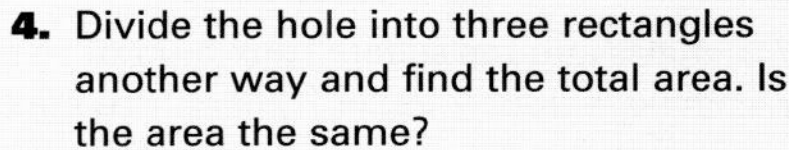

4. Divide the hole into three rectangles another way and find the total area. Is the area the same?
5. Suppose this hole has a windmill whose triangular base is cut out of the middle of the carpet. How would you find the area of the carpeted part of the hole?

Learn Problem Solving: Areas of Irregular Figures

You can find the area of an irregular figure by dividing it into familiar figures, then adding the area of each part. There are often several different ways to divide an irregular figure.

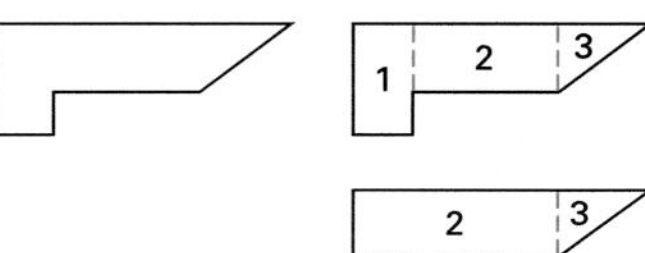

MEETING INDIVIDUAL NEEDS

Resources

5-10 Practice
5-10 Reteaching
5-10 Problem Solving
5-10 Enrichment
5-10 Daily Transparency
- Problem of the Day
- Review
- Quick Quiz

Lesson Enhancement Transparency 26
Chapter 5 Project Master

Learning Modalities

Kinesthetic Have students use chalk to draw a large irregular shape on the floor. Then have them use newspapers in various arrangements to show how the figure can be divided in various ways into familiar shapes.

Social Have students work together to help students who may be having trouble in finding the areas of irregular figures.

Challenge

Have students divide the figure into two congruent figures.

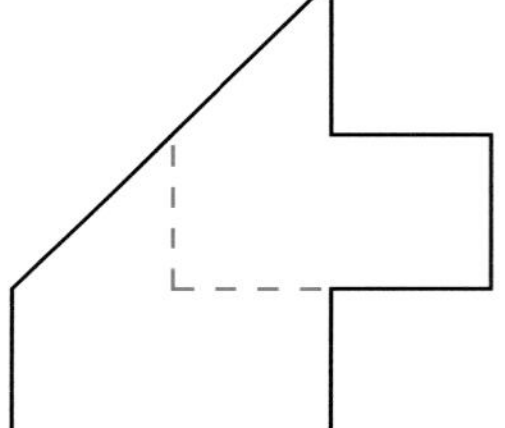

Example 1

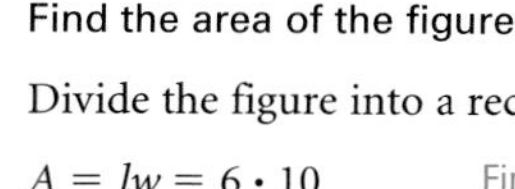

Find the area of the figure.

Divide the figure into a rectangle and a triangle.

$A = lw = 6 \cdot 10$ Find the area of the rectangle.

$= 60$ Multiply.

$\frac{1}{2}bh = \frac{1}{2} \cdot 8 \cdot 5$ Find the area of the triangle.

$= 20$ Multiply.

Total area = area of rectangle + area of triangle

$= 60 + 20$

$= 80$

The area is 80 ft^2.

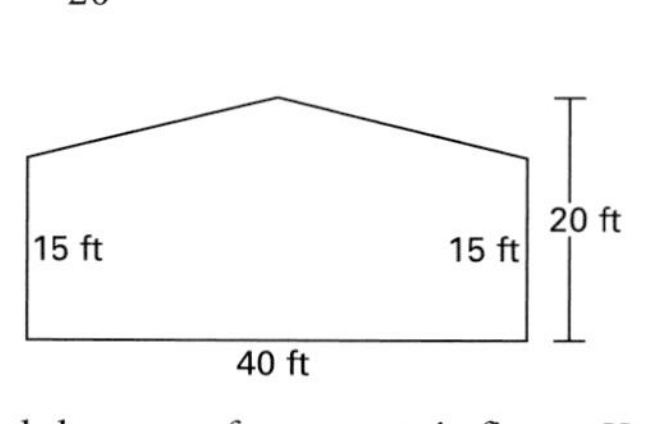

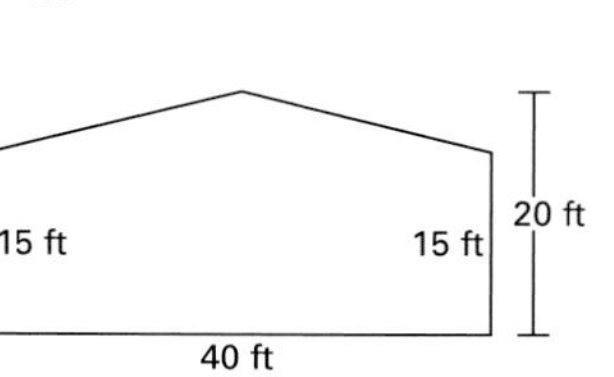

Try It

Find the area of the figure. 700 ft^2

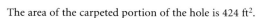

Sometimes you need to subtract to find the area of a geometric figure. You can find the area of a figure with a hole or opening in it by finding the total area of the figure and subtracting the area of the hole or opening.

Example 2

Find the area of the carpeted portion of the miniature golf hole shown. Find the total area, then subtract the area of the square.

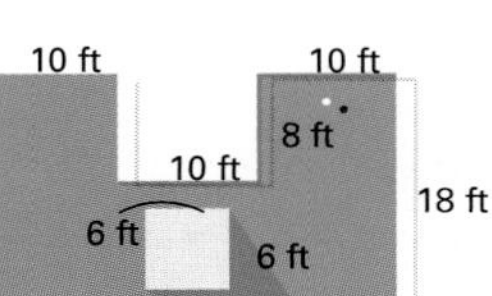

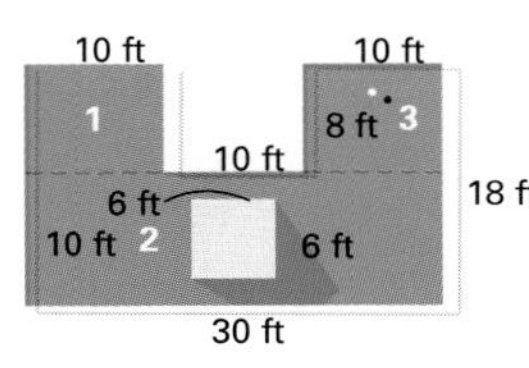

Rectangle 1	Rectangle 2	Rectangle 3
$lw = 10 \cdot 8$	$lw = 30 \cdot 10$	$lw = 10 \cdot 8$
$= 80$	$= 300$	$= 80$

Area of rectangles = 80 + 300 + 80 = 460

Area of square = $s^2 = 6^2 = 36$

Total area = area of rectangles − area of square

= 460 − 36 = 424

The area of the carpeted portion of the hole is 424 ft^2.

Study TIP

Always remember to check for any common factors and reduce if possible.

2 Teach

Learn

Alternate Examples

1. Find the area of the figure.

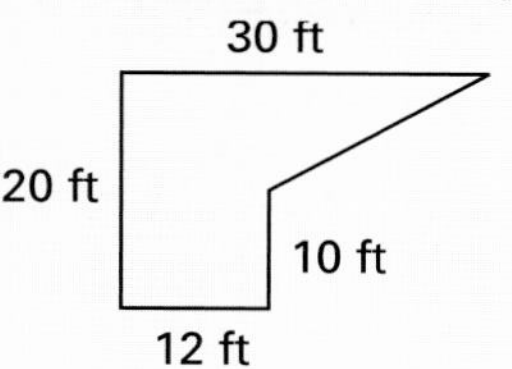

Find the area of the rectangle, then the triangle. Add the two areas.

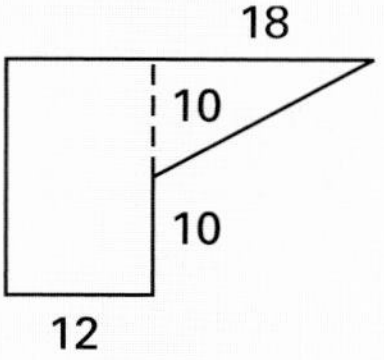

$A = lw = 12 \cdot 20 = 240$

$\frac{1}{2}bh = \frac{1}{2} \cdot 10 \cdot 18 = 90$

Total area = 240 + 90 = 330

The area is 330 ft^2.

2. Find the area of the room that must be carpeted except for the square atrium.

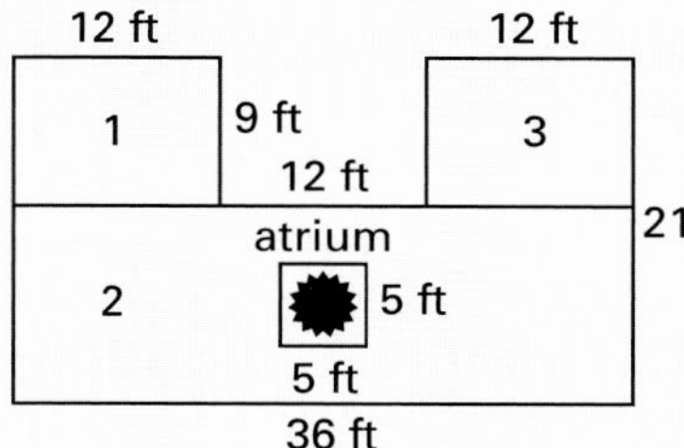

Rectangles 1 and 3 each:
$lw = 9 \cdot 12$
$= 108$

Rectangle 2:
$lw = 36 \cdot 12$
$= 432$

Area of rectangles = 108 + 432 + 108 = 648

Area of square = $s^2 = 5^2 = 25$

Total area = 648 − 25 = 623

The area of the carpeted portion is 623 ft^2.

MATH EVERY DAY

Problem of the Day

In the numbers below, find four consecutive whole numbers whose sum is exactly one half of the other eight numbers.

1 2 3 4 5 6 7 8 9 10 11 12

$5 + 6 + 7 + 8 = \frac{1}{2}(1 + 2 + 3 + 4 + 9 + 10 + 11 + 12) = 26$

Available on Daily Transparency 5-10

An Extension is provided in the transparency package.

Fact of the Day

Miniature golf has been a popular pastime for children and adults since the 1930s. Many courses are beautifully designed.

Mental Math

Do these mentally.

1. 1 + 9 + 22 + 8 + 18 + 2 60
2. 34 + 6 + 47 + 3 + 9 99
3. 7 + 156 + 44 + 305 + 95 607
4. 910 + 90 + 850 + 150 + 234 2234

Students see two methods of solving a problem. One method uses the area of a trapezoid and a rectangle. The other method uses the area of a triangle and two rectangles. Students can decide which of the two correct methods is easier for them.

Answers for What Do You Think?

1. Divide the figure into a triangle, a square, and a rectangle.
2. Choose the one with the fewest calculations to perform.

3 Practice and Assess

Check

Point out that any polygon, no matter how many sides it has, can be divided into triangles.

Answers for Check Your Understanding

1. Possible answer: Because I already know the formulas for areas of rectangles and triangles.
2. Possible answer: Parallelograms and trapezoids.

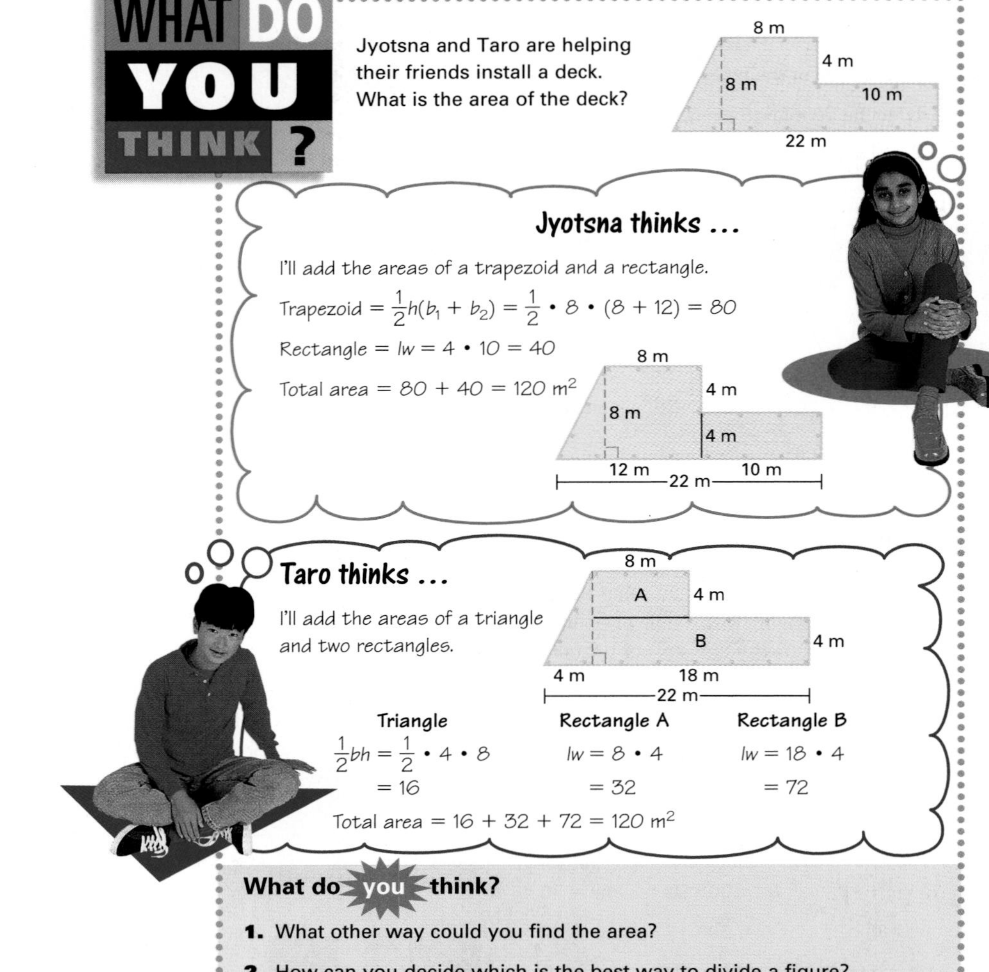

WHAT DO YOU THINK?
Jyotsna and Taro are helping their friends install a deck. What is the area of the deck?
8 m
4 m
8 m
10 m
22 m
Jyotsna thinks ...
I'll add the areas of a trapezoid and a rectangle.
Trapezoid = $\frac{1}{2}h(b_1 + b_2) = \frac{1}{2} \cdot 8 \cdot (8 + 12) = 80$
Rectangle = $lw = 4 \cdot 10 = 40$
Total area = $80 + 40 = 120$ m^2
8 m
4 m
8 m
4 m
12 m
22 m
10 m
Taro thinks ...
I'll add the areas of a triangle and two rectangles.
8 m
A
4 m
B
4 m
4 m
18 m
22 m
Triangle
$\frac{1}{2}bh = \frac{1}{2} \cdot 4 \cdot 8$
$= 16$
Rectangle A
$lw = 8 \cdot 4$
$= 32$
Rectangle B
$lw = 18 \cdot 4$
$= 72$
Total area = $16 + 32 + 72 = 120$ m^2

What do you think?

1. What other way could you find the area?
2. How can you decide which is the best way to divide a figure?

Check Your Understanding

1. Why is it helpful to divide an irregular figure into rectangles and triangles to find the area?
2. Name some other familiar figures you can divide irregular figures into.

MEETING MIDDLE SCHOOL CLASSROOM NEEDS

Tips from Middle School Teachers

I have students design their own miniature golf holes. They must provide a diagram and then determine the area of the portion to be covered with carpet.

Geography Connection

Maps of cities are good sources of examples of irregular shapes such as parks, plazas, or suburbs. Of course, most countries and states have irregular shapes.

Students could trace an irregularly shaped state or country onto graph paper and estimate its area in terms of grid squares. Advanced students might want to convert this area to actual area by using scale.

Cooperative Learning

Many of the exercises in this lesson can be solved by using more than one method. Have students work together to compare the methods they used.

5-10 Exercises and Applications

Practice and Apply

1. **Getting Started** Follow these steps to find the area of the irregular figure shown.

a. Divide the figure into two rectangles.

b. Find the area of each rectangle.

c. Add the areas of the rectangles to determine the area of the irregular figure.

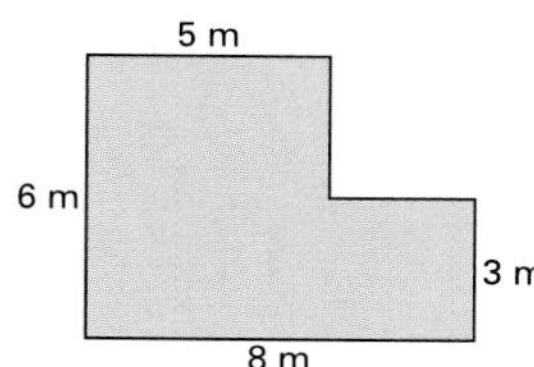

Find the area of each shaded region.

2.
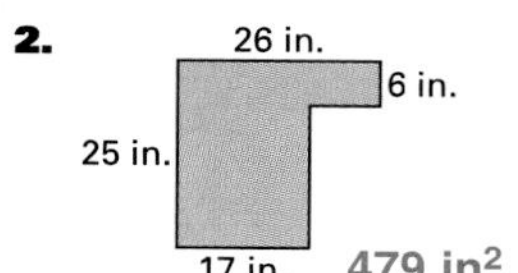

479 in²

3.
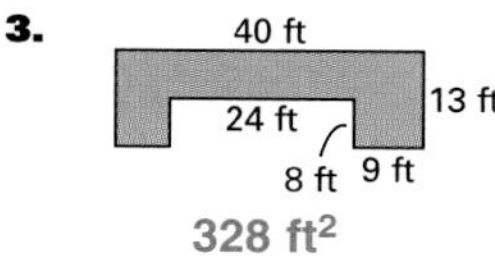

328 ft²

4.
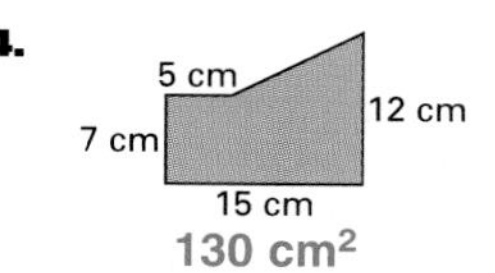

130 cm²

5.
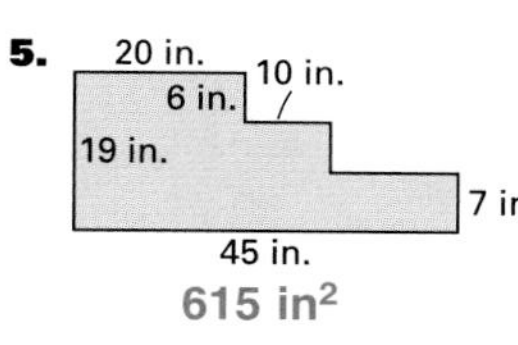

615 in²

6.
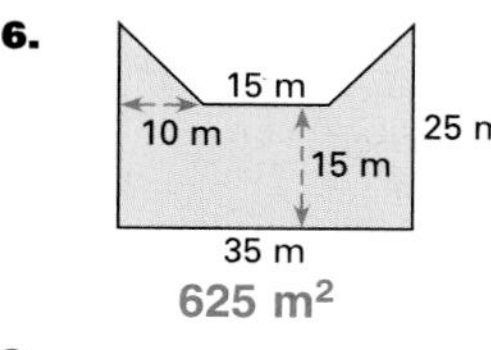

625 m²

7.
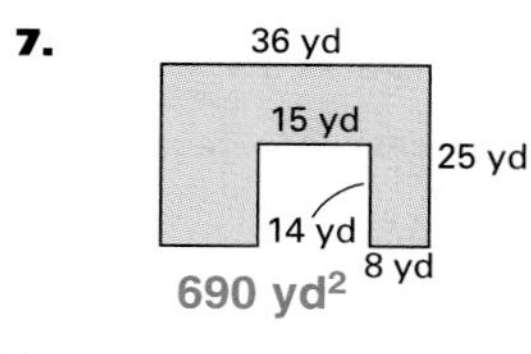

690 yd²

8.
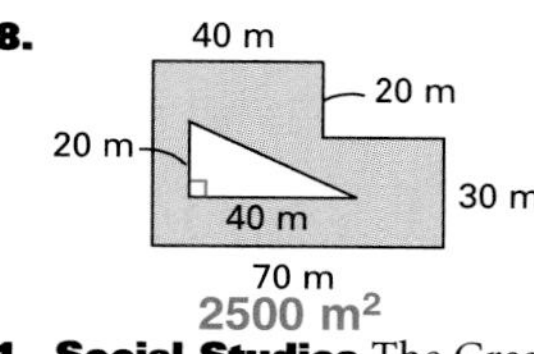

2500 m²

9.
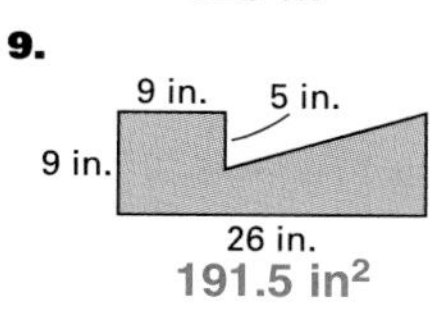

191.5 in²

10.
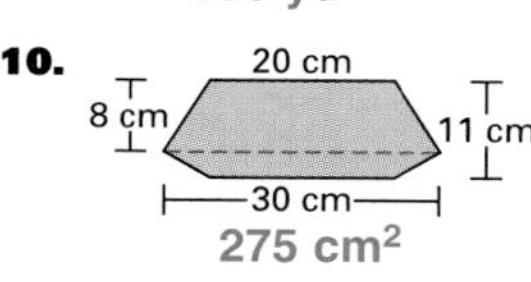

275 cm²

11. **Social Studies** The Great Ball Court at Chichen Itza, in Mexico, was the site of ceremonial Mayan ball games. Use the diagram to find the area of the Great Ball Court.
6144 m²

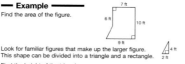

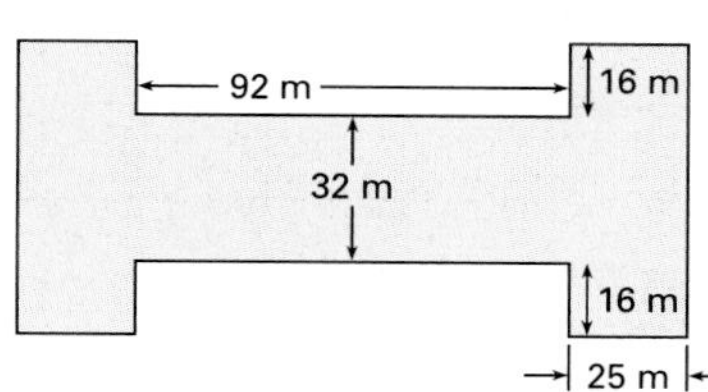

PRACTICE

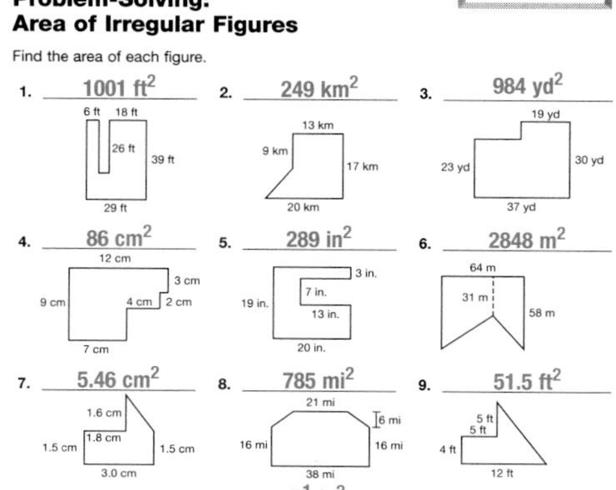

Name ______

Practice 5-10

Problem-Solving: Area of Irregular Figures

Find the area of each figure.

1. 1001 ft²
2. 249 km²
3. 984 yd²
4. 86 cm²
5. 289 in²
6. 2848 m²
7. 5.46 cm²
8. 785 mi²
9. 51.5 ft²
10. 7800 m²
11. $5\frac{1}{4}$ in²
12. 33 cm²

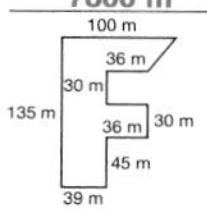

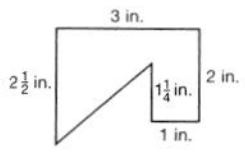

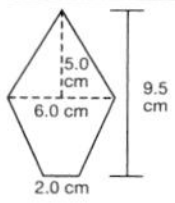

13. The flag of Switzerland features a white cross on a red background.

a. Each of the 12 sides of the cross has length 15 cm. Find the area of the white cross. 1125 cm²

b. The flag has dimensions 60 cm by 60 cm. Find the area of the red region. 2475 cm²

RETEACHING

Name ______

Alternative Lesson 5-10

Problem-Solving: Areas of Irregular Figures

Not all geometric figures are shapes with which you are familiar. Some of them, however, can be divided into familiar shapes.

Example

Find the area of the figure.

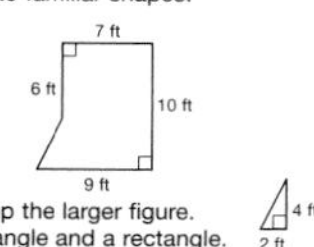

Look for familiar figures that make up the larger figure. This shape can be divided into a triangle and a rectangle.

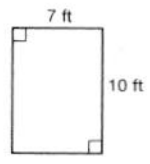

Find the height of the triangle.
Since the height is part of the side of the rectangle, subtract the length of the known portion from the length of the opposite side: $10 - 6 = 4$.

Find the base of the triangle.
A side of the rectangle makes up part of the base of the figure. Subtract the side of the rectangle from the base of the figure: $9 - 7 = 2$.

Use the area formulas to find the areas of the triangle and the rectangle.

Area of a triangle $= \frac{1}{2}(b \times h) = \frac{1}{2}(2 \times 4) = \frac{1}{2}(8) = 4 \text{ ft}^2$

Area of a rectangle $= b \times h = 7 \times 10 = 70 \text{ ft}^2$

Find the total area by adding the area of each figure.

Total area = area of triangle + area of rectangle $= 4 + 70 = 74$

The total area is 74 ft².

Try It Find the area of the figure shown.

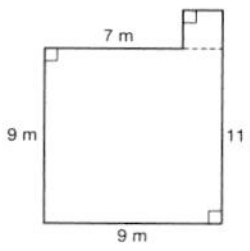

a. Divide the figure into two squares.

b. Find the length of a side of the large square. 9 m

c. Find the length of a side of the small square. 2 m

d. Find the area of the large square. 81 m²

e. Find the area of the small square. 4 m²

f. Find the total area: 81 m² + 4 m² = 85 m²

Assignment Guide

- **Basic**
  1–11 odds, 12–13, 15–29 odds
- **Average**
  2–13, 16–30 evens
- **Enriched**
  2–14, 16–30 evens

Exercise Notes

Exercise 11

Social Studies The archaeological remains at Chichen Itza are in Yucatan state, Mexico. Some of the ruins date from around 1000 A.D. An astronomical observatory and huge pyramidal temples were built at a later date.

Exercise Answers

1. a. Possible answer:

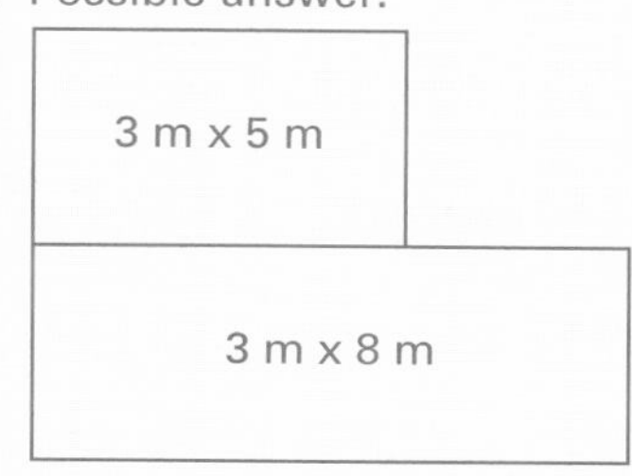

b. Possible answer: 15 m²; 24 m²

c. Area = 39 m²

Reteaching

Activity

Materials: Geoboard, rubber bands

- Work with a partner. Each person should draw a large irregular figure on paper. Exchange papers and make each other's figure on a geoboard.
- Count squares or half-squares to find the area.
- Repeat with other irregular figures.

Project Progress

You may want to have students use Chapter 5 Project Master.

Exercise Answers

14. 16 cm²; Area of square = 64 cm² and each triangle is one fourth of the square; 64 ÷ 4 = 16.

Alternate Assessment

Interview Have students conduct an interview with one or more adults to determine some cases where they need to find areas of irregular figures in daily life. Have students report how the methods of this lesson might be useful in such cases.

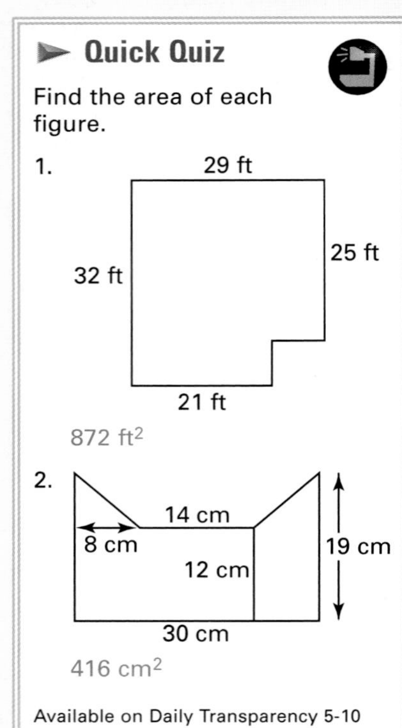

▶ Quick Quiz

Find the area of each figure.

1.

872 ft²

2.

416 cm²

Available on Daily Transparency 5-10

---

12. **Test Prep** Which of these areas could be divided into a square and a trapezoid? A

Ⓐ
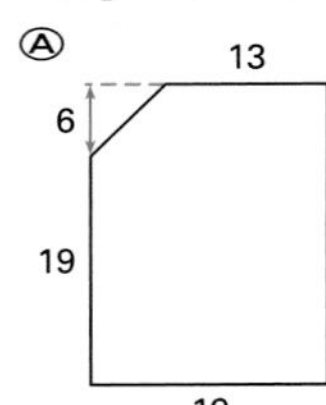

Ⓑ
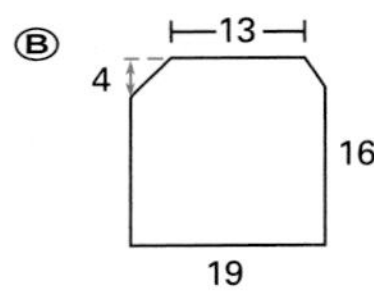

Ⓒ
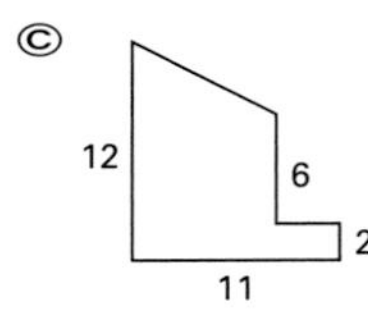

Ⓓ
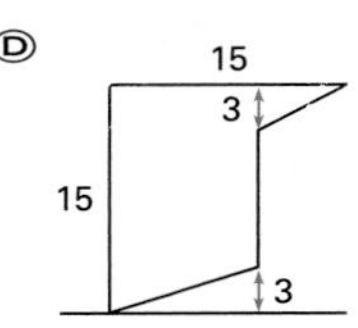

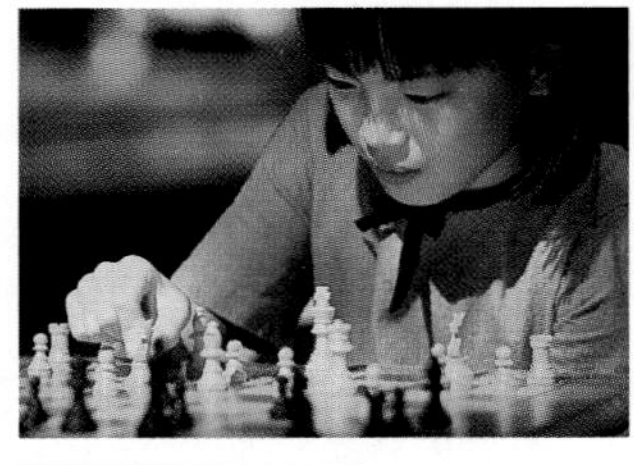

Problem Solving and Reasoning

13. **Critical Thinking** A rectangular table measures 48 in. by 30 in. A square chessboard 24 in. on a side is set on the table. What amount of the table's area is *not* covered by the chessboard? 864 in²

GPS

14. **Communicate** This 8 cm by 8 cm square has been divided into four triangles of equal size. What is the area of one of the triangles? Explain how you found your answer.

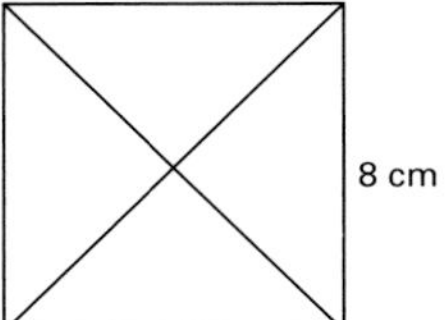

PROBLEM SOLVING 5-10

Mixed Review

Express each fraction in lowest terms. *[Lesson 3-8]*

15. $\frac{25}{35}$ $\frac{5}{7}$ **16.** $\frac{16}{42}$ $\frac{8}{21}$ **17.** $\frac{12}{54}$ $\frac{2}{9}$ **18.** $\frac{49}{84}$ $\frac{7}{12}$

19. $\frac{63}{96}$ $\frac{21}{32}$ **20.** $\frac{38}{95}$ $\frac{2}{5}$ **21.** $\frac{52}{100}$ $\frac{13}{25}$ **22.** $\frac{75}{375}$ $\frac{1}{5}$

Find each quotient. Rewrite in lowest terms. *[Lesson 4-6]*

23. $\frac{3}{7} \div \frac{8}{9}$ $\frac{27}{56}$ **24.** $\frac{5}{6} \div \frac{2}{3}$ $1\frac{1}{4}$ **25.** $\frac{6}{7} \div \frac{3}{14}$ 4 **26.** $\frac{1}{3} \div \frac{3}{4}$ $\frac{4}{9}$

27. $2\frac{3}{4} \div 5\frac{2}{5}$ $\frac{55}{108}$ **28.** $3\frac{2}{7} \div 2\frac{4}{9}$ $1\frac{53}{154}$ **29.** $1\frac{7}{8} \div 4\frac{1}{2}$ $\frac{5}{12}$ **30.** $9\frac{3}{4} \div 3\frac{1}{4}$ 3

Project Progress

Calculate the area of your school's ground floor. Then prepare a report explaining how you made your measurements and how you calculated the area. Be sure to include the floor plan you drew in your report.

Problem Solving
Understand
Plan
Solve
Look Back

PROBLEM SOLVING

Name ______________________

Guided Problem Solving 5-10

GPS **PROBLEM 13, STUDENT PAGE 262**

A rectangular table measures 48 in. by 30 in. A square chessboard 24 in. on a side is set on the table. What amount of the table's area is *not* covered by the chessboard? Possible answers: Items 5 and 10

— Understand —

1. What are the dimensions of the table? 48 in. by 30 in.
2. What are the dimensions of the chessboard? 24 in. by 24 in.

— Plan —

3. Draw a diagram of the chessboard on the table. Shade the area you are trying to find.

48 in.
24 in.
30 in.
24 in.

4. Which formula will you use to find the area of the table? $A = bh$
5. Which formula will you use to find the area of the chessboard? $A = s^2$
6. After you know the areas of the table and the chessboard, which operation will you use to find the area *not* covered? Subtraction.

— Solve —

7. What is the area of the table? 1440 in²
8. What is the area of the chessboard? 576 in²
9. Write a sentence giving the area not covered. Possible answer: The chessboard does not cover 864 in² of the table.

— Look Back —

10. Why is it easier to solve the problem by drawing a diagram? Explain. It helps visualize area of the table not covered by chessboard.

SOLVE ANOTHER PROBLEM

One wall measures 12 ft by 8 ft and contains a window measuring 3 ft by 4 ft. How much wallpaper will be needed to cover the wall? 84 ft²

ENRICHMENT

Name ______________________

Extend Your Thinking 5-10

Decision Making

The students in a wood working class are making toddlers' puzzles to sell at a craft fair.

Possible answers: Items 3–5

1. Find the area of each puzzle piece. Then find the area of the puzzle. 144 in.²

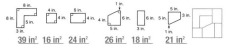

39 in² 16 in² 24 in² 26 in² 18 in² 21 in²

2. The prices of different types of wood is given in the table below. Their supplier sells the wood in either 4 or 8 board foot sections. One board foot measures 1 square foot.

Type of Wood	Cost per board foot	Board feet per section	Cost per section	Puzzles per section
Cherry	$5.50	4	$22	4
Maple	$3.80	8	$30.40	8
Red Oak	$4.00	8	$32	8
White Oak	$3.50	4	$14	4

3. What things in addition to cost would you consider when setting a price for each puzzle? Time to make, uniqueness of product, price of similar products, profit desired.
4. What price would you set for each puzzle? Explain. Cherry $16.50, maple $11.50, red oak $12, white oak $11; To allow for profit, price set at three times cost of wood.
5. You plan to make 52 puzzles to sell at the fair. You want to make some puzzles from each type of wood, and you don't want any wood left over. How many of each puzzle will you make? 12 cherry, 16 maple, 16 red oak, 8 white oak

Section 5B Connect

5B Connect

You've used formulas to find the areas and sides of some geometric figures. You've used estimation to find others. Now you'll apply what you've learned to the design of a multi-game play area.

Shaping Up

Materials: Graph paper

You've been hired to create the ground plan for a game park containing five play areas.

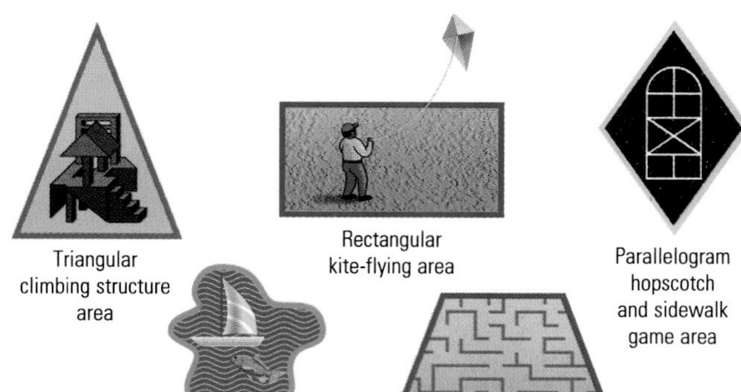

1. Geometric Park is a square with an area of 1024 yd^2. Draw the boundaries of the park on graph paper. Let each square represent an area of 1 square yard.
2. Decide where you will put each of the five play areas and how big each will be. Then draw the outline of each area within the park boundaries. Most of the park should be occupied by the five areas, with only a few small walkways and resting areas separating them.
3. Describe each play area as fully as possible in terms of topics you have studied in this section. Some of the things you might want to describe, calculate, or estimate are lengths, widths, bases, heights, perimeters, areas, and side lengths.

Shaping Up

The Point

In *Shaping Up* on page 239, students discussed geometric shapes used in play areas. Now they will design a multi-game play area.

Materials

Graph paper

Resources

Teaching Tool Transparency 7: $\frac{1}{4}$-Inch Graph Paper

About the Page

- Students might first research the areas of such things as ball fields, tennis courts, swimming pools, and the width of sidewalks.
- Remind students that 1 yd^2 = 9 ft^2. Make sure they are aware they have an area of 1024 yd^2 or 9,216 ft^2 with which to work.

Ongoing Assessment

Check that students have drawn a reasonable plan with appropriate boundaries and play areas.

Extension

Suppose that an acre (4840 yd^2) of property became available to add to the park. Have students discuss other things they would add to make the play area more useful and attractive.

Answers for Connect

1–3. Answers may vary.

5B Review

Review Correlation

Item(s)	Lesson(s)
1–3	5-5
4–8	5-6
9–12	5-7
13,15	5-9
14	5-8
16	5-10
17	5-8, 5-9
18	5-5
19	5-8

Test Prep

Test-Taking Tip

Tell students that making up numbers can sometimes help to solve a problem. Here students can use 24 for the area of the rectangle. The answers for A, B, and C are 12, 48, and 576. Since the triangle is smaller than the rectangle, 12 is the only answer that makes sense.

Answers for Review

1. Perimeter = 74 m; Area = 300 m^2.
2. Perimeter = 12.6 cm; Area = 9.36 cm^2.
3. Perimeter = $15\frac{1}{4}$ in; Area = $14\frac{7}{32}$ in^2.

17. Possible answer: Similarities: Both multiply heights by $\frac{1}{2}$. Difference: Triangle multiplies by the base, trapezoid multiplies by the sum of the bases.

Section 5B Review

REVIEW 5B

Find the perimeter and area for each rectangle.

1. $l = 25$ m; $w = 12$ m **2.** $l = 3.9$ cm; $w = 2.4$ cm **3.** $l = 4\frac{3}{8}$ in.; $w = 3\frac{1}{4}$ in.

Find the value of each expression.

4. 12^2 144 **5.** $\sqrt{121}$ 11 **6.** $(0.27)^2$ 0.0729 **7.** $\left(\frac{9}{10}\right)^2$ $\frac{81}{100}$ **8.** $\sqrt{169}$ 13

Find the missing length in each right triangle.

9. 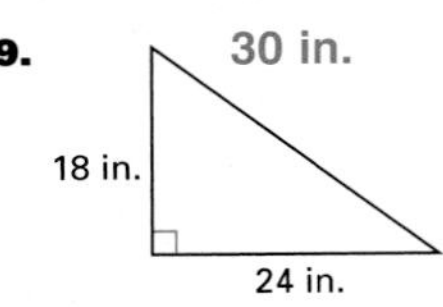

10. 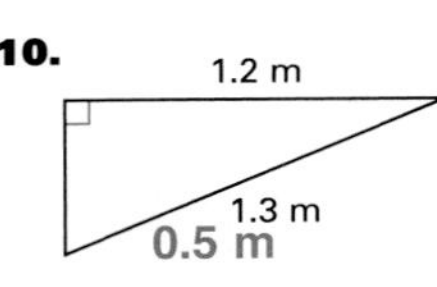

11. 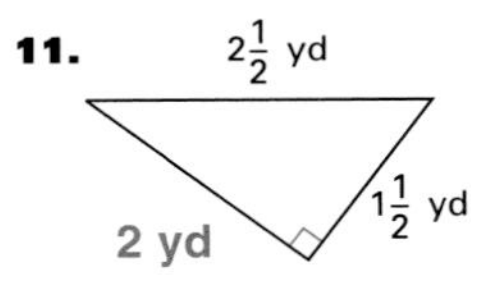

12. 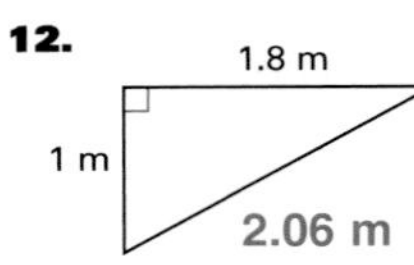

Find the area of each figure.

13. 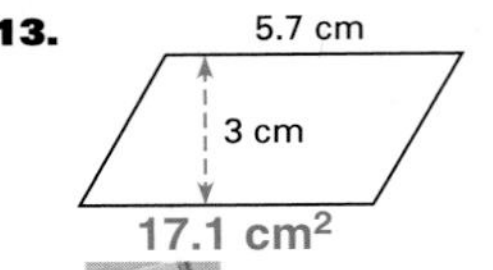

14. 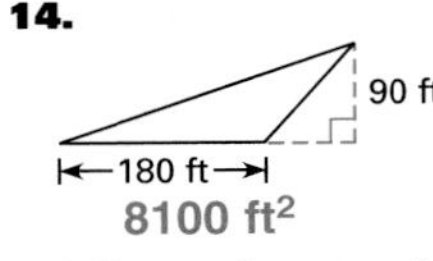

15. 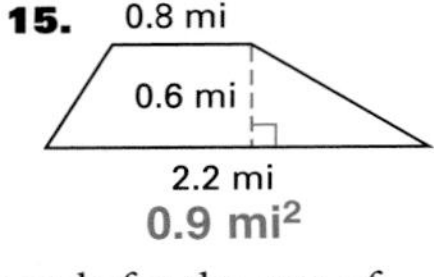

16. 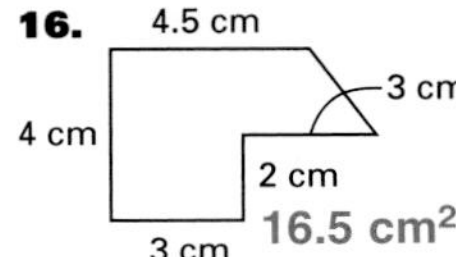

17. 

Write about the difference between the formula for the area of a triangle and the formula for the area of a trapezoid.

18. Measurement A swimming pool measures 50 m by 21 m. A typical water polo playing area measures 30 m by 20 m. How much greater than the water polo playing area is the area of the pool? 450 m^2

Test Prep

On a multiple choice test on which you are asked to find the area of a figure, recognizing that certain figures can be divided into smaller areas will help you work more quickly.

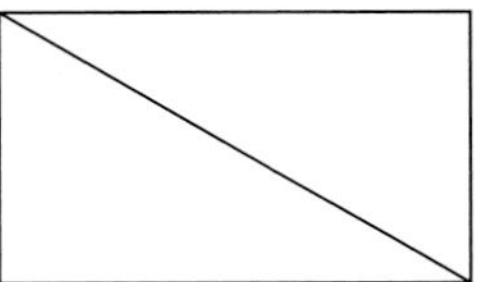

19. This rectangle is divided into two triangles of equal size. If you are given the area of the rectangle, how do you determine the area of one of the triangles? A

Ⓐ Divide the given area by 2. Ⓑ Multiply the given area by 2.

Ⓒ Square the given area. Ⓓ The answer is not given here.

Resources

Practice Masters
Section 5B Review

Assessment Sourcebook
Quiz 5B

TestWorks
Test and Practice Software

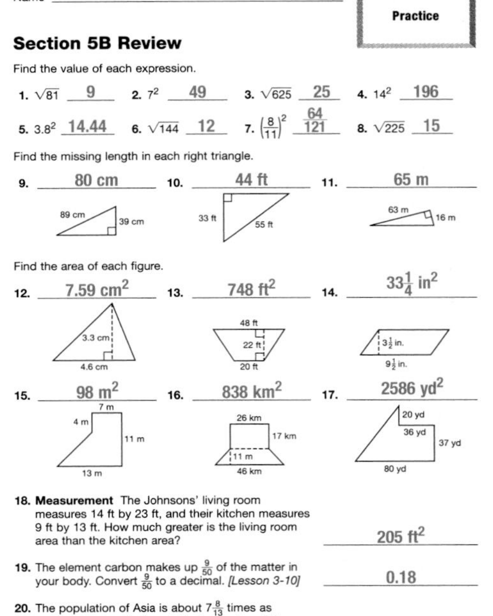
Name ______

Practice

Section 5B Review

Find the value of each expression.

1. $\sqrt{81}$ 9 2. 7^2 49 3. $\sqrt{625}$ 25 4. 14^2 196

5. 3.8^2 14.44 6. $\sqrt{144}$ 12 7. $\left(\frac{8}{11}\right)^2$ $\frac{64}{121}$ 8. $\sqrt{225}$ 15

Find the missing length in each right triangle.

9. 80 cm 10. 44 ft 11. 65 m

Find the area of each figure.

12. 7.59 cm^2 13. 748 ft^2 14. $33\frac{1}{4}$ in^2

15. 98 m^2 16. 838 km^2 17. 2586 yd^2

18. **Measurement** The Johnsons' living room measures 14 ft by 23 ft, and their kitchen measures 9 ft by 13 ft. How much greater is the living room area than the kitchen area? 205 ft^2

19. The element carbon makes up $\frac{9}{50}$ of the matter in your body. Convert $\frac{9}{50}$ to a decimal. *[Lesson 3-10]* 0.18

20. The population of Asia is about $7\frac{8}{13}$ times as great as the population of North America. If the population of North America was 436,000,000 in 1992, what was the population of Asia? About 3,320,000,000

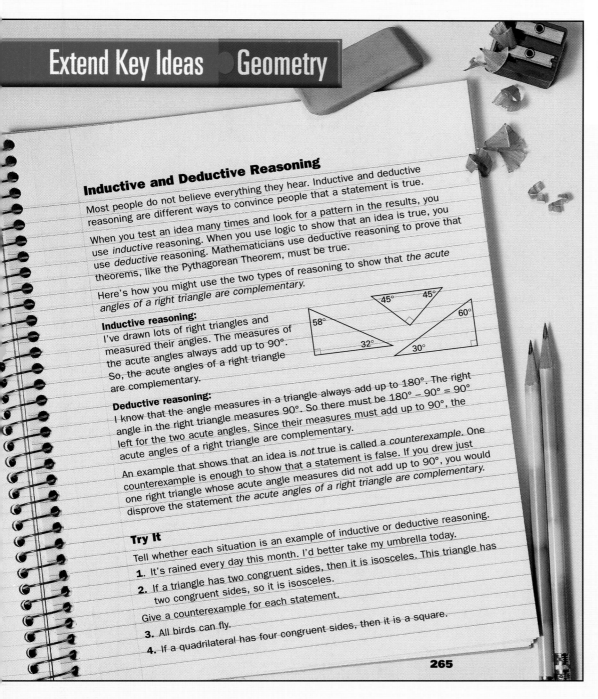

Extend Key Ideas Geometry

Inductive and Deductive Reasoning

Most people do not believe everything they hear. Inductive and deductive reasoning are different ways to convince people that a statement is true.

When you test an idea many times and look for a pattern in the results, you use *inductive* reasoning. When you use logic to show that an idea is true, you use *deductive* reasoning. Mathematicians use deductive reasoning to prove that theorems, like the Pythagorean Theorem, must be true.

Here's how you might use the two types of reasoning to show that *the acute angles of a right triangle are complementary.*

Inductive reasoning:
I've drawn lots of right triangles and measured their angles. The measures of the acute angles always add up to 90°. So, the acute angles of a right triangle are complementary.

Deductive reasoning:
I know that the angle measures in a triangle always add up to 180°. The right angle in the right triangle measures 90°. So there must be 180° – 90° = 90° left for the two acute angles. Since their measures must add up to 90°, the acute angles of a right triangle are complementary.

An example that shows that an idea is *not* true is called a *counterexample.* One counterexample is enough to show that a statement is false. If you drew just one right triangle whose acute angle measures did not add up to 90°, you would disprove the statement *the acute angles of a right triangle are complementary.*

Try It

Tell whether each situation is an example of inductive or deductive reasoning.

1. It's rained every day this month. I'd better take my umbrella today.
2. If a triangle has two congruent sides, then it is isosceles. This triangle has two congruent sides, so it is isosceles.

Give a counterexample for each statement.

3. All birds can fly.
4. If a quadrilateral has four congruent sides, then it is a square.

265

Inductive and Deductive Reasoning

The Point
Students learn the difference between inductive and deductive reasoning.

About the Page

Students may not be familiar with the terms *inductive* and *deductive reasoning*, or even that there are different ways people reason. Explain that in mystery stories, detectives often *deduce* conclusions from the clues; they make *deductions.* Scientists who conduct experiments may base their conclusions on repeatedly observed data; they are using inductive reasoning.

Ask ...

- In the example presented, which reasoning seems more sound? Possible answer: Deductive, since the result is shown to be a certainty for all right triangles. The inductive reasoning leaves open the possibility that the next right triangle might be a counterexample.

Extension

Have students think of two situations, one in which only inductive reasoning can be used, and one in which only deductive reasoning can be used. Possible answers: Inductive: Conducting surveys to determine the probabilities of people's responses. Deductive: Solving equations.

Answers for Try It

1. Inductive
2. Deductive
3. An ostrich cannot fly.
4. 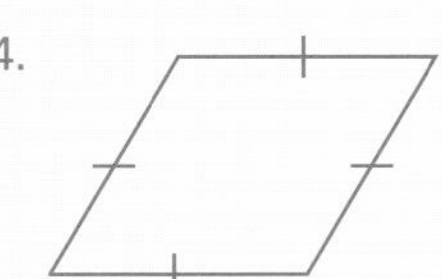

Chapter 5 Summary and Review

Review Correlation

Item(s)	Lesson(s)
1	5-1
2	5-4
3	5-1
4	5-2
5	5-5
6	5-3, 5-4
7, 8	5-6
9	5-7
10	5-9
11	5-8
12	5-10

For additional review, see page 676.

Answers for Review

1. Possible answer:

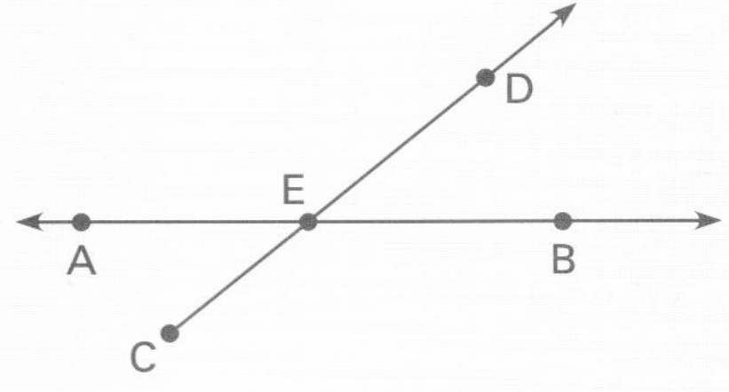

4. $\angle EFD$, an alternate interior angle.
5. Perimeter: 20 ft; Area: 24 ft^2
6. Right; Acute; Obtuse.

Chapter 5 Summary and Review

Graphic Organizer

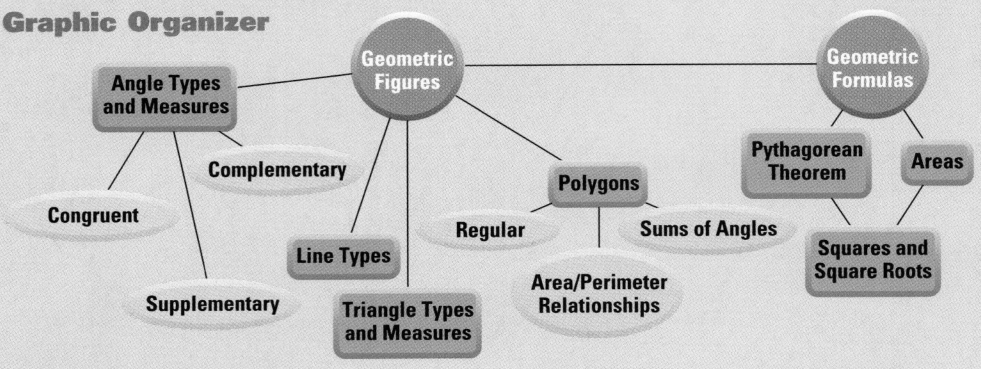

Section 5A Geometric Figures

Summary

- Two **rays** with a common endpoint form an **angle.**
- An **acute** angle measures less than 90°, a **right** angle measures 90°, and an **obtuse** angle measures between 90° and 180°. A **straight** angle measures 180°. **Complementary** angles add up to 90°; **supplementary** ones add up to 180°. **Congruent** angles have the same measure.
- Lines in a plane that never meet are **parallel. Perpendicular** lines, rays, and segments form right angles.
- A triangle may be classified by its sides, as **equilateral, isosceles,** or **scalene,** or by its angles, as **acute, right,** or **obtuse.**
- A **rhombus** is a **quadrilateral** with all sides congruent. A **trapezoid** is a quadrilateral with just one pair of parallel sides. The angles of a triangle total 180° and the angles of a quadrilateral total 360°. In **regular polygons,** all sides and angles are congruent.
- The area of a rectangle is the base (length) times the height (width): $A = bh$. The perimeter of a figure is the distance around its edge.

Review

1. Draw a line $\overleftrightarrow{AB}$ and a ray $\overrightarrow{CD}$ intersecting to form $\angle AED$.

2. What is the sum of the measures of the angles of a 10-sided polygon? **1440°**

Resources

Practice Masters
Cumulative Review Chapters 1–5

PRACTICE

Name ______________ **Practice**

Cumulative Review Chapters 1–5

Use the given formula to complete each table. *[Lesson 2-3]*

1. $y = 5x + 8$

x	4	5	6	7
y	28	33	38	43

2. $D = 60t$

D	3	4	5	6
t	180	240	300	360

Find the GCF and LCM of each pair of numbers. *[Lesson 3-7]*

3. 14, 49 GCF: 7 LCM: 98
4. 65, 26 GCF: 13 LCM: 130
5. 24, 60 GCF: 12 LCM: 120
6. 32, 45 GCF: 1 LCM: 1440

Solve each equation. *[Lesson 4-3]*

7. $5\frac{7}{8} + x = 10\frac{1}{4}$ $x =$ $4\frac{3}{8}$
8. $p - 12\frac{1}{3} = 6\frac{5}{6}$ $p =$ $19\frac{1}{6}$
9. $z + 3\frac{1}{4} = 10$ $z =$ $6\frac{3}{4}$
10. $c - 12\frac{1}{2} = 2\frac{1}{3}$ $c =$ $14\frac{5}{6}$
11. $k + 5\frac{3}{11} = 8\frac{1}{2}$ $k =$ $3\frac{5}{22}$
12. $d - 7\frac{3}{10} = 4\frac{1}{5}$ $d =$ $11\frac{1}{2}$
13. $4\frac{2}{3} + u = 6\frac{4}{15}$ $u =$ $1\frac{3}{5}$
14. $t - 9\frac{1}{8} = 7\frac{5}{12}$ $t =$ $16\frac{13}{24}$

Find the sum of the measures of the angles of each polygon. *[Lesson 5-4]*

15. octagon 1080°
16. 14-sided polygon 2160°
17. 18-sided polygon 2880°
18. 29-sided polygon 4860°
19. 36-sided polygon 6120°
20. 57-sided polygon 9900°

Find the missing length in each right triangle. *[Lesson 5-7]*

21. $n =$ 53 (28 cm, 45 cm, n cm)
22. $u =$ 11 (u ft, 60 ft, 61 ft)
23. $p =$ 77 (p m, 85 m, 36 m)

Chapter 5 Summary and Review

Section 5A Geometric Figures *continued*

3. If $\angle RST$ measures 48°:

a. What is the measure of an angle supplementary to $\angle RST$? 132°

b. What is the measure of an angle complementary to $\angle RST$? 42°

4. Lines $\overleftrightarrow{AB}$ and $\overleftrightarrow{CD}$ are parallel. Name an angle congruent to $\angle AEF$ and explain why it is congruent to $\angle AEF$.

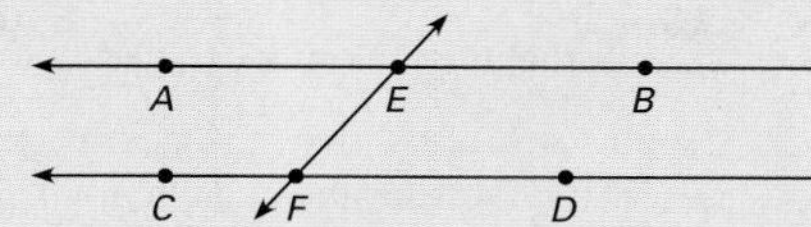

5. Find the perimeter and area of the rectangular floor of a storage shed 4 ft wide and 6 ft long.

6. Fill in the blanks with *acute, right,* or *obtuse:* All angles of a square are ______ angles. All angles of an equilateral triangle are ______ angles. The angles of any other regular polygon are ______ angles.

Section 5B Geometric Formulas

Summary

- A **perfect square** is the square of a whole number. The **square root** of a number is the length of the side of a square whose area is that number.
- The **hypotenuse** of a right triangle is the side opposite the right angle. The other sides are called **legs**. The **Pythagorean Theorem** says that the sum of the squares of the lengths of the legs of a right triangle is equal to the square of the length of the hypotenuse.
- A triangle's area is half the product of its base length and height: $A = \frac{1}{2}bh$. The area of a parallelogram is the product of the length of its base and its height: $A = bh$. The area of a trapezoid is half its height multiplied by the sum of the lengths of its bases: $A = \frac{1}{2}h(b_1 + b_2)$.

Review

7. Find a perfect square between 45 and 55. 49

8. Find $\sqrt{17}$ to three decimal places. 4.123

9. Find the length of the hypotenuse of a triangle whose legs measure 6 ft and 8 ft. 10 ft

10. Find the area of a trapezoid whose height is 4 cm and whose bases are 3 and 11 cm long. 28 cm²

11. Find the area of the obtuse triangle. 5.425 cm²

5.5 cm

3.1 cm

3.5 cm

12. Find the area of the side of the building. 260 ft²

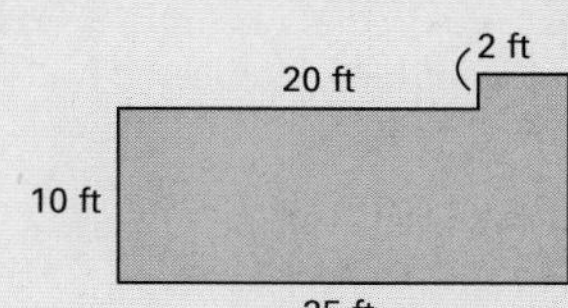

Chapter 5 Assessment

Assessment Correlation

Item(s)	Lesson(s)
1, 2	5-3
3	5-1, 5-3
4	5-7
5	5-9
6	5-10
7	5-1
8	5-4
9, 10	5-6
11	5-8
12	5-9
13	5-1, 5-3
14	5-2

Answers for Assessment

1. 22°
2. Isosceles, acute; Scalene, right.
3. 68°; Complementary.
4. 215.41 ft
5. 12,000 ft^2
6. Find the areas of both triangles and add or find the area of the trapezoid and subtract the area of the parallelogram (passage-way); 24,000 ft^2.
8. 900°
11. 112.5 cm^2
13. Possible answer:

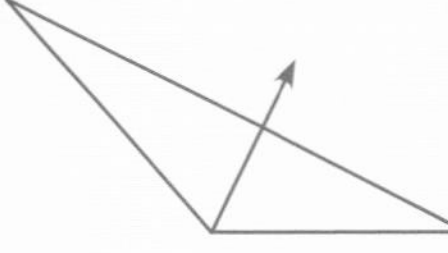

14. Possible answer (drawn here to scale):

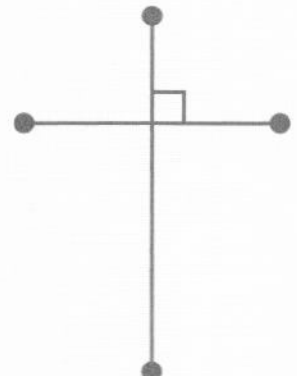

Answers for Performance Task

Triangle; 180°; 1440°

Chapter 5 Assessment

The floor plans for two triangular buildings with a passageway between them is shown. Use them to answer Questions 1–6.

1. What is the measure of the angle at corner *A*?

2. Classify each of the two triangles as equilateral, isosceles, or scalene and as acute, right, or obtuse.

3. What is the measure of ∠*B*? What is true about angles *A* and *B*?

4. Find the length, to two decimal places, of one side of the passage between the two parts of the building.

5. Find the floor area of the passage.

6. What two methods would give you the total area of both buildings? Use either method to find that area.

7. If ∠*ABC* measures 81°:

a. What is the measure of an angle complementary to ∠*ABC*? 9°

b. What is the measure of an angle supplementary to ∠*ABC*? 99°

8. Find the sum of the angles of a regular heptagon (seven-sided polygon).

9. List all of the perfect squares between 60 and 130. 64, 81, 100, 121

10. Find $\sqrt{225}$. 15

11. Find the area of an isosceles right triangle with legs measuring 15 cm.

12. Find the area of a trapezoid whose bases are 4 cm and 12 cm and whose height is 6 cm. 48 cm^2

13. Draw an obtuse triangle with a ray bisecting the obtuse angle.

14. Draw a 3 in. line segment with a 5 in. perpendicular bisector.

Performance Task

This is a three-dimensional shape called an *octahedron*. What shape does each of its eight outside surfaces have? (Be as specific as you can.) What is the sum of the angle measures on one of these surfaces? What is the sum of the angle measures on all of these surfaces?

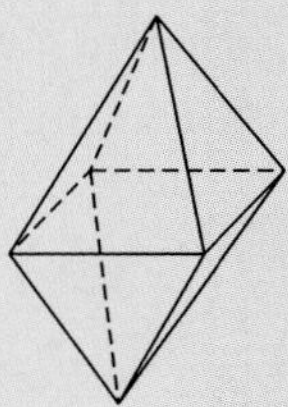

268 *Chapter 5 • Geometry and Measurement*

Resources

Assessment Sourcebook

Chapter 5 Tests
- Forms A and B (free response)
- Form C (multiple choice)
- Form D (performance assessment)
- Form E (mixed response)
- Form F (cumulative chapter test)

TestWorks
Test and Practice Software

Home and Community Connections
- Letter Home for Chapter 5 in English and Spanish

Cumulative Review Chapters 1–5 Test Prep

Performance Assessment

Choose one problem.

Saying More with Less

Draw the outline of a floor plan for a building that uses three different regular polygons. Using the smallest number of lengths possible, describe the dimensions of the building completely. Explain how you can use those measurements to find the others and calculate the area of the plan.

You Can Run, and Hide

According to legend, Queen Dido fled to Africa after her husband was killed. There, she begged a king for land. He granted her only as much as she could enclose with an oxhide.

Queen Dido sliced the oxhide into strips, then used the strips to surround a large area. According to the story, this land became the city of Carthage.

Suppose you have a 24-foot-long strip of hide. If you made an equilateral triangle out of the strip, how much area would it enclose? What area would you get if you made a square? A regular hexagon? If you were Queen Dido, which of these shapes would you choose for your city and why?

THE MYSTERY OF METER MOUNTAIN

Meter Mountain is 10 km across, but no one knows how tall it is. It's an easy 8 km hike to the top of the mountain on its west side. No one has ever climbed the steeper east side. Find:

e, the length of the hike up the east side.

h, the height of Meter Mountain.

Explain how you found your answers.

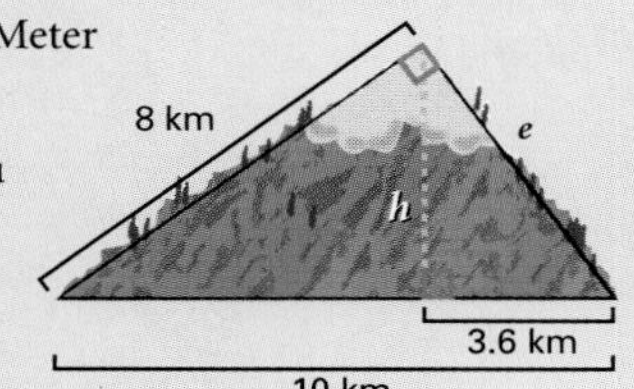

Cold Facts

If two buildings are identical except for the shapes of their bases, the one with the greater perimeter loses more heat. On graph paper, draw a square with an area of 64 square units, then experiment with a compass to draw a circle with about the same area. Compare their perimeters. If you lived in a cold climate, which shape would you prefer for a home? Why?

Answers for Assessment

- **You Can Run, and Hide**

Triangle area ≈ 27.6 ft^2; Square area = 36 ft^2; Regular hexagon area ≈ 42 ft^2; Hexagon, because it would enclose the most land.

- **The Mystery of Meter Mountain**

$e = 6$ km

$h = 4.8$ km

Used the Pythagorean Theorem.

- **Cold Facts**

The perimeter of the circle will be about 28 units, compared to 32 for the square. The circle gives the same area for a smaller perimeter, so it is the more efficient shape in cold climates.

Cumulative Review

About Performance Assessment

The Performance Assessment options ...

- provide teachers with an alternate means of assessing students.
- address different learning modalities.
- allow students to choose one problem.

Teachers may encourage students to choose the most challenging problem.

Learning Modalities
Saying More with Less **Visual** Students visualize relationships of regular polygons in floor plans.
You Can Run, and Hide **Individual** Students use critical thinking to maximize area.
Cold Facts **Kinesthetic** Students investigate shapes of buildings and classify each as to heat efficiency.
The Mystery of Meter Mountain **Logical** Students explain how to find various measurements in a triangle.

Suggested Scoring Rubric

See key on page 209.

Saying More with Less

4	•Floor plan clearly shows three different regular polygons. •Demonstrates an understanding of how to find missing dimensions and total area.
3	•Floor plan clearly shows three different regular polygons. •Demonstrates an understanding of how to find most missing dimensions.
2	•Plan attempts to show three different regular polygons. •Has some difficulty explaining how to find the missing dimensions and areas.
1	•Shows little understanding of regular polygons. •Has difficulty explaining how to find the missing dimensions and areas.

Ratios, Rates, and Proportions

Section 6A

Ratios and Rates: Students use ratios to compare quantities of all kinds. Students learn to find a ratio or rate that is equivalent to a given ratio or rate.

6-1 Exploring and Estimating Ratios

6-2 Exploring and Estimating Rates

6-3 Equivalent Ratios and Rates

6-4 Using Tables to Explore Ratios and Rates

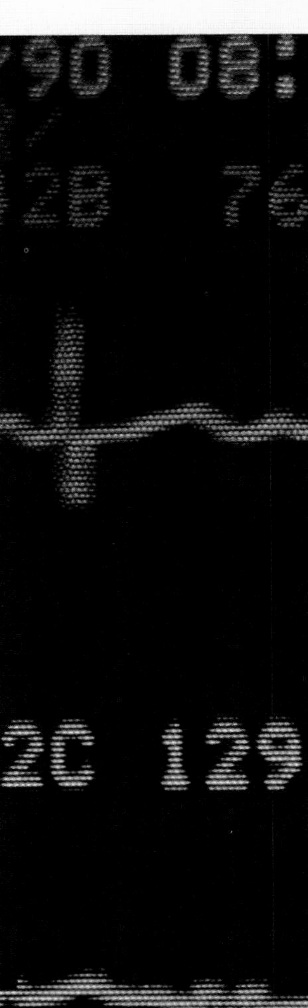

Section 6B

Proportional Quantities: Students investigate equations involving equivalent ratios. They learn how to evaluate and solve proportions.

6-5 Creating Proportions

6-6 Testing for Proportionality

6-7 Solving Proportions Using Unit Rates

6-8 Cross Multiplication

Meeting NCTM Standards

Curriculum Standards

STANDARD			pages
1	**Problem Solving**	Skills and Strategies	271, 272, 277, 287, 290, 296, 307, 312
		Applications	276–277, 280–281, 284–285, 289–290, 291, 296–297, 301–302, 306–307, 311–312, 313
		Exploration	274, 278, 282, 286, 294, 298, 304, 308
2	**Communication**	Oral	273, 276, 279, *281*, 283, 288, *290*, 293, 295, 300, 305, *307*, 310
		Written	277, 281, 285, 290, 292, 297, *302*, 307, 312, 314
		Cooperative Learning	*273, 274, 278, 282, 286, 291, 294, 298, 304, 308*
3	**Reasoning**	Critical Thinking	281, 285, 290, 297, 302, 307, 312
4	**Connections**	Mathematical	See Standards 5, 7, 8, 11–13 below.
		Interdisciplinary	Health 273, 284, 292; Language 305, *310;* Entertainment 270; Arts & Literature 270, 275, 297, 306, 312; Social Studies 271, 295; History 275, 311; Consumer 289, 292, 314; Industry 281; Sports 281, 306; Science 271, *273*, 274, 276, *277*, 279, 280, *281*, 283, *284*, 285, *288*, *290*, 292, 293, 297, *300*, 301, 305, *310*, 311, 312, 314
		Technology	272, 285, 295, 298, 303, 312
		Cultural	270, *276*, 279, *281*
5	**Number and Number Relationships**		274–313
7	**Computation and Estimation**		276, 277, 278–281, *283*, 289, *299*, 306, 312
8	**Patterns and Functions**		286–290, *302*, 307
10	**Statistics**		267, *277*, 300
11	**Probability**		284, 302
12	**Geometry**		277, 281, 285, *302*, 315
13	**Measurement**		278–291, 297–298, 304–307, 315

Italic type indicates Teacher Edition reference.

Teaching Standards

Focus on Inclusion

It is essential that schools and communities accept the goal of mathematical education for every child. This includes

- students for whom English is not their first language.
- students with hearing or sight impairments.
- students with physical disabilities.

Assessment Standards

Focus on Learning

Performance One focus of the Learning Standard is the view that assessment activities can be learning activities as well as demonstrations of what students know and can do. Performance tasks can be constructed to naturally extend from showing learned knowledge to exploring further mathematics. In Chapter 6 students show they can

- find ratio relationships.
- determine best buys.

TECHNOLOGY

For the Teacher

- **Teacher Resource Planner CD-ROM**
  Use the teacher planning CD-ROM to view resources available for Chapter 6. You can prepare custom lesson plans or use the default lesson plans provided.

- **World Wide Web**
  Visit **www.teacher.mathsurf.com** for links to lesson plans from teachers and other professionals, NCTM information, and other sites.

- **TestWorks**
  TestWorks provides ready-made tests and can create custom tests and practice worksheets.

For the Parent

- **World Wide Web**
  Parents can use the Web site at **www.parent.mathsurf.com.**

For the Student

- **Interactive CD-ROM**
  Lesson 6-6 has an *Interactive CD-ROM Lesson*. The *Interactive CD-ROM Journal* is also used in Chapter 6.

- **Wide World of Mathematics**
  Lesson 6-2 Algebra: Traveling the Oregon Trail
  Lesson 6-7 Middle School: New York City Marathon

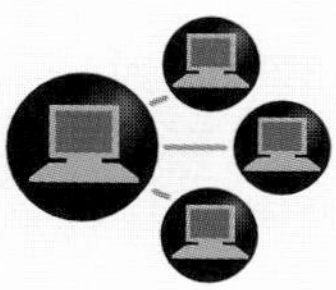

- **World Wide Web**
  Use with Chapter and Section Openers; Students can go online to the Scott Foresman-Addison Wesley Web site at **www.mathsurf.com/7/ch6** to collect information about chapter themes.

STANDARDIZED - TEST CORRELATION

SECTION 6A

LESSON	OBJECTIVE	ITBS Form M	CTBS 4th Ed.	CAT 5th Ed.	SAT 9th Ed.	MAT 7th Ed.	Your Form
6-1	• Know what a ratio is.	✘	✘	✘	✘	✘	
	• Compare quantities using division.	✘	✘	✘	✘	✘	
6-2	• Compare two quantities with different units of measure.			✘		✘	
	• Make comparisons to one unit.			✘		✘	
6-3	• Find equivalent ratios and rates.	✘		✘		✘	
6-4	• Use a table to find equivalent ratios and rates.					✘	

SECTION 6B

LESSON	OBJECTIVE	ITBS Form M	CTBS 4th Ed.	CAT 5th Ed.	SAT 9th Ed.	MAT 7th Ed.	Your Form
6-5	• Use equivalent ratios to write proportions.		✘	✘	✘	✘	
6-6	• Recognize proportional relationships.	✘	✘	✘	✘	✘	
6-7	• Use unit rates to solve a proportion.			✘	✘	✘	
6-8	• Use cross multiplication to solve a proportion.						
	• Use cross multiplication to check whether two ratios form a proportion.						

Key: ITBS - Iowa Test of Basic Skills; CTBS - Comprehensive Test of Basic Skills; CAT - California Achievement Test; SAT - Stanford Achievement Test; MAT - Metropolitan Achievement Test

ASSESSMENT PROGRAM

Traditional Assessment

QUICK QUIZZES	SECTION REVIEW	CHAPTER REVIEW	CHAPTER ASSESSMENT FREE RESPONSE	CHAPTER ASSESSMENT MULTIPLE CHOICE	CUMULATIVE REVIEW
TE: pp. 277, 281, 285, 290, 297, 302, 307, 312	SE: pp. 292, 314 *Quiz 6A, 6B	SE: pp. 316–317	SE: p. 318 *Ch. 6 Tests Forms A, B, E	*Ch. 6 Tests Forms C, E	SE: p. 319 *Ch. 6 Test Form F

Alternate Assessment

INTERVIEW	JOURNAL	ONGOING	PERFORMANCE	PORTFOLIO	PROJECT	SELF
TE: pp. 281, 290, 307	SE: pp. 277, 285, 290, 292, 297, 307, 314 TE: pp. 273, 285, 302, 312	TE: pp. 274, 278, 281, 286, 294, 298, 304, 308	SE: p. 318 TE: p. 277 *Ch. 6 Tests Forms D, E	TE: p. 297	SE: pp. 290, 307 TE: p. 271	

*Tests and quizzes are in *Assessment Sourcebook*. Test Form E is a mixed response test. Forms for Alternate Assessment are also available in *Assessment Sourcebook*.

TestWorks: Test and Practice Software

MIDDLE SCHOOL PACING CHART

REGULAR PACING

Day	5 classes per week
1	Chapter 6 Opener; Problem Solving Focus
2	Section **6A** Opener; Lesson **6-1**
3	Lesson **6-2**
4	Lesson **6-3**
5	Lesson **6-4**
6	**6A** Connect; **6A** Review
7	Section **6B** Opener; Lesson **6-5**
8	Lesson **6-6**; Technology
9	Lesson **6-7**
10	Lesson **6-8**
11	**6B** Connect; **6B** Review; Extend Key Ideas
12	Chapter 6 Summary and Review
13	Chapter 6 Assessment
14	Cumulative Review, Chapters, 1–6

BLOCK SCHEDULING OPTIONS

Block Scheduling for Complete Course

Chapter 6 may be presented in

- eight 90-minute blocks
- eleven 75-minute blocks

Each block consists of a combination of

- Chapter and Section Openers
- Explores
- Lesson Development
- Problem Solving Focus
- Technology
- Extend Key Ideas
- Connect
- Review
- Assessment

For details, see *Block Scheduling Handbook.*

Block Scheduling for Interdisciplinary Course

Each block integrates math with another subject area.

In Chapter 6, interdisciplinary topics include

- The Human Body
- Whales

Themes for Interdisciplinary Team Teaching 6A and 6B are

- The Cardiovascular System
- Blue Whale Population

For details, see *Block Scheduling Handbook.*

Block Scheduling for Lab-Based Course

In each block, 30–40 minutes is devoted to lab activities including

- Explores in the Student Edition
- Connect pages in the Student Edition
- Technology options in the Student Edition
- Reteaching Activities in the Teacher Edition

For details, see *Block Scheduling Handbook.*

Block Scheduling for Course with *Connected Mathematics*

In each block, investigations from **Connected Mathematics** replace or enhance the lessons in Chapter 6.

Connected Mathematics topics for Chapter 6 can be found in

- *Comparing and Scaling*

For details, see *Block Scheduling Handbook.*

INTERDISCIPLINARY BULLETIN BOARD

Set Up

Prepare a bulletin board that lists the following ratios: number of right-handers to number of left-handers, number of right-handers to total number of students, and number of left-handers to total number of students.

Procedure

- Right-handed students should outline their right hand on paper, and left-handed students outline their left hand.
- Students embellish the hand outlines, write their names on them, cut them out, and hang them on the bulletin board.
- The class determines the ratio of right-handers to left-handers, ratio of right-handers to total number of students, and ratio of left-handers to total number of students.

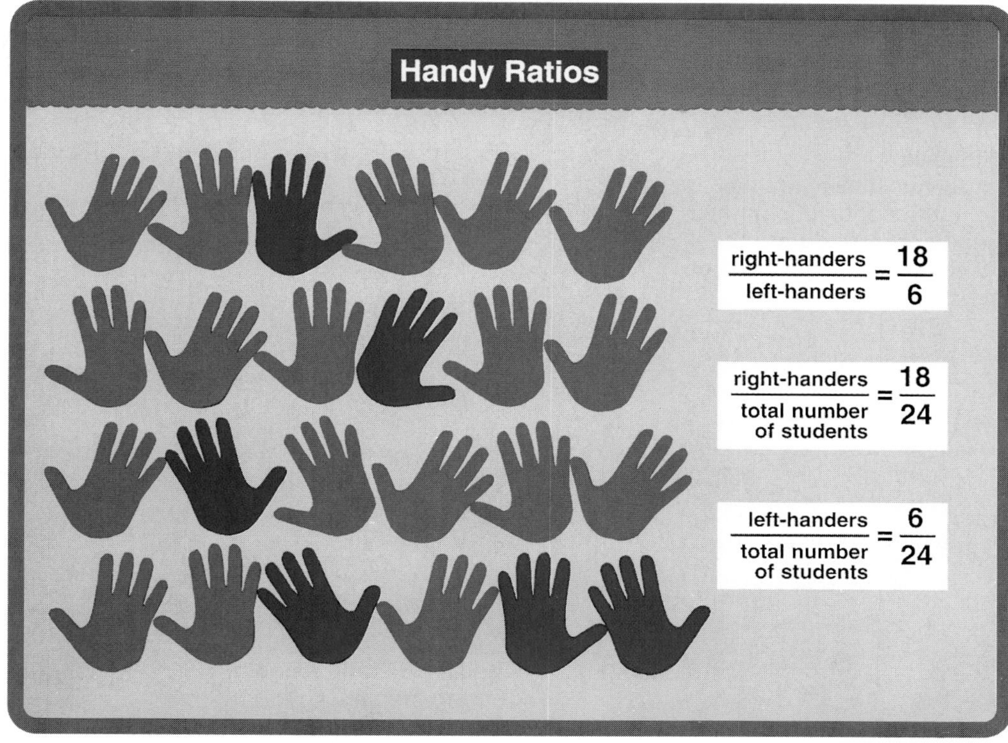

Handy Ratios
right-handers / left-handers = 18 / 6
right-handers / total number of students = 18 / 24
left-handers / total number of students = 6 / 24

Chapter 6

The information on these pages shows how to apply ratios, rates, and proportions to real-life situations.

World Wide Web

If your class has access to the World Wide Web, you might want to use the information found at the Web site addresses given.

Extensions

The following activities do not require access to the World Wide Web.

People of the World
Ask students to discuss what they think the effect the inability to read in English would have on a person's life in the United States.

Arts & Literature
Students might research Tchaikovsky's life and the kind of music he wrote. If possible, play a piece of his music for the students.

Entertainment
Have groups of students pick a favorite movie, determine how many minutes the movie runs, and find out how many frames the movie contains.

Science
Have students find how many calories per hour various activities use, especially their favorite sport or activity.

Social Studies
Have students investigate the change in the population in their community or state during the past 10 years. Did the population increase or decrease?

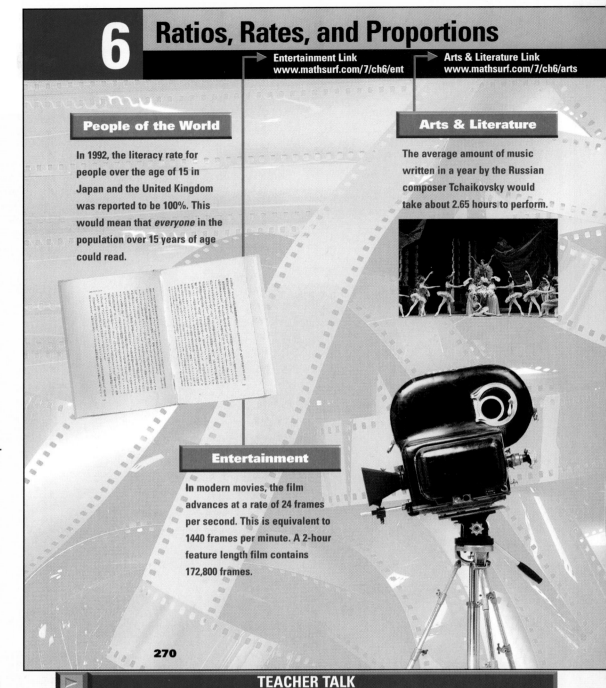

6 Ratios, Rates, and Proportions

Entertainment Link
www.mathsurf.com/7/ch6/ent

Arts & Literature Link
www.mathsurf.com/7/ch6/arts

People of the World

In 1992, the literacy rate for people over the age of 15 in Japan and the United Kingdom was reported to be 100%. This would mean that *everyone* in the population over 15 years of age could read.

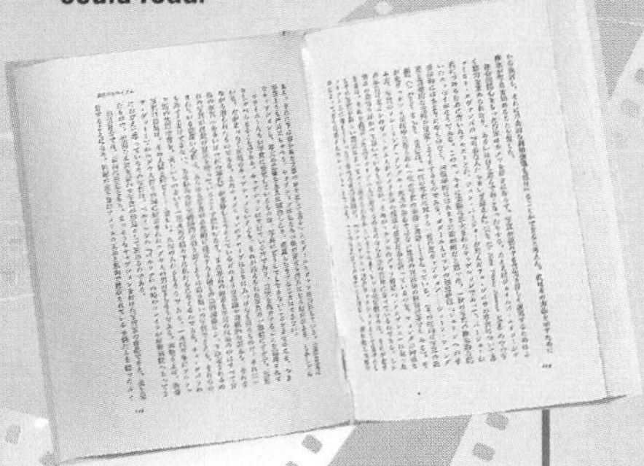

Arts & Literature

The average amount of music written in a year by the Russian composer Tchaikovsky would take about 2.65 hours to perform.

Entertainment

In modern movies, the film advances at a rate of 24 frames per second. This is equivalent to 1440 frames per minute. A 2-hour feature length film contains 172,800 frames.

270

TEACHER TALK

Meet Charlotte Jenkins

Ulysses S. Grant School
Chicago, Illinois

To introduce a chapter on ratios, I have students look at newspapers and find as many examples of ratios as they can. The examples might come from advertisements, news articles, or the sports page. As students report their findings, the class discusses the types of things being compared.

I look for a teachable moment during the discussion to stress the significance of order when two or more ratios are involved. I choose a sports example like hits for the number of times at bat, a consumer example such as cost per pound, or a school news item such as the ratio of boys to girls in each 7th grade class. Students quickly see the need to set up ratios in the same order when two or more ratios are used for the same situation.

Social Studies Link
www.mathsurf.com/7/ch6/social

Science

When sitting quietly, the average 150-pound adult burns about 50 calories an hour.

Social Studies

Between 1980 and 1990 the population of Los Angeles, California, grew at a rate of 17.41% per decade, while the population of Houston grew at a rate of 2.22%.

KEY MATH IDEAS

Ratios can be used to compare any two numbers.

Rates compare numbers whose units are different. Different rates related to the human body help doctors test a patient's health.

A unit rate compares a number to 1. Unit rates are convenient to work with when solving problems.

A proportion is an equation with equal ratios. By using proportions, you can use a small number of tests to make predictions about a larger population.

There are several ways to solve a proportion. You can use tables, unit rates, or cross multiplication.

CHAPTER PROJECT

Problem Solving

Understand
Plan
Solve
Look Back

In this project, you will conduct a price survey of different stores in your neighborhood and decide which one has the best prices. Begin the project by identifying the six to ten grocery items that your family buys most often.

271

PROJECT ASSESSMENT

You may choose to use this project as a performance assessment for the chapter.

Performance Assessment Key

Level 4 Full Accomplishment

Level 3 Substantial Accomplishment

Level 2 Partial Accomplishment

Level 1 Little Accomplishment

Suggested Scoring Rubric

4
- Records all necessary information for 6–10 grocery items.
- Correctly finds unit prices and justifies "best buys" in a report.

3
- Records most necessary information for 6–10 grocery items.
- Finds unit prices and tries to justify "best buys" in a report.

2
- Records some information for 4–6 grocery items.
- Attempts to find unit prices but has difficulty justifying "best buys."

1
- Records some information for 1–3 grocery items.
- Fails to identify "best buys."

Chapter Project

Students research prices in neighborhood grocery stores to determine which store or stores offer the best prices.

Resources
Chapter 6 Project Master

Introduce the Project

- Talk about why comparison shopping is a good idea.
- Ask students how they would go about comparing the prices of two products, such as two brands of cereal.
- Talk about how unit prices can help when comparison shopping. Alert students to the fact that sometimes the unit price is given with the displayed price of an item.
- Talk about how students can identify the items their families purchase most often and then how they can go about collecting the data.

Project Progress

Section A, page 290 Students visit two or more grocery stores and, for each of 6 to 10 items, record the price, weight, and capacity or volume of the item.

Section B, page 307 Students decide which grocery stores have the lowest prices and prepare a report to justify their results.

Community Project

A community project for Chapter 6 is available in *Home and Community Connections.*

Cooperative Learning

You may want to use Teaching Tool Transparency 1: Cooperative Learning Checklist with **Explore** and other group activities in this chapter.

Problem Solving Focus

Interpreting Mathematical Phrases

The Point

Students focus on interpreting mathematical phrases as a way to determine what operation is needed to solve the problem.

Resources

Teaching Tool Transparency 16: Problem-Solving Guidelines

 *Interactive CD-ROM Journal*

About the Page

Using the Problem-Solving Process

In these problems, students focus on phrases that suggest various operations. Discuss the following suggestions.

- Look for words like "more than," "less than," "times as many," and "divided by." Decide what operation the words suggest. Decide if it makes sense to use this operation to solve the problem.

Ask ...

- In Problem 1 will you add or subtract to find Hurricane Donna's wind speed? Why? Add; The phrase "more than the minimum" suggests addition.
- What phrase tells the operation to use in Problem 2? What operation is suggested? "Were less than"; Subtraction
- What key phrases can you use in Problem 3 to determine what operations to use? "More than" suggests addition; "Three times as fast as" suggests multiplication.
- What does "$\frac{1}{2}$ of" suggest in Problem 4? Multiplication

Answers for Problems

1. $75 + 105 = 180$ mi/hr
2. $180 - 40 = 140$ mi/hr
3. $20 + (140 \times 2) = 300$ mi/hr
4. $\frac{1}{2} \times 300 = 150$ mi/hr

Journal

Have students identify key phrases that they associate with each of the following words: addition, subtraction, multiplication, division, and equal.

Problem Solving
Understand
Plan
Solve
Look Back

Interpreting Mathematical Phrases

When you make a problem solving plan, you may need to translate words into mathematical symbols. For example, the phrase "more than" may mean "+", and "is" or "was" may mean "=".

Problem Solving Focus

For each problem below, write the answer and the arithmetic you used to find the answer. (For example, if you added 5 to 7 to get 12, write "5 + 7 = 12.")

1. A tropical storm is classified as a hurricane when its maximum wind speed reaches at least 75 mi/hr. In 1960, Hurricane Donna's winds were 105 mi/hr more than the minimum. How fast were Hurricane Donna's winds?
2. The maximum winds of 1996's Hurricane Edouard were 40 mi/hr less than those of Hurricane Donna. How fast were Hurricane Edouard's winds?
3. Wind speeds inside a tornado may be 20 mi/hr more than twice as fast as Hurricane Edouard's winds. What is the wind speed in a tornado?
4. A wind whose speed is $\frac{1}{2}$ of a tornado's is powerful enough to uproot trees. Find the speed of this wind.

272

Additional Problem

The Beaufort Wind Scale is a way of estimating wind speed. Admiral Sir Francis Beaufort developed the scale in 1805, listing wind speeds according to their effects. The scale has a series of numbers from 0 to 17, each standing for visible effects of wind. At Beaufort 0–1, wind speed is less than 1 mi/hr, and a flag hangs down, not moving. At Beaufort 4, wind speed is about 15 mi/hr, so small tree branches move. At Beaufort 6, wind speed is about 27 mi/hr, so a flag is extended outward and large branches sway. At Beaufort 10, winds are about 4 times as strong as at Beaufort 4 and trees can be uprooted. About what would be the wind speed at Beaufort 10?

1. What is the problem about? Possible answer: Estimating wind speed.
2. What does the problem ask you to do? Possible answer: Find the wind speed at Beaufort number 10.
3. What operations will you need to solve this problem? How can you tell? Multiply to find the wind speed at Beaufort 10 because "four times as strong as" suggests multiplication.
4. Does the problem have unnecessary information? Yes: Wind speeds at Beaufort 1 and 6 are unnecessary.
5. What is the wind speed at Beaufort 10? About 60 mi/hr.

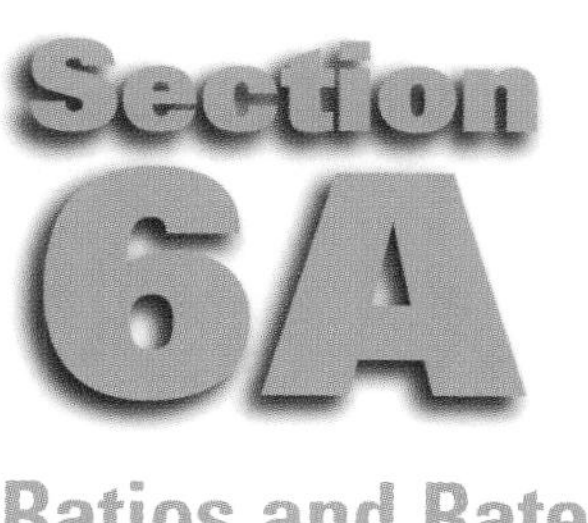

Ratios and Rates

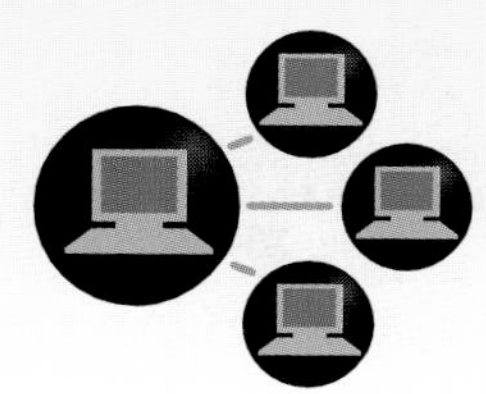

Visit www.teacher.mathsurf.com for links to lesson plans from teachers and other professionals, NCTM information, and other sites.

LESSON PLANNING GUIDE

Student Edition / Ancillaries*

LESSON		MATERIALS	VOCABULARY	DAILY	OTHER
	Chapter 6 Opener				Ch. 6 Project Master Ch. 6 Community Project Teaching Tool Transparency 1
	Problem Solving Focus				Teaching Tool Trans. 16 *Interactive CD-ROM Journal*
	Section 6A Opener				
6-1	**Exploring and Estimating Ratios**	metric ruler	ratio	6–1	Teaching Tool Trans. 2, 3, 20 Lesson Enhancement Trans. 27
6-2	**Exploring and Estimating Rates**		rate, unit rate, unit price	6–2	Teaching Tool Trans. 24 Technology Trans. 25 *WW Math*—Algebra
6-3	**Equivalent Ratios and Rates**	watch with a second hand	equivalent ratios, equivalent rates	6–3	Technology Master 26
6-4	**Using Tables to Explore Ratios and Rates**			6–4	Technology Master 27 Ch. 6 Project Master
	Connect	ruler			Interdisc. Team Teaching 6A
	Review				Practice 6A; Quiz 6A; *TestWorks*

* Daily Ancillaries include Practice, Reteaching, Problem Solving, Enrichment, and Daily Transparency. Teaching Tool Transparencies are in *Teacher's Toolkits*. Lesson Enhancement Transparencies are in *Overhead Transparency Package*.

SKILLS TRACE

LESSON	SKILL	FIRST INTRODUCED GR. 5	GR. 6	GR. 7	DEVELOP	PRACTICE/ APPLY	REVIEW
6-1	**Using ratios to compare quantities.**	✗			pp. 274–275	pp. 276–277	pp. 316, 336, 436
6-2	**Comparing quantities involving measures.**	✗			pp. 278–279	pp. 280–281	pp. 316, 340, 348, 441
6-3	**Finding equivalent ratios and rates.**	✗			pp. 282–283	pp. 284–285	pp. 316, 446
6-4	**Using tables to analyze ratios and rates.**	✗			pp. 286–288	pp. 289–290	pp. 316, 352, 454

CONNECTED MATHEMATICS

The unit *Comparing and Scaling (Ratio Proportion and Percent)*, from the **Connected Mathematics** series, can be used with Section 6A.

INTERDISCIPLINARY TEAM TEACHING

Math and Science/Technology

(Worksheet pages 21–22: Teacher pages T21–T22)

In this lesson, students use equivalent ratios and tables with cardiovascular data.

Name ______________________ *Math and Science/Technology*

This Beat Rates

Use equivalent ratios and rate tables with cardiovascular data.

Do you know how many times your heart beats every minute? The number depends on a variety of factors. These include whether you are a boy or a girl, your age and body type, your health, fitness, and activity level. Even the temperature of the room and how hard you are thinking affect the rate at which your heart beats!

When you were a newborn, your heart rate was about 135 beats per minute. By the time you were 10 years old it was about 84 beats per minute. The heart of the average fifteen year old beats about 78 times a minute. These numbers are averages. Some teens have a heartbeat rate as low as 60, while others have rates close to 100. These rates are all within a normal range. Adult rates average around 72 beats per minute.

Your heart is part of your cardiovascular system. *Cardio* means heart. *Vascular* refers to your blood vessels. The cardiovascular system carries blood to your cells, delivering the food and oxygen they need. During exercise, your need for energy increases, and your heart beats faster to bring vital nutrients and oxygen to your hard-working muscles. But how much can your heart rate go up without damaging your heart?

The American College of Sports Medicine uses a formula that provides the answer. Using the formula, an aerobics instructor or athletic trainer can decide just the right workout level for a person at a certain level of fitness. A good cardiovascular workout is intended to make the heart rate go up, but then recover, or go back down again, a short time afterwards.

1. **a.** Most people can figure out their heart rate by checking their pulse. You can feel your pulse by pressing the middle and index fingers of one hand against an artery, either in the side of your neck or the inner part of your wrist behind your thumb. Using a stopwatch, count your pulse for 15 seconds. Then multiply by 4 to find your pulse rate for one minute. What is it?

   probably between 60 and 100

   b. What are some factors that could be making your pulse different from that of your classmates?

   age, activity, fitness, gender

   c. What could increase your pulse right away?

   See below.

2. A fitness trainer is going to begin working with a 40-year-old woman named Jacki. She has a normal resting heart rate of 72 beats per minute. Jacki usually takes her pulse for 10, 15, or 30 seconds. Fill in the rest of the table to show the number of times Jacki's heart beats during 10-, 15-, and 30-second intervals.

Resting Heartbeat Rate						
Number of seconds	10	15	30	40	50	60
Number of heartbeats	**12**	**18**	**36**	48	60	72

Name ______________________ *Math and Science/Technology*

3. The trainer uses a formula to come up with a "target" heartbeat rate for Jacki when she is exercising strenuously. The formula is $t = 220 - \text{age}$.

   Jacki's target formula can be expressed as: $t = 220 - 40 =$ 180 heartbeats per minute. This number is pretty high. It is the absolute highest that Jacki would ever want her heartbeat to go. The rate for 30–60 seconds is shown in the table. However, Jacki does not want to wait that long to check her heart rate. She'd rather measure it in 10 or 15 seconds. Fill in the rest of the table with the rates for 10 and 15 seconds.

High Target Heartbeat Rate for Trained Athlete						
Number of seconds	10	15	30	40	50	60
Number of heartbeats during exercise	**30**	**45**	90	120	150	180

4. Since Jacki has not been involved in vigorous athletics for a while, the trainer chooses to start Jacki at a lower target heart rate that is 60% of the old target. The new target $= \frac{6}{10} \times t$.

   a. What is Jacki's new target heartbeat rate per minute?

   new target = 108 beats per minute

   b. One afternoon, Jacki began with a 30-second resting pulse of 36. As she ran, she took her pulse for 10 seconds. She counted 18 beats. After her cool down, her pulse for a minute was 72. Did she meet her target? Did she recover completely?

   18 beats per 10 seconds is equivalent to 108 beats per minute, which was her target rate. She recovered completely, as 72 beats per minute is the same rate as her resting pulse of 36 per 30 seconds.

6. **a.** Using a stopwatch, count your heartbeats for 30 seconds. Make a table to show the number of beats after 10, 20, 30, 40, 50, and 60 seconds. (Round your numbers.)

   See below.

   b. With teacher or parental permission, do some vigorous exercise (jog, do jumping jacks, climb stairs, etc.) for a few minutes. Take your pulse for 10 seconds while you are moving in place and record the data.

   Data will vary.

   c. Stop your activity and rest for 3 minutes. Take your pulse for 10 seconds. Calculate the number of beats per minute. How well did your heart recover? Explain.

   See below.

Answers

1. c. Possible answers: increase in activity, fear, excitement.

6. a. Tables will vary but should have the generic form of the one shown on page 22.

   c. Answers will vary. A return to the original resting rate is a sign of recovery.

BIBLIOGRAPHY

FOR TEACHERS

Edwards, Ronald. *Alge-Cadabra! Algebra Magic Tricks*. Palo Alto, CA: Dale Seymour, 1996.

Perkins, D., H. Goodrich, J. Owen, and S. Tishman. *Thinking Connections*. Reading, MA: Innovative Learning Publications, 1996.

Smith, David Eugene. *Number Stories of Long Ago*. Reston, VA: NCTM, 1996.

Spangler, David. *Math for Real Kids*. Glenview, IL: Good Year Books, 1997.

FOR STUDENTS

Lafferty, Peter. *Force and Motion*. London, England: Dorling Kindersley, 1992.

Morgan, Sally. *Movement*. New York, NY: Facts on File, 1993.

Muhlberger, Richard. *What Makes a Leonardo a Leonardo?* New York, NY: Viking, 1994.

Thorn, John ed. *Total Baseball: Ultimate Encyclopedia of Baseball*. New York, NY: Harper Perennial, 1993.

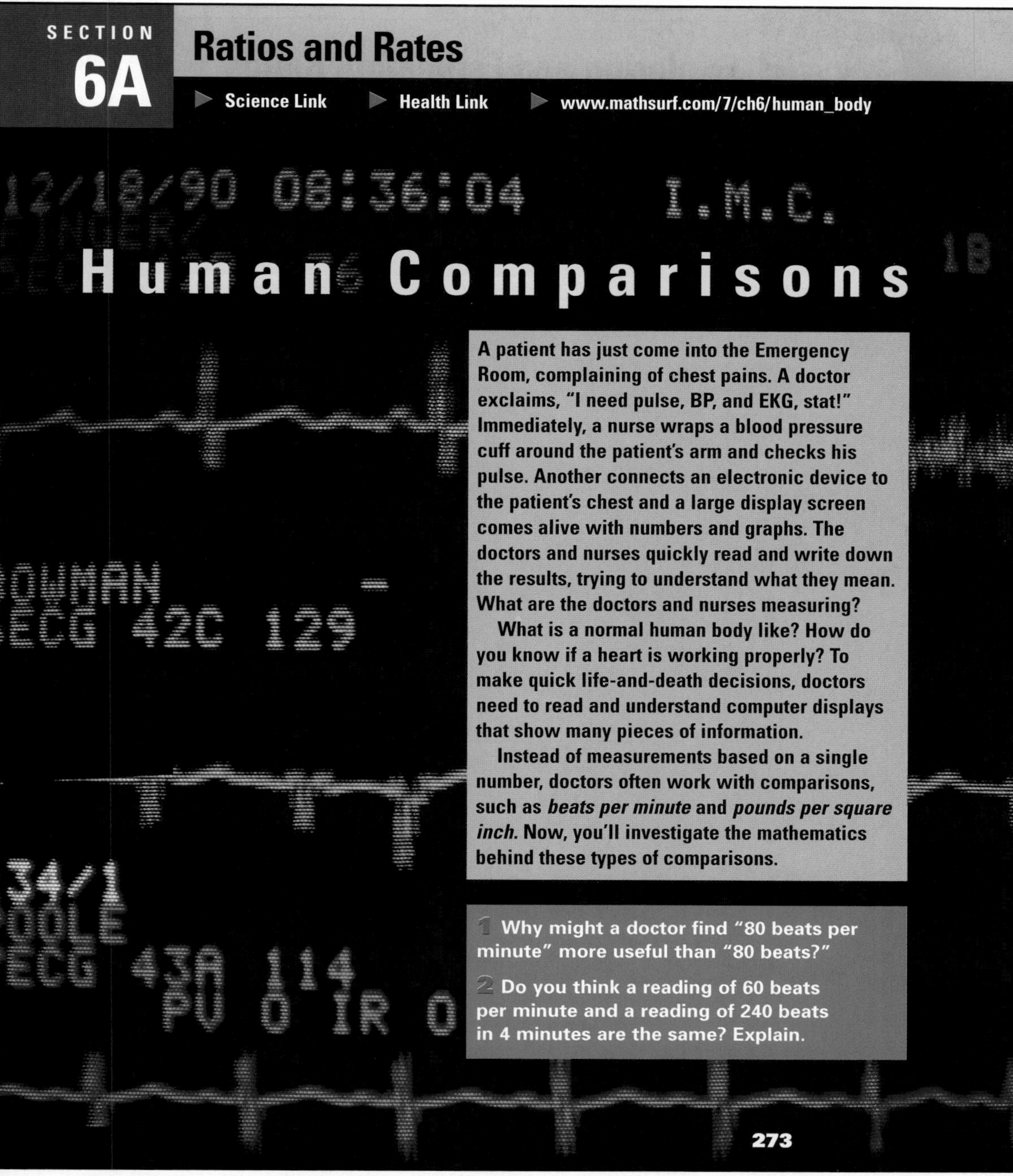

SECTION 6A

Ratios and Rates

▶ Science Link ▶ Health Link ▶ www.mathsurf.com/7/ch6/human_body

Human Comparisons

A patient has just come into the Emergency Room, complaining of chest pains. A doctor exclaims, "I need pulse, BP, and EKG, stat!" Immediately, a nurse wraps a blood pressure cuff around the patient's arm and checks his pulse. Another connects an electronic device to the patient's chest and a large display screen comes alive with numbers and graphs. The doctors and nurses quickly read and write down the results, trying to understand what they mean. What are the doctors and nurses measuring?

What is a normal human body like? How do you know if a heart is working properly? To make quick life-and-death decisions, doctors need to read and understand computer displays that show many pieces of information.

Instead of measurements based on a single number, doctors often work with comparisons, such as *beats per minute* and *pounds per square inch.* Now, you'll investigate the mathematics behind these types of comparisons.

1 Why might a doctor find "80 beats per minute" more useful than "80 beats?"

2 Do you think a reading of 60 beats per minute and a reading of 240 beats in 4 minutes are the same? Explain.

273

Where are we now?

In Grade 6, students learned the meaning of ratio, rate, and proportion.

They learned how to

- test to see if two ratios form a proportion.
- solve proportions using cross products and using unit rates.
- apply ratio and proportion concepts to similar figures and to percents.

Where are we going?

In Grade 7, Section 6A, students will

- determine whether or not a pair of ratios are equivalent.
- find missing terms in pairs of equivalent ratios.
- deal with rates as special ratios.
- use a table to find equivalent ratios and rates.

Theme: The Human Body

World Wide Web

If your class has access to the World Wide Web, you might want to use the information found at the Web site address given. The interdisciplinary links relate to the topics discussed in this section.

About the Page

This page introduces the theme of the section, the human body, and discusses the measurements that doctors and nurses use.

Ask ...

- Has the doctor ever checked your temperature, your blood pressure, or your pulse? Why do you think health professionals need this information?

Extensions

The following activities do not require access to the World Wide Web.

Science

The human body is made up of several major systems of organs: skeletal-muscular, digestive, urinary, respiratory, circulatory, nervous, and reproductive. Have groups of students research one of the systems to determine its major functions.

Health

Ask students to find out what is meant in the medical profession by pulse, BP, EKG, MRI, and stat. Heartbeat, Blood Pressure, Electrocardiogram, Magnetic Resonance Image, immediately.

Answers for Questions

1. Possible answer: 80 beats/min can be used to tell if the heart is beating too quickly.
2. Possible answer: On average they are the same, but 240 beats in 4 minutes does not have to mean that there were 60 beats every minute.

Connect

On page 291, students examine the Golden Ratio relationships in the human figure.

Lesson Organizer

Objectives

- Identify ratios.
- Compare quantities using division.

Vocabulary

- Ratio

Materials

- Explore: Metric rulers

NCTM Standards

- 1–2, 4–6

Review

On this number line, the distance from zero to one is divided into 8 equal parts. Write a fraction for each point named.

0 D A C E B 1

1. A $\frac{3}{8}$ 2. B $\frac{7}{8}$
3. C $\frac{5}{8}$ 4. D $\frac{1}{8}$
5. E $\frac{6}{8}$ or $\frac{3}{4}$

Available on Daily Transparency 6-1

1 Introduce

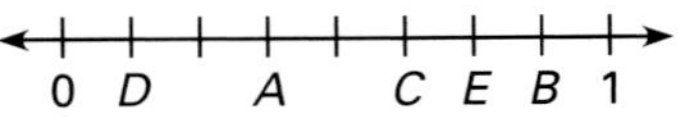

You may wish to use Lesson Enhancement Transparency 27 with **Explore**.

The Point
Students measure sketches of humans at various ages to explore ways to generate and compare ratios.

Ongoing Assessment
Be sure that students' measurements are fairly accurate so that their fractions are reasonable.

6-1 Exploring and Estimating Ratios

You'll Learn ...

- what a ratio is
- to compare quantities using division

... How It's Used

Transportation planners need to compare the number of drivers to the number of cars.

Vocabulary

ratio

► Lesson Link You've learned how to compare whole numbers, decimals, and fractions. Now you'll use ratios to compare quantities of all kinds. ◄

Explore Comparing Quantities

Materials: Metric ruler

Do Your Chin-Ups!

1. For each figure, find and record measurements for the height from the chin up, the height from the chin down, and the total height. Round to the nearest millimeter.
2. Choose one figure. Write as many fractions as you can to compare the measurements you made.

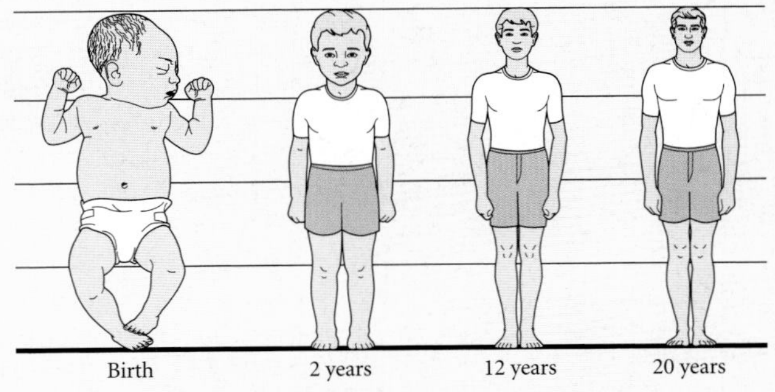

3. Use your fractions to describe the way people change as they age.

Learn Exploring and Estimating Ratios

A **ratio** compares two quantities. There are three ways to write a ratio comparing the number of cranial bones to the number of facial bones in a human skull:

$\frac{8}{14}$ 8:14 8 to 14 All of these ratios are read "8 to 14."

► Science Link

The 8 cranial bones enclose the brain.

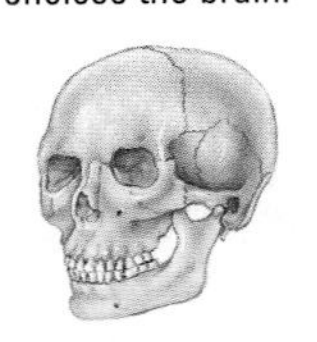

MEETING INDIVIDUAL NEEDS

Resources

- **6-1** Practice
- **6-1** Reteaching
- **6-1** Problem Solving
- **6-1** Enrichment
- **6-1** Daily Transparency
  - Problem of the Day
  - Review
  - Quick Quiz

Teaching Tool Transparencies 2, 3, 20

Lesson Enhancement Transparency 27

Learning Modalities

Logical Take a count of right- and left-handers in your class. Have students write the ratio of right-handers to left-handers, left-handers to right-handers, and right-and left-handers to the entire class. They should notice that the first two ratios are reciprocals of each other, while the denominator of the last two is the sum of the two categories.

Visual Using diagrams or objects is a visual way to help students with the concept of ratio.

Inclusion

Have students give ratios comparing various items in the classroom, for instance, the number of doors to the number of windows. Have them give the ratios in lowest terms, if appropriate. Then reverse the procedure: give ratios and have students describe items in the room that exhibit the ratios. Have students write the ratios as fractions. Then model how to read a ratio, e.g., 3:8 = 3 to 8 = $\frac{3}{8}$.

Add new vocabulary to reference book.

Example 1

In a group of 7th graders, 34 were right-handed and 5 were left-handed. Find the ratio of right-handers to left-handers.

$\frac{\text{right-handers}}{\text{left-handers}} = \frac{34}{5}$ Write the ratio in words, then substitute numbers.

The ratio of right-handers to left-handers is $\frac{34}{5}$.

Ratios are left as improper fractions and not rewritten as mixed numbers.

In Example 1, the ratio compared two quantities. In Example 2, you'll see how a ratio can compare a part to a whole.

Examples

2 Write a ratio comparing the number of squares with checkers on them to the total number of squares.

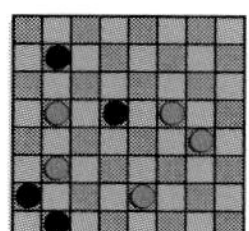

$\frac{\text{9 squares with pieces}}{\text{64 squares}} = \frac{9}{64}$ Write the ratio using words, then use only numbers.

The ratio of squares with checkers to the total number of squares is $\frac{9}{64}$.

3 The painting is the *Mona Lisa* by the Italian artist Leonardo da Vinci (1452–1519). Estimate the ratio of the length of Mona Lisa's nose to the length of her face.

Imagine Mona Lisa's face divided into three equal sections. The length of the nose is approximately equal to the length of the middle section. The ratio of the length of the nose to the length of the face is about 1:3.

Try It

The photo shows the Capitol in Washington, DC. Estimate the ratio of the height of the dome to the height of the entire building. 1:2

▶ History Link

The game of checkers is over 3,000 years old. It was first played by aristocrats in ancient Egypt.

▶ Art Link

The *Mona Lisa* is also known as *La Gioconda,* which means "the Smiling Lady." The portrait hangs in the Louvre in Paris, France.

MATH EVERY DAY

▶ Problem of the Day

You can use four 4s and mathematical symbols to write the value of some numbers. For example, $5 = \sqrt{4} + \sqrt{4} + \frac{4}{4}$. Use four 4s to write an expression equal to 15. Then use the fours to write another expression equal to 32. Possible answers:

$\frac{44}{4} + 4 = 15$; $4 \times 4 \times (\sqrt{4})^{4} = 32$

Available on Daily Transparency 6-1

An Extension is provided in the transparency package.

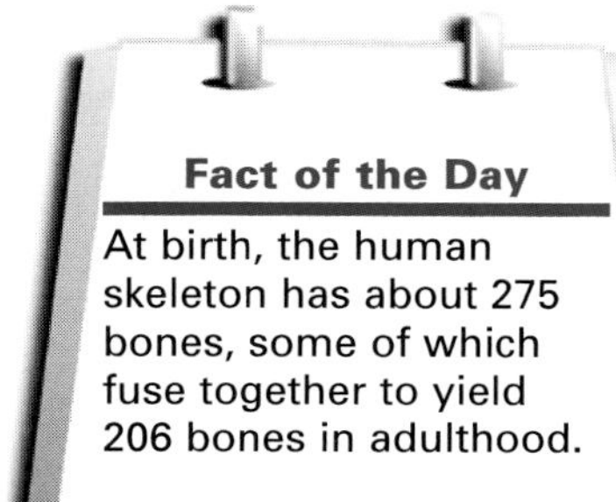

Fact of the Day

At birth, the human skeleton has about 275 bones, some of which fuse together to yield 206 bones in adulthood.

Mental Math

Find each quotient mentally.

1. 48 ÷ 12 4
2. 96 ÷ 32 3
3. 128 ÷ 4 32
4. 287 ÷ 7 41

For Groups That Finish Early

Help each other measure from elbow to wrist, elbow to tip of thumb, wrist to first knuckle on the thumb, and first knuckle on the thumb to tip of thumb. Write as many fractions as possible and compare your fractions with one another.

Answers for Explore

1. Possible answers:
   Birth: 14 mm; 36 mm; 50 mm
   2 years: 11 mm; 39 mm; 50 mm
   12 years: 7 mm; 43 mm; 50 mm
   20 years: 6 mm; 44 mm; 50 mm
2. Possible answer: Birth: $\frac{14}{36}$, $\frac{14}{50}$, $\frac{36}{50}$, $\frac{36}{14}$, $\frac{50}{14}$, $\frac{50}{36}$
3. Possible answer: As a person grows, the ratio of the length of head to total height decreases.

2 Teach

Learn

Stress that the order in the three forms of the ratio corresponds to the order stated: number of cranial bones (8) to number of facial bones (14). In the fractional form, the first quantity is the numerator and the second is the denominator.

Alternate Examples

1. There are 96 girls and 84 boys in the seventh grade. Find the ratio of girls to boys.

   Write the ratio in words, then substitute numbers. Rewrite in lowest terms. Do not write as a mixed number.

   $\frac{\text{girls}}{\text{boys}} = \frac{96}{84} = \frac{8}{7}$

   The ratio of girls to boys is $\frac{8}{7}$.

2. Use the checkerboard picture in Example 2. Write the ratio of the number of empty squares to the total number of squares.

   $\frac{\text{55 empty squares}}{\text{64 squares}} = \frac{55}{64}$

   The ratio of the number of empty squares to the total number of squares is $\frac{55}{64}$.

3. Look at the picture of the *Mona Lisa* in Example 3. Estimate the ratio of the length of Mona Lisa's forehead to the length of the rest of her face.

   Imagine Mona Lisa's face divided into 3 sections of equal length. The length of her forehead is about one of those lengths and the rest of her face is about two of those lengths. So, the ratio is about 1:2.

6-1 Exercises and Applications

Assignment Guide

- **Basic**
  1, 2–14 evens, 15, 17, 19–24
- **Average**
  1–19 odds, 20–24
- **Enriched**
  1–15 odds, 16–19, 21, 23

3 Practice and Assess

Check

Answers for Check Your Understanding

1. Like: Ratios can be written as fractions; Ratios usually compare quantities with real-world meanings; Different: Fractions tell parts of a whole; Ratios compare two quantities.
2. Because the numbers being compared could not be read easily.

Exercise Notes

Exercise 14

Cultural The Taj Mahal was built by Shah Jahan, who was the Mogul emperor of India from 1628 to 1658.

You may wish to use Teaching Tool Transparency 20: Map of the World with Exercise 14.

Reteaching

Activity

Materials: Two-color counters

Take a handful of each color of counters. Draw a line on your paper and put all the counters of one color above the line and all of the other color below the line.

- Count the number of each color and write the ratio in fraction form, using words, for example, $\frac{\text{9 yellow}}{\text{5 red}}$.
- Turn your paper around so the counters that were above the line are now below the line. Write the new ratio.
- Write the ratio of one color of counters to the total number of counters, for example, $\frac{\text{9 yellow}}{\text{14 in all}}$.

Check Your Understanding

1. How is a ratio like a fraction? How is it different?
2. Why do you think ratios are not written as mixed numbers?

6-1 Exercises and Applications

Practice and Apply

1. **Getting Started** Follow these steps to write the ratio of the number of shaded squares to the total number of squares.
   a. Find the number of shaded squares in the pattern. 12
   b. Find the total number of squares in the pattern. 36
   c. Write a ratio comparing the number of shaded squares to the total number of squares. Rewrite the ratio in lowest terms. $\frac{12}{36}; \frac{1}{3}$

$\frac{12}{36}; \frac{1}{3}$

Number Sense Write each ratio three ways. Write in lowest terms if possible.

2. 8 months out of 12 months $\frac{2}{3}$; 2:3; 2 to 3
3. 14 dogs to 16 cats $\frac{7}{8}$; 7:8; 7 to 8
4. 3 computers out of 8 computers $\frac{3}{8}$; 3:8; 3 to 8
5. 36 shoes to 27 socks $\frac{4}{3}$; 4:3; 4 to 3
6. 9 runs in 4 innings $\frac{9}{4}$; 9:4; 9 to 4
7. 88¢ for 2 oranges $\frac{44}{1}$; 44:1; 44 to 1

Science The table gives the number of bones found in the human *axial skeleton,* which is made up of the head, neck, and trunk. Write each of the following ratios in lowest terms.

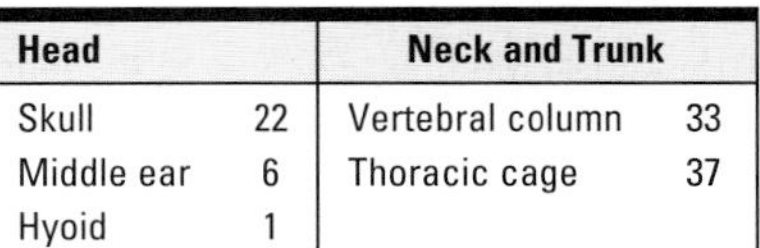

Head		Neck and Trunk	
Skull	22	Vertebral column	33
Middle ear	6	Thoracic cage	37
Hyoid	1		

8. Middle ear to vertebral column $\frac{6}{33}$
9. Thoracic cage to hyoid $\frac{37}{1}$
10. Skull to head $\frac{22}{29}$
11. Skull to neck and trunk $\frac{22}{70}$
12. Head to neck and trunk $\frac{29}{70}$
13. Head to total axial skeleton $\frac{29}{99}$
14. **Estimation** The Taj Mahal, in Agra, India, is considered by many people to be the world's most beautiful building. Estimate the ratio of the height of the main dome to the height of the entire building. 1:3

PRACTICE 6-1

PRACTICE

Name ____________________

Practice 6-1

Exploring and Estimating Ratios

Write each ratio in three ways. Write in lowest terms if possible.

1. 8 jazz CDs to 14 rock CDs $\frac{4}{7}$, 4 : 7, 4 to 7
2. 25 oranges to 45 apples $\frac{5}{9}$, 5 : 9, 5 to 9
3. \$12 for 8 sandwiches $\frac{3}{2}$, 3 : 2, 3 to 2
4. 8 dentists out of 10 dentists $\frac{4}{5}$, 4 : 5, 4 to 5
5. 32 points in 18 games $\frac{16}{9}$, 16 : 9, 16 to 9
6. 21 boys to 24 girls $\frac{7}{8}$, 7 : 8, 7 to 8

A bag contains 5 red, 6 yellow, 8 green, 10 blue, and 15 clear marbles. Write each of the following ratios in lowest terms.

7. yellow to blue $\frac{3}{5}$
8. green to yellow $\frac{4}{3}$
9. blue to clear $\frac{2}{3}$
10. blue to red $\frac{2}{1}$
11. yellow to clear $\frac{2}{5}$
12. red to clear $\frac{1}{3}$

The table shows several popular TV programs and the number of years that each was produced. Write each of the following ratios in lowest terms.

Program	Number of Years
Walt Disney	33
Ed Sullivan	24
Gunsmoke	20
Meet the Press	18
Lassie	17

13. *Lassie* to *Gunsmoke* $\frac{17}{20}$
14. *Walt Disney* to *Meet the Press* $\frac{11}{6}$
15. *Ed Sullivan* to *Walt Disney* $\frac{8}{11}$
16. A vase of flowers is shown. Estimate the ratio of the width of the vase to the total height of the vase and flowers. About $\frac{2}{5}$

RETEACHING

Name ____________________

Alternative Lesson 6-1

Exploring and Estimating Ratios

A **ratio** compares two quantities and is often written as a fraction. Ratios that appear as improper fractions are not rewritten as mixed numbers. However, you can rewrite ratios in lowest terms.

Example 1

Write a ratio to compare the number of shaded squares to the number of unshaded squares.

Number of shaded squares → 4
Number of unshaded squares → 11

The ratio can be written as 4 to 11, $\frac{4}{11}$, or 4:11.

Try It

a. Write the ratio in three ways that compares the number of shaded sections in the circle to the number of unshaded sections.
   3 to 2 $\frac{3}{2}$ 3:2

Example 2

Write a ratio for each situation in three ways. Write in lowest terms if possible.

Most students are in school 9 months out of 12 months each year.

Months in school → 9
Months in a year → 12
$\frac{9}{12} = \frac{3}{4}$

The ratio is 3 to 4, $\frac{3}{4}$, or 3:4.

A snail moved 9 inches in 5 hours.

Inches → 9
Hours → 5

The ratio is 9 to 5, $\frac{9}{5}$, or 9:5.

Try It Write the ratio for each situation in three ways. Write in lowest terms if possible.

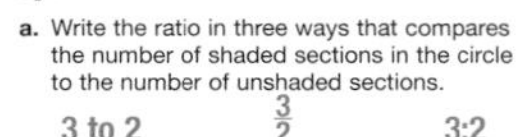
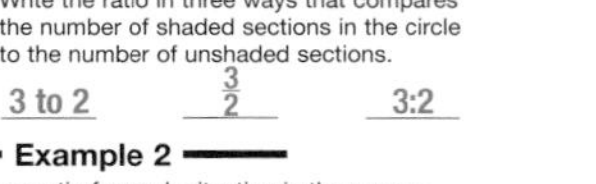
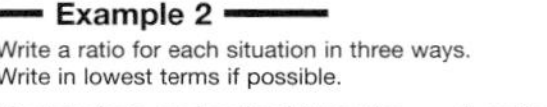

b. 25 boys to 26 girls 25 to 26; $\frac{25}{26}$; 25:26
c. 12 months in 1 year 12 to 1; $\frac{12}{1}$; 12:1
d. 4 wins to 6 losses 2 to 3; $\frac{2}{3}$; 2:3
e. 24 sit-ups in 60 seconds 2 to 5; $\frac{2}{5}$; 2:5
f. 24 lions per 80 square miles 3 to 10; $\frac{3}{10}$; 3:10
g. 168 miles per 6 gallons of gas 28 to 1; $\frac{28}{1}$; 28:1

15. Estimation The horse pictured stands 16 *hands* tall at the shoulders. Estimate the ratio of the horse's height from the shoulders up to its height from the shoulders down. Use hands as the unit of measurement. About 1:7–1:8

shoulders

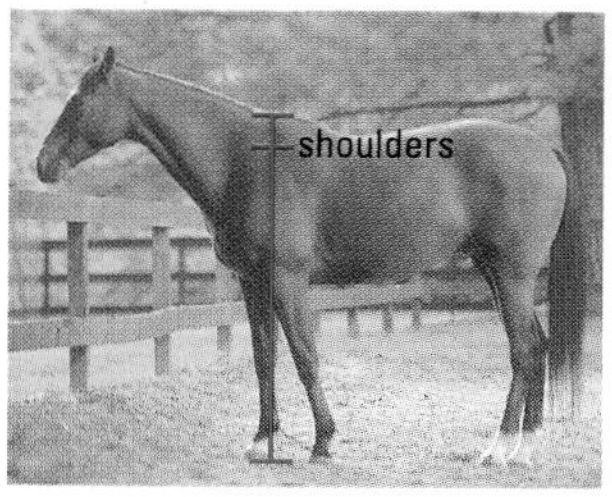

16. Science Many household cleaning solutions contain hazardous chemicals. Safe substitutes for these solutions can be made using simple ingredients. Write a ratio to describe each of these recipes for safe household cleaners.

a. Vinyl cleaner: 1 ounce vinegar, 32 ounces water $\frac{1}{32}$

b. Window cleaner: $\frac{1}{4}$ cup vinegar, 1 cup water $\frac{1}{4}$

17. Test Prep Write the ratio 400 to 150 in lowest terms. B

Ⓐ 40 to 15 Ⓑ 8 to 3 Ⓒ 4 to 1 Ⓓ 4 to 15

Problem Solving and Reasoning

18. Choose a Strategy Last year, the Brown Middle School basketball team won 8 games and lost 4. This year, the team won 10 games and lost 2. $\frac{2}{3}, \frac{5}{6}$

a. Write a ratio comparing the number of wins to the number of games played in each season. Remember to rewrite each ratio in lowest terms.

b. Did the team improve from last year to this year? Explain. Yes; $\frac{5}{6} > \frac{2}{3}$

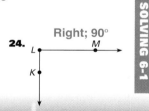

Problem Solving STRATEGIES

- Look for a Pattern
- Make an Organized List
- Make a Table
- Guess and Check
- Work Backward
- Use Logical Reasoning
- Draw a Diagram
- Solve a Simpler Problem

19. Communicate Leonardo da Vinci, Michelangelo and other artists made careful studies of the mathematical relationships of the human body. One of the ratios they used was $\frac{\text{height of head}}{\text{height of entire body}} = \frac{2}{15}$. Find several magazine or newspaper photos and measure the people to find the ratio. Is it always $\frac{2}{15}$?

Mixed Review

Science The formula $t = \frac{d}{r}$ gives the time (t) it takes to travel a distance (d) at a given rate (r). Substitute the given values into the formula. Then use the formula to find t. *[Lesson 2-1]*

20. $d = 140$ mi, $r = 40$ mi/hr 3.5 hr **21.** $d = 2000$ ft, $r = 50$ ft/sec 40 sec

Classify each angle and give its measure. *[Lesson 5-1]*

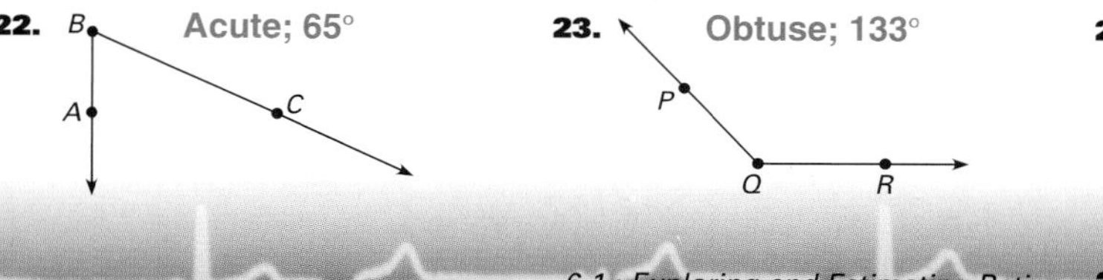

22. Acute; 65° **23.** Obtuse; 133° **24.** Right; 90°

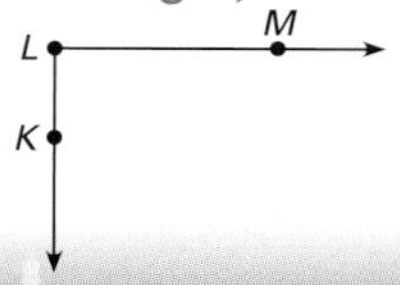

PROBLEM SOLVING 6-1

PROBLEM SOLVING

Name ______

Guided Problem Solving 6-1

GPS PROBLEM 15, STUDENT PAGE 277

The horse pictured stands 16 *hands* tall at the shoulders. Estimate the ratio of the horse's height from the shoulders up to its height from the shoulders down. Use hands as the unit of measurement.

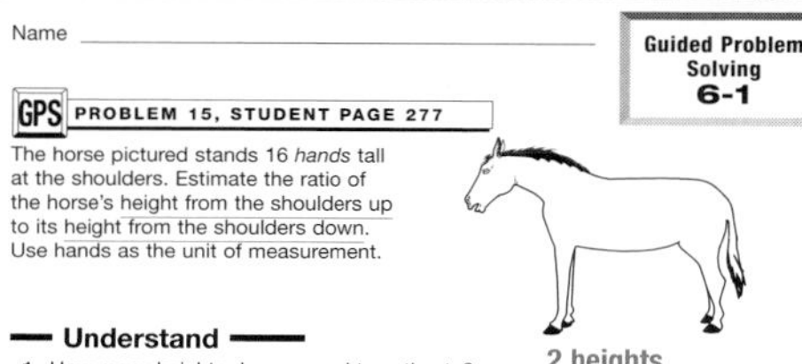

— Understand —

1. How many heights do you need to estimate? 2 heights.
2. Underline what each part of the ratio represents.

— Plan —

3. How can you divide the horse's entire height into 16 hands? Draw a horizontal line to divide height of horse in half. Then divide halves into quarters, quarters into eighths, and eighths into sixteenths.
4. About how many hands is the horse's height from the shoulders up? About 2 hands.
5. About how many hands is the horse's height from the shoulders down? About 16 hands.
6. Which measure will you use in your ratio for the
   a. numerator? 2 b. denominator? 16

— Solve —

7. Give the estimate of the ratio of the horse's height from the shoulders up to its height from the shoulders down. $\frac{2}{16}$ or $\frac{1}{8}$

— Look Back —

8. Write the ratio in two other ways. 2:16 or 1:8; 2 to 16 or 1 to 8

SOLVE ANOTHER PROBLEM

The vase and its flowers pictured at the right measure 15 inches high. Estimate the ratio of height of the vase to the height of the flowers above the vase. $\frac{3}{2}$

ENRICHMENT

Name ______

Extend Your Thinking 6-1

Patterns in Numbers

An Italian mathematician, Leonardo Fibonacci, discovered this interesting number pattern around A.D. 1200. The numbers in the pattern are called Fibonacci numbers and appear quite frequently in nature.

Use the diagram of the tree to help you complete the table.

Year	Number of branches
First	1
Second	1
Third	2
Fourth	3
Fifth	5
Sixth	8
Seventh	13

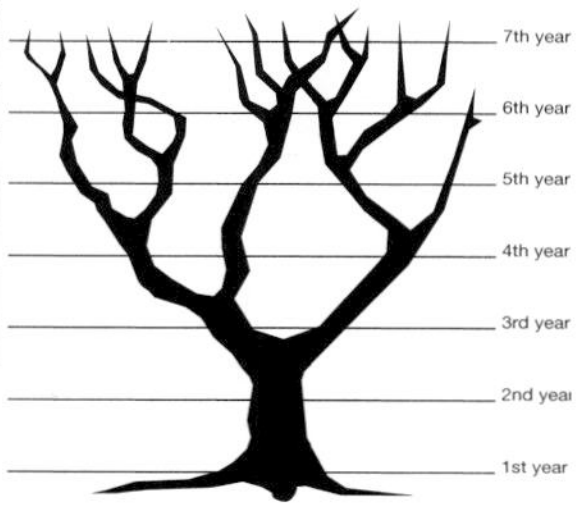

1. Choose any two consecutive years and add the number of branches. What do you notice about the sum? Repeat using two other consecutive numbers. Does the same thing occur? The sum is equal to the number of branches for the next year. Yes.
2. If the tree continues to grow at the same rate, what would be the number of branches for the eighth year? The ninth year? The tenth year? 21 branches, 34 branches, 55 branches
3. Find the missing numbers for this number pattern: 1, 1, 2, 3, *n*, *n*, 13, *n*, 34, *n*, *n*, *n*, 233 . . . 1, 1, 2, 3, 5, 8, 13, 21, 34, 55, 89, 144, 233

Exercise Notes

■ Exercise 15

Estimation A *hand* is the width of a human hand, about 4 inches.

■ Exercise 16

Science Students may not be familiar with the use of vinegar in cleaning solutions, as it is primarily used as a condiment or a preservative. It contains acetic acid, and effectively dissolves many substances.

■ Exercise 18

Problem-Solving Tip You may want to use Teaching Tool Transparencies 2 and 3: Guided Problem Solving, pages 1 and 2.

Exercise Answers

19. Answers may vary.

Alternate Assessment

Performance Have students give ratios comparing various items in the classroom, for instance, the number of doors to the number of windows. Have them give the ratios in lowest terms, if appropriate.

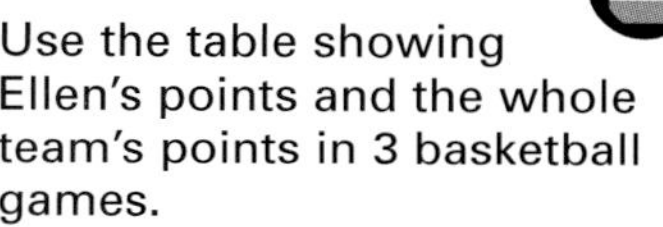

Quick Quiz

Use the table showing Ellen's points and the whole team's points in 3 basketball games.

	Game 1	Game 2	Game 3
Ellen	12	16	15
Team	32	34	39

Give each ratio of points.

1. Ellen's to team's, Game 1 $\frac{12}{32}$, or $\frac{3}{8}$
2. Team's to Ellen's, Game 3 $\frac{39}{15}$, or $\frac{13}{5}$
3. Ellen's to rest of team's, Game 2 $\frac{16}{18}$, or $\frac{8}{9}$
4. Ellen's total to team's total, Games 1–3 $\frac{43}{105}$

Available on Daily Transparency 6-1

6-2 Lesson Organizer

Objectives

- Compare two quantities with different units of measure.
- Make comparisons to one unit.

Vocabulary

- Rate, unit rate, unit price

NCTM Standards

- 1–5, 7, 13

Review

Write each fraction in lowest terms.

1. $\frac{9}{12}$ $\frac{3}{4}$
2. $\frac{8}{10}$ $\frac{4}{5}$
3. $\frac{12}{30}$ $\frac{2}{5}$
4. $\frac{18}{15}$ $\frac{6}{5}$

Available on Daily Transparency 6-2

1 Introduce

Explore

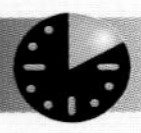

The Point
Students estimate rates for a variety of situations in order to understand rates as comparisons.

Ongoing Assessment
Check that students' estimates are reasonable. They may have to draw upon one another's experiences to make the estimates.

For Groups That Finish Early
Estimate how fast you can run or walk. Give your rate in terms of 1 mile in ______ minutes. Then tell how many miles that is in 1 hour

Possible answer: $\frac{1 \text{ mi}}{15 \text{ min}} = \frac{4 \text{ mi}}{1 \text{ hr}}$

6-2 Exploring and Estimating Rates

You'll Learn ...

- to compare two quantities with different units of measure
- to make comparisons to one unit

... How It's Used

Police officers watch for cars whose rate of speed is above the legal limit.

Vocabulary

rate

unit rate

unit price

Lesson Link You've learned that a ratio is a comparison of two quantities. Now you'll see how to compare two quantities with different units of measure.

Explore Estimating Rates

How Fast Does Your Hair Grow?

1. Answer each question by making a reasonable estimate. Give estimates in terms that are easy to understand. For example, an estimate such as "1 mile in 6 hours" is easier to understand than "five-millionths of a mile in one-tenth of a second."
2. Explain how you made each estimate.
3. Compare your estimates with the ones your classmates made. Are they about the same? Why or why not?

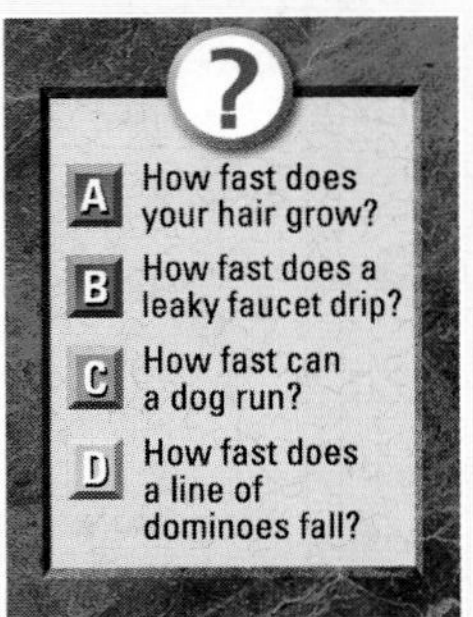

?
A How fast does your hair grow?
B How fast does a leaky faucet drip?
C How fast can a dog run?
D How fast does a line of dominoes fall?

Learn Exploring and Estimating Rates

A ratio is called a **rate** when the units of measure of the quantities are different. A rate shows how quantities with different units are related to each other.

$\frac{6 \text{ miles}}{5 \text{ miles}}$ Both measured in miles → Not a rate

$\frac{6 \text{ miles}}{5 \text{ hours}}$ One measured in miles, one measured in hours → Rate

You can read the rate as "6 miles *per* 5 hours." It means "6 miles in 5 hours."

If the measure of the second quantity in a rate is one unit, the rate is called a **unit rate**. Unit rates allow you to compare rates easily.

Rate	Unit Rate
$\frac{40 \text{ points}}{5 \text{ games}}$	$\frac{8 \text{ points}}{1 \text{ game}}$
40 points per 5 games	8 points per game, or 8 points/game

MEETING INDIVIDUAL NEEDS

Resources

- 6-2 Practice
- 6-2 Reteaching
- 6-2 Problem Solving
- 6-2 Enrichment
- 6-2 Daily Transparency
  - Problem of the Day
  - Review
  - Quick Quiz
- Teaching Tool Transparency 24
- Technology Master 25

Wide World of Mathematics Algebra: Traveling the Oregon Trail

Learning Modalities

Musical The notes in a musical scale are related by frequencies, which are rates. Frequency, or pitch, is the number of vibrations per second of a string, drum head, column of air, and so on. When two notes are an octave apart, the frequency of the higher note is twice that of the lower one.

Kinesthetic If it is feasible, students could time a dripping faucet to make an accurate estimate for Question B in **Explore**. Likewise, you might provide dominoes for them to estimate the answer to Question D.

English Language Development

Help students with limited English proficiency relate to the term *unit rate* by connecting *unit* to the word for *one* in their language, such as *un* or *uno*. Be sure they understand that the denominator in a unit rate is one.

To convert a rate to a unit rate, divide both its numerator and denominator by the number in the denominator.

Example 1

Your respiration rate measures the number of breaths you take per minute. Reggie counted 48 breaths in 3 minutes and Toan counted 34 breaths in 2 minutes. Who has the higher respiration rate?

Reggie: $\frac{48 \text{ breaths}}{3 \text{ minutes}} = \frac{16 \text{ breaths}}{1 \text{ minute}}$ Divide numerator and denominator by 3.

Toan: $\frac{34 \text{ breaths}}{2 \text{ minutes}} = \frac{17 \text{ breaths}}{1 \text{ minute}}$ Divide numerator and denominator by 2.

Reggie's respiration rate is 16 breaths per minute. Toan's respiration rate is 17 breaths per minute. Toan's respiration rate is higher.

A unit rate that gives the cost of one item is called a **unit price**. You can use unit prices when you want to compare prices of different quantities of an item.

Example 2

Super Sports sells 5 table tennis balls for $1.95. Sports City sells 6 table tennis balls for $2.28. Which is the better price?

$\frac{\$1.95}{5 \text{ balls}} = \frac{\$0.39}{1 \text{ ball}}$ Divide numerator and denominator by 5.

$\frac{\$2.28}{6 \text{ balls}} = \frac{\$0.38}{1 \text{ ball}}$ Divide numerator and denominator by 6.

$0.38 < $0.39, so $2.28 for 6 table tennis balls is the better price.

Try It

a. Four inches of rain fell in 16 hours. Find the amount of rainfall per hour. $\frac{1}{4}$ inch per hour

b. Which is the better price: $5.12 for 3 videotapes or $8.42 for 5 videotapes? $8.42 for 5 videotapes

Science Link

Medical professionals often count a patient's breaths for 10 to 15 seconds, then multiply to calculate the respiration rate.

DID YOU KNOW?

In China, table tennis players are among the best-known athletes.

Check Your Understanding

1. Is a rate a ratio? Is a ratio a rate? Explain.

2. How do you use division when you're working with rates?

3. Is an item with a lower unit price always the better buy? Explain why or why not.

MATH EVERY DAY

Problem of the Day

Copy and cut out this figure nine times. Then use the pieces to construct a larger figure that has the same shape.

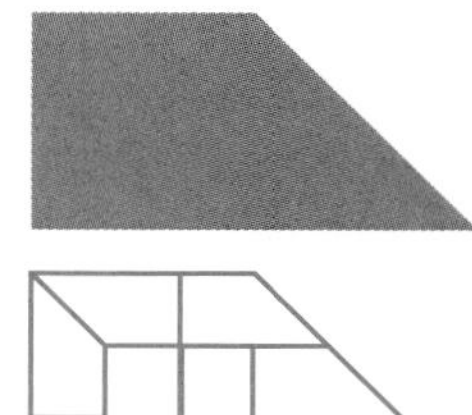

Available on Daily Transparency 6-2

An Extension is provided in the transparency package.

Fact of the Day

Respiration provides the oxygen required by the brain to sustain life. If no oxygenated blood reaches the brain for 4 to 6 minutes, brain cells begin to die.

Mental Math

Find each answer mentally.

1. 1.5 lb = ______ oz 24
2. $3\frac{1}{2}$ ft = ______ in. 42
3. 90 min = ______ hr $1\frac{1}{2}$
4. 30 in. = ______ ft $2\frac{1}{2}$

Answers for Explore

1. Possible answers:
   A. 0.5 inch in one month
   B. 1 cup in 1 hour
   C. 10 miles in 1 hour
   D. 1 line in 10 seconds
2. Possible answers:
   A. Observation
   B. By experiment
   C. Estimation
   D. By experiment
3. Answers may vary.

2 Teach

Learn

Alternate Examples

1. Which is the faster running speed, 200 meters in 25 seconds or 400 meters in 80 seconds?

   $\frac{200 \text{ m}}{25 \text{ sec}} = \frac{8 \text{ m}}{1 \text{ sec}}$

   $\frac{400 \text{ m}}{80 \text{ sec}} = \frac{5 \text{ m}}{1 \text{ sec}}$

   $\frac{200 \text{ m}}{25 \text{ sec}}$ is faster.

2. Which is the better price, 12 golf balls for $15 or 18 golf balls for $27?

   $\frac{\$15}{12 \text{ balls}} = \frac{\$1.25}{1 \text{ ball}}$

   $\frac{\$27}{18 \text{ balls}} = \frac{\$1.50}{1 \text{ ball}}$

   12 golf balls for $15 is the better price.

3 Practice and Assess

Check

Answers for Check Your Understanding

1. A rate is a ratio, because two quantities are being compared; A ratio may be a rate, but if the two quantities have the same units, it is not.
2. To compare different rates or change a rate to a unit rate.
3. No; The quality may not be as good, or the quantity may be more than you can use.

Assignment Guide

- **Basic**
  1–23 odds, 24–26, 29–37 odds
- **Average**
  1, 2–24 evens, 25–38
- **Enriched**
  2–24 evens, 25–38

Exercise Notes

Exercises 2–4

Error Prevention Be sure that students write their rates in the correct order and that they give the rates in lowest terms. Note that Exercise 3 is not a unit rate.

You may wish to use Teaching Tool Transparency 24: Calculator with Exercises 2–4.

Reteaching

Activity

Materials: Play money—dollars, half dollars, quarters, dimes, nickels

- Draw a line on your paper, and place several dollar bills below the line. Then put enough quarters above the line to make the money amounts equal. This models a rate of quarters to dollars.
- Now separate the dollars and quarters so that there are the same number of quarters for each one dollar. Each group now models the unit rate of quarters to dollars. $\frac{\text{quarters}}{\text{dollars}} = \frac{4}{1}$
- Repeat the process with dimes and dollars, and then nickels and dollars. Always start with the dollar bills below the line.
  $\frac{\text{dimes}}{\text{dollars}} = \frac{10}{1}$, $\frac{\text{nickels}}{\text{dollars}} = \frac{20}{1}$

6-2 Exercises and Applications

Practice and Apply

1. **Getting Started** Follow these steps to find the unit rate for a car that traveled 480 miles in 8 hours.
   a. Write the ratio of the two quantities. $\frac{480}{8}$
   b. Rewrite the ratio so the denominator is 1 hour. $\frac{60}{1}$
   c. Write the unit rate, using the numerator and the word *per.* **60 miles per hour**

Write each expression as a rate. Remember to include units in your rates.

2. 96 students in 3 classrooms $\frac{\text{32 students}}{\text{1 classroom}}$
3. 260 miles using 8 gallons $\frac{\text{65 miles}}{\text{2 gallons}}$
4. 44 breaths in 2 minutes $\frac{\text{22 breaths}}{\text{1 minute}}$

Express each rate as a unit rate.

5. $12.00 for 3 notebooks **$4.00 per notebook**
6. 48 chairs for 6 tables **8 chairs per table**
7. 54 cookies for 18 students **3 cookies per student**
8. 50 jumping jacks in 50 seconds **1 jumping jack per second**
9. $22.00 paid for 4 hours work **$5.50 per hour of work**
10. 56 points in 4 quarters **14 points per quarter**

Consumer Use unit prices to find the better buy.

11. Strawberries: $1.48 for 2 baskets or $2.07 for 3 baskets **$2.07 for 3 baskets**
12. Potatoes: $1.60 for 5 pounds or $0.90 for 3 pounds **$0.90 for 3 pounds**
13. Cheese: $1.80 for 12 slices or $3.36 for 24 slices **$3.36 for 24 slices**
14. Soda: 6 bottles for $2.16 or 8 bottles for $2.96 **$2.16 for 6 bottles**

Determine whether each ratio is a rate.

15. $\frac{\text{70 eighth-graders}}{\text{80 seventh-graders}}$ **No**
16. $\frac{\text{30 miles traveled}}{\text{gallon of fuel}}$ **Yes**
17. $\frac{\text{40 sit-ups}}{\text{30 seconds}}$ **Yes**
18. $\frac{\text{16 cats}}{\text{14 dogs}}$ **No**
19. $\frac{\text{3 cans red paint}}{\text{2 cans yellow paint}}$ **No**
20. $\frac{125}{500}$ **No**
21. **Science** Births of two or more babies at one time are called *multiple births.* In the United States, about 1% of all births are multiple births. Suppose one hospital has 12 sets of twins out of 1000 births. Write this information as a rate.
    $\frac{\text{12 sets of twins}}{\text{1000 births}} = \frac{\text{3 sets of twins}}{\text{250 births}}$

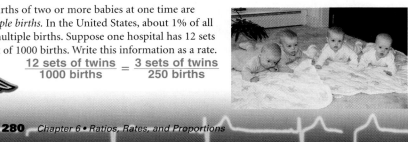

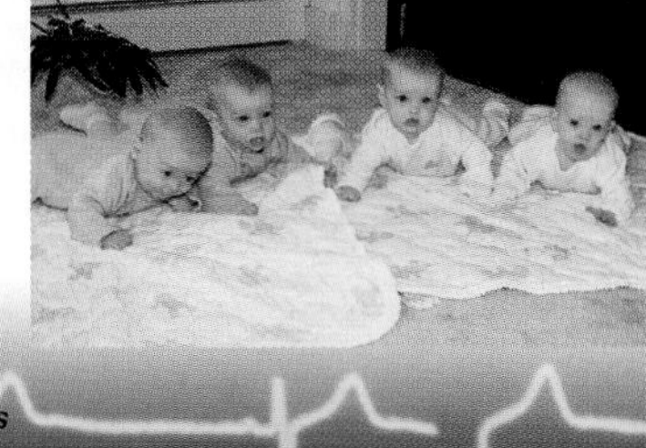

PRACTICE 6-2

PRACTICE

Name ______________________

Practice 6-2

Exploring and Estimating Rates

Find each rate. Remember to include units in your rates.

1. 60 students for 3 teachers $\frac{\text{60 students}}{\text{3 teachers}}$
2. $8 for 4 books $\frac{\$8}{\text{4 books}}$
3. 200 sit-ups in 5 minutes $\frac{\text{200 sit-ups}}{\text{5 minutes}}$
4. $36.00 paid for 6 hours work $\frac{\$36}{\text{6 hours}}$

Express each rate as a unit rate.

5. 48 inches in 4 feet $\frac{\text{12 inches}}{\text{1 foot}}$
6. $15 for 5 keychains $\frac{\$3}{\text{1 keychain}}$
7. 80 pages in 5 hours $\frac{\text{16 pages}}{\text{1 hour}}$

Consumer Use unit prices to find the better buy. Underline the correct choice.

8. Peaches: 87¢ for 3 peaches or <u>$1.12 for 4 peaches</u>
9. Video game tokens: $1.00 for 5 tokens or <u>$5.00 for 30 tokens</u>
10. Facial tissue: <u>$3.50 for 2 boxes</u> or $9.00 for 5 boxes

Determine whether each ratio is a rate. Explain. **Possible answers:**

11. $\frac{\$5}{\text{20 oranges}}$ This is a rate because it is a ratio of quantities with different units of measure.
12. $\frac{14}{21}$ This is not a rate because there are no units.
13. $\frac{\text{32 ounces}}{\text{1 pint}}$ This is a rate because it is a ratio of quantities with different units of measure.
14. **Science** A black-billed cuckoo bird can eat 48 caterpillars in 6 minutes. Find the unit rate. $\frac{\text{8 caterpillars}}{\text{1 minute}}$
15. The population of Stockton, California increased by 62,660 people during the 10 years from 1980 to 1990. Find the unit rate. $\frac{\text{6,266 people}}{\text{1 year}}$

RETEACHING

Name ______________________

Alternative Lesson 6-2

Exploring and Estimating Rates

A ratio is called a **rate** when the units of measure of the quantities are different. A rate shows how quantities with different units are related to each other. You use unit labels in rates.

If the measure of the second quantity in a rate is one unit, the rate is called a **unit rate**. Unit rates allow you to compare rates easily.

— Example 1 —

Tell whether the situation expresses a rate.

Takima walked 6 miles in the same time Bernard walked 5 miles.

Takima → 6 miles
Bernard → 5 miles

Since measurements (in miles) are the same, this is *not* a rate.

Fatihia walked 6 miles in 5 hours.

Distance → 6 miles
Time → 5 hours

Since measurements (in miles and hours) are different, this is a rate.

Try It Tell whether each situation expresses a rate.

a. $\frac{\text{61 sit-ups}}{\text{2 minutes}}$ Yes.
b. $\frac{\text{8 questions}}{\text{13 questions}}$ No.

— Example 2 —

The coach called 8 time-outs in 4 quarters. Write the ratio of time-outs to quarters. Then write the unit rate.

Write the ratio of time-outs to quarters. $\frac{\text{8 time-outs}}{\text{4 quarters}}$

Divide numerator and denominator by 4 to get 1 as a denominator. $\frac{\text{8 time-outs} \div \mathbf{4} = \text{2 time-outs}}{\text{4 quarters} \div \mathbf{4} = \text{1 quarter}}$

Write the unit rate. $\frac{\text{2 time-outs}}{\text{1 quarter}}$

Try It Write each expression as a ratio. Then express the ratio as a unit rate.

c. $72 for 9 pizzas $\frac{\$72}{\text{9 pizzas}}$; $\frac{\$8}{\text{1 pizza}}$
d. $2 for 4 oranges $\frac{\$2}{\text{4 oranges}}$; $\frac{\$0.50}{\text{1 orange}}$
e. 120 miles in 2 hours $\frac{\text{120 miles}}{\text{2 hours}}$; $\frac{\text{60 miles}}{\text{1 hour}}$
f. $135 for 27 tickets $\frac{\$135}{\text{27 tickets}}$; $\frac{\$5}{\text{1 ticket}}$
g. $3 for 15 kiwis $\frac{\$3}{\text{15 kiwis}}$; $\frac{\$0.20}{\text{1 kiwi}}$
h. 210 km in 3 hours $\frac{\text{210 km}}{\text{3 hours}}$; $\frac{\text{70 km}}{\text{1 hour}}$

22. **Industry** Vermont leads the United States in maple syrup production. Sap from maple trees is boiled to make the syrup. As the sap boils, water evaporates until pure maple syrup remains. If it takes 120 gallons of sap to make 3 gallons of maple syrup, find the unit ratio.
40 gallons of sap per gallon of maple syrup

23. **Science** The planet Mercury travels about 756,000 miles in its orbit in the 7 hours that make up a typical school day. Find the unit rate. **10,800 mi/hr**

24. **Sports** Basketball players often use unit rates to compare statistics. Which represents the higher unit rate, 210 points in 8 games or 153 points in 6 games? **210 points in 8 games**

25. **Test Prep** Find the best unit price for apples. **A**

Ⓐ \$0.79 per pound Ⓑ $\frac{\$2.40}{\text{3-pound bag}}$ Ⓒ $\frac{\$4.10}{\text{5-pound bag}}$ Ⓓ $\frac{\$8.00}{\text{10-pound bag}}$

Problem Solving and Reasoning

26. **Critical Thinking** Some jobs pay hourly wages; other jobs pay a salary for a week's work. One job pays \$7.00 for each hour's work. A second job pays \$320.00 for 40 hours of work each week. Which job has a higher unit rate? Explain.

GPS

27. **Communicate** A friend was absent from school, so he wants you to explain the difference between a rate and a ratio. Explain to your friend how a rate is a special kind of ratio.

Mixed Review

Find the value of each expression. *[Lesson 2-2]*

28. $41 + 27 \div 3$ **50**
29. $3 \times (62 - 14)$ **144**
30. $2 \times 5 + 6 \times 7$ **52**
31. $(24 + 28) \div 4$ **13**
32. $\frac{14 + 7}{3} - \frac{30}{10}$ **4**
33. $17 - 56 \div 7$ **9**
34. $\frac{56 - 4 \times 5}{2 \times 4 + 4}$ **3**
35. $\frac{64 \div (8 - 6)}{10 - 2 \times 3}$ **8**

Use the figure to name each pair of lines. *[Lesson 5-2]*

36. A pair of parallel lines **$\overleftrightarrow{BD}$ and $\overleftrightarrow{CE}$**

37. A pair of perpendicular lines **$\overleftrightarrow{AD}$ and $\overleftrightarrow{AC}$**

38. A pair of lines that are neither parallel nor perpendicular **$\overleftrightarrow{AD}$ and $\overleftrightarrow{CE}$**

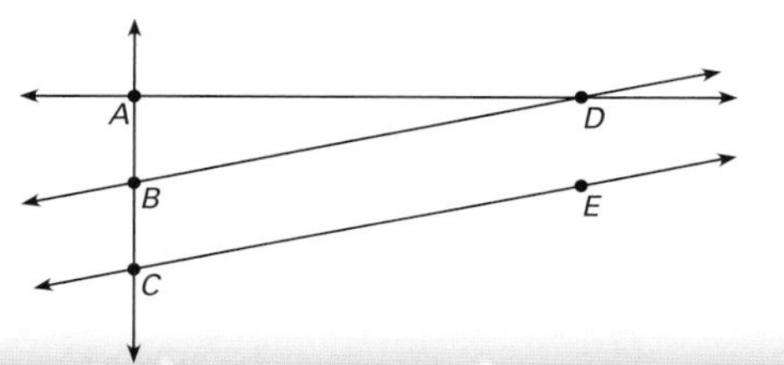

PROBLEM SOLVING 6-2

Exercise Notes

■ Exercise 22

Cultural Native Americans taught early immigrants the process of making maple syrup. Today, the Canadian province of Quebec is the leading producer of maple syrup, processing 3 million gallons a year.

■ Exercise 23

Science Mercury has the fastest orbital rate of all the planets, traveling at nearly 30 miles per second, while Pluto is the slowest at a little under 3 miles per second.

Exercise Answers

26. The second job; It pays \$8.00 per hour.

27. Possible answer: A rate is a ratio comparing two quantities using different units of measure.

Alternate Assessment

Interview Ask students to describe the difference between ratios and rates, giving examples of each. Have them explain what a unit rate is and give an example.

▶ Quick Quiz

Tell whether each ratio is a rate. If your answer is yes, express the rate as a unit rate.

1. $\frac{\$2.70}{3 \text{ lb}}$ **Yes; $\frac{\$0.90}{1 \text{ lb}}$**
2. $\frac{25 \text{ students}}{100 \text{ students}}$ **No**

Tell which is the better price.

3. $\frac{\$5}{2 \text{ pair}}$ or $\frac{\$8.25}{3 \text{ pair}}$ $\frac{\$5}{2 \text{ pair}}$
4. $\frac{\$0.59}{1 \text{ lb}}$ or $\frac{\$1}{2 \text{ lb}}$ $\frac{\$1}{2 \text{ lb}}$

Available on Daily Transparency 6-2

PROBLEM SOLVING

Name ____________ **Guided Problem Solving 6-2**

GPS PROBLEM 26, STUDENT PAGE 281

Some jobs pay hourly wages; other jobs pay a salary for a week's work. One job pays \$7.00 for each hour's work. A second job pays \$320.00 for 40 hours of work each week. Which job has a higher unit rate? Explain.

— Understand —

1. Circle the information you will need to use to solve the problem.
2. A unit rate is a rate where the **b**
   a. first quantity is one unit. b. second quantity is one unit.

— Plan —

3. Which rate has a unit rate of one hour? **\$7.00 per hour.**
4. Write the other rate as an hourly rate. **\$320 per 40 hours.**
5. What operation will you use to change the rate in Item 4 to a unit rate? **Division. Divide numerator and denominator by 40.**

— Solve —

6. Find the unit rate for the rate in Item 4. **\$8.00 per hour.**
7. Compare the unit rates. Which job has the higher unit rate? Explain. **The second job since it pays more money per hour.**

— Look Back —

8. How could you check your answer to see if it is reasonable? **Find how much the first job pays for 40 hours work and compare the totals.**

SOLVE ANOTHER PROBLEM

One job pays an annual salary of \$24,000 for 12 months' work. Another job pays \$1700 per month. Which job has a higher unit rate? Explain.
First job, since \$2000 per month > \$1700 per month.

ENRICHMENT

Name ____________ **Extend Your Thinking 6-2**

Decision Making

Caroline earned \$100. She decided to spend some of it on computer games. Help her choose which of these games she can purchase.

1. Caroline plans to buy at least two different games. Complete the table to list the possible combinations of games that she might choose.

Space Arena	Falling Shapes	Racing Stripes	Air Thrill	Money Left
	1	1	1	\$3.67
		1	1	\$41.56
	1	1		\$36.12
1		1		\$30.62
1	1			\$18.72
1			1	\$24.16
	1		1	\$29.66

2. Which will she buy if she spends the most money possible? **Falling Shapes, Racing Stripes, and Air Thrill**
3. Caroline's hobby is aviation. How might this affect her decision? **Possible answer: She may choose Space Arena and Air Thrill.**
4. If Caroline decides to buy a sweater priced at \$39.48, what games can she still buy? **Racing Stripes, Air Thrill**
5. Do you think she should buy 2 or 3 computer games? Why? **Possible answer: 2, so she has money left to buy other items.**

Lesson Organizer

Objective

- Find equivalent ratios and rates.

Vocabulary

- Equivalent ratios, equivalent rates

Materials

- Explore: Watch with a second hand

NCTM Standards

- 1–5, 7, 11, 13

► Review

For each fraction, give two equivalent fractions. Possible answers are given.

1. $\frac{8}{12}$ $\frac{2}{3}$, $\frac{16}{24}$
2. $\frac{6}{10}$ $\frac{3}{5}$, $\frac{18}{30}$
3. $\frac{6}{2}$ $\frac{3}{1}$, $\frac{12}{4}$

Available on Daily Transparency 6-3

1 Introduce

Explore

The Point
Students find a rate by experimentation. Then they use that rate to find a unit rate as well as several equivalent rates.

Ongoing Assessment
Check that students are able to estimate the unit rate correctly.

For Groups That Finish Early
Work in pairs, timing each other to see how many times each of you can write the name of your state in 15 seconds. Then estimate a unit rate and rates per 30 seconds and per minute.

6-3 Equivalent Ratios and Rates

You'll Learn ...

■ to find equivalent ratios and rates

... How It's Used

Physicians' assistants use equivalent rates when they take a patient's pulse.

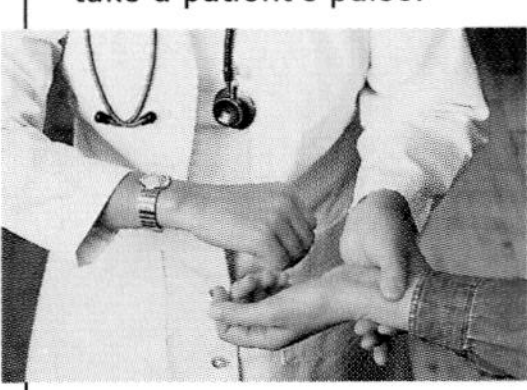

Vocabulary

equivalent ratios

equivalent rates

► Lesson Link You've seen that two fractions or decimals can be equivalent. In this lesson, you'll find equivalent ratios and equivalent rates. ◄

Explore Equivalent Rates

Knock on Wood

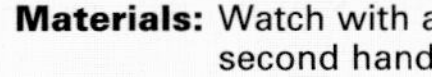

Materials: Watch with a second hand

1. Determine your "tapping rate" by counting the number of times you can tap your finger rapidly on your desk in 5 seconds. Have a partner time you.
2. Use your tapping rate to estimate the number of times you can tap your finger in 1 second. Explain how you found the number.
3. Estimate how long it would take you to tap 200 times. Explain how you found your answer. Are you making any assumptions?
4. Can you tap your finger 1000 times in 3 minutes? Explain.

Learn Equivalent Ratios and Rates

Recall that equivalent fractions name the same number. **Equivalent ratios** and **equivalent rates** also name the same number. The ratio $\frac{3 \text{ bones}}{1 \text{ ear}}$ is equivalent to $\frac{6 \text{ bones}}{2 \text{ ears}}$.

You can find equivalent ratios and equivalent rates the same way as you find equivalent fractions—by multiplying or dividing both parts of the ratio or rate by the same number.

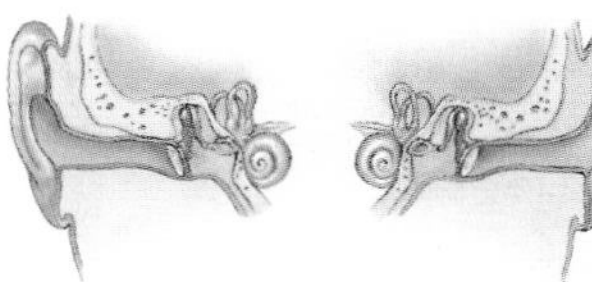

The middle ear has 3 bones.

MEETING INDIVIDUAL NEEDS

Resources

6-3 Practice
6-3 Reteaching
6-3 Problem Solving
6-3 Enrichment
6-3 Daily Transparency
Problem of the Day
Review
Quick Quiz
Technology Master 26

Learning Modalities

Logical Stress that finding equivalent ratios and equivalent rates is just like finding equal fractions.

Verbal Have students discuss situations in which they might have had to find equivalent ratios or rates. They might suggest changing amounts in recipes for more or fewer servings, determining traveling times at given rates per hour, and so on.

Challenge

Show students that they need not multiply or divide the terms of a ratio by a whole number to get an equivalent ratio.

For the following pairs of ratios, have students explain how the second is obtained from the first. Then have them make up similar pairs.

1. $\frac{8}{10} = \frac{20}{25}$ Multiply by 2.5 or divide by 0.4.
2. $\frac{5.6}{10.4} = \frac{3.5}{6.5}$ Multiply by 0.625 or divide by 1.6.

Examples

1 Find two ratios equivalent to $\frac{9}{15}$.

Multiply or divide the numerator and denominator by the same number.

Multiply: $\frac{9 \times 2}{15 \times 2} = \frac{18}{30}$

Divide: $\frac{9 \div 3}{15 \div 3} = \frac{3}{5}$

The ratios $\frac{18}{30}$ and $\frac{3}{5}$ are equivalent to $\frac{9}{15}$.

2 As José jogged at a steady rate on a treadmill, his heart beat 420 times in 4 minutes. Find the number of times his heart would beat in triple that amount of time. (Assume that the rate stays the same.)

$\text{rate} = \frac{420 \text{ beats}}{4 \text{ minutes}}$

To find an equivalent rate over *3 times* the time, multiply both parts of the rate by 3.

$\frac{420 \text{ beats} \times 3}{4 \text{ minutes} \times 3} = \frac{1260 \text{ beats}}{12 \text{ minutes}}$

José's heart would beat 1260 times in 12 minutes.

3 A 6-pack of boxed orange juice sells for \$2.45. Predict the price of a 24-pack by creating equal rates.

The price is $\frac{\$2.45}{6 \text{ boxes}}$. Notice that 24 is 4 × 6. So to predict the price of 24 boxes, multiply both parts of the rate by 4.

$\frac{\$2.45 \times 4}{6 \text{ boxes} \times 4} = \frac{\$9.80}{24 \text{ boxes}}$

A 24-pack of juice should cost \$9.80.

Science Link

A heart rate that is too rapid can put extra stress on the heart. Regular exercise can help lower your resting heart rate.

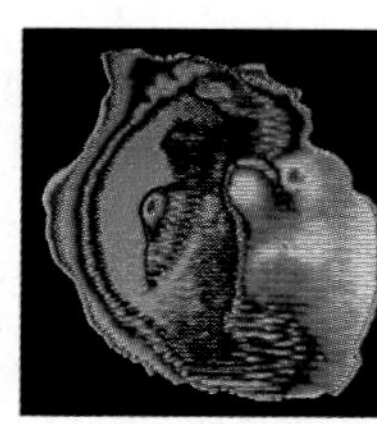

Remember

Multiplying or dividing the numerator and the denominator of a fraction by the same number does not change the value of the fraction. [Page 145]

Try It

a. Use multiplication and division to find two ratios equivalent to $\frac{6}{14}$. Possible answer: $\frac{3}{7}$ and $\frac{12}{28}$

b. The last time Jason made buttermilk biscuits, he used 8 cups of flour to make 60 biscuits. Today he plans to make one-fourth as many biscuits. If the flour-to-biscuit rate remains the same, how much flour should he use? 2 cups

Check Your Understanding

1. How can you tell if two ratios or two rates are equivalent?
2. Give an example showing how you can use equivalent ratios or rates in everyday life.

MATH EVERY DAY

Problem of the Day

Two years ago, Kevin was four times as old as Aretha. Six years ago, he was seven times as old. In how many years will the ratio be 2:1? 14 years

Available on Daily Transparency 6-3

An Extension is provided in the transparency package.

Fact of the Day

The heart rate is controlled by a knot of tissue called the sinoatrial node. This node is the body's natural pacemaker.

Estimation

Estimate each answer.

1. 2.3 × 5.8 12
2. 0.9 × 48.93 50
3. 57.45 ÷ 6.8 8
4. 44.6 ÷ 5.8 8

Answers for Explore

1. Possible answer: 30 taps in 5 sec.
2. Possible answer: 6 taps per sec; Used division to find the unit tapping rate.
3. Possible answer: About 33 sec; Divided 200 by the unit tapping rate; Assumed constant rate.
4. Possible answer: Yes; 3 min = 180 sec; 180 × 6 = 1080.

2 Teach

Learn

Alternate Examples

1. Find two ratios equivalent to $\frac{8}{10}$.

   Multiply $\frac{8 \times 3}{10 \times 3} = \frac{24}{30}$

   Divide $\frac{8 \div 2}{10 \div 2} = \frac{4}{5}$

   $\frac{24}{30}$ and $\frac{4}{5}$ are equivalent to $\frac{8}{10}$.

2. Maria jogged 700 steps in 4 minutes. At the given rate, how many steps does Maria take in half the time?

   Divide both parts of the rate by 2.

   $\frac{700 \text{ steps} \div 2}{4 \text{ min} \div 2} = \frac{350 \text{ steps}}{2 \text{ min}}$.

   Maria takes 350 steps in half the time.

3. How many steps would Maria take in 12 minutes?

   Since 12 is 3 times 4, multiply both parts of the rate by 3.

   $\frac{700 \text{ steps} \times 3}{4 \text{ min} \times 3} = \frac{2100 \text{ steps}}{12 \text{ min}}$.

   Maria would take 2100 steps in 12 min.

3 Practice and Assess

Check

Answers for Check Your Understanding

1. Write both in lowest terms.
2. Possible answer: When shopping for the best buy.

6-3 Exercises and Applications

Assignment Guide

- **Basic** 1–15 odds, 16, 18, 21–29 odds
- **Average** 1, 2–16 evens, 17, 18, 20–30 evens
- **Enriched** 2–18 evens, 19, 20–30 evens

Exercise Notes

Exercises 2–11

Error Prevention Ask students what is similar about the ratios in these exercises. They are not in lowest terms. Be sure students recognize that there are many correct answers for each exercise.

Exercise Answers

14. Ring the Bell has a 3 in 12 chance of winning, and Race the Rocket has a 4 in 12 chance of winning. So you'd be more likely to win Race the Rocket.

Reteaching

Activity

Materials: Play money—quarters, dimes, nickels, pennies

Possible answers are given.

- Write equivalent ratios for these ratios comparing values. Then model the ratios with the play money.

$\frac{2\text{ dimes}}{4\text{ nickels}}$ $\frac{1\text{ dime}}{2\text{ nickels}}$, $\frac{4\text{ dimes}}{8\text{ nickels}}$, $\frac{6\text{ dimes}}{12\text{ nickels}}$

$\frac{2\text{ quarters}}{10\text{ nickels}}$ $\frac{1\text{quarter}}{5\text{ nickels}}$, $\frac{3\text{ quarters}}{15\text{ nickels}}$, $\frac{4\text{ quarters}}{20\text{ nickels}}$

a30 pen- nies $\frac{10\text{ pennies}}{1\text{ dime}}$, $\frac{20\text{ pennies}}{2\text{ dimes}}$, $\frac{60\text{ pennies}}{6\text{ dimes}}$

- Write other pairs of equivalent ratios using dollar and coin amounts.

6-3 Exercises and Applications

Practice and Apply

1. **Getting Started** Follow these steps to find two ratios equivalent to $\frac{8}{20}$.
   a. Choose a number. Multiply the numerator and the denominator by the number you chose. 2
   b. Write the equivalent ratio. $\frac{16}{40}$
   c. Try to find a number that both the numerator and denominator are divisible by. 4
   d. Divide the numerator and the denominator by the number, then write the equivalent ratio. $\frac{2}{5}$

Multiply and divide to find two ratios equivalent to each ratio. Possible answers:

2. $\frac{6}{9}$ $\frac{12}{18}, \frac{2}{3}$
3. $\frac{10}{14}$ $\frac{20}{28}, \frac{5}{7}$
4. $\frac{15}{20}$ $\frac{30}{40}, \frac{3}{4}$
5. $\frac{22}{24}$ $\frac{44}{48}, \frac{11}{12}$
6. $\frac{25}{35}$ $\frac{50}{70}, \frac{5}{7}$
7. $\frac{27}{45}$ $\frac{54}{90}, \frac{3}{5}$
8. $\frac{36}{54}$ $\frac{72}{108}, \frac{2}{3}$
9. $\frac{40}{75}$ $\frac{80}{150}, \frac{8}{15}$
10. $\frac{64}{80}$ $\frac{128}{160}, \frac{4}{5}$
11. $\frac{100}{175}$ $\frac{200}{350}, \frac{4}{7}$
12. **Health** The human body gets energy from food. This energy is measured in calories. If a person burns 2.9 calories per minute while walking, how many calories would that person burn during a 20-minute walk? 58 calories
13. Suppose one U.S. dollar can be exchanged for 125 Spanish pesetas. At this rate of exchange, how many pesetas would you receive for eight U.S. dollars? 1000 pesetas
14. **Chance** Use equivalent rates to explain which game you would have a better chance of winning.

PRACTICE 6-3

PRACTICE

Name ______________________

Practice 6-3

Equivalent Ratios and Rates

Multiply and divide to find two ratios equivalent to each ratio. Possible answers:

1. $\frac{12}{15}$ $\frac{24}{30}, \frac{4}{5}$
2. $\frac{6}{9}$ $\frac{24}{36}, \frac{2}{3}$
3. $\frac{8}{14}$ $\frac{24}{42}, \frac{4}{7}$
4. $\frac{6}{12}$ $\frac{30}{60}, \frac{1}{2}$
5. $\frac{10}{12}$ $\frac{20}{24}, \frac{5}{6}$
6. $\frac{6}{8}$ $\frac{18}{24}, \frac{3}{4}$
7. $\frac{5}{10}$ $\frac{15}{30}, \frac{1}{2}$
8. $\frac{16}{22}$ $\frac{64}{88}, \frac{8}{11}$
9. $\frac{6}{12}$ $\frac{12}{24}, \frac{1}{2}$
10. $\frac{8}{30}$ $\frac{40}{150}, \frac{4}{15}$
11. $\frac{20}{34}$ $\frac{60}{102}, \frac{10}{17}$
12. $\frac{15}{18}$ $\frac{30}{36}, \frac{5}{6}$
13. $\frac{16}{36}$ $\frac{32}{72}, \frac{4}{9}$
14. $\frac{9}{12}$ $\frac{27}{36}, \frac{3}{4}$
15. $\frac{24}{27}$ $\frac{48}{54}, \frac{8}{9}$
16. $\frac{6}{10}$ $\frac{24}{40}, \frac{3}{5}$
17. $\frac{6}{33}$ $\frac{30}{165}, \frac{2}{11}$
18. $\frac{30}{42}$ $\frac{90}{126}, \frac{5}{7}$
19. $\frac{10}{16}$ $\frac{20}{32}, \frac{5}{8}$
20. $\frac{24}{28}$ $\frac{72}{84}, \frac{6}{7}$
21. $\frac{16}{18}$ $\frac{64}{72}, \frac{8}{9}$
22. $\frac{6}{15}$ $\frac{30}{75}, \frac{2}{5}$
23. $\frac{14}{16}$ $\frac{56}{64}, \frac{7}{8}$
24. $\frac{8}{10}$ $\frac{24}{30}, \frac{4}{5}$
25. $\frac{20}{50}$ $\frac{40}{100}, \frac{2}{5}$
26. $\frac{15}{30}$ $\frac{75}{150}, \frac{1}{2}$
27. $\frac{19}{38}$ $\frac{57}{114}, \frac{1}{2}$
28. $\frac{28}{30}$ $\frac{140}{150}, \frac{14}{15}$
29. $\frac{10}{18}$ $\frac{30}{54}, \frac{5}{9}$
30. $\frac{8}{12}$ $\frac{16}{24}, \frac{2}{3}$
31. $\frac{12}{57}$ $\frac{24}{114}, \frac{4}{19}$
32. $\frac{16}{20}$ $\frac{48}{60}, \frac{4}{5}$
33. $\frac{26}{44}$ $\frac{78}{132}, \frac{13}{22}$
34. $\frac{14}{24}$ $\frac{70}{120}, \frac{7}{12}$
35. $\frac{35}{42}$ $\frac{70}{84}, \frac{5}{6}$
36. $\frac{28}{34}$ $\frac{84}{102}, \frac{14}{17}$
37. $\frac{13}{65}$ $\frac{65}{325}, \frac{1}{5}$
38. $\frac{52}{78}$ $\frac{260}{390}, \frac{2}{3}$
39. $\frac{10}{52}$ $\frac{20}{104}, \frac{5}{26}$
40. $\frac{12}{18}$ $\frac{48}{72}, \frac{2}{3}$
41. $\frac{6}{82}$ $\frac{24}{328}, \frac{3}{41}$
42. $\frac{24}{48}$ $\frac{96}{192}, \frac{1}{2}$
43. $\frac{25}{45}$ $\frac{100}{180}, \frac{5}{9}$
44. $\frac{12}{68}$ $\frac{60}{340}, \frac{3}{17}$
45. $\frac{20}{30}$ $\frac{40}{60}, \frac{2}{3}$
46. $\frac{24}{39}$ $\frac{48}{78}, \frac{8}{13}$
47. $\frac{12}{36}$ $\frac{48}{144}, \frac{1}{3}$
48. $\frac{33}{44}$ $\frac{66}{88}, \frac{3}{4}$
49. $\frac{46}{72}$ $\frac{92}{144}, \frac{23}{36}$
50. $\frac{14}{54}$ $\frac{42}{162}, \frac{7}{27}$
51. $\frac{18}{27}$ $\frac{90}{135}, \frac{2}{3}$
52. $\frac{10}{15}$ $\frac{50}{75}, \frac{2}{3}$
53. $\frac{6}{38}$ $\frac{30}{190}, \frac{3}{19}$
54. $\frac{24}{26}$ $\frac{72}{78}, \frac{12}{13}$
55. $\frac{18}{28}$ $\frac{36}{56}, \frac{9}{14}$
56. $\frac{8}{56}$ $\frac{40}{280}, \frac{1}{7}$
57. $\frac{6}{14}$ $\frac{12}{28}, \frac{3}{7}$
58. $\frac{26}{32}$ $\frac{52}{64}, \frac{13}{16}$
59. $\frac{35}{40}$ $\frac{70}{80}, \frac{7}{8}$
60. $\frac{30}{96}$ $\frac{120}{384}, \frac{5}{16}$
61. **Science** Neptune rotates 12 times in 18 Earth days. How many times will Neptune rotate in 6 Earth days? 4 times
62. **Measurement** There are 8 pints in a gallon. How many pints are in 7 gallons? 56 pints

RETEACHING

Name ______________________

Alternative Lesson 6-3

Equivalent Ratios and Rates

Recall that equivalent fractions name the same number. You can find **equivalent ratios** and **equivalent rates** the same way you find equivalent fractions–by multiplying or dividing both parts of the ratio or rate by the same number.

Example 1

Use multiplication to find two ratios equivalent to $\frac{8}{12}$.

$\frac{8 \times 2}{12 \times 2} = \frac{16}{24}$ $\frac{8 \times 5}{12 \times 5} = \frac{40}{60}$

$\frac{16}{24}$ and $\frac{40}{60}$ are equivalent to $\frac{8}{12}$.

Use division to find two ratios equivalent to $\frac{8}{12}$.

$\frac{8 \div 2}{12 \div 2} = \frac{4}{6}$ $\frac{8 \div 4}{12 \div 4} = \frac{2}{3}$

$\frac{4}{6}$ and $\frac{2}{3}$ are equivalent to $\frac{8}{12}$.

Try It Possible answers:

a. Use multiplication to find two ratios equivalent to $\frac{3}{5}$. $\frac{6}{10}$ $\frac{9}{15}$

b. Use division to find two ratios equivalent to $\frac{12}{18}$. $\frac{6}{9}$ $\frac{4}{6}$

Example 2

Margo jogs 10 miles in 2 hours. Assuming her rate stays the same, find the number of miles she would jog in twice that amount of time.

Since twice means *2 times*, multiply both parts of the rate by 2.

$\frac{10\text{ miles} \times 2}{2\text{ hours} \times 2} = \frac{20\text{ miles}}{4\text{ hours}}$

Margo would jog 20 miles in 4 hours.

Try It Jo does 20 sit-ups in 40 seconds. At this rate, how many can she do in half that time?

c. Write the rate. $\frac{20\text{ sit-ups}}{40\text{ seconds}}$

d. Divide by 2. $\frac{20\text{ sit-ups} \div 2}{40\text{ seconds} \div 2} = \frac{10\text{ sit-ups}}{20\text{ seconds}}$

e. How many sit-ups can Jo do in half the time? 10 sit-ups

Ken spends $2.50 for 3 pens. At this rate, what will he spend for 5 times as many pens?

f. Write the rate. $\frac{\$2.50}{3\text{ pens}}$

g. Multiply by 5. $\frac{\$2.50 \times 5}{3\text{ pens} \times 5} = \frac{\$12.50}{15\text{ pens}}$

h. What will Ken spend for 5 times as many pens? $12.50

15. Science It takes 10 seconds for sound to travel 9 miles underwater. How long does it take sound to travel 6 times that distance? **60 sec**

16. Test Prep The number of breaths per minute for a person at rest is about 16. About how many breaths are taken in 30 minutes by a person at rest? **D**

Ⓐ 8   Ⓑ 14   Ⓒ 46   Ⓓ 480

Problem Solving and Reasoning

17. Critical Thinking Some animated films, such as the film *A Close Shave*, by Nick Park, are made by using clay models. At the beginning of a scene, the models are placed in position and a picture is taken. The models are then moved slightly—a finger curls, an eye opens wider—and the next picture is taken. Each picture, or *frame*, is seen for only $\frac{1}{24}$ of a second on the movie screen. How many frames are needed to make 30 seconds of animated film using this method? Write an equivalent ratio to show this quantity. **720; $\frac{720 \text{ frames}}{30 \text{ seconds}}$**

©Aardman Animations/ Wallace and Gromit Ltd.1995

18. Critical Thinking GPS It is estimated that 13 out of every 100 pounds of garbage in the United States is recycled. An average person in the United States throws away about 4 pounds of garbage per day. About how many pounds of garbage does an average person recycle in 50 days? 100 days? **26 pounds; 52 pounds**

19. Journal Identify a ratio that describes something in your classroom, such as the number of legs per desk. Write the unit ratio for the item. Then count the total number of items and write the equivalent ratio based on the number you count. (Remember to include units!)

Mixed Review

Compare using <, >, or =. *[Lesson 3-9]*

20. $\frac{6}{13} > \frac{7}{26}$ **21.** $\frac{10}{13} < \frac{11}{14}$ **22.** $\frac{16}{24} = \frac{22}{33}$ **23.** $\frac{16}{21} < \frac{33}{40}$

24. $\frac{20}{32} > \frac{9}{15}$ **25.** $\frac{32}{50} > \frac{40}{64}$ **26.** $\frac{5}{17} > \frac{4}{15}$ **27.** $\frac{18}{42} < \frac{35}{80}$

Classify each triangle by its sides and by its angles. *[Lesson 5-3]*

28.

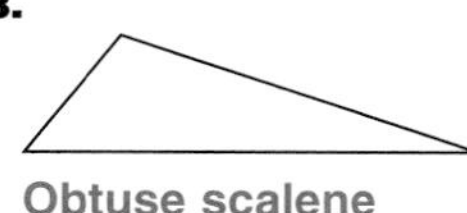

Obtuse scalene

29.

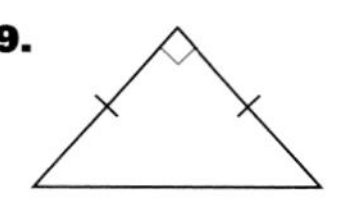

Right isosceles

30.

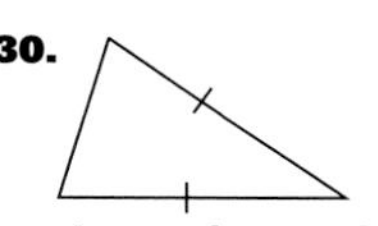

Acute isosceles

PROBLEM SOLVING

Name ______________________

Guided Problem Solving 6-3

GPS **PROBLEM 18, STUDENT PAGE 285**

It is estimated that 13 out of every 100 pounds of garbage in the United States is recycled. An average person in the United States throws away about 4 pounds of garbage per day. About how many pounds of garbage does an average person recycle in 50 days? 100 days?

— Understand —

1. Circle the information you will need to use to solve the problem.

— Plan —

2. About how many pounds of garbage does an average person throw away in 50 days? **200 pounds.**
3. About how many pounds of garbage does an average person throw away in 100 days? **400 pounds.**

— Solve —

4. Choose an equivalent ratio that gives the approximate number of pounds of garbage recycled by an average person in 50 days. **a**

   a. $\frac{13}{100} = \frac{26}{200}$ **b.** $\frac{13}{100} = \frac{52}{100}$

5. Write an equivalent ratio that gives the approximate number of pounds of garbage recycled by an average person in 100 days. **$\frac{13}{100} = \frac{52}{400}$**
6. About how many pounds of garbage does an average person recycle in 50 days? In 100 days? **26 lb; 52 lb**

— Look Back —

7. Does it make sense that the number of pounds of garbage recycled in 100 days is double that recycled in 50 days? Explain.

   Yes, since 100 days is double 50 days and the rate of garbage that is recycled is constant.

SOLVE ANOTHER PROBLEM

Out of every 4 books read by Janelle, 3 are fiction. She reads 14 books each semester. How many fiction books does she read in 6 semesters? **63 fiction books.**

ENRICHMENT

Name ______________________

Extend Your Thinking 6-3

Critical Thinking

The table on the right shows exchange rates for several foreign currencies.

Country	Currency	Rate Per Dollar
Mexico	Peso	7.52
Britain	Pound	0.64
Germany	Mark	1.53
France	Franc	5.18

1. For each country, give the exchange rate as a unit rate in foreign currency per dollar. Then find an equivalent rate to show how much foreign currency you would receive for the given amount of U. S. dollars. The first one is done for you.

	Unit rate	Foreign currency
a. Mexican pesos, 10 dollars	$\frac{7.52 \text{ pesos}}{1 \text{ dollar}}$	$\frac{75.2 \text{ pesos}}{10 \text{ dollars}}$
b. British pounds, 5 dollars	**$\frac{0.64 \text{ pound}}{1 \text{ dollar}}$**	**$\frac{3.2 \text{ pounds}}{5 \text{ dollars}}$**
c. German marks, 7 dollars	**$\frac{1.53 \text{ marks}}{1 \text{ dollar}}$**	**$\frac{10.71 \text{ marks}}{7 \text{ dollars}}$**
d. French francs, 3 dollars	**$\frac{5.18 \text{ francs}}{1 \text{ dollar}}$**	**$\frac{15.54 \text{ francs}}{3 \text{ dollars}}$**

2. Suppose your company wants to sell a software package in Mexico and in Germany. It sells for $250 in the United States. What will you charge in each country?

   a. Write an equivalent ratio to show how many pesos are in $250.
   $\frac{7.52 \text{ pesos}}{1 \text{ dollar}} = \frac{1880 \text{ pesos}}{250 \text{ dollars}}$

   b. Write an equivalent ratio to show how many marks are in $250.
   $\frac{1.53 \text{ marks}}{1 \text{ dollar}} = \frac{382.5 \text{ marks}}{250 \text{ dollars}}$

3. Suppose your marketing manager travels from Great Britain to Germany to meet you.

   a. Write a rate comparing German marks to British pounds. Then give the unit rate per pound. Round your answer to the nearest hundredth.
   $\frac{1.53 \text{ marks}}{0.64 \text{ pound}}$; 2.39 marks per pound.

   b. Write an equivalent ratio to show the cost in German marks of a software package that costs 48 British pounds.
   $\frac{2.39 \text{ marks}}{1 \text{ pound}}, \frac{114.72 \text{ marks}}{48 \text{ pounds}}$

Exercise Notes

Exercise 15

Science It would take sound more than 40 seconds to travel 9 miles in air.

Exercise 17

Error Prevention Students might make the mistake of finding a ratio equivalent to $\frac{1}{24}$. Help them see that if 24 frames are seen in a second, then the unit ratio is $\frac{24 \text{ frames}}{1 \text{ second}}$. They can then find an equivalent ratio with 30 seconds as the desired time.

Exercise Answers

19. Possible answer: $\frac{32 \text{ students}}{1 \text{ classroom}}$, $\frac{64 \text{ students}}{2 \text{ classrooms}}$.

Alternate Assessment

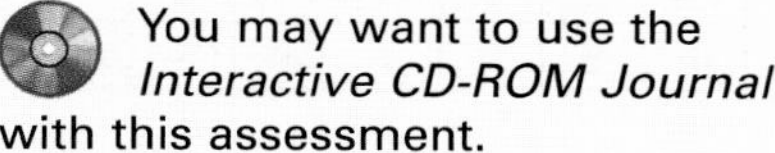

You may want to use the *Interactive CD-ROM Journal* with this assessment.

Journal Have students describe how to find ratios and rates equivalent to given ratios and rates. Have them include appropriate examples.

Quick Quiz

Find two ratios equivalent to the given ratio.

Possible answers are given.

1. $\frac{4}{3}$ $\frac{8}{6}, \frac{20}{15}$
2. $\frac{18}{27}$ $\frac{2}{3}, \frac{36}{54}$
3. $\frac{24}{30}$ $\frac{4}{5}, \frac{12}{15}$
4. $\frac{12}{28}$ $\frac{3}{7}, \frac{6}{14}$
5. $\frac{25}{75}$ $\frac{5}{15}, \frac{50}{150}$

Available on Daily Transparency 6-3

6-4 Lesson Organizer

Objective

- Use a table to find equivalent ratios and rates.

NCTM Standards

- 1–5, 7, 8, 13

Review

Find the pattern and complete the table.

1.

m	2	3	4	5	6	7
n	5	6	7	8	9	10

$n = m + 3$ or $m = n - 3$

2.

a	16	22	28	34	40	46
b	8	11	14	17	20	23

$b = \frac{a}{2}$ or $a = 2b$

Available on Daily Transparency 6-4

1 Introduce

Explore

The Point
Students see how to use the patterns in a table to generate rates equivalent to a given rate.

Ongoing Assessment
Observe students' responses to Step 4. Be sure they understand that the number of breaths per minute can be found by *dividing* the heart rate by 4.

For Groups That Finish Early
Use a timing device to determine if your pattern of breaths and heartbeats is the same or similar to that given in **Explore**.

6-4 Using Tables to Explore Ratios and Rates

You'll Learn ...

- to use a table to find equivalent ratios and rates

... How It's Used

Manufacturers use tables to make sure parts are distributed correctly throughout the manufacturing process.

▶ Lesson Link You know how to find a ratio or a rate that is equivalent to a given ratio or rate. Now you'll see how to use a table to find as many equivalent ratios or rates as you want. ◀

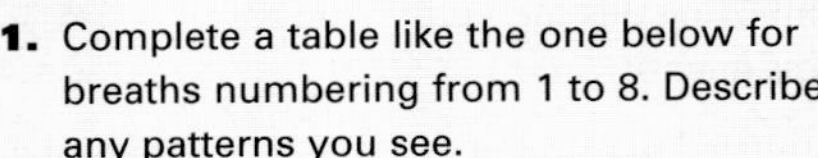

Explore Rate Tables

Grizzlies, Mice, and You

Biologists have discovered that nearly all mammals, regardless of size, breathe about once for every 4 heartbeats.

1. Complete a table like the one below for breaths numbering from 1 to 8. Describe any patterns you see.

No. of Breaths	1	2	3	4	5	6	7	8
No. of Heartbeats	4							

2. A grizzly bear breathes about 10 times per minute. Find the grizzly's heart rate. How did you find the answer?
3. A mouse's heart beats about 700 times in 1 minute. How many times does a mouse breathe in 1 minute? How did you find the answer?
4. Give a method for finding a mammal's heart rate if you know how many times it breathes in a minute. Can you use this method to find the number of breaths per minute if you know the heart rate? Explain.

Learn Using Tables to Explore Ratios and Rates

To create a table of equivalent ratios or rates, use the same method you use to create equivalent fractions. Multiply or divide the numerator and the denominator of a known ratio or rate by the same number. The table shows that $\frac{3}{4}$ is equal to $\frac{6}{8}$.

$3 \cdot 2$

3	6	
4	8	

$4 \cdot 2$

MEETING INDIVIDUAL NEEDS

Resources

- 6-4 Practice
- 6-4 Reteaching
- 6-4 Problem Solving
- 6-4 Enrichment
- 6-4 Daily Transparency
  - Problem of the Day
  - Review
  - Quick Quiz
- Technology Master 27
- Chapter 6 Project Master

Learning Modalities

Logical Give students a ratio and have them add the same number to both parts of the ratio. Ask if the resulting ratio is equivalent to the original. No Then have them subtract the same number from both parts and ask if this results in a ratio equivalent to the original. No Repeat the process with a variety of ratios to reinforce the notion that equivalent ratios can be found only by multiplying or dividing parts of a ratio by the same number.

Visual You might illustrate the table in **Explore** using symbols or letters to show the ratios; for instance, you could use *B*s for breaths and *H*s for heartbeats.

Inclusion

Students might benefit from working with concrete materials. Have them work with two-color counters to find equivalent ratios.

Remind students that equivalent ratios are like equivalent fractions.

Example 1

Complete the table to create five ratios equivalent to $\frac{4}{9}$.

4	8	12	16	20	24
9					

To find the first equivalent ratio, notice that the second number in the top row, 8, is 4×2. To find the second number in the bottom row, multiply 9 by 2: $9 \times 2 = 18$.

	4 × 2	4 × 3	4 × 4	4 × 5	4 × 6
4	8	12	16	20	24
9	18	27	36	45	54
	9 × 2	9 × 3	9 × 4	9 × 5	9 × 6

The five ratios are $\frac{8}{18}$, $\frac{12}{27}$, $\frac{16}{36}$, $\frac{20}{45}$, and $\frac{24}{54}$.

Try It

Use the table to create five ratios equivalent to $\frac{2}{5}$.

2	4	6	8	10	12
5	10	15	20	25	30

Problem Solving TIP

A row in a table is a horizontal line of entries. A vertical line of entries is called a column. To remember this, think of the up-and-down *columns* in famous buildings.

You can also use tables to estimate and make predictions about ratios and rates. First find the number you know (or numbers close to it) in one row of the table. Then find the corresponding number(s) in the other row.

Example 2

The table gives the number of sit-ups Laurie did during three workouts last week. Estimate how long it will take her to complete 35 sit-ups.

Sit-Ups	20	30	40
Time (sec)	24	36	48

To estimate the time it takes Laurie to do 35 sit-ups, think:

The number of sit-ups is in the top row of the table. Although 35 is not in the top row, 35 is halfway between 30 and 40. So the time is the number halfway between 36 and 48 in the bottom row. 42 is halfway between 36 and 48.

A good estimate for the time to complete 35 sit-ups is 42 seconds.

MATH EVERY DAY

Problem of the Day

Neck scarves at Accessories Galore sell for $8.50 each. At the store's most recent sale, they were priced at 2 for $16.00. How much money can you save by buying ten scarves at the sale price of 2 for $16.00 rather than buying ten scarves at the original price of $8.50 each? How many sale scarves would you have to buy to get a "free" or "extra" scarf? $5; 16 scarves

Available on Daily Transparency 6-4

An Extension is provided in the transparency package.

Fact of the Day

A grizzly bear may grow to a length of 9 feet and weigh up to 900 pounds.

Mental Math

Complete each equation mentally.

1. $\frac{7 \times \square}{8 \times \square} = \frac{14}{16}$ 2; 2
2. $\frac{36 \div \square}{16 \div \square} = \frac{9}{4}$ 4; 4
3. $\frac{12 \times \square}{10 \times \square} = \frac{36}{30}$ 3; 3

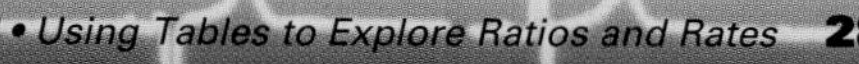

Answers for Explore

1. 8; 12; 16; 20; 24; 28; 32. Four times the number of breaths equals the number of heartbeats; Numbers of heartbeats are multiples of 4.
2. 40 heartbeats per minute; 1 breath is 4 heartbeats, so 10 breaths in one minute is 40 heartbeats in one minute.
3. 175; 4 heartbeats is 1 breath, so 700 heartbeats in one minute is 175 breaths in one minute, $700 \div 4 = 175$.
4. Multiply the number of breaths in a minute by 4 to find the heart rate; No, divide the heart rate by 4 to find the number of breaths per minute.

2 Teach

Learn

Alternate Examples

1. Complete the table to create five ratios equivalent to $\frac{3}{7}$.

3	6	9	12	15	18
7					

Notice that the second number in the top row, 6, is 3×2. Multiply 7×2 to find the second number in the bottom row. $9 = 3 \times 3$. so multiply 7×3, and so on.

3	6	9	12	15	18
7	14	21	28	35	42

The five ratios are $\frac{6}{14}$, $\frac{9}{21}$, $\frac{12}{28}$, $\frac{15}{35}$, and $\frac{18}{42}$.

2. The table gives the number of pushups Toby did. Estimate how long it would take him to do 450 pushups.

Pushups	300	400	500
Time (sec)	750	1000	1250

Think: 450 is halfway between 400 and 500, so the time is halfway between 1000 and 1250 seconds, or 1125 seconds.

It would take Toby about 1125 seconds to do 450 pushups.

Students see two methods for finding a ratio equivalent to a given ratio. One method involves making a table of ratios equivalent to the given ratio, and the other involves multiplying the numerator and denominator of the given ratio by the same number.

Answers for What Do You Think?

1. Paula's is easier; She only needs to divide 46 by 11 and multiply the answer by 5.
2. 100 is about 11×10, so multiply 5 by 10. The volume of 100 grams of sulfur is about 50 cm^3.

3 Practice and Assess

Check

Be sure that students are able to estimate values that are not in ratio tables. You might ask them to extend the table in Example 2 and then find other intermediate values, such as number of sit-ups in 30 seconds, number of seconds for 45 sit-ups, and so on.

Answers for Check Your Understanding

1. Estimate by what number you need to multiply both the numerator and denominator to get the given numerator or denominator. Then multiply to find the missing number.
2. Possible answer: Multiply both the numerator and denominator by 2 and then by 3.

Ramon and Paula are lab partners in science class. They find that a volume of 5 cubic centimeters (cm^3) of sulfur has a mass of 11 grams (g). They need to find the volume of 55 g of sulfur.

Ramon thinks ...

I'll make a table.

Volume (cm^3)	5	10	15	20	25
Weight (g)	11	22	33	44	55

From the $\frac{25}{55}$ column of my table, I can tell that 55 g of sulfur has a volume of 25 cm^3.

Paula thinks ...

The ratio of the volume to the weight is $\frac{5\ cm^3}{11\ g}$. I know that 55 is 11×5. So I can multiply both parts of the ratio by 5.

$$\frac{5\ cm^3 \times 5}{11\ g \times 5} = \frac{25\ cm^3}{55\ g}$$

So 55 g of sulfur has a volume of 25 cm^3.

What do you think?

1. Suppose Ramon and Paula needed to find the volume of 46 g of sulfur. Whose method would be more helpful? Explain why you think so.
2. Describe a method you could use to *estimate* the volume of 100 g of sulfur. What is your estimate?

Check Your Understanding

1. Suppose you know one out of two numbers in a ratio. With a table of ratios equivalent to that ratio, how can you use the table to find the missing number?
2. How can you find two rates that are equivalent to 1.2 miles in 15 minutes?

MEETING MIDDLE SCHOOL CLASSROOM NEEDS

Tips from Middle School Teachers

Developing proportional thinking is a main goal of the middle-school curriculum. Seventh graders should be familiar with ratios and proportions, and the content in this chapter will reinforce their understanding and help to prepare them for their work with percents and with similar figures.

Team Teaching

Have the health teacher discuss with students the importance of maintaining a healthy pulse rate and the problems associated with too rapid a pulse.

Science Connection

Sulfur is a nonmetallic element which is very flammable. It is used in, among other things, sulfa drugs, insecticides, fungicides, and plant fertilizers.

6-4 Exercises and Applications

Practice and Apply

1. **Getting Started** Follow these steps to make a table of five ratios equivalent to $\frac{4}{7}$.

a. Make a table containing 6 columns and 2 rows.

b. In the column at the far left of the table, write 4 in the top row and 7 in the bottom row.

c. Multiply both the numerator and the denominator by 2 and enter the result in the second column of your table.

d. Multiply the 4 and the 7 by 3, 4, 5, and 6 to complete your table.

2. Using multiplication, complete the table to find five ratios equivalent to $\frac{5}{8}$.

5	10	15	20	25	30
8	16	24	32	40	48

3. Using division, complete the table to find five ratios equivalent to $\frac{48}{72}$.

48	24	16	12	8	6
72	36	24	18	12	9

Fill in each table to find four ratios equivalent to the ratio in the first column.

4.

3	6	9	12	21
5	10	15	20	35

5.

32	16	4	1	64
64	32	8	2	128

Use the table to make an estimate.

6. **Estimation** In 1984, Paul Forthomme of Belgium set the record for the greatest distance walked in a day. Forthomme averaged about 29 miles every 5 hours. Estimate how long it took him to walk 100 miles. About 17 hours

Distance Walked (mi)	29	58	87	116	145
Time (hr)	5	10	15	20	25

7. **Consumer** Used video games are on sale at 2 for $17. Estimate how many you could buy for $100. 11 video games

Video Games	2	4	6	8	10
Cost ($)	17	34	51	68	85

PRACTICE 6-4

PRACTICE

Name ______________________

Practice 6-4

Using Tables to Explore Ratios and Rates

1. Using multiplication, complete the table to find 5 ratios equivalent to $\frac{3}{11}$.

3	6	9	12	15	18
11	22	33	44	55	66

Ratios: $\frac{6}{22}, \frac{9}{33}, \frac{12}{44}, \frac{15}{55}, \frac{18}{66}$

2. Using division, complete the table to find 5 ratios equivalent to $\frac{90}{225}$.

90	30	18	10	6	2
225	75	45	25	15	5

Ratios: $\frac{30}{75}, \frac{18}{45}, \frac{10}{25}, \frac{6}{15}, \frac{2}{5}$

Fill in each table to find four ratios equal to the ratio in the first column.

3.

5	10	15	30	40
8	16	24	48	64

Ratios: $\frac{10}{16}, \frac{15}{24}, \frac{30}{48}, \frac{40}{64}$

4.

21	7	42	63	84
36	12	72	108	144

Ratios: $\frac{7}{12}, \frac{42}{72}, \frac{63}{108}, \frac{84}{144}$

5. In 1946, Stella Pajunas set a record by typing 216 words in a minute on an electric typewriter. Use the table to estimate how long it took her to type 100 words. About 28 seconds

Number of words	36	72	108	144	180	216
Number of seconds	10	20	30	40	50	60

Use a table to find two rates equivalent to each rate. Possible answers:

6. $15 per CD

Price ($1)	15	30	45
CDs	1	2	3

Rates: $\frac{\$30}{2\text{ CDs}}, \frac{\$45}{3\text{ CDs}}$

7. 16 pages typed in 4 hours

Pages	16	8	4
Hours	4	2	1

Rates: $\frac{8\text{ pages}}{2\text{ hours}}, \frac{4\text{ pages}}{1\text{ hour}}$

8. A walrus can swim at a rate of 24 kilometers per hour. Make a table to find five rates equivalent to this unit rate. Possible answer:

Distance (km)	24	48	72	96	120	144
Time (hr)	1	2	3	4	5	6

Rates: $\frac{48\text{ km}}{2\text{ hr}}, \frac{72\text{ km}}{3\text{ hr}}, \frac{96\text{ km}}{4\text{ hr}}, \frac{120\text{ km}}{5\text{ hr}}, \frac{144\text{ km}}{6\text{ hr}}$

RETEACHING

Name ______________________

Alternative Lesson 6-4

Using Tables to Explore Ratios and Rates

You can multiply or divide to create a table of equivalent ratios or rates.

Example 1

Use multiplication to complete the table to find ratios equivalent to $\frac{5}{8}$.

	5 × 2	5 × 3	5 × 4	5 × 5	5 × 6	5 × 7	5 × 8
5	10	15	20	25	30	35	40
8	16	24	32	40	48	56	64
	8 × 2	8 × 3	8 × 4	8 × 5	8 × 6	8 × 7	8 × 8

Try It

a. Use multiplication to complete the table to find ratios equivalent to $\frac{3}{5}$.

	3 × 2	3 × 3	3 × 4	3 × 5	3 × 6	3 × 7	3 × 8
3	6	9	12	15	18	21	24
5	10	15	20	25	30	35	40
	5 × 2	5 × 3	5 × 4	5 × 5	5 × 6	5 × 7	5 × 8

b. Use multiplication to complete the table to find ratios equivalent to $\frac{7}{9}$.

	7 × 2	7 × 3	7 × 4	7 × 5	7 × 6	7 × 7	7 × 8
7	14	21	28	35	42	49	56
9	18	27	36	45	54	63	72
	9 × 2	9 × 3	9 × 4	9 × 5	9 × 6	9 × 7	9 × 8

Example 2

Use division to complete the table to find ratios equivalent to $\frac{32}{48}$.

	32 ÷ 2	32 ÷ 4	32 ÷ 8	32 ÷ 16
32	16	8	4	2
48	24	12	6	3
	48 ÷ 2	48 ÷ 4	48 ÷ 8	48 ÷ 16

Try It

c. Use division to complete the table to find ratios equivalent to $\frac{54}{72}$.

	54 ÷ 2	54 ÷ 3	54 ÷ 6	54 ÷ 9
54	27	18	9	6
72	36	24	12	8
	72 ÷ 2	72 ÷ 3	72 ÷ 6	72 ÷ 9

d. Use division to complete the table to find ratios equivalent to $\frac{80}{96}$.

	80 ÷ 2	80 ÷ 4	80 ÷ 8	80 ÷ 16
80	40	20	10	5
96	48	24	12	6
	96 ÷ 2	96 ÷ 4	96 ÷ 8	96 ÷ 16

6-4 Exercises and Applications

Assignment Guide

- **Basic**
  1–4, 6–12 evens, 15, 16–28 evens
- **Average**
  1–13 odds, 14–17, 19–27 odds
- **Enriched**
  2–14 evens, 15–17, 18–28 evens

Exercise Answers

1.

4	8	12	16	20	24
7	14	21	28	35	42

Possible answers for 8-11:

8. 6 runs in 14 games; 9 runs in 21 games.
9. 50 words typed in 2 minutes; 75 words typed in 3 minutes.
10. 5 miles in 1 hour; 10 miles in 2 hours.
11. 7 points in 8 minutes played; 14 points in 16 minutes played.

Reteaching

Activity

Materials: Index cards

Mark five index cards "3 sit-ups" and five "2 sit-ups." Use them to model this situation, and complete the table below.

- May can do 3 sit-ups for every 2 that Jon can do. How many sit-ups can May do when Jon does 4? When Jon does 6? When he does 8? When he does 10?

Jon	2	4	6	8	10
May	3	6	9	12	15

- How could you find the number Jon does if May does 24? How could you find the number May does if Jon does 20? Possible answers: Extend the table by multiplying; Use the ratio $\frac{2}{3}$ and find equivalent ratios with the desired denominator and numerator.

Exercise Notes

■ Exercise 15

Test Prep Choice A implies that students have not distinguished between numerator and denominator.

■ Exercises 26–28

Error Prevention You may need to remind students of the formula to use for these exercises: $S = (n - 2)180°$.

Project Progress

You may want to have students use Chapter 6 Project Master.

Exercise Answers

Answers for Exercises 8–11 are on page 289.

12.

14	21	28	35	42
2	3	4	5	6

13.

30	45	60	75	90
2	3	4	5	6

14.

5	7.5	10	12.5	15
2	3	4	5	6

16. No; No; None of these ratios is equivalent to $\frac{12}{18}$: $\frac{11}{17}, \frac{10}{16}, \frac{a9}{15}, \frac{8}{14}, \frac{7}{13}, \frac{6}{12}, \frac{5}{11}, \frac{4}{10}, \frac{3}{9}, \frac{2}{8}, \frac{1}{7}$.

17. Possible answer:

Hours	1	2	3	4	5
1930s	.25	.50	.75	1	1.25
Now	3.50	7	10.50	14	17.50

Baby-sitting or lawn mowing for only $3.50 per hour or $17.50 for 5 hours. Call XXX-XXXX.

Alternate Assessment

Interview Have students describe how they might use tables of equivalent ratios in a real-world situation and why making tables might be easier than other methods for finding equivalent ratios.

➤ Quick Quiz

Fill in the table with equivalent ratios.

12	6	4	2	1	24
48	24	16	8	4	96

Available on Daily Transparency 6-4

Use a table to find two rates equivalent to each rate.

8. 3 home runs in 7 games

9. 25 words typed per minute

10. 15 miles in 3 hours

11. 21 points in 24 minutes played

Science Make a table for each animal to find five rates equivalent to its unit rate.

12. Three-toed sloth: 7 feet per minute

13. Tortoise: 15 feet per minute

14. Snail: $2\frac{1}{2}$ feet per minute

15. **Test Prep** A ratio is equivalent to $\frac{3}{8}$. The numerator is 24. Which of these numbers is the denominator? B

Ⓐ 9 Ⓑ 64 Ⓒ 72 Ⓓ 192

Problem Solving and Reasoning

16. **Critical Thinking** GPS Estelle has built two towers of blocks. There are 12 blocks in Tower A and 18 blocks in Tower B. If she takes one block from each tower, will the ratio of blocks remain the same? Is there any number she could remove from each tower to keep the ratio the same? Explain.

17. Journal In the 1930s, most teenagers were paid about 25¢ an hour to baby-sit or mow lawns. Make a table using this rate showing the total amount charged for 5 hours of baby-sitting or for mowing 5 lawns. Then make a second table using a rate you might charge now. Choose one of your tables and write an advertisement for your own baby-sitting or lawn-mowing service, using the rates in your table.

Mixed Review

Convert to a fraction in lowest terms. *[Lesson 3-10]*

18. 0.375 $\frac{3}{8}$

19. 0.25 $\frac{1}{4}$

20. 0.42 $\frac{21}{50}$

21. 0.671 $\frac{671}{1000}$

22. 0.15 $\frac{3}{20}$

23. 0.38 $\frac{19}{50}$

24. 0.33 $\frac{33}{100}$

25. 0.1234 $\frac{617}{5000}$

Find the sum of the measures of the angles of each polygon. *[Lesson 5-4]*

26. Parallelogram 360°

27. Pentagon 540°

28. 9-sided polygon 1260°

Project Progress

Go to two or more stores in your neighborhood, and record the prices of the 6–10 items on your grocery list. Be sure you record each item's weight, capacity, or volume.

Problem Solving
Understand
Plan
Solve
Look Back

PROBLEM SOLVING 6-4

PROBLEM SOLVING

Name ____________

Guided Problem Solving 6-4

GPS PROBLEM 16, STUDENT PAGE 290

Estelle has built two towers of blocks. There are 12 blocks in Tower A and 18 blocks in Tower B. If she takes one block from each tower, will the ratio of blocks remain the same? Is there any number she could remove from each tower to keep the ratio the same? Explain.

— Understand —

1. Circle the number of blocks in Tower A.
2. Underline the number of blocks in Tower B.

— Plan —

3. Write the current ratio of number of blocks in Tower A to the number of blocks in Tower B in lowest terms. $\frac{12}{18} = \frac{2}{3}$
4. Complete the table to show the number of blocks in each tower if Estelle removes more than one block from the tower.

Tower A	12	11	10	9	8	7	6	5	4	3	2	1
Tower B	18	17	16	15	14	13	12	11	10	9	8	7

— Solve —

5. Is the ratio the same if she removes one block from each tower? No.
6. Is there any number of blocks she can remove from each tower to keep the same ratio? Explain.
No. None of the ratios are equivalent to $\frac{2}{3}$.

— Look Back —

7. How can a table of ratios equivalent to $\frac{2}{3}$ help you check your answer?
Since no ratios in the table above are in the table of ratios equivalent to $\frac{2}{3}$, no number of blocks can be removed from both towers that will keep the ratio the same as $\frac{2}{3}$.

SOLVE ANOTHER PROBLEM

Tower X has 15 blocks and Tower Y has 20 blocks. Is there any number of blocks that can be removed from each tower to keep the ratio of blocks the same? No.

ENRICHMENT

Name ____________

Extend Your Thinking 6-4

Visual Thinking

The following diagram shows what happens when holes are punched in a piece of paper that is folded two times.

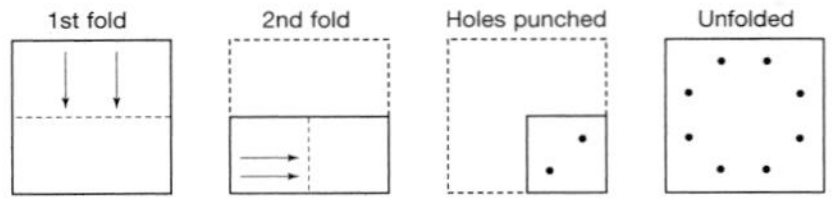

1st fold   2nd fold   Holes punched   Unfolded

Sketch the holes in the unfolded paper for the drawings in each row.

1st fold   2nd fold   Holes punched   Unfolded

1.

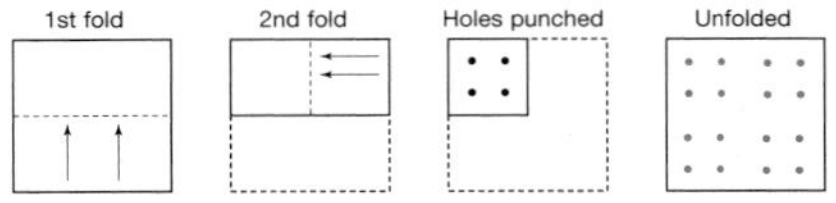

2.

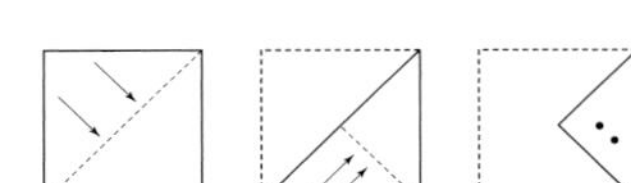

3.

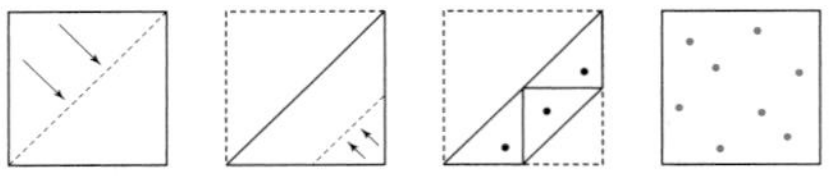

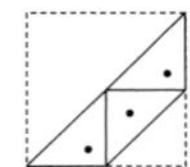

Section 6A Connect

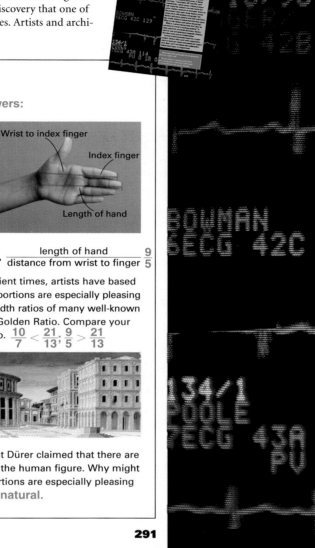

During the Renaissance, artists such as Leonardo da Vinci and Albrecht Dürer worked out ratios that describe the human figure. One unexpected result of their work was the discovery that one of those ratios had been known since ancient times. Artists and architects call it the Golden Ratio.

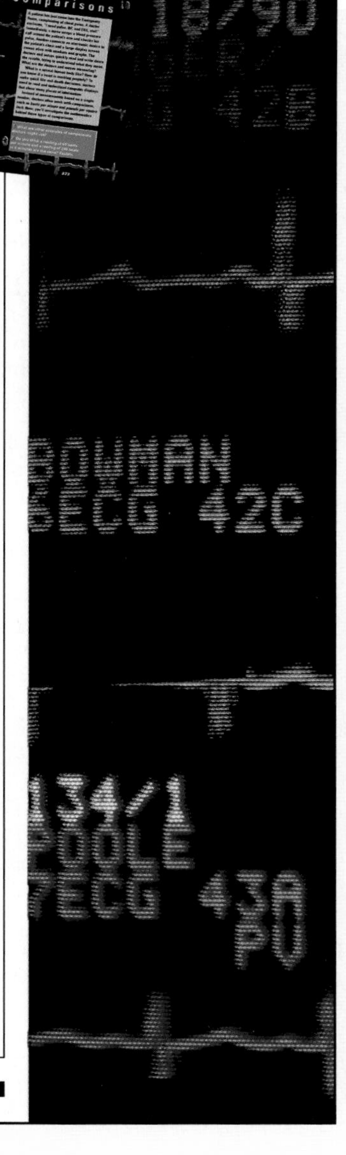

Human Comparisons

Materials: Ruler 1–4. Possible answers:

1. Measure each of the following lengths on one hand as accurately as possible:

a. Distance from wrist to index finger 10 cm

b. Length of the index finger 7 cm

c. Length of hand 18 cm

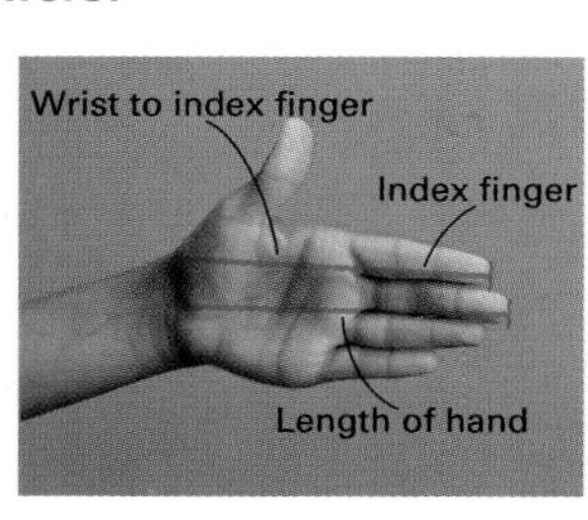

2. Calculate each ratio.

a. $\frac{\text{distance from wrist to finger}}{\text{length of finger}}$ $\frac{10}{7}$ **b.** $\frac{\text{length of hand}}{\text{distance from wrist to finger}}$ $\frac{9}{5}$

3. The Golden Ratio is about $\frac{21}{13}$. Since ancient times, artists have based works on this ratio, believing that its proportions are especially pleasing to the eye. For example, the length-to-width ratios of many well-known buildings and designs are equal to the Golden Ratio. Compare your ratios from Step 2 with the Golden Ratio. $\frac{10}{7} < \frac{21}{13}$, $\frac{9}{5} > \frac{21}{13}$

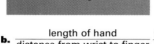

4. Although other artists disagree, Albrecht Dürer claimed that there are dozens of Golden Ratio relationships in the human figure. Why might people believe that Golden Ratio proportions are especially pleasing to look at? Because they seem so natural.

Human Comparisons

The Point

In *Human Comparisons* on page 273, students discussed the human body. Now they will see how the Golden Ratio occurs in certain body measurements.

Materials

Ruler

About the Page

Pair students so they can measure each other's hands for Exercise 1.

- Illustrate exactly how the measurements should be made so that the students get the most accurate results possible.
- Students should compare the results of their measurement with the Golden Ratio by expressing the results as decimals.

Ongoing Assessment

Check that students have measured accurately and have expressed and calculated the ratios correctly.

Extension

Have students compare the ratio of their total height to their waist height (the distance from their waist to the floor). Ask students to compare this measurement to the Golden Ratio. This ratio is usually very close to the Golden Ratio.

6A Review

Review Correlation

Item(s)	Lesson(s)
1–5	6-1
6–9	6-2
10–14	6-3
15–17	6-4
18	6-3

Test Prep

Test-Taking Tip

Tell students that they may not need to work through a problem completely in order to eliminate an answer.

Answers for Review

15. a.

Fly					
Flaps	200	400	600	800	1000
Sec	1	2	3	4	5

b.

Mosquito					
Flaps	600	1200	1800	2400	3000
Sec	1	2	3	4	5

17. Answers may vary.

Section 6A Review

Number Sense Write each ratio in lowest terms.

1. 3:15 1:5 **2.** 27 to 21 9 to 7 **3.** $\frac{9}{63}$ $\frac{1}{7}$ **4.** 16:56 2:7 **5.** $\frac{75}{90}$ $\frac{5}{6}$

Express each rate as a unit rate.

6. Read 64 pages in 4 hours 16 pages per hour **7.** Do 84 push-ups in 4 minutes 21 push-ups per minute **8.** Earn \$56 for 7 hours of work \$8 per hour

9. Consumer Which is the better price, \$2.22 for 2 baskets of blueberries or \$3.54 for 3 baskets? \$2.22 for 2 baskets

Operation Sense Multiply and divide to find two ratios equivalent to each ratio. Possible answers:

10. $\frac{42}{63}$ $\frac{84}{126}, \frac{14}{21}$ **11.** 49:70 98:140; 7:10 **12.** $\frac{81}{108}$ $\frac{243}{324}, \frac{9}{12}$ **13.** 150:225 300:450; 30:45 **14.** $\frac{320}{740}$ $\frac{1600}{3700}, \frac{16}{37}$

15. Science Many small insects flap their wings very quickly. Make a table for each insect to find five rates equivalent to each rate.

a. Fly: 200 flaps per second **b.** Mosquito: 600 flaps per second

16. Health The table shows how quickly a swimmer expends calories. Estimate the number of calories you expend if you swim for one hour. 600

Calories Expended	250	500	750	1000	1250
Time (min)	25	50	75	100	125

17. 

Use an advertisement to find the price of an item you would like to buy. Construct a table to show how much it would cost to purchase different quantities of the item. Find another ad for the same item and construct another table using a different price for the item.

REVIEW 6A

Test Prep

On a multiple choice test where you need to decide if two ratios are equivalent, use mental math to multiply or divide the numbers in the ratios.

18. Choose the ratio equivalent to $\frac{13}{4}$. C

Ⓐ $\frac{50}{16}$ Ⓑ $\frac{26}{7}$ Ⓒ $\frac{39}{12}$ Ⓓ $\frac{65}{15}$

Resources

Assessment Sourcebook
Quiz 6A
Practice Masters
Section 6A Review
TestWorks
Test and Practice Software

PRACTICE

Name ____________ Practice

Section 6A Review

Write each ratio in lowest terms.

1. $\frac{8}{10}$ $\frac{4}{5}$ 2. 36 to 48 3 to 4 3. 16 : 20 4 : 5

Express each rate as a unit rate.

4. baked 72 cookies in 3 hours $\frac{24 \text{ cookies}}{1 \text{ hour}}$
5. played 6 games in 2 hours $\frac{3 \text{ games}}{1 \text{ hour}}$
6. \$45 to 5 hours work $\frac{\$9}{1 \text{ hour}}$
7. 60 students for 12 computers $\frac{5 \text{ students}}{1 \text{ computer}}$
8. Which price is better, \$4.32 for 2 pounds of granola or \$6.51 for 3 pounds? \$4.32 for 2 pounds

Multiply and divide to find two ratios equivalent to each ratio. Possible answers:

9. $\frac{18}{24}$ $\frac{90}{120}, \frac{3}{4}$ 10. $\frac{22}{36}$ $\frac{66}{108}, \frac{11}{18}$ 11. $\frac{12}{15}$ $\frac{24}{30}, \frac{4}{5}$

12. **Consumer** When buying a car, it is important to consider fuel efficiency. A more efficient car will travel a greater distance per gallon of gas. Make a table for each car to find five rates equivalent to each unit rate. Possible answers:

a. Yachtomobile: 13 miles per gallon

Mi	13	26	39	52	65	78
Gal	1	2	3	4	5	6

Rates: $\frac{26 \text{ mi}}{2 \text{ gal}}, \frac{39 \text{ mi}}{3 \text{ gal}}, \frac{52 \text{ mi}}{4 \text{ gal}}, \frac{65 \text{ mi}}{5 \text{ gal}}, \frac{78 \text{ mi}}{6 \text{ gal}}$

b. Pepster: 45 miles per gallon

Mi	45	90	135	180	225	270
Gal	1	2	3	4	5	6

Rates: $\frac{90 \text{ mi}}{2 \text{ gal}}, \frac{135 \text{ mi}}{3 \text{ gal}}, \frac{180 \text{ mi}}{4 \text{ gal}}, \frac{225 \text{ mi}}{5 \text{ gal}}, \frac{270 \text{ mi}}{6 \text{ gal}}$

13. The Tremendous T-shirt Co. sells T-shirts by mail for \$7.00 each. Since there is a \$5.00 shipping charge, the price for n T-shirts is given by the formula $P = 7n + 5$. If Maria paid \$47, how many T-shirts did she order? *[Lesson 2-8]* 6 T-shirts

14. **Science** A typical male elk weighs about $\frac{7}{20}$ of a ton. How many elk would weigh 21 tons altogether? *[Lesson 4-6]* 60 male elk

Section 6B

Proportional Quantities

Visit www.teacher.mathsurf.com for links to lesson plans from teachers and other professionals, NCTM information, and other sites.

LESSON PLANNING GUIDE

Student Edition / **Ancillaries***

LESSON		MATERIALS	VOCABULARY	DAILY	OTHER
	Section 6B Opener				
6-5	**Creating Proportions**	graph paper	proportion	6-5	Teaching Tool Trans. 7
6-6	**Testing for Proportionality**	graphing utility		6-6	Technology Master 28 *Interactive CD-ROM Lesson*
	Technology	World Wide Web access			
6-7	**Solving Proportions Using Unit Rates**	watch with a second hand		6-7	Technology Master 29 Ch. 6 Project Master *WW Math*—Middle School
6-8	**Cross Multiplication**		cross product	6-8	
	Connect	plastic chips, bowl, marking pen			Interdisc. Team Teaching 6B
	Review				Practice 6B; Quiz 6B; *TestWorks*
	Extend Key Ideas				
	Chapter 6 Summary and Review				
	Chapter 6 Assessment				Ch. 6 Tests Forms A–F *TestWorks*; Ch. 6 Letter Home
	Cumulative Review, Chapters 1–6				Cumulative Review Ch. 1–6 Quarterly Tests Ch. 1–6

* Daily Ancillaries include Practice, Reteaching, Problem Solving, Enrichment, and Daily Transparency. Teaching Tool Transparencies are in *Teacher's Toolkits*. Lesson Enhancement Transparencies are in *Overhead Transparency Package*.

SKILLS TRACE

LESSON	SKILL	FIRST INTRODUCED GR. 5	GR. 6	GR. 7	DEVELOP	PRACTICE/ APPLY	REVIEW
6-5	**Writing proportions.**		✗		pp. 294–295	pp. 296–297	pp. 317, 356, 528
6-6	**Recognizing proportional relationships.**		✗		pp. 298–300	pp. 301–302	pp. 317, 364, 533
6-7	**Using unit rates to solve proportions.**		✗		pp. 304–305	pp. 306–307	pp. 317, 370, 538
6-8	**Using cross multiplication.**		✗		pp. 308–310	pp. 311–312	pp. 317, 374, 542

CONNECTED MATHEMATICS

The unit *Comparing and Scaling (Ratio Proportion and Percent)*, from the **Connected Mathematics** series, can be used with Section 6B.

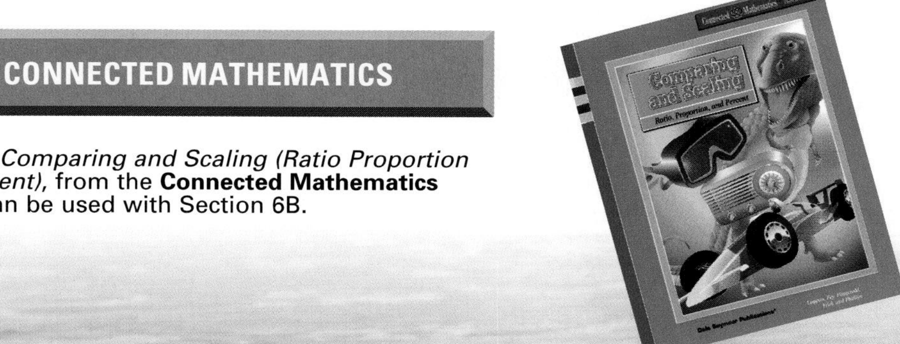

INTERDISCIPLINARY TEAM TEACHING

Math and Science/Technology

(Worksheet pages 23–24: Teacher pages T23–T24)

In this lesson, students use proportionality in blue whale population data.

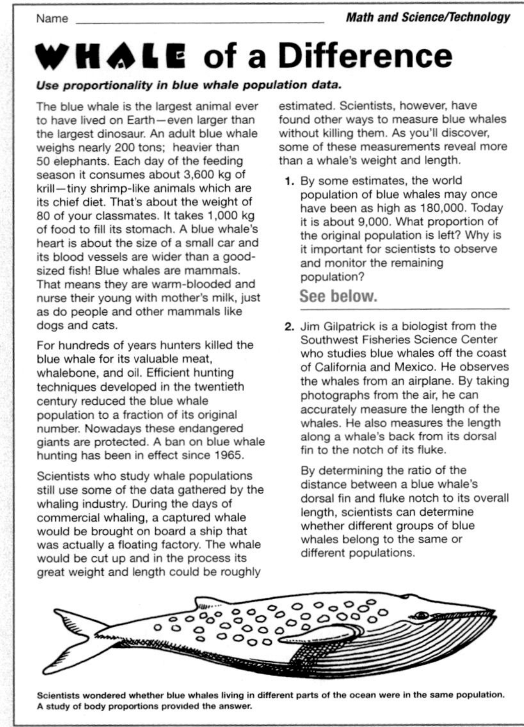

Name ______________________ *Math and Science/Technology*

WHALE of a Difference

Use proportionality in blue whale population data.

The blue whale is the largest animal ever to have lived on Earth—even larger than the largest dinosaur. An adult blue whale weighs nearly 200 tons; heavier than 50 elephants. Each day of the feeding season it consumes about 3,600 kg of krill—tiny shrimp-like animals which are its chief diet. That's about the weight of 80 of your classmates. It takes 1,000 kg of food to fill its stomach. A blue whale's heart is about the size of a small car and its blood vessels are wider than a good-sized fish! Blue whales are mammals. That means they are warm-blooded and nurse their young with mother's milk, just as do people and other mammals like dogs and cats.

For hundreds of years hunters killed the blue whale for its valuable meat, whalebone, and oil. Efficient hunting techniques developed in the twentieth century reduced the blue whale population to a fraction of its original number. Nowadays these endangered giants are protected. A ban on blue whale hunting has been in effect since 1965.

Scientists who study whale populations still use some of the data gathered by the whaling industry. During the days of commercial whaling, a captured whale would be brought on board a ship that was actually a floating factory. The whale would be cut up and in the process its great weight and length could be roughly estimated. Scientists, however, have found other ways to measure blue whales without killing them. As you'll discover, some of these measurements reveal more than a whale's weight and length.

1. By some estimates, the world population of blue whales may once have been as high as 180,000. Today it is about 9,000. What proportion of the original population is left? Why is it important for scientists to observe and monitor the remaining population?
   See below.

2. Jim Gilpatrick is a biologist from the Southwest Fisheries Science Center who studies blue whales off the coast of California and Mexico. He observes the whales from an airplane. By taking photographs from the air, he can accurately measure the length of the whales. He also measures the length along a whale's back from its dorsal fin to the notch of its fluke.

   By determining the ratio of the distance between a blue whale's dorsal fin and fluke notch to its overall length, scientists can determine whether different groups of blue whales belong to the same or different populations.

Scientists wondered whether blue whales living in different parts of the ocean were in the same population. A study of body proportions provided the answer.

Name ______________________ *Math and Science/Technology*

The data table shows several whales of similar lengths from the Pacific Ocean off the coast of California and Mexico and from the waters around Antarctica. Write in the missing ratios in the appropriate columns. Then convert each ratio to a percent ($\frac{a}{b} \times 100$).

California Blue Whales			
Length from dorsal fin to fluke notch	Total length	Ratio	Percent
a	b	$\frac{a}{b}$	($\frac{a}{b} \times 100$)
4.6 m	19.9 m	$\frac{46}{199}$	23.1%
4.6 m	20.9 m	$\frac{46}{209}$	22.0%
5.1 m	23.4 m	$\frac{51}{234}$	21.8%

Antarctic Blue Whales			
Length from dorsal fin to fluke notch	Total length	Ratio	Percent
a	b	$\frac{a}{b}$	($\frac{a}{b} \times 100$)
4.9 m	19.9 m	$\frac{49}{199}$	24.6%
5.3 m	20.9 m	$\frac{53}{209}$	25.4%
5.9 m	23.4 m	$\frac{59}{234}$	25.2%

3. Which group's ratio was greatest?
   See below.

4. The total length of one of the California whales was 19.7 meters. The distance from the dorsal fin to fluke notch was 4.2 meters.
   a. Write a ratio that shows this distance compared to the entire length.
   $\frac{42}{197}$
   b. Round the numerator to the nearest ten and the denominator to the nearest hundred. Write the new ratio and reduce to lowest terms.
   $\frac{40}{200}$; $\frac{1}{5}$

5. Whaling data from the Antarctic shows one blue whale measured a total of 19.9 meters with a dorsal fin to fluke notch measurement of 4.9 meters. Write a ratio of dorsal fin to fluke notch length to total length. Round the fraction as you did above and simplify. How does the ratio compare to the one for the whale from California in Item 4?
   $\frac{49}{199}$; $\frac{50}{200}$; $\frac{1}{4}$; larger.

6. For years, scientists assumed that the blue whales from the Arctic to the Antarctic were all the same population. Explain why you agree or disagree.
   Students should site the data derived for Item 2 as evidence that blue whales form different populations.

7. What might account for the conclusion you reached for Item 6?
   Possible answer: Antarctic blue whales do not interbreed with California blue whales so their characteristics are different.

Answers

1. The present population is 9,000/180,000 of its original size. Scientists study the remaining population in order to prevent further decreases in population so the species will not become extinct.

3. The ratio was greater in the Antarctic blue whale.

BIBLIOGRAPHY

FOR TEACHERS

Edwards, Ronald. *Alge-Cadabra! Algebra Magic Tricks.* Palo Alto, CA: Dale Seymour, 1996.

Perkins, D., H. Goodrich, J. Owen, and S. Tishman. *Thinking Connections.* Reading, MA: Innovative Learning Publications, 1996.

Smith, David Eugene. *Number Stories of Long Ago.* Reston, VA: NCTM, 1996.

Spangler, David. *Math for Real Kids.* Glenview, IL: Good Year Books, 1997.

FOR STUDENTS

Bramwell, Martyn. *The Oceans.* New York: Watts, 1994.

Patent, Dorothy Henshaw. *Whales, Giants of the Deep.* New York, NY: Holiday House, 1984.

SECTION 6B

Proportional Quantities

▶ Science Link ▶ www.mathsurf.com/7/ch6/whales

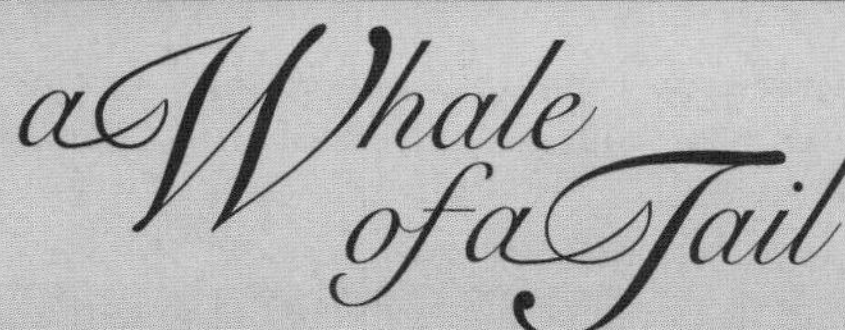

Do you think you could count the whales in the ocean without counting the same one twice? Marine biologists such as Gretchen Steiger of Cascadia Research are faced with this problem.

Luckily, whales do have identifying "fingerprints." Each whale has different markings on its flukes (tail fins). Gretchen photographs these flukes so she can identify individual whales. Since 1986, Cascadia Research has identified more than 600 individual humpback whales. By comparing pictures of whale flukes, Gretchen can see if a whale has been photographed before or if it is a new addition to the collection of photos.

Even with this method, it is not possible to count every single whale in an area. Biologists use a "photo-rephoto" method to estimate the whale population. After you have learned about proportional quantities, you will discover how this method works.

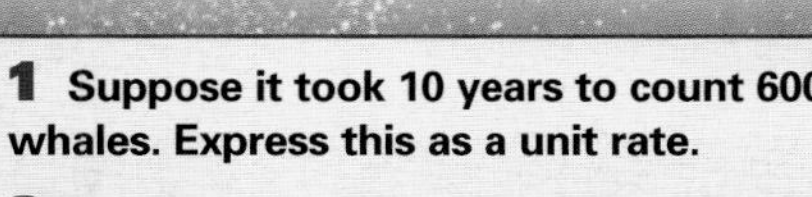

1 Suppose it took 10 years to count 600 whales. Express this as a unit rate.

2 Why do you think it would be difficult to count every whale in an area of the ocean? Try to give at least three reasons.

3 Name some other types of animals that might be hard to count and explain why.

Where are we now?

In Section 6A, students explored the idea of using a ratio to compare quantities.

They learned how to

- determine whether or not a pair of ratios are equivalent.
- find missing terms in pairs of equivalent ratios.
- deal with rates as special ratios.
- use a table to find equivalent ratios and rates.

Where are we going?

In Section 6B, students will

- use ratios to create proportions.
- test pairs of ratios for proportionality.
- use equal ratios to solve proportions.
- solve proportions by using cross-products.

In Chapters 7 and 8, students will apply their proportional reasoning skills to scale, similarity, and percent.

Section 6B

Theme: Whales

World Wide Web

If your class has access to the World Wide Web, you might want to use the information found at the Web site address given. The interdisciplinary link relates to the topics discussed in this section.

About the Page

This page introduces the theme of the section, whales, and discusses counting the number of whales in the ocean.

Ask ...

- Have you ever tried to count the number of fish in a large fish tank filled with fish?
- What clues would you use to make sure you have counted almost all of the fish?

Extension

The following activity does not require access to the World Wide Web.

Science

Whales are mammals that resemble fish. Have students list ways that whales differ from fish. Students might then investigate how the flukes of various whales differ, and how they are catalogued by scientists.

Answers for Questions

1. 60 whales per year.
2. Possible answers: Whales are always swimming around; It would be easy to count the same whale twice; Whales might deliberately stay away from the research vessel.
3. Possible answers: Fish, because they are underwater; Insects, because they are so small.

Connect

On page 313, students will use ratios and proportions to simulate the "photo-rephoto" technique.

Lesson Organizer

Objective

- **Use equivalent ratios to write proportions.**

Vocabulary

- **Proportion**

Materials

- **Explore: Graph paper**

NCTM Standards

- **1–5**

Review

For each ratio, give two equivalent ratios.

Possible answers are given.

1. $\frac{3}{5}$ $\frac{6}{10}, \frac{9}{15}$
2. $\frac{10}{16}$ $\frac{5}{8}, \frac{20}{32}$
3. $\frac{20}{12}$ $\frac{10}{6}, \frac{5}{3}$

Available on Daily Transparency 6-5

1 Introduce

Explore

You may wish to use Teaching Tool Transparency 7: $\frac{1}{4}$-Inch Graph Paper with **Explore**.

The Point
Students visualize proportions by making rectangles on graph paper to represent various areas proportional to a given area.

Ongoing Assessment
Check that students are able to see the relationship between 2 whales in 9 grid squares and 4 whales in 18 grid squares.

For Groups That Finish Early
Make a poster using your drawings from Steps 1 and 2. You might color the background blue for water and sketch the appropriate number of whales in the area. If time allows you could also draw rectangles for Step 4 and include these as well.

6-5 Creating Proportions

You'll Learn ...

- to use equivalent ratios to write proportions

... How It's Used

Magazine designers use proportions to scale photographs so that they fill the right amount of space.

Vocabulary

proportion

Lesson Link You've created equivalent ratios, such as $\frac{2}{3}$ and $\frac{4}{6}$, by multiplying or dividing both parts of a ratio by the same number. Now you'll investigate equations involving equivalent ratios.

Explore Proportions

Materials: Graph paper

Antarctic Blues

The blue whale is the largest animal on earth. A blue whale can weigh 160 tons! An area of the ocean near Antarctica contains an average of 2 blue whales in every 9 square miles. Use this rate to answer the following questions.

1. On graph paper, draw a rectangle with an area of 18 square units. Let each square represent 1 square mile. How many blue whales would you expect to be in an area of the ocean this size? Explain.
2. Draw a rectangle that you would expect to contain 10 blue whales. What is its area? Explain.
3. The rate $\frac{\text{2 whales}}{\text{9 square miles}}$ is one way to represent the concentration of blue whales. Using your results from Steps 1 and 2, write two other rates that represent this concentration.
4. Create three more rates equivalent to $\frac{\text{2 whales}}{\text{9 square miles}}$. Explain what each means by describing the number of whales in each area.
5. A marine biologist surveyed an area of 140 square miles. Estimate the number of blue whales she counted.

Learn Creating Proportions

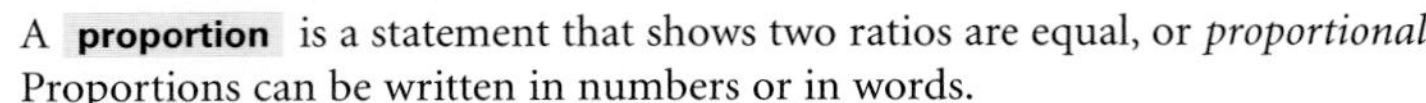

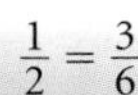

A **proportion** is a statement that shows two ratios are equal, or *proportional.* Proportions can be written in numbers or in words.

$\frac{1}{2} = \frac{3}{6}$ "One is to two as three is to six."

MEETING INDIVIDUAL NEEDS

Resources

- **6-5** Practice
- **6-5** Reteaching
- **6-5** Problem Solving
- **6-5** Enrichment
- **6-5** Daily Transparency
  - Problem of the Day
  - Review
  - Quick Quiz
- Teaching Tool Transparency 7

Learning Modalities

Visual To further reinforce the concept of equivalent rates, have students draw rectangles on graph paper to illustrate their equivalent rates in **Explore** Step 4.

Kinesthetic Have students act out **Explore** Steps 1, 2, and 4 by placing objects or standing on squares of paper. Each square of paper represents 1 square mile and each object or person represents a blue whale.

English Language Development

Students whose knowledge of English is limited can benefit from working with pictures to grasp the concepts of equal ratios. Ask a student who can draw simple, but clear, diagrams to prepare cards illustrating a variety of ratios using the same pair of symbols or objects. Then have the students with limited English skills find equivalent ratios.

For journal writing activities, such as Exercise 27, provide help with vocabulary and spelling as requested by these students.

Example

Complete the table to create three ratios equivalent to $\frac{3}{4}$. Then write three proportions using $\frac{3}{4}$.

3	6	9	12
4			

Use multiplication to complete the table.

	3•2	3•3	3•4
3	6	9	12
4	8	12	16
	4•2	4•3	4•4

The proportions are $\frac{3}{4} = \frac{6}{8}$, $\frac{3}{4} = \frac{9}{12}$, and $\frac{3}{4} = \frac{12}{16}$.

Try It

a. Complete the table to create three ratios equivalent to $\frac{2}{5}$. Then write three proportions using $\frac{2}{5}$.

2	4	6	8
5	10	15	20

b. In the Sea of Cortez, marine biologists counted 3 gray whales for every 8 killer whales. Make a table of values and write two proportions related to the survey.

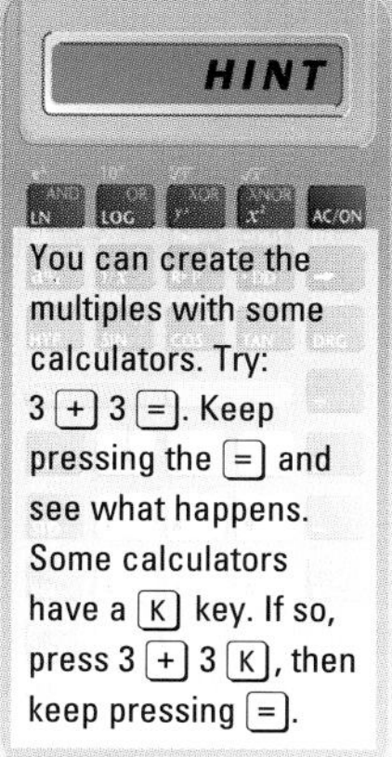

You can create the multiples with some calculators. Try: 3 [+] 3 [=]. Keep pressing the [=] and see what happens. Some calculators have a [K] key. If so, press 3 [+] 3 [K], then keep pressing [=].

You can use the table in the Example to write other proportions.

$\frac{6}{8} = \frac{9}{12}$ $\frac{6}{8} = \frac{12}{16}$ $\frac{9}{12} = \frac{12}{16}$

A proportion can be written in several correct ways. Four ways to write a proportion from the data in the table are shown.

Television Sets	3	6
Homes	2	4

$\frac{\text{3 television sets}}{\text{2 homes}} = \frac{\text{6 television sets}}{\text{4 homes}}$ $\frac{\text{2 homes}}{\text{3 television sets}} = \frac{\text{4 homes}}{\text{6 television sets}}$

$\frac{\text{2 homes}}{\text{4 homes}} = \frac{\text{3 television sets}}{\text{6 television sets}}$ $\frac{\text{4 homes}}{\text{2 homes}} = \frac{\text{6 television sets}}{\text{3 television sets}}$

However, be careful that the numerators and the denominators match up properly! The equation $\frac{\text{3 television sets}}{\text{2 homes}} = \frac{\text{4 homes}}{\text{6 television sets}}$ is *not* a proportion.

Social Studies Link

The Sea of Cortez is another name for the Gulf of California. It is on the west coast of Mexico, between the mainland and the Baja California peninsula. Many species of marine life are found there.

Check Your Understanding

1. How can you write two proportions using the ratio $\frac{5}{8}$?
2. Give an example of a proportion you find in your daily life.
3. In your own words, explain the difference between a ratio and a proportion.

MATH EVERY DAY

Problem of the Day

Write the numbers 15 through 31 in the circles so that the sum of the circles in each straight line is 69.

Possible answer:

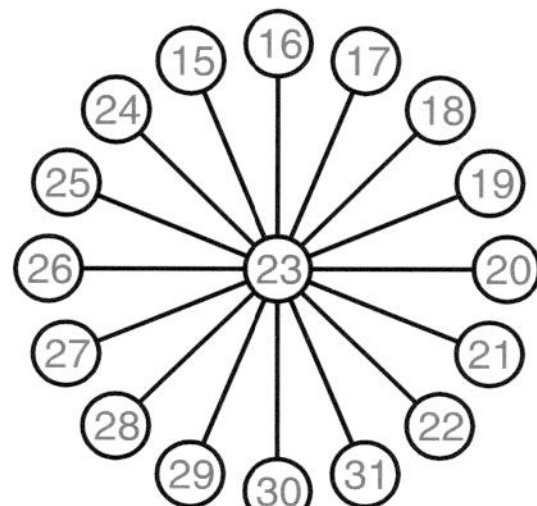

Available on Daily Transparency 6-5

An Extension is provided in the transparency package.

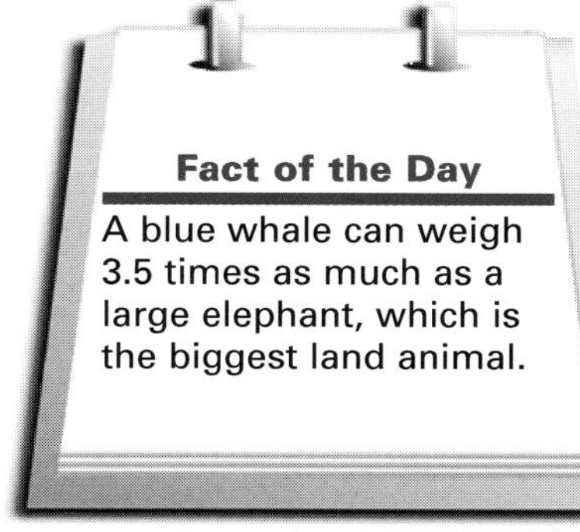

Fact of the Day
A blue whale can weigh 3.5 times as much as a large elephant, which is the biggest land animal.

Mental Math

Write the next four multiples of each number.

1. 8, 16, 24, 32, 40, 48
2. 12, 24, 36, 48, 60, 72
3. 21, 42, 63, 84, 105, 126

Answers for Explore

Diagrams for Steps 1–2 on page C7.

1. Possible answer: 4 whales; $\frac{2}{9} = \frac{4}{18}$
2. Possible answer: 45 sq mi; $\frac{2}{9} = \frac{10}{45}$
3. $\frac{\text{4 whales}}{\text{18 sq mi}}, \frac{\text{10 whales}}{\text{45 sq mi}}$
4. Possible answers: $\frac{\text{6 whales}}{\text{27 sq mi}}, \frac{\text{12 whales}}{\text{54 sq mi}}, \frac{\text{8 whales}}{\text{36 sq mi}}$
5. $\approx$ 31 whales; $140 \div 9 \approx 15.5$, $15.5 \times 2 = 31$

2 Teach

Learn

Alternate Example

Using multiplication, complete the table to create three ratios equivalent to $\frac{2}{3}$. Then write three proportions using $\frac{2}{3}$.

2	4	6	8
3			

	2•2	2•3	2•4
2	4	6	8
3	6	9	12
	3•2	3•3	3•4

The proportions are $\frac{2}{3} = \frac{4}{6}$, $\frac{2}{3} = \frac{6}{9}$, and $\frac{2}{3} = \frac{8}{12}$.

Answer for Try It

a. $\frac{2}{5} = \frac{4}{10}$; $\frac{2}{5} = \frac{6}{15}$; $\frac{2}{5} = \frac{8}{20}$

b. Possible answer: $\frac{3}{8} = \frac{6}{16}$, $\frac{3}{8} = \frac{9}{24}$

3 Practice and Assess

Check

Answers for Check Your Understanding

1. Possible answer: Multiply or divide numerator and denominator by the same number. Do this twice to find 2 ratios equal to $\frac{5}{8}$. Then write two equations using $\frac{5}{8}$.
2. Possible answer: $\frac{\text{1 teacher}}{\text{32 students}} = \frac{\text{2 teachers}}{\text{64 students}}$
3. Possible answer: A ratio compares two numbers. A proportion is an equation involving two ratios.

6-5 Exercises and Applications

Assignment Guide

- **Basic**
  1–13 odds, 14, 15–37 odds
- **Average**
  2–18 evens, 19–24, 28–40 evens
- **Enriched**
  3–41 odds

Exercise Notes

Exercises 15–18

Error Prevention Explain that you can use the same four terms to write four different ratios, but that the order of the terms is important.

Exercise Answers

1. a–c.

2	4	6	8
7	14	21	28

Possible answers: $\frac{2}{7} = \frac{4}{14}$, $\frac{2}{7} = \frac{6}{21}$, $\frac{2}{7} = \frac{8}{28}$, $\frac{4}{14} = \frac{6}{21}$

2.

6	12	18	24
7	14	21	28

Possible answers: $\frac{6}{7} = \frac{12}{14}$, $\frac{6}{7} = \frac{18}{21}$, $\frac{6}{7} = \frac{24}{28}$, $\frac{12}{14} = \frac{18}{21}$

Answers for Exercises 3–18 on pages C7–C8.

Reteaching

Activity

Materials: Water, 2 colors of food coloring, 3 plastic cups

- Put $\frac{1}{2}$ cup of water into each cup.
- Put 2 drops of one color into the first cup, 4 drops into the second cup, and 6 drops into the third cup.
- Then put 3 drops of the second color into the first cup, 6 drops into the second cup, and 9 drops into the third cup. Compare the colors in the cups.
- Write three ratios for the number of drops of food coloring in the three cups. $\frac{2}{3}, \frac{4}{6}, \frac{6}{9}$ Write three proportions using these three ratios. Possible answers: $\frac{2}{3} = \frac{4}{6}$, $\frac{2}{3} = \frac{6}{9}$, $\frac{4}{6} = \frac{6}{9}$

6-5 Exercises and Applications

Practice and Apply

1. **Getting Started** Follow these steps to complete the table with equivalent ratios. Then use the table to write three proportions.

2			
7			

   a. Make a table with four columns and two rows. In the left-hand column, write 2 in the top row and 7 in the bottom row.

   b. Multiply both the numerator and the denominator by 2. Put the results in the second column. Complete the third and fourth columns by multiplying the first entries by 3 and by 4.

   c. All of the ratios in the table are equivalent. Choose pairs of these ratios to create the three proportions.

Complete each table. Then write four proportions involving ratios in the table.

2.

6	12	18	24
7			

3.

5	10	20	50
9			

For each ratio, make a table and create three equal ratios. Then use your ratios to write three proportions.

4. $\frac{9}{20}$ 5. $\frac{7}{8}$ 6. $\frac{3}{11}$ 7. $\frac{13}{15}$ 8. $\frac{20}{7}$

9. $\frac{10}{14}$ 10. $\frac{12}{13}$ 11. $\frac{2}{100}$ 12. $\frac{11}{5}$ 13. $\frac{17}{19}$

14. **Problem Solving** A coleslaw recipe that serves 4 calls for $\frac{1}{3}$ cup of mayonnaise, $1\frac{1}{2}$ tablespoons of vinegar, and 3 cups of sliced cabbage. Change these amounts so the recipe serves 2, 3, and 4 times as many people.

Use each proportion to write two other proportions.

15. $\frac{1 \text{ yard}}{3 \text{ feet}} = \frac{7 \text{ yards}}{21 \text{ feet}}$

16. $\frac{3}{4} = \frac{15}{20}$

17. $\frac{2 \text{ teachers}}{7 \text{ teachers}} = \frac{16 \text{ students}}{56 \text{ students}}$

18. $\frac{60 \text{ calories}}{1 \text{ apple}} = \frac{180 \text{ calories}}{3 \text{ apples}}$

PRACTICE 6-5

PRACTICE

Name ____________________

Practice 6-5

Creating Proportions

Complete each table. Then write four proportions involving ratios in the table.

1.

3	6	9	12
5	10	15	20

Possible answer: $\frac{3}{5} = \frac{6}{10}$, $\frac{9}{15} = \frac{12}{20}$, $\frac{9}{15} = \frac{3}{5}$, $\frac{6}{10} = \frac{12}{20}$

2.

4	8	20	32
11	22	55	88

Possible answer: $\frac{4}{11} = \frac{8}{22}$, $\frac{20}{55} = \frac{8}{22}$, $\frac{4}{11} = \frac{32}{88}$, $\frac{32}{88} = \frac{20}{55}$

For each ratio, make a table and create three equal ratios. Then use your ratios to write three proportions. Possible answers:

3. $\frac{5}{7}$

5	10	15	20
7	14	21	28

$\frac{5}{7} = \frac{10}{14}$, $\frac{15}{21} = \frac{20}{28}$, $\frac{15}{21} = \frac{5}{7}$

4. $\frac{11}{15}$

11	22	33	44
15	30	45	60

$\frac{11}{15} = \frac{22}{30}$, $\frac{33}{45} = \frac{44}{60}$, $\frac{22}{30} = \frac{33}{45}$

5. $\frac{16}{20}$

16	32	48	64
20	40	60	80

$\frac{16}{20} = \frac{32}{40}$, $\frac{16}{20} = \frac{48}{60}$, $\frac{16}{20} = \frac{64}{80}$

6. $\frac{8}{6}$

8	16	24	32
6	12	18	24

$\frac{8}{6} = \frac{16}{12}$, $\frac{24}{18} = \frac{8}{6}$, $\frac{16}{12} = \frac{32}{24}$

Use each proportion to write two other proportions. Possible answers:

7. $\frac{5}{8} = \frac{15}{24}$ $\frac{8}{5} = \frac{24}{15}$, $\frac{5}{15} = \frac{8}{24}$

8. $\frac{4}{18} = \frac{6}{27}$ $\frac{27}{6} = \frac{18}{4}$, $\frac{4}{6} = \frac{18}{27}$

9. $\frac{\$2}{7 \text{ apples}} = \frac{\$6}{21 \text{ apples}}$ $\frac{\$6}{\$2} = \frac{21 \text{ apples}}{7 \text{ apples}}$, $\frac{21 \text{ apples}}{\$6} = \frac{7 \text{ apples}}{\$2}$

10. $\frac{80 \text{ miles}}{15 \text{ hours}} = \frac{32 \text{ miles}}{6 \text{ hours}}$ $\frac{15 \text{ hours}}{80 \text{ miles}} = \frac{6 \text{ hours}}{32 \text{ miles}}$, $\frac{6 \text{ hours}}{15 \text{ hours}} = \frac{32 \text{ miles}}{80 \text{ miles}}$

11. An electronics kit contains 7 resistors, 3 capacitors, and 2 transistors. Tell how many of each part would be in 2, 3, and 4 kits.

2 kits: 14 resistors, 6 capacitors, 4 transistors

3 kits: 21 resistors, 9 capacitors, 6 transistors

4 kits: 28 resistors, 12 capacitors, 8 transistors

RETEACHING

Name ____________________

Alternative Lesson 6-5

Creating Proportions

A **proportion** is a statement that shows two ratios are equal. Proportions can be written in numbers, such as $\frac{3}{5} = \frac{6}{10}$; or in words such as "Three is to five as six is to ten." You can use tables of equivalent ratios to create proportions.

Example

Multiply to complete the table. Then write three proportions using $\frac{1}{4}$.

	1 × 2	1 × 3	1 × 4
1	2	3	4
4	8	12	16
	4 × 2	4 × 3	4 × 4

The proportions are $\frac{1}{4} = \frac{2}{8}$, $\frac{1}{4} = \frac{3}{12}$, and $\frac{1}{4} = \frac{4}{16}$.

Try It

a. Multiply to complete the table. Then write three proportions using $\frac{2}{5}$.

2	4	6	8
5	10	15	20

The three proportions are: $\frac{2}{5} = \frac{4}{10}$; $\frac{2}{5} = \frac{6}{15}$; $\frac{2}{5} = \frac{8}{20}$

b. Multiply to complete the table. Then write three proportions using $\frac{3}{8}$.

3	6	9	12
8	16	24	32

The three proportions are: $\frac{3}{8} = \frac{6}{16}$; $\frac{3}{8} = \frac{9}{24}$; $\frac{3}{8} = \frac{12}{32}$

c. Multiply to complete the table. Then write three proportions using $\frac{5}{6}$.

5	10	15	20
6	12	18	24

The three proportions are: $\frac{5}{6} = \frac{10}{12}$; $\frac{5}{6} = \frac{15}{18}$; $\frac{5}{6} = \frac{20}{24}$

d. Multiply to complete the table. Then write three proportions using $\frac{2}{7}$.

2	4	6	8
7	14	21	28

The three proportions are: $\frac{2}{7} = \frac{4}{14}$; $\frac{2}{7} = \frac{6}{21}$; $\frac{2}{7} = \frac{8}{28}$

e. Multiply to complete the table. Then write three proportions using $\frac{7}{10}$.

7	14	21	28
10	20	30	40

The three proportions are: $\frac{7}{10} = \frac{14}{20}$; $\frac{7}{10} = \frac{21}{30}$; $\frac{7}{10} = \frac{28}{40}$

19. **Test Prep** Which proportion is made up of ratios equivalent to $\frac{2}{3}$? C

Ⓐ $\frac{4}{9} = \frac{8}{18}$ Ⓑ $\frac{6}{9} = \frac{9}{12}$ Ⓒ $\frac{10}{15} = \frac{12}{18}$ Ⓓ $\frac{20}{30} = \frac{21}{32}$

20. **Science** A fully grown fin whale weighs about 80 tons. A bowhead whale weighs about 50 tons. At these weights, 5 fin whales weigh about as much as 8 bowhead whales. Use this ratio to create three equivalent ratios, then use the ratios to write three proportions.

Bowhead whale

Problem Solving and Reasoning

Critical Thinking Write a proportion suggested by each figure.

21. 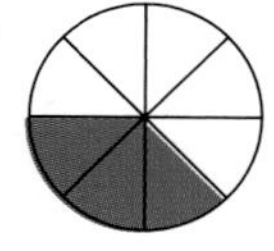 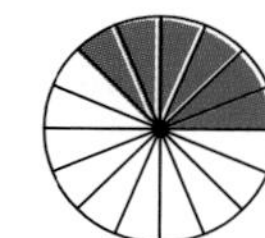 $\frac{3}{8} = \frac{6}{16}$

22. 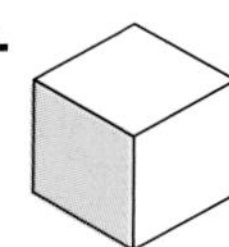 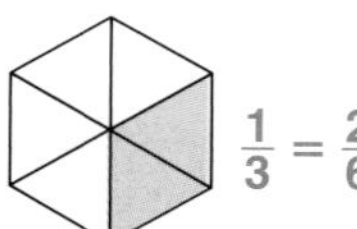 $\frac{1}{3} = \frac{2}{6}$

Critical Thinking Find values of the variables so that the three ratios are equivalent.

 23. $\frac{2}{9}, \frac{x}{45}$, and $\frac{14}{y}$ $x = 10; y = 63$

24. $\frac{7}{12}, \frac{a}{60}$, and $\frac{63}{b}$ $a = 35; b = 108$

25. $\frac{12}{25}, \frac{48}{g}$, and $\frac{h}{300}$ $g = 100; h = 144$

26. $\frac{75}{120}, \frac{25}{s}$, and $\frac{t}{24}$ $s = 40; t = 15$

27. **Journal** The ratio of humpback whales to blue whales seen on a series of whale-watching trips averaged 8 to 3. Can you tell how many whales of each type were seen on a particular trip? Explain.

Mixed Review

For each equation, make a table to show the value of y when $x = 2, 3, 4, 5,$ and 6. *[Lesson 2-3]*

28. $y = x - 2$
29. $y = 4x$
30. $y = x + 17$
31. $y = 8x + 3$
32. $y = 4x - 5$
33. $y = 5x + 6$
34. $y = 10x - 5$
35. $y = 3x - 4$

Find the perimeter and area of each rectangle. *[Lesson 5-5]*

36. Length 8 cm, width 5 cm Perimeter = 26 cm; Area = 40 cm^2
37. Length 20 ft, width 14 ft Perimeter = 68 ft; Area = 280 ft^2
38. Base 14 in., height 23 in. Perimeter = 74 in.; Area = 322 in^2
39. Base 9 m, height 8 m Perimeter = 34 m; Area = 72 m^2
40. Base $\frac{1}{4}$ mm, height $\frac{2}{7}$ mm $P = 1\frac{1}{14}$ mm; $A = \frac{1}{14}$ mm^2
41. Length 2.4 mi, width 3.5 mi $P = 11.8$ mi; $A = 8.4$ mi^2

PROBLEM SOLVING 6-5

Exercise Notes

Exercise 20

Literature Many literary works have described whales and their relationship to humans. Have students do research to find stories and myths about how people have interacted with whales and other sea creatures.

Exercises 36–41

Error Prevention Remind students to give the area in square units.

Exercise Answers

20. Possible answers: $\frac{10 \text{ fin whales}}{16 \text{ bowhead whales}}$, $\frac{15 \text{ fin whales}}{24 \text{ bowhead whales}}$, $\frac{20 \text{ fin whales}}{32 \text{ bowhead whales}}$; $\frac{5 \text{ fin}}{8 \text{ bowhead}} = \frac{15 \text{ fin}}{24 \text{ bowhead}}$; $\frac{5 \text{ fin}}{8 \text{ bowhead}} = \frac{20 \text{ fin}}{32 \text{ bowhead}}$; $\frac{15 \text{ fin}}{24 \text{ bowhead}} = \frac{20 \text{ fin}}{32 \text{ bowhead}}$

27. Possible answer: No; All we know is that during a series of excursions, for every 3 blue whales, 8 humpback whales were seen.

Answers for Exercises 28–35 on page C8.

Alternate Assessment

Portfolio Have students include in their portfolio one of the tables they made in this lesson. Students should also write an explanation of a proportion.

PROBLEM SOLVING

Name ______________________

Guided Problem Solving 6-5

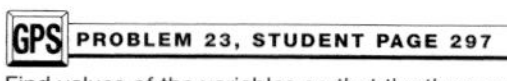

GPS PROBLEM 23, STUDENT PAGE 297

Find values of the variables so that the three ratios are equivalent.
$\frac{2}{9}, \frac{x}{45}$, and $\frac{14}{y}$

Understand

1. What are you asked to find?
The values of the variables in three equivalent ratios.

Plan

2. All three ratios must be equivalent to what given ratio? $\frac{2}{9}$

Solve

3. Complete the table to find ratios equivalent to $\frac{2}{9}$. Let x represent the top number of the ratios and y represent the bottom number of the ratios in the table.

x	2	4	6	8	10	12	14	16	18	20
y	9	18	27	36	45	54	63	72	81	90

4. What is the value of x when the bottom number is 45? $x = 10$
5. What is the value of y when the top number is 14? $y = 63$
6. Write the three equivalent ratios. $\frac{2}{9} = \frac{10}{45} = \frac{14}{63}$

Look Back

6. How can you tell if all three ratios are equivalent?
Possible answer: Write a proportion and check to see that all the ratios can be written in lowest terms as $\frac{2}{9}$.

SOLVE ANOTHER PROBLEM

Find values of the variables so these three ratios are equivalent.
$\frac{5}{9}, \frac{20}{c}$, and $\frac{d}{63}$.
$c = 36; d = 35$

ENRICHMENT

Name ______________________

Extend Your Thinking 6-5

Decision Making

Suppose your family needs to buy the following grocery items: an 8-pound rib roast, 10 pounds of potatoes, 2 packages of frozen broccoli, 2 pints of strawberries, and 12 dinner rolls. Read these advertisements to find the cost of each item at Best Supermarket and at Top Value Supermarket.

BEST SUPERMARKET		TOP VALUE SUPERMARKET	
Rib roast	$3.89 per pound	Rib roast	$3.96 per pound
Potatoes	10 pounds for $2.00	Potatoes	5 pounds for $1.48
Broccoli	1 package for $0.99	Broccoli	3 packages for $2.89
Strawberries	2 pints for $1.98	Strawberries	4 pints for $3.87
Dinner rolls	6 rolls for $0.90	Dinner rolls	15 rolls for $1.50

1. Find the unit price for each item at each store. Round answers to nearest cent.

	Best Supermarket	Top Value Supermarket
Rib roast	$3.89/1 pound	$3.96/1 pound
Potatoes	$0.20/1 pound	$0.30/1 pound
Broccoli	$0.99/package	$0.96/package
Strawberries	$0.99/pint	$0.97/pint
Dinner rolls	$0.15/roll	$0.10/roll

2. Determine the cost of purchasing all the items on your list for each market.
Best, $38.88; Top Value, $39.74

3. Which market offers the better buy? Best Supermarket.

4. It is 20 miles to Best Supermarket and 5 miles to Top Value Supermarket. Your car uses 1 gallon of gas for each 20 miles it travels. If a gallon of gas costs $1.28, how much will you spend to get to and from each supermarket?
Best, $2.56; Top Value, $0.64

5. Explain how this might affect your choice of supermarkets. Possible answer: Actual cost: Best - $41.44, Top Value - $40.38; Buying at Top Value is less expensive and saves time.

Quick Quiz

Write three ratios equivalent to $\frac{3}{5}$ and then write three proportions using those ratios. Possible answers: $\frac{6}{10}, \frac{9}{15}, \frac{18}{30}$; $\frac{3}{5} = \frac{6}{10}, \frac{3}{5} = \frac{9}{15}, \frac{3}{5} = \frac{18}{30}$

Available on Daily Transparency 6-5

INTERACTIVE LESSON

6-6 Lesson Organizer

Objective

- **Recognize proportional relationships.**

Materials

- **Explore: Graphing utility**

NCTM Standards

- **1–5, 11**

Review

Find the GCF of the numerator and denominator. Then write the fraction in lowest terms.

1. $\frac{28}{35}$ 7; $\frac{4}{5}$
2. $\frac{12}{48}$ 12; $\frac{1}{4}$
3. $\frac{24}{54}$ 6; $\frac{4}{9}$

Available on Daily Transparency 6-6

1 Introduce

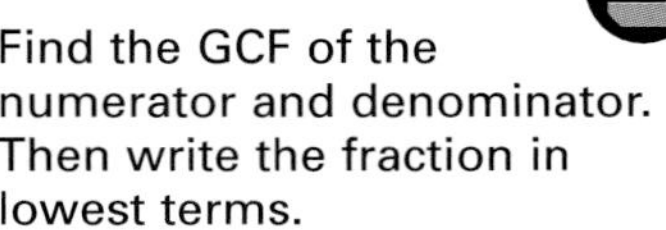

Explore

The Point
Students investigate how a graph can be used to identify proportional data.

Ongoing Assessment
Be sure the rates that students enter in their tables are equivalent to $\frac{54}{3}$.

For Groups That Finish Early
Choose any one of the whales in the table for Step 3 and graph five rates equal to the rate of that whale. What do you notice now? For each whale, the points fall in a straight line.

Answers for Explore on page C8.

6-6 Testing for Proportionality

You'll Learn ...

- to recognize proportional relationships

... How It's Used

Officers investigating traffic accidents understand that a vehicle's stopping distance is proportional to the square of the speed at which it was traveling.

► Lesson Link You've learned to create a proportion. Now you will see how to tell whether a relationship is proportional. ◄

Explore Proportionality

Materials: Graphing utility

Whales to Scale

While migrating, a group of killer whales might move 54 feet in 3 seconds (12 mi/hr).

Gray whale

1. Create a table of five rates that are equivalent to the killer whale's rate.
2. Use a graphing utility to make a scatterplot of your data. Each of your rates will represent a point. Describe the scatterplot.
3. The table lists typical speeds for three other whale species. Add these points to your scatterplot. What do you notice? Explain how you can use a scatterplot to decide whether the ratios in a data set are proportional.

Species	Rate
Gray	36 ft/4 sec
Fin	36 ft/3 sec
Right	29 ft/4 sec

Learn Testing for Proportionality

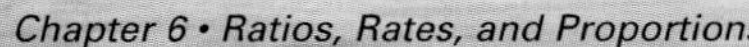

There are many ways to check whether two ratios are proportional. One is to rewrite the ratios in lowest terms and see if they are equivalent.

Example 1

Decide if the ratios $\frac{4}{12}$ and $\frac{8}{24}$ are proportional.

$\frac{4}{12} = \frac{4 \div 4}{12 \div 4} = \frac{1}{3}$ Rewrite in lowest terms by dividing by the greatest common factor.

$\frac{8}{24} = \frac{8 \div 8}{24 \div 8} = \frac{1}{3}$ Rewrite in lowest terms by dividing by the greatest common factor.

Since both ratios are equal to $\frac{1}{3}$, they are proportional.

MEETING INDIVIDUAL NEEDS

Resources

6-6 Practice
6-6 Reteaching
6-6 Problem Solving
6-6 Enrichment
6-6 Daily Transparency
Problem of the Day
Review
Quick Quiz
Technology Master 28

Interactive CD-ROM Lesson

Learning Modalities

Visual To further reinforce the concept of scatterplots, you may wish to have students make some of the graphs by hand. You may need to review with students the procedure for plotting points.

Social For **Explore,** have students use the calculators in pairs if individual calculators are not available.

English Language Development

Have an artistic student help you prepare cards with drawings of things or animals. Begin with two sets of 20 cards showing, for example, from 1 to 20 whales and from 1 to 20 elephants. Work individually with students who have limited English ability and discuss such problems as these: There are 2 whales for every 3 elephants. How many whales are there if there are 6 elephants? Help students show the problem and solution by choosing the appropriate cards and positioning them so that 2 whales are over 3 elephants and 4 whales are over 6 elephants.

Example 2

Two migrating gray whales were traveling at the same speed but started at different times. When the first whale had traveled 7 miles, the second whale had traveled 2 miles. When the first whale had traveled 15 miles, the second whale had traveled 10 miles. Is this a proportional relationship?

Substitute numbers in the ratio $\frac{\text{1st whale}}{\text{2nd whale}}$. The ratios are $\frac{7}{2}$ and $\frac{15}{10}$.

Notice that $\frac{7}{2}$ is already in lowest terms.

$\frac{15}{10} = \frac{15 \div 5}{10 \div 5} = \frac{3}{2}$ Rewrite in lowest terms by dividing by the greatest common factor.

$\frac{3}{2}$ is not equal to $\frac{7}{2}$.

The relationship is not proportional.

DID YOU KNOW?

After spending the summer off the coast of Alaska, gray whales migrate to Baja California for the winter months. It is one of the longest migrations in the animal kingdom.

Another way to check whether two ratios are proportional is to check whether the numerators or denominators are related by multiplication.

$\frac{4}{12} \stackrel{?}{=} \frac{8}{24}$ (• 2 on numerators and denominators)

Both parts of the second fraction are 2 times the first.

$\frac{4}{12} \stackrel{?}{=} \frac{8}{24}$ (• 3 from numerator to denominator)

Each denominator is 3 times the numerator.

Example 3

Decide if the ratios $\frac{6}{9}$ and $\frac{24}{36}$ are proportional.

Since $6 \cdot 4 = 24$ and $9 \cdot 4 = 36$, the ratios are equivalent.

$\frac{6}{9} \stackrel{?}{=} \frac{24}{36}$ (• 4)

$\frac{6}{9}$ and $\frac{24}{36}$ are proportional.

Try It

a. Decide if the ratios $\frac{3}{15}$ and $\frac{10}{50}$ are proportional by rewriting them in lowest terms. Yes; both are equal to $\frac{1}{5}$.

b. Is the rate 32 apples in 6 boxes proportional to the rate 20 apples in 4 boxes? No

c. Decide if the ratios $\frac{7}{10}$ and $\frac{21}{30}$ are proportional by seeing if they are related by multiplication. Yes: $21 = 7 \cdot 3$ and $30 = 10 \cdot 3$

MATH EVERY DAY

Problem of the Day

THE PURPOSE OF THIS TEST IS TO COUNT AS MANY E'S AS POSSIBLE IN TWENTY SECONDS. THERE ARE MORE THAN FIFTEEN E'S IN THIS BOX. CAN YOU FIND THEM ALL? IF YOU DO, YOU ARE BETTER THAN AVERAGE.

20 E'S

Available on Daily Transparency 6-6

An Extension is provided in the transparency package.

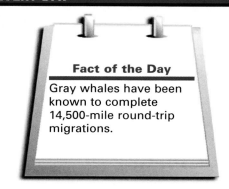

Fact of the Day

Gray whales have been known to complete 14,500-mile round-trip migrations.

Estimation

Estimate each answer.

1. 58×4 240
2. $456 \div 48$ 9
3. 385×53 20,000
4. $5280 \div 252$ 20

2 Teach

Learn

Alternate Examples

1. Decide if the ratios $\frac{16}{20}$ and $\frac{20}{25}$ are proportional.

   Rewrite each ratio in lowest terms.

   $\frac{16}{20} = \frac{16 \div 4}{20 \div 4} = \frac{4}{5}$

   $\frac{20}{25} = \frac{20 \div 5}{25 \div 5} = \frac{4}{5}$

   Since both ratios are equal to $\frac{4}{5}$, they are proportional.

2. In one day, Lourdes decorates 15 sweatshirts and Sonia decorates 12. In a week, Lourdes decorates 120 sweatshirts and Sonia decorates 100. Is this a proportional relationship?

   Substitute numbers in the ratio $\frac{\text{Lourdes}}{\text{Sonia}}$

   The ratios are $\frac{15}{12}$ and $\frac{120}{100}$.

   Rewrite each ratio in lowest terms.

   $\frac{15}{12} = \frac{15 \div 3}{12 \div 3} = \frac{5}{4}$

   $\frac{120}{100} = \frac{120 \div 20}{100 \div 20} = \frac{6}{5}$

   Since $\frac{5}{4}$ is not equal to $\frac{6}{5}$, the relationship is not proportional.

3. Decide if the ratios $\frac{4}{12}$ and $\frac{8}{24}$ are proportional.

   Since $\frac{4 \cdot 2}{12 \cdot 2} = \frac{8}{24}$, the ratios are equivalent and therefore proportional.

Alternate Examples

4. Gary plans to go whale watching. The fee is \$20 plus \$2 an hour to rent binoculars. Make a table to find his total cost for 2, 4, 6, and 8 hours. Then make a scatterplot to see if the relationship between time and cost is proportional.

Time (hr)	2	4	6	8
Cost (\$)	\$24	\$28	\$32	\$36

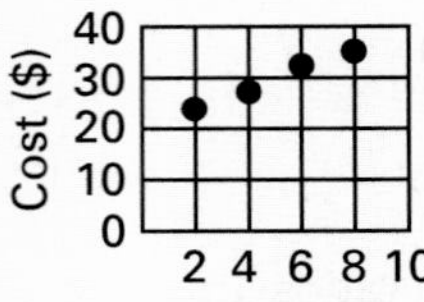

The line does not pass through (0, 0), so the relationship is not proportional.

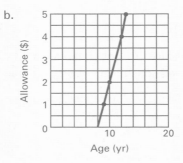

Answers for Try It

a.

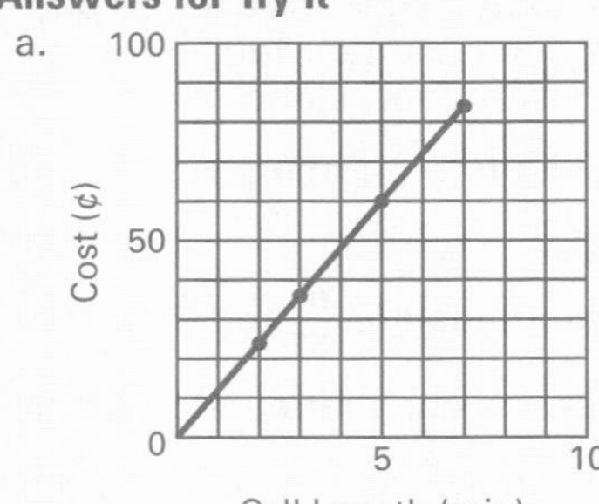

b. Allowance (\$) vs. Age (yr)

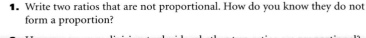

3 Practice and Assess

Check

Answers for Check Your Understanding

1. Possible answer: $\frac{8}{12}$ and $\frac{15}{20}$; They are not proportional because they are not equal when reduced to lowest terms.
2. Possible answer: Divide one numerator by the other numerator, then do the same for the denominators in the same order. If the quotients are the same, the ratios are proportional.

Ernest Everett Just (1883–1941) was a prominent African American scientist. He graduated from Dartmouth College in 1907, and was the only student that year to graduate *magna cum laude* (with great honor). Dr. Just researched marine biology—the study of underwater life—in Massachusetts and Italy.

You can also use a scatterplot to test for proportionality. When you graph equivalent ratios, a straight line through all the points will also pass through the point (0, 0).

Gasoline (gal)	2	4	5
Distance (mi)	40	80	100

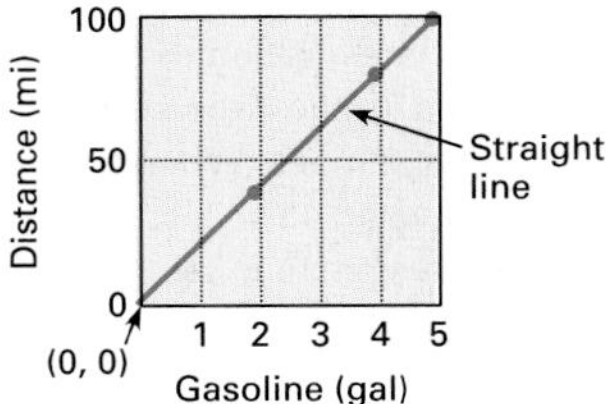

Example 4

A marine biologist plans to photograph whales. She will pay \$50 to rent special photography equipment and \$25 per hour for a boat. Make a table to find her total cost for 2, 4, 6, and 8 hours. Then make a scatterplot to see if the relationship between time and cost is proportional.

Time (hr)	2	4	6	8
Cost (\$)	100	150	200	250

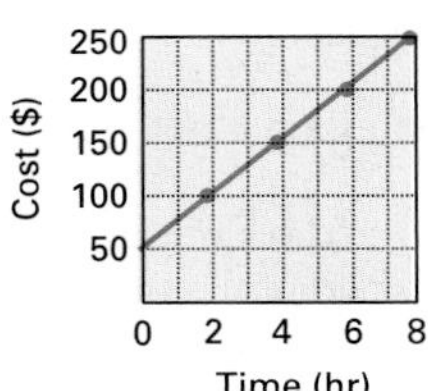

A line through the points on the scatterplot does not pass through the point (0, 0).

The relationship is not proportional.

Try It

Make a scatterplot to see if each relationship is proportional.

a.

Length of Call (min)	2	3	5	7
Cost (¢)	24	36	60	84

Proportional

b.

Age	9	10	12	13
Allowance (\$)	1	2	4	5

Not proportional

Check Your Understanding

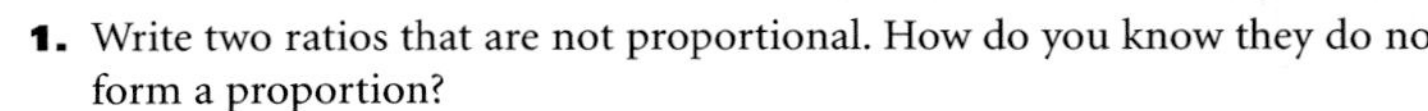

1. Write two ratios that are not proportional. How do you know they do not form a proportion?
2. How can you use division to decide whether two ratios are proportional?

MEETING MIDDLE SCHOOL CLASSROOM NEEDS

Tips from Middle School Teachers

I use the overhead or a chalkboard grid to make scatterplots that exhibit a linear relationship. For some, the related line passes through the origin, and for others it does not. I have students verify that those scatterplots whose line passes through the origin show a proportional relationship, while the others do not.

Team Teaching

Ask the science teachers to discuss with students the various types of insects, fish, and mammals that migrate.

Science Connection

The blue whale and humpback whale spend the warmer season in the polar oceans, where more plankton is available, and migrate to tropical waters during winter to give birth to their young.

6-6 Exercises and Applications

Practice and Apply

1. **Getting Started** Follow these steps to decide if $\frac{6}{8}$ and $\frac{9}{12}$ are proportional.

   a. Rewrite $\frac{6}{8}$ in lowest terms by dividing the numerator and denominator by the same number. $\frac{3}{4}$

   b. Rewrite $\frac{9}{12}$ in lowest terms by dividing the numerator and denominator by the same number. $\frac{3}{4}$

   c. Compare the ratios in lowest terms to decide if $\frac{6}{8}$ and $\frac{9}{12}$ are proportional. They are equal and proportional.

Decide if the ratios are proportional.

2. $\frac{1}{2} \stackrel{?}{=} \frac{3}{6}$ Yes
3. $\frac{3}{9} \stackrel{?}{=} \frac{5}{15}$ Yes
4. $\frac{5}{8} \stackrel{?}{=} \frac{2}{3}$ No
5. $\frac{3}{1} \stackrel{?}{=} \frac{12}{4}$ Yes
6. $\frac{54}{2} \stackrel{?}{=} \frac{108}{3}$ No
7. $\frac{3}{4} \stackrel{?}{=} \frac{27}{36}$ Yes
8. $\frac{12}{18} \stackrel{?}{=} \frac{48}{72}$ Yes
9. $\frac{42}{7} \stackrel{?}{=} \frac{12}{2}$ Yes
10. $\frac{7}{9} \stackrel{?}{=} \frac{25}{27}$ No
11. $\frac{9}{18} \stackrel{?}{=} \frac{9}{27}$ No
12. $\frac{14}{17} \stackrel{?}{=} \frac{56}{68}$ Yes
13. $\frac{4.8}{48} \stackrel{?}{=} \frac{3.02}{302}$ No
14. $\frac{12}{13} \stackrel{?}{=} \frac{60}{78}$ No
15. $\frac{3}{5} \stackrel{?}{=} \frac{12}{20}$ Yes
16. $\frac{6}{18} \stackrel{?}{=} \frac{27}{81}$ Yes

Make a scatterplot to see if each relationship is proportional.

17.

Mike's Age	4	6	8	12
Ted's Age	6	8	10	14

18.

Dog's Weight (lb)	10	20	45	90
Amount of Food (cans)	0.5	1.5	2.5	4.5

19. **Science** Researchers tracking a pod (group) of killer whales found that the whales swam 30 miles in 4 hours on Monday, 45 miles in 6 hours on Tuesday, and 60 miles in 8 hours on Wednesday. Make a scatterplot to find out if these rates are proportional.

GPS

20. **Science** An elephant's heart rate was measured at 26 beats in 1 minute and 102 beats in 4 minutes. Are the rates proportional? No

Pod of killer whales

PRACTICE 6-6

PRACTICE

Name ____________

Practice 6-6

Testing for Proportionality

Decide if each pair of ratios is proportional.

1. $\frac{14}{10} \stackrel{?}{=} \frac{9}{7}$ Not proportional
2. $\frac{18}{8} \stackrel{?}{=} \frac{36}{16}$ Proportional
3. $\frac{6}{10} \stackrel{?}{=} \frac{15}{25}$ Proportional
4. $\frac{7}{16} \stackrel{?}{=} \frac{4}{9}$ Not proportional
5. $\frac{6}{4} \stackrel{?}{=} \frac{12}{8}$ Proportional
6. $\frac{19}{3} \stackrel{?}{=} \frac{114}{18}$ Proportional
7. $\frac{5}{14} \stackrel{?}{=} \frac{6}{15}$ Not proportional
8. $\frac{6}{27} \stackrel{?}{=} \frac{8}{36}$ Proportional
9. $\frac{27}{15} \stackrel{?}{=} \frac{45}{25}$ Proportional
10. $\frac{3}{18} \stackrel{?}{=} \frac{4}{20}$ Not proportional
11. $\frac{5}{2} \stackrel{?}{=} \frac{15}{6}$ Proportional
12. $\frac{20}{15} \stackrel{?}{=} \frac{4}{3}$ Proportional

Make a scatterplot to see if each relationship is proportional.

13.

Oranges	2	4	6	8
Price ($)	0.50	1.00	1.50	2.00

Proportional

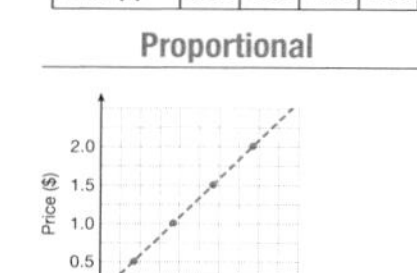

14.

Oats (cups)	0.50	1	2	3
Water (cups)	1	1.75	3.5	5

Not proportional

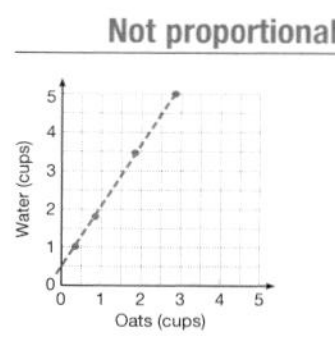

15. During the breaststroke competitions of the 1992 Olympics, Nelson Diebel swam 100 meters in 62 seconds, and Mike Bowerman swam 200 meters in 130 seconds. Are the rates proportional? No

16. During a vacation, the Vasquez family traveled 174 miles in 3 hours on Monday, and 290 miles in 5 hours on Tuesday. Are the rates proportional? Yes

RETEACHING

Name ____________

Alternative Lesson 6-6

Testing for Proportionality

One way to decide if two ratios are proportional is to rewrite the ratios in lowest terms and see if they are equivalent. Another way is to check whether the numerators and denominators are related by multiplication.

Example 1

Decide if the ratios $\frac{6}{14}$ and $\frac{9}{21}$ are proportional.

Rewrite both ratios in lowest terms. $\frac{6}{14} = \frac{6 \div 2}{14 \div 2} = \frac{3}{7}$, $\frac{9}{21} = \frac{9 \div 3}{21 \div 3} = \frac{3}{7}$

Since both ratios are equal to $\frac{3}{7}$, they are proportional.

Try It Decide if the ratios $\frac{8}{14}$ and $\frac{20}{35}$ are proportional.

a. Rewrite each ratio in lowest terms. $\frac{8}{14} = \frac{4}{7}$; $\frac{20}{35} = \frac{4}{7}$

b. Are they equal? Yes.

c. Are they proportional? Yes.

Example 2

Decide if the ratios $\frac{9}{16}$ and $\frac{45}{80}$ are proportional.

Step 1: How is 9 related to 45 by multiplication? Think: $9 \cdot \mathbf{5} = 45$

Step 2: How is 16 related to 80 by multiplication? Think: $16 \cdot \mathbf{5} = 80$

Since the numerators and denominators are related by multiplication, the ratios are proportional.

Try It Decide if the ratios $\frac{5}{8}$ and $\frac{45}{64}$ are proportional.

d. How is 5 related to 45 by multiplication? Think: $5 \cdot 9 = 45$

e. How is 8 related to 64 by multiplication? Think: $8 \cdot 8 = 64$

f. Are the ratios proportional? No.

Decide if the ratios $\frac{8}{5}$ and $\frac{56}{35}$ are proportional.

g. How is 8 related to 56 by multiplication? Think: $8 \cdot 7 = 56$

h. How is 5 related to 35 by multiplication? Think: $5 \cdot 7 = 35$

i. Are the ratios proportional? Yes.

6-6 Exercises and Applications

Assignment Guide

- **Basic** 1–21 odds, 22, 24, 27–39 odds
- **Average** 2–18 evens, 19–25 odds, 28–36 evens
- **Enriched** 8–18 evens, 19–26, 28–40 evens

Exercise Answers

17. Not proportional.

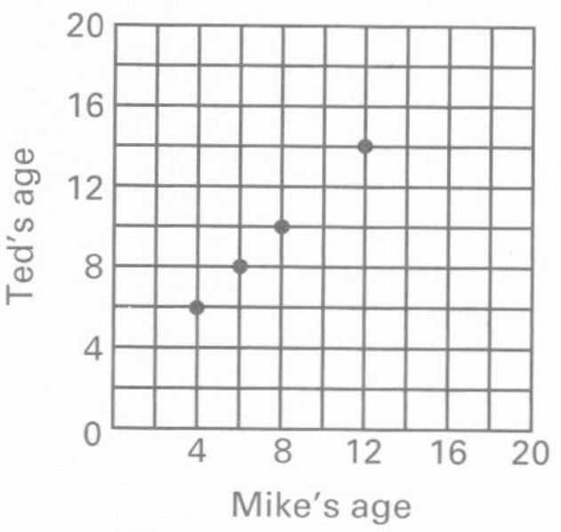

Answers for Exercises 18 and 19 on next page.

Reteaching

Activity

Materials: 20 index cards

- On each card write one of the following fractions: $\frac{1}{2}$, $\frac{3}{6}$, $\frac{5}{10}$, $\frac{10}{20}$, $\frac{50}{100}$, $\frac{3}{4}$, $\frac{6}{8}$, $\frac{15}{20}$, $\frac{30}{40}$, $\frac{75}{100}$, $\frac{1}{4}$, $\frac{2}{8}$, $\frac{3}{12}$, $\frac{5}{20}$, $\frac{25}{100}$, $\frac{1}{5}$, $\frac{2}{10}$, $\frac{3}{15}$, $\frac{10}{50}$, $\frac{20}{100}$.

  Play the following game with a partner:

- Shuffle the cards and then pick two of them. Decide if the two ratios are proportional. If yes, remove both cards from play and reshuffle. Then take another turn. If the ratios are not proportional, replace the cards and reshuffle. Your partner gets a turn.
- The person removing the most cards from play is the winner.

Exercise Notes

■ Exercises 31-32

Be sure students write the inverse operations in the correct order.

Exercise Answers

18. Not proportional.

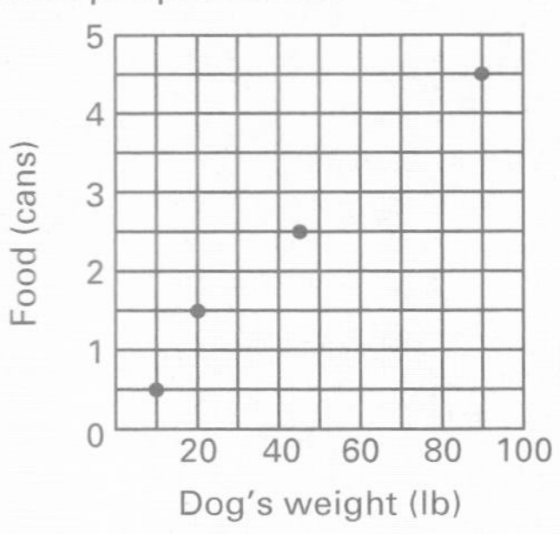

19. Proportional.

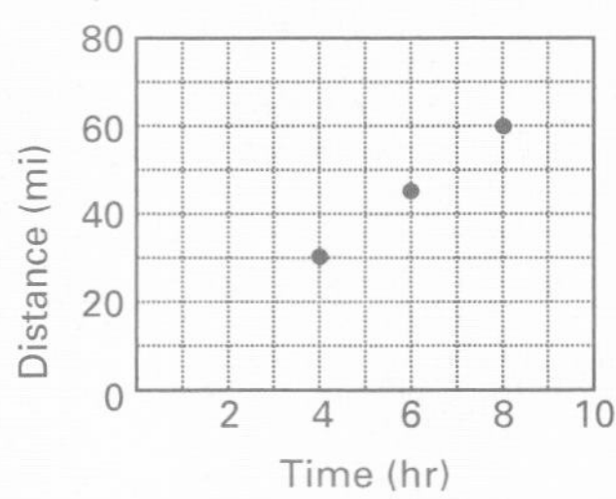

23. No; The ratio of green to total marbles in the first bag is $\frac{3}{12}$ and in the second bag, the ratio is $\frac{6}{25}$; These do not form a proportion.

24. Punch; Because $4\frac{1}{3} \cdot 3 = 13$.

25. Possible answers: $\frac{2}{3} = \frac{4}{6}$, $\frac{4}{6} = \frac{2}{3}$, $\frac{2}{4} = \frac{4}{8}$, $\frac{6}{3} = \frac{8}{4}$, $\frac{3}{2} = \frac{6}{4}$.

26. No; The ratios are all different.

Alternate Assessment

You may want to use the *Interactive CD-ROM Journal* with this assessment.

Journal Have students write a description of all the methods they have learned for checking if ratios are proportional.

▶ Quick Quiz

Decide if the ratios are proportional.

1. $\frac{3}{4}, \frac{24}{28}$ No
2. $\frac{24}{18}, \frac{36}{27}$ Yes
3. $\frac{12}{13}, \frac{52}{48}$ No
4. $\frac{15}{18}, \frac{10}{12}$ Yes
5. $\frac{12}{48}, \frac{5}{20}$ Yes

Available on Daily Transparency 6-6

---

21. **Test Prep** Choose the ratio that is proportional to $\frac{5}{9}$. D

Ⓐ $\frac{1}{3}$ Ⓑ $\frac{2}{6}$ Ⓒ $\frac{7}{12}$ Ⓓ $\frac{15}{27}$

22. Use the data in the table to decide whether the ratios of brain to body weights are equal for humans and dolphins. No

	Body Weight (lb)	Brain Weight (lb)
Human	150	3.1
Dolphin	300	3.5

23. **Chance** There are 3 green marbles in a bag of 12 marbles. A larger bag has a total of 25 total marbles, including 6 green marbles. Are the chances of choosing a green marble from each bag the same? Explain.

Problem Solving and Reasoning

24. **Communicate** The directions on a can of frozen orange juice say to mix 3 cans of cold water with each can of concentrate. The directions on a can of frozen orange punch say to mix $4\frac{1}{3}$ cans of cold water with each can of concentrate. Marsha correctly used 13 cans of water for 3 cans of concentrate. Did she make orange juice or punch? How do you know?

25. **Critical Thinking** Create as many proportions as you can using the numbers 2, 3, 4, 6, and 8. Show why each is a proportion.

26. **Communicate** A dolphin researcher collected the data on bottle-nosed dolphins shown in the table. Are the dolphins' weights roughly proportional to their lengths? Explain.

Length (m)	1.626	2.159	2.337	2.400	2.565
Weight (kg)	45.5	97.7	117.3	140.0	153.6

Bottle-nosed dolphin

Mixed Review

Name the inverse action of each. *[Lesson 2-4]*

27. Add 45 Subtract 45
28. Multiply by 20 Divide by 20
29. Divide by 10 Multiply by 10
30. Subtract 15 Add 15
31. Add 24, then divide by 7 Multiply by 7, then subtract 24
32. Multiply by 5, then add 14 Subtract 14, then divide by 5

Find each square root. *[Lesson 5-6]*

33. $\sqrt{81}$ 9
34. $\sqrt{225}$ 15
35. $\sqrt{3600}$ 60
36. $\sqrt{729}$ 27
37. $\sqrt{100}$ 10
38. $\sqrt{49}$ 7
39. $\sqrt{289}$ 17
40. $\sqrt{6400}$ 80

PROBLEM SOLVING

Name ______________________

Guided Problem Solving 6-6

GPS PROBLEM 19, STUDENT PAGE 301

Researchers tracking a pod (group) of killer whales found that the whales swam 30 miles in 4 hours on Monday, 45 miles in 6 hours on Tuesday, and 60 miles in 8 hours on Wednesday. Make a scatterplot to find out if these rates are proportional.

— Understand —

1. Underline what you are asked to do.
2. Circle the information you will use.

— Plan —

3. Make a table to show the values you will plot.

Miles	30	45	60
Hours	4	6	8

4. Make a scatterplot of the values in your table. Connect the points.

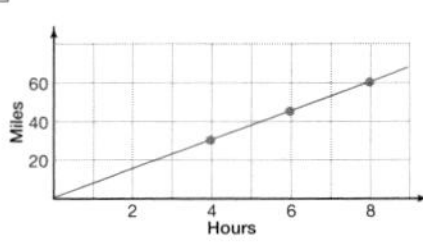

— Solve —

5. Are these rates proportional? Explain. Possible answer: Yes, the connected points form a line passing through origin.

— Look Back —

6. How can you determine if the rates are proportional without making a scatterplot? Check to see if the ratios are equivalent.

SOLVE ANOTHER PROBLEM

A gazelle travels 25 miles in 2 hours on Monday, 36 mi in 5 hours on Tuesday, and 37 mi in 1 hour on Wednesday. Make a scatterplot to find out if these rates are proportional.

Not proportional because connected points do not form a line going through the origin; $\frac{25}{2} \neq \frac{36}{5} \neq \frac{37}{1}$.

ENRICHMENT

Name ______________________

Extend Your Thinking 6-6

Patterns in Geometry

Every right triangle has two acute angles. In the right triangle at the right, the acute angles are angle *A* and angle *B*. The ratio of the length of the opposite side to the length of the adjacent side of a right triangle is called the **tangent ratio**.

In triangle *ABC*, the tangent ratio for angle *A* is $\frac{a}{b}$, and the tangent ratio for angle *B* is $\frac{b}{a}$.

In the table below, each right triangle has one acute angle that measures 57° and another that measures 33°. Find the tangent ratio for the acute angles in each triangle. Use your calculator to divide. Round each answer to the nearest hundredth.

1.	tangent ratio for angle *A* 0.65 tangent ratio for angle *B* 1.54	$a = 6$, $b = 9.24$
2.	tangent ratio for angle *A* 0.65 tangent ratio for angle *B* 1.54	$a = 2.6$, $b = 4$
3.	tangent ratio for angle *A* 0.65 tangent ratio for angle *B* 1.54	$a = 7.79$, $b = 12$
4.	tangent ratio for angle *A* 0.65 tangent ratio for angle *B* 1.54	$a = 3$, $b = 4.62$
5.	tangent ratio for angle *A* 0.65 tangent ratio for angle *B* 1.54	$a = 24$, $b = 36.96$
6.	tangent ratio for angle *A* 0.65 tangent ratio for angle *B* 1.54	$a = 11.04$, $b = 17$

7. Describe the pattern. The tangent ratio for angles having the same measure is the same regardless of the length of the sides.

TECHNOLOGY

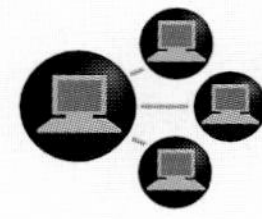

Searching the World Wide Web • Using Search Engines

Problem: What is the difference between using the words "or" and "and" when searching for information on the World Wide Web?

You can use one of the many *search engines* available on the Internet to investigate the solution to this problem. (A search engine is a program that searches Web pages for the information you've asked for.)

1. **Get onto the Internet and select a search engine. Type "blue AND whale" into the search text box, then click on Search. Notice the number of documents found that match your request.**

2. **Now, search for "blue OR whale." Compare the number of matches for this request to the results for "blue AND whale."**

Solution: Using "and" locates documents that contain both "blue" and "whale"; using "or" locates documents that contain either word. (Note: There are differences between search engines; for instance, some use a plus sign to mean "and.")

TRY IT

a. If you wanted information about "great white sharks," would you use "and" or "or"? Try your idea.

b. If you were choosing between two topics for a science project, would you search for "whales and dolphins" or "whales or dolphins"? Explain your answer.

ON YOUR OWN

▶ What are some advantages and disadvantages of researching a topic using the World Wide Web instead of using an encyclopedia (in book form)?

303

Technology

Searching the World Wide Web • Using Search Engines

The Point
Students see how using "and" or "or" affects a search for topics on the Internet.

Materials
Computer with access to the World Wide Web.

About the Page
- Conducting each search will likely result in a very large number of references. Students should note the numbers carefully for comparison purposes.
- There is a dual emphasis in this lesson: the use of the Internet and the meaning of "and" and "or." This is an important concept, as it relates to intersection and union of sets.

Ask ...
- Which conjunction instructs the search to identify sources with both reference words? And
- Which conjunction instructs the search to identify sources with either of the two reference words? Or

Answers for Try It
a. "And"; You only want to look at documents that contain all three words.

b. Possible answer: Whales or dolphins. You want to compare the information available about each topic before deciding between them.

On Your Own
The Web might offer more diverse or elaborate information, rather than just a collection of facts, as might be found in an encyclopedia.

Answer for On Your Own
On the World Wide Web, you can narrow or expand your search quickly, but you cannot be sure that all of the documents you find will be useful. With an encyclopedia, you can be more certain of finding relevant information, but it is more difficult and time-consuming to search for related topics.

Lesson Organizer

Objective

- Use unit rates to solve a proportion.

Materials

- Explore: Watch with a second hand

NCTM Standards

- 1–5, 7, 13

Review

For each ratio, give an equivalent ratio with a denominator of 1.

1. $\frac{12}{6}$ $\frac{2}{1}$
2. $\frac{18}{3}$ $\frac{6}{1}$
3. $\frac{48}{16}$ $\frac{3}{1}$
4. $\frac{5.5}{5}$ $\frac{1.1}{1}$

Available on Daily Transparency 6-7

1 Introduce

Explore

The Point
Students use pulse rates to experiment with unit rates and equivalent rates.

Ongoing Assessment
Check that students are writing correct proportions for Steps 1–3.

For Groups That Finish Early
Count your heartbeats for a minute and check whether the rates agree with the rate you calculated in Step 1.

Answers for Explore

1. Possible answer: 11 beats in 10 seconds; 66 beats per minute; Since 1 minute is 60 seconds, multiply 11 by 6.
2. 12; 20; Find ratios with denominators of 10 that are equivalent to $\frac{72}{60}$ and $\frac{120}{60}$.
3. 100 beats per minute.
4. An estimate; You would have to count heartbeats for a full minute to get an exact rate.

6-7 Solving Proportions Using Unit Rates

You'll Learn ...

- to use unit rates to solve a proportion

... How It's Used

Hardware store clerks use proportions when they mix paints. They need to calculate exactly the right amount of each color.

▶ Lesson Link You've learned how to write proportions and how to decide whether a relationship is proportional. Now you'll see how to use unit rates to find a missing part of a proportion. ◀

Explore Solving Proportions

How Do You Rate?

Materials: Watch with a second hand

Your *pulse rate* is the number of times your heart beats in 1 minute. A typical pulse rate for a person at rest is 72 beats per minute.

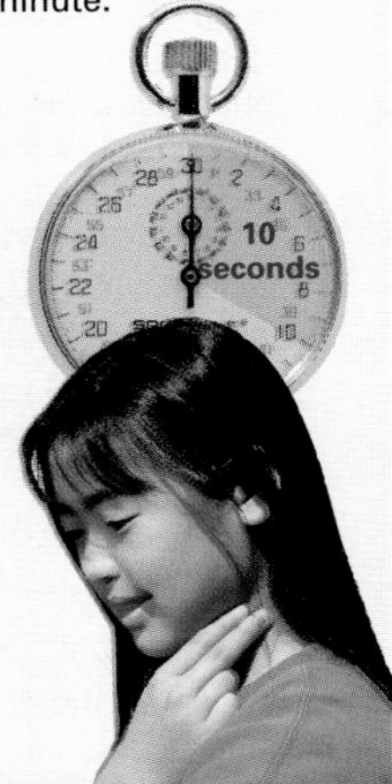

1. To find your pulse rate, place your index and middle fingers on your carotid artery (at the side of your neck) and count the number of beats in 10 seconds. Work out your pulse rate. Explain your calculation.
2. How many beats in 10 seconds would give a pulse rate of 72 beats per minute? Of 120 beats per minute? Explain.
3. Suppose you count 10 beats in 6 seconds. What is your pulse rate?
4. Does the method you're using give an estimate of the actual pulse rate, or does it give the exact rate? Explain why.

Learn Solving Proportions Using Unit Rates

Solving a proportion means finding a missing part of the proportion. You can use unit rates to solve a proportion. First find the unit rate. Then multiply to solve the proportion.

For instance, if you know that you can read 30 pages per hour, you can quickly predict how many pages you could read in other amounts of time.

In 2 hours I can read 30 • 2 = 60 pages.

In 5 hours I can read 30 • 5 = 150 pages.

MEETING INDIVIDUAL NEEDS

Resources

- 6-7 Practice
- 6-7 Reteaching
- 6-7 Problem Solving
- 6-7 Enrichment
- 6-7 Daily Transparency
  - Problem of the Day
  - Review
  - Quick Quiz
- Technology Master 29
- Chapter 6 Project Master

Wide World of Mathematics Middle School: New York City Marathon

Learning Modalities

Kinesthetic Demonstrate for students how to take one another's or their own pulse, either at the carotid artery or in the wrist. Explain that it is best to use the index and middle fingers to feel the pulse.

Social Have students work in pairs to find pulse rates for the **Explore** exercises.

Challenge

Materials: Several sheets of notebook paper

Work with a group of three or four students. Demonstrate the correct way to fold a business letter into thirds. Have the students fold the papers and pretend to stuff them into envelopes. Students then might write addresses on the outside of the papers. See how many "letters" they can have ready to mail in 15 seconds. Then, have students write and solve a proportion to determine how long it would take to have 1 million letters ready for a mass mailing.

Examples

1 Size D batteries cost $2.19 for 3 batteries. At this rate, how much will 5 batteries cost?

> Estimate: Using compatible numbers, 1 battery costs about $2.10 ÷ 3, or $0.70. Five batteries cost about 5 • $0.70, or $3.50.

$\frac{2.19 \text{ dollars}}{3 \text{ batteries}} = \frac{2.19 \div 3}{3 \div 3}$ Divide by the denominator to find the unit rate.

$= \frac{0.73 \text{ dollars}}{1 \text{ battery}}$ The unit rate is $0.73 per battery.

$0.73 \cdot 5 = 3.65$ Multiply the unit rate by 5.

The cost of 5 batteries is $3.65.

2 A bottle-nosed dolphin can travel about 2.25 miles in 5 minutes. At this rate, how long does it take the dolphin to travel 8 miles?

$\frac{5 \text{ minutes}}{2.25 \text{ miles}} = \frac{5 \div 2.25}{2.25 \div 2.25}$ Divide by the denominator to find the unit rate.

$\approx \frac{2.22 \text{ minutes}}{1 \text{ mile}}$ The unit rate is about 2.22 minutes per mile.

$2.22 \cdot 8 \approx 17.8$ Multiply the unit rate by 8 to find the time for 8 miles.

The dolphin takes about 17.8 minutes to travel 8 miles.

Try It

Five CDs cost $42. At that rate, how much will 7 CDs cost? $58.80

▶ Science Link

The electric battery was invented by the Italian Alessandro Volta in 1800.

▶ Language Link

Unit means one of anything. The French word for "one" is *un.* In Spanish, *uno* means "one." When a word starts with *uni,* think ONE!

Check Your Understanding

1. What do car salespeople mean by their "sales per day" rate? By their "days per sale" rate?
2. Why are the words "at this rate" included in the Examples? What would happen if they weren't included?

MATH EVERY DAY

▶ Problem of the Day

Ronna planted flowers in a bed that was the shape of an equilateral triangle. The perimeter of the bed is 18 feet. What is the area? Round your answer to the nearest tenth. 15.6 square feet; Each side is 6 ft. Use the Pythagorean Theorem to find the height of the triangle: $3^2 + b^2 = 6^2$, $b = 5.2$. Then use the formula for the area of a triangle: $\frac{1}{2} \times 6 \times 5.2 = 15.6$.

Available on Daily Transparency 6-7

An Extension is provided in the transparency package.

Fact of the Day

The amount of food a dolphin eats in a day amounts to almost $\frac{1}{3}$ of its body weight.

Mental Math

Solve each problem mentally.

Pencils are 3 for 29¢. Estimate the cost of

1. 2 pencils. 20¢
2. 5 pencils. 50¢
3. 10 pencils $1.00

2 Teach

Learn

Alternate Examples

1. Light bulbs cost $3 for 4 bulbs. At this rate, how much will 6 bulbs cost?

   Estimate: Using compatible numbers, 1 bulb costs about $3.20 ÷ 4 , or $0.80. 6 bulbs cost about 6 × $0.80, or $4.80.

   Divide both parts of the ratio by the denominator to find the unit rate.

   $\frac{3 \text{ dollars}}{4 \text{ bulbs}} = \frac{3 \div 4}{4 \div 4} = \frac{0.75 \text{ dollars}}{1 \text{ bulb}}$

   Multiply the unit rate by 6.
   $0.75 \cdot 6 = 4.50$

   The cost of 6 light bulbs is $4.50.

2. A cheetah can run 35 miles in 30 minutes. At this rate, how far could a cheetah run in 45 minutes?

   Divide both parts of the ratio by the denominator to find the unit rate.

   $\frac{35}{30} = \frac{35 \div 30}{30 \div 30} \approx \frac{1.17 \text{ mi}}{1 \text{ min}}$

   Multiply the unit rate by 45.
   $45 \cdot 1.17 = 52.7$

   In 45 minutes, the cheetah could run about 52.7 miles.

3 Practice and Assess

Check

Answers for Check Your Understanding

1. "Sales per day" means how many cars they will sell in one day, while "days per sale" means how many days it takes to make a sale.
2. To make clear what rate to use. Since rates such as animal speed are not constant, there would be no basis for answering the question.

6-7 Exercises and Applications

Assignment Guide

- **Basic**
  1–10, 12–22 evens
- **Average**
  1–9 odds, 10–22
- **Enriched**
  5–22

Exercise Notes

Exercise 7

Sports The 1990 Indy 500 was won by Arie Luyendyk with an average speed of 186 miles per hour. Some of the fastest rates for 1-mile auto races exceed 600 miles per hour.

Exercise 9

Literature Jules Verne's books were written in the late 1800s. In 1889, Nellie Bly, a journalist, tried to match the fictional feat. She traveled around the world in about 72 days, using ships, trains, carts, and burros. In 1933 Wiley Post made a solo airplane flight around the world in 115 hours.

Reteaching

Activity

Materials: Red and yellow counters

- Draw a line on your paper and use counters to model the ratio $\frac{\text{20 yellow counters}}{\text{5 red counters}}$.
- To model the unit rate, separate the counters into five equivalent ratios, each with 1 red counter as the denominator. How many yellow counters would be in each numerator? 4 What is the rate? $\frac{4}{1}$
- Now use the unit rate and more counters to model an equivalent ratio. With 8 red counters as the denominator, how many yellow counters would be in the numerator? 32 What is the rate? $\frac{32}{8}$

6-7 Exercises and Applications

Practice and Apply

Getting Started Find each unit rate.

1. 24 pages in 6 minutes **4 pages per minute**
2. 500 miles in 12 hours **$41.\overline{6}$ miles per hour**
3. $1.44 per dozen **$0.12 for one**
4. $1.89 for 3 **$0.63 for one**
5. Oranges are on sale at 6 for $0.99.
   a. Find the cost of 2 oranges. **$0.33**
   b. Find the cost of 4 oranges. **$0.66**
6. Jake earned $51.20 in 8 hours.
   a. Find his hourly rate. **$6.40**
   b. Find his earnings in 7 hours. **$44.80**
7. **Sports** Driving a Marmon Wasp race car, Ray Harroun completed the first 500-mile Indianapolis 500 auto race in 1911 in 6.7 hours.
   a. Find Harroun's rate in miles per hour. Round to the nearest tenth. **74.6 miles per hour**
   b. At this rate, how far did Harroun drive in 2 hours? **149.2 miles**
   c. Find Harroun's rate in hours per mile. **0.0134 hours per mile**
   d. How long did it take Harroun to drive 400 miles? **5.36 hours**

Ray Harroun

8. **Estimation** Your body weight is a measure of the force of gravity. Jupiter's gravitational pull is 2.64 times that of Earth. Imagine that a scale on Jupiter shows that a whale weighs 8712 pounds. Estimate the whale's weight on Earth. **3300 pounds**
9. **Literature** Phileas Fogg was the hero of Jules Verne's adventure novel *Around the World in Eighty Days.* The distance around the earth is about 25,000 miles. GPS
   a. Assuming Fogg traveled at a steady rate, how long did it take him to travel the 4000 miles from London to India? **12.8 days**
   b. How far did Fogg travel during the final week of his trip? **2187.5 miles**
10. **Test Prep** Lea earned $25.50 in 5 hours. How much did she earn per hour? **B**
    Ⓐ $102.50 Ⓑ $5.10 Ⓒ $5.50 Ⓓ None of these
11. **Sports** Olympic volleyball player Bev Oden averaged 3.42 "kills" (spikes that end a rally) per game. Predict her number of kills in a 5-game match. **17**

PRACTICE 6-7

PRACTICE

Name ______ **Practice 6-7**

Solving Proportions Using Unit Rates

1. Bananas are on sale at 8 for $0.96.
   a. Find the cost of 1 banana. **$0.12**
   b. Find the cost of 7 bananas. **$0.84**
2. Sylvia earned $199.20 for 24 hours of work.
   a. Find her hourly rate. **$8.30 per hour**
   b. Find her earnings for 15 hours of work. **$124.50**
3. History In 1927, Charles Lindbergh flew 3600 miles from New York to Paris in $33\frac{2}{3}$ hours.
   a. Find Lindbergh's rate in miles per hour. Round to the nearest tenth. **106.9 mi/hr**
   b. At this rate, how far did Lindbergh fly in 24 hours? **2565.6 mi**
   c. Find Lindbergh's rate in hours per mile. **About 0.00935 hr/mi**
   d. How long did it take Lindbergh to travel 1600 miles? **About 15.0 hours**
4. Health A 4.3-ounce raw tomato has about 24 calories.
   a. Find the unit rate in calories per ounce. **About 5.6 calories per oz**
   b. How many calories are in a pound (16 oz) of tomatoes? **About 90 calories**
5. The hair in a typical man's beard grows about 3.5 mm per week.
   a. Find the unit rate in mm per day. **0.5 mm per day**
   b. October has 31 days. How long will the hair grow in October? **15.5 mm**
6. In 1993, President Clinton received an average of 25,000 letters per day. How many letters did he receive during the entire year? **9,125,000**

RETEACHING

Name ______ **Alternative Lesson 6-7**

Solving Proportions Using Unit Rate

Solving a proportion means finding a missing part of the proportion. You can use unit rates to solve a proportion. First find the unit rate. Then multiply to solve the proportion.

Example

Shawn filled 8 bags of leaves in 2 hours. At this rate, how many bags would he fill in 6 hours?

Step 1: Find a unit rate for the number of bags per hour. Divide by the denominator.

$\frac{8 \text{ bags}}{2 \text{ hours}} = \frac{8 \text{ bags} \div 2}{2 \text{ hours} \div 2} = \frac{4 \text{ bags}}{1 \text{ hour}}$ The unit rate is 4 bags per hour.

Step 2: Multiply the unit rate by 6 to find the number of bags he will fill in 6 hours.

Unit rate		Number of hours		Total
4	×	6	=	24

At this rate, Shawn can fill 24 bags in 6 hours.

Try It The bookstore advertises 5 notebooks for $7.75. At this rate, how much will 7 notebooks cost?

a. Find a unit rate for the cost per notebook.

$\frac{\$7.75}{5 \text{ notebooks}} = \frac{\$7.75 \div 5}{5 \text{ notebooks} \div 5} = \frac{\$1.55}{1 \text{ notebook}}$

The unit rate is **$1.55** per notebook.

b. Multiply the unit rate by the number of notebooks to find the cost of 7 notebooks.

Unit rate		Number of notebooks		Cost for 7 notebooks
$1.55	×	**7**	=	**$10.85**

At this rate, 7 notebooks will cost **$10.85**.

Alta makes $16.25 for baby-sitting 5 hours. At this rate, how much will she make if she baby-sits 8 hours?

c. Unit rate **$\frac{\$3.25}{1 \text{ hour}}$** d. Earnings for 8 hours **$26**

Leroy can lay 144 bricks in 3 hours. At this rate, how many bricks can he lay in 7 hours?

e. Unit rate **$\frac{48 \text{ bricks}}{1 \text{ hour}}$** f. Bricks laid in 7 hours **336 bricks**

Problem Solving and Reasoning

12. Communicate In 1991, Mike Powell of the United States set a world long-jump record of 29 ft 4.5 in. Powell is 6 ft 4 in. tall. A 5-foot-tall kangaroo can jump more than 40 feet. If Powell could jump the same distance in proportion to his height as the kangaroo can, how far could he jump? Explain how you found your answer.

13. Journal A 20-year-old man is 6 ft tall. Does that mean that a 40-year-old man is 12 ft tall? Explain why or why not.

14. Critical Thinking Gloria paid \$14.99 for a new CD with 10 songs. Another CD by the same artist has 12 songs and sells for \$17.99.

a. Is the price for the second CD fair? Explain.

b. Besides the number of songs, what other factors might help Gloria decide whether to buy the second CD?

Mixed Review

Write an algebraic expression for each phrase. *[Lesson 2-5]*

15. 5 less than a number (u) $u - 5$

16. 7 more than a number (x) $7 + x$

17. A number (g) increased by 12 $g + 12$

18. The product of a number (z) and 10 $10z$

Find the length of the unknown side. *[Lesson 5-7]*

19.
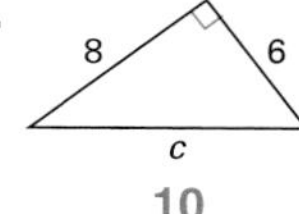

10

20.
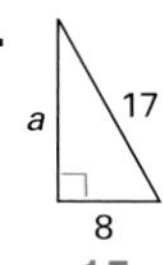

15

21.
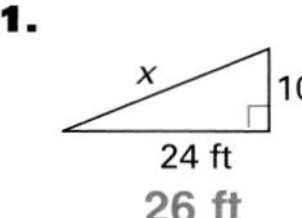

26 ft

22.
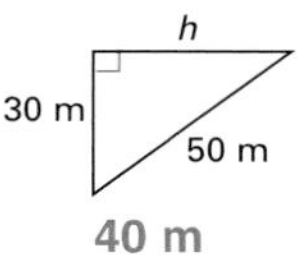

40 m

Project Progress

Decide which of the grocery stores you surveyed has the lowest overall prices. Prepare a report for your class to show your results and to explain how you decided on the lowest-priced store.

Problem Solving
Understand
Plan
Solve
Look Back

PROBLEM SOLVING 6-7

Project Progress

You may want to have students use Chapter 6 Project Master.

Exercise Answers

12. 50 ft 8 in.; I converted the measurements to inches and solved the proportion $\frac{60 \text{ in. tall}}{480\text{-in. long-jump}} = \frac{76 \text{ in. tall}}{x\text{-in. long-jump}}$.

13. No; People do not grow at the same rate throughout their lives; Ratios of height to age are not proportional.

14. a. Yes; The prices and numbers of songs are proportional when the prices are rounded to the nearest dollar.

b. Possible answers: If she likes the songs, if the songs are old or new, if she already has the CD or not.

Alternate Assessment

Interview Have students describe purchasing situations in which they would determine unit rates and use the rates to influence their buying.

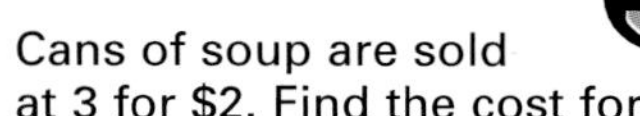

Quick Quiz

Cans of soup are sold at 3 for \$2. Find the cost for

1. 1 can. \$0.67
2. 2 cans. \$1.34
3. 4 cans. \$2.68
4. 6 cans. \$4.00

Available on Daily Transparency 6-7

PROBLEM SOLVING

Name ____________

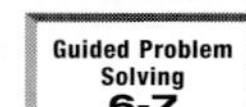

Guided Problem Solving 6-7

GPS PROBLEM 9, STUDENT PAGE 306

Phileas Fogg was the hero of Jules Verne's adventure novel *Around the World in Eighty Days.* The distance around the earth is about 25,000 miles.

a. Assuming Fogg traveled at a steady rate, how long did it take him to travel the 4000 miles from London to India?

b. How far did Fogg travel during the final week of his trip?

— Understand —

1. Underline the two things you are asked to find.
2. What is the distance around the earth? 25,000 miles.

— Plan —

3. What is the unit rate in miles per day traveled by Phileas Fogg? b
   a. $\frac{50 \text{ mi}}{1 \text{ day}}$ b. $\frac{312.5 \text{ mi}}{1 \text{ day}}$ c. $\frac{6.25 \text{ mi}}{1 \text{ day}}$
4. Which proportion would you use to find how many days it took Fogg to travel 4000 miles? b
   a. $\frac{50 \text{ mi}}{1 \text{ day}} = \frac{? \text{ days}}{4000 \text{ mi}}$ b. $\frac{312.5 \text{ mi}}{1 \text{ day}} = \frac{4000 \text{ mi}}{? \text{ days}}$
5. How can you find how many days it took Phileas Fogg to travel 4000 miles? Find number times 312.5 that equals 4000.
6. How can you use the unit rate to find how far Fogg traveled during the final week? Multiply both numbers in the unit rate by 7.

— Solve —

7. How long did it take Fogg to get from London to India? 12.8 days
8. How far did Fogg travel during the final week? 2187.5 miles.

— Look Back —

9. How can you determine if your answers are reasonable? Estimate and work backward: 13×300 is close to 4000 mi; $2100 \div 7$ is close to $\frac{312.5 \text{ mi}}{\text{day}}$.

SOLVE ANOTHER PROBLEM

Suppose a traveler covers 9800 miles in 35 days. At this rate, how far can she travel in 50 days? 14,000 miles.

ENRICHMENT

Name ____________

Extend Your Thinking 6-7

Visual Thinking

Circle the letter of the figure on the right that completes the pattern on the left.

1.
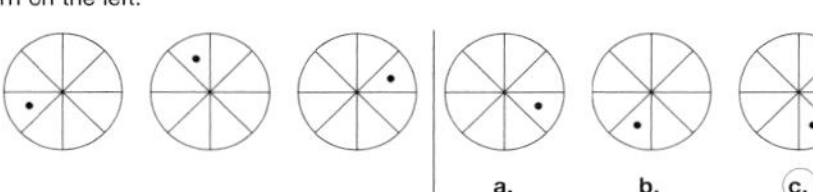

2.
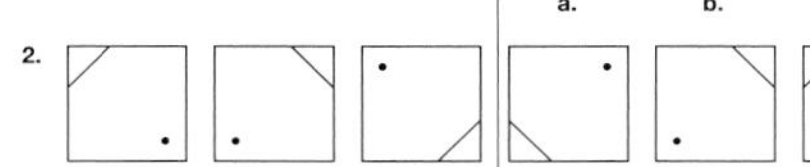

3.
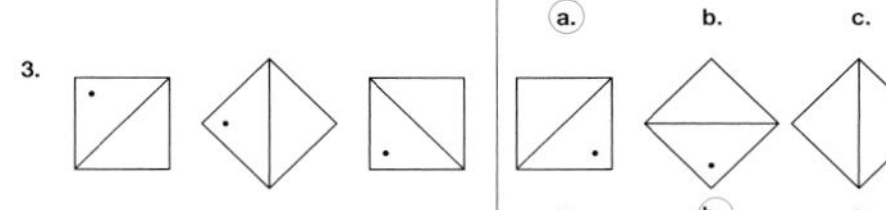

4.
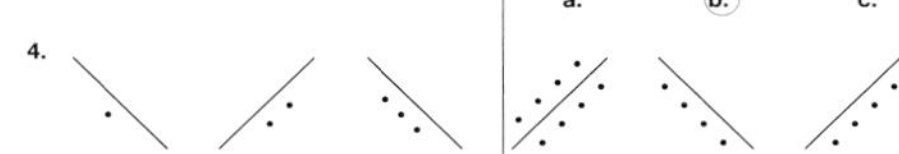

5.
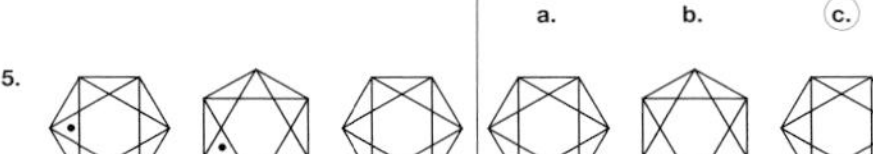

6.
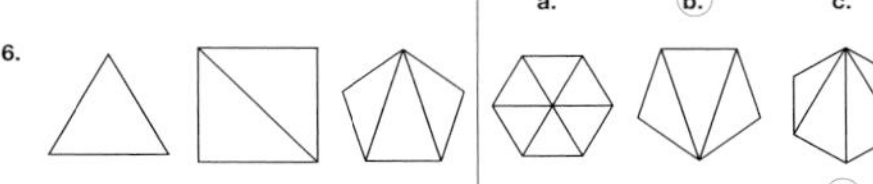

Lesson Organizer

Objectives

- Use cross multiplication to solve a proportion.
- Use cross multiplication to check whether two ratios form a proportion.

Vocabulary

- Cross product

NCTM Standards

- 1-5, 7

Review

Find each product.

1. 12 × 8 96
2. 1.8 × 6 10.8
3. 250 × 5 1250
4. 2.4 × 3.2 7.68

Available on Daily Transparency 6-8

1 Introduce

Explore

The Point
Students experiment pairing the four terms of a ratio to find patterns in their products. By investigating these patterns, students see that proportions have equal cross products.

Ongoing Assessment
Check that students multiply correctly.

For Groups That Finish Early
Follow the steps in **Explore** using the ratio $\frac{12}{8}$.

Possible answers: $\frac{12}{8} = \frac{3}{2}, \frac{3}{2} = \frac{6}{4}$;
$12 \cdot 3 = 36$, $12 \cdot 2 = 24$, $12 \cdot 8 = 96$, $8 \cdot 3 = 24$, $8 \cdot 2 = 16$, $3 \cdot 2 = 6$; $3 \cdot 6 = 18$, $3 \cdot 4 = 12$, $3 \cdot 2 = 6$, $2 \cdot 6 = 12$, $2 \cdot 4 = 8$, $6 \cdot 4 = 24$

Do your results match those in **Explore**? Yes

6-8 Cross Multiplication

You'll Learn ...

- to use cross multiplication to solve a proportion
- to use cross multiplication to check whether two ratios form a proportion

... How It's Used

When photographers set up photos, they use proportions to determine a good exposure.

Vocabulary

cross product

► Lesson Link You've used unit rates to solve proportions and to help decide if two ratios form a proportion. Now you'll use a method that can do both. ◄

Explore Cross Multiplication

Reinventing the Whale

An aquarium has models of humpback whales hanging from the ceiling of the ticket area and the gift shop.

1. One whale in the aquarium is 45 feet long. Its flippers are 15 feet long.

   Write this as a ratio: $\frac{\text{actual flipper length}}{\text{actual body size}} = \frac{?\text{ ft}}{?\text{ ft}}$

2. The whale model in the ticket area is 21 ft long and its flippers are 7 ft long. The model in the gift shop is 12 ft long and its flippers are 4 ft long. Use this information to write two more ratios like the one you wrote in Step 1.
3. Are all three of your ratios equivalent? How do you know? Use your ratios to write two different proportions.
4. For each proportion, use its four numbers to write as many different pairs of numbers as you can. Find the product of each pair.
5. What do you notice about the pairs that give equal products? Write a sentence describing any patterns you found.

Learn Cross Multiplication

In a proportion, the product of one numerator and the other denominator is a **cross product**. Notice that the cross products in the proportion $\frac{3}{4} = \frac{6}{8}$ are equal.

$3 \cdot 8 = 24$
$4 \cdot 6 = 24$

MEETING INDIVIDUAL NEEDS

Resources

- 6-8 Practice
- 6-8 Reteaching
- 6-8 Problem Solving
- 6-8 Enrichment
- 6-8 Daily Transparency
  - Problem of the Day
  - Review
  - Quick Quiz

Learning Modalities

Logical Stress with students that there are two parts to the property of cross products. First, if two ratios are proportional, their cross products are equal. Conversely, if the cross products of two ratios are equal, the ratios are proportional.

Visual Reinforce the concept of cross multiplication by pointing out that the arrows connecting the pairs of numbers form a large multiplication sign.

Inclusion

Students with learning disabilities may have difficulty visualizing equal ratios. Have them continue to use manipulatives or draw pictures to represent the equal ratios until they are confident enough to work without them.

Break down the steps for finding proportions and have students follow them consistently. For example: (1) write the ratios as fractions; (2) write a proportion; (3) cross multiply (can use a calculator); (4) compare the cross products.

PROPERTY OF CROSS PRODUCTS

If two ratios form a proportion, the cross products are equal. If two ratios have equal cross products, they form a proportion.

Example 1

Check cross products to decide if the ratios $\frac{9}{21}$ and $\frac{7}{16}$ form a proportion.

$\frac{9}{21} \stackrel{?}{=} \frac{7}{16}$ — Write the ratios as if they are a proportion.

$\frac{9}{21} = \frac{7}{16}$ — Identify the cross products.

$9 \cdot 16 \stackrel{?}{=} 21 \cdot 7$ — Write the cross products.

$144 \neq 147$ — Multiply. Compare the cross products.

Since the cross products are not equal, the ratios do not form a proportion.

You can use cross products to find an unknown number in a proportion.

Example 2

Crustaceans called krill are some whales' only food. A 150-ton blue whale can eat 8 tons of krill a day. How many tons might a 130-ton whale eat?

Let n stand for the number of tons of krill a 130-ton whale might eat in a day.

wt. of 150-ton whale → $\frac{150}{8} = \frac{130}{n}$ ← wt. of 130-ton whale
tons of krill → ← tons of krill — Write the ratios as a proportion.

$150 \cdot n = 8 \cdot 130$ — Write the cross products.

$150n = 1040$ — Multiply.

$\frac{150n}{150} = \frac{1040}{150}$ — To undo multiplying by 150, divide both sides by 150.

$n \approx 6.9$ — Divide.

A 130-ton blue whale might eat 6.9 tons of krill in a day.

Try It

Decide whether each pair of ratios forms a proportion.

a. $\frac{4}{5} \stackrel{?}{=} \frac{11}{13}$ No **b.** $\frac{5}{8} \stackrel{?}{=} \frac{15}{24}$ Yes

Solve each proportion. **c.** $\frac{4}{7} = \frac{x}{84}$ 48 **d.** $\frac{8}{3} = \frac{192}{k}$ 72 **e.** $\frac{51}{35} = \frac{8.5}{n}$ $5.8\overline{3}$

Test Prep

When a test asks you to compare two fractions, you can use cross products. When you find the cross products, "move" the denominators, not the numerators. If the cross products are not equal, the greater product will be on the same side as the greater fraction.

Answers for Explore

1. $\frac{15 \text{ ft}}{45 \text{ ft}}$
2. $\frac{7 \text{ ft}}{21 \text{ ft}}, \frac{4 \text{ ft}}{12 \text{ ft}}$
3. Yes; they all reduce to $\frac{1}{3}$; $\frac{15}{45} = \frac{7}{21}, \frac{15}{45} = \frac{4}{12}$.
4. $\frac{15}{45} = \frac{7}{21}$: $15 \cdot 7 = 105$, $15 \cdot 21 = 315$, $15 \cdot 45 = 675$, $45 \cdot 7 = 315$, $45 \cdot 21 = 945$, $7 \cdot 21 = 147$
   $\frac{15}{45} = \frac{4}{12}$: $15 \cdot 4 = 60$, $15 \cdot 12 = 180$, $15 \cdot 45 = 675$, $45 \cdot 4 = 180$, $45 \cdot 12 = 540$, $4 \cdot 12 = 48$
5. Products involving the numerator of one ratio and the denominator of the other are always equal.

2 Teach

Learn

Alternate Examples

1. Check cross products to decide if the ratios $\frac{8}{12}$ and $\frac{18}{27}$ form a proportion.

   Write the two ratios.

   $\frac{8}{12} = \frac{18}{27}$

   Identify and write the cross products.

   $8 \cdot 27 \stackrel{?}{=} 18 \cdot 12$

   Multiply and compare the cross products.

   $216 = 216$

   Since the cross products are equal, the ratios form a proportion.

2. A 220-pound dolphin eats about 66 pounds of food a day. About how much might a 200-pound dolphin eat in a day?

   Let n stand for the number of pounds a 200-pound dolphin would eat in a day. Write the ratios as a proportion.

   $\frac{220}{66} = \frac{200}{n}$

   Write the cross products and multiply.

   $220 \cdot n = 66 \cdot 200$
   $220n = 13{,}200$

   Divide both sides by 220.

   $\frac{220n}{220} = \frac{13{,}200}{220}$

   $n = 60$

   A 200-pound dolphin might eat 60 pounds of food in a day.

MATH EVERY DAY

Problem of the Day

A Brazilian flag is the largest flag in regular use today. When folded in half four times, its dimensions are 50 ft by 75 ft. Its area is slightly larger than that of a regular football field. What is the area when it is unfolded? 60,000 ft^2

Available on Daily Transparency 6-8

An Extension is provided in the transparency package.

Fact of the Day

A nighthawk, a bird about the size of a robin, can eat more than 2000 flying ants a day.

Mental Math

Find each product mentally.

1. 200×40 8000
2. 32×300 9600
3. $71 \times 2{,}000$ 142,000

Students see two methods used to solve a problem involving ratios. The first solves a proportion. The second uses multiplication to find a ratio equivalent to a given ratio.

Answers for What Do You Think?

1. Yes; Yes; For both methods the math would have involved using fractions.
2. Find out how long it took them to swim 1 meter, then multiply by 800.

3 Practice and Assess

Check

Have students give examples of proportions that are easily solved using cross multiplication and examples that are more easily solved using other methods.

Answers for Check Your Understanding

1. When the numbers do not share common factors; Other methods work well when one numerator or denominator divides easily into the other numerator or denominator, respectively.
2. No; There is an infinite number of pairs that would solve the proportion.

Kimberly and Andy are on a swim team. Their training swim is 200 meters and usually takes them 3 minutes. How long, at this rate, would it take them to complete an 800-meter swim?

Kimberly thinks ...

$\frac{200 \text{ meter}}{3 \text{ minutes}} = \frac{800 \text{ meters}}{n \text{ minutes}}$ Write the ratios as a proportion.

$200 \cdot n = 3 \cdot 800$ Write the cross products.

$200n = 2400$ Multiply.

$\frac{200n}{200} = \frac{2400}{200}$ To undo multiplying by 200, divide both sides by 200.

$n = 12$ Divide.

An 800-meter swim will take 12 minutes.

Andy thinks ...

Since 800 is 4 • 200, an 800-meter swim is 4 times the length of our 200-meter swim. It should take us 4 times as long as our 3 minute training swim.

4 • 3 minutes = 12 minutes

An 800-meter swim will take 12 minutes.

What do you think?

1. Would Andy's method have worked for a distance of 700 meters? Would Kimberly's? Explain.
2. How could you solve this problem using unit rates?

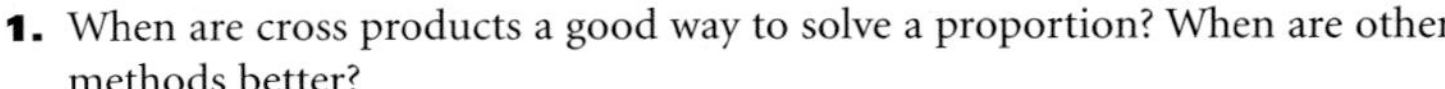

Check Your Understanding

1. When are cross products a good way to solve a proportion? When are other methods better?
2. If you know only two of the four numbers in a proportion, can you find the other two? Why or why not?

MEETING MIDDLE SCHOOL CLASSROOM NEEDS

Tips from Middle School Teachers

I find that many of my students need a great deal of extra reinforcement when using cross products to solve proportions. I try to solidify their comprehension by having them write problems for others in the class to solve.

Science Connection

Many people, describing someone with a small appetite, say that the person "eats like a bird." Actually, birds have a very large appetite. In comparison with whales, whose daily food intake is $\frac{1}{25}$ of their body weight, some birds' daily food intake is $\frac{1}{3}$ of their body weight.

Team Teaching

Ask the science teachers to discuss with students the diets of various insects, birds, fish, and mammals.

6-8 Exercises and Applications

Practice and Apply

1. **Getting Started** Follow the steps to solve the proportion $\frac{5}{x} = \frac{4}{3}$.
   a. Complete the cross products: $5 \cdot$ ____ $= 4 \cdot x$ **3**
   b. Multiply: ____ $= 4x$ **15**
   c. To undo multiplying by 4, divide both sides by 4. $\frac{15}{4} = \frac{4x}{4}$
   d. Write and check the solution. $x = 3.75$

Find the cross products for each proportion.

2. $\frac{4}{14} = \frac{2}{7}$ **28**
3. $\frac{2}{3} = \frac{6}{9}$ **18**
4. $\frac{5}{8} = \frac{25}{40}$ **200**
5. $\frac{32}{40} = \frac{8}{10}$ **320**
6. $\frac{18}{30} = \frac{9}{15}$ **270**

Decide whether each pair of ratios forms a proportion.

7. $\frac{6}{8} \stackrel{?}{=} \frac{10}{15}$ **No**
8. $\frac{5}{15} \stackrel{?}{=} \frac{3}{9}$ **Yes**
9. $\frac{9}{15} \stackrel{?}{=} \frac{15}{25}$ **Yes**
10. $\frac{6}{10} \stackrel{?}{=} \frac{25}{42}$ **No**
11. $\frac{7}{9} \stackrel{?}{=} \frac{20}{27}$ **No**
12. $\frac{8}{22} \stackrel{?}{=} \frac{28}{77}$ **Yes**
13. $\frac{15}{12} \stackrel{?}{=} \frac{4.5}{3.6}$ **Yes**
14. $\frac{1.9}{2.4} \stackrel{?}{=} \frac{5.7}{7.2}$ **Yes**

Solve each proportion.

15. $\frac{x}{6} = \frac{1}{3}$ **2**
16. $\frac{1}{6} = \frac{k}{12}$ **2**
17. $\frac{3}{x} = \frac{11}{20}$ **$5.\overline{45}$**
18. $\frac{5}{2} = \frac{6}{x}$ **2.4**
19. $\frac{9}{1} = \frac{t}{4}$ **36**
20. $\frac{y}{10} = \frac{3}{5}$ **6**
21. $\frac{4}{9} = \frac{10}{x}$ **22.5**
22. $\frac{5}{2} = \frac{2}{x}$ **0.8**

23. **Test Prep** What is the value of x in the proportion $\frac{5}{8} = \frac{10}{x}$? **C**
    Ⓐ 8 Ⓑ 15 Ⓒ 16 Ⓓ None of these

24. **Science** An adult blue whale can be about 100 ft long and weigh about 150 tons. An adult beluga whale can be about 15 ft long and weigh about 1.5 tons. Do the ratios of the whales' lengths to weights form a proportion? **No**

Beluga whale

25. **History** In 1890, the United States had an area of about 3.0 million square miles and a population of about 62.9 million. In 1990, the area was about 3.5 million square miles and the population was about 248.7 million. Do the ratios of the areas to the populations form a proportion? Explain. **No; Possible explanation: The cross products are not equal.**

PRACTICE 6-8

PRACTICE

Name ____________________

Practice 6-8

Cross Multiplication

Find the cross products for each proportion.

1. $\frac{6}{16} = \frac{9}{24}$ **$6 \cdot 24 = 144$; $16 \cdot 9 = 144$**
2. $\frac{21}{49} = \frac{3}{7}$ **$21 \cdot 7 = 147$; $49 \cdot 3 = 147$**
3. $\frac{4}{3} = \frac{16}{12}$ **$4 \cdot 12 = 48$; $3 \cdot 16 = 48$**

Decide whether each pair of ratios forms a proportion.

4. $\frac{2}{10} \stackrel{?}{=} \frac{4}{16}$ **Not a proportion**
5. $\frac{12}{7} \stackrel{?}{=} \frac{34}{20}$ **Not a proportion**
6. $\frac{20}{18} \stackrel{?}{=} \frac{30}{27}$ **Proportion**
7. $\frac{40}{45} \stackrel{?}{=} \frac{8}{9}$ **Proportion**
8. $\frac{7}{14} \stackrel{?}{=} \frac{3}{7}$ **Not a proportion**
9. $\frac{2}{6} \stackrel{?}{=} \frac{3}{9}$ **Proportion**
10. $\frac{10}{11} \stackrel{?}{=} \frac{18}{20}$ **Not a proportion**
11. $\frac{5}{13} \stackrel{?}{=} \frac{2}{6}$ **Not a proportion**
12. $\frac{4}{28} \stackrel{?}{=} \frac{2}{14}$ **Proportion**
13. $\frac{12}{9} \stackrel{?}{=} \frac{4}{3}$ **Proportion**
14. $\frac{18}{16} \stackrel{?}{=} \frac{45}{40}$ **Proportion**
15. $\frac{19}{18} \stackrel{?}{=} \frac{9}{8}$ **Not a proportion**

Solve each proportion.

16. $\frac{k}{8} = \frac{14}{4}$ $k =$ **28**
17. $\frac{u}{3} = \frac{10}{5}$ $u =$ **6**
18. $\frac{14}{6} = \frac{d}{15}$ $d =$ **35**
19. $\frac{5}{1} = \frac{m}{4}$ $m =$ **20**
20. $\frac{36}{32} = \frac{n}{8}$ $n =$ **9**
21. $\frac{5}{30} = \frac{1}{x}$ $x =$ **6**
22. $\frac{t}{4} = \frac{5}{10}$ $t =$ **2**
23. $\frac{9}{2} = \frac{v}{4}$ $v =$ **18**
24. $\frac{x}{10} = \frac{6}{4}$ $x =$ **15**
25. $\frac{8}{12} = \frac{2}{b}$ $b =$ **3**
26. $\frac{v}{15} = \frac{4}{6}$ $v =$ **10**
27. $\frac{3}{18} = \frac{2}{s}$ $s =$ **12**

28. The 1991 income for a typical 8-acre cotton farm was \$3040. Estimate the income for a 13-acre cotton farm. **\$4940**
29. A 150-pound person contains about 97.5 pounds of the element oxygen. Estimate the amount of oxygen in a 216-pound person. **140.4 lb**

RETEACHING

Name ____________________

Alternative Lesson 6-8

Cross Multiplication

In a proportion, the product of one numerator and the other denominator is a **cross product**. The cross products in the proportion at the right are equal.

$\frac{2}{3} \times \frac{6}{9}$ $2 \cdot 9 = 18$ $3 \cdot 6 = 18$

PROPERTY OF CROSS PRODUCTS
If two ratios form a proportion, then the cross products are equal.
If the two ratios have equal cross products, then they form a proportion.

Example 1

Check cross products to decide whether $\frac{6}{7}$ and $\frac{18}{21}$ form a proportion.

Step 1:	Step 2:	Step 3:	Step 4:
Write the ratios as if they are a proportion.	Identify the cross products.	Write the cross products.	Multiply. Compare the cross products.
$\frac{6}{7} \stackrel{?}{=} \frac{18}{21}$	$\frac{6}{7} \times \frac{18}{21}$	$6 \cdot 21 \stackrel{?}{=} 7 \cdot 18$	$126 = 126$ ✔

Since the cross products are equal, the ratios form a proportion.

Try It Tell whether each of the following forms a proportion.

a. $\frac{3}{4} = \frac{4}{6}$ **No.**
b. $\frac{8}{9} = \frac{80}{99}$ **No.**
c. $\frac{75}{81} = \frac{50}{54}$ **Yes.**
d. $\frac{4}{7} = \frac{24}{42}$ **Yes.**
e. $\frac{3}{8} = \frac{15}{36}$ **No.**
f. $\frac{16}{21} = \frac{48}{63}$ **Yes.**

Example 2

Solve the proportion $\frac{4}{9} = \frac{32}{x}$.

Step 1:	Step 2:	Step 3:
Identify the cross products.	Write the cross products.	Solve the equation. $4x = 288$
$\frac{4}{9} \times \frac{32}{x}$	$4 \cdot x = 9 \cdot 32$ or $4x = 288$	To undo the multiplication, divide both sides by 4. $\frac{4x}{4} = \frac{288}{4}$ $x = 72$

The solution is $x = 72$.

Try It Solve each proportion.

g. $\frac{8}{3} = \frac{x}{9}$ **$x = 24$**
h. $\frac{10}{55} = \frac{4}{b}$ **$b = 22$**
i. $\frac{12}{18} = \frac{t}{15}$ **$t = 10$**
j. $\frac{10}{30} = \frac{40}{y}$ **$y = 120$**
k. $\frac{g}{18} = \frac{3}{2}$ **$g = 27$**
l. $\frac{5}{16} = \frac{d}{24}$ **$d = 7.5$**

6-8 Exercises and Applications

Assignment Guide

- **Basic**
  1–25 odds, 28, 31–35 odds
- **Average**
  2–22 evens, 23–28, 30–36 evens
- **Enriched**
  2–22 evens, 23–30, 32–36 evens

Exercise Notes

Exercises 7–22

Extension You may wish to have students use calculators for many of these exercises.

Reteaching

Activity

Materials: Play money—pennies, nickels, dimes, quarters

Model each of these examples and decide if the ratios form a proportion, using the values of the coins. Then use cross products to verify your answer.

1. $\frac{2 \text{ nickels}}{10 \text{ pennies}}, \frac{3 \text{ nickels}}{20 \text{ pennies}}$
   No; $10 \cdot 20 \neq 15 \cdot 10$
2. $\frac{4 \text{ nickels}}{20 \text{ pennies}}, \frac{2 \text{ nickels}}{10 \text{ pennies}}$
   Yes; $20 \cdot 10 = 20 \cdot 10 = 200$
3. $\frac{2 \text{ quarters}}{10 \text{ nickels}}, \frac{3 \text{ quarters}}{15 \text{ nickels}}$
   Yes; $50 \cdot 75 = 75 \cdot 50 = 3750$
4. $\frac{3 \text{ dimes}}{6 \text{ nickels}}, \frac{8 \text{ dimes}}{16 \text{ nickels}}$
   Yes; $30 \cdot 80 = 80 \cdot 30 = 2400$

Model other ratios that form proportions and some that do not, and check in the same way by using cross products.

Exercise Notes

Exercise 30

Literature Mark Twain was the pseudonym of Samuel Langhorne Clemens. The name Mark Twain is a term meaning two fathoms deep, ensuring safe passage for a riverboat.

Exercises 35–36

Error Prevention Be sure students remember the formula for the area of a triangle, $A = \frac{1}{2}bh$.

Exercise Answers

28. 4 teachers; For 720 students, 20 teachers are needed for a ratio of $\frac{1}{36}$ and 24 teachers are needed for a ratio of $\frac{a1}{30}$; $24 - 20 = 4$.

29. Yes; A and C; $\frac{4}{18} = \frac{10}{45}$

30. Yes; Both Twain and Snodgrass wrote about $\frac{1}{2}$ one-syllable and $\frac{1}{4}$ two-syllable words.

Alternate Assessment

You may want to use the Interactive *CD-ROM Journal* with this assessment.

Journal Give students a proportion with one term missing and have them write the steps they would follow to solve it.

Quick Quiz

Solve each proportion.

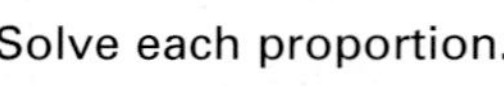

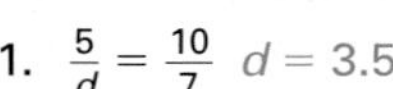

1. $\frac{5}{d} = \frac{10}{7}$ $d = 3.5$
2. $\frac{18}{81} = \frac{a}{63}$ $a = 14$
3. $\frac{p}{11} = \frac{49}{77}$ $p = 7$
4. $\frac{10}{24} = \frac{z}{84}$ $z = 35$
5. $\frac{r}{9} = \frac{70}{30}$ $r = 21$

Available on Daily Transparency 6-8

26. Estimation According to 1993 figures from the A. C. Nielsen Company, nearly 60 million of the 95 million U.S. households own two or more television sets. Use the data shown to estimate the number of households in Texas with two or more sets. 4–5 million

= 1 million households

27. Science A 380-cubic-centimeter sample of titanium has a mass of 1710 g. Find the weight of a titanium sample that has a volume of 532 cubic centimeters. 2394 g

Problem Solving and Reasoning

28. Choose a Strategy GPS The ratio of teachers to students at Sam Houston Middle School is 1 to 36. If there are 720 students, how many more teachers are needed to make the teacher-to-student ratio 1 to 30? Explain.

29. Critical Thinking A chemist analyzed samples of three substances. If two samples do not contain the same proportions of carbon and hydrogen, they cannot be the same substance. Could any of these samples be the same substance? Explain.

	Sample A	Sample B	Sample C
Carbon (g)	4	6	10
Hydrogen (g)	18	25	45

Problem Solving STRATEGIES

- Look for a Pattern
- Make an Organized List
- Make a Table
- Guess and Check
- Work Backward
- Use Logical Reasoning
- Draw a Diagram
- Solve a Simpler Problem

30. Communicate Some linguists believe that the works of 19th-century writer Thomas Jefferson Snodgrass were actually written by Mark Twain. The table shows a count of 1- and 2-syllable words in similar passages by the two writers. Does the data support the theory that Twain was Snodgrass? Explain.

	Total No. of Words	1-Syllable Words	2-Syllable Words
Twain	916	525	231
Snodgrass	655	362	179

PROBLEM SOLVING 6-8

Mixed Review

Solve each equation. *[Lesson 2-6]*

31. $x - 9 = 24$ 33 **32.** $f + 25 = 67$ 42 **33.** $34 = y - 18$ 52 **34.** $659 = p + 345$ 314

Find the missing measurements of the following triangles. *[Lesson 5-8]*

35. Base = 8, height = 6, area = ? 24 **36.** Base = ?, height = 24 in., area = 96 in^2 8 in.

PROBLEM SOLVING

Name ____________

Guided Problem Solving 6-8

GPS PROBLEM 28, STUDENT PAGE 312

The ratio of teachers to students at Sam Houston Middle School is 1 to 36. If there are 720 students, how many more teachers are needed to make the teacher-to-student ratio 1 to 30? Explain.

— Understand —

1. What is the current ratio of teachers to students? $\frac{1}{36}$
2. What is the proposed ratio of teachers to students? $\frac{1}{30}$

— Plan —

3. Which proportion would you use to find the number of teachers currently at Sam Houston Middle School. c
   a. $\frac{1}{30} = \frac{x}{720}$ b. $\frac{1}{36} = \frac{720}{x}$ c. $\frac{1}{36} = \frac{x}{720}$
4. Which proportion would you use to find the number of teachers needed to make the teacher-to-student ratio 1 to 30. b
   a. $\frac{1}{36} = \frac{x}{720}$ b. $\frac{1}{30} = \frac{x}{720}$ c. $\frac{1}{30} = \frac{720}{x}$

— Solve —

5. How many teachers are currently teaching at Sam Houston Middle School? 20 teachers.
6. How many teachers are needed if the teacher-to-student ratio is 1 to 30? 24 teachers.
7. How many more teachers are needed to make the teacher-to-student ratio 1 to 30? 4 teachers.

— Look Back —

7. How can you check your answers? Possible answer: Write the first answer as a ratio of 20:720 to see if it is equal to the ratio 1:36 and the second answer as a ratio of 24:720 to see if it is equal to the ratio 1:30.

SOLVE ANOTHER PROBLEM

The ratio of computers to printers in Juan's computer classroom is 5 to 1. There are 60 computers. How many more printers are needed to make the ratio 4 to 1? 3 printers.

ENRICHMENT

Name ____________

Extend Your Thinking 6-8

Critical Thinking

The Parthenon is an ancient, very famous temple built in Athens, Greece, to honor Athena, the goddess of wisdom. It has the proportions of the *Golden Ratio*, which is often considered to be the most visually pleasing shape for a rectangle. Such a rectangle is called a *Golden Rectangle*.

1. Find the dimensions of the Golden Rectangle around the Parthenon.

   Length: 72 mm Width: 45 mm

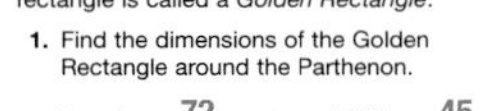

2. Use your answer to Question 1 to find the Golden Ratio. Then write the ratio as a decimal. $\frac{8}{5} = 1.6$
3. Without measuring, which of the rectangles below do you think is a Golden Rectangle? Answers will vary.

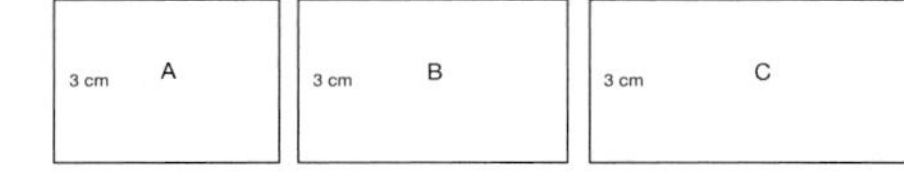

4. Measure the length of each rectangle above. Find the ratio of the length to the width and write it as a decimal. Circle the letter of the Golden Rectangle.

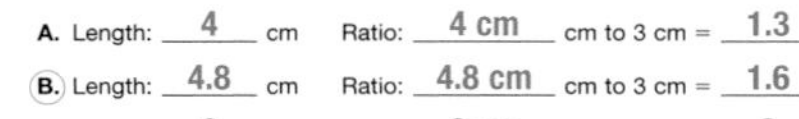

   A. Length: 4 cm Ratio: 4 cm cm to 3 cm = 1.3
   (B.) Length: 4.8 cm Ratio: 4.8 cm cm to 3 cm = 1.6
   C. Length: 6 cm Ratio: 6 cm cm to 3 cm = 2

5. Design a small picture frame in the shape of a Golden Rectangle. Label the dimensions. Check students' drawings.

At the beginning of this section, you read about the *photo-rephoto* method that researchers use to estimate the number of whales in a particular region. You can model this technique using chips as "whales" and a bowl as an "ocean."

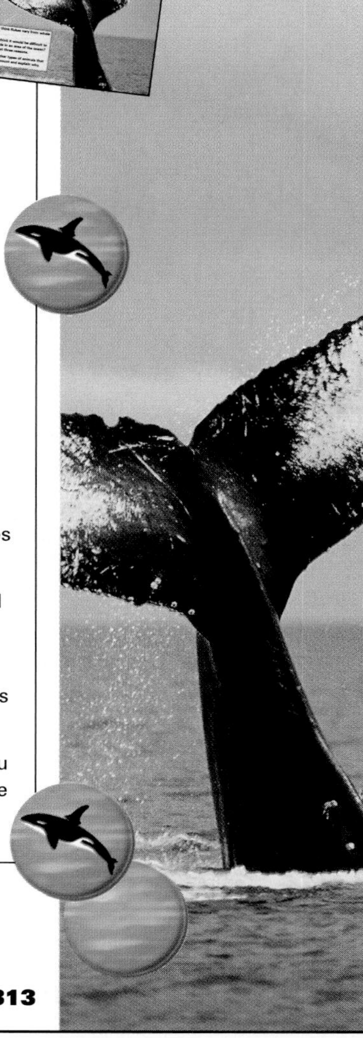

A Whale of a Tail

Materials: Large number of plastic chips, Bowl, Marking pen

Put the whales (chips) into the ocean (bowl). Do not count the whales.

1. **Photo** Grab a small handful of chips. Mark each of these chips with a felt-tipped pen. Count and record the number of marked chips. This number is the *first number of whales photographed.* Return the chips to the bowl and mix thoroughly.
2. **Rephoto** Grab another small handful of chips. Count and record the number of chips grabbed (the *second number of whales photographed*) and the number of marked chips in the second handful (the *number of whales rephotographed*).
3. Solve the proportion:

$$\frac{\text{number of whales rephotographed}}{\text{second number of whales photographed}} = \frac{\text{first number of whales photographed}}{x}$$

   The value of x you obtain will be an estimate of the number of whales in your ocean.
4. Return the chips to the bowl and mix thoroughly. Repeat Steps 2 and 3 four more times. Each time, you'll obtain an estimate of the total number of whales.
5. Find the mean of your five estimates. Then count the number of chips in the bowl and compare the total with the mean you calculated.
6. Explain why it is important to mix the chips thoroughly each time you return them to the bowl. What can biologists do to make sure that the whales they photograph and rephotograph are thoroughly "mixed"?

Answers for Connect

1–5. Answers may vary.

6. Possible answers: So you don't keep picking up the same chips; Biologists shouldn't photograph whales in the same place every time.

A Whale of a Tail

The Point

In *A Whale of a Tail* on page 293, students discussed counting the whales in the ocean. Now they will simulate the "photo-rephoto" method of estimating animal populations.

Materials

Large number of plastic chips, bowl, marking pen

About the Page

- Do not tell students how many chips you put in the bowl initially, since this is what you want them to estimate.
- The number of chips in the bowl can vary, but using 100 or more will yield better results.
- Students should mark about 10 chips in the "photo" step (more if there are more than 100 chips in the bowl), and about 30 chips for the "rephoto" step.
- If students' answers to Steps 4 and 5 are not similar, have them repeat the "rephoto" a few more times and use the combined results of all the samples.
- Discuss why estimates based on large samples are usually more accurate. A large sample is a better representation of the population.

Ongoing Assessment

Check that students have set up and solved the proportion correctly.

Extension

A method similar to "photo-rephoto" is the capture-recapture method. Have students research the capture-recapture method and find when the method is used. Possible answers: Animals in an area are captured, tagged, and released. Later a number of animals are recaptured and the number of tagged animals are counted. Ideally, the ratio of recaptured-tagged to original-tagged is similar to the ratio of total recaptured to the total population; This method is used to determine the status of endangered species, to follow the migration of birds, to predict how a species of fish is adapting to a new habitat, and to estimate the deer population in an area.

6B Review

Review Correlation

Item(s)	Lesson(s)
1–6	6-5
7–11	6-6
12–16	6-8
17, 18	6-7
19, 20	6-8

Test Prep

Test-Taking Tip

Tell students that sometimes finding decimal equivalents can help them solve proportions. Here, $\frac{4}{5} = 0.8$, so they can substitute each value for *x*, divide, and find the denominator that gives a decimal equal to 0.8.

Answers for Review

2. Possible answers:

3	6	9
7	14	21

$\frac{3}{7} = \frac{6}{14}; \frac{3}{7} = \frac{9}{21}; \frac{9}{21} = \frac{6}{14}$.

3. Possible answers:

9	18	27
8	16	24

$\frac{9}{8} = \frac{a1}{8}; \frac{9}{8} = \frac{27}{24}; \frac{27}{24} = \frac{18}{16}$.

4. Possible answers:

6	3	1.5
11	5.5	2.75

$\frac{6}{11} = \frac{3}{5.5}; \frac{6}{11} = \frac{1.5}{2.75}; \frac{1.5}{2.75} = \frac{3}{5.5}$.

5. Possible answers:

5	10	15
2	4	6

$\frac{5}{2} = \frac{10}{4}; \frac{5}{2} = \frac{15}{6}; \frac{15}{6} = \frac{10}{4}$.

6. Possible answers:

9	18	27
20	40	60

$\frac{9}{20} = \frac{18}{40}; \frac{9}{20} = \frac{27}{60}; \frac{27}{60} = \frac{18}{40}$.

19. 640; Solved the proportion $\frac{200}{x} = \frac{5}{16}$.

Section 6B Review

1. Complete the table with equivalent ratios. Then write four proportions using ratios in the table.

3	6	9	12	15	18
5	10	15	20	25	30

$\frac{3}{5} = \frac{6}{10}; \frac{3}{5} = \frac{9}{15}; \frac{3}{5} = \frac{12}{20}; \frac{3}{5} = \frac{15}{25}$

Make a table and create three equal ratios. Use the ratios to write three proportions.

2. $\frac{3}{7}$ **3.** $\frac{9}{8}$ **4.** $\frac{6}{11}$ **5.** $\frac{5}{2}$ **6.** $\frac{9}{20}$

Decide whether each pair of ratios forms a proportion.

7. $\frac{9}{14} \stackrel{?}{=} \frac{25}{39}$ No **8.** $\frac{10}{35} \stackrel{?}{=} \frac{8}{28}$ Yes **9.** $\frac{6}{9} \stackrel{?}{=} \frac{12}{18}$ Yes **10.** $\frac{7}{8} \stackrel{?}{=} \frac{49}{56}$ Yes **11.** $\frac{18}{36} \stackrel{?}{=} \frac{9}{18}$ Yes

Solve each proportion.

12. $\frac{3}{5} = \frac{12}{x}$ 20 **13.** $\frac{5}{4} = \frac{y}{10}$ 12.5 **14.** $\frac{n}{27} = \frac{8}{18}$ 12 **15.** $\frac{18}{36} = \frac{10}{a}$ 20 **16.** $\frac{4}{9} = \frac{20}{q}$ 45

17. Consumer Report covers sell for 8 for \$5.20. Find the unit price. Then tell how many covers you can buy for \$78.00. \$0.65; 120

18. Science In 1996, Keiko, the killer whale used in the filming of *Free Willy*, was moved from Mexico to Oregon. It cost \$9,000,000 to airlift the 7,000 pound whale to his new home. How much did it cost per pound to move Keiko? \$1,285.71

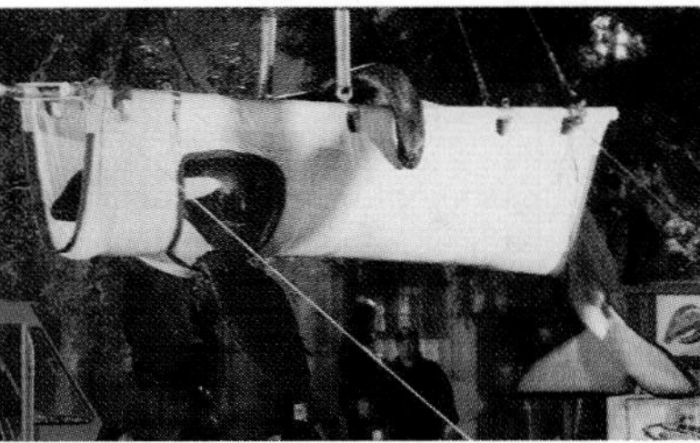

19. 

A researcher tagged 200 bass and released them into a lake. A month later, he netted 16 bass and found that 5 of them were tagged. Estimate the bass population of the lake. Describe the process you used.

REVIEW 6B

Test Prep

To solve a proportion on a multiple choice test, substitute each answer and check the cross products. The answer giving equal cross products is correct.

20. Solve for *x*. $\frac{4}{5} = \frac{6}{x}$ B

Ⓐ 7 Ⓑ 7.5 Ⓒ 9 Ⓓ 9.5

Resources

Assessment Sourcebook
Quiz 6B

Practice Masters
Section 6B Review

TestWorks
Test and Practice Software

PRACTICE

Name ______________________

Practice

Section 6B Review

1. Complete the table with equivalent ratios. Then write four proportions using ratios in the table.

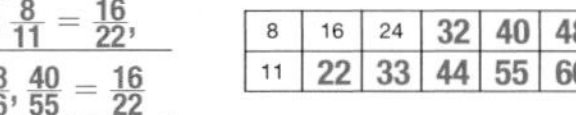

8	16	24	32	40	48
11	22	33	44	55	66

Possible answer: $\frac{8}{11} = \frac{16}{22}$, $\frac{24}{33} = \frac{40}{55}$, $\frac{32}{44} = \frac{48}{66}$, $\frac{40}{55} = \frac{16}{22}$

Decide whether each pair of ratios forms a proportion.

2. $\frac{14}{2} \stackrel{?}{=} \frac{35}{5}$ Proportion
3. $\frac{2}{6} \stackrel{?}{=} \frac{7}{18}$ Not a proportion

Solve each proportion.

4. $\frac{35}{30} = \frac{28}{j}$ $j =$ 24
5. $\frac{8}{20} = \frac{d}{5}$ $d =$ 2
6. $\frac{1}{x} = \frac{5}{10}$ $x =$ 2
7. $\frac{16}{n} = \frac{40}{15}$ $n =$ 6

8. Make a scatterplot to see if the relationship is proportional.

Boys	5	9	13	17
Girls	4	7	10	13

Not proportional

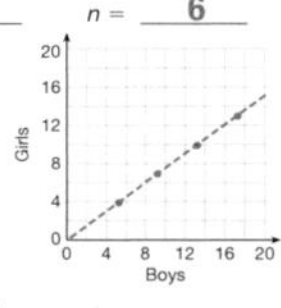

9. A certain brand of pen is priced at 5 for \$2.90. Find the unit price. Then tell how many pens you can buy for \$10.44. \$0.58; 18 pens

10. In 1991, the average household received 10 mail-order catalogs every 26 days. How many catalogs did the average household receive in 91 days? 35 catalogs

For Exercises 11–12, use the picture showing the approximate shape of Samuel Crawford Memorial Park in Dallas, Texas.

$\frac{1}{2}$ mi, $\frac{5}{8}$ mi, 1 mi

11. The perimeter of the polygon is $2\frac{3}{4}$ mi. Write and solve an equation to find the length of the unknown side. *[Lesson 4-3]*

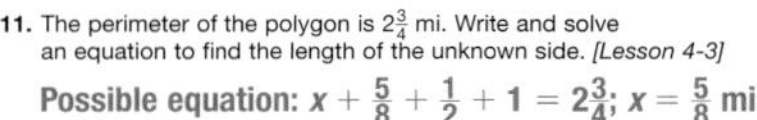

Possible equation: $x + \frac{5}{8} + \frac{1}{2} + 1 = 2\frac{3}{4}$; $x = \frac{5}{8}$ mi

12. Classify the polygon in as many ways as you can. *[Lesson 5-3]*

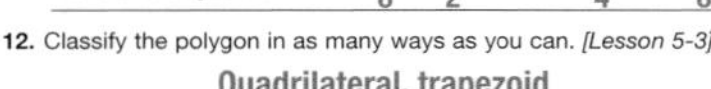

Quadrilateral, trapezoid

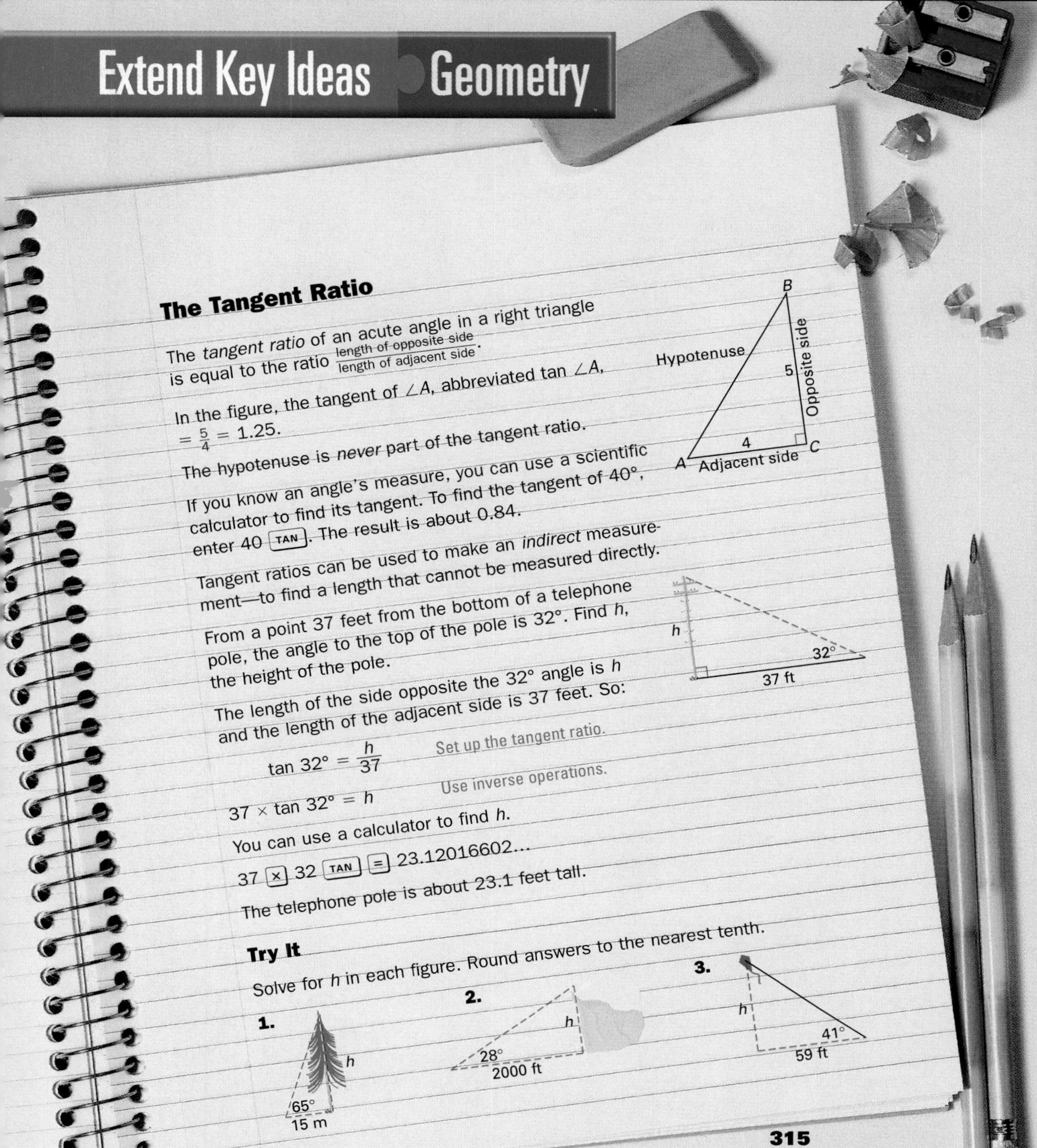

Extend Key Ideas ● Geometry

The Tangent Ratio

The *tangent ratio* of an acute angle in a right triangle is equal to the ratio $\frac{\text{length of opposite side}}{\text{length of adjacent side}}$.

In the figure, the tangent of $\angle A$, abbreviated tan $\angle A$, $= \frac{5}{4} = 1.25$.

The hypotenuse is *never* part of the tangent ratio.

If you know an angle's measure, you can use a scientific calculator to find its tangent. To find the tangent of 40°, enter 40 [TAN]. The result is about 0.84.

Tangent ratios can be used to make an *indirect* measurement—to find a length that cannot be measured directly.

From a point 37 feet from the bottom of a telephone pole, the angle to the top of the pole is 32°. Find *h*, the height of the pole.

The length of the side opposite the 32° angle is *h* and the length of the adjacent side is 37 feet. So:

$\tan 32° = \frac{h}{37}$ Set up the tangent ratio.

$37 \times \tan 32° = h$ Use inverse operations.

You can use a calculator to find *h*.

37 [×] 32 [TAN] [=] 23.12016602...

The telephone pole is about 23.1 feet tall.

Try It

Solve for *h* in each figure. Round answers to the nearest tenth.

Extend Key Ideas

The Tangent Ratio

The Point

Students use the tangent ratio to find lengths that cannot be measured directly.

About the Page

- The tangent ratio is one of the important ratios in the study of trigonometry; it involves the legs of a right triangle. Two other ratios in trigonometry, the sine ratio and the cosine ratio, involve one of the legs and the hypotenuse.
- Students with graphing calculators might enter:

  37 [TAN] [×] 32 [ENTER]

  With this key sequence, the calculator will perform the calculation for the height of the telephone pole. You may need to point out that the calculator must be set to degree measure, rather than radian measure.

Ask ...

- How is the tangent of an angle defined? For a right triangle, the ratio of the length of the side opposite the angle to the length of the side adjacent to the angle.
- The tangent ratio is defined for the acute angles of a right triangle. Can a right triangle have an obtuse angle? Why or why not? No; The sum of the angle measures of a triangle is 180°, so a right triangle can have only one right angle and two acute angles.

Answers for Try It

1. 32.2 m
2. 1063.4 ft
3. 51.3 ft

Extension

A ladder leans against the side of a house. It makes a 50° angle with the ground and touches the house 12 feet above the ground. How far from the house is the base of the ladder? About 10.1 feet

Chapter 6 Summary and Review

Review Correlation

Item(s)	Lesson(s)
1	6-1
2–5	6-2
6	6-7
7	6-3
8–10	6-4
11	6-6
12, 13	6-5
14	6-6
15	6-7
16, 17	6-8
18	6-7

For additional review, see page 677.

Chapter 6 Summary and Review

Graphic Organizer

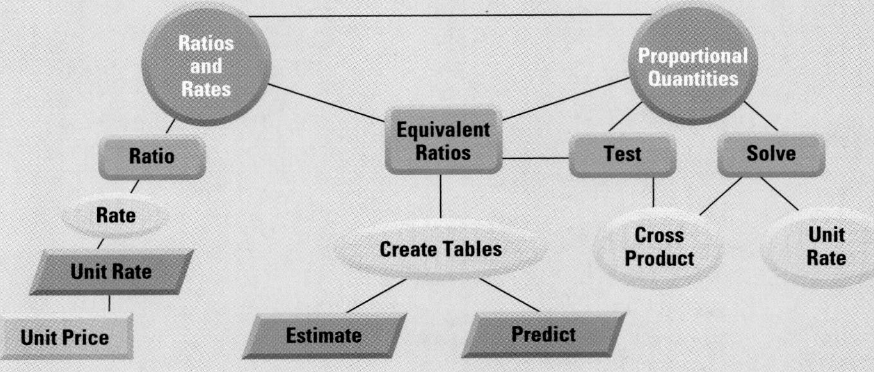

Section 6A Ratios and Rates

Summary

- A **ratio** compares two quantities. There are three ways to write a ratio; for example, the ratios 2 to 3, $\frac{2}{3}$, and 2:3 all have the same meaning.
- A ratio is called a **rate** when the units of measure of the quantities are different. A rate shows how quantities with different units are related.
- A **unit rate** is a rate in which the measure of the second quantity is 1 unit. A **unit price** is a unit rate that gives the cost of one item.
- To find **equivalent ratios** or **equivalent rates**, multiply or divide the numerator and denominator of a given ratio or rate by the same number. You can use this method to create a table of equivalent ratios or rates.
- You can use tables to estimate and predict ratios and rates.

Review

1. Write the ratio 8 forks to 6 spoons in three ways. Write in lowest terms if possible. 4 to 3; 4:3; $\frac{4}{3}$

2. Estimate the ratio of the height to the base of the triangle. Possible answer: $\frac{3}{5}$

3. Find the unit rate: 130 miles in 2 hours. Remember to include units in your rate. 65 miles per hour

4. Express the rate as a unit rate: 102 houses along a 6-mile road. 17 houses per mile

Resources

Practice Masters
Cumulative Review Chapters 1–6

Assessment Sourcebook
Quarterly Test Chapters 1–6

PRACTICE

Name ______________________

Practice

Cumulative Review Chapters 1–6

Express each fraction in lowest terms. *[Lesson 3-8]*

1. $\frac{27}{72}$ $\frac{3}{8}$ 2. $\frac{12}{18}$ $\frac{2}{3}$ 3. $\frac{20}{28}$ $\frac{5}{7}$ 4. $\frac{21}{70}$ $\frac{3}{10}$

5. $\frac{24}{52}$ $\frac{6}{13}$ 6. $\frac{32}{88}$ $\frac{4}{11}$ 7. $\frac{45}{90}$ $\frac{1}{2}$ 8. $\frac{48}{120}$ $\frac{2}{5}$

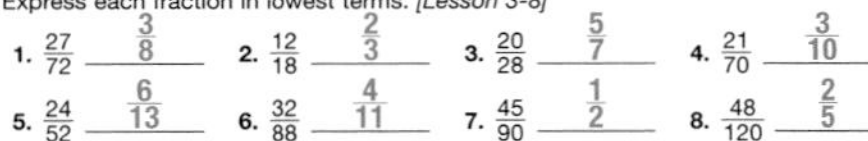

Find each sum or difference. *[Lesson 4-3]*

9. $2\frac{1}{2} + 7\frac{3}{4}$ $10\frac{1}{4}$ 10. $8\frac{2}{3} - 5\frac{1}{9}$ $3\frac{5}{9}$ 11. $7\frac{1}{6} + 4\frac{1}{2}$ $11\frac{2}{3}$

12. $7\frac{3}{8} - 1\frac{3}{4}$ $5\frac{5}{8}$ 13. $6\frac{4}{7} + 9\frac{5}{7}$ $16\frac{2}{7}$ 14. $4\frac{2}{5} - 2\frac{7}{10}$ $1\frac{7}{10}$

15. $\frac{15}{16} + 3\frac{5}{8}$ $4\frac{9}{16}$ 16. $14\frac{5}{7} - 8\frac{1}{2}$ $6\frac{3}{14}$ 17. $6\frac{5}{9} + 3\frac{7}{11}$ $10\frac{19}{99}$

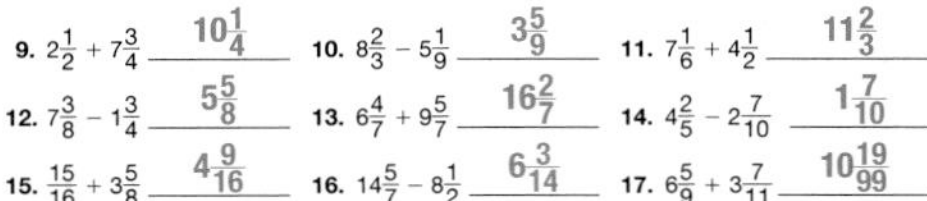

Use the figure to name each pair of angles or lines if it is possible. *[Lesson 5-2]*

18. a pair of parallel lines None

19. a pair of perpendicular lines $\overleftrightarrow{AB}$ and $\overleftrightarrow{BC}$

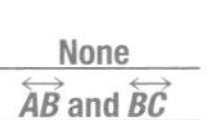

20. a pair of vertical angles Possible answer: ∠2 and ∠4

21. a pair of supplementary angles Possible answer: ∠6 and ∠7

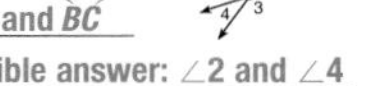

Consumer Use unit prices to find the better buy. Underline the correct choice. *[Lesson 6-2]*

22. Used books: $1.00 for 5 books or $1.47 for 7 books

23. Candied apples: $9.60 for 8 apples or $7.32 for 6 apples

24. Ribbon: $2.82 for 60 ft or $3.68 for 80 ft

25. Baseball cards: $8.19 for 7 cards or $12.98 for 11 cards

Solve each proportion. *[Lesson 6-8]*

26. $\frac{3}{7} = \frac{x}{21}$ $x =$ 9 27. $\frac{n}{16} = \frac{15}{24}$ $n =$ 10 28. $\frac{6}{u} = \frac{14}{35}$ $u =$ 15 29. $\frac{42}{24} = \frac{28}{r}$ $r =$ 16

Section 6A Ratios and Rates *continued*

5. Find the better buy for bread: $3.20 for 2 loaves or $5.10 for 3 loaves. $3.20 for 2 loaves

6. Hugo's car travels 108 miles on 4 gallons of gas. How far will it travel on 7 gallons of gas? 189 miles

7. Multiply and divide to find two ratios equivalent to the ratio $\frac{16}{20}$.

8. Use a table to find two rates equivalent to 15 points in 4 games.

9. Using multiplication, complete the table to find 5 ratios equivalent to $\frac{3}{4}$.

3	6	9	12	15	18
4	8	12	16	20	24

10. Using division, complete the table to find 5 ratios equivalent to $\frac{120}{80}$.

120	60	30	24	12	6
80	40	20	16	8	4

Section 6B Proportional Quantities

Summary

- A **proportion** is an equation or statement that shows two ratios are equal.
- To test two ratios to see if they are proportional, you can reduce each ratio to lowest terms and see if they are equivalent.
- You can use unit rates to solve a proportion. First find the unit rate. Then multiply to solve the proportion.
- A **cross product** of two ratios is the product of the numerator of one ratio and the denominator of the other ratio.
- If two ratios form a proportion, the cross products are equal. If two ratios have equal cross products, they form a proportion. You can use cross products to find an unknown number in a proportion.

Review

11. Steve baked one loaf of bread using 3 cups of flour and 5 teaspoons of yeast, and another loaf using 4 cups of flour and 7 teaspoons of yeast. Are these ratios proportional? No

12. Complete the ratio table. Then write four proportions involving the ratios in the table.

4	8	12	16
7			

13. Make a table and create three ratios equal to $\frac{5}{13}$. Use your ratios to write three proportions.

14. Decide if the ratios are proportional and give a reason: $\frac{9}{14} \stackrel{?}{=} \frac{13}{21}$.

15. Find the unit rate: $7.65 for 9 muffins. $0.85 per muffin

16. Solve the proportion: $\frac{12}{26} = \frac{n}{65}$. $n = 30$

17. Decide whether the ratios form a proportion: $\frac{98}{112} \stackrel{?}{=} \frac{63}{72}$. Yes

18. Anna earned $123.75 in 15 hours. Find her hourly rate. $8.25 per hour

Answers for Review

7. Possible answer: $\frac{32}{40}, \frac{4}{5}$.

8. Possible answer: $\frac{30 \text{ points}}{8 \text{ games}}, \frac{45 \text{ points}}{12 \text{ games}}$

12. Possible answers:

4	8	12	16
7	14	21	28

$\frac{4}{7} = \frac{8}{14}$; $\frac{4}{7} = \frac{12}{21}$; $\frac{4}{7} = \frac{16}{28}$; $\frac{8}{14} = \frac{12}{21}$

13. Possible answers:

5	10	15	20
13	26	39	52

$\frac{5}{13} = \frac{10}{26}$, $\frac{5}{13} = \frac{15}{39}$, $\frac{5}{13} = \frac{20}{52}$

14. No; Their cross products are not equal.

Chapter 6 Assessment

Assessment Correlation

Item(s)	Lesson(s)
1	6-4
2, 3	6-1
4, 5	6-2
6	6-7
7	6-2
8	6-4
9	6-3
10	6-5
11	6-4
12	6-5
13, 14	6-6
15–17	6-8

Answers for Assessment

Possible answers:

8. $\frac{10 \text{ feet}}{17 \text{ seconds}}, \frac{40 \text{ feet}}{68 \text{ seconds}}$

10.

3	6	9	12
8	16	24	32

$\frac{3}{8} = \frac{6}{16}, \frac{3}{8} = \frac{9}{24}, \frac{3}{8} = \frac{12}{32}$

12. $\frac{6}{11} = \frac{12}{22}, \frac{12}{22} = \frac{18}{33},$
$\frac{18}{33} = \frac{24}{44}, \frac{6}{11} = \frac{24}{44}$

Answers for Performance Task

Ratio of short sides:

A to B = $\frac{1}{2}$

B to C = $\frac{2}{3}$

A to C = $\frac{1}{3}$

Ratio of long sides:

A to B = $\frac{1}{2}$

B to C = $\frac{2}{3}$

A to C = $\frac{1}{3}$

Ratio of areas:

A to B = $\frac{1}{4}$

B to C = $\frac{4}{9}$

A to C = $\frac{1}{9}$

Ratios of short sides and ratios of long sides for each rectangle are the same for each pair. The ratio of the areas is the square of the ratio of the sides.

Chapter 6 Assessment

1. Using multiplication, complete the table by finding 5 ratios equivalent to $\frac{5}{9}$.

5	10	15	20	25	30
9	18	27	36	45	54

2. Estimate the ratio of the height to the width of the building. **1 to 3**

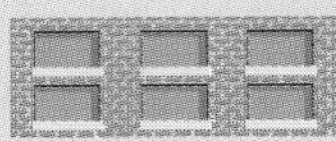

3. Write the ratio 10 cats to 25 dogs in three ways. Write in lowest terms if possible. **2 to 5; 2:5; $\frac{2}{5}$**

4. Express the rate as a unit rate: 385 raisins in 7 pounds of cereal. **55 raisins per pound**

5. Use unit rates to find the better buy for dog food: 98 cents for 14 oz or 64 cents for 8 oz. **98 cents for 14 oz**

6. Morris was paid $34.00 for 5 hours of work. If he is paid an hourly wage, how much will he be paid for 12 hours of work? **$81.60**

7. Find the rate: 5 tons in 18 days. Remember to include units in your rate. $\frac{5 \text{ tons}}{18 \text{ days}}$

8. Use a table to find two rates equivalent to 20 feet in 34 seconds.

9. Multiply and divide to find two ratios equivalent to the ratio $\frac{12}{21}$. $\frac{4}{7}$ **and** $\frac{24}{42}$

10. Make a table and create three ratios equal to $\frac{3}{8}$. Use your ratios to write three proportions.

11. Using division, complete the table by finding 5 ratios equivalent to $\frac{72}{126}$.

72	36	24	12	8	4
126	63	42	21	14	7

12. Complete the ratio table. Then write four proportions involving the ratios in the table.

6	12	18	24
11	22	33	44

13. Hulleah ran 100 m in 15 sec, 200 m in 30 sec, and 400 m in 70 sec. Use a scatterplot to decide whether these rates are proportional. **No**

14. Mr. Sanderson's class has 20 boys and 16 girls. Ms. Trevino's class has 15 boys and 12 girls. Are these ratios proportional? **Yes**

15. Decide whether the ratios form a proportion: $\frac{75}{120} \stackrel{?}{=} \frac{96}{144}$. **No**

16. Decide if the ratios are proportional and give a reason: $\frac{40}{56} \stackrel{?}{=} \frac{45}{63}$. **Yes; cross products are equal**

17. Solve the proportion: $\frac{16}{x} = \frac{12}{8}$. $x = 10\frac{2}{3}$

Performance Task

Draw rectangles of dimensions 3 by 5, 6 by 10, and 9 by 15. For each pair of rectangles, find the ratio of the short sides, the ratio of the long sides, and the ratio of the areas. What do you notice?

Performance Assessment Key

See key on page 271.

Resources

Assessment Sourcebook
Chapter 6 Tests
- Forms A and B (free response)
- Form C (multiple choice)
- Form D (performance assessment)
- Form E (mixed response)
- Form F (cumulative chapter test)

TestWorks
Test and Practice Software

Home and Community Connections
Letter Home for Chapter 6 in English and Spanish

Suggested Scoring Rubric

4
- Accurately draws and labels three rectangles.
- Correctly calculates the ratios.
- Notes the correct relationship between pairs of ratios.

3
- Draws three rectangles with labels.
- Calculates the ratios.
- Notes a relationship between pairs of ratios.

2
- Draws three rectangles.
- Attempts to calculate the ratios.
- Notes a relationship between some pairs of ratios.

1
- Attempts to sketch rectangles.
- Makes some attempt to calculate ratios.
- Fails to notice a relationship between pairs of ratios.

Cumulative Review Chapters 1–6

Test Prep

Multiple Choice

Choose the best answer.

1. Solve $5z + 8 = 43$. *[Lesson 2-7]* B

Ⓐ $z = 6$ Ⓑ $z = 7$

Ⓒ $z = 8$ Ⓓ $z = 9$

2. Express the number 3,800,000 in scientific notation. *[Lesson 3-5]* C

Ⓐ 38×10^5 Ⓑ 3.8×10^5

Ⓒ 3.8×10^6 Ⓓ 3.8×10^7

3. Find the quotient $6\frac{2}{3} \div 2\frac{1}{7}$. *[Lesson 4-5]* B

Ⓐ $2\frac{6}{7}$ Ⓑ $3\frac{1}{9}$ Ⓒ $7\frac{1}{3}$ Ⓓ $14\frac{2}{7}$

4. Which of the following is not correct? *[Lesson 5-1]* D

Ⓐ A 95° angle is obtuse.

Ⓑ A 90° angle is a right angle.

Ⓒ An 84° angle is acute.

Ⓓ A 91° angle is acute.

5. What is the sum of the angles in a quadrilateral? *[Lesson 5-3]* B

Ⓐ 180°

Ⓑ 360°

Ⓒ 540°

Ⓓ It depends on the quadrilateral.

6. Which rectangle has a perimeter of 18? *[Lesson 5-5]* A

Ⓐ 4 by 5 Ⓑ 7 by 11

Ⓒ 2 by 9 Ⓓ 4 by 18

7. Between which consecutive whole numbers does $\sqrt{183}$ lie? *[Lesson 5-6]* B

Ⓐ 12 and 13 Ⓑ 13 and 14

Ⓒ 14 and 15 Ⓓ 15 and 16

8. Which trapezoid has the smallest area? *[Lesson 5-9]* D

Ⓐ Bases 7 and 8, height 19

Ⓑ Bases 12 and 18, height 6

Ⓒ Bases 3 and 7, height 16

Ⓓ Bases 4 and 12, height 9

9. Which of the following does *not* represent a ratio of 12 to 8? *[Lesson 6-1]* C

Ⓐ 12:8 Ⓑ 3 to 2

Ⓒ $\frac{8}{12}$ Ⓓ $\frac{12}{8}$

10. Express as a unit rate: 64 gallons in 16 hours. *[Lesson 6-2]* A

Ⓐ $\frac{4 \text{ gallons}}{1 \text{ hour}}$ Ⓑ $\frac{64 \text{ gallons}}{16 \text{ hours}}$

Ⓒ $\frac{4 \text{ hours}}{1 \text{ gallon}}$ Ⓓ $\frac{8 \text{ gallons}}{1 \text{ hour}}$

11. Which rate is equivalent to 24 feet in 64 seconds? *[Lesson 6-6]* A

Ⓐ $\frac{6 \text{ ft}}{16 \text{ sec}}$ Ⓑ $\frac{12 \text{ ft}}{15 \text{ sec}}$

Ⓒ $\frac{30 \text{ ft}}{84 \text{ sec}}$ Ⓓ $\frac{40 \text{ ft}}{108 \text{ sec}}$

12. Frederic bought 3 pounds of onions for \$0.63. How many pounds of onions could he buy for \$2.94? *[Lesson 6-7]* B

Ⓐ 12 pounds Ⓑ 14 pounds

Ⓒ 15 pounds Ⓓ 16 pounds

13. Solve the proportion: $\frac{8}{3} = \frac{12}{p}$. *[Lesson 6-8]* B

Ⓐ $p = 4$ Ⓑ $p = 4.5$

Ⓒ $p = 5.5$ Ⓓ $p = 6.5$

Cumulative Review Test Prep

About Multiple-Choice Tests

The Cumulative Review found at the end of Chapters 2, 4, 6, 8, 10, and 12 can be used to prepare students for standardized tests.

Students sometimes do not perform as well on standardized tests as they do on other tests. There may be several reasons for this related to the format and content of the test.

- **Format**
Students may have limited experience with multiple-choice tests. For some questions, such tests are harder because having options may confuse the student.

- **Content**
A standardized test may cover a broader range of content than normally covered on a test, and the relative emphasis given to various strands may be different from that given in class. Also, some questions may assess general aptitude or thinking skills and not include specific pieces of mathematical content.

It is important not to let the differences between standardized tests and other tests shake your students' confidence.

STUDENT RESOURCES

CONTENTS

Chapter 1 Review

Answers

1. June
2. 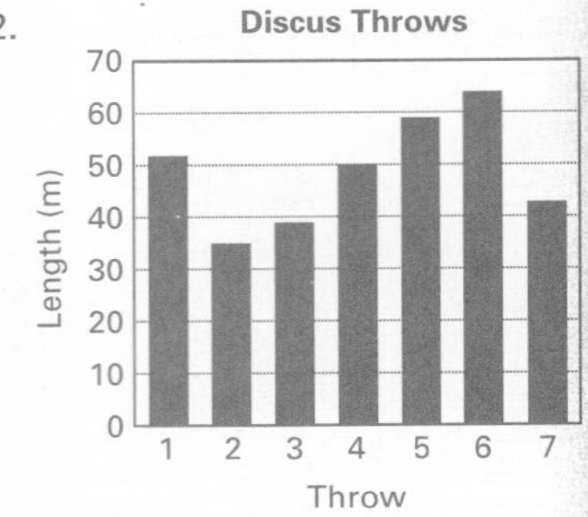

3. Mean: 14; Median: 15; Mode: 15
4.

Stem	Leaf
5	3 7 9
6	1 4 7 8
7	5 5 6

5. Possible answer:

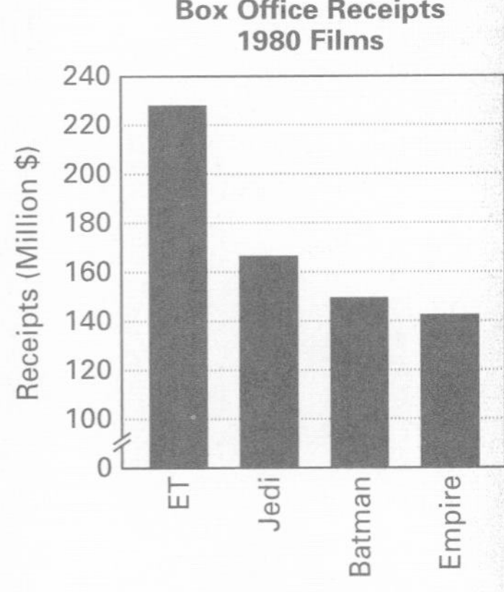

The graph exaggerates the differences between the movie receipts.

6. Median: 97; Modes: 90, 103; Outlier: 118
7. 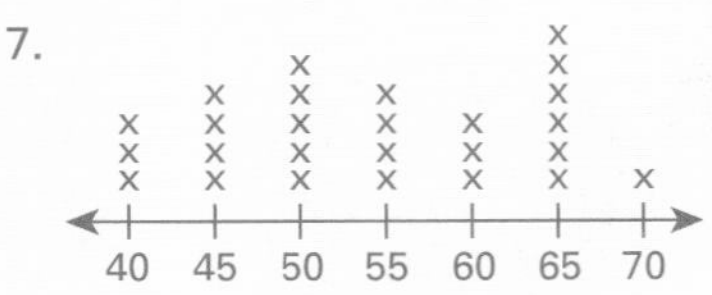
8. 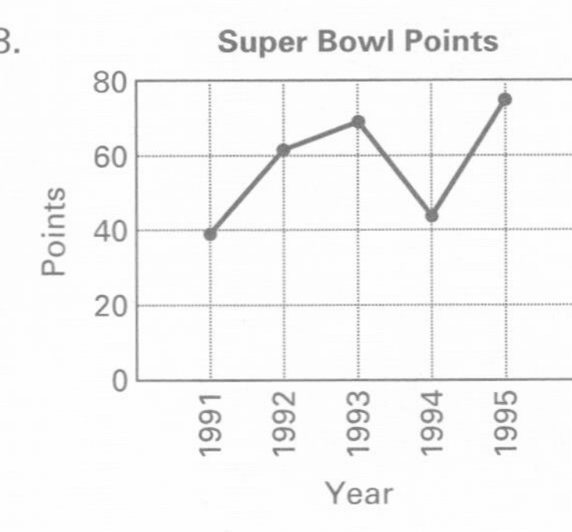

9. 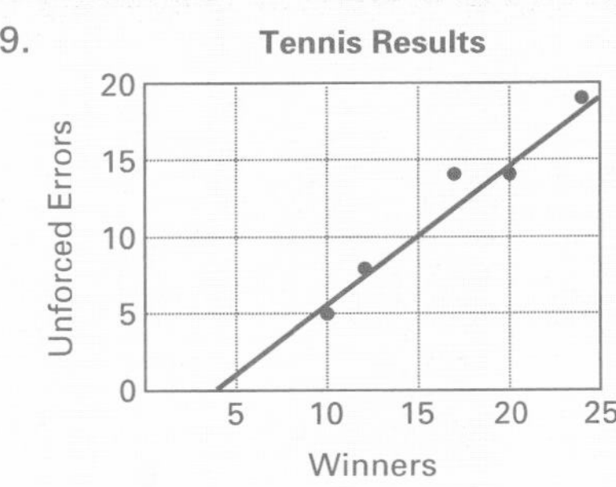

About 20 winners

Chapter Review

CHAPTER 1 REVIEW

Chapter 1 Review

1. Use estimation to identify the month with the largest difference between cost and revenue.

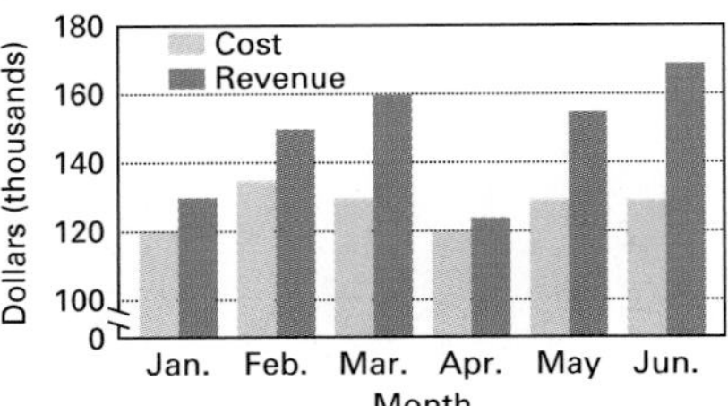

2. The lengths of seven discus throws, in meters, were 52, 34, 39, 50, 59, 64, 43. Make a bar graph of the data.
3. Find the mean, median, and mode(s) of the data values: 9, 19, 15, 4, 23, 14, 20, 15, 7
4. Make a stem-and-leaf diagram of the data: 57, 76, 75, 61, 53, 68, 75, 59, 64, 67
5. Make a bar graph with a broken vertical axis to display this data for the four most popular films of the 1980s. Explain why your graph could be misleading.

Box Office Receipts—1980s Films

Movie	Receipts ($ million)
E.T.—The Extra-Terrestrial	228
Return of the Jedi	168
Batman	151
The Empire Strikes Back	142

6. Find the median and mode(s) of the data values displayed in the stem-and-leaf diagram. Are there any outliers?

Stem	Leaf
8	4 5 5 6 9 9
9	0 0 0 1 4 5 7 7 9 9
10	1 1 2 3 3 3 5 6
11	8

7. Make a line plot to show the finishing times of swimmers in a race.

Seconds	40	45	50	55	60	65	70
Finishers	3	4	5	4	3	6	1

8. The table gives the total number of points scored in the Super Bowl for each year. Make a line graph to display the data.

Total Points Scored in Super Bowl

Year	1991	1992	1993	1994	1995
Points	39	61	69	43	75

9. Make a scatterplot of the data for the players on a tennis team. Draw a trend line and use it to predict the expected number of winners for a player with 15 unforced errors.

Winners	24	12	17	20	10
Unforced Errors	19	8	14	14	5

CHAPTER REVIEW

Chapter 2 Review

1. A long distance call costs \$1.50 plus \$0.80 for each minute. Let $C = 0.8m + 1.5$, where C is the cost and m is the number of minutes. How much would a 12-minute call cost?

Evaluate each expression.

2. $7 + 3 \times 5$
3. $48 - 36 \div (11 - 2)$
4. Tell which operation you would do first to evaluate $\frac{3 \times (9 - 5)}{6}$.
5. Find a formula relating the variables.

x	1	2	3	4	5	6	7
y	5	6	7	8	9	10	11

6. Which property is suggested by the formulas $A = lw$ and $A = wl$?
7. Use the formula $r = \frac{d}{t}$ to make a table of values showing the speed (r) needed to travel a distance (d) of 120 miles in 2, 3, 4, 5, and 6 hours (t).
8. Name the inverse action of walking 3 miles west.

Tell if the number in bold is a solution to the equation.

9. $x - 24 = 9$; **15**
10. $j \cdot 14 = 56$; **4**

Solve each equation. Check your answer.

11. $a - 31 = 47$
12. $53 = c + 17$
13. $18m = 396$
14. $\frac{n}{7} = 6$
15. $15k + 32 = 77$
16. $7 = \frac{n}{3} - 5$
17. A number is multiplied by 2, then 13 is added to the result. What operations are needed to return the original number?
18. Write an equation for this statement: The number of students decreased by 4 is 31.
19. Write an algebraic expression for the product of 8 and a number (n).
20. Lauren bought 6 chewing bones for each of her dogs. She bought 24 bones all together. Write and solve an equation to find the number of dogs (d) she has.

Write a phrase for each algebraic expression.

21. $a + 4$
22. $8n - 1$
23. $\frac{h}{3} - 2$
24. $\frac{5}{x + 9}$

CHAPTER 2 REVIEW

Chapter 2 Review

Answers

1. \$11.10
2. 22
3. 44
4. $9 - 5$
5. $y = x + 4$
6. The Commutative Property of Multiplication
7.

Time (hr)	2	3	4	5	6
Speed (mi/hr)	60	40	30	24	20

8. Walking 3 miles east
9. No
10. Yes
11. $a = 78$
12. $c = 36$
13. $m = 22$
14. $n = 42$
15. $k = 3$
16. $n = 36$
17. Subtract 13, then divide by 2
18. $s - 4 = 31$
19. $8n$
20. $6d = 24$; $d = 4$
21. Four more than a number a
22. One less than 8 times a number n
23. Two less than a number h divided by 3
24. Five divided by the sum of a number x and 9

CHAPTER REVIEW

Chapter 3 Review

Answers

1. The first 6 represents 60; The second represents $\frac{6}{10000}$.
2. 2.89 > 2.091
3. 4.928
4. 1800
5. 450
6. 220
7. 25
8. $x = 266.99$
9. $y = 13.4$
10. $n = 47.32$
11. $x = 33.4$
12. $x = 101$
13. $w = 480.703$
14. 4,597,000
15. 3.85×10^5
16. $2^2 \cdot 3 \cdot 5^2$
17. 24
18. 80
19. Possible answer: $\frac{8}{13}, \frac{16}{26}$
20. $\frac{8}{11}$
21. $\frac{5}{8}$
22. $\frac{1}{3}$
23. $\frac{2}{11}$
24. $\frac{1}{4}$
25. $\frac{9}{20}$
26. $\frac{8}{11} < \frac{16}{21}$
27. $\frac{15}{24} = \frac{35}{56}$
28. $\frac{18}{45} = \frac{24}{60}$
29. $\frac{31}{250}$
30. $\frac{17}{20}$
31. $\frac{1}{4}$
32. $\frac{5}{8}$
33. $\frac{8}{25}$
34. $\frac{1}{20}$
35. 0.777...; Repeats

CHAPTER REVIEW

Chapter 3 Review

CHAPTER 3 REVIEW

1. Give the value of each 6 in 4168.9206.

2. Use <, >, or = to compare: 2.89 ☐ 2.091

3. Round 4.9275 to the nearest thousandth.

Estimate.

4. $294.91 \cdot 5.81$

5. $141.83 + 308.11$

6. Find the sum: $129.56 + 85.403$

7. Find the quotient: $\frac{766.38}{31.8}$

Solve each equation.

8. $x + 64.1 = 331.09$

9. $129.98 = 9.7y$

10. $\frac{n}{5.2} = 9.1$

11. $x - 10.5 = 22.9$

12. $1.01x = 102.01$

13. $\frac{w}{35.74} = 13.45$

14. Write 4.597×10^6 in standard form.

15. Write 385,000 in scientific notation.

16. Use a factor tree to find the prime factorization of 300.

17. Find the GCF of 120 and 144.

18. Find the LCM of 16 and 20.

19. Give two fractions that are equivalent to $\frac{24}{39}$.

Rewrite each fraction in lowest terms.

20. $\frac{56}{77}$ **21.** $\frac{40}{64}$ **22.** $\frac{75}{225}$ **23.** $\frac{18}{99}$ **24.** $\frac{13}{52}$ **25.** $\frac{72}{160}$

Compare using <, >, or =.

26. $\frac{8}{11}$ ☐ $\frac{16}{21}$ **27.** $\frac{15}{24}$ ☐ $\frac{35}{56}$ **28.** $\frac{18}{45}$ ☐ $\frac{24}{60}$

Convert each decimal to a fraction in lowest terms.

29. 0.124 **30.** 0.85 **31.** 0.25 **32.** 0.625 **33.** 0.32 **34.** 0.05

35. Convert $\frac{14}{18}$ to a decimal. Tell if the decimal terminates or repeats.

Chapter 4 Review

Estimate each sum or difference.

1. $\frac{4}{5} + \frac{1}{10}$ **2.** $\frac{7}{15} - \frac{1}{4}$

3. Use compatible numbers to estimate the quotient $48\frac{1}{3} \div 5\frac{5}{8}$.

4. About how many $4\frac{3}{4}$-inch pieces can be cut from a string measuring $32\frac{7}{8}$ inches? Estimate to find your answer.

Find each sum or difference. Write answers in lowest terms.

5. $\frac{4}{15} + \frac{8}{15}$ **6.** $\frac{7}{8} - \frac{2}{3}$ **7.** $\frac{2}{5} + \frac{1}{4}$

8. $\frac{5}{6} - \frac{1}{3}$ **9.** $\frac{7}{18} + \frac{11}{24}$ **10.** $\frac{10}{50} - \frac{1}{10}$

11. Solve the equation: $x - \frac{1}{4} = \frac{2}{5}$

12. Write $4\frac{5}{6}$ as an improper fraction.

Find each sum or difference.

13. $6\frac{7}{9} - 4\frac{8}{9}$ **14.** $14\frac{3}{5} + 9\frac{2}{3}$ **15.** $9\frac{1}{6} - 8\frac{1}{3}$

16. $22\frac{3}{7} + 19\frac{8}{21}$ **17.** $9\frac{9}{99} - 8\frac{8}{88}$ **18.** $1\frac{17}{18} + 3\frac{2}{3}$

19. Find the area of a picture frame with dimensions $\frac{11}{12}$ ft by $\frac{3}{4}$ ft.

20. One package is $2\frac{1}{3}$ times as heavy as another. If the lighter package weighs 9 lb, how much does the heavier package weigh?

Find each product or quotient. Write answers in lowest terms.

21. $\frac{4}{5} \cdot \frac{7}{12}$ **22.** $6\frac{2}{5} \cdot 4\frac{7}{8}$ **23.** $\frac{5}{7} \div \frac{25}{4}$

24. $4\frac{5}{8} \div 1\frac{7}{12}$ **25.** $1\frac{2}{5} \cdot 3\frac{3}{4}$ **26.** $\frac{1}{4} \div \frac{16}{64}$

27. The area of one plot of land is $1\frac{1}{4}$ acres. How many plots with this area are contained in 20 acres of land?

28. A jar holds $\frac{7}{8}$ of a gallon. How many jars of this size are needed to hold 28 gallons?

Chapter 4 Review

Answers

1. ≈ 1
2. $\approx \frac{1}{4}$
3. About 8
4. About 6
5. $\frac{4}{5}$
6. $\frac{5}{24}$
7. $\frac{13}{20}$
8. $\frac{1}{2}$
9. $\frac{61}{72}$
10. $\frac{1}{10}$
11. $x = \frac{13}{20}$
12. $\frac{29}{6}$
13. $1\frac{8}{9}$
14. $24\frac{4}{15}$
15. $\frac{5}{6}$
16. $41\frac{17}{21}$
17. 1
18. $5\frac{11}{18}$
19. $\frac{11}{16}$ ft^2
20. 21 lb
21. $\frac{7}{15}$
22. $31\frac{1}{5}$
23. $\frac{4}{35}$
24. $2\frac{35}{38}$
25. $5\frac{1}{4}$
26. 1
27. 16 plots
28. 32 jars

Chapter 5 Review

Answers

1. Possible answer:

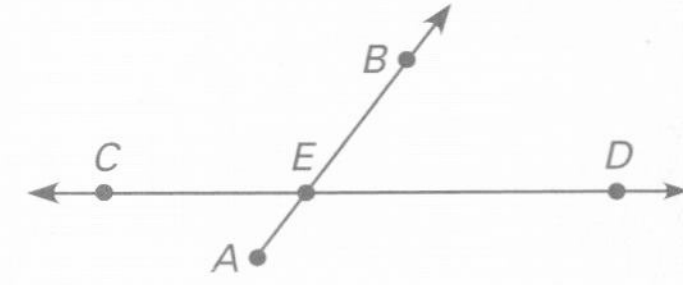

2. 1080°
3. a. 27°

   b. 117°
4. $\angle CFE \cong \angle BEF$ because they are alternate interior angles, $\angle CFE \cong \angle AGE$ because they are corresponding angles, $\angle CFE \cong \angle DFH$ because they are vertical angles.
5. Area: 1872 ft^2; Perimeter: 176 ft
6. Congruent; Congruent; Congruent
7. 64
8. 6.481
9. 5 m
10. 16 in^2
11. 115 cm^2
12. 1068 ft^2

CHAPTER REVIEW

Chapter 5 Review

CHAPTER 5 REVIEW

1. Draw a ray $\overrightarrow{AB}$ and a line $\overleftrightarrow{CD}$ intersecting to form $\angle BEC$.
2. What is the sum of the measures of the angles of an octagon?
3. If $\angle ABC$ measures 63°:
   a. What is the measure of an angle complementary to $\angle ABC$?
   b. What is the measure of an angle supplementary to $\angle ABC$?
4. Lines $\overleftrightarrow{AB}$ and $\overleftrightarrow{CD}$ are parallel. List the angles congruent to $\angle CFE$, and explain why they are congruent.

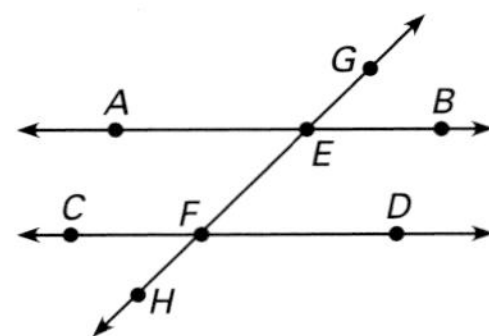

5. Find the area and perimeter of the base of a rectangular building 36 ft wide and 52 ft long.
6. Fill in the blanks: All sides of a square are _____. All sides of an equilateral triangle are _____. The sides of any other regular polygon are _____.
7. Find a perfect square between 60 and 70.
8. Find $\sqrt{42}$ to three decimal places.
9. Find the length of the shorter leg of a right triangle whose hypotenuse is 13 m long and whose longer leg is 12 m long.
10. Find the area of a triangle whose height is 6.4 in. and whose base is 5 in.
11. Find the area of the trapezoid.

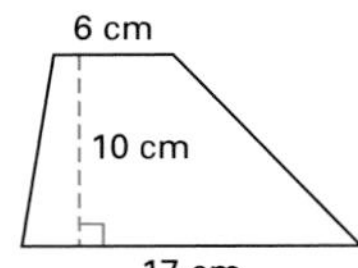

12. Find the area of the stage.

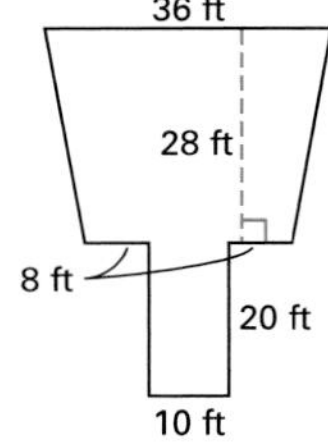

Chapter 6 Review

1. Estimate the ratio of the width to the length of the rectangle shown.

2. Find the rate: 144 feet in 6 seconds. Remember to include units in your rate.
3. Express the rate as a unit rate: $46.00 for 8 hours of work
4. Use unit rates to find the better gas mileage: 162 miles on 6 gallons of gas or 203 miles on 7 gallons
5. Corner Market sells 3 pounds of apples for $6.45. At this rate, how much will 5 pounds of apples cost?
6. Multiply and divide to find two ratios equivalent to $\frac{14}{24}$.
7. Use a table to find two rates equivalent to 45 jumping jacks in 2 minutes.
8. Using multiplication, complete the table to find five ratios equivalent to $\frac{2}{5}$.

2	4	6	8	10	12
5					

9. Using division, complete the table to find five ratios equivalent to $\frac{288}{216}$.

288	144	48	16	8	4
216					

10. Complete the ratio table. Then write four proportions involving the ratios.

5	10	15	20
6			

11. Sam baked one apple pie using 4 apples and 3 tablespoons of sugar, and a larger pie using 6 apples and 5 tablespoons of sugar. Are these ratios proportional?
12. Decide whether these ratios form a proportion: $\frac{84}{124} \stackrel{?}{=} \frac{42}{60}$
13. Decide if these ratios are proportional and give a reason: $\frac{5}{8} \stackrel{?}{=} \frac{17}{24}$
14. Find the unit rate: 54 pages in 9 minutes
15. Kamilah's mother drove 138 miles on 6 gallons of gas. Find the gas mileage for her car.
16. Solve the proportion: $\frac{16}{20} = \frac{n}{35}$

Chapter 6 Review

Answers

1. 2:1
2. $\frac{24 \text{ ft}}{1 \text{ sec}}$
3. $\frac{\$5.75}{1 \text{ hr}}$
4. 203 miles on 7 gallons
5. $10.75
6. Possible answer: $\frac{28}{48}, \frac{7}{12}$
7. Possible answer:

min	2	4	6
jumps	45	90	135

8.

2	4	6	8	10	12
5	10	15	20	25	30

$\frac{4}{10}, \frac{6}{15}, \frac{8}{20}, \frac{10}{25}, \frac{12}{30}$

9.

288	144	48	16	8	4
216	108	36	12	6	3

$\frac{144}{108}, \frac{48}{36}, \frac{16}{12}, \frac{8}{6}, \frac{4}{3}$

10.

5	10	15	20
6	12	18	24

Possible answer: $\frac{5}{6} = \frac{10}{12}$, $\frac{10}{12} = \frac{15}{18}$, $\frac{10}{12} = \frac{20}{24}$, $\frac{20}{24} = \frac{5}{6}$

11. No
12. No
13. No. Possible reason: because $\frac{5}{8} = \frac{15}{24}$
14. 6 pages per minute
15. 23 miles per gallon
16. $n = 28$

Chapter 7 Review

Answers

1. Possible answer: 1 cm:4 m; 15 cm:60 m
2. 3 cm:14 km
3. 21 ft
4. $x = 21$ mi
5. At or before 8:18 A.M.
6. 5:00 P.M.
7. Possible answer: 1 in.:1 ft
8. 1:14
9. Possible answer: Centimeters per month
10. \$0.25 per 1 gal
11. 7 ft per sec
12. $29\frac{1}{3}$ ft per sec
13. No; $\frac{10}{6} = \frac{20}{12} \neq \frac{26}{12}$
14. Perimeter: 45 cm; Area: 180 cm^2
15. Perimeter ratio: 6:1; Scale factor: 6
16. 15 cm

CHAPTER REVIEW

CHAPTER 7 REVIEW

Chapter 7 Review

1. Write 5 cm:20 m in two other ways.

2. Find the scale of a map if a 42 km wide lake is 9 cm wide on the map.

3. A scale model of a truck is 3.5 in. long. Find the length of the actual truck if the scale is 1 in.:6 ft.

4. Solve the proportion: $\frac{8 \text{ in.}}{6 \text{ mi}} = \frac{28 \text{ in.}}{x}$

5. Paul needs to be at school at 8:30 A.M. If the school is 6 miles away from his home and the bus travels at 30 mi/hr, when does the bus need to leave his home?

6. Anne begins running at 4:15 P.M. and runs at a rate of 8 km/hr. If she runs 6 km, what time does she finish?

7. A model of an 82 ft long train has to fit in a display case that is 10 in. long. Suggest an appropriate scale for the model.

8. A photograph is 4 in. by 6 in. What is the largest scale that can be used to make an enlargement to fit in a 60 in. by 85 in. frame?

9. Suggest appropriate units for the rate at which your hair grows.

10. Give a reciprocal unit rate that has the same meaning as 4 gal for \$1.

11. Convert 84 inches per second to feet per second.

12. Ting bicycles at a speed of 20 miles per hour. Convert this rate to feet per second.

13. Tell whether the triangles at right are similar. If they are, write a similarity statement using ~ and give the scale factor. If they are not, explain why not.

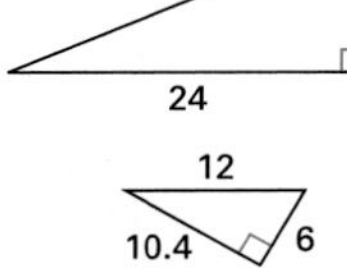

14. Two trapezoids are similar, with scale factor 3:1. The smaller trapezoid has perimeter 15 cm and area 20 cm^2. Find the perimeter and area of the larger trapezoid.

15. Two similar pentagons have an area ratio of 36:1. Find the ratio of their perimeters and the scale factor.

16. Rectangle *ABCD* has an area of 44 cm^2 and a perimeter of 30 cm. Rectangle *EFGH* is similar to *ABCD*. If the area of *EFGH* is 11 cm^2, what is its perimeter?

Chapter 8 Review

1. Rewrite $\frac{19}{25}$ as a percent. **2.** Rewrite 56% as a fraction. **3.** Rewrite 31% as a decimal.

Rewrite each decimal as a fraction and a percent.

4. 0.24 **5.** 1.5 **6.** 0.002 **7.** 0.75

Rewrite each percent as a fraction and a decimal.

8. 0.2% **9.** 96% **10.** 120% **11.** 36%

Find each of the following mentally.

12. 10% of 340 **13.** 50% of 410 **14.** 1% of $50

15. 80% of 35 is what number? **16.** What percent of 72 is 40?

17. 12% of what number is 60? **18.** 220% of 145 is what number?

19. A compact disc player is on sale for $119. This is 85% of the regular price. Find the regular price.

20. In one town, 20% of the 165 restaurants sell pizza. How many restaurants sell pizza?

21. Of the 700 students at Central School, 112 went on a field trip. What percent of the students went on the field trip?

22. A $15 book is on sale at a 30% discount. What is the sale price of the book?

23. Nate bought a $42 sweater on sale for $36.96. What percent is this of the regular price? What percent discount did he get?

24. Over a holiday weekend, the number of cats at a kennel increased from 35 to 48. What was the percent increase?

25. After Janine received a salary increase of 6%, her salary was $44,520. What was her salary before the raise?

26. Maria was given 120 raffle tickets to sell. She sold 29 of them in one week. What percent decrease in the tickets was this?

27. The number of birds on a nature reserve increased from 2980 to 3610. What was the percent increase?

28. There were 650 students at an all-day concert. By the time the last band played, 480 students were left. Find the percent decrease in the number of students.

Chapter 8 Review

Answers

1. 76%
2. $\frac{14}{25}$
3. 0.31
4. $\frac{6}{25}$, 24%
5. $\frac{3}{2}$, 150%
6. $\frac{1}{500}$, 0.2%
7. $\frac{3}{4}$, 75%
8. $\frac{1}{500}$, 0.002
9. $\frac{24}{25}$, 0.96
10. $\frac{6}{5}$, 1.2
11. $\frac{9}{25}$, 0.36
12. 34
13. 205
14. $0.50
15. 28
16. About 55.6%
17. 500
18. 319
19. $140
20. 33 restaurants
21. 16%
22. $10.50
23. 88%; 12%
24. About 37.1%
25. $42,000
26. About 24.2%
27. About 21.1%
28. About 26.2%

Answers

1. No
2. −2000 ft
3. 19
4. 53
5. $-47 < -35$
6. −13, −6, −2, 7, 24
7. Sometimes
8.

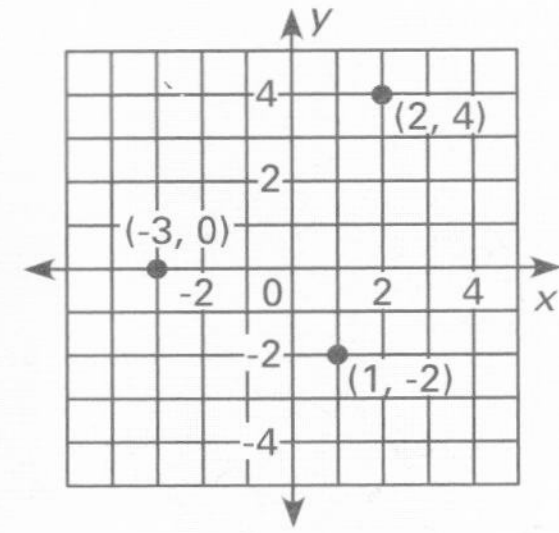

9. Quadrant III
10. Possible answer:

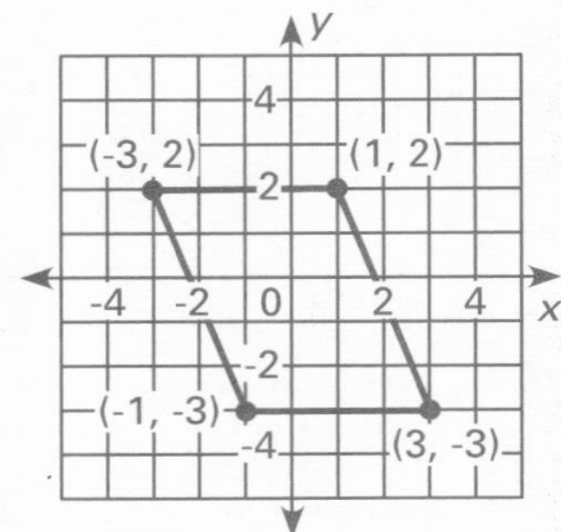

11. 4+ −7 = −3
12. 13
13. 13
14. −16
15. 28
16. −1
17. −7
18. 3
19. −74
20. 0
21. 167°F
22. 40
23. −36
24. −180
25. −504
26. −7
27. 9
28. 6
29. −13
30. −$500

Chapter 9 Review

1. Tell whether −4.5 is an integer.

2. Use a sign to write this number: 2000 feet below sea level

3. Write the opposite of −19.

4. Find the absolute value: $|-53|$

5. Use $>$, $<$, or $=$ to compare: −47 ☐ −35

6. Order this set of numbers from least to greatest: 24, −6, 7, −13, −2

7. Fill in the blank with *sometimes, always,* or *never:* An integer is ____ equal to its absolute value.

8. Plot each point on the same coordinate plane.

a. (2, 4) **b.** (1, −2) **c.** (−3, 0)

9. Name the quadrant or axis that contains the point (−4, −7).

10. Draw a parallelogram so that each of its vertices is in a different quadrant. Label the coordinates of each point.

11. Write the addition problem and the sum modeled in the picture.

12. Write the next integer in the pattern: −14, −5, 4, ____.

Find each sum or difference.

13. 24 + (−11)	**14.** −9 + (−7)	**15.** −63 + 91	**16.** 37 + (−38)
17. 8 − 15	**18.** −4 − (−7)	**19.** −29 − 45	**20.** −18 − (−57) − 39

21. The highest average temperature in the world is 95°F, in Dalol Danakil Depression, Ethiopia. The lowest average temperature is −72°F, in Plateau Station, Antarctica. Subtract to find the range of average temperatures.

Find each product or quotient.

22. −8 • (−5)	**23.** −12 • 3	**24.** 15 • (−4) • 3	**25.** −7 • (−9) • (−8)
26. 84 ÷ (−12)	**27.** −54 ÷ (−6)	**28.** −90 ÷ 3 ÷ (−5)	**29.** −39 ÷ 3

30. The profits from Rocia's business for the first five months of 1996 were $3500, −$2200, −$2900, $800, and −$1700. What was the average monthly profit?

Chapter 10 Review

1. Tell a story that fits the graph at right.

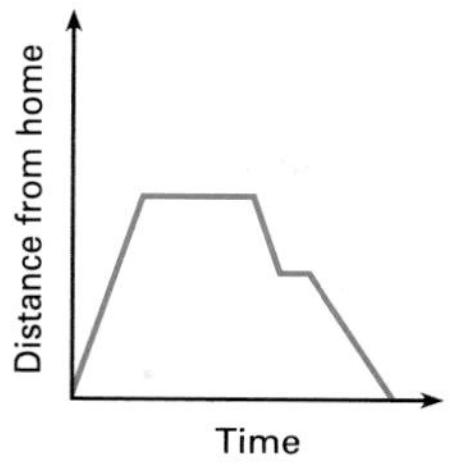

Distance from home

Time

2. Define a variable and give a reasonable range of values for the height of a car.

3. Name a quantity that the volume of a cone might depend on.

4. Write a rule for the sequence 5, 10, 15, 20, ..., and give the 100th term of the sequence.

5. For the table below, write an equation to show the relationship between x and y. Use the equation to find y when $x = 7$.

x	1	2	3	4
y	3	4	5	6

6. Make a table of six pairs of values for the equation $y = 3x - 7$.

Graph each equation on a coordinate plane.

7. $y = x + 2$ **8.** $y = x^2 + 1$

9. The table below was created from the equation $y = -4x + 2$. Use it to solve each related equation.

x	0	1	2	3	4
y	2	−2	−6	−10	−14

a. $-2 = -4x + 2$ **b.** $-14 = -4x + 2$

10. Use a graph to solve $-11 = 2x - 5$.

11. Write the equation modeled in the equation box. Solve the equation. Sketch your steps.

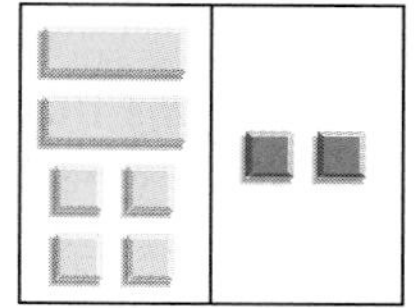

12. Write and graph an inequality to show that at least 150 students attended a play.

Solve each equation. Check your solution.

13. $p - 14 = -6$ **14.** $a + 11 = 36$ **15.** $\frac{d}{-6} = -72$

16. $-9r = 63$ **17.** $3x + 4 = 1$ **18.** $\frac{c}{3} - 2 = 5$

19. A cab ride costs $3 plus $2 per mile. Alonzo paid $17 for a cab ride. How many miles did he travel?

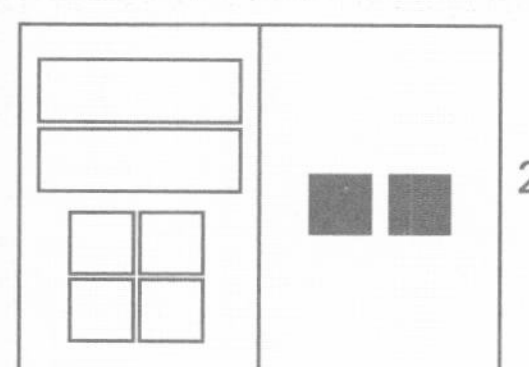

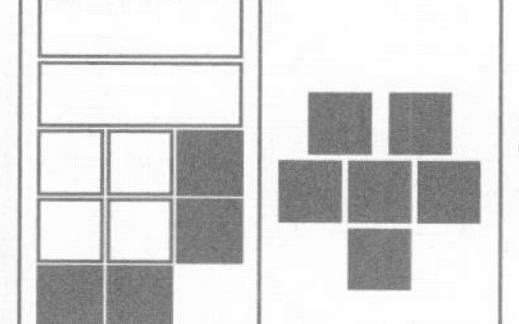

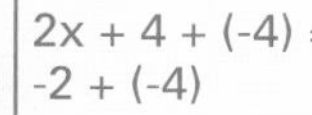

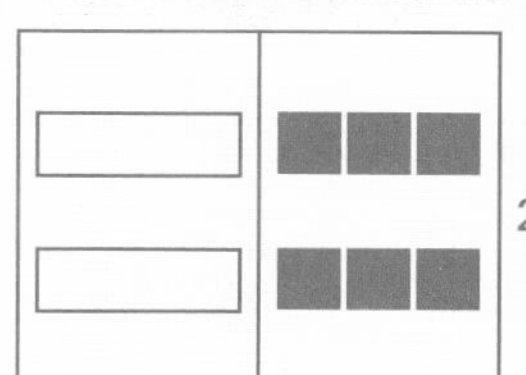

2x = -6

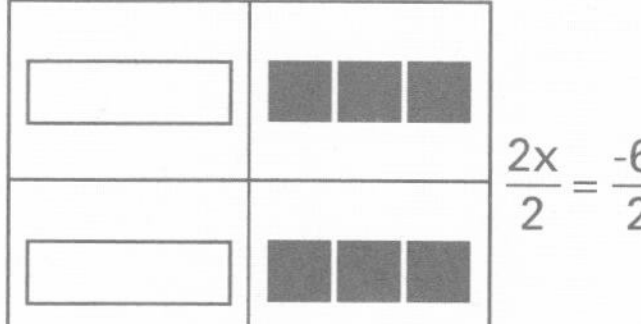

$\frac{2x}{2} = \frac{-6}{2}$

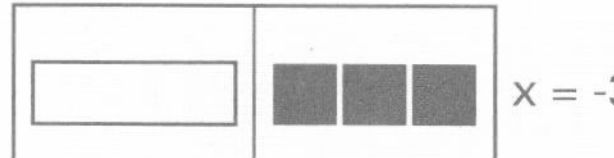

x = -3

CHAPTER 10 REVIEW

Chapter 10 Review

Answers

1. Possible answer: A boy walked to a friend's house, stayed there a while, then went home, stopping to get a drink of water at a park.
2. Possible answer: h = height; Range = 4 to 6 ft
3. Possible answers: Height, area of base, radius of base
4. $5n$; 500
5. $y = x + 2$; 9
6. Possible answer:

x	0	1	2	3	4	5
y	-7	-4	-1	2	5	8

7\.

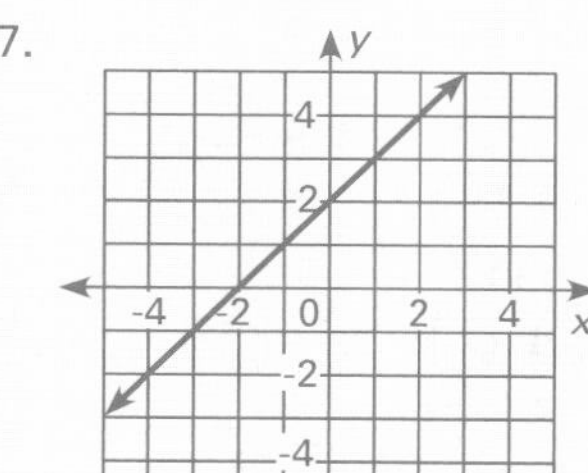

8\.

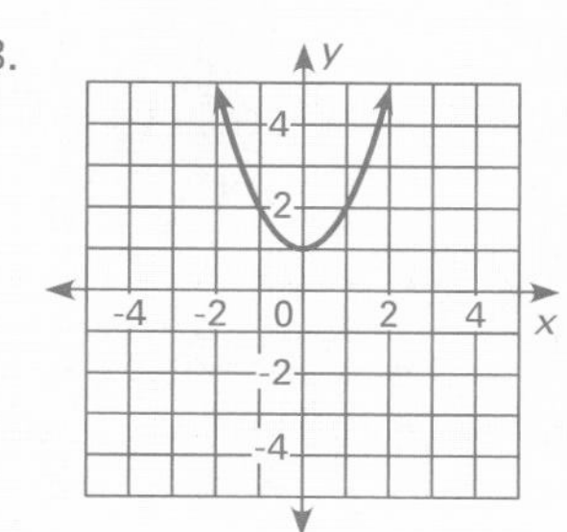

9\. a. $x = 1$

b. $x = 4$

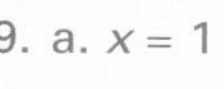

10\.

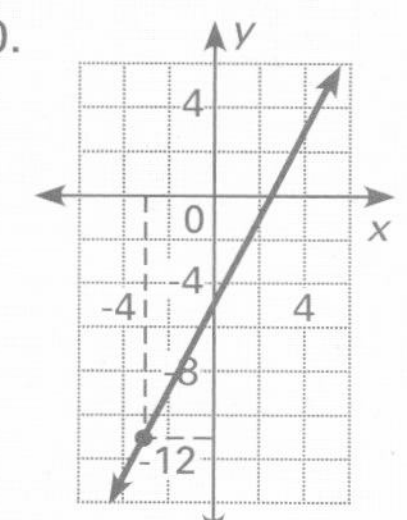

When $y = -11$, $x = -3$

11\. $2x + 4 = -2$
Steps shown at the left.

12\. $s \geq 150$

13\. $p = 8$
14\. $a = 25$
15\. $d = 432$
16\. $r = -7$
17\. $x = -1$
18\. $c = 21$
19\. 7 mi

CHAPTER REVIEW

Chapter 11 Review

Answers

1.

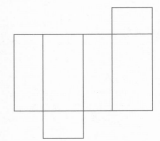

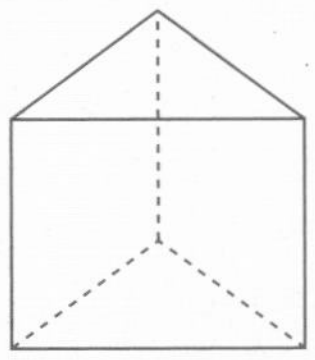

9 edges, 5 faces, 6 vertices

2. 7

3. a. Possible answer:

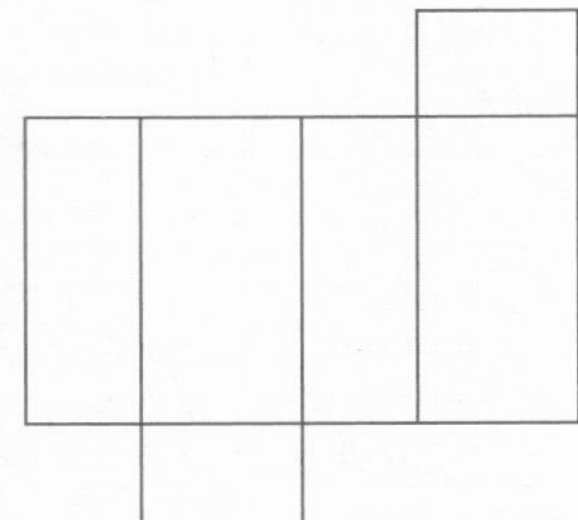

b. 82 in^2
c. 42 in^3

4.

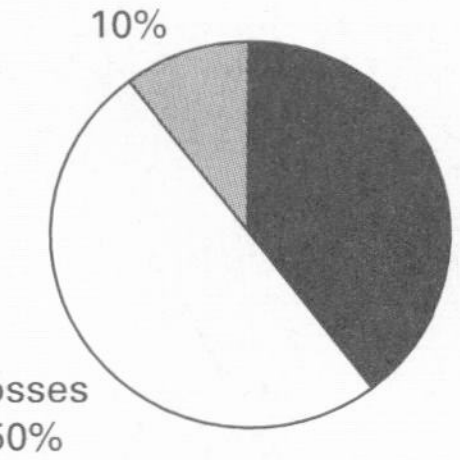

Ties 10%
Wins 40%
Losses 50%

5. Circumference: 39.38 cm; Area: 123.44 cm^2

6. Surface area: 6041.4 ft^2; Volume: 23,349.0 ft^3

7.

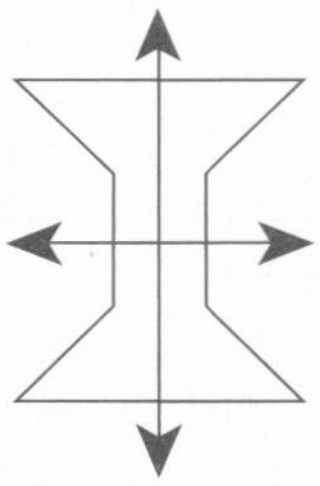

Yes, it has rotational symmetry.

8. $A'(-1, -2)$

9. a–b.

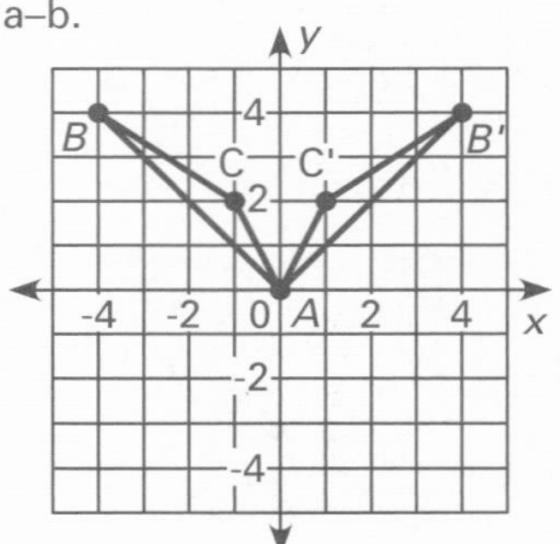

Reflection vertices:
$A'(0, 0)$, $B'(4, 4)$, $C'(1, 2)$

c. Rotation vertices:
$A'(0, 0)$, $B'(4, 4)$, $C'(2, 1)$.

CHAPTER REVIEW

Chapter 11 Review

CHAPTER 11 REVIEW

1. Sketch a triangular prism. How many edges, faces, and vertices does it have?

2. Find the number of cubes in the figure at right. Assume all cubes are visible.

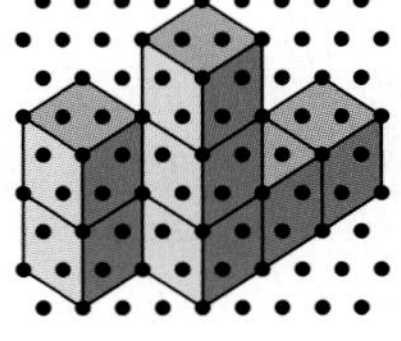

3. A rectangular prism is shown below.

a. Sketch a net for this prism.

b. Find its surface area.

c. Find its volume.

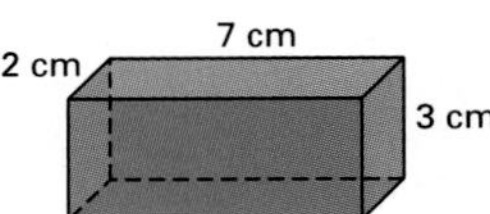

4. The data shows the season summary for Phil's baseball team. Make a circle graph. Label each sector.

Wins	Losses	Ties
40%	50%	10%

5. Find the circumference and area of a circle whose diameter is 12.54 cm. Use 3.14 for π. Round to the nearest hundredth.

6. Find the surface area and the volume of the cylinder shown. Use 3.14 for π. Round to the nearest tenth.

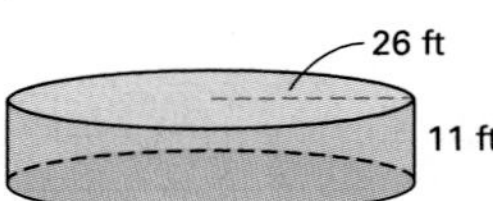

7. Copy the figure. Draw all lines of symmetry. Then tell whether or not it has rotational symmetry.

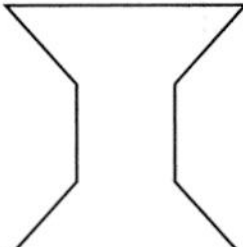

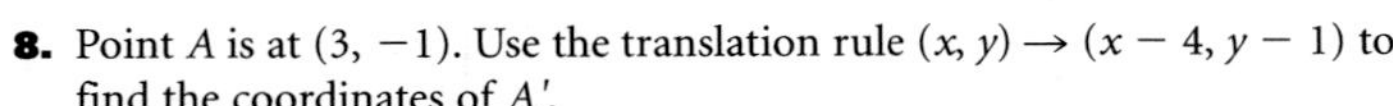

8. Point A is at $(3, -1)$. Use the translation rule $(x, y) \rightarrow (x - 4, y - 1)$ to find the coordinates of A'.

9. The coordinates of a triangle are $A(0, 0)$, $B(-4, 4)$, and $C(-1, 2)$.

a. Draw the figure on the coordinate plane.

b. Draw the reflection of ABC across the y-axis. Give the coordinates of the reflection's vertices.

c. Give the coordinates of a rotation of ABC for a 90° clockwise rotation around the origin.

Chapter 12 Review

1. Mama's Pizza Parlor offers 3 types of crust, 2 choices of cheese, and 6 choices of toppings. Use the Counting Principle to find the number of different pizzas consisting of one type of crust, cheese, and topping.
2. A bookstore has separate sections for hardcover and paperback books in each of these categories: fiction, mystery, nonfiction, science fiction, and poetry. Make a tree diagram to show the possible outcomes. How many sections does the bookstore need?
3. A contest awards four prizes. Sandra, Miguel, Tasha, and Jimmy are the four finalists. In how many ways can first, second, third, and fourth place be assigned?
4. List all of the possible orderings of the numbers 1, 2, and 3, without repeating digits.
5. Elena has 10 CDs she wants to take on a trip, but she can't fit all of them into her luggage. How many different ways can she choose 4 of the CDs to take?
6. A bag contains 4 red, 6 blue, and 3 yellow marbles. A marble is chosen at random. Find the odds that the marble is:
   a. Blue
   b. Yellow
7. A spinner has 6 equal sections, labeled A, B, C, D, E, and F. Pramit wins if a vowel is spun and Molly wins if a consonant is spun. Give each player's odds of winning. Then determine whether the game is fair.
8. A number cube is rolled. Find the probability of each event.
   a. Rolling a number greater than 4
   b. Rolling a number that is *not* greater than 4
9. Find the probability of rolling a sum of 9 when rolling two number cubes. Express your answer as a percent.
10. Mike flipped a coin 20 times and got heads 7 times. Find each of the following:
    a. Theoretical probability of getting heads
    b. Experimental probability of getting heads
11. A dart hits the dart board shown. What is the probability that it lands in the shaded region?

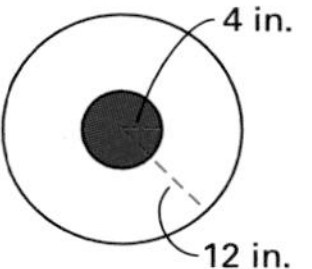

12. A number cube is rolled twice. What is the probability of getting a number less than 3 on the first roll, then a 6 on the second?
13. Roberto draws two coins from his pocket, which contains 4 quarters and 5 nickels. What is the probability that both coins are quarters?

CHAPTER 12 REVIEW

Chapter 12 Review

Answers

1. 36 different pizzas
2. 10 sections
3. 24 ways
4. 1, 2, 3; 1, 3, 2; 2, 3, 1; 2, 1, 3; 3, 1, 2; 3, 2, 1
5. 5040 ways
6. a. 6:7
   b. 3:10
7. Pramit: 1:3; Molly: 2:3; Not fair
8. a. $\frac{1}{3}$
   b. $\frac{2}{3}$
9. About 11.1%
10. a. 50%
    b. 35%
11. $\frac{1}{9}$
12. $\frac{1}{18}$
13. $\frac{1}{6}$

CHAPTER REVIEW

Geometric Formulas

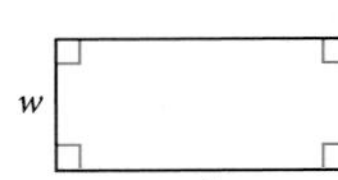 **Rectangle** Area: $A = lw$ Perimeter: $p = 2l + 2w$	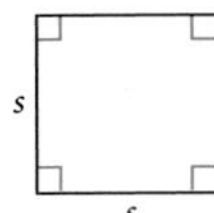 **Square** Area: $A = s^2$ Perimeter: $p = 4s$	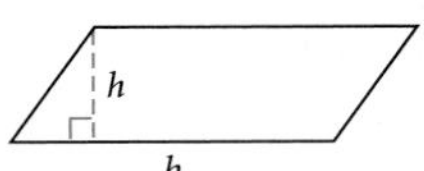 **Parallelogram** Area: $A = bh$
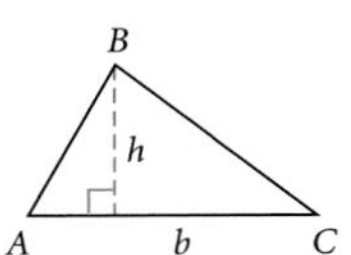 **Triangle** Area: $A = \frac{1}{2}bh$ $m\angle A + m\angle B + m\angle C = 180°$	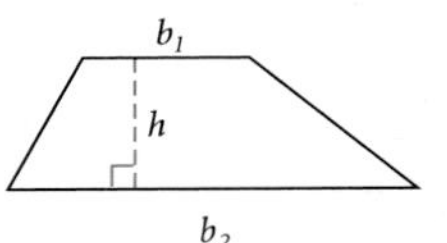 **Trapezoid** Area: $A = \frac{1}{2}h(b_1 + b_2)$	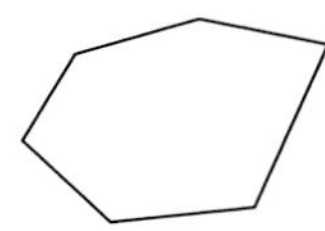 **Polygon** Sum of angle measures for n-sided polygon: $S = (n - 2)180°$ Perimeter: sum of measures of all sides
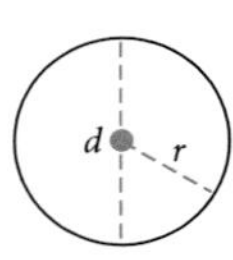 **Circle** Area: $A = \pi r^2$ Circumference: $C = \pi d = 2\pi r$	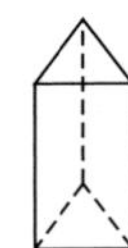 **Prism** Volume: $V = Bh$ Surface Area: $SA = ph + 2B$	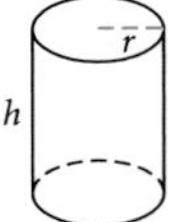 **Cylinder** Volume: $V = \pi r^2 h$ Surface Area: $SA = 2\pi rh + 2\pi r^2$

Measurement Conversion Factors

Metric Measures of Length
1000 meters (m) = 1 kilometer (km)
100 centimeters (cm) = 1 m
10 decimeters (dm) = 1 m
1000 millimeters (mm) = 1 m
10 cm = 1 decimeter (dm)
10 mm = 1 cm

Customary Measures of Length
12 inches (in.) = 1 foot (ft)
3 ft = 1 yard (yd)
36 in. = 1 yd
5280 ft = 1 mile (mi)
1760 yd = 1 mi
6076 ft = 1 nautical mile

Area
100 square millimeters (mm^2) = 1 square centimeter (cm^2)
10,000 cm^2 = 1 square meter (m^2)
10,000 m^2 = 1 hectare (ha)

Area
144 square inches (in^2) = 1 square foot (ft^2)
9 ft^2 = 1 square yard (yd^2)
43,560 sq ft^2 = 1 acre (A)

Volume
1000 cubic millimeters (mm^3) = 1 cubic centimeter (cm^3)
1000 cm^3 = 1 cubic decimeter (dm^3)
1,000,000 cm^3 = 1 cubic meter (m^3)

Volume
1728 cubic inches (cu in.) = 1 cubic foot (cu ft)
27 cu ft = 1 cubic yard (cu yard)

Capacity
1000 milliliters (mL) = 1 liter (L)
1000 L = 1 kiloliter (kL)

Capacity
8 fluid ounces (fl oz) = 1 cup (c)
2 c = 1 pint (pt)
2 pt = 1 quart (qt)
4 qt = 1 gallon (gal)

Mass
1000 kilograms (kg) = 1 metric ton (t)
1000 grams (g) = 1 kg
1000 milligrams (mg) = 1 g

Weight
16 ounces (oz) = 1 pound (lb)
2000 lb = 1 ton (T)

Temperatures in Degrees Celsius (°C)
0°C = freezing point of water
37°C = normal body temperature
100°C = boiling point of water

Temperatures in Degrees Fahrenheit (°F)
32°F = freezing point of water
98.6°F = normal body temperature
212°F = boiling point of water

Time
60 seconds (sec) = 1 minute (min)
60 min = 1 hour (hr)
24 hr = 1 day

TABLES

TABLES

Symbols

$+$	plus or positive
$-$	minus or negative
$\cdot$	times
$\times$	times
$\div$	divided by
$\pm$	positive or negative
$=$	is equal to
$\neq$	is not equal to
$<$	is less than
$>$	is greater than
$\leq$	is less than or equal to
$\geq$	is greater than or equal to
$\approx$	is approximately equal to
%	percent
$a:b$	the ratio of a to b, or $\frac{a}{b}$
$\cong$	is congruent to
$\sim$	is similar to
$^\circ$	degree(s)
$\overleftrightarrow{AB}$	line containing points A and B
$\overline{AB}$	line segment with endpoints A and B
$\overrightarrow{AB}$	ray with endpoint A and containing B
∟	right angle
$\perp$	is perpendicular to
$\parallel$	is parallel to
AB	length of $\overline{AB}$; distance between A and B
$\triangle ABC$	triangle with vertices A, B, and C
$\angle ABC$	angle with sides $\overrightarrow{BA}$ and $\overrightarrow{BC}$
$\angle B$	angle with vertex B
$m\angle ABC$	measure of angle ABC
$'$	prime
a^n	the nth power of a
$\lvert x \rvert$	absolute value of x
$\sqrt{x}$	principal square root of x
π	pi (approximately 3.1416)
(a, b)	ordered pair with x-coordinate a and y-coordinate b
$P(A)$	the probability of event A
$n!$	n factorial

TABLES

TABLES

Squares and Square Roots

N	N^2	$\sqrt{N}$	N	N^2	$\sqrt{N}$
1	1	1	51	2,601	7.141
2	4	1.414	52	2,704	7.211
3	9	1.732	53	2,809	7.280
4	16	2	54	2,916	7.348
5	25	2.236	55	3,025	7.416
6	36	2.449	56	3,136	7.483
7	49	2.646	57	3,249	7.550
8	64	2.828	58	3,364	7.616
9	81	3	59	3,481	7.681
10	100	3.162	60	3,600	7.746
11	121	3.317	61	3,721	7.810
12	144	3.464	62	3,844	7.874
13	169	3.606	63	3,969	7.937
14	196	3.742	64	4,096	8
15	225	3.873	65	4,225	8.062
16	256	4	66	4,356	8.124
17	289	4.123	67	4,489	8.185
18	324	4.243	68	4,624	8.246
19	361	4.359	69	4,761	8.307
20	400	4.472	70	4,900	8.367
21	441	4.583	71	5,041	8.426
22	484	4.690	72	5,184	8.485
23	529	4.796	73	5,329	8.544
24	576	4.899	74	5,476	8.602
25	625	5	75	5,625	8.660
26	676	5.099	76	5,776	8.718
27	729	5.196	77	5,929	8.775
28	784	5.292	78	6,084	8.832
29	841	5.385	79	6,241	8.888
30	900	5.477	80	6,400	8.944
31	961	5.568	81	6,561	9
32	1,024	5.657	82	6,724	9.055
33	1,089	5.745	83	6,889	9.110
34	1,156	5.831	84	7,056	9.165
35	1,225	5.916	85	7,225	9.220
36	1,296	6	86	7,396	9.274
37	1,369	6.083	87	7,569	9.327
38	1,444	6.164	88	7,744	9.381
39	1,521	6.245	89	7,921	9.434
40	1,600	6.325	90	8,100	9.487
41	1,681	6.403	91	8,281	9.539
42	1,764	6.481	92	8,464	9.592
43	1,849	6.557	93	8,649	9.644
44	1,936	6.633	94	8,836	9.695
45	2,025	6.708	95	9,025	9.747
46	2,116	6.782	96	9,216	9.798
47	2,209	6.856	97	9,409	9.849
48	2,304	6.928	98	9,604	9.899
49	2,401	7	99	9,801	9.950
50	2,500	7.071	100	10,000	10

TABLES

687

Glossary

absolute value A number's distance from zero, shown by | |. Example: |–7| = 7 [p. 434]

acute angle An angle that measures less than 90°. [p. 213]

acute triangle A triangle with three acute angles. [p. 223]

addend A number added to one or more others.

additive inverse A number's opposite. Example: The additive inverse of 2 is –2. [p. 451]

algebraic expression An expression containing a variable. Example: $2(x - 9)$ [p. 78]

alternate interior angles A pair of angles formed by two lines and a transversal. In the figure below, ∠1 and ∠3 are a pair of alternate interior angles, and ∠2 and ∠4 are a pair of alternate interior angles. [p. 218]

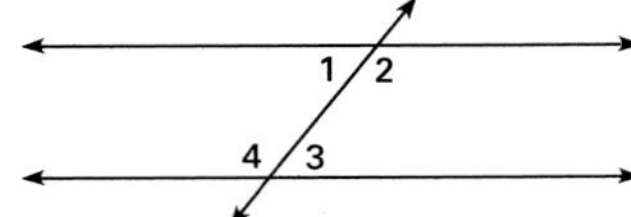

angle Two rays with a common endpoint. [p. 213]

angle bisector A ray bisecting an angle. [p. 214]

area The number of square units needed to cover a figure. [p. 233]

arithmetic sequence A sequence where the difference between consecutive terms is always the same. Example: 3, 6, 9, ... [p. 492]

Associative Property of Addition The fact that grouping does not affect the sum of three or more numbers. $a + (b + c) = (a + b) + c$ [p. 62]

Associative Property of Multiplication The fact that grouping does not affect the product of three or more numbers. $a(bc) = (ab)c$ [p. 62]

average See *mean*.

axes See *x-axis* and *y-axis*.

bar graph A graph that uses bars to display data. [p. 7]

base (in numeration) A number multiplied by itself the number of times shown by an exponent. Example: $5^2 = 5 \cdot 5$, where 5 is the base and 2 is the exponent. [p. 125]

base (of a polygon) Any side of the polygon, or the length of that side. [pp. 233, 249]

base (of a solid) See examples below. [pp. 555, 587]

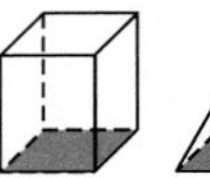
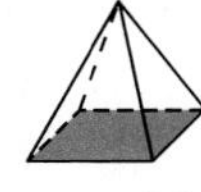

binary number system A base-two place value system. [p. 159]

bisect To divide an angle or segment into two congruent angles or segments. [pp. 214, 218]

box-and-whisker plot A graph showing how a collection of data is distributed. [p. 26]

capacity The volume of a figure, given in terms of liquid measure. [p. 594]

center The point at the exact middle of a circle or sphere. [pp. 574, 587]

central angle An angle whose vertex is at the center of a circle. [p. 574]

circle A plane figure whose points are all the same distance from its center. [p. 574]

circle graph A circular graph that uses wedges to represent portions of the data set. [p. 7]

circumference The perimeter of a circle. [p. 578]

circumscribed figure A figure containing another. A polygon is circumscribed around a circle if the circle touches each of its sides. [p. 617]

combination A selection of items where the order does not matter. [p. 636]

common denominator A denominator that is the same in two or more fractions. [p. 150]

common factor If a number is a factor of two or more numbers, it is a common factor of that set of numbers. [p. 139]

common multiple A number that is a multiple of each of two given numbers. Example: 24 is a common multiple of 4 and 3. [p. 141]

Commutative Property of Addition The fact that ordering does not affect the sum of two or more numbers. $a + b = b + a$ [p. 62]

Commutative Property of Multiplication The fact that ordering does not affect the product of two or more numbers. $ab = ba$ [p. 62]

complementary angles Two angles whose measures add up to 90°. [p. 214]

composite number A whole number greater than 1 that has more than two factors. [p. 136]

GLOSSARY

GLOSSARY

688

cone A solid with one circular base. [p. 587]

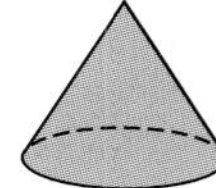

congruent angles Two angles that have equal measures. [p. 214]

congruent segments Two segments that have equal lengths. [p. 218]

constant A quantity whose value cannot change. [p. 482]

constant graph A graph in which the height of the line does not change. [p. 486]

conversion factor A fraction, equal to 1, whose numerator and denominator represent the same quantity but use different units. [p. 349]

coordinates A pair of numbers used to locate a point on a coordinate plane. [p. 443]

coordinate system (coordinate plane) A system of intersecting horizontal and vertical number lines, used to locate points. [p. 443]

corresponding angles Angles formed by two lines and a transversal. ∠1 and ∠5, ∠2 and ∠6, ∠4 and ∠8, and ∠3 and ∠7 are corresponding angles. [p. 218]

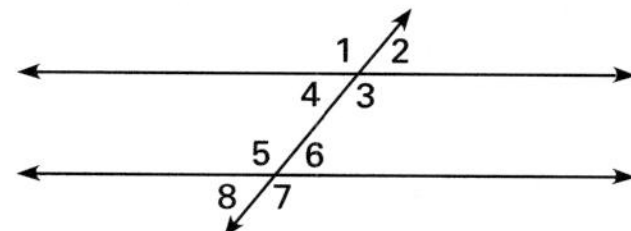

corresponding angles (in similar figures) Matching angles on similar figures. [p. 361]

corresponding sides Matching sides on similar figures. [p. 361]

counterexample An example that shows a statement is false. [p. 265]

Counting Principle To find the number of outcomes for selecting several items, multiply the number of possibilities for each item. [p. 627]

cross product In a proportion, the product of a numerator on one side with the denominator on the other. [p. 308]

cube (geometric figure) A 6-sided prism whose faces are congruent squares.

cube (in numeration) A number raised to the third power.

customary system of measurement The measurement system often used in the United States: inches, feet, miles, ounces, pounds, tons, cups, quarts, gallons, etc.

cylinder A solid with two parallel circular bases with the same radius. [p. 587]

decagon A polygon with 10 sides.

decimal system A base-10 place value system.

decreasing graph A graph in which the height of the line decreases from left to right. [p. 486]

deductive reasoning Using logic to show that a statement is true. [p. 265]

degree (°) A unit of measure for angles. [p. 213]

denominator The bottom number in a fraction. [p. 144]

dependent events Events for which the outcome of one affects the probability of the other. [p. 660]

diameter The distance across a circle through its center. [p. 578]

difference The answer to a subtraction problem.

Distributive Property The fact that $a(b + c) = ab + ac$. [p. 62]

dividend The number to be divided in a division problem. In 8 ÷ 4 = 2, 8 is the dividend, 4 is the *divisor,* and 2 is the *quotient.*

divisible A number is divisible by a second number if it can be divided by that number with no remainder. [p. 134]

divisor See *dividend.*

double-bar graph A single graph comparing bar graphs for two related data sets. [p. 12]

double-line graph A single graph comparing line graphs for two related data sets. [p. 32]

edge A segment joining two faces of a polyhedron. [p. 554]

equally-likely outcomes Outcomes that have the same probability.

equation A mathematical statement that two expressions are equal. Example: $x - 10 = 6$ [p. 82]

equilateral triangle A triangle whose sides are all the same length. [p. 222]

equivalent fractions Two fractions representing the same number, such as $\frac{1}{2}$ and $\frac{8}{16}$. [p. 144]

equivalent rates Rates corresponding to equivalent fractions. [p. 282]

equivalent ratios Ratios corresponding to equivalent fractions. [p. 282]

estimate An approximation for the result of a calculation.

event An outcome or set of outcomes of an experiment or situation. Example: Rolling a 3 or higher is one possible event produced by a dice roll. [p. 645]

GLOSSARY

GLOSSARY

689

experiment In probability, any activity involving chance (such as a dice roll). [p. 644]

experimental probability A probability based on the statistical results of an experiment. [p. 654]

exponent A number telling how many times the base is being multiplied by itself. Example: $8^3 = 8 \cdot 8 \cdot 8$, where 3 is the exponent and 8 is the base. [p. 125]

expression A mathematical phrase made up of variables and/or numbers and operations. Example: $3x - 11$ [p. 60]

face A flat surface on a solid. [p. 554]

factor A whole number that divides another whole number evenly. Example: 8 is a factor of 48. [p. 134]

factorial The factorial of a number is the product of all whole numbers from 1 to that number. The symbol for factorial is an "!" [p. 633]

factor tree A diagram showing how a whole number breaks down into its prime factors. [p. 136]

fair games Games where all players have the same odds of winning. [p. 645]

formula A rule showing relationships among quantities. Example: $A = bh$ [p. 56]

fractal A pattern with self-similarity. If you zoom in on a small part of a fractal, the enlarged region looks similar to the original figure. [p. 377]

fraction A number in the form $\frac{a}{b}$. [p. 144]

function A rule that matches two sets of numbers. [p. 97]

geometric probability A probability based on comparing measurements of geometric figures. [p. 656]

geometric sequence A sequence where the ratio between consecutive terms is always the same. Example: 3, 6, 12, ... [p. 492]

greatest common factor (GCF) The largest factor two numbers have in common. Example: 6 is the GCF of 24 and 18. [p. 139]

height On a triangle or quadrilateral, the distance from the base to the opposite vertex or side. On a prism or cylinder, the distance between the bases. [pp. 233, 249, 567, 587]

heptagon A seven-sided polygon.

hexadecimal number system A base-16 place value system. [p. 159]

hexagon A six-sided polygon. [p. 227]

histogram A type of bar graph where the categories are equal ranges of numbers. [p. 47]

hypotenuse The side opposite the right angle in a right triangle. [p. 244]

if-then statement A logical statement that uses *if* and *then* to show a relationship between two conditions. Example: *If* a triangle is scalene, *then* none of its sides are congruent. [p. 667]

improper fraction A fraction greater than 1. [p. 178]

increasing graph A graph in which the height of the line increases from left to right. [p. 486]

independent events Events for which the outcome of one does not affect the probability of the other. [p. 660]

inductive reasoning Using a pattern to draw a conclusion. [p. 265]

inequality A statement that two expressions are not equal. Examples: $3x < 11$, $x + 2 \leq 6$ [p. 517]

inscribed figure A figure that just fits inside another. A polygon is inscribed in a circle if all of its vertices lie on the circle. [p. 617]

integer A whole number, its opposite, or zero. The integers are the numbers ... −3, −2, −1, 0, 1, 2, 3, ... [p. 433]

interval The space between marked values on a bar graph's scale. [p. 11]

inverse operations Operations that "undo" each other, such as addition and subtraction. [p. 75]

isometric drawing A perspective drawing. [p. 559]

isosceles triangle A triangle with at least two congruent sides. [p. 222]

least common denominator (LCD) The least common multiple (LCM) of two or more denominators. [p. 174]

least common multiple (LCM) The smallest common multiple of two numbers. Example: 56 is the LCM of 8 and 14. [p. 141]

leg A side of a right triangle other than the hypotenuse. [p. 244]

line A straight set of points that extends without end in both directions. [p. 212]

line graph A graph that uses a line to show how data changes over time. [p. 30]

line of symmetry The imaginary "mirror" in line symmetry. [p. 605]

line plot A plot, using stacked ×'s, showing the distribution of values in a data set. [p. 17]

line segment Two points, called the *endpoints* of the segment, and all points between them. [p. 218]

line symmetry A figure has line symmetry if one half is the mirror image of the other half. [p. 605]

lowest terms A fraction with a numerator and denominator whose only common factor is 1. [p. 145]

GLOSSARY

690

mean The sum of the values in a data set divided by the number of values. Also known as the *average.* [p. 22]

measurement error The uncertainty in a measurement. The greatest possible error in a measurement is half the smallest unit used. [p. 203]

median The middle value in a data set when the values are arranged in order. [p. 22]

metric system of measurement The most commonly used measurement system throughout the world: centimeters, meters, kilometers, grams, kilograms, milliliters, liters, etc.

midpoint The point that divides a segment into two congruent smaller segments. [p. 218]

mixed number A number made up of a whole number and a fraction. [p. 169]

mode The value(s) that occur most often in a data set. [p. 22]

multiple The product of a given number and another whole number. Example: Since $3 \cdot 7 = 21$, 21 is a multiple of both 3 and 7. [p. 141]

negative numbers Numbers that are less than zero. [p. 433]

negative relationship Two data sets have a negative relationship when the data values in one set increase as the values in the other decrease. [p. 37]

no relationship Two data sets have no relationship when there is no positive or negative relationship. [p. 37]

numerator The top number in a fraction. [p. 144]

obtuse angle An angle that measures more than 90° and less than 180°. [p. 213]

obtuse triangle A triangle with one obtuse angle. [p. 223]

octagon An eight-sided polygon. [p. 227]

odds The ratio of the number of ways an event can happen to the number of ways it cannot. [p. 645]

opposite numbers Numbers that are the same distance from zero but on opposite sides, such as 5 and –5. [p. 433]

ordered pair A pair of numbers, such as (12, –8), used to locate points on a coordinate plane. [p. 443]

order of operations A rule telling in what order a series of operations should be done. The order of operations is (1) compute within grouping symbols; (2) compute powers; (3) multiply and divide from left to right; (4) add and subtract from left to right. [p. 61]

origin The zero point on a number line, or the point (0, 0) where the axes of a coordinate system intersect. [pp. 433, 443]

orthographic drawing A drawing of an object using front, side, and top views. [p. 559]

outcome (in probability) One way an experiment or situation could turn out. [p. 627]

outlier A value widely separated from the others in a data set. [p. 17]

parallel lines Lines in a plane that never meet. [p. 217]

parallelogram A quadrilateral with parallel and congruent opposite sides. [p. 223]

pentagon A five-sided polygon. [p. 227]

percent A ratio comparing a number to 100. Example: $29\% = \frac{29}{100}$ [p. 386]

percent change The amount of a change, divided by the original amount, times 100. [p. 415]

percent decrease A percent change describing a decrease in a quantity. [p. 415]

percent increase A percent change describing an increase in a quantity. [p. 415]

perfect square The square of a whole number. [p. 240]

perimeter The distance around the outside of a figure. [p. 233]

permutation One of the ways to order a set of items. [p. 631]

perpendicular Lines, rays, or line segments that intersect at right angles. [p. 219]

perpendicular bisector A line, ray, or segment that intersects a segment at its midpoint and is perpendicular to it. [p. 219]

pi (π) The ratio of a circle's circumference to its diameter: $\pi \approx 3.14159265....$ [p. 579]

place value The value given to the place a digit occupies.

plane A flat surface that extends forever. [p. 217]

point symmetry A figure has point symmetry if it looks unchanged after a 180° rotation. [p. 611]

polygon A geometric figure with at least three sides. [p. 227]

polyhedron A solid whose faces are polygons. [p. 554]

positive numbers Numbers greater than zero. [p. 433]

positive relationship Two data sets have a positive relationship when their data values increase or decrease together. [p. 37]

GLOSSARY

691

power A number produced by raising a base to an exponent. Example: $16 = 2^4$, so 16 is the 4th power of 2. [p. 125]

prime factorization Writing a number as a product of prime numbers. Example: $60 = 2^2 \cdot 3 \cdot 5$ [p. 136]

prime number A whole number greater than 1 whose only factors are 1 and itself. The primes start with 2, 3, 5, 7, 11, ... [p. 136]

prism A polyhedron whose bases are congruent and parallel. [p. 555]

probability The number of ways an event can occur divided by the total number of possible outcomes. [p. 650]

product The answer to a multiplication problem.

proportion A statement showing two ratios are equal. [p. 294]

protractor A tool for measuring angles. [p. 213]

pyramid A polyhedron with one polygonal base. [p. 555]

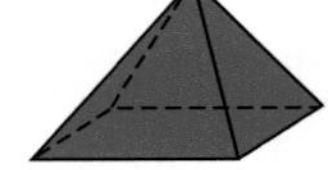

Pythagorean Theorem In a right triangle where *c* is the length of the hypotenuse and *a* and *b* are the lengths of the legs, $a^2 + b^2 = c^2$. [p. 245]

quadrants The four regions determined by the axes of a coordinate plane. [p. 443]

quadratic equation An equation with squared terms. Example: $x^2 + 3 = 12$ [p. 545]

quadrilateral A four-sided polygon. [p. 223]

quotient See *dividend.*

radical sign $\sqrt{}$, used to represent a square root. [p. 241]

radius The distance from the center of a circle to a point on the circle. [p. 578]

range (in statistics) The difference between the least and greatest numbers in a data set. [p. 22]

rate A ratio showing how quantities with different units are related. Example: $\frac{72 \text{ dollars}}{8 \text{ hours}}$ [p. 278]

ratio A comparison of two quantities, often written as a fraction. [p. 274]

ray Part of a line that has one endpoint and extends forever. [p. 212]

reciprocals Two numbers whose product is 1. Example: $\frac{5}{7}$ and $\frac{7}{5}$ are reciprocals. [p. 198]

rectangle A quadrilateral with four right angles. [p. 223]

reflection A transformation that flips a figure over a line. [p. 606]

regular polygon A polygon with all sides and angles congruent. [p. 228]

repeating decimal A decimal number that repeats a pattern of digits. Example: $2.313131... = 2.\overline{31}$ [p. 154]

rhombus A parallelogram with all sides congruent. [p. 223]

right angle An angle that measures 90°. [p. 213]

right triangle A triangle with one right angle. [p. 223]

rotation A transformation that turns a figure around a point. [p. 610]

rotational symmetry A figure has rotational symmetry if it looks unchanged after a rotation of less than 360°. [p. 611]

rounding Estimating a number to a given place value. Example: 2153 rounded to the nearest hundred is 2200. [p. 110]

scale (graphical) The evenly spaced marks on a bar graph's vertical axis, used to measure the heights of the bars. [p. 11]

scale (in scale drawings and maps) The ratio of the distance between two points on the map or drawing to the actual distance. [p. 324]

scale drawing A drawing that uses a scale to make an enlarged or reduced picture of an object. [p. 328]

scale factor The ratio used to enlarge or reduce similar figures. [p. 361]

scalene triangle A triangle whose sides have different lengths. [p. 222]

scatterplot A graph showing paired data values as points. [p. 35]

scientific notation A number written as a decimal greater than or equal to 1 and less than 10, times a power of 10. Example: $937 = 9.37 \times 10^2$ [p. 126]

sector A wedge-shaped part of a circle. [p. 7]

segment See *line segment.*

segment bisector A line, ray, or segment through the midpoint of a segment. [p. 218]

sequence A list of numbers, such as –1, 4, 9, 14, ... [p. 490]

similar figures Figures with the same shape but not necessarily the same size. [p. 360]

simulation (in probability) A model of a probability experiment. [p. 664]

solid A three-dimensional object. [p. 554]

solutions of an equation or inequality Values of a variable that make an equation or inequality true. [pp. 82, 517]

GLOSSARY

GLOSSARY

692

solve To find the solutions of an equation or inequality. [p. 82]

sphere A solid whose points are all the same distance from the center. [p. 587]

square (geometric figure) A quadrilateral with four congruent sides and four right angles. [p. 223]

square (in numeration) A number raised to the second power. [p. 240]

square root The length of the side of a square with an area equal to a given number. [p. 240]

standard form The usual way of writing numbers (in contrast to scientific notation). [p. 126]

stem-and-leaf diagram A table showing the distribution of values in a data set by splitting each value into a stem and a leaf. [p. 17]

straight angle An angle that measures 180°. [p. 213]

substitute To replace a variable with a known value. [p. 57]

sum The answer to an addition problem.

supplementary angles Two angles whose measures add up to 180°. [p. 214]

surface area For a solid, the sum of the areas of its surfaces. [p. 563]

symmetry See *line symmetry, point symmetry,* and *rotational symmetry.*

tangent line A line that touches a circle at only one point. [p. 582]

tangent ratio In a right triangle, the tangent of an angle is the ratio of the length of the side opposite the angle to the length of the side adjacent to it. [p. 315]

term One number in a sequence. [p. 490]

terminating decimal A decimal number that ends. Example: 2.31 [p. 154]

tessellation A set of repeating figures that fills a flat surface with no gaps or overlaps. [p. 615]

theoretical probability The ratio of the number of ways an event can happen to the total number of possible outcomes. [p. 654]

transformation A change in the size or position of a figure. [p. 600]

translation A transformation that slides a figure. [p. 600]

transversal A line intersecting two or more lines. [p. 217]

trapezoid A quadrilateral with exactly two parallel sides. [p. 223]

tree diagram A branching diagram showing all possible outcomes for a given situation. [p. 627]

trend A clear direction in a line graph suggesting how the data will behave in the future. [p. 31]

trend line A line drawn through a set of data points to show a trend in the data values. [p. 41]

triangle A three-sided polygon.

unit price A unit rate giving the cost of one item. [p. 279]

unit rate A rate in which the second quantity is one unit. Example: $\frac{55 \text{ miles}}{1 \text{ hour}}$ [p. 278]

variable A quantity whose values may vary. [p. 56]

Venn diagram A diagram that uses regions to show relationships. [p. 667]

vertex On an angle, the endpoint of the rays forming the angle. On a polygon, a corner where two sides meet. On a polyhedron, a corner where edges meet. [pp. 213, 227, 554]

vertical angles Angles on opposite sides of the intersection of two lines. $\angle 1$ and $\angle 2$ are a pair of vertical angles. [p. 218]

volume The amount of space taken up by a solid. [p. 567]

whole number A number in the set {0, 1, 2, 3, ...}.

***x*-axis** The horizontal line in an *x-y* coordinate system. [p. 443]

***x*-coordinate** The first number in an ordered pair. [p. 443]

***x-y* coordinate plane** A coordinate system for locating points based on two number lines, the *x*- and *y*-axes. [p. 443]

***y*-axis** The vertical line in an *x-y* coordinate system. [p. 443]

***y*-coordinate** The second number in an ordered pair. [p. 443]

zero pair A number and its opposite. Example: 23 and (–23) [p. 451]

GLOSSARY

693

Selected Answers

Chapter 1

1-1 Try It (Examples 1–2)

Public service and trade

Try It (Examples 3–4)

A bar graph

1-1 Exercises & Applications

1. a. Ruiz; Hekla **b.** Colima and Etna **c.** Height in feet **3. a.** Bar graph **b.** Circle graph **c.** Circle graph **5.** C **7.** Gardening **13.** 16,002 **15.** 133 **17.** 938 **19.** 108

1-2 Try It

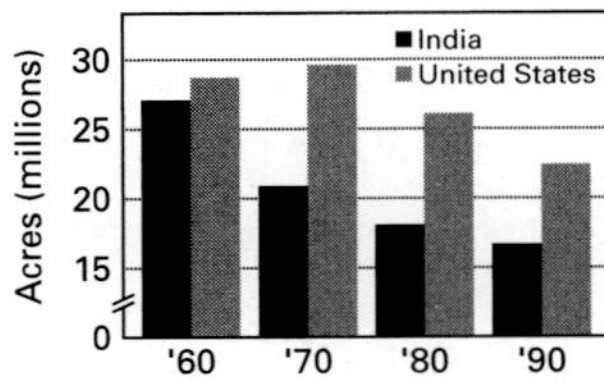

1-2 Exercises & Applications

1. a. 250,000,000 **b.** 50,000,000 **3.** B **5.** Possible answer: Scale 1000–5000, Interval 1000. **7.** Possible answer: Scale 120–360, Interval 40. **13.** four hundred twenty-eight **15.** forty-three thousand one hundred eighty-five **17.** three million seven hundred thirty-four thousand seven hundred ninety **19.** 16 **21.** 186

1-3 Try It

a.

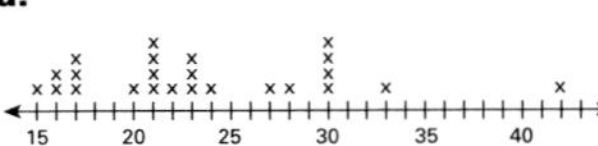

b.

Stem	Leaf
4	2
3	0, 0, 0, 0, 3
2	0, 1, 1, 1, 1, 2, 3, 3, 3, 4, 7, 8
1	5, 6, 6, 7, 7, 7

1-3 Exercises & Applications

1. a. 29 **b.** 36

c.

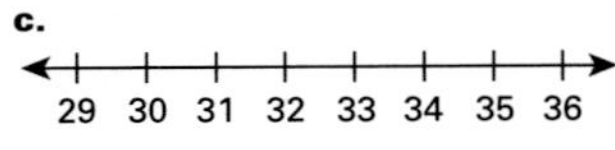

d. 1

e.

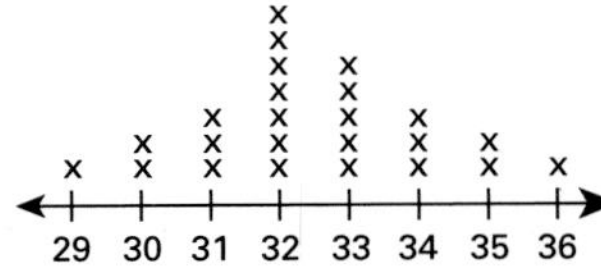

f. No **3.** 47; 0 **5.** D

7.

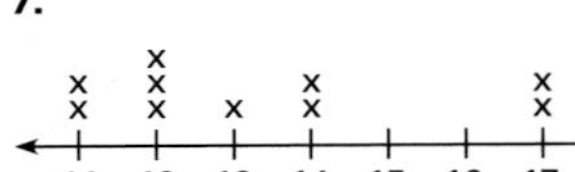

9.

Stem	Leaf
3	8
2	0 3 3 5 5 8
1	2 4 6 7 9
0	5 8

11. a.

Stem	Leaf
6	1 1 4 5 8
5	0 1 2 4 4 6 7 7 7 7 8
4	6 8 9 9

13. 410 **15.** 3560 **17.** 8060 **19.** 354,450 **21.** 20,861 **23.** 101,000 **25.** 24,000 **27.** 4000 **29.** 0 **31.** 10,000

1-4 Try It

a. Mean 38.4, median 41, range 45. **b.** Mean 46, median 40.5, range 67.

1-4 Exercises & Applications

1. a. 5, 6, 17, 19, 23, 26, 34; Median is 19. **b.** 27, 38, 39, 45, 47, 48, 49, 52; Median is 46. **3. a.** Mean ≈ 59.7 in., median 59.5 in., range 7 in., mode 59 in. **5.** Mean ≈ 320.1; Median 321.5; Modes 320 and 327; Range 202. **7. a.** ≈ 6,000,000 people **9.** Mean 11.87, median 10, mode 6. **11.** C **17.** 9 R2 **19.** 97 R3 **21.** 6999; 7286; 8003 **23.** 28; 82; 288; 2228; 8282; 8822; 8882

Section 1A Review

1. 25% **3.** Yes

5.

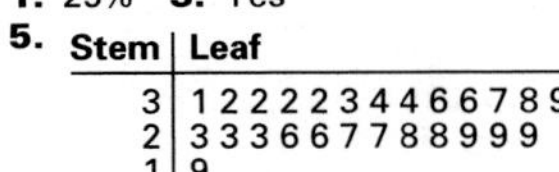

Stem	Leaf
3	1 2 2 2 2 2 3 4 4 6 6 7 8 9
2	3 3 3 6 6 7 7 8 8 9 9 9
1	9

7. China

1-5 Try It

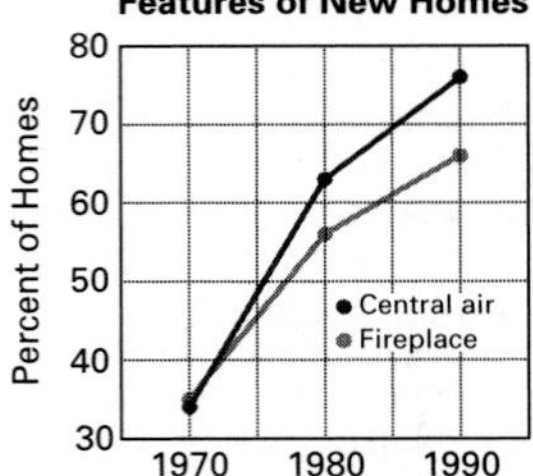

1-5 Exercises & Applications

1. An increasing trend—more nations compete each time.

3.

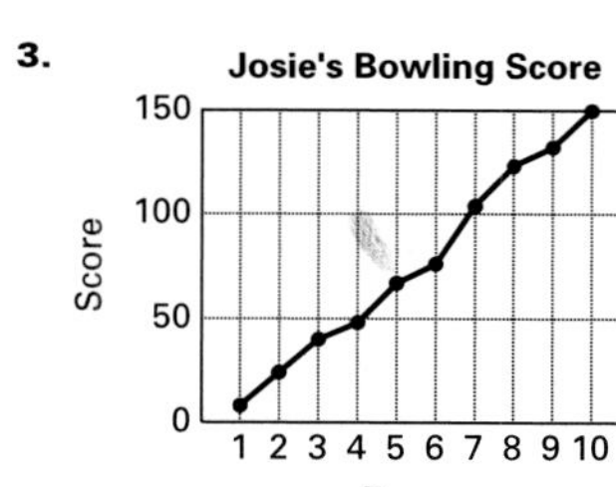

9. C **13.** 13,951 **15.** 101,555 **17.** 771,936 **19.** Possible answer: Scale 100–700, Interval 50. **21.** Possible answer: Scale 0–150, Interval 10. **23.** Possible answer: Scale 0–50, Interval 5.

1-6 Try It (Example 1)

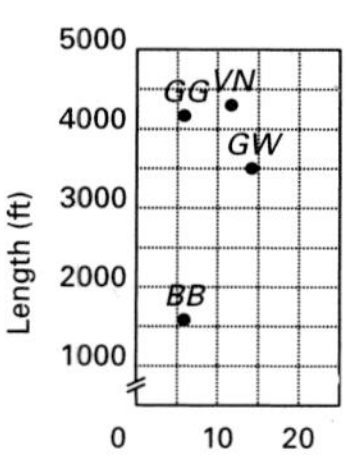

1-6 Try It (Examples 2–3)

a. Negative **b.** Positive

1-6 Exercises & Applications

3. Gorilla: 50; Rhinoceros: 72

5.

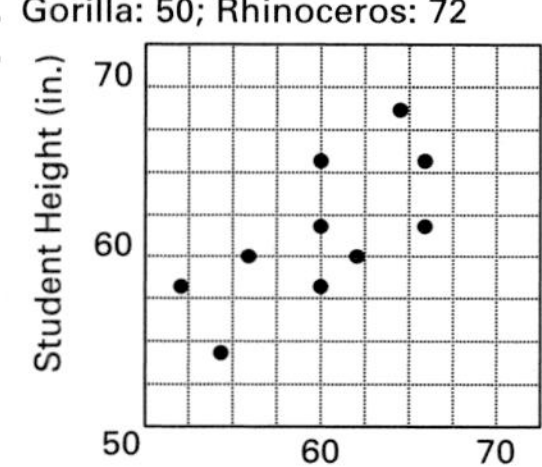

7. Negative **9.** D **15.** 38 R6 **17.** 118 R24 **19.** 17,269,827

21.

Stem	Leaf
2	1, 1, 3
1	0, 1, 2, 2, 4, 6, 7, 9
0	4, 7, 8, 9

1-7 Try It

a.

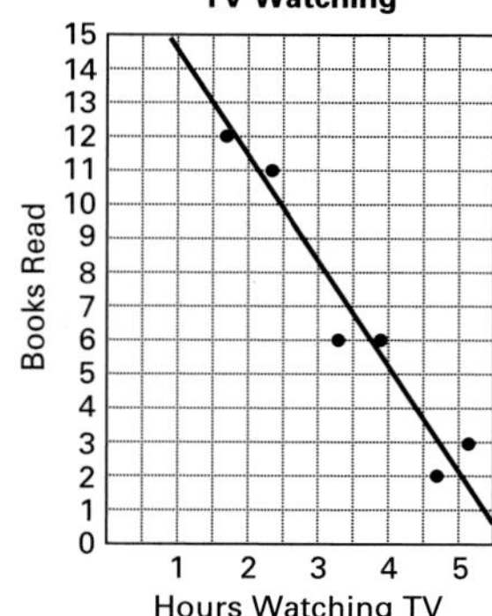

b. About 1

1-7 Exercises & Applications

3.

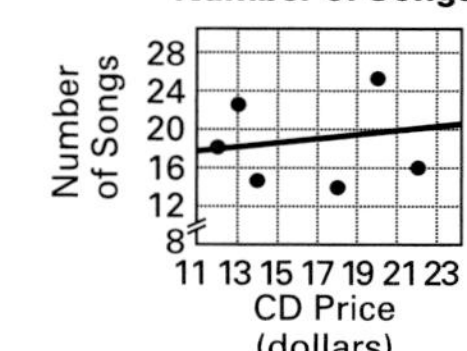

5. a.

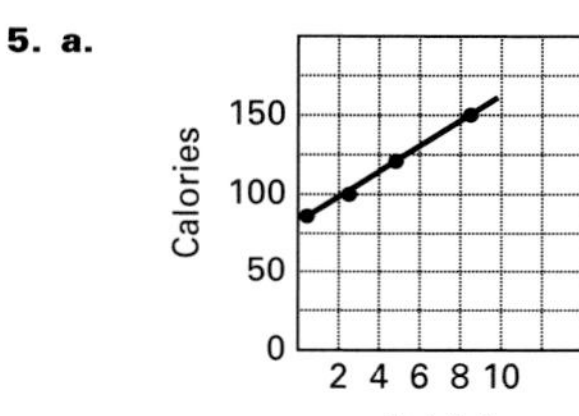

11. 3530 **13.** 54,566 **15.** 1,521,688 **17.** Mean 34.67, median 36.5, mode 38. **19.** Mean 101, median 98, no mode.

Section 1B Review

1. a.

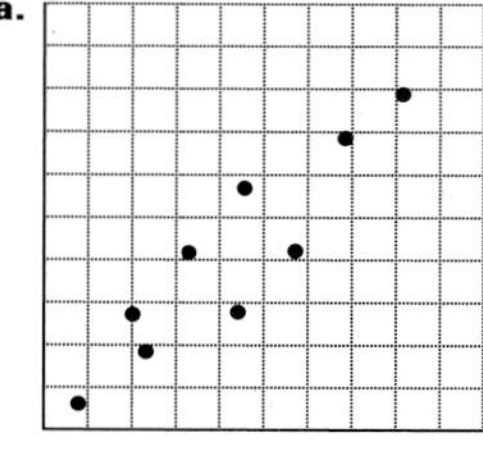

b.

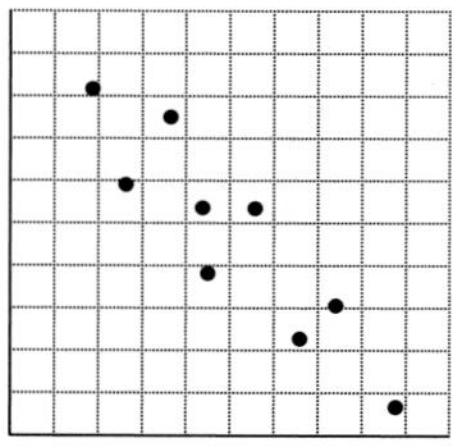

c.

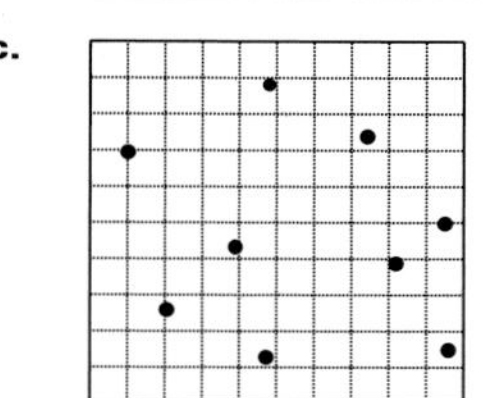

5.

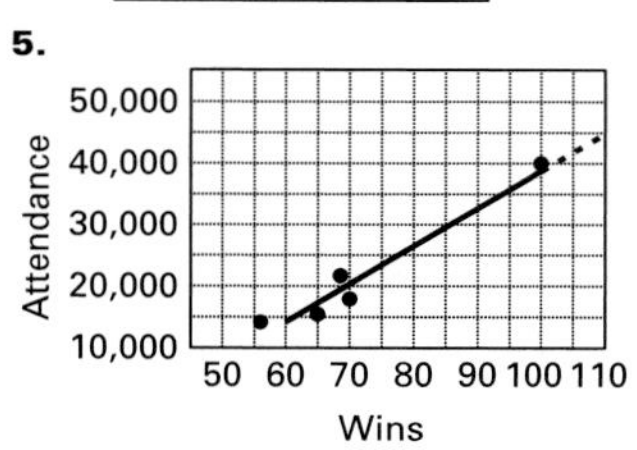

Chapter 1 Summary & Review

1.

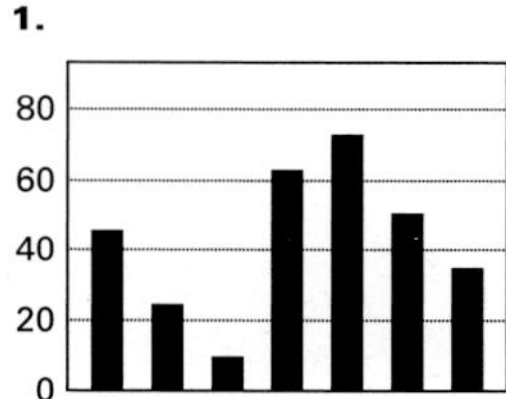

SELECTED ANSWERS

2. Mean 20.3, median 21, mode 23, range 44
3.

Stem	Leaf
4	1 2 5
3	2 3 4 7
2	2 3 8

4. A circle graph **5.** Asia and Africa
6.

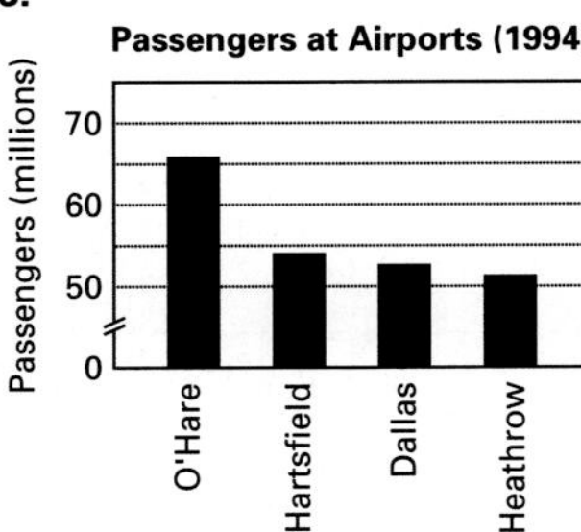

7.

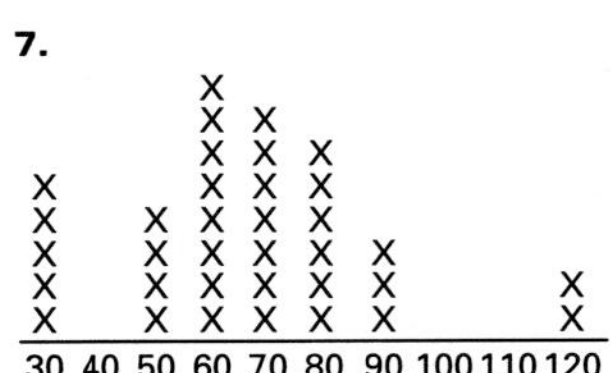

8. c
9.

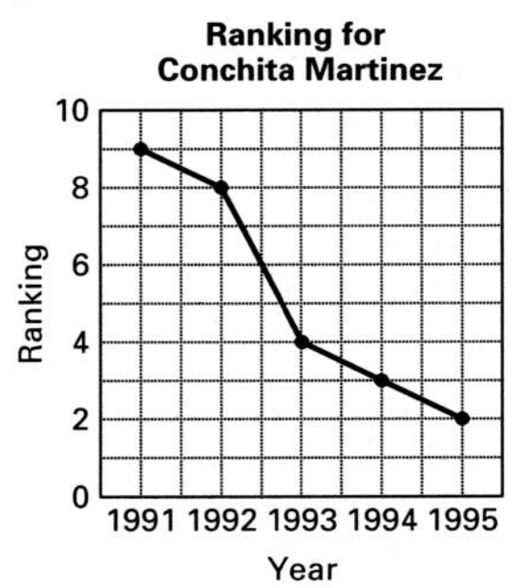

10.

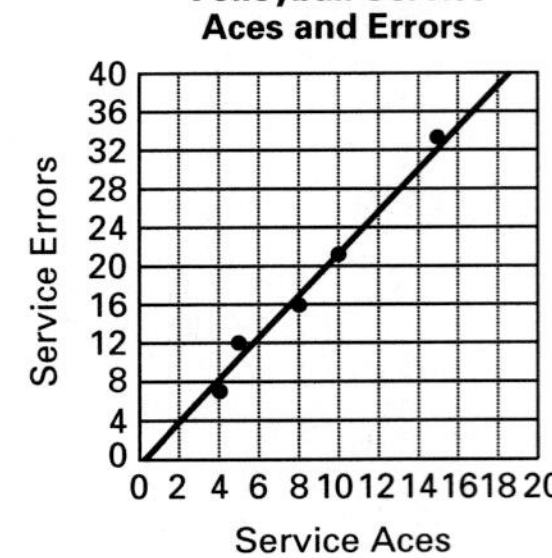

Chapter 2

2-1 Try It

a. 14 **b.** $160

2-1 Exercises & Applications

1. a. *p*, *l* and *w* **b.** 20 cm **3.** 230 m² **5.** 240 ft² **7.** ≈ 0.435 km/hr **9.** 0.6 km/hr **11.** 9 miles **13.** B **17.** 24,000 **19.** 7,500 **21.** 296,000 **23.** 74,600 **25.** 146,000 **27.** 3,820,000

2-2 Try It (Examples 1–2)

a. 7 **b.** 2 **c.** 14 **d.** 26

2-2 Try It (Example 3)

a. 2430 **b.** 2456 **c.** 2460

2-2 Exercises & Applications

1. Multiplication **3.** Division **5.** Yes; Parentheses **7.** Yes; Division bar **9.** 13 **11.** 89 **13.** 66 **15.** B **17.** $18 + 12 \div (3 + 1) = 21$ **19.** $7 \times (2 + 3 \times 6) = 140$ **21.** Associative Property of Multiplication **23.** Commutative Property of Multiplication **25.** Commutative Property of Multiplication **27. a.** $65.10 **b.** $71.40 **31.** 80 **33.** 190 **35.** 170 **37.** 220

2-3 Try It (Example 1)

s (in.)	2	3	5	8	10	12
A (in²)	4	9	25	64	100	144

2-3 Try It (Example 2)

a. $y = 8x$ **b.** $n = m - 4$

2-3 Exercises & Applications

1. a. 72 **b.** 96
c.

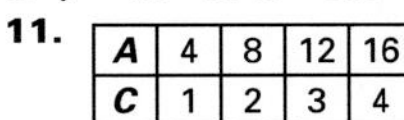

Days	3	4	5	6	7	8
Hours	72	96	120	144	168	192

3.

C	0°	20°	40°	60°	80°	100°
K	273°	293°	313°	333°	353°	373°

5. $y = 5x$ **7.** $n = 6m$ **9.** $v = 0.1w$
11.

A	4	8	12	16
C	1	2	3	4

15. 50 **17.** 170 **19.** 270 **21.** 4600

Section 2A Review

1. 10 **3.** 7 **5.** 16 **7.** $9 \times (9 - 9) \div 9 = 0$ **9.** $(9 \times 9) - (9 \div 9) = 80$ **11.** 120 **13.** $y = 3x$ **16.** B

2-4 Try It

a. 12 **b.** Subtract 3, then multiply by 2

2-4 Exercises & Applications

1. Drive 5 mi west **3.** Run down 3 flights of stairs **5.** Subtract $4.50 **7.** 25, 30, 240, 30, 25 **9.** 44, 49, 392, 49, 44 **11.** Multiply by 4, subtract 7 **13.** Set his watch ahead 3 hours **15.** 2 **19.** 240 **21.** 1500 **23.** 52,000 **25.** 3,000,000 **27.** 1000 **29.** 125 **31.** 10,000 **33.** 100,000 **35.** 32,768

2-5 Try It (Examples 1–2)

a. $h \div 2$ **b.** $\$25 + d$ **c.** $d(v - 5)$

2-5 Try It (Examples 3–4)

a. Twelve decreased by a number (*g*) **b.** The sum of the products of 3 and a number (*a*) and 4 and a number (*b*) **c.** The product of 11 and the difference between 5 and a number (*r*).

2-5 Exercises & Applications

1. Subtraction **3.** Addition **5.** $2k$ **7.** $u - 4$ **9.** $2c + 8$ **11.** $4(n - 6)$ **13.** $3(x + 15)$ **15.** 6 decreased by a number (x) **17.** The sum of twice a number (r) and 3 **19.** Half a number (f) **21.** The product of 3 and the sum of a number (d) and 3 **23.** 4 more than the quotient of 3 and the sum of a number (c) and 2 **25. a.** $267n$ **b.** $267n - 25$ **27.** $5 + 2y$ **29. a.** $2x + 6$ **b.** $2(x + 3)$ **33.** 16 **35.** 4 **37.** 20 **39.** 40 **41.** $P = 102$ ft; $A = 620$ ft^2 **43.** $P = 204$ m; $A = 2480$ m^2

2-6 Try It

a. $x = 181$ **b.** $b + 67 = 122$; $b = 55$; $55

2-6 Exercises & Applications

1. Add 80 to both sides: $d - 80 + 80 = 70 + 80$ **3.** Subtract 16 from both sides: $f + 16 - 16 = 32 - 16$ **5.** Yes **7.** No **9.** $d = 9$ **11.** $f = 9$ **13.** $x = 88$ **15.** $p = 0$ **17.** $h = 68$ **19.** $f = 1000$ **21.** $g = 12$ **23.** $c = 149$ **25.** D **27.** $p - 25 = 180$ **29.** $n = 59 - 17$; $n = 42$ **31.** $n + 127 = 250$; $n = 123$ **33.** $t \approx 1400$ **35.** $s \approx 6000$ **37.** 13 was added to both sides. **39.** $h = 1300 - 115$, $h = 1185$ **41.** Add 17 **43.** Divide by 20 **45.** 7 **47.** 3 **49.** 16 **51.** 18

2-7 Try It

a. $x = 245$ **b.** $s = 222$ **c.** 120 kilowatts

2-7 Exercises & Applications

1. Divide both sides by 15: $15d \div 15 = 1200 \div 15$ **3.** Multiply both sides by 16: $\frac{f}{16} \times 16 = 32 \times 16$ **5.** No **7.** No **9.** $m = 2$ **11.** $p = 1$ **13.** $d = 15$ **15.** $y = 1$ **17.** $r = 21$ **19.** $h = 3484$ **21.** A **23.** Rectangle with 4 cm base has a height of 3 cm and rectangle with 6 cm base has a height of 2 cm. **25.** About 3,775,000 mi^2 **27.** $k \approx 30$ **29.** $t \approx 20{,}000$ **31.** C **35.** $n = 1235 \div 36$; $n \approx 34.31$; Hua must buy 35 rolls of film. **37.** About $\frac{1}{4}$ mi **41.** $2c - 3$ **43.** $r - 10$

2-8 Try It

a. $x = 51$ **b.** $5t + 48 = 73$. He worked 5 hours.

2-8 Exercises & Applications

1. Addition **3.** Subtraction **5.** $n = 1$ **7.** $u = 1$ **9.** $m = 7.5$ **11.** $s = 1$ **13.** $u = 4$ **15.** $s = 5$ **17.** $x = 7$ **19.** $s = 16$ **21.** $8 = 4 + 2x$; 2 oz **23. a.** 176 chirps per minute **b.** 16 chirps per minute **25.** No **27.** 4 days **29.** First 6 was subtracted from both sides, then both sides were multiplied by 4. **31.** $x = 26$ **33.** $x = 76$ **35.** $x = 63$ **37.** $x = 857$ **39.** $e = d + 4$ **41.** $y = 9x$

Section 2B Review

1. She unfastens her seatbelt, opens the door, stands up, gets out of the car, closes the door. **3.** $32 + y$ **5.** 28 decreased by a number (f) **7.** The product of 6 and the difference of g and 8 **9.** 1 **11.** 21 **15.** $k = 8$ **17.** $z = 38$ **19.** $x = 2$ **21.** $k = 49$ **23.** $m = 4$

Chapter 2 Summary & Review

1. 20 ft^2 **2.** It will cost $20 to travel 6 miles. **3.** 23 **4.** 10 **5.** Addition **6.** The distributive property **7.** $y = 4x$
8.

Time (t) in hr	0	1	2	3	4	5
Distance (d) in mi	0	40	80	120	160	200

9. Flying 260 miles south. **10.** Yes, $35 \div 5 = 7$ **11.** $d + 7 = 23$; $d = 16$ **12.** Multiplication by 11 **13.** No, $18 + 6 \neq 26$. **14.** $x = 13$ **15.** $a = 17$ **16.** $n = 96$ **17.** $x = 135$ **18.** $x = 120$ **19.** Division by 3, and subtraction of 18. **20. a.** $k + 21$ **b.** $10u$ **21.** $x = 7$ **22. a.** The product of 5 and a number (z). **b.** The product of 12 and 4 less than a number (j). **c.** The quotient of 5 more than a number (d) and 14.

Cumulative Review Chapters 1–2

1. B **2.** B **3.** C **4.** A **5.** B **6.** D **7.** C **8.** A **9.** C **10.** A

Chapter 3

3-1 Try It

a. > **b.** =

3-1 Exercises & Applications

1. Thirty-six and five-tenths **3.** Four thousand, seven hundred ninety-two and six hundred thirty-nine thousandths **5.** $\frac{6}{100}$ **7.** $\frac{6}{10}$ **9.** 6 thousands, 6 hundreds, $\frac{6}{10}$, $\frac{6}{100}$ **11.** < **13.** < **15.** < **17.** Greatest: 1993; Least: 1991 **19. a.** Country Yogurt **25.** 23, 29, 34, 43, 45, 46, 65, 78, 89; Median is 45 **27.** 2, 3, 3, 3, 4, 5, 5, 6, 6, 6, 7, 8, 8, 9; Median is 5.5 **29.** 7 less than a number (x) **31.** The product of 8 and 4 less than a number (n) **33.** The quotient of 3 more than a number (d) and 4 **35.** 5 reduced by a number (n)

3-2 Try It (Example 1)

7.9; 7.87; 7.865

3-2 Try It (Examples 2–4)

a. $\approx 68 - 32 = 36$ **b.** $\approx 10 \times 60 = 600$ **c.** $\approx 450 \div 90 \approx 5$

3-2 Exercises & Applications

1. 3.1 **3.** 17.5 **5.** 15 **7.** 10 **9.** 15, 1; 15 **11.** 2, 9; 18 **13.** ≈ 800 **15.** ≈ 9 **17.** ≈ 290 **19.** ≈ 240 **21.** ≈ 9600 **23.** ≈ 7 **25.** ≈ 2.5 **27.** ≈ 550 **29. a.** 23.38 **b.** 23.4 **c.** 23.383 **31. a.** 19.01 **b.** 19.0 **c.** 19.010 **33. a.** 0.05 **b.** 0.0 **c.** 0.046 **35. a.** 43.43 **b.** 43.4 **c.** 43.434 **37.** $\approx$ $240 **39.** B **41.** Mars: 0.2 years; Jupiter: 1.3 years; Saturn: 2.7 years; Neptune: 9.3 years **47.** $x = 22$ **49.** $m = 197$ **51.** $y = 3$ **53.** $n = 55$

3-3 Try It

a. $x = 13.1$ **b.** $x = 21.35$

SELECTED ANSWERS

697

3-3 Exercises & Applications

1. a. $42.4 > 42.268$ **d.** 0.132 **3.** ≈ 170 **5.** ≈ 0.4 **7.** ≈ 0.6 **9.** ≈ 0.01 **11.** ≈ 0.04 **13.** ≈ 0.26 **15.** $x = 84.304$ **17.** $x = 16.395$ **19.** $x = 0.015667$ **21.** A **23.** 2.3125 points **25.** Fuel used = 33.39 kg; Fuel remaining = 22.31 kg **31.** $v = 12$ **33.** $c = 140$ **35.** $w = 60$ **37.** $d = 72$

3-4 Try It (Example 1)

a. $x = 1.6173$ **b.** $x = 152.165$

3-4 Try It (Examples 2–3)

a. 34.5 **b.** 0.66

3-4 Try It (Example 4)

a. $x \approx 9.47$ **b.** $n \approx 197.95$

3-4 Exercises & Applications

1. a. $\frac{x}{9} \approx 4$; $x \approx 36$ **b.** 38.22 **c.** 38.22 and 36 are close, so the answer is reasonable. **3.** ≈ 36 **5.** ≈ 12.5 **7.** 2 **9.** 20 **11.** 0.5 **13.** ≈ 0.4 **15.** ≈ 0.004 **17.** ≈ 20 **19.** ≈ 24 **21.** ≈ 0.05 **23.** $u = 0.46552$ **25.** $x \approx 2.8147$ **27.** $a = 0.9968$ **29.** $k = 0.5068$ **31.** B **33.** \$10.68 **35.** $w \approx 3.0698$ **37.** 364 **39.** 1 **41.** $g = 7$ **43.** $x = 14$ **45.** $w = 826$ **47.** $c = 306$

3-5 Try It

a. 3.17×10^{10} **b.** 9.6005×10^{3} **c.** 410,000 **d.** 2,894,000,000,000

3-5 Exercises & Applications

1. a. 1.6120000 **b.** 7 **c.** 1.612×10^{7} **3.** 9 **5.** 10,000 **7.** 9.37×10^{9} **9.** 1.75×10^{2} **11.** 1.01×10^{9} **13.** 3.654×10^{7} **15.** 9.9×10^{17} **17.** 2.43×10^{8} **19.** C **21.** 600,000,000 **23.** 1,200,000,000,000 **25.** 498,000 **27.** 5,690,000 **29.** \$18,157.69 **31.** 2.2744×10^{9} **33.** \$5,446 **37.** Subtract 5 **39.** Sit down **41.** 12.0 **43.** 6.5 **45.** 109 **47.** 88

Section 3A Review

1. a. > **b.** < **c.** = **3.** ≈ 69 **5.** ≈ 82 **7.** 2 **9.** 0.2 **11.** $x \approx 9$; $x = 8.96$ **13.** $x \approx 5.3$; $x \approx 4.90$ **15. a.** 1.21×10^{4} **b.** 5.206×10^{6} **c.** 4.86×10^{9} **19.** About \$6 **21.** C

3-6 Try It (Example 2)

a. 2, 3, 4, and 6 **b.** 5 **c.** 2, 4, and 8 **d.** 2, 3, 6, and 9

3-6 Try It (Example 3)

a. $2^2 \times 31$ **b.** $3^2 \times 7$ **c.** $2^2 \times 7 \times 11$ **d.** $2 \times 3 \times 17$

3-6 Exercises & Applications

1. No **3.** Yes **5.** Yes **7.** Yes **9.** 3 **11.** 3, 5, and 9 **13.** 2, 4, 5, 8, and 10 **15.** 2, 3, 6, and 9 **17.** Composite **19.** Composite **21.** Composite **23.** Composite **25.** 2×3^2 **27.** 5×37 **29.** $2^3 \times 3^2 \times 5$ **31.** $3^2 \times 5^3$ **33.** C **35.** 2, 3, 6, 7, 9, 14, 18, 21, 27, 42, 54, 63, 126, and 189 seconds **43.** 1,758,289,144

45.

Stem	Leaf
4	1 3
3	1 8
2	3 6 9
1	5 7

47.

Stem	Leaf
11	7
10	3 5
9	4 5 9
8	6 7

49. > **51.** < **53.** > **55.** >

3-7 Try It (Example 2)

a. 18 **b.** 24 **c.** 13 **d.** 2

3-7 Try It (Examples 3–4)

a. 15 **b.** 48 **c.** 60 **d.** 63

3-7 Exercises & Applications

1. a. 1, 2, 3, 6, 7, 14, 21, 42 **b.** 1, 3, 7, 9, 21, 63 **c.** 1, 3, 7, 21 **d.** 21 **3.** 12 **5.** 17 **7.** 54 **9.** 81 **11.** 45 **13.** 60 **15.** 56 **17.** 120 **19.** The 300th customer **21.** 85 bars **31.** ≈ 160 **33.** ≈ 0.28 **35.** ≈ 4 **37.** ≈ 100

3-8 Try It (Example 1)

Possible answers: **a.** $\frac{2}{3}, \frac{12}{18}$ **b.** $\frac{5}{6}, \frac{50}{60}$ **c.** $\frac{5}{6}, \frac{30}{36}$ **d.** $\frac{5}{7}, \frac{30}{42}$

3-8 Try It (Example 2)

a. No **b.** No **c.** Yes **d.** Yes

3-8 Exercises & Applications

1. a. 1, 2, 4, 8, 16 **b.** 1, 2, 3, 4, 6, 8, 12, 24 **c.** GCF = 8 **d.** $\frac{2}{3}$ **3.** $\frac{5}{9}, \frac{30}{54}$ **5.** $\frac{8}{11}, \frac{32}{44}$ **7.** $\frac{2}{3}$ **9.** $\frac{7}{9}$ **11.** $\frac{4}{5}$ **13.** $\frac{2}{3}$ **15.** $\frac{3}{4}$ **17.** $\frac{3}{4}$ **19.** $\frac{2}{3}$ **21.** $\frac{1}{7}$ **23.** $\frac{13}{27}$ **25.** $\frac{18}{25}$ **27.** $\frac{5}{22}$ **29.** $\frac{24}{53}$ **31.** C **33.** About $\frac{11}{20}$ **35.** $x = 21$ **37.** $x = 75$ **41.** $t = 9$ **43.** $x = 2$ **45.** $n = 204$ **47.** $y = 408$ **49.** 31 **51.** 470 **53.** 87 **55.** 56

3-9 Try It

a. > **b.** > **c.** <

3-9 Exercises & Applications

1. a. $\frac{48}{56}$ **b.** $\frac{49}{56}$ **c.** $\frac{7}{8} > \frac{6}{7}$ **3.** = **5.** < **7.** > **9.** > **11.** = **13.** = **15.** = **17.** = **27.** 4.756×10^{5} **29.** 9.3×10^{7} **31.** 8.3×10^{2} **33.** 5.0×10 **35.** 46,000 **37.** 620,000,000 **39.** 347,000 **41.** 749,000,000,000,000 **43.** $\frac{25}{51}$

3-10 Try It (Example 1)

a. $\frac{3}{10}$ **b.** $\frac{3}{4}$ **c.** $\frac{46}{125}$

3-10 Try It (Examples 2–3)

a. 0.85; terminating **b.** $0.\overline{6}$; repeating **c.** 0.28125; terminating

3-10 Exercises & Applications

1. a. $\frac{25}{1000}$ **b.** $\frac{1}{40}$ **3.** $\frac{3}{25}$ **5.** $\frac{1}{25}$ **7.** $\frac{27}{250}$ **9.** $\frac{203}{250}$ **11.** $0.\overline{571428}$, repeating **13.** $0.\overline{6}$, repeating **15.** 0.8, terminating **17.** 0.52, terminating

SELECTED ANSWERS

698

19. C **21.** $\frac{5}{6}$ **23.** $\frac{2}{11}$ **27.** 63.25
29. 56.625
31.

Gallons	1	2	3	4	5
Miles	36	72	108	144	180

Section 3B Review

1. $<$ **3.** $>$ **5.** $>$ **7.** $>$ **9.** $w = 8.5$ **11.** $c = 26.72$ **13.** 2×3^3 **15.** $5^2 \times 7$ **17.** $2^4 \times 3^2$ **19.** GCF: 9; LCM: 810 **21.** GCF: 27; LCM: 810
23. $\frac{1}{32}$; one thirty-second
25. $0.\overline{428571}$ **27.** $0.\overline{6}$

Chapter 3 Summary & Review

1. 400, $\frac{4}{1000}$ **2.** $8.041 > 8.04$
3. 18.64 **4.** ≈ 840 **5.** ≈ 6
6. 343.615 **7.** $y = 43.783$
8. 29.555 **9.** $e = 58.824$ **10.** $p = 45.3$ **11.** 723,400 **12.** 1.739×10^6
13. 2, 3, 5, 6, and 10 **14.** $2^2 \times 3 \times 23$ **15.** 5 **16.** 60 **17.** Possible answer: $\frac{5}{6}, \frac{30}{36}$ **18.** $\frac{1}{4}$ **19.** $\frac{5}{11}$
20. $\frac{24}{31} > \frac{23}{31}$ **21.** $\frac{9}{16} > \frac{5}{9}$ **22.** $\frac{6}{25}$
23. $\frac{66}{125}$ **24.** $0.\overline{81}$; the decimal repeats

Chapter 4

4-1 Try It (Example 1)

a. $\approx \frac{1}{2}$ **b.** ≈ 1 **c.** ≈ 2

4-1 Try It (Example 2)

a. ≈ 9 **b.** ≈ 4 **c.** ≈ 21

4-1 Try It (Examples 3–4)

a. ≈ 5 **b.** ≈ 5 **c.** ≈ 176

4-1 Exercises & Applications

1. $\frac{1}{2}$ **3.** 0 **5.** 0 **7.** $\approx \frac{1}{2}$ **9.** ≈ 0
11. ≈ 1 **13.** $\approx \frac{1}{2}$ **15.** ≈ 1
17. ≈ 12 **19.** ≈ 1 **21.** ≈ 14
23. ≈ 4 **25.** ≈ 4 **27.** ≈ 8
29. ≈ 7 **31.** ≈ 9 **33.** 30–35 times
35. ≈ 5 pieces **39.** South; Mountain **41.** $>$ **43.** $>$ **45.** $<$

4-2 Try It

a. $d = \frac{7}{12}$ **b.** $w = \frac{14}{15}$ **c.** $h = \frac{1}{3}$

4-2 Exercises & Applications

1. As written **3.** Rewritten **5.** As written **7.** 12 **9.** 24 **11.** 20
13. $\frac{4}{5}$ **15.** $\frac{7}{8}$ **17.** $\frac{5}{12}$ **19.** $\frac{13}{18}$ **21.** $\frac{1}{2}$
23. $y = \frac{2}{9}$ **25.** $n = \frac{9}{28}$ **27.** $\frac{7}{8}$
29. A **31.** Stock A **33.** $p = 7$
35. $u \approx 7.\overline{09}$ **37.** $a = 996$ **39.** $x = 2976$ **41.** ≈ 49 **43.** ≈ 1260
45. ≈ 111 **47.** ≈ 1500 **49.** ≈ 55
51. ≈ 470 **53.** ≈ 130 **55.** ≈ 5000

4-3 Try It

a. $8\frac{1}{8}$ **b.** $1\frac{2}{3}$ **c.** $3\frac{9}{10}$

4-3 Exercises & Applications

1. $3\frac{3}{7}$ **3.** $3\frac{7}{9}$ **5.** $4\frac{7}{8}$ **7.** $\frac{25}{8}$ **9.** $\frac{31}{4}$
11. $\frac{55}{8}$ **13.** $4\frac{1}{4}$ **15.** $2\frac{2}{7}$ **17.** $6\frac{4}{5}$
19. $2\frac{7}{8}$ **21.** $n = 3\frac{5}{21}$ **23.** $y = 6\frac{13}{20}$
25. a. $1\frac{4}{5}$ in. **b.** $1\frac{3}{4}$ in. **27.** $5\frac{1}{5}$ AU
29. a. $\frac{1}{8}$ **b.** $\frac{1}{16}$ **33.** $d = 50$ mi
35. $d = 375$ km **37.** $d = 220$ mi
39. $x = 68.86$ **41.** $x = 45.56$
43. $x = 0.049$

Section 4A Review

1. ≈ 1 **3.** $\approx 1\frac{1}{2}$ **5.** ≈ 0 **7.** ≈ 8
9. ≈ 21 **11.** $\frac{19}{24}$ **13.** $\frac{43}{45}$ **15.** $8\frac{1}{5}$
17. $4\frac{4}{5}$ **19.** $6\frac{5}{8}$ **21.** $z = 3\frac{7}{20}$
23. $x = 9\frac{7}{8}$ **25.** 2 ft $5\frac{1}{4}$ in. **27.** D

4-4 Try It (Examples 1–2)

a. $\frac{15}{56}$ **b.** $\frac{2}{3}$ **c.** $\frac{1}{4}$ **d.** $\frac{1}{6}$ **e.** $\frac{1}{10}$

4-4 Try It (Examples 3–4)

a. $\frac{8}{9}$ **b.** $\frac{1}{3}$ **c.** $\frac{27}{125}$ **d.** $\frac{1}{2}$ **e.** $\frac{1}{4}$

4-4 Exercises & Applications

1. $\frac{1}{3}$ **3.** $\frac{8}{45}$ **5.** $\frac{3}{20}$ **7.** $\frac{2}{5}$ **9.** $\frac{1}{3}$
11. $\frac{3}{10}$ **13.** $\frac{1}{7}$ **15.** $\frac{1}{6}$ **17.** $\frac{1}{4}$ **19.** $\frac{5}{14}$
21. $\frac{4}{25}$ **23.** $\frac{3}{14}$ **25.** $\frac{1}{5}$ **27.** B
29. $\approx 13{,}000$ **31.** $1\frac{1}{3}$ **37.** $p = 1.15$
39. $u = 3.8$ **41.** $x = 2.65$
43. $y = 9.26$

4-5 Try It

a. 18 **b.** 6 **c.** $4\frac{1}{2}$ **d.** $16\frac{1}{2}$ **e.** $17\frac{1}{3}$

4-5 Exercises & Applications

1. $\frac{27}{8}$ **3.** $\frac{71}{8}$ **5.** $\frac{13}{6}$ **7.** 14
9. 16 **11.** 16 **13.** 56 **15.** 9
17. $6\frac{2}{3}$ **19.** $73\frac{1}{8}$ **21.** $3\frac{23}{27}$ **23.** $43\frac{1}{2}$
25. $9\frac{2}{7}$ **29.** 26 **31.** $6\frac{3}{8}$ grams
39. 1.8×10^1 **41.** 4.21×10^7
43. 1.27×10^8 **45.** 1.933×10^4
47. 2.7×10^2 **49.** 9.3×10^7

4-6 Try It

a. 35 **b.** $\frac{3}{4}$ **c.** $1\frac{1}{3}$

4-6 Exercises & Applications

1. 2 **3.** $\frac{10}{3}$ **5.** 4 **7.** $\frac{7}{2}; \frac{2}{7}$ **9.** $\frac{19}{4}; \frac{4}{19}$
11. $\frac{3}{8} \times 4 = 1\frac{1}{2}$ **13.** $\frac{3}{5} \times 3 = 1\frac{4}{5}$
15. $\frac{5}{8} \times \frac{2}{7} = \frac{5}{28}$ **17.** $\frac{12}{5} \times \frac{6}{5} = 2\frac{22}{25}$
19. $\frac{5}{7}$ **21.** $2\frac{1}{2}$ **23.** $1\frac{25}{44}$ **25.** $4\frac{13}{20}$
27. C **29.** $13\frac{1}{3}$ or 14 hats
31. Possible answer: A whole number is the sum of that many ones. A proper fraction is less than one, so there must be more of them contained in the whole number.
33. a. $x = 1\frac{5}{9}$ **b.** $x = 8\frac{8}{25}$ **37.** 2, 3, 6 **39.** 2, 5, 10

Section 4B Review

1. $\frac{5}{21}$ **3.** $3\frac{7}{8}$ **5.** $\frac{1}{8}$ **7.** $1\frac{7}{10}$ **9.** $\frac{7}{12}$
11. $1\frac{2}{25}$ **13.** $5\frac{4}{9}$ **15.** 2 **17.** $\frac{1}{8}$
19. $\frac{8}{25}$ **21.** $\frac{203}{325}$ **23.** $\frac{65}{96}$ **25.** ≈ 42 ft
27. A

Chapter 4 Summary & Review

1. $\approx 1\frac{1}{2}$ **2.** ≈ 0 **3.** ≈ 5
4. ≈ 29 **5.** $1\frac{17}{30}$ **6.** $\frac{13}{18}$ **7.** $\frac{19}{60}$
8. $\frac{31}{8}$ **9.** $9\frac{3}{8}$ **10.** $5\frac{13}{15}$ **11.** $\frac{6}{11}$
12. $1\frac{3}{7}$ **13.** $\frac{5}{16}$ ft² **14.** 36 yr
15. 18 **16.** $61\frac{39}{40}$ **17.** $\frac{9}{16}$
18. $1\frac{13}{55}$ **19.** $41\frac{2}{3}$ or 42 disks
20. 8

SELECTED ANSWERS

699

Cumulative Review Chapters 1–4

1. C **2.** C **3.** B **4.** C **5.** B **6.** C **7.** B **8.** C **9.** C **10.** B **11.** A **12.** D **13.** C **14.** C

Chapter 5

5-1 Try It

Complement: 47°; Supplement: 137°

5-1 Exercises & Applications

3. $\angle XYZ$; 140° **5.** $\angle LMN$; 100° **7.** None; 45° **9.** 56°; 146° **11.** 145° **13.** 13° **15.** Obtuse **17.** Acute **19.** A **23.** < **25.** > **27.** > **29.** > **31.** GCF = 5; LCM = 2805 **33.** GCF = 12; LCM = 672 **35.** GCF = 33; LCM = 2178 **37.** GCF = 4; LCM = 504

5-2 Try It (Example 1)

a. Corresponding **b.** Vertical **c.** Alternate Interior **d.** 59° **e.** 121° **f.** 121° **g.** 59°

5-2 Try It (Example 2)

a. The midpoint of the shorter "stick" is at the point where it is intersected by the longer one.
b. The longer stick is the perpendicular bisector of the shorter; The longer stick intersects the shorter at its midpoint and forms a right angle.

5-2 Exercises & Applications

1. Parallel **3.** Perpendicular **5.** Parallel **7.** Perpendicular **9.** Perpendicular **11.** $\overleftrightarrow{EF}$ and $\overleftrightarrow{GH}$ **13.** Possible answer: $\angle 1$ and $\angle 2$ **19.** A **25.** ≈ 85 **27.** ≈ 15 **29.** ≈ 35 **31.** ≈ 1000 **33.** $\frac{1}{3}$ **35.** $\frac{6}{13}$ **37.** $\frac{24}{35}$ **39.** $\frac{9}{16}$

5-3 Try It

a. 90°

5-3 Exercises & Applications

1. a. Known: 87°, 76°, 98°; Unknown: m **b.** $87 + 76 + 98 + m = 360$ **c.** $261 - 261 + m = 360 - 261$ **d.** 99 **3.** Right scalene **5.** Right isosceles **7.** Quadrilateral, parallelogram **9.** Quadrilateral, rectangle, parallelogram **11.** Quadrilateral, rhombus, parallelogram **13.** $t =$ 38° **15.** $x =$ 177° **21.** $y = 31.95$ **23.** $x = 12.78$ **25.** $k = 106.575$ **27.** > **29.** < **31.** < **33.** <

5-4 Try It

a. 1080° **b.** 1800°

5-4 Exercises & Applications

1. Regular hexagon **3.** Nonregular quadrilateral **5.** Sides are not congruent. **7.** Sides and angles not congruent. **11.** 900° **13.** 3240° **17.** C **19.** 13 **21.** 108° **23.** 135° **27.** $m = 3.6$ **29.** $y = 1.46$ **31.** $x =$ 9.84 **33.** $b = 12.8$ **35.** 0.4375; Terminates **37.** $0.\overline{428571}$; Repeats **39.** 0.13125; Terminates **41.** 0.875; Terminates

5-5 Try It

a. 268 ft **b.** 4200 ft^2

5-5 Exercises & Applications

1. a. 48 ft **b.** $A =$ 14 ft × 10 ft **c.** 140 ft^2 **3.** P: 80 m; A: 364 m^2 **5.** P: 346 yd; A: 6360 yd^2 **7.** P: 9,232 ft; A: 5,270,220 ft^2 **9.** P: 42 ft; A: 108 ft^2 **11.** 2760 m^2 **17.** 10% **19.** ≈ 12 **21.** ≈ 16 **23.** ≈ 12 **25.** ≈ 34 **27.** ≈ 35

Section 5A Review

1. 143° **3.** 13° **5.** Nonregular hexagon **7.** 1260° **9.** 2520° **11.** P: 800 ft; A: 33,600 ft^2

5-6 Try It (Example 1)

a. 9 **b.** 11 **c.** 15 **d.** 100 **e.** 8

5-6 Try It (Examples 2–3)

a. 9.22 **b.** 6.40 **c.** 8.54 **d.** 9.49 **e.** 17.32

5-6 Exercises & Applications

1. 16 **3.** 625 **5.** 81 **7.** 0.0121 **9.** $\frac{9}{64}$ **11.** Yes **13.** Yes **15.** No **17.** 10 **19.** 9 **21.** 15 **23.** 100 **25.** 25 **27.** 23.32 **29.** 27.04 **31.** 9.90 **33.** 7.55 **35.** 3.46 **37.** 1 **39.** ≈ 115 ft **41.** B **43.** 36 and 64 **47.** $\frac{1}{6}$ **49.** $\frac{43}{75}$ **51.** $1\frac{1}{80}$ **53.** $\frac{87}{91}$ **55.** $\frac{11}{60}$ **57.** $\frac{189}{1100}$

5-7 Try It

a. $c = 25$ ft **b.** $b \approx 10.39$ ft

5-7 Exercises & Applications

1. Hypotenuse r; legs p and q **3.** Hypotenuse s; legs t and u **5.** $j^2 + h^2 = k^2$ **7.** $w^2 + v^2 = u^2$ **9.** Yes **11.** No **13.** $a = 9$ in. **15.** $y = 35$ cm **17.** ≈ 127.3 ft **19.** C **25.** $20\frac{7}{48}$ **27.** $22\frac{18}{35}$ **29.** $3\frac{51}{70}$ **31.** $36\frac{1}{21}$

5-8 Try It

a. 42 in^2 **b.** 152 in^2 **c.** 60 ft^2

5-8 Exercises & Applications

1. a. 9 **b.** 4 **c.** 36 **d.** 18 sq. units **3.** $62\frac{1}{2}$ ft^2 **5.** $6\frac{2}{3}$ in^2 **7.** 22 ft^2 **9.** 810 m^2 **11.** 18 ft **13.** 90 in. **15.** 18 yd **17.** 26 in. **19.** 7 in^2 **25.** 3 **27.** 5 **29.** 2, 4 **31.** None **33.** $\frac{7}{12}$ **35.** $\frac{7}{15}$ **37.** $\frac{2}{9}$ **39.** $\frac{56}{225}$ **41.** $\frac{55}{96}$ **43.** 1

5-9 Try It (Example 1)

a. $\frac{15}{4}$ in^2 **b.** 253 m^2 **c.** 2.88 km^2

5-9 Try It (Example 3)

a. 19.5 in^2 **b.** 13.25 cm^2 **c.** 8.4375 in^2

5-9 Exercises & Applications

1. Height n; base m **3.** Height x; base y **5.** $A = \frac{1}{2}h(b_1 + b_2)$ **7.** $A = bh$ **9.** 175.2 cm^2 **11.** $\frac{2}{9}$ in^2 **13.** 96 cm^2 **15.** $\frac{9}{16}$ in^2 **17.** 64 cm^2 **19.** A **25.** GCF = 2; LCM = 2376 **27.** GCF = 42; LCM = 840 **29.** GCF = 30; LCM = 13,260 **31.** GCF = 30; LCM = 3780

SELECTED ANSWERS

700

33. $18\frac{6}{7}$ **35.** $55\frac{1}{4}$ **37.** $16\frac{11}{18}$
39. $14\frac{7}{12}$

5-10 Try It

700 ft^2

5-10 Exercises & Applications

1. c. Area = 39 m^2 **3.** 328 ft^2
5. 615 in^2 **7.** 690 yd^2 **9.** 191.5 in^2
11. 6144 m^2 **13.** 864 in^2 **15.** $\frac{5}{7}$
17. $\frac{2}{9}$ **19.** $\frac{21}{32}$ **21.** $\frac{13}{25}$ **23.** $\frac{27}{56}$
25. 4 **27.** $\frac{55}{108}$ **29.** $\frac{5}{12}$

Section 5B Review

1. Perimeter = 74 m; Area = 300 m^2
3. Perimeter = $15\frac{1}{4}$ in.; Area = $14\frac{7}{32}$ in^2 **5.** 11 **7.** $\frac{81}{100}$ **9.** 30 in.
11. 2 yd **13.** 17.1 cm^2 **15.** 0.9 mi^2
19. A

Chapter 5 Summary & Review

1.

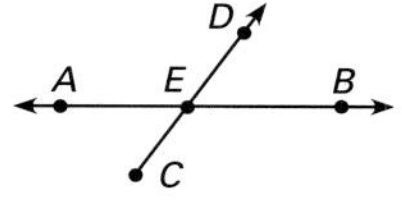

2. 1440° **3. a.** 132° **b.** 42°
4. ∠*EFD*, an alternate interior angle
5. Area: 24 ft^2; Perimeter: 20 ft
6. Right; acute; obtuse **7.** 49
8. 4.123 **9.** 10 ft **10.** 28 cm^2
11. 5.425 cm^2 **12.** 260 ft^2

Chapter 6

6-1 Try It

1:2

6-1 Exercises & Applications

1. a. 12 **b.** 36 **c.** $\frac{12}{36}$; $\frac{1}{3}$ **3.** $\frac{7}{8}$; 7:8; 7 to 8 **5.** $\frac{4}{3}$; 4:3; 4 to 3 **7.** 44; 44:1; 44 to 1 **9.** $\frac{37}{1}$ **11.** $\frac{22}{70}$ **13.** $\frac{29}{99}$
15. 1:7 **17.** B **21.** 40 sec
23. Obtuse; 133°

6-2 Try It

a. $\frac{1}{4}$ inch per hour **b.** $8.42 for 5 videotapes

6-2 Exercises & Applications

1. a. $\frac{480}{8}$ **b.** $\frac{60}{1}$ **c.** 60 miles per hour **3.** $\frac{65 \text{ miles}}{2 \text{ gallons}} = \frac{32.5 \text{ miles}}{1 \text{ gallon}}$
5. $4.00 per notebook **7.** 3 cookies per student **9.** $5.50 per hour of work **11.** $2.07 for 3 baskets
13. $3.36 for 24 slices **15.** No
17. Yes **19.** No **21.** $\frac{12}{1000} = \frac{3}{250}$
23. 10,800 mi/hr **25.** A **29.** 144
31. 13 **33.** 9 **35.** 8
37. $\overleftrightarrow{AD}$ and $\overleftrightarrow{AC}$

6-3 Try It

a. Possible answer: $\frac{3}{7}$ and $\frac{12}{28}$
b. 2 cups

6-3 Exercises & Applications

1–11. Possible answers given.
1. a. 2 **b.** $\frac{16}{40}$ **c.** 4 **d.** $\frac{4}{10}$ **3.** $\frac{20}{28}$; $\frac{5}{7}$
5. $\frac{44}{48}$; $\frac{11}{12}$ **7.** $\frac{54}{90}$; $\frac{3}{5}$ **9.** $\frac{80}{150}$; $\frac{8}{15}$
11. $\frac{200}{350}$; $\frac{4}{7}$ **13.** 1000 pesetas
15. 60 sec **17.** 720; $\frac{720 \text{ frames}}{30 \text{ seconds}}$
21. $<$ **23.** $<$ **25.** $>$ **27.** $<$
29. Right isosceles

6-4 Try It

$\frac{4}{10}$; $\frac{6}{15}$; $\frac{8}{20}$; $\frac{10}{25}$; $\frac{12}{30}$

6-4 Exercises & Applications

1. a–d.

4	8	12	16	20	24
7	14	21	28	35	42

3. $\frac{24}{36}$; $\frac{16}{24}$; $\frac{12}{18}$; $\frac{8}{12}$; $\frac{6}{9}$ **5.** $\frac{16}{32}$; $\frac{4}{8}$; $\frac{1}{2}$; $\frac{64}{128}$
7. 11 video games **15.** B **19.** $\frac{1}{4}$
21. $\frac{671}{1000}$ **23.** $\frac{19}{50}$ **25.** $\frac{617}{5000}$ **27.** 540°

Section 6A Review

1. 1:5 **3.** $\frac{1}{7}$ **5.** $\frac{5}{6}$ **7.** 21 push-ups per minute **9.** $2.22 for 2 baskets

6-5 Try It

a. Missing table entries are 10, 15, 20; $\frac{2}{5} = \frac{4}{10}$; $\frac{2}{5} = \frac{6}{15}$; $\frac{2}{5} = \frac{8}{20}$
b. $\frac{3 \text{ gray whales}}{8 \text{ killer whales}} = \frac{6 \text{ gray whales}}{16 \text{ killer whales}}$; $\frac{3 \text{ gray whales}}{8 \text{ killer whales}} = \frac{9 \text{ gray whales}}{24 \text{ killer whales}}$

6-5 Exercises & Applications

1. a–b.

2	4	6	8
7	14	21	28

c. $\frac{2}{7} = \frac{4}{14}$; $\frac{2}{7} = \frac{6}{21}$; $\frac{2}{7} = \frac{8}{28}$

3.

5	10	20	50
9	18	36	90

$\frac{5}{9} = \frac{10}{18}$; $\frac{5}{9} = \frac{20}{36}$; $\frac{5}{9} = \frac{50}{90}$; $\frac{10}{18} = \frac{20}{36}$

5.

7	14	21	28
8	16	24	32

$\frac{7}{8} = \frac{14}{16}$; $\frac{7}{8} = \frac{21}{24}$; $\frac{7}{8} = \frac{28}{32}$

7.

13	26	39	52
15	30	45	60

$\frac{13}{15} = \frac{26}{30}$; $\frac{13}{15} = \frac{39}{45}$; $\frac{13}{15} = \frac{52}{60}$

9.

10	20	30	40
14	28	42	56

$\frac{10}{14} = \frac{20}{28}$; $\frac{10}{14} = \frac{30}{42}$; $\frac{10}{14} = \frac{40}{56}$

11.

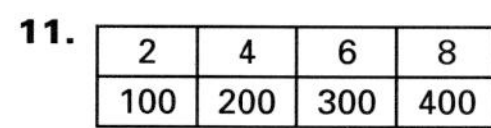

2	4	6	8
100	200	300	400

$\frac{2}{100} = \frac{4}{200}$; $\frac{2}{100} = \frac{6}{300}$; $\frac{2}{100} = \frac{8}{400}$

13.

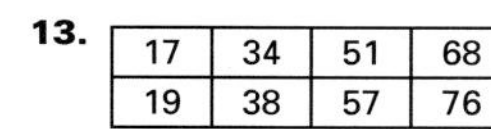

17	34	51	68
19	38	57	76

$\frac{17}{19} = \frac{34}{38}$; $\frac{17}{19} = \frac{51}{57}$; $\frac{17}{19} = \frac{68}{76}$ **19.** C
23. $x = 10$; $y = 63$ **25.** $g = 100$; $h = 144$ **37.** P = 68 ft; A = 280 ft^2
39. P = 34 m; A = 72 m^2

6-6 Try It (Example 3)

a. Yes, both are equal to $\frac{1}{5}$. **b.** No
c. Yes: 7 • 3 = 21 and 10 • 3 = 30

SELECTED ANSWERS

SELECTED ANSWERS

SELECTED ANSWERS

6-6 Try It (Example 4)

a. Proportional

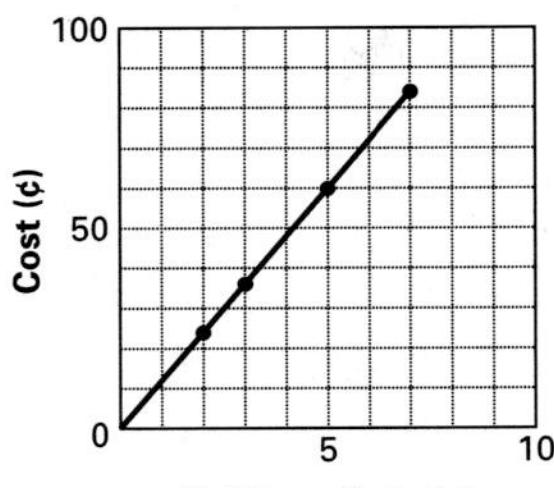

b. Not proportional

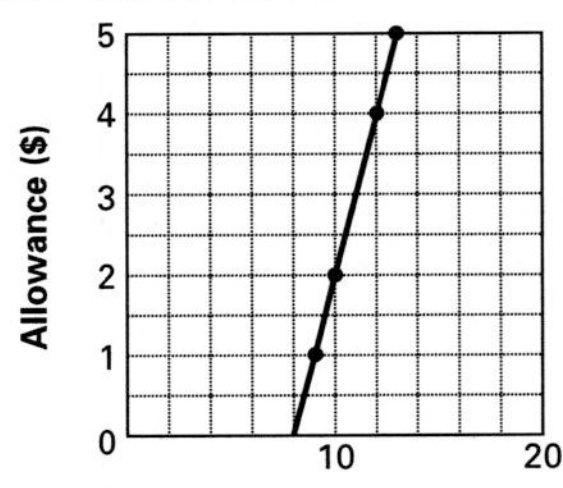

6-6 Exercises & Applications

1. a. $\frac{3}{4}$ **b.** $\frac{3}{4}$ **c.** They are equal and proportional. **3.** Yes **5.** Yes **7.** Yes **9.** Yes **11.** No **13.** No **15.** Yes **19.** Yes **21.** D **23.** No **27.** Subtract 45 **29.** Multiply by 10 **31.** Multiply by 7, then subtract 24 **33.** 9 **35.** 60 **37.** 10 **39.** 17

6-7 Try It

$58.80

6-7 Exercises & Applications

1. 4 pages per minute **3.** $0.12 for one **5. a.** $0.33 **b.** $0.66 **7. a.** 74.6 miles per hour **b.** 149.2 miles **c.** 0.0134 hours per mile **d.** 5.36 hours **9. a.** 12.8 days **b.** 2187.5 miles **11.** 17 **15.** $u - 5$ **17.** $g + 12$ **19.** 10 **21.** 26 ft

6-8 Try It

a. No **b.** Yes **c.** $x = 48$ **d.** $k = 72$ **e.** $n = 5.8\overline{3}$

6-8 Exercises & Applications

1. a. 3 **b.** 15 **d.** $x = 3.75$ **3.** 18 **5.** 320 **7.** No **9.** Yes **11.** No **13.** Yes **15.** $x = 2$ **17.** $x = 5.\overline{45}$ **19.** $t = 36$ **21.** $x = 22.5$ **23.** C **25.** No **27.** 2394 g **31.** $x = 33$ **33.** $y = 52$ **35.** 24

Section 6B Review

7. No **9.** Yes **11.** Yes **13.** 12.5 **15.** 20 **17.** $0.65; 120

Chapter 6 Summary & Review

1. 4 to 3; 4:3; $\frac{4}{3}$ **2.** $\frac{3}{5}$ **3.** 65 miles per hour **4.** 17 houses per mile **5.** $3.20 for 2 loaves **6.** 189 miles **7.** Possible answer: $\frac{32}{40}, \frac{8}{10}$ **8.** Possible answer: $\frac{30 \text{ points}}{8 \text{ games}}, \frac{45 \text{ points}}{12 \text{ games}}$ **9.** $\frac{6}{8}, \frac{9}{12}, \frac{12}{16}, \frac{15}{20}, \frac{18}{24}$ **10.** $\frac{60}{40}, \frac{30}{20}, \frac{24}{16}, \frac{12}{8}, \frac{6}{4}$ **11.** No

12.

4	8	12	16
7	14	21	28

$\frac{4}{7} = \frac{8}{14}; \frac{4}{7} = \frac{12}{21}; \frac{4}{7} = \frac{16}{28}; \frac{8}{14} = \frac{12}{21}$

13.

5	10	15	20
13	26	39	52

$\frac{5}{13} = \frac{10}{26}; \frac{5}{13} = \frac{15}{39}; \frac{5}{13} = \frac{20}{52}$ **14.** No; Their cross products are not equal. **15.** $0.85 per muffin **16.** $n = 30$ **17.** Yes **18.** $8.25 per hour

Cumulative Review Chapters 1–6

1. B **2.** C **3.** B **4.** D **5.** B **6.** A **7.** B **8.** D **9.** C **10.** A **11.** A **12.** B **13.** B

Chapter 7

7-1 Try It (Examples 1–2)

A little less than 2 inches: ≈ 1.9 inches

7-1 Try It (Example 3)

≈ 150 km

7-1 Exercises & Applications

1. a. 75 miles **b.** ≈ 1.9 miles **c.** ≈ 76.9 miles **3.** 1 in.:225 mi, $\frac{1 \text{ in.}}{225 \text{ mi}}$ **5.** 6 cm = 100 km, $\frac{6 \text{ cm}}{100 \text{ km}}$ **7.** 1 in.:10–12 mi **9.** 1 in.:7–8 mi **11.** ≈ 2 cm **13.** ≈ 9000 km **15.** ≈ 100 mi **17.** 25 ft:3000 mi ≈ 1 ft:100 mi **19.** ≈ 7 in. long, ≈ 5 in. wide **21.** 1 in.:100 ft **23.** $\approx \frac{1}{2}$ **25.** ≈ 1 **27.** ≈ 0 **29.** $\approx \frac{1}{2}$ **31.** ≈ 1 **33.** 36 sq. units

7-2 Try It

5 feet

7-2 Exercises & Applications

1. a. 3 cm **b.** $\frac{3 \text{ cm}}{x \text{ m}} = \frac{1 \text{ cm}}{3 \text{ m}}$ **c.** 9 m **3.** 12.75 ft **5.** 18.375 ft **7.** 20 m **9.** 250 mi **11.** $x = 20$ ft **13.** $x = 125$ mi **15.** 2860 km **17.** 160 ft × 255 ft **21.** $\frac{1}{30}$ **23.** $\frac{59}{60}$ **25.** 82.5 sq. units **27.** 71 sq. units

7-3 Try It

About 5:35 P.M.

7-3 Exercises & Applications

1. a. 6 km **b.** $1\frac{1}{2}$ hours **c.** 5:00 P.M. **3.** 8:00 P.M. **5.** ≈ 5:45 P.M. **7. a.** ≈ 30 mi **b.** ≈ 45 min **c.** ≈ 7:15 P.M. **9. a.** 12:30 P.M. **b.** 7:50 P.M. **11. a.** 1,375 mi **b.** 125 gallons **c.** $162.50 **15.** $2\frac{4}{5}$ **17.** $1\frac{11}{56}$ **19.** $16\frac{19}{63}$ **21.** $18\frac{2}{21}$ **23.** 3 pounds:1 dollar; $\frac{3 \text{ pounds}}{1 \text{ dollar}}$; 3 pounds = 1 dollar

7-4 Try It

1:11

7-4 Exercises & Applications

1. a. 2.5 in. **b.** 14.4:1 **c.** 2 in.; 10.5:1 **d.** Scale is 10.5:1 **3.** 1 ft:3 ft **5.** 1 in.:3.6 ft **7.** ≈ 4.25:1 **9.** 1 in.:200 mi **11.** 27 ft:5 in. = 1 ft:0.185 in. **13. a.** ≈ 1:7,326,300,000 **b.** ≈ 20.4 m **c.** ≈ 812.1 m **d.** ≈ 0.06 m = 6 cm **15.** $q = 60$ **17.** $n = 5$ **19.** $t = 21$ **21.** $r = 2$ **23.** $w = 40$ **25.** 3 sections per day

702

27. 33.4 miles per gallon **29.** 24 cans per case

Section 7A Review

1. $\frac{4 \text{ in.}}{200 \text{ mi}}$, 4 in. = 200 mi **3.** 10 cm:4 km, 10 cm = 4 km **5.** 2 cm:400 km **7.** 60 in.

7-5 Try It (Example 1)

a. Miles per hour **b.** Problems per hour

7-5 Try It (Example 2)

Yes

7-5 Try It (Example 3)

$\frac{1 \text{ wk}}{25 \text{ lbs}}$; $\frac{0.04 \text{ wk}}{1 \text{ lb}}$

7-5 Exercises & Applications

1. a. $\frac{20 \text{ miles}}{1 \text{ gallon}}$ **b.** $\frac{1 \text{ gallon}}{20 \text{ miles}}$ **c.** $\frac{0.05 \text{ gallons}}{\text{mile}}$ **3–5.** Possible answers given: **3.** Gallons per mile **5.** Dollars per hour **7.** $\frac{1}{2}$ quart of soup per student **9.** 10 meters per second **11.** Yes **13.** Yes **15.** $\frac{\$0.20}{1 \text{ lb}}$ **17.** $\frac{0.5 \text{ ton}}{\text{week}}$ **19.** No **23.** Yes **25.** $q = 75$ **27.** $n = 3$ **29.** 3 mm per second **31.** 33 desks per classroom **33.** 1000 mL per L

7-6 Try It

a. 3 hrs **b.** 30 yds

7-6 Exercises & Applications

1. a. $\frac{1000 \text{ m}}{1 \text{ km}}$ and $\frac{1 \text{ km}}{1000 \text{ m}}$ **b.** $\frac{1 \text{ km}}{1000 \text{ m}}$ **c.** 3 km **3.** $\frac{365 \text{ days}}{1 \text{ year}}$, $\frac{1 \text{ year}}{365 \text{ days}}$ **5.** $\frac{1 \text{ pound}}{16 \text{ ounces}}$, $\frac{16 \text{ ounces}}{1 \text{ pound}}$ **7.** $\frac{1000 \text{ grams}}{1 \text{ kilogram}}$, $\frac{1 \text{ kilogram}}{1000 \text{ grams}}$ **9.** 240 inches **11.** 42 pounds **13.** 2 gallons **15.** 12.5 feet **17.** 40 quarts **21.** C **25.** 4.00452×10^4 **27.** 4.3567×10^1 **29.** 5.77×10^2 **31.** 4.03770×10^2

7-7 Try It (Example 1)

a. ≈ 29,762 trees per hour
b. 12,000 millimeters per second
c. 720,000 millimeters per minute

7-7 Try It (Example 2)

a. ≈ 1083.3 meters per minute
b. 15 cents per ounce

7-7 Exercises & Applications

1. a. $\frac{1 \text{ gal}}{4 \text{ qt}}$; $\frac{4 \text{ qt}}{1 \text{ gal}}$ **b.** $\frac{4 \text{ qt}}{1 \text{ gal}}$ **c.** $\frac{64 \text{ qt}}{1 \text{ day}}$ **3.** $10\frac{2}{3}$ feet per second **5.** $4\frac{1}{2}$ cups per day **7.** ≈ 137,000 flea collars per day **9.** ≈ 46,000 ounces per hour **11.** A **13.** ≈ 216.8 miles per hour **17.** $\frac{13}{52} < \frac{5}{16}$ **19.** $\frac{23}{92} = \frac{1}{4}$ **21.** $\frac{5}{3} = \frac{10}{6}$; $\frac{10}{6} = \frac{15}{9}$; $\frac{15}{9} = \frac{20}{12}$ **23.** $\frac{11}{44} = \frac{22}{88}$; $\frac{22}{88} = \frac{33}{132}$; $\frac{33}{132} = \frac{44}{176}$ **25.** $\frac{27}{36} = \frac{9}{12}$; $\frac{9}{12} = \frac{3}{4}$; $\frac{3}{4} = \frac{54}{72}$

Section 7B Review

1. Possible answer: Pages per hour **3.** $\frac{2.5 \text{ pizzas}}{1 \text{ student}}$; $\frac{0.4 \text{ pizza}}{1 \text{ student}}$ **5.** No **7.** Yes **9.** 3.5 days **11.** 600 miles per day **13.** 2880 gallons per day **15.** 208 ounces per year **17.** B

7-8 Try It

Yes; Scale factor is $\frac{4}{3}$; $\triangle UVW \sim \triangle XZY$

7-8 Exercises & Applications

1. a. $\angle E$, $\angle D$, $\angle F$ **b.** Corresponding angles are congruent. **c.** $\overline{ED}$, $\frac{1}{3}$; $\overline{DF}$, $\frac{1}{3}$; $\overline{EF}$, $\frac{1}{3}$ **d.** The ratios are equal; scale factor is $\frac{1}{3}$. **3.** Not similar **7.** $m\angle U = 38°$; $m\angle V = 46°$; $m\angle W = 96°$ **9.** $\frac{1}{960}$ **11.** B **13.**

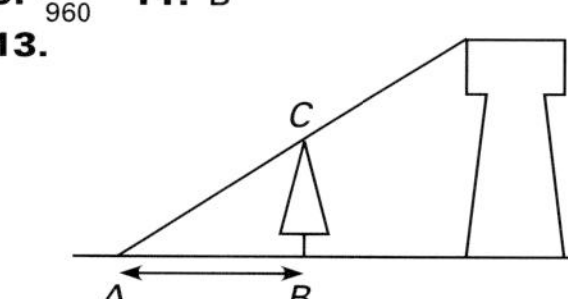

Anywhere on line segment $\overline{AB}$.

15. $\frac{2}{15}$ **17.** 1 **19.** 1 **21.** Yes **23.** Yes

7-9 Try It

$a = 9$, $b = 18$, $c = 21$

7-9 Exercises & Applications

1. a. $\overline{AB}$ **b.** $\frac{x}{18}$ **c.** $\overline{HE}$ **d.** $\overline{DA}$; $\frac{1}{3}$ **e.** $\frac{x}{18} = \frac{1}{3}$; $x = 6$ **3.** $x = 45$ **5.** 50 m **7.** $t = 3$, $s = 5$, $u = 3$ **9.** A **13.** Yes **15.** $25\frac{11}{24}$ **17.** $24\frac{7}{10}$ **19.** 40 words per minute **21.** $1.699 per gallon

7-10 Try It

Perimeter = 96 units; Area = 99 square units

7-10 Exercises & Applications

1. a. 42 **b.** 9 **c.** 252 sq. units **3.** 16 **5.** Perimeter = 30 cm; Area = 54 cm^2 **7.** Perimeter = 21 ft; Area = 58.5 ft^2 **9.** 5 **11.** 0.62 **13.** B **15.** 1875 m^2 **17.** $\frac{9}{20}$ **19.** $3\frac{1}{3}$ **21.** 64 **23.** $p = 9$ **25.** $n = 10$

Section 7C Review

1. Yes; $\triangle XYZ \sim \triangle RQP$; 2 **3.** No **5.** Perimeter = 40 ft; Area = 96 ft^2 **7.** $12\frac{1}{3}$ miles per minute

Chapter 7 Summary & Review

1. 1 in.:25 mi; 1 in. = 25 mi **2.** $x = 8$ yd **3.** 450 ft **4.** 14 cm = 63 km or 1 cm = 4.5 km **5.** 4:27 p.m. **6.** About 1:3 **7.** Answers may vary. **8.** $\frac{0.2 \text{ sec}}{\text{foot}}$ **9.** 6 miles per minute **10.** ≈ 1.5 cents per second **11.** Similar **12.** Perimeter = 28 in.; Area = 80 in^2 **13.** Perimeter ratio = 9; Scale factor = 9

Chapter 8

8-1 Try It

a. $\frac{1}{2} = 50\%$; $\frac{3}{5} = 60\%$; $\frac{1}{2} < \frac{3}{5}$ **b.** $\frac{7}{10} = 70\%$; $\frac{3}{4} = 75\%$; $\frac{7}{10} < \frac{3}{4}$ **c.** $\frac{13}{20} = 65\%$; $\frac{16}{25} = 64\%$; $\frac{13}{20} > \frac{16}{25}$

SELECTED ANSWERS

SELECTED ANSWERS

703

8-1 Exercises & Applications

1. a. 4 **b.** $\frac{28}{100}$ **c.** 28% **3.** 75% **5.** 48.3% **7.** 75% **9.** 13.5% **11.** 80% **13.** $\frac{11}{25} = 44\%$, $\frac{1}{2} = 50\%$; $\frac{11}{25} < \frac{1}{2}$ **15.** $\frac{3}{4} = 75\%$, $\frac{4}{5} = 80\%$; $\frac{3}{4} < \frac{4}{5}$ **17.** 9% < 15% **19.** 16% < 28% **21.** 1% **23.** 63% **25.** 100% **27.** 1% of a dollar **29.** 100% of a dollar **31.** D **35.** $\frac{44}{125}$ **37.** $\frac{1101}{2000}$ **39.** $\frac{49}{80}$ **41.** 0.375 **43.** 0.46 **45.** $0.\overline{3}$ **47.** 1 cm:20 m **49.** 1 in.:20 ft

8-2 Try It

a. $\frac{27}{50}$ **b.** 91% **c.** 60% **d.** 13.5%

8-2 Exercises & Applications

1. a. 0.1875 **b.** 18.75% **3.** 0.75 **5.** 0.05 **7.** 1.0 **9.** 0.143 **11.** 0.475 **13.** $\frac{1}{5}$ **15.** $\frac{17}{20}$ **17.** $\frac{11}{20}$ **19.** $\frac{7}{25}$ **21.** $\frac{3}{8}$ **23.** 8% **25.** 87.5% **27.** 50% **29.** $44.\overline{4}\%$ **31.** 80% **33.** 45% **35.** 15.5% **37.** ≈ 3% **39.** C **41.** No; 54 of the 130 calories ≈ 41.5%. **43.** ≈ 1 **45.** $\approx \frac{3}{4}$ **47.** $\approx \frac{1}{2}$ **49.** $\approx \frac{1}{2}$ **51.** $\approx \frac{1}{3}$ **53.** $x = 25$ in. **55.** $x = 0.8$ in. **57.** $x = 250$ m **59.** $x = 52.5$ mm **61.** $x = 110$ km

8-3 Try It

a. $\frac{1}{250}$, 0.004 **b.** $1\frac{1}{4}$, 1.25

8-3 Exercises & Applications

1. a. $\frac{0.8}{100}$ **b.** $\frac{8}{1000}$ **c.** $\frac{1}{125}$ **3.** A **5.** B **7.** C **9.** A **11.** B **13.** > **15.** < **17.** 0.03% **19.** 350% **21.** 130% **23.** 280% **25.** 0.8% **27.** 0.7% **29.** 0.125% **31.** 6.04% **33.** 1.25 **35.** 0.002 **37.** 0.065 **39.** 0.00375 **41.** 0.000067 **43.** ≈ 0.27% **45.** B **49.** $\frac{11}{12}$ **51.** $\frac{25}{36}$ **53.** $\frac{19}{21}$ **55.** $\frac{5}{39}$ **57.** $\frac{11}{30}$ **59.** 3:20 **61.** 2:45

8-4 Try It

a. 3 **b.** 16 **c.** 15 **d.** 450

8-4 Exercises & Applications

1. a. 3,400 **b.** 1,700 **c.** 5,100 **3.** 2,900; 580; 58 **5.** 122; 24.4; 2.44 **7.** 1,230 **9.** 5,740 **11.** 3,280 **13.** 125 **15.** $56 **17.** 105 **19.** 240 **21.** 35 **23.** ≈ 4 **25.** ≈ 12 **27.** ≈ 2000 **29.** C **31. a.** 2,000,000 died; 2,000,000 survived **b.** 500,000 died; 1,500,000 returned to Texas. **c.** 37.5 **33.** 256 **35.** 529 **37.** 1 **39.** 22 **41.** 19 **43.** 14 in.:100 mi ≈ 1 in.:7.1 mi

Section 8A Review

1. 17% **3.** 30% **5.** 71.6% **7.** 60% **9.** 45.6% **11.** 89% **13.** 49.8% **15.** 307% **17.** 0.3 **19.** 4.23 **21.** 0.001 **23.** $\frac{7}{10}$ **25.** $3\frac{3}{50}$ **27.** 85 **29.** $5.40 **31.** 305

8-5 Try It

a. 30% **b.** 75

8-5 Exercises & Applications

1. a. Let regular price be *r*. **b.** $25.20 is 60% of the regular price. **c.** $25.20 = 0.6 \cdot r$ **d.** $\frac{25.20}{0.6} = \frac{0.6}{0.6} \cdot r$ **e.** $r = 42$. The regular price is $42.00. **3.** 31.4% **5.** 54 **7.** 327.3 **9.** 38 **11.** 200 **13.** 12,000 **15. a.** 75% **b.** $5.25 **17.** It is not possible to tell. **21.** Greater than 45; Less than 45 **23.** Yes Possible answers for Exercises 25 and 27: **25.** Breaths per minute **27.** Cubic centimeters per minute

8-6 Try It (Examples 1–2)

a. 172.38 **b.** $53.\overline{3}\%$

8-6 Try It (Example 3)

a. 164 **b.** 1,312,500 African elephants

8-6 Exercises & Applications

1. a. x **b.** $\frac{38}{100} = \frac{52}{x}$ **c.** $38x = 5200$ **d.** $\frac{38x}{38} = \frac{5200}{38}$ **e.** 136.8 **3.** 17.3 **5.** 9.1% **7.** 238.9 **9.** 240% **11.** 3.3% **13.** 2.5 **15.** 7,500,000% **17.** Possible answer: $\frac{4}{12}$, $\frac{8}{24}$, $\frac{16}{48}$ **19. a.** 6.25 grams **b.** 2.5 grams **23.** $b = 10$ cm **25.** $h = 12$ m **27.** 120 feet per minute **29.** 30.48 centimeters per foot

8-7 Try It

a. 60% **b.** 29¢

8-7 Exercises & Applications

1. a. 119 **b.** $\frac{c}{100} = \frac{119}{140}$ **c.** $140c = 11{,}900$ **d.** 85% **3.** 25% **5.** 98.4% **7.** 66.7% **9.** 30 **11.** 42 **13.** 9.4 **15.** 40.1 **17.** ≈ 23.1% **19.** Tax: $4.41; Price: $57.90 **21.** Tax: $5.20; Price: $85.18 **23.** 56.25% **25.** 224% **27.** C **29.** $7{,}499{,}9\overline{00}\%$ **31.** 48 yd^2 **33.** 21 in^2 **35.** $28.\overline{63}$ miles per hour

Section 8B Review

1. 22.2% **3.** 105.4 **5.** 125% **7.** 67.2 **9.** $23.76 **11.** $83\frac{1}{9}\%$ **13.** $5 **15.** $4.80

Chapter 8 Summary & Review

1. 27% **2.** $\frac{1}{4} = 25\%$; $\frac{1}{5} = 20\%$; $\frac{1}{4} > \frac{1}{5}$ **3.** $\frac{11}{50}$ **4.** 0.86 **5.** 73%, $\frac{73}{100}$ **6.** $\frac{9}{20}$, 0.45 **7.** $\frac{1}{125}$, 0.008 **8.** $\frac{5}{4}$, 1.25 **9.** 240, 24 **10.** 276 **11.** 14 **12.** $6.60 **13.** 20 **14.** ≈ 46.2% **15.** $66\frac{2}{3}$ **16.** 184 **17.** $212.50 **18.** $15.00 **19.** 99 **20.** ≈ 21.5% **21.** 84%; 16% **22.** ≈ 23.1% **23.** $31\frac{1}{9}\%$ **24.** ≈ 74.2%

Cumulative Review Chapters 1–8

1. C **2.** B **3.** C **4.** D **5.** A **6.** B **7.** B **8.** C **9.** C **10.** B **11.** C **12.** B **13.** C

SELECTED ANSWERS

704

Chapter 9

9-1 Try It (Examples 1–2)

3, 4, 5; −1, −3, −5; −3 and 3, −5 and 5

9-1 Try It (Example 3)

a. 17 **b.** 5.25 **c.** 3298 **d.** 0

9-1 Exercises & Applications

1. a.

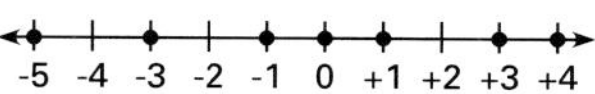

b. 1, 3, 4 **c.** −1, −3, −5 **d.** −1 and 1, −3 and 3 **3.** No **5.** Yes **7.** −31,441 **9.** −6 **11.** −2 **13.** −3 **15.** 222 **17.** −5640 **19.** 23 **21.** 66 **23.** 4771 **25.** 2435 **27.** 90,121 **29.** 136°; 129°; −129° **31.** 13,796; −19,680 **35.** $\frac{2}{1}$, 2:1, 2 to 1 **37.** $\frac{12}{10}$, 12:10, 12 to 10 **39.** $x = 15$

9-2 Try It

a. 45°F **b.** −1 > −22 **c.** −313, −262, −252, −245

9-2 Exercises & Applications

1. a.

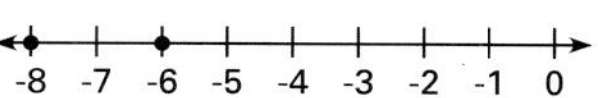

b. −6 **3.** −5 > −7 **5.** 5 > −8 **7.** −7 > −9 **9.** −2 > −3 **11.** 3 > −4 **13.** < **15.** > **17.** = **19.** > **21.** \$12, \$11, \$8, \$0, −\$2, −\$5, −\$7 **23.** −3151, −3155, −3515, −3551, −3555 **25. a.** Always **b.** Sometimes **c.** Never **d.** Always **27.** B **29. a.** Lost \$2.75 **b.** Lost \$3.25 **c.** Gained \$1.25 **d.** Lost \$4.00 **31.** A half a page per minute **33.** 2 hours per day **35.** Perimeter of first: 24; Area of first: 36; Perimeter of second: 72; Area of second: 324

9-3 Try It (Examples 1–2)

a–d.

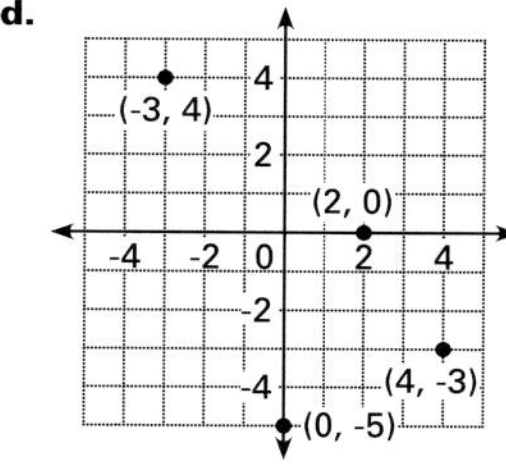

e. II **f.** IV **g.** x-axis **h.** y-axis

9-3 Try It (Example 3)

$B(-4, 1)$, $C(1, 3)$, $D(0, -3)$, $E(2, -2)$

9-3 Try It (Example 4)

They are negative.

9-3 Exercises & Applications

1. a–d.

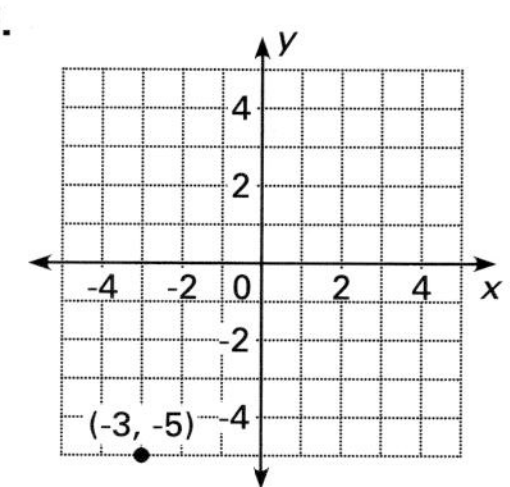

3. (0, 0) **5.** (−2, 0) **7.** (3, −1) **19. a.** (200, −100); (500, −200) **b.**

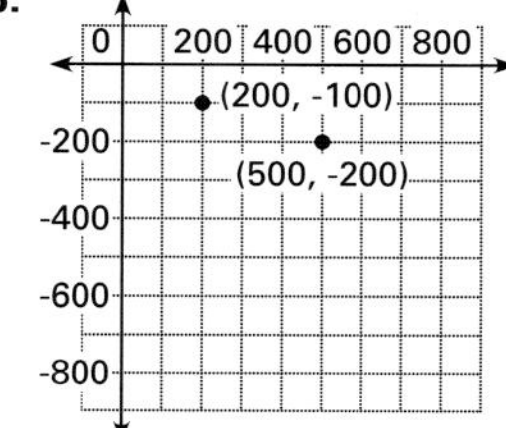

21. IV **23.** I **25.** III **27.** IV **29.** I **31.** C **33.** Cairo: 30° north, 31° east; Zanzibar: 6° south, 39° east Possible answers for 35–39: **35.** $\frac{4}{11}$, $\frac{16}{44}$ **37.** $\frac{10}{21}$, $\frac{40}{84}$ **39.** $\frac{21}{50}$, $\frac{84}{200}$ **41.** 67% **43.** 34%

Section 9A Review

1. 4 **3.** 0 **5.** −201 **7.** 6 **9.** 613 **11.** > **13.** > **15.** −5, −25 **23.** C

9-4 Try It (Example 1)

a. −3 **b.** 5 **c.** −8 **d.** 6

9-4 Try It (Examples 2–3)

a. 3 **b.** −1 **c.** −1 **d.** 0

9-4 Exercises & Applications

1. a–b. □□ ■■■■■

c.

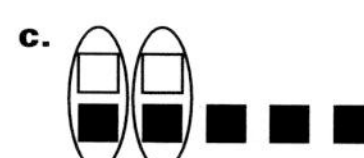

d. −3 **3.** 4 + (−6) = −2 **5.** 6 **7.** 15 **9.** 0 **11.** −10 **13.** 5 **15.** 4 **17.** −10 **19.** 0 **21.** 11 **23.** −46 **25.** 22 **27.** −110 **29.** 4 tokens **31.** −10 **33.** B **35. a.** 264 + (−127) **b.** 137 ft **37.** $\frac{6}{14}$, $\frac{9}{21}$, $\frac{12}{28}$, $\frac{15}{35}$, $\frac{18}{42}$ **39.** $\frac{1}{2}$ **41.** $\frac{1}{20}$ **43.** $\frac{9}{20}$ **45.** $\frac{14}{125}$ **47.** $\frac{13}{25}$

9-5 Try It (Example 1)

a. 1 **b.** −3 **c.** −6 **d.** 4

9-5 Try It (Example 2)

a. 2 **b.** −5 **c.** 3 **d.** 2

9-5 Try It (Example 3)

69 feet

9-5 Exercises & Applications

1. a–b. □□□□□ ■■■■

c. □□□□□

d. 5 **3.** −9 **5.** 10 **7.** 12 **9.** 56 **11.** 60 **13.** −21 **15.** −30 **17.** −91 **19.** 583 **21.** 130 **23.** −14 **25.** 12 **27.** −7 **29.** Alaska: 180; California: 179; Hawaii: 86; North Dakota: 181; West Virginia: 149; Widest: North Dakota; Narrowest: Hawaii **31. a.** −10 − 20 = −30

SELECTED ANSWERS

SELECTED ANSWERS

705

b. 20 − (−10) = 30 **c.** −10 − (−10) = 0 **d.** 20 − 20 = 0 **33.** 2^{10}
35. 2 × 3 × 11 **37.** $2^4 \times 3^2$
39. 2 × 3 × 5 × 7 × 13 **41.** $2^5 \times 3$
43. 52% **45.** 90% **47.** 243%
49. 987.654% **51.** 1020%

9-6 Try It (Examples 1–3)

a. −16 **b.** 20 **c.** −54 **d.** −33 **e.** −140 **f.** 0

9-6 Try It (Examples 4–6)

a. 64 **b.** −30 **c.** 24

9-6 Exercises & Applications

1. 8, 4, −4, −8 **3.** −27, 0, 9, 18
5. − **7.** + **9.** 72 **11.** −72
13. 45 **15.** −100 **17.** −135
19. 125 **21.** −112 **23.** −8
25. −84 **27.** −512 **29.** −136
31. C **33.** You can multiply integers as you would whole numbers, but you have to look at the signs to figure out what sign the product is.
35. 15 **37.** 17 **39.** 21 **41.** 3
43. 60 **45.** 90 **47.** 1.5 **49.** $5.40

9-7 Try It (Examples 1–4)

a. 4 **b.** 5 **c.** −2 **d.** −3

9-7 Try It (Example 5)

−4

9-7 Exercises & Applications

1. a. −724 **b.** −181 **c.** −181 **d.** a drop **3.** − **5.** + **7.** −3 **9.** 8
11. −2 **13.** −8 **15.** 81 **17.** −16
19. 15 **21.** −8 **23.** 4 **25.** −1
27. 0 **29.** $\frac{11}{25}$ **31.** $\frac{1}{5}$ **33.** $\frac{4}{5}$ **35.** $\frac{1}{5}$
37. 50% **39.** 22 **41.** 25%

Section 9B Review

1. 0 **3.** −50 **5.** 9 **7.** 150
9. −240 **11.** 382 **13.** −16
15. −170,017 **17.** −160 **19.** 0
27. 265°F; 147°C

Chapter 9 Summary & Review

1. No **2.** −$25 **3.** −42 **4.** 87
5. > **6.** −8, −4, 0, 10, 18

7. Possible answer:

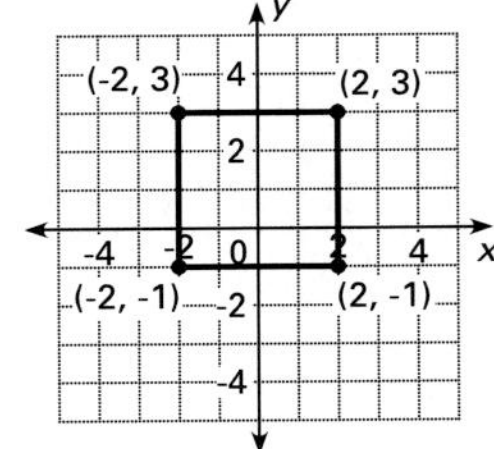

8.

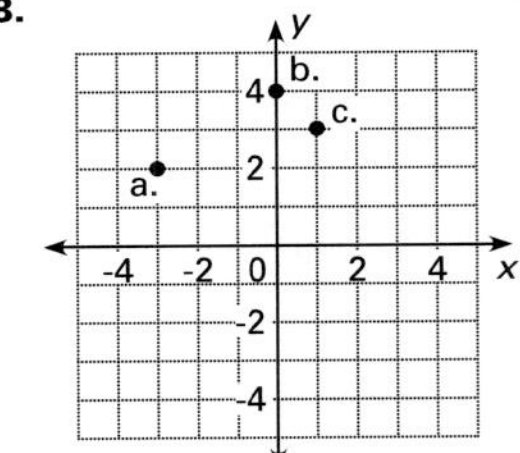

9. 5 + (−9) = −4
10. Possible answer:

□□□
■■■■■■■

Sum is −4.
11. 2 **12. a.** 6 **b.** −11 **c.** −65 **d.** −62 **13. a.** −3 **b.** 4 **c.** −101 **d.** 0 **14. a.** −84 **b.** 40 **c.** −252 **d.** 480 **15. a.** −22 **b.** 4 **c.** −6 **d.** 21 **16.** −$5250 **17.** 20,602 ft

Chapter 10

10-1 Try It (Examples 1–2)

a. Variable **b.** Constant
c. Variable **d.** Constant

10-1 Try It (Examples 3–4)

Possible answers: **a.** Let T = the time it takes to get to school; Between 5 and 60 minutes **b.** Let W = wingspan of a butterfly; Between 1 cm and 10 cm

10-1 Exercises & Applications

1. a. Variables **b.** Constants
3. Variable **5.** Variable
7. Variable Possible answers for Exercises 9–17: **9.** Let W = weight of newborn; Between 5 and 12 lb
11. Let T = time it takes to eat lunch; Between 5 and 45 min
13. Let H = height of desk; Between 2 and 4 ft **15.** Feet or meters
17. Minutes or hours **19.** The measurements of the area, the base, and the height can change; The $\frac{1}{2}$ is constant. **21.** D **23.** The length is constant. **25.** About 12 in.
27. 41°, 32°, 3°, −3°, −15°, −42°
29. −4111, −4122, −4212, −4221, −4222

10-2 Try It (Example 1)

b

10-2 Try It (Example 2)

There were no students at the start of the day, a few students arrived and stayed for the first class, more students came and stayed for a second class, some students left before a third class, then everyone left the room.

10-2 Exercises & Applications

1. a. Decreases **b.** Decreases **c.** Stays constant **d.** Increases
Possible answers for Exercises 3 and 5: **3.** The length of a side **5.** The age of the teenager **7.** a
9. Possible answer: You start with a full tank. You stop driving for a while, then drive for a bit longer. Then you fill the tank. **13.** b
15. 8 m **17.** 14 m

10-3 Try It (Examples 1–3)

$3n$

10-3 Try It (Example 4)

x	1	2	3	4	5	6
$10x$	10	20	30	40	50	60

10-3 Exercises & Applications

1.

Term #	1	2	3	4	5	n
# in Seq.	7	14	21	28	35	$7n$

SELECTED ANSWERS

706

3. 0 **5.** 5 **7.** 16 **11.** $n + 10$; 110 **13.** $\frac{n}{2}$; 50 **15.** $\frac{n}{10}$; 10 **17.** n^2; 10,000 **19. a.** $8000n$ **b.** 2,920,000 **25. b.** $3n$ **c.** 300 **27.** Arithmetic; 9, 11 **29.** Arithmetic; 55, 66 **31.** Geometric; 100,000; 1,000,000 **33.** Neither; $\frac{5}{6}$, $\frac{6}{7}$ **35.** 1,250,000,000 **37.** 9:00 P.M. **39.** 5:24 P.M. **41.** 8 **43.** −27 **45.** −48 **47.** −179 **49.** −468

10-4 Try It (Examples 1–2)

$y = \frac{x}{4}$; $y = 4.25$

10-4 Try It (Example 3)

Possible answers:

y	1	2	3	4	5	6
p	20 kg	40 kg	60 kg	80 kg	100 kg	120 kg

10-4 Exercises & Applications

1. Possible answer:

x	1	2	3	4	5
y	-1	2	5	8	11

3. $y = -5x$; $y = -35$ **5.** $C = 21.00$, $C = 28.00$; $C = 3.5n$ **7.** $d = 105$, $d = 140$, $d = 175$; $d = 35t$ **19.** C **23.** 1 in.:4 ft **25.** 1 in.:2.4 ft **27.** 5 **29.** 102 **31.** 789

10-5 Try It (Example 1)

a.

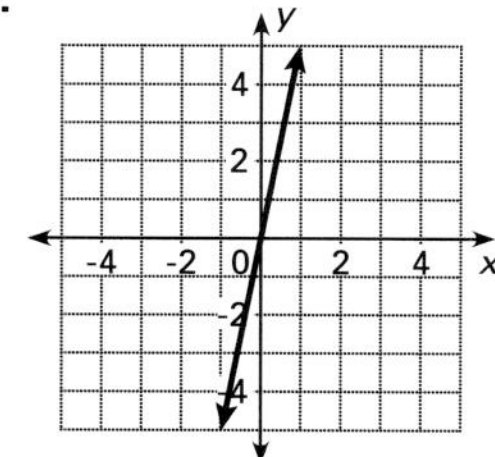

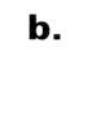

b.

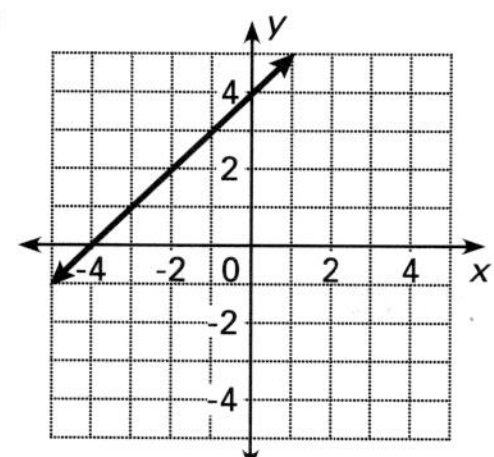

c.

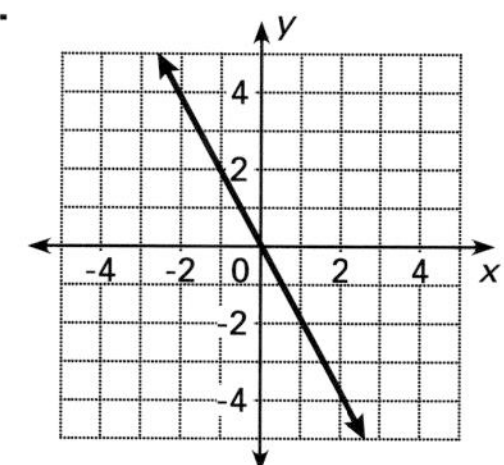

10-5 Try It (Example 2)

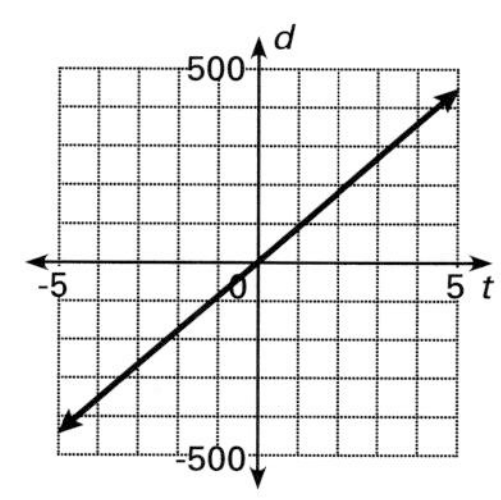

10-5 Exercises & Applications

1.

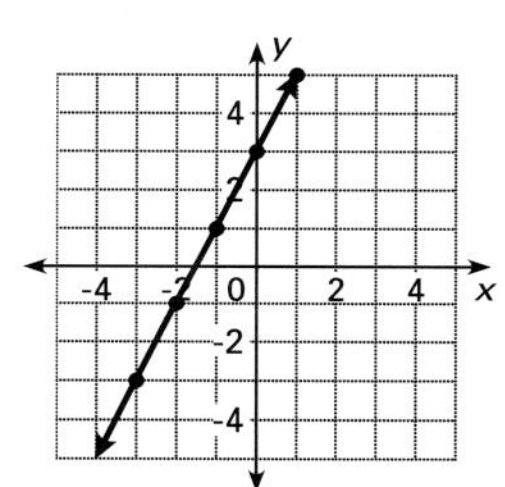

3.

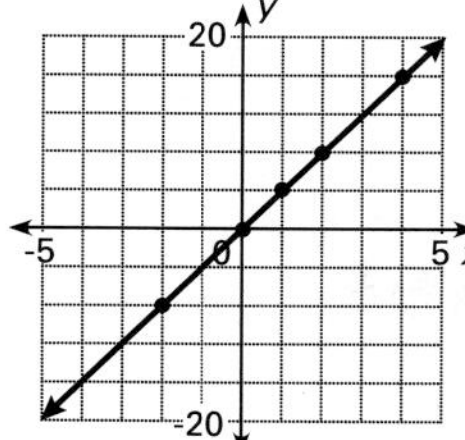

11. The graphs that go through the origin don't have a number subtracted or added at the end of the equation.
13, 15.

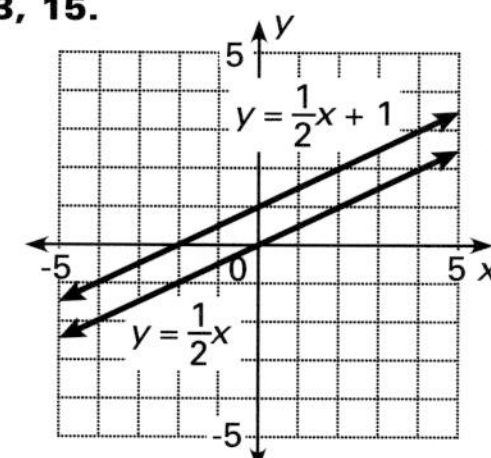

17. They are parallel lines. **19. a.** Let r = rate and m = minutes; r = 140m and $r = \frac{m}{60}$. **b.** The line with the steeper slope represents the greater rate. **21. d.** The lines are images of each other reflected over the y-axis. **23.** $\frac{9}{20} = 45\%$; $\frac{1}{2} = 50\%$; $\frac{9}{20} < \frac{1}{2}$ **25.** $\frac{1}{4} = 25\%$; $\frac{1}{5} = 20\%$; $\frac{1}{4} > \frac{1}{5}$ **27.** 63 **29.** −44 **31.** 0 **33.** 108 **35.** −270

Section 10A Review

1. b **3.** $2n$; 200 **5.** $-5n$; -500 **7.** $y = x - 6$; 3 **9.**

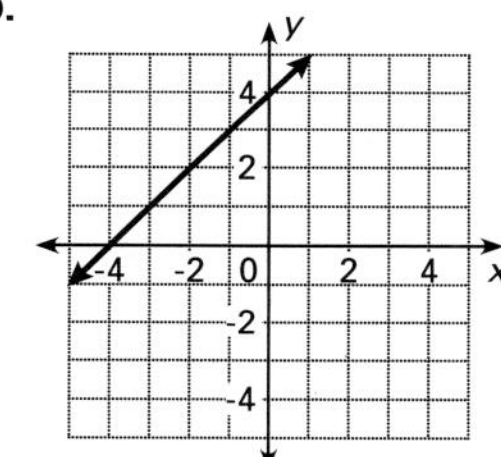

SELECTED ANSWERS

707

SELECTED ANSWERS

11.

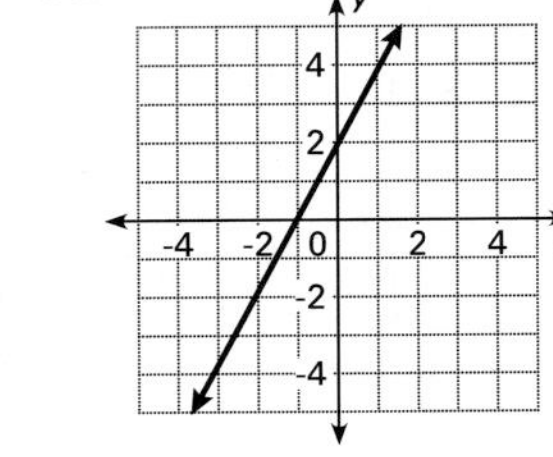

10-6 Try It

a. $x = 10$ **b.** $x = -6$ **c.** $k = 4\frac{1}{3}$
d. $x = -7$

10-6 Exercises & Applications

1. a. $y = x + 3$ **c.** $x = 5$ **3.** $x = -2$ **5.** $x = 4$ **7.** $x = 6$ **9.** $r = -4$ **11.** $x = 3\frac{1}{2}$ **13.** $z = -5$ **15. b.** $d \approx 3\frac{1}{2}$cm **17.** 200 times **19.** Possible answer: About 63.4% **21.** 0.5 **23.** 0.9 **25.** 0.07 **27.** 0.056 **29.** 0.8462 **31.** 3 **33.** 0 **35.** 7 **37.** −4 **39.** −34

10-7 Try It

a. $x = 6$ **b.** $x = -4$ **c.** $x = -3$

10-7 Exercises & Applications

1. $x = -1$ **3.** $x = 1$ **5.** $x = -2\frac{1}{2}$ **7.** $x = 2$ **9.** $p = -1$ **11.** $x = 4\frac{1}{2}$ **13.** $t \approx -15\frac{1}{3}$ **15.** 10 months **17. a.** $2n$ **b.** $1200 **c.** $y = 2n - 1200$ **d.** 2100 items **19. a.** $A = 5 + 0.25c$ **b.** $7.50 **c.** 15 checks **21.** 135% **23.** 0.5% **25.** −7 **27.** 417 **29.** 114 **31.** 22,714 **33.** -4×10^4

10-8 Try It (Examples 1–2)

a.

-5 -4 -3 -2 -1 0 1 2 3

b. $x > -3$

10-8 Try It (Examples 3–4)

$A < 450$

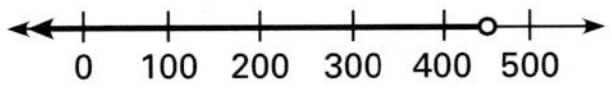

0 100 200 300 400 500

10-8 Exercises & Applications

1. a–c.

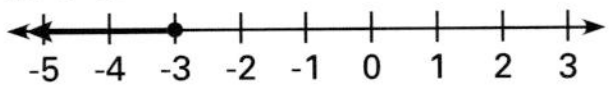

-5 -4 -3 -2 -1 0 1 2 3

3.

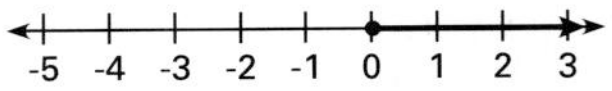

-5 -4 -3 -2 -1 0 1 2 3

5.

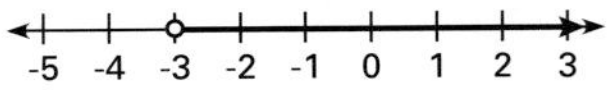

-5 -4 -3 -2 -1 0 1 2 3

13. No **15.** Yes **17.** $x \geq -2$ **19.** $x > 40$ **21.** The number of tickets sold was greater than 150. **23.** The plane needed at least 90 gallons of fuel. **25.** There were no more than 65 sofas in the shipment. **27.** $C \leq 1$ **29.** No **31.** A **33.** Tables may vary; Any values of x greater than 4 solve the inequality. **35.** ≈ 4 **37.** ≈ $2.10 **39.** $<$ **41.** $<$ **43.** $>$ **45.** $>$

Section 10B Review

1. $x = 0$ **3.** $x = -2$ **5.** $x = 0$ **7.** $x = -4$ **11. a.** $m = 72p$ **b.** Need to sell about 55 pillows to make $4000. **13.** $6n$; 600 **15.** n^3; 1,000,000

10-9 Try It

a. $x = -5$ **b.** $x = -7$ **c.** $x = -40$
d. $x = 48$

10-9 Exercises & Applications

1. a. $x + (-2) + 2 = (-11) + 2$ **b.** $x = -9$ **c.** $(-9) + (-2) = (-11)$; $-11 = -11$ **3.** $x + (-5) = -3$; $x = 2$ **5.** No **7.** No **9.** $x = -5$ **11.** $z = -1$ **13.** $k = 27$ **15.** $x = -5$ **17.** $x = -11$ **19.** $x = -60$ **21.** −4°F **23.** 1021 millibars **25.** $x = -60$ **27. a.** The variable is preceded by a minus sign. **b.** $x = 59$ **29.** 15, 20, 35; Possible answers: $\frac{1}{5} = \frac{3}{15}$, $\frac{3}{15} = \frac{4}{20}$, $\frac{4}{20} = \frac{7}{35}$, $\frac{3}{15} = \frac{7}{35}$ **31.** $\frac{1}{5} = \frac{12}{x}$; $x = 60$ **33.** $\frac{1}{1000} = \frac{57}{m}$; $m = 57{,}000$

10-10 Try It (Examples 1–2)

a. $x = -2$ **b.** $h = 4.\overline{4}$ **c.** $x = -4.\overline{3}$

10-10 Try It (Examples 3–4)

a. $y = -150$ **b.** $w = 1320$
c. $m = 448$

10-10 Exercises & Applications

1. a. $\frac{-3x}{-3} = \frac{-15}{-3}$ **b.** $x = 5$ **c.** $-3(5) = -15$, $-15 = -15$ **3.** $2x = -8$; $x = -4$ **5.** No **7.** Yes **9.** $m = 33$ **11.** $z = 10$ **13.** $c = -64$ **15.** $d = 36$ **17.** $x = -19$ **19.** $x = 3.5$ **21.** 0.5 mm **23.** Possible answers: $\frac{12}{m} = -3$ and $\frac{n}{-2} = 2$ **25.** 24 **29.** No **31.** 158 **33.** $71.30

10-11 Try It (Examples 1–2)

a. $x = -3$ **b.** $c = -8$ **c.** $x = 30$
d. $x = -20$

10-11 Try It (Example 3)

a. 2 km **b.** 5 km

10-11 Exercises & Applications

1. a. $-4x - 2 + 2 = -14 + 2$ **b.** −12 **c.** $\frac{-4x}{-4} = \frac{-12}{-4}$ **d.** $x = 3$ **e.** $-4(3) - 2 = -14$, $-12 - 2 = -14$, $-14 = -14$ **3.** $3x + 2 = -1$; $x = -1$ **5.** Yes **7.** No **9.** $x = 1$ **11.** $t = -36$ **13.** $g = -3$ **15.** $n = -8$ **17.** $x = 80$ **19.** $f = -1120$ **21.** 43 inches **23.** A **25.** Possible answers: $3m + 11 = 2$ and $3 - 2n = 9$ **27.** $0.\overline{2}$; Repeats **29.** 0.875; Terminates **31.** 0.4375; Terminates **33.** $3.00

10-12 Try It

a. $9494 **b.** 5 weeks

10-12 Exercises & Applications

1. $h + 2 = 14$ **3.** $2t - 7 = -27$ **5.** 5°F **7.** 14 years **9.** B **11. a.** In 200 years **b.** In 600 years **c.** In 800 years **d.** $0.000\overline{3}$°C per year; This is $\frac{1}{15}$ of the current rate. **13.** $k = 3$ **15.** $x = 60$ **17.** $y = 4$ **19.** $x = 1.\overline{3}$ **21.** 10 **23.** 0 **25.** 75 **27.** 32 **29.** 101 **31.** 14 **33.** 4

708

Section 10C Review

1. $x - 2 = 6$; $x = 8$ **3.** $-5 = 2x - 3$; $x = -1$ **5.** No **7.** Yes **9.** $p = -22$ **11.** $x = 180$ **13.** $d = 128$ **15.** $x = -32$ **17.** $x = 5$ **19.** $x = 4$ **21.** D

Chapter 10 Summary & Review

1. Possible answer: p = number of petals on a flower; 5–50 petals
2. Possible answers: diameter, circumference, height **3.** $6n$; 600
4. Possible table values for (x, y): (1, 7), (2, 9), (3, 11), (4, 13), (5, 15), (6, 17) **5.** Possible answer: Over a 3-month period a plant grew to 3 feet and then with lack of water over the next 3 months withered down to the ground. **6.** $y = 4x$; 36
7. a.

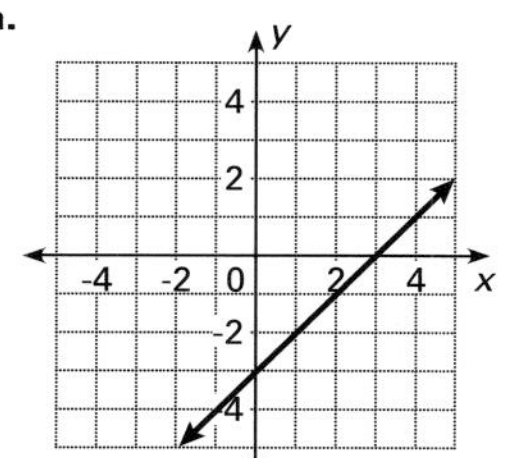

b.

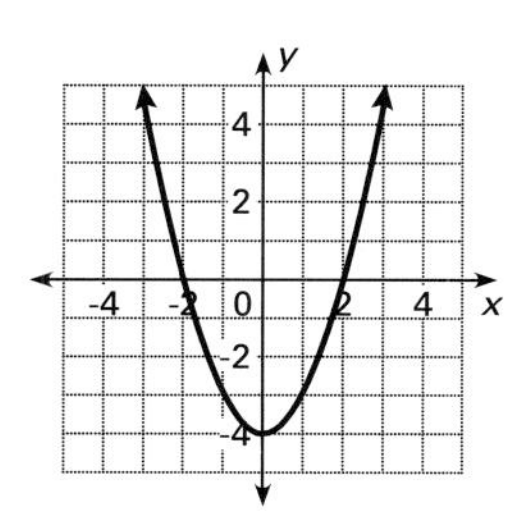

8. a. $x = 3$ **b.** $x = 0$ **9.** $x = -4$
10. $y < 7$

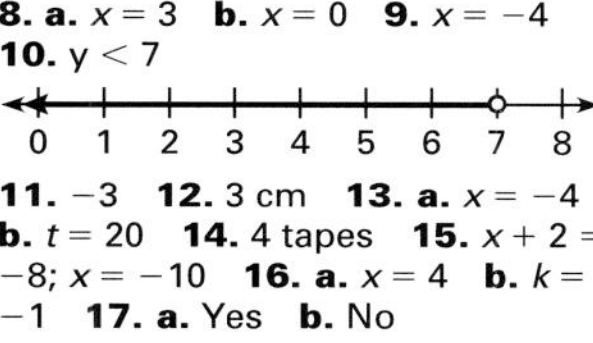

11. −3 **12.** 3 cm **13. a.** $x = -4$ **b.** $t = 20$ **14.** 4 tapes **15.** $x + 2 = -8$; $x = -10$ **16. a.** $x = 4$ **b.** $k = -1$ **17. a.** Yes **b.** No

Cumulative Review Chapters 1–10

1. A **2.** A **3.** B **4.** B **5.** C **6.** B **7.** C **8.** C **9.** D **10.** B **11.** D **12.** A **13.** C **14.** C **15.** C **16.** B

Chapter 11

11-1 Try It

a. Triangular prism **b.** Pentagonal pyramid
c.

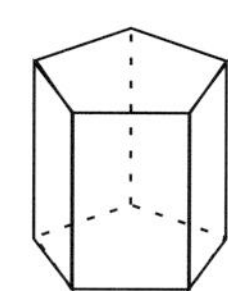

11-1 Exercises & Applications

1. Possible answer:

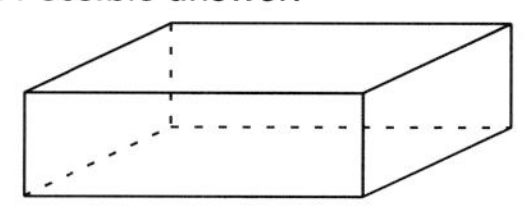

3. 2 triangles, 3 rectangles
5. Pentagonal prism **7.** Right triangular prism **11.** Rectangular pyramid **13.** C **15. a.** Tetrahedron: 4 faces, 6 edges, 4 vertices; Hexahedron: 6 faces, 12 edges, 8 vertices; Octahedron: 8 faces, 12 edges, 6 vertices **b.** Number of faces + Number of vertices − Number of edges = 2 **17.** 60 faces, 120 edges, 80 vertices
19.

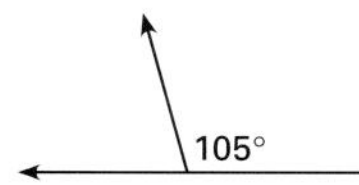

21. II **23.** III **25.** I

11-2 Try It (Example 1)

1. A **2.** B

11-2 Try It (Examples 2–3)

a.

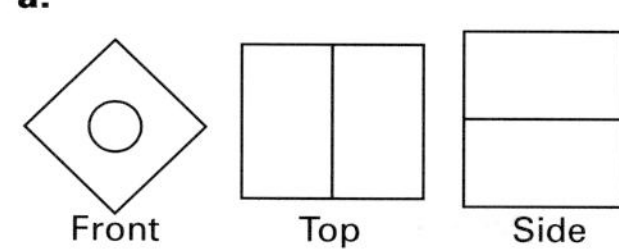

b.

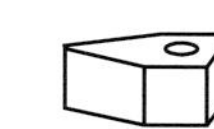

11-2 Exercises & Applications

1. a–c.

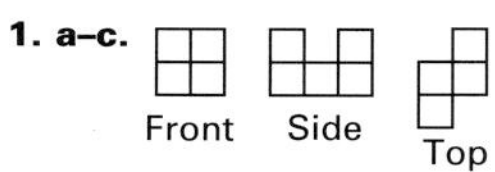

3. 7 **5.** C **7.** A **17.** Perpendicular **19.** Perpendicular **21.** Constant **23.** Variable

11-3 Try It

a.

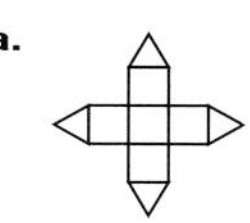

112 ft^2 **b.** 610 mm^2

11-3 Exercises & Applications

1. a. 40 cm^2 **b.** 130 cm^2 **c.** 150 cm^2 **d.** 48 cm^2 **e.** 368 cm^2 **5.** 184 cm^2 **7.** 168 cm^2 **9.** 7 gal **11.** C **13.** a and c **15. a.** Yes; Any piece other than a corner **b.** No **c.** Yes; Any corner piece **17.** Quadrilateral, parallelogram, rectangle, rhombus, square **19.** Obtuse, scalene triangle **21.** Measure of base or height

11-4 Try It

a. 48 ft^3 **b.** 55,000 cm^3

11-4 Exercises & Applications

1. a. 24 cm^2 **b.** $24 \cdot 9 = 216$ **c.** 216 cm^3 **3.** 42 in^3 **5.** 450 mm^3 **7.** 160 m^3 **9.** A **11.** The volume of the prism would be 3 times the volume of the pyramid. **13.** 1800° **15.** 2700° **17.** 3; Always 3 **19.** $\frac{1}{14}$; $\frac{1}{2n+4}$

SELECTED ANSWERS

SELECTED ANSWERS

709

SELECTED ANSWERS

Section 11A Review

1. True **3.** True **9.** Area: 30 cm^2; Volume: 7 cm^3 **11.** Area: ≈ 339.048 in^2; Volume: 339.184 in^3

11-5 Try It

a.

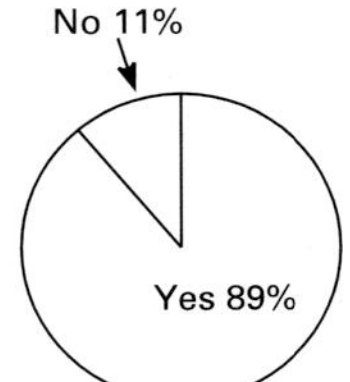

People who've heard of Slinky

b.

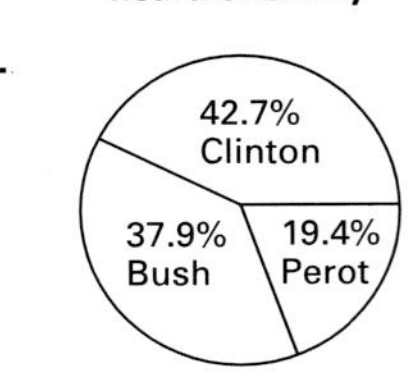

11-5 Exercises & Applications

1. a. 104.4° **b.** 40% is 144°; 31% is 111.6°
c–e.

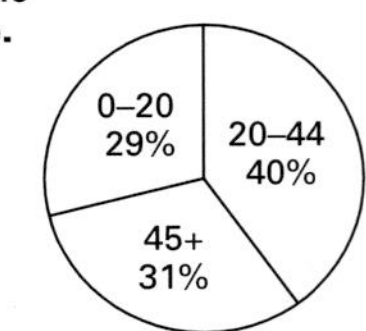

Ages of People in the US, 1990

3. Republican; The sector is greater than 50% of the circle. **7.** 864 **15.** $A = 68$ in^2; $P = 42$ in. **17.** $A = 7.2$ cm^2; $P = 36.8$ cm **19.** $A = 10{,}875$ mi^2; $P = 440$ mi **21.** $y = -8, -9, -10, -11, -12, -13$

11-6 Try It

$d = 64$ in.; $C \approx 201$ in.

11-6 Exercises & Applications

1. a. 10 cm **b.** 31.4 cm **3.** $d = 8$ cm; $C = 25.1$ cm **5.** $d = 16.4$ m; $C = 51.5$ m **7.** $23\frac{4}{7}$ ft **9.** $d = 16$ cm; $C \approx 50.2$ cm **11.** $d \approx 1.9$ mm; $r \approx 1.0$ mm **13.** $r = 25.5$ ft; $C \approx 160.1$ ft **15.** $d = 200$ in.; $C \approx 628.0$ in. **17.** $d \approx 28.0$ ft; $r \approx 14.0$ ft **19.** D **21.** 157 in. **23.** The $\frac{\text{circumference}}{\text{diameter}}$ ratio for all circles is π. It doesn't matter how big or small the circle is. **25.** 51 mi/hr **27.** 17 students for 1 teacher

11-7 Try It

a. 1256 in^2 **b.** 122.7 cm^2

11-7 Exercises & Applications

1. a. 8 in. **b.** A ≈ 200.96 in^2 **3.** 28.3 cm^2 **5.** 1589.6 ft^2 **7.** $38\frac{1}{2}$ ft^2 **9.** 12.6 cm^2 **11.** 73,504.3 ft^2 **13.** 78.5 cm^2 **15.** 60.8 m^2 **17.** ≈ 113.04 ft^2 **19.** $\frac{22}{7} = 3.1428571...$ is closer. **23.** ≈ 286 in^2 **25.** 48 hr **27.** 5 lb **29.** 42 gallons **31.** $x = 5$ **33.** $x = -25$

11-8 Try It

a. 81.6 in^2 **b.** 366.2 in^2

11-8 Exercises & Applications

1. a. 78.5 cm^2 **b.** 157 cm^2 **c.** 31.4 cm **d.** 628 cm^2 **e.** 785 cm^2 **5.** D **7.** 113.0 cm^2 **9.** 117.8 m^2 **11.** ≈ 25.1 in^2 **13.** ≈ 125.6 in^2 **17.** 184,800 ft/hr **19.** $x = 3$ **21.** $x = 2$

11-9 Try It (Examples 1–2)

a. ≈ 1152 cm^3 **b.** 1384.7 in^3

11-9 Try It (Example 3)

577 mL

11-9 Exercises & Applications

1. a. ≈ 28.26 in^2 **b.** ≈ 113.04 in^3 **c.** 113.0 in^3 **3.** 300 cm^3 **5.** 8164 mm^3 **7.** 1256 in^3 **9.** 52.2 cm^3 **11.** About 15.3 in^3 **13.** 1130.4 mL **15.** 879.6 mL **17.** Liquid foods, or foods packed in liquid, tend to come in cans; dry foods tend to come in boxes. Liquids need to be packed in metal (or plastic), not cardboard, and metal boxes are difficult to make (and dangerous to have on tall shelves). **19.** No **21.** Yes

Section 11B Review

3. $C = 56.5$ cm; $A = 254.3$ cm^2 **5.** About 1.6 ft **7.** $V = 141.3$ in^3; $SA = 150.7$ in^2 **9.** A

11-10 Try It (Example 1)

C and D

11-10 Try It (Examples 2–3)

(−5, 1), (−5, 5), (−3, 4)

11-10 Exercises & Applications

1. a-c.

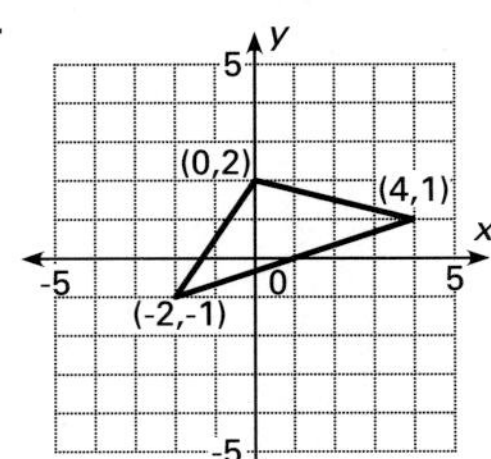

3. C **5.** The image shows horizontal translations of a basic pattern. **7.** $(x, y) \rightarrow (x - 5, y + 7)$ **9.** $(x, y) \rightarrow (x, y - 3)$ **11.** (0, 0) **13.** (−3, 4) **15.** (−1, 4), (4, 4), (−1, 2), and (4, 2) **17.** (−5, 3), (0, 3), (−5, 1), and (0, 1) **19.** No **21.** x and z are 9 cm, y is 18 cm **23.** $a = 3$ **25.** $c = 20$ **27.** $m = 4$ **29.** $f = 9.5$ **31.** $c = -21$ **33.** $k = -2$

11-11 Try It (Examples 1–3)

a.

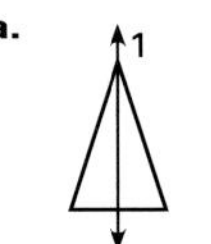

b.

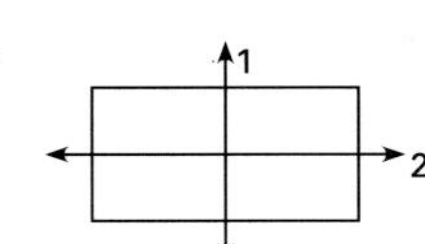

SELECTED ANSWERS

710

c.

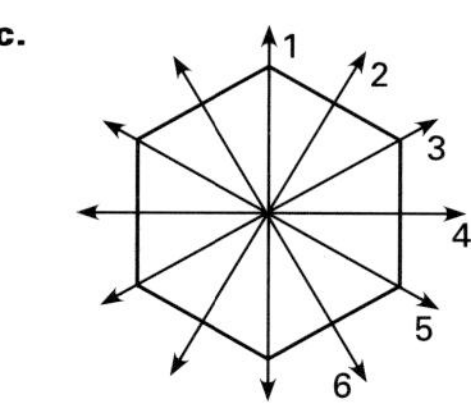

11-11 Try It (Example 4)

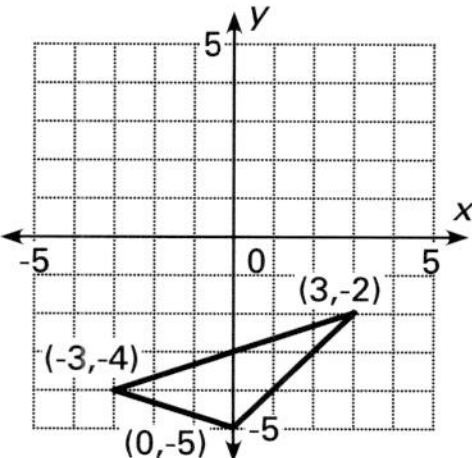

$A'(3, -2)$, $B'(-3, -4)$, $C'(0, -5)$

11-11 Exercises & Applications

1. a–c.

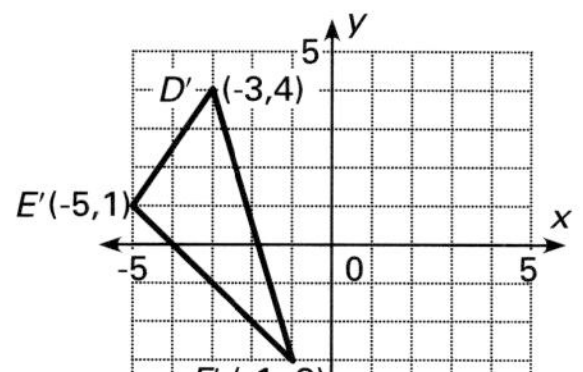

3. Yes **5.** Yes **7.** B **9.** (0, 4), (3, 1), and (5, 2) **13.** Regular polygons have the same number of lines of symmetry as they have sides. **17.** Perimeter: 30 in.; Area: 50 in^2 **19.** $m = -45$ **21.** $y = 0$ **23.** $d = 42$ **25.** $z = 52$

11-12 Try It

No

11-12 Exercises & Applications

1. Yes, it has 180° rotational symmetry. **3.** $\frac{1}{2}$ **5.** $\frac{1}{4}, \frac{1}{2}, \frac{3}{4}$ **7.** 2, 3, 5 **9.** C **11.** 180° **13. a.** $D'(0, 0)$, $E'(4, -1)$, $F'(0, -3)$ **b.** $D'(0, 0)$, $E'(-1, -4)$, $F'(-3, 0)$ **c.** $D'(0, 0)$, $E'(-4, 1)$, $F'(0, 3)$ **15. a.** $\frac{1}{3}, \frac{2}{3}$ **b.** $\frac{1}{4}, \frac{1}{2}, \frac{3}{4}$ **c.** $\frac{1}{5}, \frac{2}{5}, \frac{3}{5}, \frac{4}{5}$ **d.** $\frac{1}{6}, \frac{1}{3}, \frac{1}{2}, \frac{2}{3}, \frac{5}{6}$ **e.** A regular polygon with n sides has rotational symmetry for every multiple of the quotient of $\frac{360°}{n}$. **17.** $\frac{x}{100} = \frac{25}{125}$; $x = 20$ **19.** $x = 21$ **21.** $m = 13$ **23.** $v = 8$ **25.** $x = -1$

Section 11C Review

1. (0, 0), (4, 0), and (1, −5) **3.** (1, 2) **7.** D

Chapter 11 Summary & Review

1. 6
2.

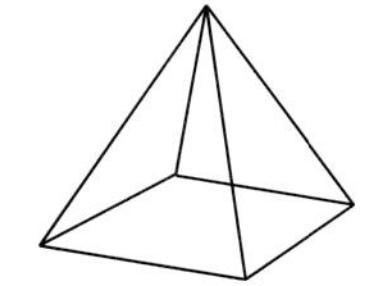

8 edges, 5 faces, 5 vertices
3. a. Answers will vary. **b.** SA = 520 in^2, V = 600 in^3
4.

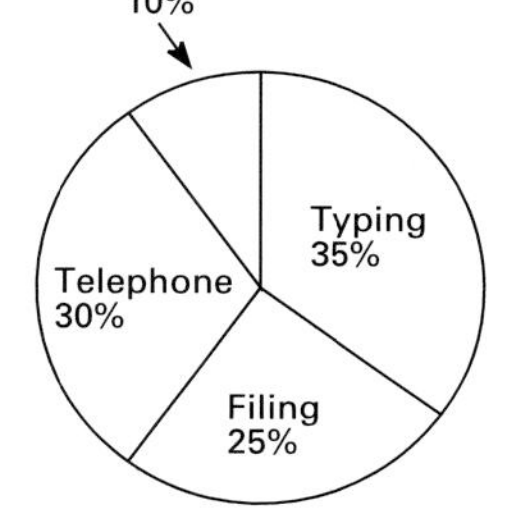

5. Circumference, 138.0 m; Area, 1517.0 m^2 **6.** Surface area, 533.8 cm^2; Volume, 942 cm^3

7.

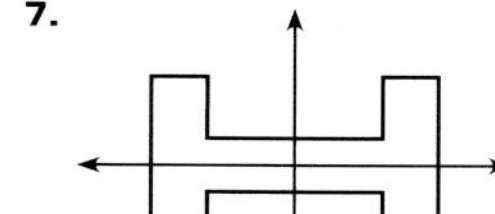

Yes **8.** $A'(-7, 1)$ **9. b.** $A'(0, 0)$, $B'(4, 0)$, $C'(6, -3)$, and $D'(2, -5)$ **c.** $A'(0, 0)$, $B'(0, -4)$, $C'(3, -6)$, and $D'(5, -2)$

Chapter 12

12-1 Try It (Example 1)

There are 6 different outcomes for juice orders.

12-1 Try It (Examples 2–3)

20

12-1 Exercises & Applications

1. a. 12 **b.** 36 **c.** Counting Principle **3.** 24 **5.** 24 **7.** 120 **9.** 144 **11.** 144

12-2 Try It (Examples 1–2)

120

12-2 Try It (Examples 3–5)

a. 24 **b.** 3,628,800 **c.** 3024

12-2 Exercises & Applications

1. a. 4 **b.** 3 **c.** 2 **d.** 1 **e.** 24 **3.** 5040 **5.** 362,880 **7.** ARY, AYR, RAY, RYA, YAR, YRA (A = Arimora, R = Roba, Y = Yegorova) **9.** ABCD, ABDC, ACBD, ACDB, ADBC, ADCB, BACD, BADC, BCAD, BCDA, BDAC, BDCA, CABD, CADB, CBAD, CBDA, CDAB, CDBA, DABC, DACB, DBAC, DBCA, DCAB, DCBA; None of the orderings form words. **11.** C **13.** The factorial product $x!$ increases very quickly as x increases. **15.** Surface area = 216 cm^2 **17.** Surface area = 56 in^2 **19.** 168 m^3

12-3 Try It

a. 3 **b.** 10

SELECTED ANSWERS

711

12-3 Exercises & Applications

1. a. Alex and Bess, Alex and Chandra **b.** Bess and Chandra **c.** 3 **3.** Yes **5.** 6 **7.** 1 **9.** 20 **11.** B **13. a.** 20 **b.** 120 **c.** The number in b is greater **17.** 25.1 in. **19.** 34.5 mm

Section 12A Review

1. 12 **3.** There are 8 possibilities. **5.** 40,320 **7.** 720 **9. a.** 1000 **b.** 720 **11.** A

12-4 Try It (Examples 3–4)

a. 1:1 **b.** 2:4

12-4 Try It (Examples 5–6)

a. 1:1 odds for both; Fair **b.** Odds for A = 2:1, odds for B = 1:2; Unfair **c.** Odds for Evan = 3:3, odds for Primo = 3:3, odds for Trace = 2:4; Unfair

12-4 Exercises & Applications

1. a. 2 **b.** 4 **c.** 2:4 **3.** 1, 2, 3, 4, 5, 6, 7, or 8 **5.** 1:1 **7.** 2:3 **9.** 104:66 **11.** 2:52 **13.** 26:28 **15.** 16:38 **17.** Odds for A = 1:5, odds for B = 4:2, odds for C = 1:5; Unfair **21.** Yes **23.** 706.5 in^2 **25.** 0.8 m^2

12-5 Try It (Examples 1–3)

a. $\frac{1}{3} \approx 33.3\% = 0.333$ **b.** $\frac{1}{2} = 50\% = 0.5$ **c.** $\frac{3}{10} = 30\% = 0.3$

12-5 Try It (Examples 4–5)

a. $\frac{7}{8}$ **b.** $\frac{1}{100}$; 1:99

12-5 Exercises & Applications

1. a. 12 **b.** $\frac{3}{12}$ **c.** $\frac{1}{4}$ **3.** $\frac{1}{6} \approx 16.7\% = 0.167$ **5. a.** 75.1% **b.** 24.9% **c.** 18.4% **7.** Probability does not = $\frac{7}{8}$; Odds = 1:7 **9.** Probability = $\frac{1}{2}$; Odds = 1:1 **11.** $\frac{1}{2}$ **13.** $\frac{1}{8}$ **15.** $\frac{55}{99} = \frac{5}{9}$ **17.** 1% **19.** 56%

21. Possible answers: A dropped ball will fall down (probability 1); A person will jump to the moon tomorrow (probability 0). **23.** 9118.6 cm^3 **25.** 1356.5 in^3 **27.** $(x + 4, y - 6)$ **29.** $(x - 0.2, y + 7)$

12-6 Try It (Examples 1–2)

a. 0.58 **b.** $\frac{8}{72} = \frac{1}{9}$; Less than the theoretical probability of $\frac{6}{36} = \frac{1}{6}$

12-6 Try It (Examples 3–4)

$\frac{6}{128} = \frac{3}{64}$

12-6 Exercises & Applications

1. a. 10 in^2 **b.** 60 in^2 **c.** $\frac{10}{60} = \frac{1}{6}$ **3.** $\frac{9}{72} = \frac{1}{8}$ **5.** $\frac{15}{72} = \frac{5}{24}$ **7.** $\frac{1}{72}$ **9.** $\frac{3}{36} = \frac{1}{12}$; Less than experimental **11.** $\frac{6}{36} = \frac{1}{6}$; Less than experimental **13.** $\frac{1}{36}$; Greater than experimental **15.** $\frac{48}{80} = 60\%$ **17.** An estimate from 1000 trials would give more confidence. **19.** $\frac{9}{144} = \frac{1}{16}$ **21. a.** Experimental **b.** Possible data set: 10 injured fire fighters, 36 uninjured **23.** Figure has one line of symmetry. **25.** Figure has one line of symmetry.

12-7 Try It (Examples 1–2)

a. Dependent **b.** Independent

12-7 Try It (Examples 4–5)

a. $\frac{1}{10}$ **b.** $\frac{7}{30}$

12-7 Exercises & Applications

1. a. $\frac{5}{10}$ **b.** 4 green cubes; 9 cubes **c.** $\frac{4}{9}$ **d.** $\frac{2}{9}$ **3.** Independent **5.** $\frac{1}{48}$ **7.** $\frac{1}{4}$ **9. a.** $\frac{1}{16} = 6.25\%$ **b.** No **13.** D **15.** 5%, 14% **17.** 6

Section 12B Review

1. 1, 2, 3, 4, 5, 6, 7, 8, 9, 10 **3.** 4:2 **7.** $\frac{3}{10} = 30\% = 0.3$ **9.** $\frac{4}{5} = 80\% = 0.8$ **11.** Independent **13.** $\frac{1}{4}$

Chapter 12 Summary & Review

1. 60 **2.** The store needs 8 bins. **3.** 15 **4.** 24 **5.** TUV, TVU, UVT, UTV, VTU, VUT **6.** 21 **7.** 5:3 **8.** Melanie's odds = 4:3, Nathan's odds = 3:4; Unfair **9. a.** $\frac{4}{6} = \frac{2}{3}$ **b.** $\frac{2}{6} = \frac{1}{3}$ **10.** 8% **11.** $\frac{11}{25}$ **12.** $\frac{4}{9}$ **13.** $\frac{1}{12}$ **14.** $\frac{5}{11} \cdot \frac{4}{10} = \frac{2}{11}$

Cumulative Review Chapters 1–12

1. A **2.** D **3.** C **4.** C **5.** D **6.** A **7.** C **8.** B **9.** B **10.** C **11.** D **12.** D **13.** B **14.** C **15.** A

SELECTED ANSWERS

712

Photographs

Cover/Spine Dugald Bremner/Tony Stone Images

Front Matter **iii** GHP Studio* **iii (background)** John Banagan/The Image Bank **v–xvi T (border)** GHP Studio* **xviii BC** GHP Studio* **xviii TC** Thomas Johnson/Earthviews **xviii BL** David Madison **xviii BR** Adam Peiperl/The Stock Market **xix T** Parker/Boon Productions and Dorey Sparre Photography* **xix B** Dennis Geaney,* Ken Karp* and Parker/Boon Productions and Dorey Sparre Photography* **xxi** Anne Dowie* **xxii** Anne Dowie* **xxiii** Anne Dowie* **xxiv** Roz Chast © 1995 from The New Yorker Magazine, Inc. **xxv** Richard Steinheimer **xxvi** Ken Karp* **xxviii** Ken Karp* **xxix** William R. Sallaz/Duomo

Chapter 1 **2–3 (background)** Allen Lee Page/The Stock Market **2 TL** Giraudon/Art Resource, NY **2 BL** SEF/Art Resource, NY **2 R** Reed Saxon/AP Photo **2 TR** Cheryl Fenton* **3** Ken Karp* **4** Cheryl Fenton* **5 L** Don Mason/The Stock Market **5 R** Geoffrey Nilsen Photography* **6** Lawrence Migdale/Tony Stone Images **8** Shaw McCutcheon/Bruce Coleman Inc. **10** Nathan T. Wright/Bruce Coleman Inc. **11 L** J. Messerschmidt/ Bruce Coleman Inc. **11 R** ©1996, USA TODAY. Reprinted with permission. Photo by Cheryl Fenton* **12** UPI/Corbis-Bettmann **13 T** Cameramann/The Image Works **13 B** Rich Iwasaki/Tony Stone Images **15** Library of Congress **16** Tim Davis* **18** Chad Ehlers/ Tony Stone Images **19** GHP Studio* **20** Stanley King Collection **21 R** Dan Dancer/Herd/Sipa Press **21 L** Ken Karp* **24** Robie Price* **27 T** Don Mason/The Stock Market **27 R** Geoffrey Nilsen Photography* **28** Will & Deni McIntyre/Photo Researchers **29 TL** David Madison **29 TR** David Madison/ Bruce Coleman Inc. **29 B** Jim Cummins/FPG International **30** Court Mast/FPG International **31** Culver Pictures **32** Cheryl Fenton* **33** Andrea Sperling/FPG International **34** Otto Greule/ Allsport **35** Geoffrey Nilsen Photography* **36** Bill Losh/FPG International **38** Andy Lyons/ Allsport **40 R** David Madison **40 L** Clive Mason/ Allsport **41** The Image Bank **42 R** Parker/Boon Productions and Dorey Sparre Photography* **42 L** Dennis Geaney* **43 T** David Madison **43 B** Cheryl Fenton* **44 T** Stephen Dunn/Allsport **45** Jim Cummins/FPG International **46** Stephen Dunn/Allsport **47** Geoffrey Nilsen Photography* **51 TL** David Madison **51 BL (capitol)** Richard Pasley/Stock, Boston **51 BL (tiles)** Cheryl Fenton* **51 TR** Cheryl Fenton* **51 BR** George B. Fry III*

Chapter 2 **52–53 (background)** GHP Studio* **52 B** Photo © Michael Holford/Collection British Museum **52 TL** David Madison **52 TR** Jenny Thomas* **53 B** Cheryl Fenton* **53 T** Joe McDonald/Animals, Animals **54 T** E. R. Degginger/ Animals, Animals **54 B** Johnny Johnson/DRK Photo **55** Cindy Lewis **56** Will & Deni McIntyre/ Tony Stone Images **58** Renee Lynn/Davis-Lynn Images **59** Ford Motor Company **60 L** Phil Degginger/Bruce Coleman Inc. **60 R** Cheryl Fenton* **61** GHP Studio* **62** Cindy Lewis **63** Tim Davis/Davis-Lynn Images **66** Anne Dowie* **68** Ken Karp* **69** Archive Photos **70** Maxell Corporation of America **71** Cindy Lewis **72** Tony Arruza/The Image Works **73 (inset)** The Bancroft Library, University of California **73 (background)** Steve Solum/Bruce Coleman Inc. **74 L** Mindscape, Inc. **74 R** Jenny Thomas* **77** Art Wolfe/Tony Stone Images **78** Cheryl Fenton.* Drawing from the collection of Jeff Kelly **80** Detroit Industry, North Wall (detail of fresco), 1932–1933 by Diego Rivera. Accession no. 33.10N (detail). Photograph © 1996 The Detroit Institute of Arts, Gift of Edsel B. Ford. **81** Long Term Parking, sculpture by Arman. Photo by Gianfranco Gorgoni/Sygma **82** Rene Sheret/Tony Stone Images **83** Photo © Michael Holford/Collection British Museum **84 L** Charles D. Winters/ Photo Researchers **84 R** Eric Gravé/ Photo Researchers **85** Culver Pictures **86** Dr. Jeremy Burgess/SPL/Photo Researchers **87** NMAI/Smithsonian Institution **88** Ken Karp* **89** David J. Sams/Stock, Boston **90** Cheryl Fenton* **91** Jose L. Pelaez/The Stock Market **92** Corbis-Bettmann **93** GHP Studio* **94** David Madison **95** Steve Solum/Bruce Coleman Inc. **97** Geoffrey Nilsen Photography*

Chapter 3 **102–103 (background)** M. L. Sinibaldi/The Stock Market **102 TL** Cheryl Fenton* **102 TC** Ulrike Welsch **102 TR** Ulrike Welsch **102 BL** Alfred Pasieka/G&J Images/ The Image Bank **103 T** Cheryl Fenton* **103 B** Naomi Duquid/Asia Access **104 T** Cheryl Fenton* **104 B** Aneal F. Vohra/Unicorn Stock Photos **105** World Perspectives/Tony Stone Images **106** Topham/The Image Works **110 L** Richard Hutchings/Photo Researchers **110 R** USGS/NASA **111** Finley Holiday Films **113** Ken Karp* **114** Julian Baum/SPL/Photo Researchers **115 L** NASA/JPL Special Services **115 R** Cheryl Fenton* **116** James Balog/Tony Stone Images **117 T** Ken Karp* **117 B** Parker/Boon Productions and Dorey Sparre Photography* **118** fotos internacional/Archive Photos **119** Finley Holiday Film **120** John Lei* **121** NASA **123** Francois Gohier/Photo Researchers **124** Finley Holiday Film **125** John Lei* **127** Yerkes Observatory Photograph **129** Biophoto Associates/Photo Researchers **130** Cheryl Fenton* **131** World Perspectives/Tony Stone Images **132** NASA/Dan McCoy/The Stock Market **133** Ken Karp* **134 L** Peter Beck/The Stock Market **134 R** G. Holz/ The Image Works **137** Jane Lidz **139 L** GHP Studio* **139 R** Mike Greenlar/The Image Works **140** Ken Karp* **141** Ken Karp **143** Cheryl Fenton* **144 L** Mark Loader/Uniphoto Picture Agency **144 R** Cheryl Fenton* **146** Ken Karp* **147** Courtesy of The Selmer Company **148** Wolfgang Kaehler **149** Anne Dowie* **150** Cheryl Fenton* **151** G. C. Kelley/Photo Researchers **152** Bob Daemmrich/Stock, Boston **153 L** Cheryl Fenton* **153 R** Anne Dowie* **154** Richard Pasley/Liaison International **155 T** JPL/NASA **155 B** GHP Studio* **156** Cheryl Fenton* **157 L** GHP Studio* **157 R** Ken Karp* **158** Cheryl Fenton* **159** Geoffrey Nilsen Photography* **163 TL** Ken Karp* **163 TR** Cheryl Fenton* **163 BL** Renee Lynn/ Davis-Lynn Images **163 BR** GHP Studio*

Chapter 4 **164–165 (background)** Cheryl Fenton* **164 TL** Cheryl Fenton* **164 TR** GHP Studio* **164 B** Photo © Michael Holford/ Collection British Museum **165 T** Anne Dowie* **165 B T.** A. Wiewandt/DRK Photo **166 T** GHP Studio* **166 B** John Margolies/Esto **167 T** Jonathan Kirn/Liaison International **167 C** Jon Riley/Tony Stone Images **167 B** Tim Flach/Tony Stone Images **168** Ed Bock/The Stock Market **169** Ken Karp* **170** Bryan F. Peterson/The Stock Market **171 L** Joe McDonald/Animals, Animals **171 C** Stephen Green-Armytage/The Stock Market **171 R** Roy Morsch/The Stock Market **172** Roger Tully/Tony Stone Images **173** Pierre Boulat/ Cosmos/Woodfin Camp & Associates **175** Laima Druskis/Photo Researchers **176** Adam Lubroth/ Liaison International **178** Joe Quever* **179** Ed Lallo/Liaison International **180 L** Dennis Geaney* **180 R** Ken Karp* **181** UPI/Corbis-Bettmann **183 L** Ken Karp* **183 TR** Jonathan Kirn/Liaison International **183 CR** Jon Riley/Tony Stone Images **183 BR** Tim Flach/Tony Stone Images **184** Tim Davis/Photo Researchers **185** Ken Karp* **186** Crandall/The Image Works **187** Union Pacific Railroad **189** Ken Karp* **190** Tim Fitzharris/ Masterfile **191** Joe Quever* **193 L** Ken Karp* **193 R** Dennis Geaney* **194** Porter Gifford/Liaison International **195** Cheryl Fenton* **197** Cheryl Fenton* **200** Bob Daemmrich/Stock, Boston **201** Ken Karp* **202 L** Zefa Germany/The Stock Market **202 R** Tim Davis/Tony Stone Images **203** Geoffrey Nilsen Photography*

Chapter 5 **208–209 (background)** Rafael Macía/Photo Researchers **208 TR** GHP Studio* **208 L** ©1997 photo by Kunio Hirano/ORION PRESS, Tokyo **209 T** Roberto de Gugliemo/ SPL/Photo Researchers **209 B** Bob Burch/ Bruce Coleman Inc. **210 T** Cheryl Fenton* **210 B** Parker/Boon Productions and Dorey Sparre Photography* **211** Jon Simon/Liaison International **212 L** Marty Katz/Woodfin Camp & Associates **212 R** David Barnes/ Tony Stone Images **213** Cheryl Fenton* **214** Ron Sanford/Tony Stone Images **216** Ken Kay/Fundamental Photographs **217 TL** Ken Karp* **217 TR** Greg Stott/Masterfile **217 B** Robert Fried/Stock, Boston **219** GHP Studio* **220** 1994 by Rand McNally R.L. 94-S-140 **221 L** Bob Krist/The Stock Market **221 R** P. Hammerschmidt/Okapia/Photo Researchers **222 L** Lisl Dennis/The Image Bank **223** Cheryl Fenton* **224** Harvey Lloyd/The Stock Market **226 L** Rafael Macia/Photo Researchers **226 C** Catherine Karnow/Woodfin Camp & Associates **226 R** M. Granitsas/The Image Works **227 T** Michal Heron/The Stock Market **227 TL** Cheryl Fenton* **227 B** Tony Craddock/SPL/Photo Researchers **228** J. C. Carton/Bruce Coleman Inc. **229 L** Ken Karp* **229 R** Parker/Boon Productions and Dorey Sparre Photography* **230 L** Wendell Metzen/Bruce Coleman Inc. **230 R** Springer/ Liaison International **230 B** GHP Studio* **233** Charles Gupton/Stock, Boston **234** Kevin R. Morris/Tony Stone Images **235** Kay Chernush **236** Peter Mauss/Esto **237 L** Kevin Schafer/ Tony Stone Images **237 R** Jon Simon/Liaison International **239** Cheryl Fenton* **240 L** M. Douglas/The Image Works **240 R** GHP Studio* **241** Cheryl Fenton* **242 L** Ken Karp* **242 R** Miles Ertman/Masterfile **244** Renee Lynn* **247** David Madison **248** Lee Foster/Bruce Coleman Inc. **250** Cheryl Fenton* **251** Schiller/ The Image Works **252** Cheryl Fenton* **253** GHP Studio* **254** Lionello Fabbri/Photo Researchers **258 L** Baron Wolman **258 R** John Margolies/ ESTO **260** Parker/Boon Productions and Dorey Sparre Photography* **261** Kal Muller/Woodfin Camp & Associates **262** Craig Wells/Liaison International **263** Cheryl Fenton* **264** Claus Andersen/Masterfile **265** Geoffrey Nilsen Photography* **269 L** John Elk/Stock, Boston **269 TR** GHP Studio* **269 B** David Rosenberg/ Tony Stone Images

Chapter 6 **270–271 (background)** Cheryl Fenton* **270 L** Cheryl Fenton* **270 TR** Jack Vartoogian **270 BR** The Oakland Museum of California **271 T** Peter Menzel/Stock, Boston **271 B** Nancy Fix/Stock, Boston **272 B** NASA **272 T** Warren Faidley/Weatherstock **273** Will & Deni McIntyre/Photo Researchers **274** David Sailors/The Stock Market **275 T** Scala/Art Resource, NY **275 B** Jeff Hunter/The Image Bank **276** Ned Gillette/The Stock Market **277** Dale O'Dell/The Stock Market **278** David Pollack/ The Stock Market **279** Jim Pickerell/The Image Works **280** M. Siluk/The Image Works **281** William Johnson/Stock, Boston **282** Ken Karp*

283 Howard Sochurek/Woodfin Camp & Associates **284** Donald Dietz/Stock, Boston **285** © Aardman Animations/Wallace and Gromit Ltd. 1995 **286 L** Brownie Harris/The Stock Market **286 R** Erwin and Peggy Bauer/Bruce Coleman Inc. **287** Ken Karp* **288 L** Ken Karp* **288 R** Dennis Geaney* **289** David Madison **290** Art Wolfe/Tony Stone Images **291 TL** Ken Karp* **291 BL** Scala/Art Resource, NY **291 R** Will & Deni McIntyre/Photo Researchers **292** David Madison **293** Art Wolfe/ Tony Stone Images **294 L** Cheryl Fenton* **294 R** Pieter Arend Folkens **297** Richard Ellis/Photo Researchers **298 L** Alvis Upitis/The Image Bank **298 R** Thomas Johnson/Earthviews **299** Francois Gohier/Photo Researchers **301** Stuart Westmorland/Tony Stone Images **302** Joseph Van/The Image Bank **304 L** Anne Dowie* **304 BR** Tim Davis* **305** Stephen Frink/The Stock Market **306** Culver Pictures **307** Cheryl Fenton* **308 L** Ken Karp* **308 R** Paul Souders/Tony Stone Images **309** Steinhart Aquarium, photo by Tom McHugh/Photo Researchers **310** Ken Karp* **311** Nicholas Conte/Bruce Coleman Inc. **313** Art Wolfe/Tony Stone Images **314** Joe Cavaretta/Wide World Photos **315** Geoffrey Nilsen Photography*

Chapter 7 **320–321 (background)** GHP Studio* **320 TL** Katrine Naleid* **320 TR** Judith Canty/Stock, Boston **320 B** Corbis-Bettmann **321 T** European Space Agency/SPL/Photo Researchers **321 C** GHP Studio* **321 B** New York Public Library, courtesy of Map Division, Astor, Lenox & Tilden Foundations **322 T** Ken Karp* **322 B** George B. Fry III* **323** Smithsonian Institution, photo #83.3049 **324 L** © AAA, reproduced by permission. Photo by Cheryl Fenton* **324 TR** Quattrocchi Architects **324 B** Minnesota State Map ©Rand McNally 352-2-9611. Photo by Ken Karp* **325** Ken Karp* **326** RAGA/ The Stock Market **327 T** Brent Jones **327 B** Illustration from THE HOBBIT. Copyright © 1966 by J.R.R. Tolkien. Reprinted by permission of Houghton Mifflin Company. All rights reserved. **328** Bob Daemmrich/Stock, Boston **330 L** Ken Karp* **330 R** Parker/Boon Productions and Dorey Sparre Photography* **331** GHP Studio* **332 L** Blumb/Liaison International **332 R** GHP Studio* **333** Ken Karp* **335** Corbis-Bettmann **336** Courtesy Northampton East High School, Conway, North Carolina **337** Bill Gallery/Stock, Boston **339** William R. Sallaz/Duomo **340** Oscar Mayer, the Oscar Mayer Rhomboid, and the Oscar Mayer Wienermobile are registered trademarks of Kraft Foods, Inc., Madison, Wisconsin and are used with permission. **341** Smithsonian Institution, photo #83.3049 **342** Giraudon/Art Resource, NY **343** Ken Karp* **344 L** John Lei* **344 R** Katrine Naleid* **346** Liza Loeffler* **348** Cheryl Fenton* **349 L** John Lei* **349 R** Eric Carle/Stock, Boston **350 T** Hans Reinhard/Bruce Coleman Inc. **350 B** Vanessa Vick/Photo Researchers **351** Michael Holford **352** William Strode/Woodfin Camp & Associates **353** Nancy Pierce/Photo Researchers **354** Tim Bieber Inc./The Image Bank **355** Gary Holscher/Tony Stone Images **356 T** Laguna Photo/Liaison International **356 B** Katrine Naleid* **357** Ken Karp* **358** Bob Daemmrich/ Stock, Boston **359** Cheryl Fenton* **360 L** John Lei* **360 R** Alan Schein/The Stock Market **360 BR** Ken Karp* **364** Cheryl Fenton* **366** Robb Kendrick/Aurora **368 L** Parker/Boon Productions and Dorey Sparre Photography* **368 R** Ken Karp* **371 L** Steve Starr/Stock, Boston **371 R** Cheryl Fenton* **373** Archive Photos **374 T** John Elk III/Stock, Boston **374 B** Everett Collection **375** Cheryl Fenton* **376 T** Tim Davis/Tony Stone Images **376 B** Everett Collection **377** Geoffrey Nilsen Photography* **381 TL** Photofest **381 TR** California State Railroad Museum **381 BL** GHP Studio*

Chapter 8 **382–383 (background)** Tom Bean/DRK Photo **382 TL** Cheryl Fenton* **382 TR** Alan Schein/The Stock Market **382 B** Cheryl Fenton* **383 T** David Madison/Duomo **383 B** Jon Feingersh/The Stock Market **384 T** GHP Studio* **384 B** Ken Karp* **385** Jane Burton/Bruce Coleman Inc. **386 L** Joe Quever* **386 R** Merlin D. Tuttle **387** John Elk/Stock, Boston **388** ©1996 Cordon Art, Baarn, Holland **389** Merlin D. Tuttle/Bat Conservation International, Inc. **390** Cheryl Fenton* **391** J. McDonald/Bruce Coleman Inc. **393** Michael Fogden/DRK Photo **394** Mark Burnett/Stock, Boston **395** Merlin D. Tuttle **396** Ken Karp* **397** Michael Fogden/DRK Photo **398** Merlin D. Tuttle **399** Jenny Thomas* **400** Wayne Lankinen/DRK Photo **401** Mark Tomalty/ Masterfile **402** Michael Fogden/DRK Photo **403 L** Stephen J. Krasemann/DRK Photo **403 R** Jane Burton/Bruce Coleman Inc. **404** Merlin D. Tuttle **405 (background)** Kevin R. Morris/Tony Stone Images **405 (insets)** Cheryl Fenton* **406** Anne Dowie* **407** GHP Studio* **408** Anne Dowie* **409** Cheryl Fenton* **410** Cheryl Fenton* **411** Cheryl Fenton* **412** Brian Stablyk/Tony Stone Images **414** Robert A. Tyrell **414** Will & Deni McIntyre/Tony Stone Images **415** Joe Quever* **416** Marc Biggins/Liaison International **417** Parker/Boon Productions and Dorey Sparre Photography* **421 (background)** Kevin R. Morris/Tony Stone Images **421 (inset)** Cheryl Fenton* **422** Corbis-Bettmann **423** Geoffrey Nilsen Photography*

Chapter 9 **428–429 (background)** Cheryl Fenton* **428 TL** Robert Fried/Stock, Boston **428 TR** NASA **428 B** Cheryl Fenton* **429 T** Dr. Peter W. Sloss/NOAA/NGDC **429 B** Cheryl Fenton* **430** Cheryl Fenton* **432** Tom Bean/ DRK Photo **433** Barbara Gerlach/DRK Photo **434 L** Peter Essick/Aurora **434 R** Tom McHugh/ Cal. Acad. of Sciences/Photo Researchers **435** NASA, Goddard Institute for Space Studies/ SPL/Photo Researchers **436** Guido Cozzi/Bruce Coleman Inc. **437 L** Sally Beyer/Tony Stone Images **437 R** Ted Horowitz/The Stock Market **439 L** Parker/Boon Productions and Dorey Sparre Photography* **439 R** Ken Karp* **442 T** Roger Richards/Liaison International **442 B** Map Art Corporation **447 L** Leo Touchet/Woodfin Camp & Associates **449** Susan Van Etten/Stock, Boston **450** © 1996, USA TODAY. Reprinted with permission. Photo by Cheryl Fenton* **451** Liza Loeffler* **452** Liza Loeffler* **453** Liza Loeffler* **454** UPI/Corbis-Bettmann **455** Cheryl Fenton* **457** Dan Feicht/ Cedar Point **458** David M. Schleser/ Photo Researchers **461** Jeff Hunter/The Image Bank **464** Dallas & John Heaton/Stock, Boston **465 T** Rocky Widner **465 B** Jeff Greenberg/MRp/ Photo Researchers **466 L** Cheryl Fenton* **466 R** Paramount's Great America **467** Liza Loeffler* **468 L** Parker/Boon Productions and Dorey Sparre Photography* **468 R** Ken Karp* **469** J. L. Bulcao/Liaison International **470** Michele Burgess/The Stock Market **471 L** C. Bruce Forster/ Tony Stone Images **471 R** Susan Van Etten/Stock, Boston **472** Underwood Photo Archives, SF **473** Geoffrey Nilsen Photography* **477 TL** Cheryl Fenton* **477 BL** Stacy Pick/Stock, Boston **477 BR** Cheryl Fenton*

Chapter 10 **478–479 (background)** Gregory Sams/SPL/Photo Researchers **478 TL** Scala/Art Resource, NY **478 TR** GHP Studio* **478 B** Cheryl Fenton* **479** Lifesmith Classic Fractals **480 T** John Elk III **480 B** Rich Buzzelli/ Tom Stack & Associates **481** (ants) Runk-Schoenberger/Grant Heilman Photography **481** (bees) Charles Krebs/Tony Stone Images **481** Katrine Naleid* **482 L** Bryan Peterson/ The Stock Market **482 R** Dr. Jeremy Burgess/SPL/ Photo Researchers **483** Michael Lustbader/Photo Researchers **484** David Overcash/Bruce Coleman Inc. **485** Richard R. Hansen/Photo Researchers **486** Donald C. Johnson/The Stock Market **487** Aaron Strong/Liaison International **488** Wolfgang Kaehler/Liaison International **490** Phil Degginger/Bruce Coleman Inc. **491 L** ©1997 photo by Noriyuki Yoshida/ORION PRESS, Tokyo **491 R** Kim Taylor/Bruce Coleman Inc. **493** Kjell B. Sandved/Photo Researchers **494** J. M. Burnley/Bruce Coleman Inc. **495** Ken Karp* **498 T** Michael Lustbader/Photo Researchers **498 B** Daniel J. Cox/Liaison International **500** Mark Burnett/Stock, Boston **502 L** Kim Taylor/Bruce Coleman Inc. **502 R** Jeff Lepore/Photo Researchers **503** E. R. Degginger/ Bruce Coleman Inc. **504** Scott Camazine/Photo Researchers **505 L** G & J Images/The Image Bank **505 R** Katrine Naleid* **505 R(inset)** Charles Krebs/Tony Stone Images **506** Richard Hurley/ Courtesy of the John Carter Brown Library at Brown University **507** Cheryl Fenton* **508 L** GHP Studio* **508 R** David Katzenstein **509** David Katzenstein **510** Paul F. Gero/KDI-Champ Cookies **511** Cheryl Fenton* **512 L** Ted Horowitz/The Stock Market **512 R** David Katzenstein **514 L** Parker/Boon Productions and Dorey Sparre Photography* **514 R** Ken Karp* **516** John Zich **517 L** Rex Rystedt Photography **517 R** Ken Karp* **519** Katherine Lambert **520** Charles D. Winters/Photo Researchers **521 L** Jim McHugh **521 R** Cheryl Fenton* **523** NASA Space Photo/The Image Bank **524** Ken Karp* **525** Gary Withey/Bruce Coleman Inc. **526 L** Ken Karp* **526 R** Parker/Boon Productions and Dorey Sparre Photography* **527** Cheryl Fenton* **528** NASA/Liaison International **529** Mark M. Lawrence/Stock Market **530** TASS/Sovfoto/Eastfoto **531** Mike Maple/Woodfin Camp & Associates **532** Robert Caputo/Stock, Boston **533** Coco McCoy/Rainbow **534 L** Spencer Grant/Stock, Boston **534 R** Ken Karp* **536** B. Seitz/Photo Researchers **537** Dagmar Fabricius/Stock, Boston **538** Inga Spence/Tom Stack & Associates **539 L** Keith Gunnar/Bruce Coleman Inc. **539 R** Archive Photos **541** Erwin & Peggy Bauer/Bruce Coleman Inc. **543 L** Christopher Pfau/Wide World Photos **543 R** NASA Space Photo/The Image Bank **545** Geoffrey Nilsen Photography*

Chapter 11 **550–551 (background)** Ken Lax* **550 TL** GHP Studio* **550 TR** Adam Woolfitt/Woodfin Camp & Associates **550 B** GHP Studio* **551 T** Mark Newman/Photo Researchers **551 B** Keren Su/Stock, Boston **552 T** Tim Davis/ Photo Researchers **552 B** Jim Tuten/Animals, Animals **553** Dawn (1962), by Louise Nevelson. Gold painted wood, 94-1/2 × 75-1/2 × 7-3/4." Photograph courtesy PaceWildenstein, New York **554** Antonio Ribeiro/Liaison International **555** Cubi XIX (1964), by David Smith. © Copyright VAGA, NY. Tate Gallery, London/Art Resource, NY **556 L** John Elk III/Stock, Boston **556 R** Peter Menzel/Stock, Boston **557 TL** Breck P. Kent/ Earth Scenes **557 TR** Geoffrey Nilsen* **557 B** Untitled (1975), by Donald Judd. Galvanized iron in ten units, 31" × 9" × 40" each. Donald Judd Estate/VAGA. Photo by Flavin Judd **558 T** Illustration by Amanda Smith, photo by Joe Quever* **558 B** Relief from Sennacherib's Palace at Nineveh. Photo © Michael Holford/Collection British Museum **560** Coco McCoy/Rainbow

562 Black Sun (1969), by Isamu Noguchi. Courtesy of the Seattle City Light 1% for Art Collection **563** Joe Sohm/The Stock Market **566** Memories of Mike (1966), by Larry Bell. Vacuum-plated glass with metal binding. 24" × 24" × 24". Photograph courtesy PaceWildenstein, New York. Photo by Boesch **567** Cheryl Fenton* **568** Brenda Tharp/ Photo Researchers **569** Untitled (1975), by Donald Judd. Galvanized iron in ten units, 31" × 9" × 40" each. Donald Judd Estate/VAGA. Photo by Flavin Judd **571 L** Two Open Modular Cubes/Half-Off (1972) by Sol LeWitt. Tate Gallery, London/Art Resource, NY **571 R** Dawn (1962), by Louise Nevelson. Gold painted wood, 94-1/2 × 75-1/2 × 7-3/4." Photograph courtesy PaceWildenstein, New York **572 T** Kathleen Culbert-Aguilar* **572 B** Una Grande Liberta (1963), by Hubert Dalwood. Aluminum, gilt and wood. 60 × 30 × 10 3/4 (153 × 77 × 27). Collection and photo: Gimpel Fils, London **573 (background)** GHP Studio* **573 (inset)** Wooden horse on wheels from Akhmun, 200 A.D. Photo © Michael Holford/Collection British Museum **574 L** ©1996, USA TODAY. Reprinted with permission. Photo by GHP Studio* **574 R** Cheryl Fenton* **575** Cheryl Fenton* **577** Scott Halleran/Allsport **578** Joe Quever* **579** GHP Studio* **581 L** George Holton/Photo Researchers **581 R** Dr. Tom Kuhn **583** Robert Rathe/Stock, Boston **584 T** Cheryl Fenton* **584 B** GHP Studio* **585** Wolfgang Kaehler **586 T** Cheryl Fenton* **586 B** GHP Studio* **587 L** Ken Karp* **587 R** Kaz Mori/The Image Bank **588** Cheryl Fenton* **589 T** Ken Karp* **589 B** Dennis Geaney* **591 T** GHP Studio* **591 B** Rachel Canto/Rainbow **592 L** Jim Corwin/Tony Stone Images **592 R** GHP Studio* **593 T** GHP Studio* **593 C** Cheryl Fenton* **593 B** Cheryl Fenton* **594** GHP Studio* **595** GHP Studio* **596** Ken Lax* **597** GHP Studio* **598** Corbis-Bettmann **599 (background)** Adam Peiperl/The Stock Market **599 (inset)** Adam Peiperl/The Stock Market **600 T** The Kobal Collection/Touchstone Pictures **600 B** C. Bennett through Scopelens **602** Ken Karp* **605 T** John Eastcott-Yva Momatiuk/Photo Researchers **605 B** Adam Peiperl/The Stock Market **608 L** Adam Peiperl/The Stock Market **608 R** Eric Grave/Photo Researchers **610** Joe Quever* **611** Alfred Pasieka-Science Photo Library/Photo Researchers **613 L** Adam Peiperl/The Stock Market **613 R** Blue, Green, Yellow, Orange, Red (1966), by Ellsworth Kelly. Guggenheim Museum, New York. Photograph by David Heald. © The Solomon R. Guggenheim Foundation, New York. (FN 67.1833) **615 L** Viviane Moos **615 R** Adam Peiperl/The Stock Market **616** C. Bennett through Scopelens **617** Geoffrey Nilsen Photography* **621 TL** Ken Lax* **621 TR** Joe Quever* **621 B** Ken Karp*

Chapter 12 **622–623 (background)** Joe Quever* **622 TL** Jacob Lawrence: Harriet Tubman Series No. 16. Casein tempera on gessoed hardboard, 12 × 17-7/8". Hampton University Museum, Hampton, Virginia **622 TR** Lowell Observatory/NOAO **622 B** Cheryl Fenton* **623 T** Jonathan T. Wright/Bruce Coleman Inc. **623 B** Cheryl Fenton* **624 T** Cheryl Fenton* **624 B** Weinberg-Clark/The Image Bank **625** Cheryl Fenton* **626 L** Stephen J. Krasemann/DRK Photo **626 R** Jenny Thomas* **629** Elliott Smith* **630 T** Pacer Infotec Inc. **630 B** Cheryl Fenton* **631** Cheryl Fenton* **632** Jenny Thomas* **634 T** Richard Pasley/Stock, Boston **634 B** Jeff Lepore/ Photo Researchers **636** Michael Topolovac/David Madison **637** Bruce Iverson **638 L** Parker/Boon Productions and Dorey Sparre Photography* **638 R** Ken Karp* **639** Cheryl Fenton* **641** Cheryl Fenton* **642** Bert Blokhuis/Tony Stone Images **643** Joe Quever* **644 L** J. M. Labat/ Jacana/Photo Researchers **644 R** Cheryl Fenton* **647** Cesar Rubio* **649** Hires Chip/Liaison International **651** GHP Studio* **652** ©1996, USA TODAY. Reprinted with permission. Photo by GHP Studio* **653** Cheryl Fenton* **654 L** David Madison/Bruce Coleman Inc. **654 R** Cheryl Fenton* **657** Cheryl Fenton* **659** Geoff Tomkinson/SPL/Photo Researchers **662** GHP Studio* **665 L** Cheryl Fenton* **665 R** Joe Quever* **667** Geoffrey Nilsen Photography*

*Photographs provided expressly for Addison Wesley Longman, Inc.

Illustrations

Brian Evans: **93b** Terry Guyer: **3d, 9a, 9b, 10b, 12b, 33c, 35a, 36c, 38a, 39f, 43a, 44b, 108a, 109a, 115a, 128a, 138a, 163e, 218b, 219b, 249e, 341a, 347b, 361b, 370b, 381c, 431b, 432a, 432d, 448a, 477a, 479a, 486a, 500a, 500b** Gary Hallgren: **96a** Joe Heiner Studio: All icons and borders. Paul Koziarz: **106a, 173a, 178a, 233a, 248a, 248b, 248c, 248d, 248e, 253a, 253b, 360a, 372a, 375a, 375b, 430a, 430b, 430c, 430d, 563a, 563b, 583a, 583b, 583c, 600a, 610a, 610b, 610c, 659a** Maryland Cartographics: **337a** Marlene May-Howerton: **309b** Patrick Merewether: **631a, 636a, 659b** Precision Graphics: All illustrative technical artwork throughout; all generated electronically. Laurie O'Keefe: **274b, 282b** William Pasini: **7c, 14b, 16b, 24b, 25b, 76a, 172b, 187a, 187b, 192a, 198a, 235a, 257a, 312a, 325a, 326b, 330a, 332a, 336b, 339b, 342b, 392a, 398a, 402b, 403b, 434a, 440c, 442a, 446a, 446b, 540a, 542a, 543b, 544d** QYA Design: **49d, 286b, 300b, 317b, 318b, C3c, C3e, C3f, C6b** Doug Roy: **95a** Rob Schuster: **56a, 64a, 67a, 82a, 86a, 91a, 168a, 177b, 182a, 203a, 263a, 269d, 278a, 284b, 284c, 329a, 329b, 334a, 363e, 367b, 369e, 380c, 410a, 426a, 445b, 459a, 461a, 461b, 469a, 477b, 484b, 489d, 495a, 502b, 629b, 645a, 648a, 660b**

SCOPE AND SEQUENCE

CONTENTS

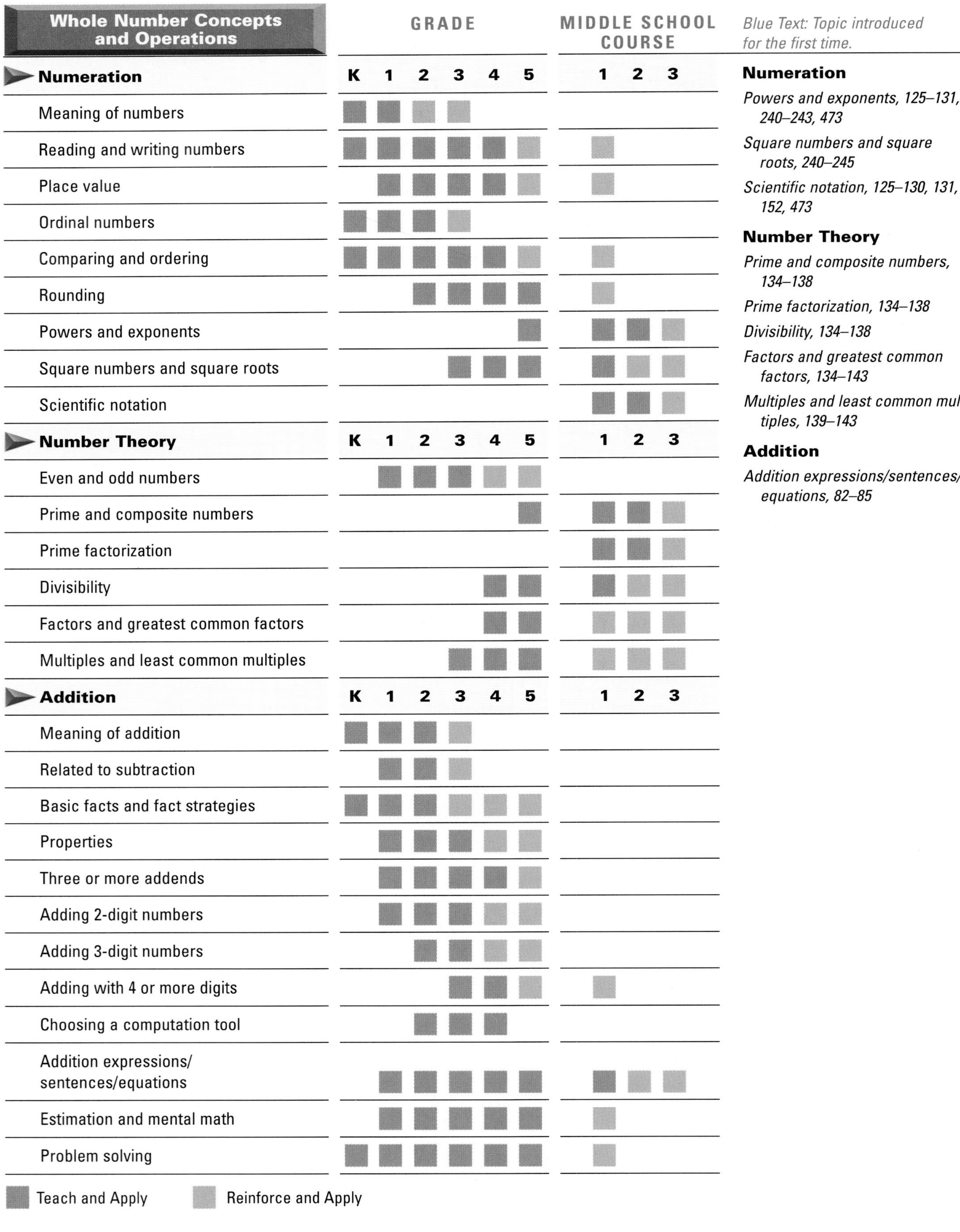

Whole Number Concepts and Operations

	GRADE K	1	2	3	4	5	MIDDLE SCHOOL COURSE 1	2	3
Numeration	**K**	**1**	**2**	**3**	**4**	**5**	**1**	**2**	**3**
Meaning of numbers	■	■	□	□					
Reading and writing numbers	■	■	■	■	■	□	□		
Place value		■	■	■	■	□	□		
Ordinal numbers	■	■	■	□					
Comparing and ordering	■	■	■	■	■	□	□		
Rounding			■	■	■	■	□		
Powers and exponents						■	■	■	□
Square numbers and square roots				■	■	■	■	□	□
Scientific notation							■	■	□
Number Theory	**K**	**1**	**2**	**3**	**4**	**5**	**1**	**2**	**3**
Even and odd numbers		■	■	■	□	□			
Prime and composite numbers						■	■	■	□
Prime factorization							■	■	□
Divisibility					■	■	■	□	□
Factors and greatest common factors					■	■	□	□	□
Multiples and least common multiples				■	■	■	□	□	□
Addition	**K**	**1**	**2**	**3**	**4**	**5**	**1**	**2**	**3**
Meaning of addition	■	■	■	□					
Related to subtraction		■	■	□					
Basic facts and fact strategies	■	■	■	□	□	□			
Properties		■	■	■	□	□			
Three or more addends		■	■	■	■	□			
Adding 2-digit numbers		■	■	■	□	□			
Adding 3-digit numbers			■	■	□	□			
Adding with 4 or more digits				■	■	□	□		
Choosing a computation tool			■	■	■				
Addition expressions/ sentences/equations		■	■	■	■	■	■	□	□
Estimation and mental math		■	■	■	■	■	□		
Problem solving	■	■	■	■	■	■	□		

■ Teach and Apply □ Reinforce and Apply

Blue Text: Topic introduced for the first time.

Numeration

Powers and exponents, 125–131, 240–243, 473

Square numbers and square roots, 240–245

Scientific notation, 125–130, 131, 152, 473

Number Theory

Prime and composite numbers, 134–138

Prime factorization, 134–138

Divisibility, 134–138

Factors and greatest common factors, 134–143

Multiples and least common multiples, 139–143

Addition

Addition expressions/sentences/equations, 82–85

Whole Number Concepts and Operations (cont'd)

	GRADE						MIDDLE SCHOOL COURSE		
Subtraction	K	1	2	3	4	5	1	2	3
Meaning of subtraction	■	■	■	□					
Related to addition		■	■	□					
Basic facts and fact strategies	■	■	■	□	□	□			
Properties		■	■	■	□	□			
Subtracting 2-digit numbers		■	■	■	□	□			
Subtracting 3-digit numbers			■	■	■	□			
Subtracting with 4 or more digits				■	■	□	□		
Choosing a computation tool			■	■	■				
Subtraction expressions/ sentences/equations		■	■	■	■	■	■	□	□
Estimation and mental math		■	■	■	■	■	□		
Problem solving	■	■	■	■	■	■	□		
Multiplication	K	1	2	3	4	5	1	2	3
Meaning of multiplication			■	■	□				
Related to addition/division			■	■	□				
Basic facts and fact strategies			■	■	■	□			
Properties			■	■	■	■			
By a 1-digit number				■	■	■			
By multiples of 10 and 100				■	■	■			
By a multi-digit number				■	■	■	□		
Choosing a computation tool					■	■			
Multiplication expressions/ sentences/equations				■	■	■	■	□	□
Estimation and mental math				■	■	■	■		
Problem solving			■	■	■	■	■		
Division	K	1	2	3	4	5	1	2	3
Meaning of division			■	■	■	□			
Related to subtraction/multiplication				■	■	□			
Basic facts and fact strategies				■	■	□			
Properties				■	■	■			
By a 1-digit divisor				■	■	■	□		
By multiples of 10 and 100				■	■	■	□		
By a multi-digit divisor					■	■	■		
Division expressions/sentences/equations				■	■	■	■	□	□
Estimation and mental math				■	■	■	■		
Problem solving			■	■	■	■	■		

■ Teach and Apply   □ Reinforce and Apply

Blue Text: Topic introduced for the first time.

Subtraction

Subtraction expressions/ sentences/equations, 82–85

Multiplication

Multiplication expressions/ sentences/equations, 86–90

Division

Division expressions/sentences/ equations, 86–90

Fraction Concepts and Operations

Blue Text: Topic introduced for the first time.

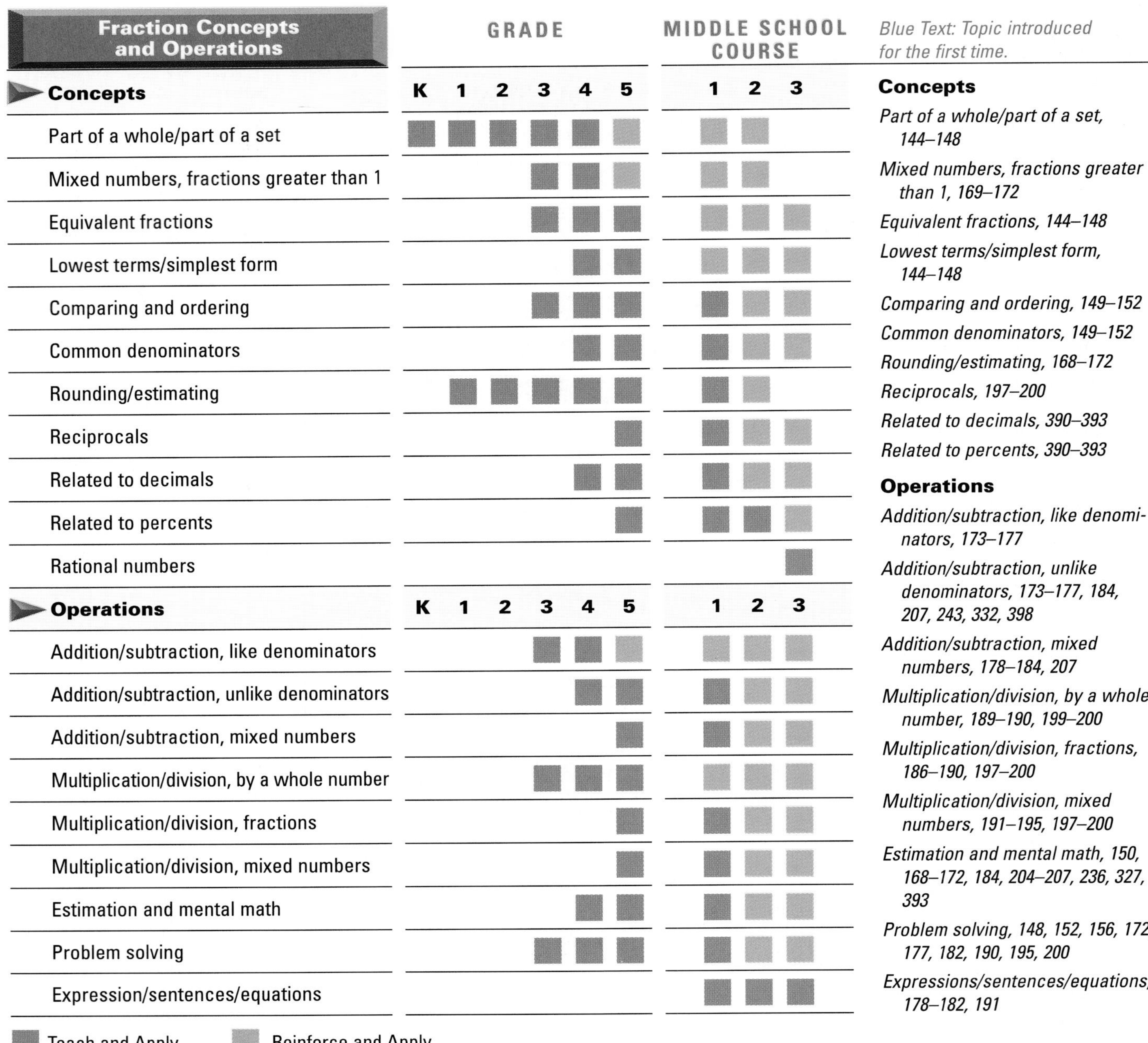

Concepts	Grade K	Grade 1	Grade 2	Grade 3	Grade 4	Grade 5	Middle School Course 1	Middle School Course 2	Middle School Course 3
Part of a whole/part of a set	T	T	T	T	T	R	R	R	
Mixed numbers, fractions greater than 1				T	T	R	R	R	
Equivalent fractions				T	T	T	R	R	R
Lowest terms/simplest form					T	T	R	R	R
Comparing and ordering				T	T	T	T	R	R
Common denominators					T	T	T	R	R
Rounding/estimating		T	T	T	T	T	T	R	
Reciprocals						T	T	R	R
Related to decimals					T	T	T	R	R
Related to percents						T	T	T	R
Rational numbers									T
Operations	**K**	**1**	**2**	**3**	**4**	**5**	**1**	**2**	**3**
Addition/subtraction, like denominators				T	T	R	R	R	R
Addition/subtraction, unlike denominators					T	T	T	R	R
Addition/subtraction, mixed numbers						T	T	R	R
Multiplication/division, by a whole number				T	T	T	R	R	R
Multiplication/division, fractions						T	T	R	R
Multiplication/division, mixed numbers						T	T	R	R
Estimation and mental math					T	T	T	R	R
Problem solving				T	T	T	T	R	R
Expression/sentences/equations							T	T	T

T = Teach and Apply R = Reinforce and Apply

Concepts

Part of a whole/part of a set, 144–148

Mixed numbers, fractions greater than 1, 169–172

Equivalent fractions, 144–148

Lowest terms/simplest form, 144–148

Comparing and ordering, 149–152

Common denominators, 149–152

Rounding/estimating, 168–172

Reciprocals, 197–200

Related to decimals, 390–393

Related to percents, 390–393

Operations

Addition/subtraction, like denominators, 173–177

Addition/subtraction, unlike denominators, 173–177, 184, 207, 243, 332, 398

Addition/subtraction, mixed numbers, 178–184, 207

Multiplication/division, by a whole number, 189–190, 199–200

Multiplication/division, fractions, 186–190, 197–200

Multiplication/division, mixed numbers, 191–195, 197–200

Estimation and mental math, 150, 168–172, 184, 204–207, 236, 327, 393

Problem solving, 148, 152, 156, 172, 177, 182, 190, 195, 200

Expressions/sentences/equations, 178–182, 191

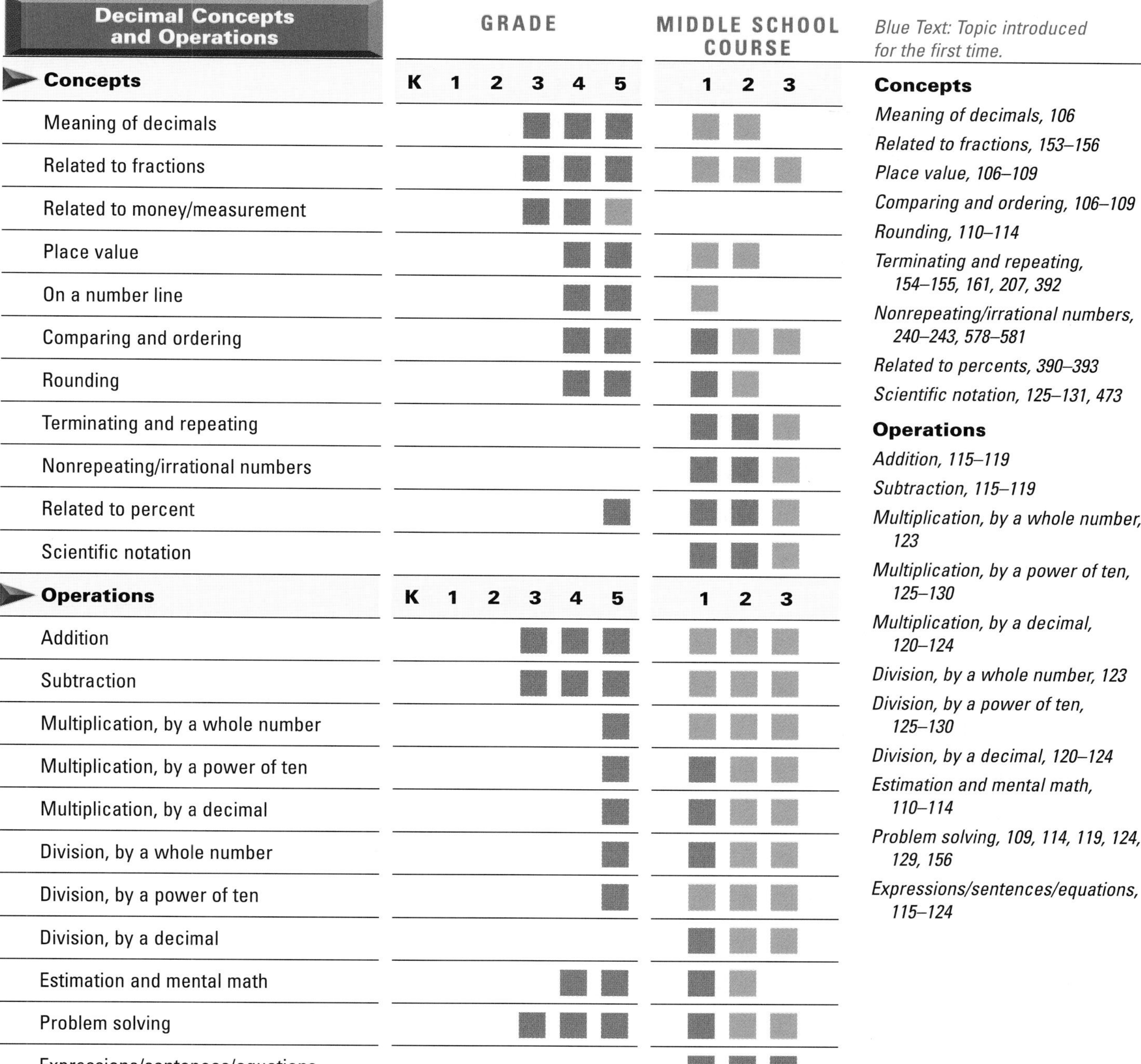

Decimal Concepts and Operations

Concepts	Grade K	1	2	3	4	5	Middle School Course 1	2	3
Meaning of decimals				T	T	T	R	R	
Related to fractions				T	T	T	R	R	R
Related to money/measurement				T	T	R			
Place value					T	T	R	R	
On a number line					T	T	R		
Comparing and ordering					T	T	T	R	R
Rounding					T	T	T	R	
Terminating and repeating							T	T	R
Nonrepeating/irrational numbers							T	T	R
Related to percent						T	T	T	R
Scientific notation							T	T	R
Operations	**K**	**1**	**2**	**3**	**4**	**5**	**1**	**2**	**3**
Addition				T	T	T	R	R	R
Subtraction				T	T	T	R	R	R
Multiplication, by a whole number						T	R	R	R
Multiplication, by a power of ten						T	T	R	R
Multiplication, by a decimal						T	T	R	R
Division, by a whole number						T	T	R	R
Division, by a power of ten						T	R	R	R
Division, by a decimal							T	R	R
Estimation and mental math					T	T	T	R	
Problem solving				T	T	T	T	R	R
Expressions/sentences/equations							T	T	T

T = Teach and Apply R = Reinforce and Apply

Blue Text: Topic introduced for the first time.

Concepts

Meaning of decimals, 106
Related to fractions, 153–156
Place value, 106–109
Comparing and ordering, 106–109
Rounding, 110–114
Terminating and repeating, 154–155, 161, 207, 392
Nonrepeating/irrational numbers, 240–243, 578–581
Related to percents, 390–393
Scientific notation, 125–131, 473

Operations

Addition, 115–119
Subtraction, 115–119
Multiplication, by a whole number, 123
Multiplication, by a power of ten, 125–130
Multiplication, by a decimal, 120–124
Division, by a whole number, 123
Division, by a power of ten, 125–130
Division, by a decimal, 120–124
Estimation and mental math, 110–114
Problem solving, 109, 114, 119, 124, 129, 156
Expressions/sentences/equations, 115–124

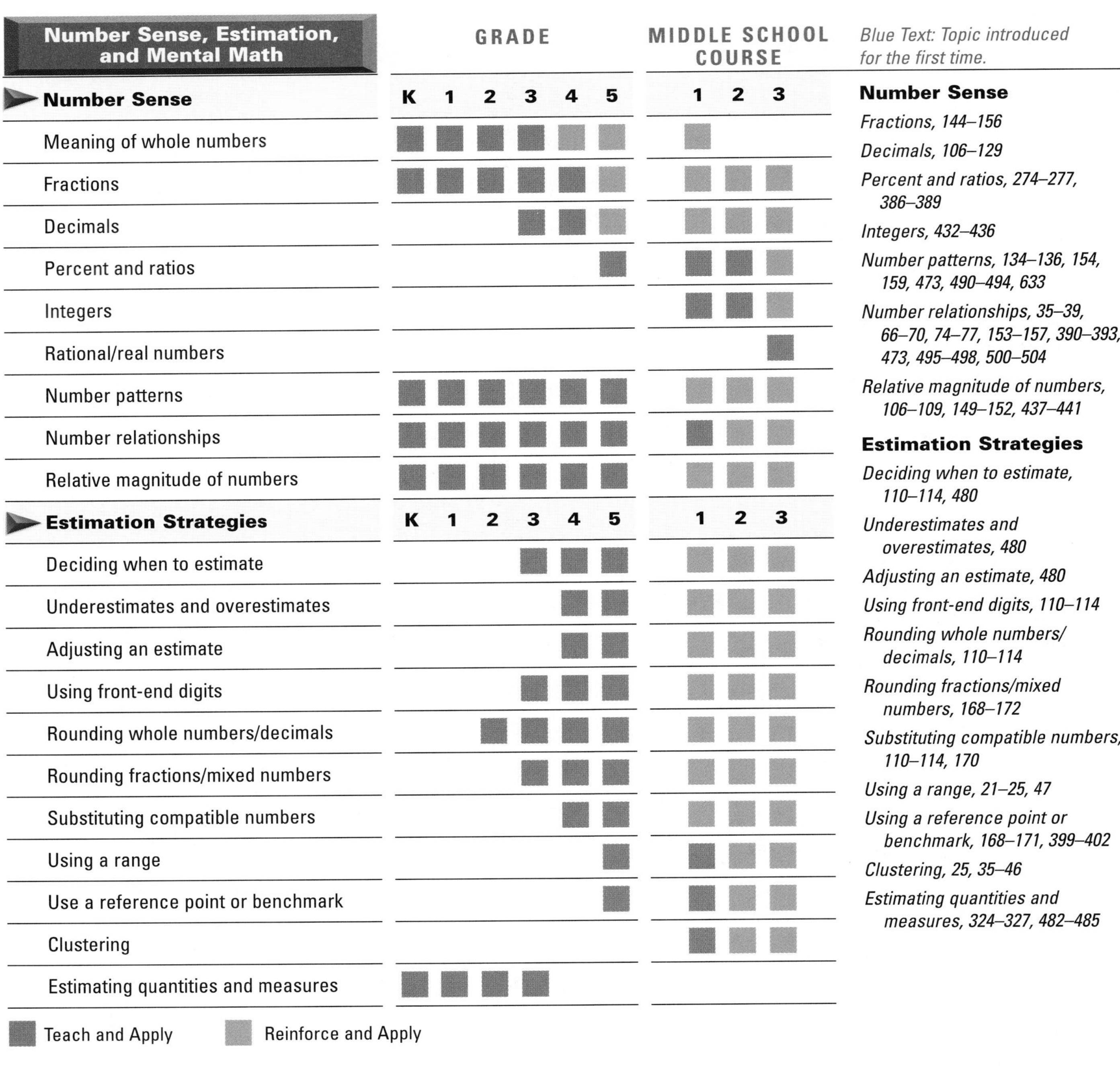

Number Sense, Estimation, and Mental Math	GRADE						MIDDLE SCHOOL COURSE		
Number Sense	**K**	**1**	**2**	**3**	**4**	**5**	**1**	**2**	**3**
Meaning of whole numbers	■	■	■	■	□	□	□		
Fractions	■	■	■	■	■	□	□	□	□
Decimals				■	■	□	□	□	□
Percent and ratios						■	■	■	□
Integers							■	■	□
Rational/real numbers									■
Number patterns	■	■	■	■	■	■	□	□	□
Number relationships	■	■	■	■	■	■	■	□	□
Relative magnitude of numbers	■	■	■	■	■	■	□	□	□
Estimation Strategies	**K**	**1**	**2**	**3**	**4**	**5**	**1**	**2**	**3**
Deciding when to estimate				■	■	■	□	□	□
Underestimates and overestimates					■	■	□	□	□
Adjusting an estimate					■	■	□	□	□
Using front-end digits				■	■	■	□	□	□
Rounding whole numbers/decimals			■	■	■	■	□	□	□
Rounding fractions/mixed numbers				■	■	■	□	□	□
Substituting compatible numbers					■	■	□	□	□
Using a range						■	■	□	□
Use a reference point or benchmark						■	■	□	□
Clustering							■	□	□
Estimating quantities and measures	■	■	■	■					

■ Teach and Apply　□ Reinforce and Apply

Blue Text: Topic introduced for the first time.

Number Sense

Fractions, 144–156

Decimals, 106–129

Percent and ratios, 274–277, 386–389

Integers, 432–436

Number patterns, 134–136, 154, 159, 473, 490–494, 633

Number relationships, 35–39, 66–70, 74–77, 153–157, 390–393, 473, 495–498, 500–504

Relative magnitude of numbers, 106–109, 149–152, 437–441

Estimation Strategies

Deciding when to estimate, 110–114, 480

Underestimates and overestimates, 480

Adjusting an estimate, 480

Using front-end digits, 110–114

Rounding whole numbers/ decimals, 110–114

Rounding fractions/mixed numbers, 168–172

Substituting compatible numbers, 110–114, 170

Using a range, 21–25, 47

Using a reference point or benchmark, 168–171, 399–402

Clustering, 25, 35–46

Estimating quantities and measures, 324–327, 482–485

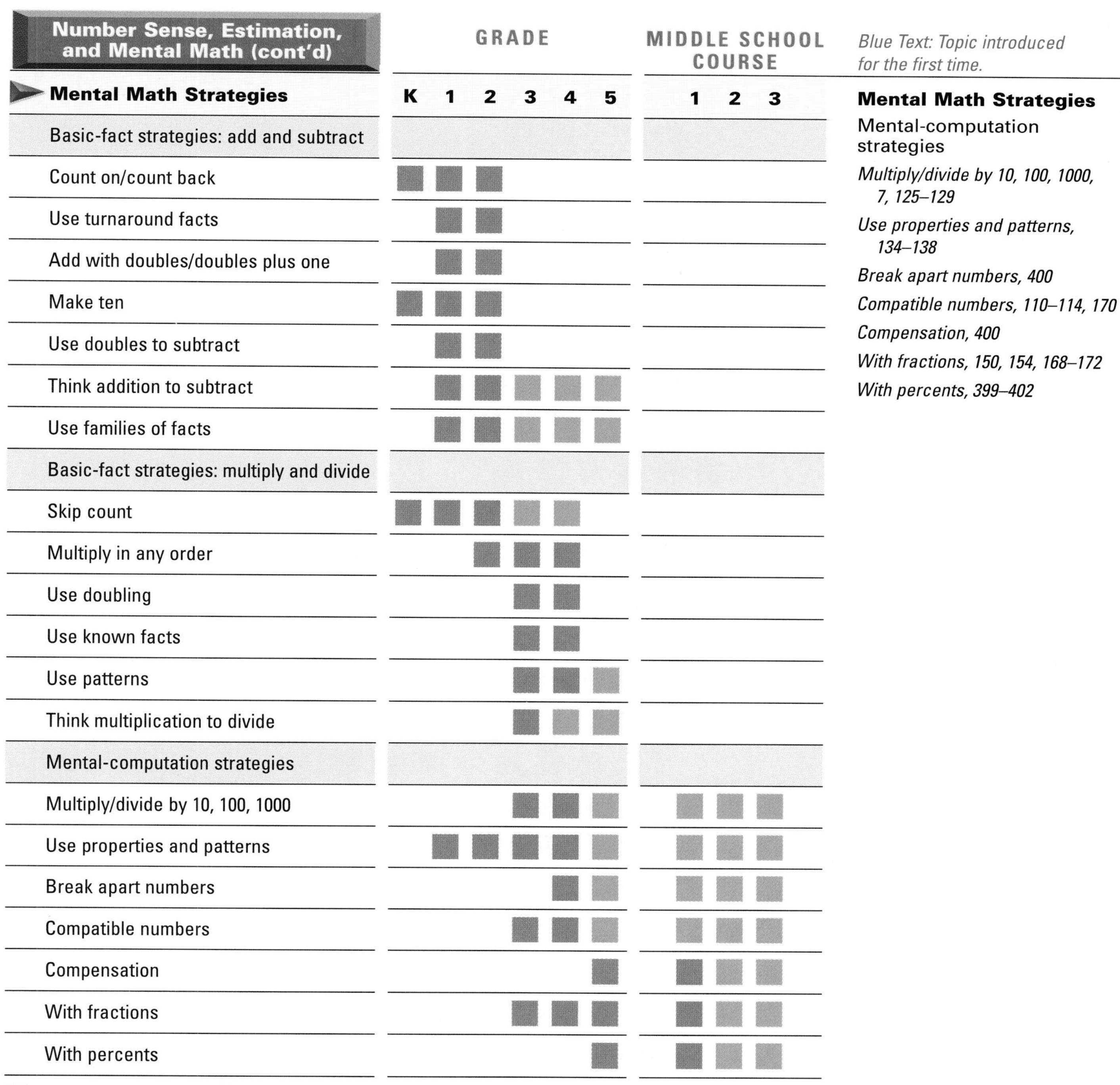

Number Sense, Estimation, and Mental Math (cont'd)

Mental Math Strategies	K	1	2	3	4	5	Middle School Course 1	2	3
Basic-fact strategies: add and subtract									
Count on/count back	■	■	■						
Use turnaround facts		■	■						
Add with doubles/doubles plus one		■	■						
Make ten	■	■	■						
Use doubles to subtract		■	■						
Think addition to subtract		■	■	□	□	□			
Use families of facts		■	■	□	□	□			
Basic-fact strategies: multiply and divide									
Skip count	■	■	■	□	□				
Multiply in any order			■	■	■				
Use doubling				■	■				
Use known facts				■	■				
Use patterns				■	■	□			
Think multiplication to divide				■	□	□			
Mental-computation strategies									
Multiply/divide by 10, 100, 1000				■	■	□	□	□	□
Use properties and patterns		■	■	■	■	□	□	□	□
Break apart numbers					■	□	□	□	□
Compatible numbers				■	■	□	□	□	□
Compensation						■	■	□	□
With fractions				■	■	■	■	□	□
With percents						■	■	□	□

■ Teach and Apply   □ Reinforce and Apply

Blue Text: Topic introduced for the first time.

Mental Math Strategies

Mental-computation strategies

Multiply/divide by 10, 100, 1000, 7, 125–129

Use properties and patterns, 134–138

Break apart numbers, 400

Compatible numbers, 110–114, 170

Compensation, 400

With fractions, 150, 154, 168–172

With percents, 399–402

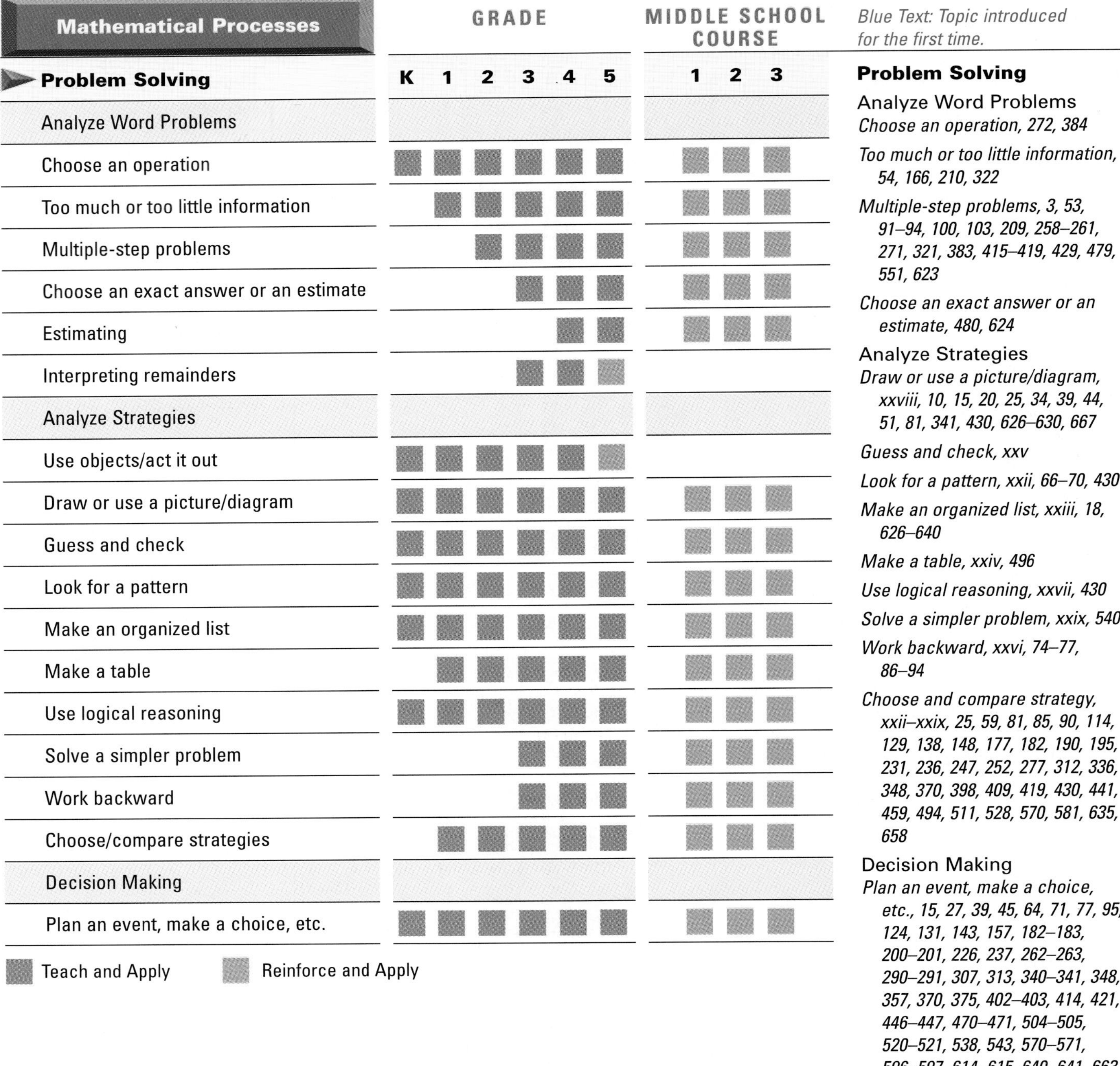

Mathematical Processes

Problem Solving	K	1	2	3	4	5	MS 1	MS 2	MS 3
Analyze Word Problems									
Choose an operation	■	■	■	■	■	■	□	□	□
Too much or too little information		■	■	■	■	■	□	□	□
Multiple-step problems			■	■	■	■	□	□	□
Choose an exact answer or an estimate				■	■	■	□	□	□
Estimating					■	■	□	□	□
Interpreting remainders				■	■	□			
Analyze Strategies									
Use objects/act it out	■	■	■	■	■	□			
Draw or use a picture/diagram	■	■	■	■	■	■	□	□	□
Guess and check	■	■	■	■	■	■	□	□	□
Look for a pattern	■	■	■	■	■	■	□	□	□
Make an organized list	■	■	■	■	■	■	□	□	□
Make a table		■	■	■	■	■	□	□	□
Use logical reasoning	■	■	■	■	■	■	□	□	□
Solve a simpler problem				■	■	■	□	□	□
Work backward				■	■	■	□	□	□
Choose/compare strategies		■	■	■	■	■	□	□	□
Decision Making									
Plan an event, make a choice, etc.	■	■	■	■	■	■	□	□	□

Columns K–5: GRADE; columns 1–3: MIDDLE SCHOOL COURSE

■ Teach and Apply □ Reinforce and Apply

Blue Text: Topic introduced for the first time.

Problem Solving

Analyze Word Problems

Choose an operation, 272, 384

Too much or too little information, 54, 166, 210, 322

Multiple-step problems, 3, 53, 91–94, 100, 103, 209, 258–261, 271, 321, 383, 415–419, 429, 479, 551, 623

Choose an exact answer or an estimate, 480, 624

Analyze Strategies

Draw or use a picture/diagram, xxviii, 10, 15, 20, 25, 34, 39, 44, 51, 81, 341, 430, 626–630, 667

Guess and check, xxv

Look for a pattern, xxii, 66–70, 430

Make an organized list, xxiii, 18, 626–640

Make a table, xxiv, 496

Use logical reasoning, xxvii, 430

Solve a simpler problem, xxix, 540

Work backward, xxvi, 74–77, 86–94

Choose and compare strategy, xxii–xxix, 25, 59, 81, 85, 90, 114, 129, 138, 148, 177, 182, 190, 195, 231, 236, 247, 252, 277, 312, 336, 348, 370, 398, 409, 419, 430, 441, 459, 494, 511, 528, 570, 581, 635, 658

Decision Making

Plan an event, make a choice, etc., 15, 27, 39, 45, 64, 71, 77, 95, 124, 131, 143, 157, 182–183, 200–201, 226, 237, 262–263, 290–291, 307, 313, 340–341, 348, 357, 370, 375, 402–403, 414, 421, 446–447, 470–471, 504–505, 520–521, 538, 543, 570–571, 596–597, 614–615, 640–641, 663, 665

Mathematical Processes (cont'd)	GRADE						MIDDLE SCHOOL COURSE		
Problem Solving (cont'd)	K	1	2	3	4	5	1	2	3
Problem-Solving Guide/Checklist									
Understand									
Determine what you know			T	T	T	R	R	R	R
Use data from pictures, graphs, . . .			T	T	T	R	R	R	R
Tell what you need to find out					T	R	R	R	R
Plan									
Choose an operation/strategy			T	T	T	R	R	R	R
Choose a computation method			T	T	T	R	R	R	R
Estimate the answer				T	T	T	R	R	R
Solve									
Carry out the plan			T	T	T	R	R	R	R
Try another strategy if needed			T	T	T	R	R	R	R
Give the answer			T	T	T	R	R	R	R
Look Back									
Check your answer			T	T	T	R	R	R	R
Check reasonableness of answer				T	T	T	R	R	R
Be sure the question is answered			T	T	T	R	R	R	R
Reasoning	K	1	2	3	4	5	1	2	3
Critical Thinking, Logical Reasoning									
Classifying/sorting	T	T	T	T	T	T	R	R	R
Comparing/contrasting	T	T	T	R	R	R	R	R	R
Finding/extending/using patterns	T	T	T	T	T	T	R	R	R
Making generalizations	T	T	T	T	T	T	R	R	R
Drawing conclusions	T	T	T	T	T	T	R	R	R
Making/testing conjectures		T	T	T	T	T	R	R	R
Explaining/justifying answers					T	T	R	R	R
Visual and Creative Thinking									
Visual patterns	T	T	T	T	T	T	R	R	R
Spatial reasoning	T	T	T	T	T	T	R	R	R
Solve nonroutine problems				T	T	T	R	R	R
Generate problems				T	T	T	R	R	R
Develop alternative ways to solve problems						T	R	R	R

T = Teach and Apply   R = Reinforce and Apply

Blue Text: Topic introduced for the first time.

Problem Solving (cont'd)

Problem-Solving Guide/Checklist

Use problem–solving guidelines, xx–xxi, 4, 15, 39, 54, 64, 77, 104, 124, 143, 166, 182, 200, 210, 226, 262, 272, 290, 307, 322, 340, 348, 370, 384, 388, 402, 414, 446, 470, 480, 504, 520, 538, 552, 570, 596, 614, 624, 640, 663

Reasoning

Critical Thinking, Logical Reasoning

Classifying/sorting, 134–144, 212–231, 554–557

Comparing/contrasting, 11–15, 106–109, 149–152, 437–441, 482–485, 667

Finding/extending/using patterns, 286–290, 377, 490–498, 508–511

Making generalizations, 30–44, 47, 649

Drawing conclusions, 30–44, 66–70, 490–498, 641, 644, 654–658

Making/testing conjectures, 139, 144, 153, 312, 563–566, 600

Explaining/justifying answers, 51, 56, 74, 77, 82, 106, 163, 237, 258, 262, 263, 286, 472, 574, 636, 649, 665

Visual and Creative Thinking

Visual patterns, 227, 430, 491, 493–494, 613, 615

Spatial patterns, 558–570, 587, 600–614

Solve nonroutine problems, 3, 50, 51, 100, 103, 162, 163, 165, 206, 209, 268, 269, 271, 318, 321, 380, 381, 383, 426, 429, 476, 477, 479, 548, 551, 620, 621, 623

Generate problems, 138, 454, 471, 524

Develop alternative ways to solve problems, 191, 197, 229, 260, 310, 330, 396, 414, 422

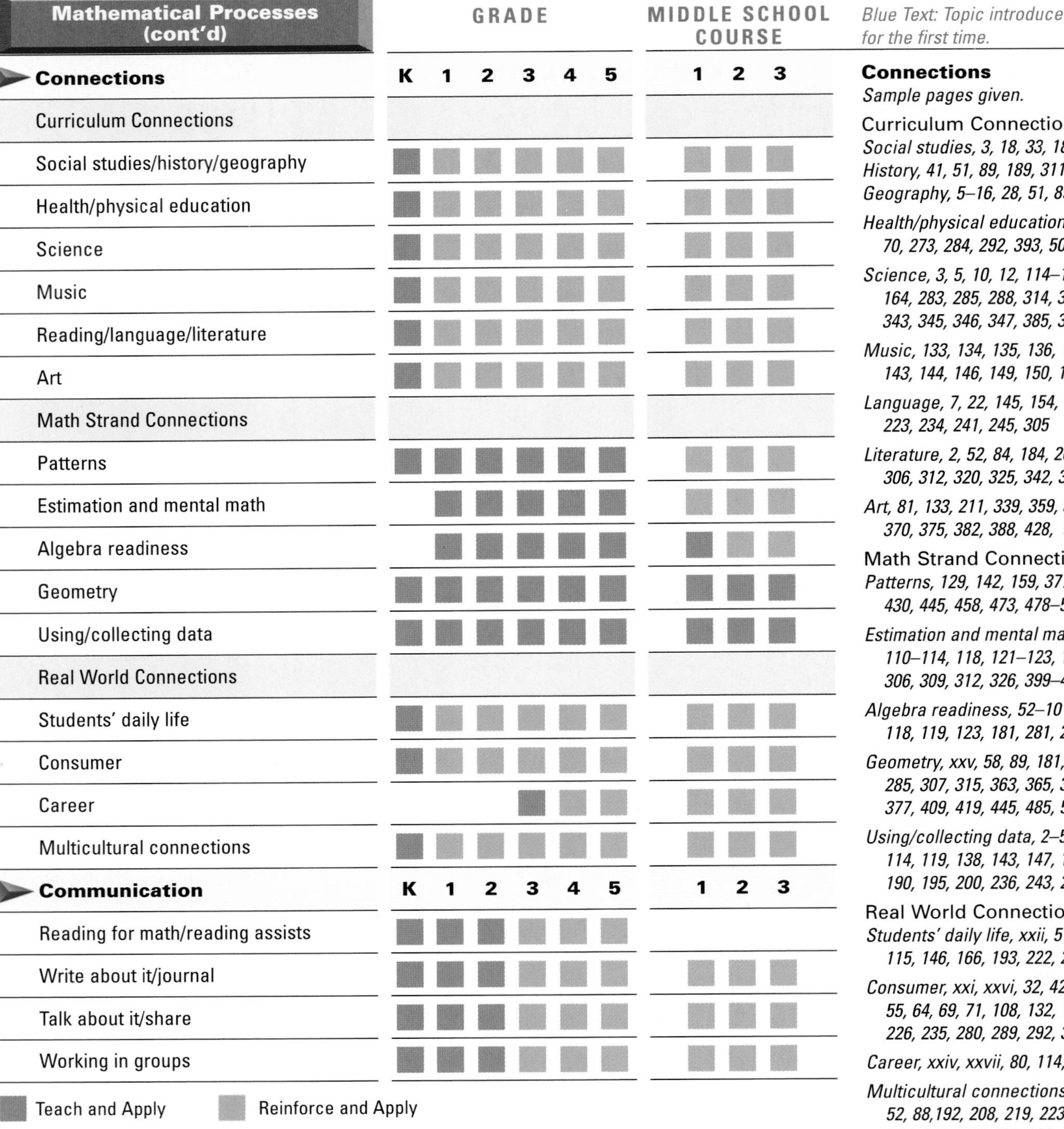

Mathematical Processes (cont'd)	GRADE						MIDDLE SCHOOL COURSE		
Connections	K	1	2	3	4	5	1	2	3
Curriculum Connections									
Social studies/history/geography	■	□	□	□	□	□	□	□	□
Health/physical education	■	□	□	□	□	□	□	□	□
Science	■	□	□	□	□	□	□	□	□
Music	■	□	□	□	□	□	□	□	□
Reading/language/literature	■	□	□	□	□	□	□	□	□
Art	■	□	□	□	□	□	□	□	□
Math Strand Connections									
Patterns	■	■	■	■	■	■	□	□	□
Estimation and mental math		■	■	■	■	■	□	□	□
Algebra readiness		■	■	■	■	■	■	□	□
Geometry	■	■	■	■	■	■	■	■	■
Using/collecting data	■	■	■	■	■	■	■	■	■
Real World Connections									
Students' daily life	■	□	□	□	□	□	□	□	□
Consumer	■	□	□	□	□	□	□	□	□
Career				■	□	□	□	□	□
Multicultural connections	■	□	□	□	□	□	□	□	□
Communication	K	1	2	3	4	5	1	2	3
Reading for math/reading assists	■	■	■	□	□	□			
Write about it/journal	■	■	■	□	□	□	□	□	□
Talk about it/share	■	■	■	□	□	□	□	□	□
Working in groups	■	■	■	□	□	□	□	□	□

■ Teach and Apply □ Reinforce and Apply

Blue Text: Topic introduced for the first time.

Connections

Sample pages given.

Curriculum Connections

Social studies, 3, 18, 33, 182, 485

History, 41, 51, 89, 189, 311

Geography, 5–16, 28, 51, 89, 458

Health/physical education, 43, 58, 70, 273, 284, 292, 393, 505

Science, 3, 5, 10, 12, 114–116, 163, 164, 283, 285, 288, 314, 320, 321, 343, 345, 346, 347, 385, 387

Music, 133, 134, 135, 136, 139, 140, 143, 144, 146, 149, 150, 151, 154

Language, 7, 22, 145, 154, 170, 213, 223, 234, 241, 245, 305

Literature, 2, 52, 84, 184, 208, 297, 306, 312, 320, 325, 342, 351

Art, 81, 133, 211, 339, 359, 364, 367, 370, 375, 382, 388, 428, 553, 556

Math Strand Connections

Patterns, 129, 142, 159, 377, 413, 430, 445, 458, 473, 478–549

Estimation and mental math, 110–114, 118, 121–123, 168–172, 306, 309, 312, 326, 399–402

Algebra readiness, 52–101, 114, 118, 119, 123, 181, 281, 297

Geometry, xxv, 58, 89, 181, 208–269, 285, 307, 315, 363, 365, 373, 376, 377, 409, 419, 445, 485, 510, 533

Using/collecting data, 2–51, 101, 114, 119, 138, 143, 147, 151, 172, 190, 195, 200, 236, 243, 247, 301

Real World Connections

Students' daily life, xxii, 51, 110, 115, 146, 166, 193, 222, 260, 271

Consumer, xxi, xxvi, 32, 42, 43, 51, 55, 64, 69, 71, 108, 132, 176, 188, 226, 235, 280, 289, 292, 314, 389

Career, xxiv, xxvii, 80, 114, 142, 189

Multicultural connections, 2, 7, 8, 52, 88,192, 208, 219, 223, 234, 243, 250, 254, 281, 320

Communication

Reading for math/reading assists, (English Language Development in Teacher's Edition) 56, 78, 86, 217, 240, 248, 386, 406, 415, 432

Write about it/journal, 10, 15, 39, 44, 49, 59, 109, 114, 119, 156, 158, 163, 172, 348, 389, 393

Talk about it/share, 42, 68, 88, 117, 146, 180, 193, 229, 260, 288, 310, 330, 368, 396, 417, 439, 468, 514, 526, 589, 602, 638

Working in groups, 6, 11, 30, 170, 186, 188, 214, 394, 529, 631, 638, 663

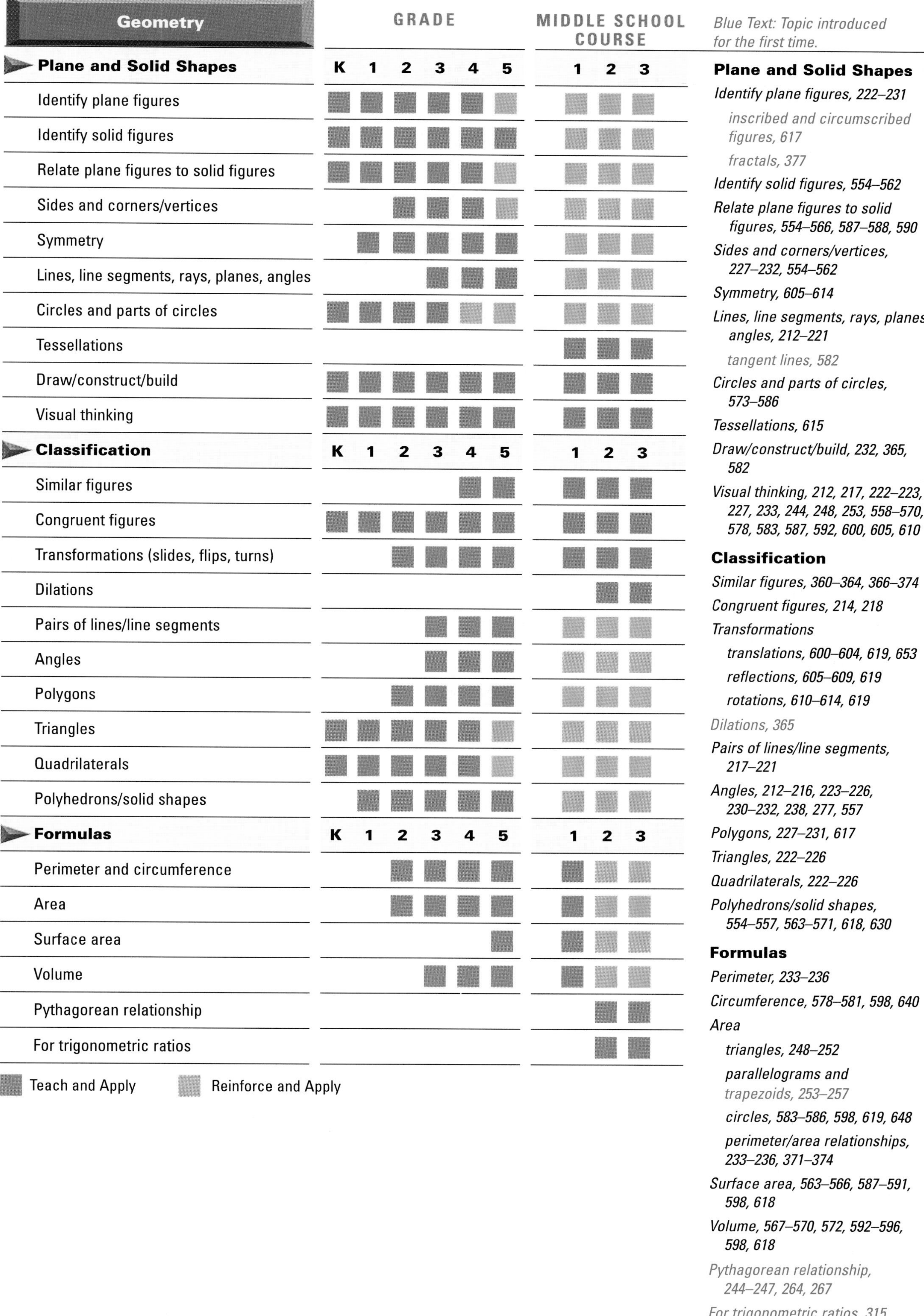

Geometry	GRADE K	1	2	3	4	5	MIDDLE SCHOOL COURSE 1	2	3
Plane and Solid Shapes	**K**	**1**	**2**	**3**	**4**	**5**	**1**	**2**	**3**
Identify plane figures	■	■	■	■	■	□	□	□	□
Identify solid figures	■	■	■	■	■	■	□	□	□
Relate plane figures to solid figures	■	■	■	■	■	□	□	□	□
Sides and corners/vertices			■	■	■	□	□	□	□
Symmetry		■	■	■	■	■	□	□	□
Lines, line segments, rays, planes, angles				■	■	■	□	□	□
Circles and parts of circles	■	■	■	■	□	□	□	□	□
Tessellations							■	■	■
Draw/construct/build	■	■	■	■	■	■	■	■	■
Visual thinking	■	■	■	■	■	■	■	■	■
Classification	**K**	**1**	**2**	**3**	**4**	**5**	**1**	**2**	**3**
Similar figures					■	■	■	■	■
Congruent figures	■	■	■	■	■	■	■	■	■
Transformations (slides, flips, turns)			■	■	■	■	■	■	■
Dilations								■	■
Pairs of lines/line segments				■	■	■	□	□	□
Angles				■	■	■	□	□	□
Polygons			■	■	■	■	□	□	□
Triangles	■	■	■	■	■	□	□	□	□
Quadrilaterals	■	■	■	■	■	□	□	□	□
Polyhedrons/solid shapes		■	■	■	■	■	□	□	□
Formulas	**K**	**1**	**2**	**3**	**4**	**5**	**1**	**2**	**3**
Perimeter and circumference			■	■	■	■	■	□	□
Area			■	■	■	■	■	□	□
Surface area						■	■	□	□
Volume				■	■	■	■	□	□
Pythagorean relationship								■	■
For trigonometric ratios								■	■

■ Teach and Apply □ Reinforce and Apply

Blue Text: Topic introduced for the first time.

Plane and Solid Shapes

Identify plane figures, 222–231

inscribed and circumscribed figures, 617

fractals, 377

Identify solid figures, 554–562

Relate plane figures to solid figures, 554–566, 587–588, 590

Sides and corners/vertices, 227–232, 554–562

Symmetry, 605–614

Lines, line segments, rays, planes, angles, 212–221

tangent lines, 582

Circles and parts of circles, 573–586

Tessellations, 615

Draw/construct/build, 232, 365, 582

Visual thinking, 212, 217, 222–223, 227, 233, 244, 248, 253, 558–570, 578, 583, 587, 592, 600, 605, 610

Classification

Similar figures, 360–364, 366–374

Congruent figures, 214, 218

Transformations

translations, 600–604, 619, 653

reflections, 605–609, 619

rotations, 610–614, 619

Dilations, 365

Pairs of lines/line segments, 217–221

Angles, 212–216, 223–226, 230–232, 238, 277, 557

Polygons, 227–231, 617

Triangles, 222–226

Quadrilaterals, 222–226

Polyhedrons/solid shapes, 554–557, 563–571, 618, 630

Formulas

Perimeter, 233–236

Circumference, 578–581, 598, 640

Area

triangles, 248–252

parallelograms and trapezoids, 253–257

circles, 583–586, 598, 619, 648

perimeter/area relationships, 233–236, 371–374

Surface area, 563–566, 587–591, 598, 618

Volume, 567–570, 572, 592–596, 598, 618

Pythagorean relationship, 244–247, 264, 267

For trigonometric ratios, 315

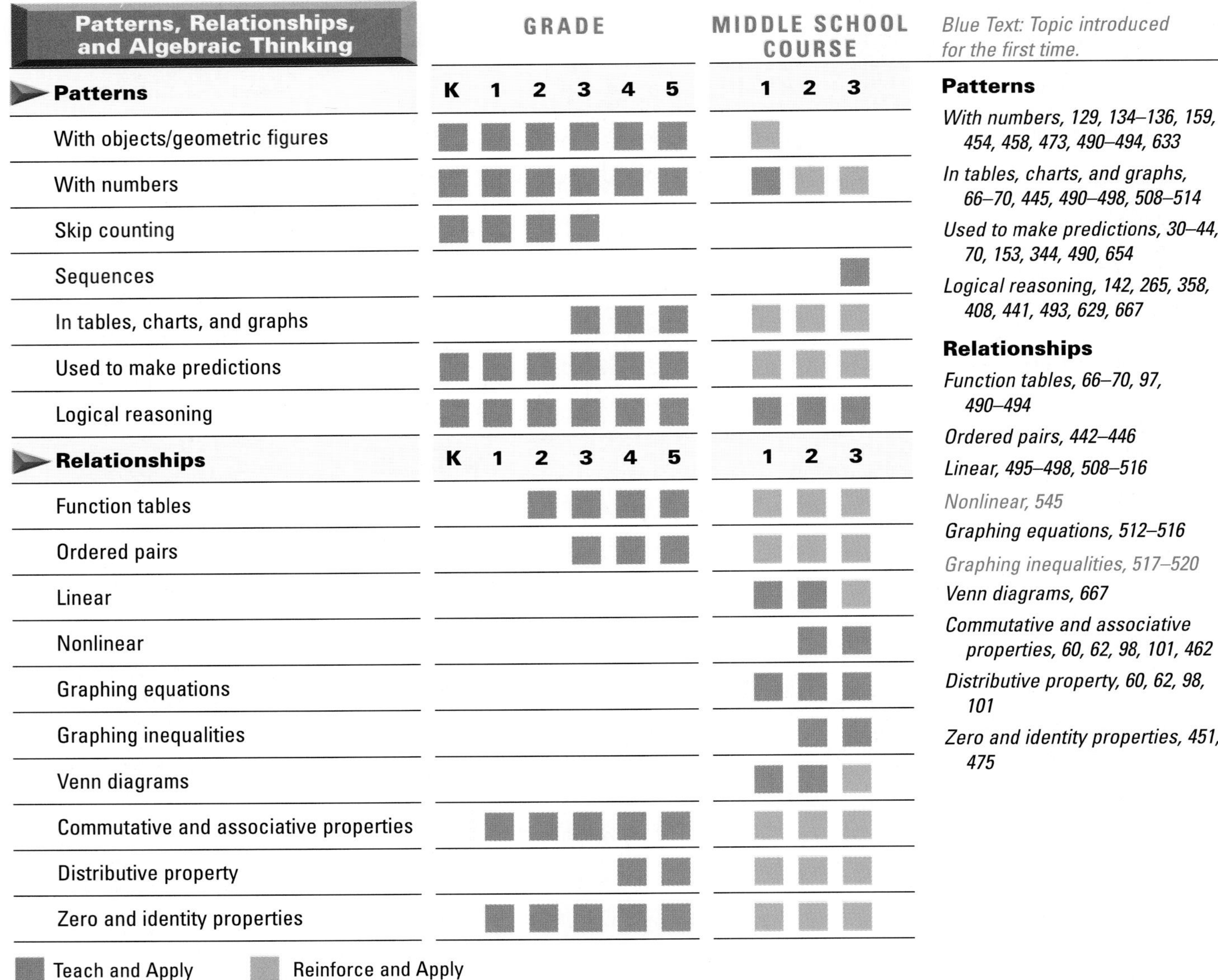

Patterns, Relationships, and Algebraic Thinking

Patterns	Grade K	Grade 1	Grade 2	Grade 3	Grade 4	Grade 5	Middle School Course 1	Course 2	Course 3
With objects/geometric figures	■	■	■	■	■	■	□		
With numbers	■	■	■	■	■	■	■	□	□
Skip counting	■	■	■	■					
Sequences									■
In tables, charts, and graphs				■	■	■	□	□	□
Used to make predictions	■	■	■	■	■	■	□	□	□
Logical reasoning	■	■	■	■	■	■	■	■	■
Relationships	**K**	**1**	**2**	**3**	**4**	**5**	**1**	**2**	**3**
Function tables			■	■	■	■	□	□	□
Ordered pairs				■	■	■	□	□	□
Linear							■	■	□
Nonlinear								■	■
Graphing equations							■	■	■
Graphing inequalities								■	■
Venn diagrams							■	■	□
Commutative and associative properties		■	■	■	■	■	□	□	□
Distributive property					■	■	□	□	□
Zero and identity properties		■	■	■	■	■	□	□	□

■ Teach and Apply □ Reinforce and Apply

Blue Text: Topic introduced for the first time.

Patterns

With numbers, 129, 134–136, 159, 454, 458, 473, 490–494, 633

In tables, charts, and graphs, 66–70, 445, 490–498, 508–514

Used to make predictions, 30–44, 70, 153, 344, 490, 654

Logical reasoning, 142, 265, 358, 408, 441, 493, 629, 667

Relationships

Function tables, 66–70, 97, 490–494

Ordered pairs, 442–446

Linear, 495–498, 508–516

Nonlinear, 545

Graphing equations, 512–516

Graphing inequalities, 517–520

Venn diagrams, 667

Commutative and associative properties, 60, 62, 98, 101, 462

Distributive property, 60, 62, 98, 101

Zero and identity properties, 451, 475

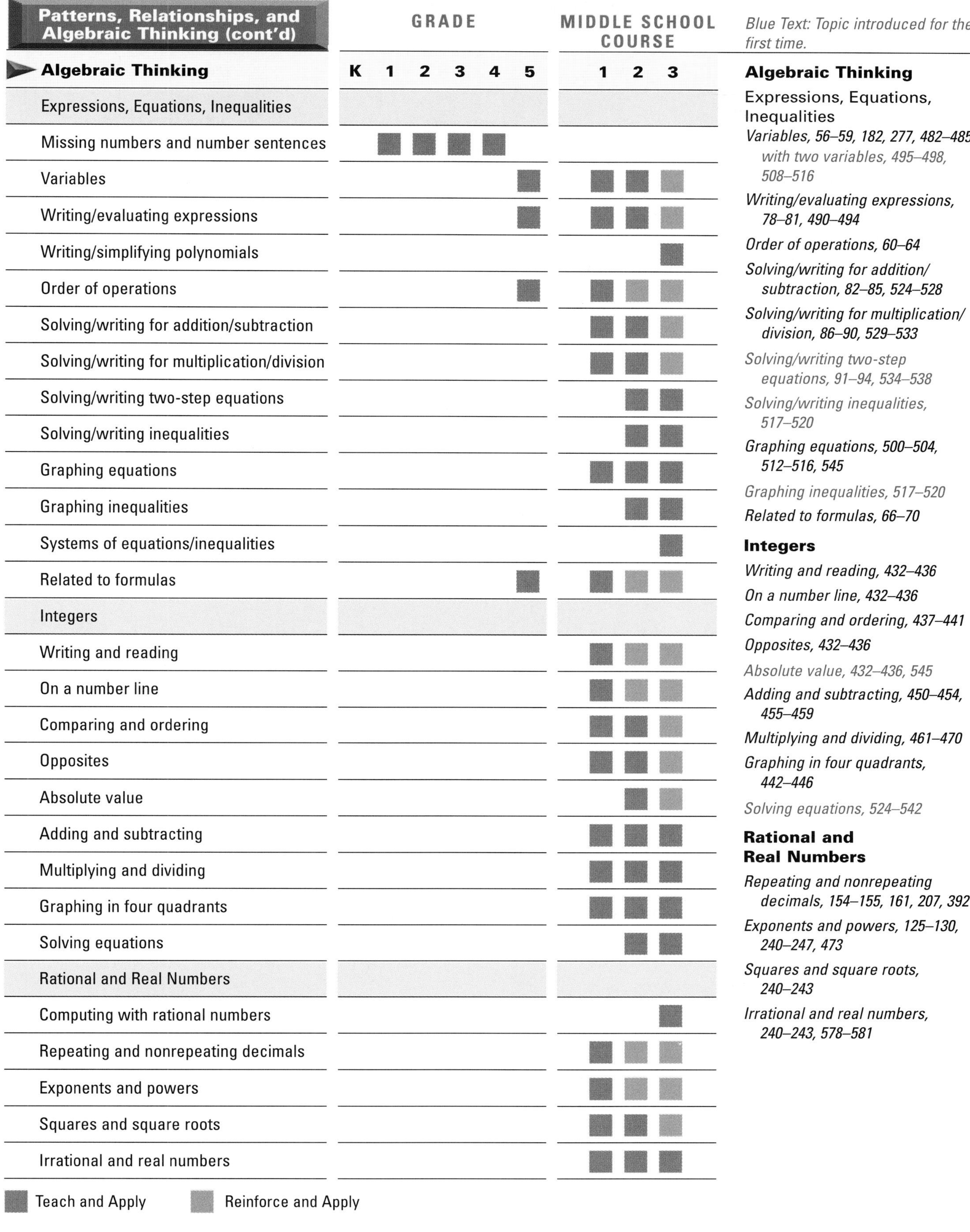

Patterns, Relationships, and Algebraic Thinking (cont'd)	GRADE						MIDDLE SCHOOL COURSE		
Algebraic Thinking	K	1	2	3	4	5	1	2	3
Expressions, Equations, Inequalities									
Missing numbers and number sentences		■	■	■	■				
Variables						■	■	■	□
Writing/evaluating expressions						■	■	■	□
Writing/simplifying polynomials									■
Order of operations						■	■	□	□
Solving/writing for addition/subtraction							■	■	□
Solving/writing for multiplication/division							■	■	□
Solving/writing two-step equations								■	■
Solving/writing inequalities								■	■
Graphing equations							■	■	■
Graphing inequalities								■	■
Systems of equations/inequalities									■
Related to formulas						■	■	□	□
Integers									
Writing and reading							■	□	□
On a number line							■	□	□
Comparing and ordering							■	■	□
Opposites							■	■	□
Absolute value								■	□
Adding and subtracting							■	■	■
Multiplying and dividing							■	■	■
Graphing in four quadrants							■	■	■
Solving equations								■	■
Rational and Real Numbers									
Computing with rational numbers									■
Repeating and nonrepeating decimals							■	□	□
Exponents and powers							■	□	□
Squares and square roots							■	■	□
Irrational and real numbers							■	■	■

■ Teach and Apply   □ Reinforce and Apply

Blue Text: Topic introduced for the first time.

Algebraic Thinking

Expressions, Equations, Inequalities

Variables, 56–59, 182, 277, 482–485
with two variables, 495–498, 508–516
Writing/evaluating expressions, 78–81, 490–494
Order of operations, 60–64
Solving/writing for addition/subtraction, 82–85, 524–528
Solving/writing for multiplication/division, 86–90, 529–533
Solving/writing two-step equations, 91–94, 534–538
Solving/writing inequalities, 517–520
Graphing equations, 500–504, 512–516, 545
Graphing inequalities, 517–520
Related to formulas, 66–70

Integers

Writing and reading, 432–436
On a number line, 432–436
Comparing and ordering, 437–441
Opposites, 432–436
Absolute value, 432–436, 545
Adding and subtracting, 450–454, 455–459
Multiplying and dividing, 461–470
Graphing in four quadrants, 442–446
Solving equations, 524–542

Rational and Real Numbers

Repeating and nonrepeating decimals, 154–155, 161, 207, 392
Exponents and powers, 125–130, 240–247, 473
Squares and square roots, 240–243
Irrational and real numbers, 240–243, 578–581

Measurement, Time, and Money

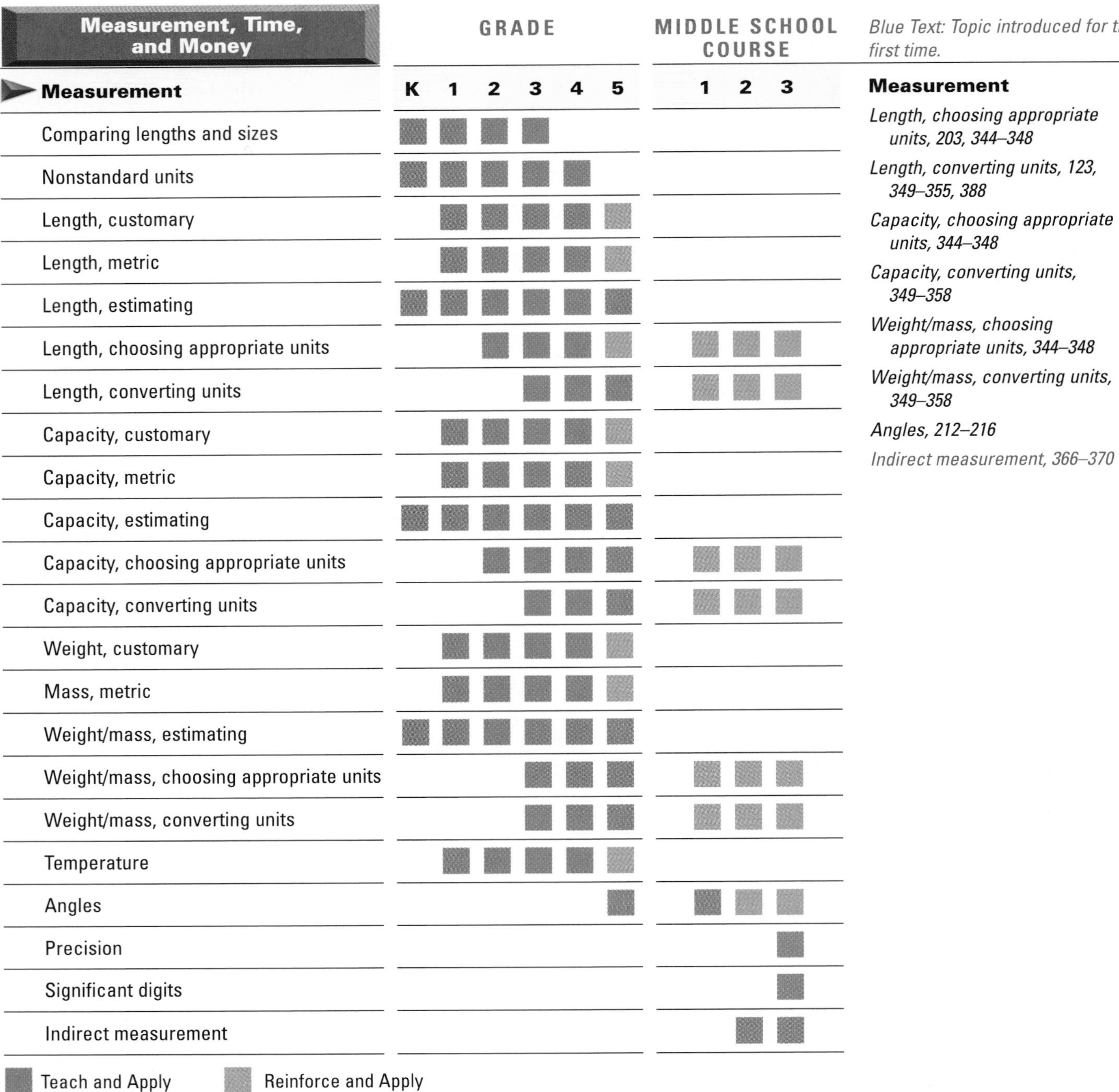

▶ Measurement	K	1	2	3	4	5	MS Course 1	MS Course 2	MS Course 3
Comparing lengths and sizes	■	■	■	■					
Nonstandard units	■	■	■	■	■				
Length, customary		■	■	■	■	□			
Length, metric		■	■	■	■	□			
Length, estimating	■	■	■	■	■	■			
Length, choosing appropriate units			■	■	■	□	□	□	□
Length, converting units				■	■	■	□	□	□
Capacity, customary		■	■	■	■	□			
Capacity, metric		■	■	■	■	□			
Capacity, estimating	■	■	■	■	■	■			
Capacity, choosing appropriate units			■	■	■	■	□	□	□
Capacity, converting units				■	■	■	□	□	□
Weight, customary		■	■	■	■	□			
Mass, metric		■	■	■	■	□			
Weight/mass, estimating	■	■	■	■	■	■			
Weight/mass, choosing appropriate units				■	■	■	□	□	□
Weight/mass, converting units				■	■	■	□	□	□
Temperature		■	■	■	■	□			
Angles						■	■	□	□
Precision									■
Significant digits									■
Indirect measurement								■	■

■ Teach and Apply　□ Reinforce and Apply

Blue Text: Topic introduced for the first time.

Measurement

Length, choosing appropriate units, 203, 344–348
Length, converting units, 123, 349–355, 388
Capacity, choosing appropriate units, 344–348
Capacity, converting units, 349–358
Weight/mass, choosing appropriate units, 344–348
Weight/mass, converting units, 349–358
Angles, 212–216
Indirect measurement, 366–370

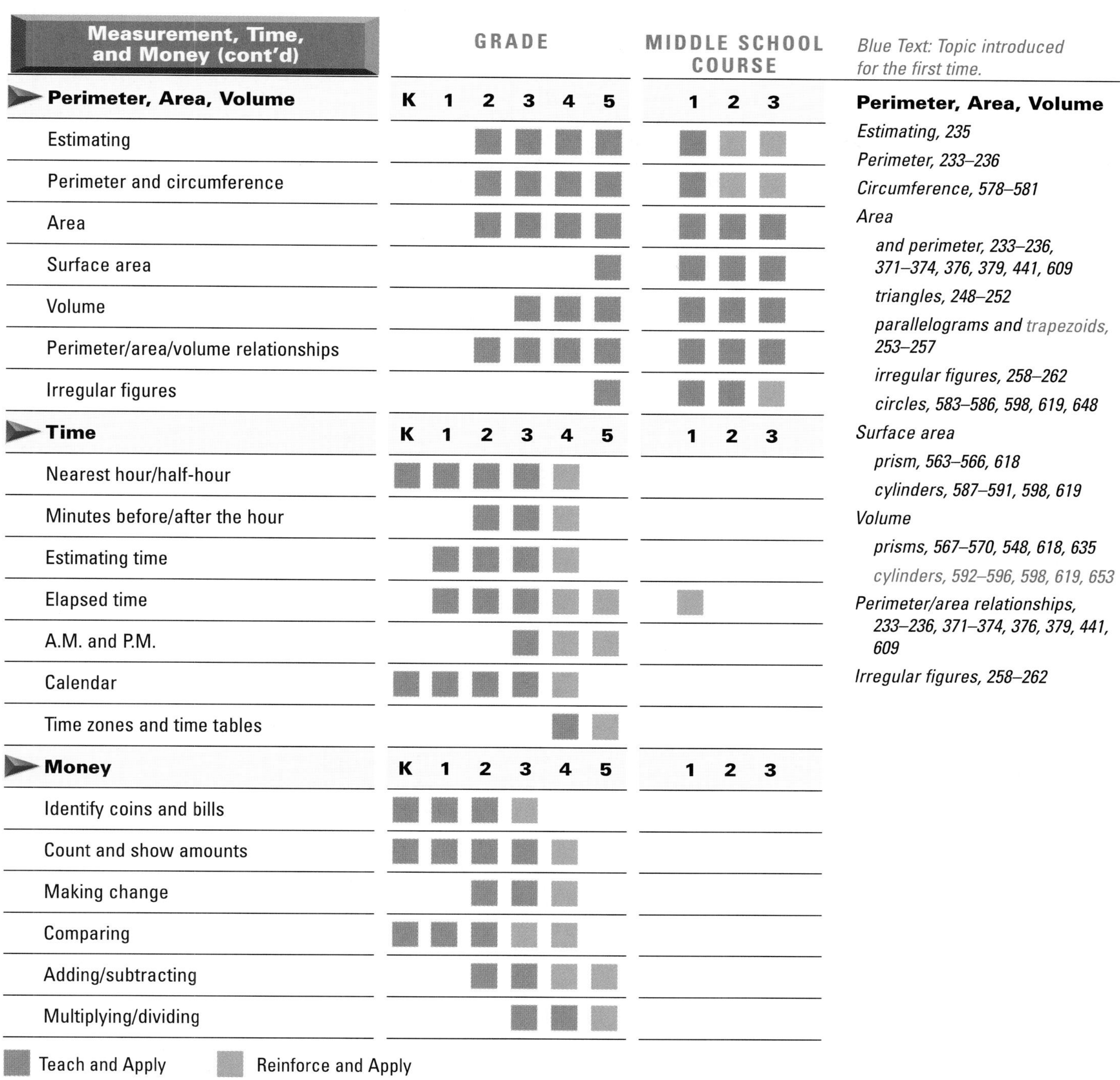

Measurement, Time, and Money (cont'd)	GRADE						MIDDLE SCHOOL COURSE		
Perimeter, Area, Volume	**K**	**1**	**2**	**3**	**4**	**5**	**1**	**2**	**3**
Estimating			■	■	■	■	■	□	□
Perimeter and circumference			■	■	■	■	■	□	□
Area			■	■	■	■	■	■	■
Surface area						■	■	■	■
Volume				■	■	■	■	■	■
Perimeter/area/volume relationships			■	■	■	■	■	■	■
Irregular figures						■	■	■	□
Time	**K**	**1**	**2**	**3**	**4**	**5**	**1**	**2**	**3**
Nearest hour/half-hour	■	■	■	■	□				
Minutes before/after the hour			■	■	□				
Estimating time		■	■	■	□				
Elapsed time		■	■	■	□	□	□		
A.M. and P.M.				■	□	□			
Calendar	■	■	■	■	□				
Time zones and time tables					■	□			
Money	**K**	**1**	**2**	**3**	**4**	**5**	**1**	**2**	**3**
Identify coins and bills	■	■	■	□					
Count and show amounts	■	■	■	■	□				
Making change			■	■	□				
Comparing	■	■	■	□	□				
Adding/subtracting			■	■	□	□			
Multiplying/dividing				■	■	□			

■ Teach and Apply □ Reinforce and Apply

Blue Text: Topic introduced for the first time.

Perimeter, Area, Volume

Estimating, 235

Perimeter, 233–236

Circumference, 578–581

Area

and perimeter, 233–236, 371–374, 376, 379, 441, 609

triangles, 248–252

parallelograms and trapezoids, 253–257

irregular figures, 258–262

circles, 583–586, 598, 619, 648

Surface area

prism, 563–566, 618

cylinders, 587–591, 598, 619

Volume

prisms, 567–570, 548, 618, 635

cylinders, 592–596, 598, 619, 653

Perimeter/area relationships, 233–236, 371–374, 376, 379, 441, 609

Irregular figures, 258–262

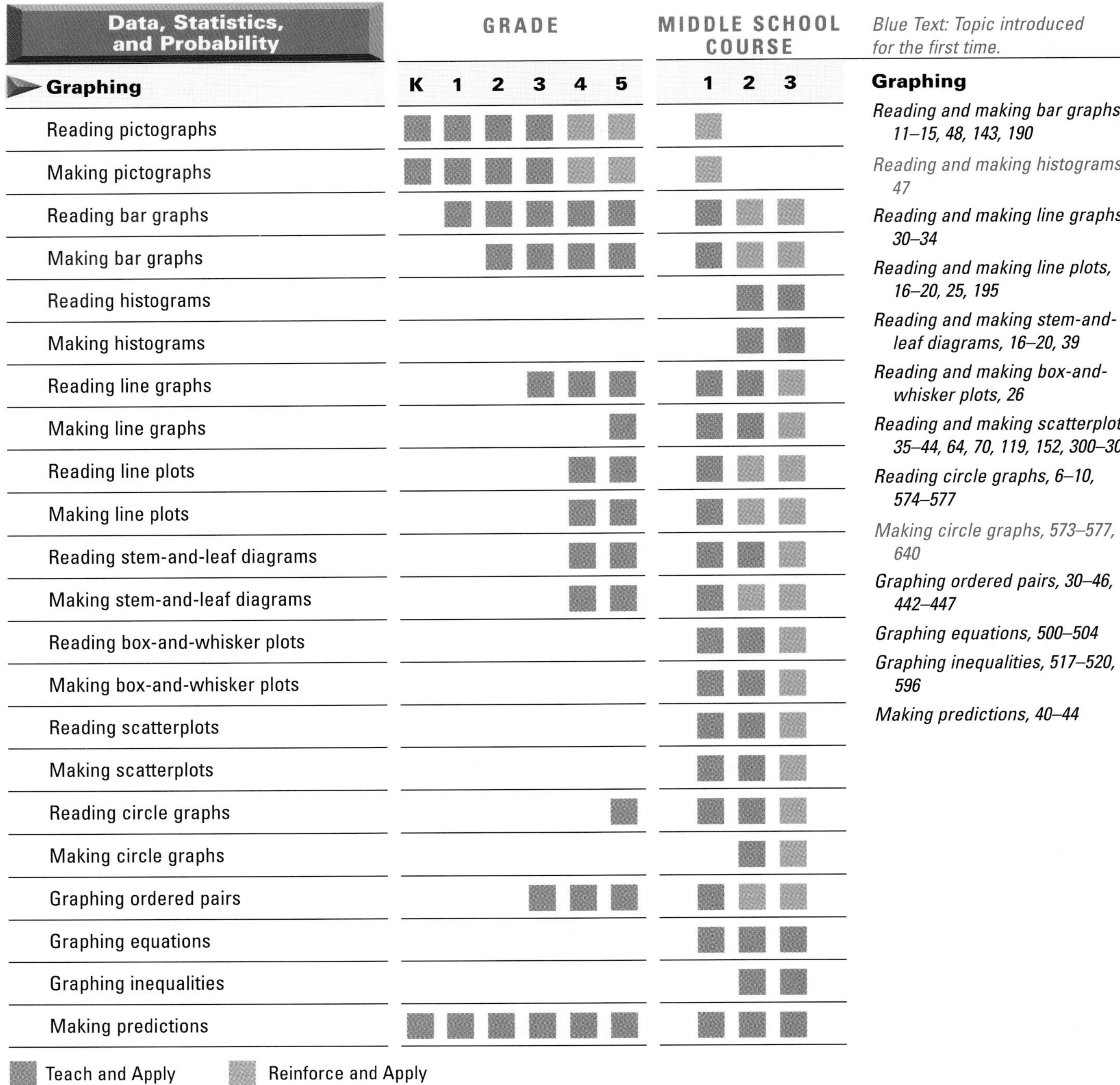

Data, Statistics, and Probability

Graphing	K	1	2	3	4	5	MS 1	MS 2	MS 3
	GRADE						**MIDDLE SCHOOL COURSE**		
Reading pictographs	■	■	■	■	□	□	□		
Making pictographs	■	■	■	■	□	□	□		
Reading bar graphs		■	■	■	■	■	■	□	□
Making bar graphs			■	■	■	■	■	□	□
Reading histograms								■	■
Making histograms								■	■
Reading line graphs				■	■	■	■	■	□
Making line graphs						■	■	■	□
Reading line plots					■	■	■	□	□
Making line plots					■	■	■	□	□
Reading stem-and-leaf diagrams					■	■	■	■	□
Making stem-and-leaf diagrams					■	■	■	□	□
Reading box-and-whisker plots							■	■	□
Making box-and-whisker plots							■	■	□
Reading scatterplots							■	■	□
Making scatterplots							■	■	□
Reading circle graphs						■	■	■	□
Making circle graphs								■	□
Graphing ordered pairs				■	■	■	■	□	□
Graphing equations							■	■	■
Graphing inequalities								■	■
Making predictions	■	■	■	■	■	■	■	■	■

■ Teach and Apply □ Reinforce and Apply

Blue Text: Topic introduced for the first time.

Graphing

Reading and making bar graphs, 11–15, 48, 143, 190

Reading and making histograms, 47

Reading and making line graphs, 30–34

Reading and making line plots, 16–20, 25, 195

Reading and making stem-and-leaf diagrams, 16–20, 39

Reading and making box-and-whisker plots, 26

Reading and making scatterplots, 35–44, 64, 70, 119, 152, 300–301

Reading circle graphs, 6–10, 574–577

Making circle graphs, 573–577, 640

Graphing ordered pairs, 30–46, 442–447

Graphing equations, 500–504

Graphing inequalities, 517–520, 596

Making predictions, 40–44

SCOPE AND SEQUENCE

Data, Statistics, and Probability (cont'd)

Blue Text: Topic introduced for the first time.

Data and Statistics	K	1	2	3	4	5	MS 1	MS 2	MS 3
Collecting and organizing data	■	■	■	■	■	■	■	■	■
Reading/making charts and tables	■	■	■	■	■	■	□	□	□
Tally charts	■	■	■	■	□	□	□		
Survey/census								■	■
Frequency distribution							■	■	■
Range, mode, median, mean					■	■	□	□	□
Sampling						■	■	■	□
Correlation/dispersed points							■	■	□
Using data in problem solving	■	■	■	■	■	■	■	■	■
Interpreting data					■	■	■	■	□
Making predictions				■	■	■	■	■	■
Misleading statistics							■	■	

Probability	K	1	2	3	4	5	MS 1	MS 2	MS 3
Outcomes			■	■	■	■	□	□	□
Tree diagrams					■	■	■	□	□
Writing probabilities		■	■	■	■	■	□	□	□
Certain/possible/impossible events				■	■	■	■	□	□
Independent/dependent events								■	■
Compound events								■	■
Experimental/theoretical probability						■	■	□	□
Simulation					■	■	■	□	□
Fair and unfair games				■	■	■	■	□	□
Making predictions		■	■	■	■	■	■	■	□
Fundamental counting principle								■	■
Permutations and combinations								■	■

■ Teach and Apply □ Reinforce and Apply

Data and Statistics

Collecting and organizing data, 3, 53, 103, 165, 209, 304, 383, 429, 479

Reading/making charts and tables, 11–25, 30–33, 35–38, 40–49, 58–59, 66–72, 286–290, 298–301, 520

Survey/census, 271

Frequency distribution, 47

Range, mode, median, mean, 21–25

Sampling, 51, 271

Correlation/dispersed points, 35–39

Using data in problem solving, 2–5, 10, 15, 25, 34, 68, 124, 131, 143, 147, 152, 156, 190, 195, 200, 243, 247, 298, 504, 520, 575–577, 654

Interpreting data, 6–25, 30–44, 71, 115, 157, 461, 500, 520

Making predictions, 30–34, 40–45, 153, 447

Misleading statistics, 8

Probability

Outcomes, 626–630, 644–658

Tree diagrams, 626–630, 632, 637

Writing probabilities, 649–653

Certain/possible/impossible events, 649–653

Independent/dependent events, 659–663

Experimental/theoretical probability, 654–658

Simulations, 664

Fair and unfair games, 644–648

Making predictions, 654

Fundamental counting principle, 626–630

Permutations and combinations, 631–640

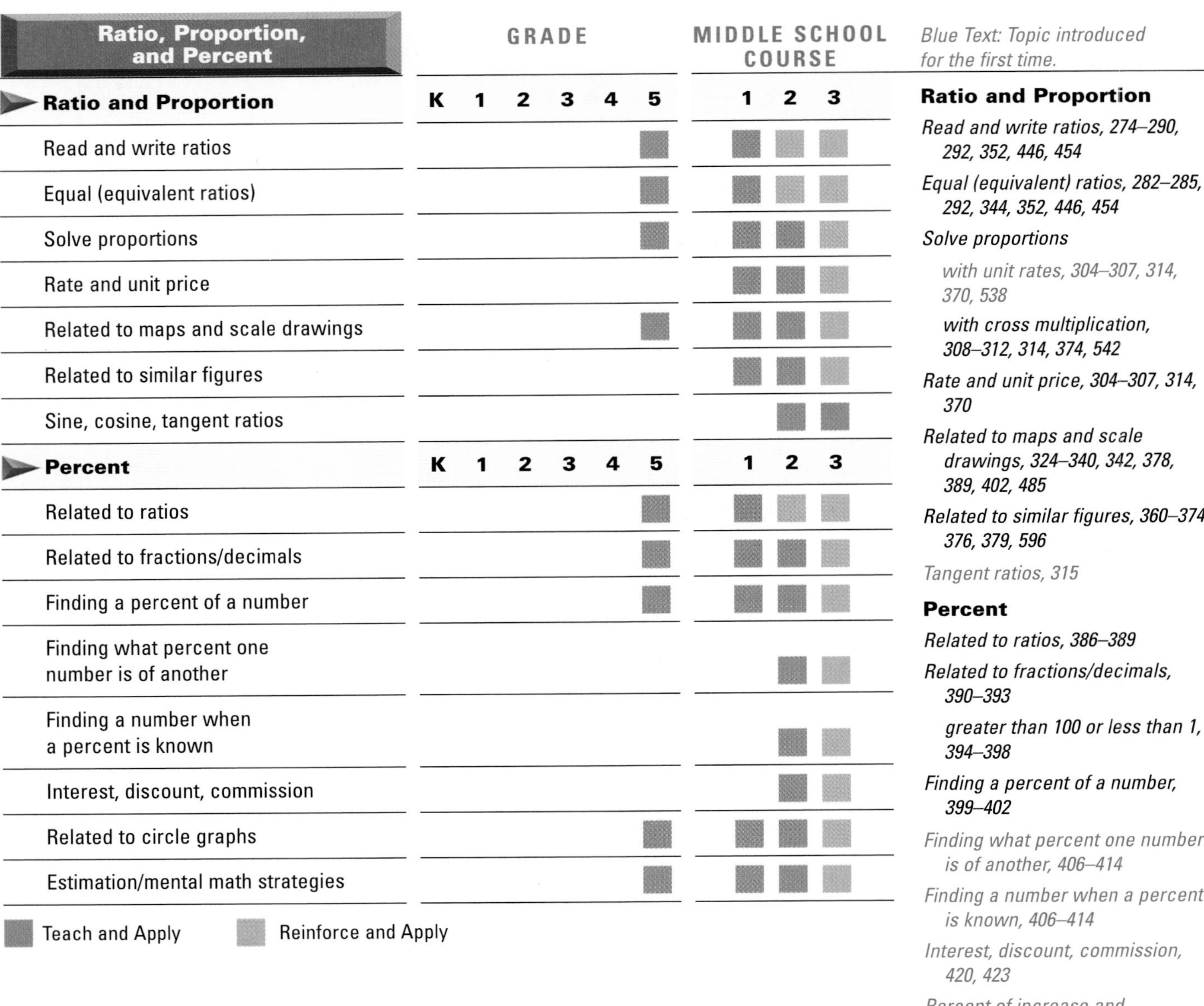

Ratio, Proportion, and Percent	GRADE						MIDDLE SCHOOL COURSE		
Ratio and Proportion	**K**	**1**	**2**	**3**	**4**	**5**	**1**	**2**	**3**
Read and write ratios						■	■	□	□
Equal (equivalent ratios)						■	■	□	□
Solve proportions						■	■	■	□
Rate and unit price							■	■	□
Related to maps and scale drawings						■	■	■	□
Related to similar figures							■	■	□
Sine, cosine, tangent ratios								■	■
Percent	**K**	**1**	**2**	**3**	**4**	**5**	**1**	**2**	**3**
Related to ratios						■	■	□	□
Related to fractions/decimals						■	■	■	□
Finding a percent of a number						■	■	■	□
Finding what percent one number is of another								■	□
Finding a number when a percent is known								■	□
Interest, discount, commission								■	□
Related to circle graphs						■	■	■	□
Estimation/mental math strategies						■	■	■	□

■ Teach and Apply   □ Reinforce and Apply

Blue Text: Topic introduced for the first time.

Ratio and Proportion

Read and write ratios, 274–290, 292, 352, 446, 454

Equal (equivalent) ratios, 282–285, 292, 344, 352, 446, 454

Solve proportions

with unit rates, 304–307, 314, 370, 538

with cross multiplication, 308–312, 314, 374, 542

Rate and unit price, 304–307, 314, 370

Related to maps and scale drawings, 324–340, 342, 378, 389, 402, 485

Related to similar figures, 360–374, 376, 379, 596

Tangent ratios, 315

Percent

Related to ratios, 386–389

Related to fractions/decimals, 390–393

greater than 100 or less than 1, 394–398

Finding a percent of a number, 399–402

Finding what percent one number is of another, 406–414

Finding a number when a percent is known, 406–414

Interest, discount, commission, 420, 423

Percent of increase and decrease, 415–419

Related to circle graphs, 574–577

Estimation/mental math strategies, 399–402

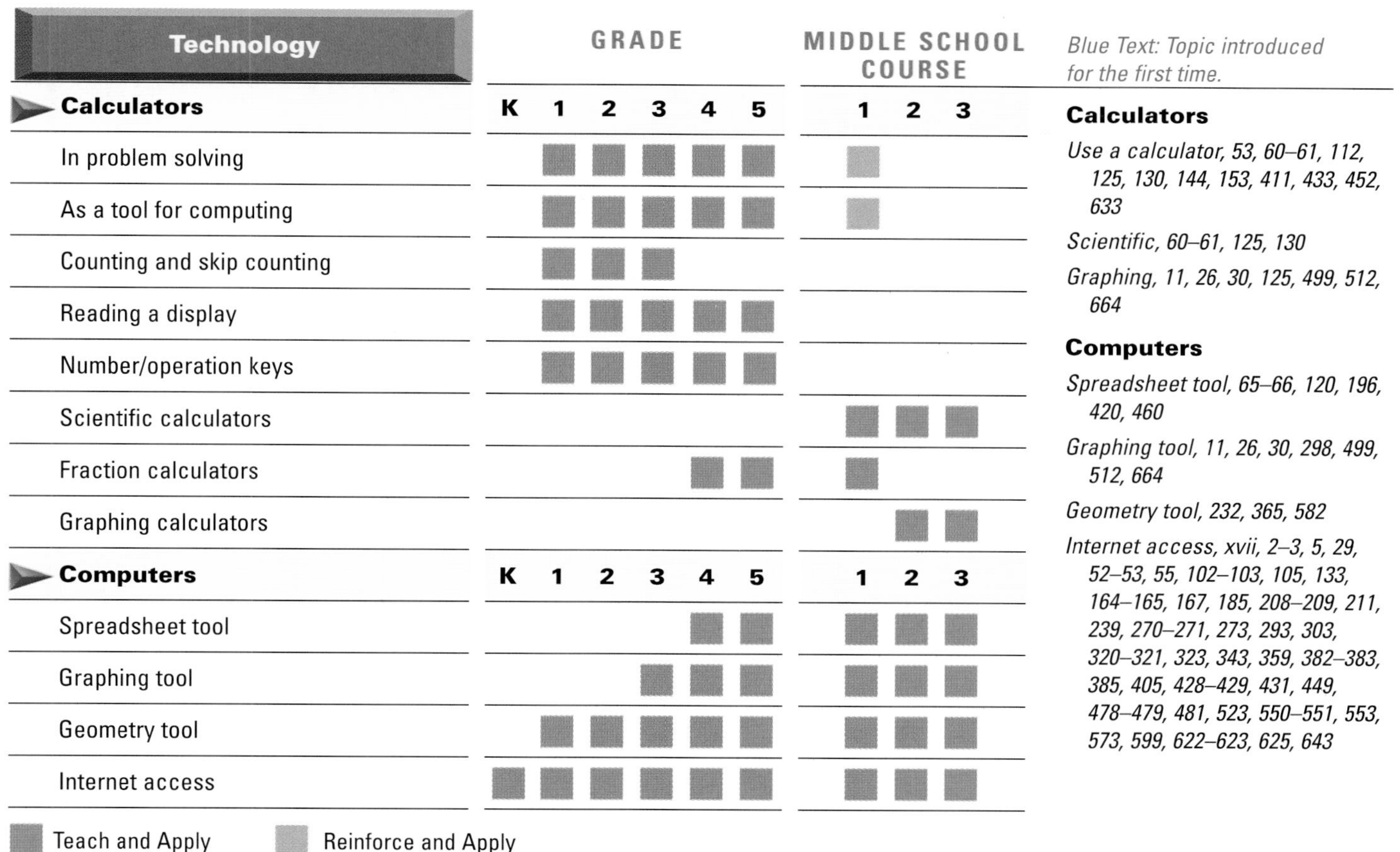

Technology	GRADE						MIDDLE SCHOOL COURSE		
Calculators	**K**	**1**	**2**	**3**	**4**	**5**	**1**	**2**	**3**
In problem solving		■	■	■	■	■	□		
As a tool for computing		■	■	■	■	■	□		
Counting and skip counting		■	■	■					
Reading a display		■	■	■	■	■			
Number/operation keys		■	■	■	■	■			
Scientific calculators							■	■	■
Fraction calculators					■	■	■		
Graphing calculators								■	■
Computers	**K**	**1**	**2**	**3**	**4**	**5**	**1**	**2**	**3**
Spreadsheet tool					■	■	■	■	■
Graphing tool				■	■	■	■	■	■
Geometry tool		■	■	■	■	■	■	■	■
Internet access	■	■	■	■	■	■	■	■	■

■ Teach and Apply　□ Reinforce and Apply

Blue Text: Topic introduced for the first time.

Calculators

Use a calculator, 53, 60–61, 112, 125, 130, 144, 153, 411, 433, 452, 633

Scientific, 60–61, 125, 130

Graphing, 11, 26, 30, 125, 499, 512, 664

Computers

Spreadsheet tool, 65–66, 120, 196, 420, 460

Graphing tool, 11, 26, 30, 298, 499, 512, 664

Geometry tool, 232, 365, 582

Internet access, xvii, 2–3, 5, 29, 52–53, 55, 102–103, 105, 133, 164–165, 167, 185, 208–209, 211, 239, 270–271, 273, 293, 303, 320–321, 323, 343, 359, 382–383, 385, 405, 428–429, 431, 449, 478–479, 481, 523, 550–551, 553, 573, 599, 622–623, 625, 643

CONTENTS

Building a Foundation for Number Sense

TAKE A MOMENT

What does "number sense" mean? Is it important? Does your class have it? How can it be taught? Some people say number sense is a way of thinking that unfolds as students explore the skills and concepts shown at the right. Stress these topics to build number sense—working with numbers, operations, basic facts, and computation in ways that make sense.

NUMBERS

Number Meanings and Uses

- *Concrete and Pictorial Models:* Models for fractions, decimals, integers.
- *Number Uses:* Quantity (5 girls), measurement (5 feet), order (the fifth day)

Number Relationships

- *Breaking Apart Numbers:* 87 = 80 + 7
- *Relative Size of Numbers:* 248 is 2 less than 250, is large compared to 4, and is small compared to 8,000,000.
- *Benchmark Numbers:* 98 is about 100.
- *Number Patterns:* Sequences, figurate numbers, divisibility, etc.

Estimation in Measurement

- *Estimates:* About 200 people, 10 to 20 feet long, about 1/2 eaten
- *Common-Object Benchmarks:* The end of your thumb is about 1 inch.
- *Checking for Sensible Answers:* A person isn't 4 meters tall.

OPERATIONS

Operation Meanings

- *Knowing When to Add or Subtract:* Joining, separating, comparing
- *Knowing When to Multiply or Divide:* Joining or forming equal groups, comparing with "times as many" or "fraction of"

Operation Relationships; Properties

- *Relationships Between Operations:* Multiplication as repeated addition and as the inverse of division
- *Properties:* Commutative, associative, distributive, identity

Effects of Operations

- Ask students if adding and multiplying always result in a larger number.
- Have students multiply two numbers, then explore the effect of doubling one factor, the other factor, both factors.
- Have students add 2 to a number ten times. Then have them multiply the same number by 2 ten times.

Try This Tomorrow

Ask students how they could estimate the thickness of a sheet of paper. [Measure a stack of 500 sheets and divide by 500.] Then have them estimate the height of a stack of paper if you start with 2 sheets and double the stack 20 times.

What are some ways you could estimate the height of a bookshelf?

Which is greater, 3,523 + 245 or 245 + 3,524?
If 6 × 452 = 2,712, what is 6 × 453?
Find 4,567 × 12.8 × 0 × 15.47.
Which is greater, 79/80 or 99/100?

How many different ways can you find 480 x 5 in your head?

"Number sense is to using numbers and operations as comprehension is to reading words and sentences."

—John Dossey

NUMBER SENSE TEACHING TIPS

Encourage Flexibility
People with good number sense use multiple strategies and can use different strategies for the same problem.

Basic-Facts Mastery
Basic-facts mastery is a key to good number sense. When appropriate, work for rapid recall of basic facts.

The Value of Estimation
Stress the value of estimates. Some students see them as wrong answers.

Put Strategies in Perspective
Point out that learning names of strategies for basic facts, mental math, and estimation is not important. Being able to use strategies is what's important.

BASIC FACTS AND COMPUTATION

Basic Facts

Rapid recall of basic facts is important for estimation, mental math, and computation. Use flash cards, software, fact strategies, etc. as needed to ensure all students know their facts.

Estimation and Mental Computation

Remind students to estimate before calculating an exact answer or when an exact answer isn't needed. Remind them of various estimation and mental-computation strategies.

Estimation Strategies in Computation
Front End 173 + 421 + 348 —> 100 + 400 + 300 = 800. Then add 150 because 73 + 21 + 48 is about 150. 800 + 150 = 950.
Rounding 28.4 – 3.9 —> 28 – 4 = 24. 425 × 28 —> 400 × 30 = 1,200.
Compatible Numbers 1/3 × 187 —> 1/3 × 180 = 60.
Clustering 627 + 658 + 589 + 613 —> 4 × 600 = 2,400.
Benchmark 46 + 38 —> 46 < 50 and 38 < 50. 46 + 38 < 100.

Mental-Computation Strategies
Compensation 57 + 29 —> 57 + 30 = 87. 87 – 1 = 86.
Breaking Apart Numbers 54 + 23 —> 54 + 20 = 74. 74 + 3 = 77. 92 × 6 = (90 × 6) + (2 × 6) = 540 + 12 = 552.
Special Numbers Look for numbers like 1, 10, 100 or 3, 30, 300. 400 × 20 = 8,000. 45 + 30 = 75. 3 + 79 + 7 = 3 + 7 + 79 = 10 + 79 = 89.

Paper-Pencil Computation

If some students have still not mastered paper-pencil computation that you consider important, provide remediation but don't deny them access to other math in the meantime. Let students use calculators as needed to solve problems and learn concepts.

Choosing a Computation Tool

Remind students to try mental math first and don't use calculators instead of mental math. Discuss the choice of calculators or paper and pencil. In real life, the choice may depend on how tedious the computation is, how many computations are needed, etc.

Scott Foresman - Addison Wesley Math

Number sense is a foundation of the program.

Student Book

- Lessons that focus on many aspects of number sense including Estimating by Rounding, Estimating: Fractions and Mixed Numbers, Exploring and Estimating Ratios, Exploring and Estimating Rates, Measurement: Estimating Actual and Scale Distances, Choosing Appropriate Rates and Units, Finding a Percent of a Number Mentally
- Exercises identified as number sense, operation sense, estimation
- Mental math notes in lesson development

Teacher's Edition

- Support for number sense in notes and activities plus special Mental Math or Estimation exercises for every lesson

Ancillaries

- Support for number sense in the program components including the Interactive CD-ROM with a Place-Value Blocks tool and a Fraction Tool.

Keys to Success in Teaching Problem Solving

TAKE A MOMENT

Many teachers ask "What can I do to help my students do better in problem solving?" There's no one simple answer. There may be a variety of reasons why students are struggling. One reason could be that students are simply having difficulty reading the problem and gaining the kind of information they need in order to understand and solve the problem. One of the keys to success in teaching problem solving is helping students learn to "read for math."

Try This Tomorrow

Give students some word problems and tell them you want to check on how effectively they read the problems. Ask questions to check their understanding of the problems. Then give some more problems and have the students ask such questions.

PROVIDE TOOLS FOR LEARNING THE PROBLEM-SOLVING PROCESS

Problem-Solving Guidelines

Introduce general problem-solving guidelines and use them to provide guided problem solving as needed.

Understand the Problem
- What do you know?
- What do you need to find out?

Develop a Plan
- Have you ever solved a similar problem?
- What strategies can you use?
- What is an estimate for the answer?

Solve the Problem
- Do you need to try another strategy?
- What is the solution?

Look Back
- Did you answer the right question?
- Does your answer make sense?

Problem-Solving Strategies

Introduce problem-solving strategies and show students examples of problems solved using the strategies.

- Look for a Pattern
- Make an Organized List
- Make a Table
- Guess and Check
- Work Backward
- Use Logical Reasoning
- Draw a Diagram
- Solve a Simpler Problem

Within daily lessons at middle school, integrate instruction of problem-solving strategies by:

- Using problems-solving strategies in lesson examples.
- Providing problem-solving tips as a regular part of instruction.

INTEGRATE PROBLEM SOLVING INTO DAILY INSTRUCTION

Teach Through Problem Solving Use real-world contexts. Introduce content with opportunities for students to explore, letting the math emerge during the problem-solving process.

Integrate Problem Solving Into Practice There's no substitute for solving lots of problems. Give routine, nonroutine, and open-ended problems. Do a problem of the day and multi-day projects.

Use Technology to Enhance Problem Solving Use calculators so students can access problems involving real data and can solve more problems in a given period of time.

"All students can think, reason, and solve problems in mathematics."

—Randy Charles

Reading for Math

Focus on ways that reading problems with math in mind can help students at various phases of the problem-solving process: doing an initial reading to understand the problem, reading to organize information and make a plan, reading to look back and compare the answer to the original problem.

Reading for Math	Is a Key to Success
To Help You Understand	
• Read the problem and then ask yourself questions.	• What is the problem about? What is it asking for?
• Read the problem looking for unnecessary information.	• Read all the data in the problem? Is some not needed?
To Help You Plan	
• As you read, interpret math phrases.	• Look for phrases like 3 more than, twice as long as, half of.
• After you read, identify any missing information.	• Is there data you need that is not stated in the problem?
To Help You Look Back	
• After you get an answer, reread for reasonableness.	• Ask if your answer is too low or too high or close enough.
• Reread to check the rules of the problem.	• Verify that your solution agrees with all the facts.

ENCOURAGE HELPFUL HABITS AND BELIEFS

Promote Good Problem-Solving Habits

- Perseverance
- Flexibility
- Confidence, risk taking
- Willingness to reflect on one's thinking

Foster Important Beliefs About Problem Solving

- There's more than one way to solve a problem.
- Some problems have more than one solution.

PROBLEM-SOLVING TEACHING TIPS

Model Good Problem Solving
Model the problem solving skills, strategies, and habits you'd like students to have.

Facilitate Class Discussions
Make students responsible for thinking. Listen to them. Ask them to explain what they did. Ask who did it a different way.

Introduce Ideas As Needed
Present math terms, symbols, content, and alternative solutions as needed within an overall role of problem-solving coach.

Assess Problem Solving Holistically
Look at the total work (the process) and not just the answer. Use scoring rubrics.

Scott Foresman - Addison Wesley Math

Problem solving is a foundation of the program.

Teaching the Problem-Solving Process

- A Problem-Solving Handbook in front of the book presents problem-solving guidelines and strategies.
- Problem-Solving Focus pages look at reading the problem, finding unnecessary information, etc.
- Problem-Solving Tips are in lesson development.

Integrating Problem Solving in Instruction

- "Explore" teaches through problem solving.
- Problem-solving exercises are one-step, multiple-step, nonroutine, and include Choose a Strategy.
- Chapter Projects are introduced and revisited.
- Problem of the Day is in the Teacher's Edition and on the Daily Transparencies.
- A Guided Problem Solving blackline master for each lesson provides a step-by-step approach to solving a problem selected from an exercise in the book.
- Calculators are assumed. An Interactive CD-ROM, Wide World of Mathematics for Middle School, and the New Adventures of Jasper Woodbury videodisc provide technology-enhanced problem solving.

Encouraging Helpful Habits and Beliefs

- "What Do You Think" in lessons throughout shows how 2 students solved the same problem and then asks questions about comparing their methods.

Technology in Math Class: What Are Your Goals?

TAKE A MOMENT

What technology is available to you as you teach math? How do you use it? Whether you have a little or a lot and use it rarely or often, take a moment to think through your technology goals. Start by thinking about your students.

- Write down the year they will turn 21 and the year they'll be 65.
- Think about the math and the technology they will use as adults.
- Now set some goals. What math content will you emphasize and how would you like to use technology in your math class? Use the information at the right to help.

Try This Tomorrow

Have each student pick 2 numbers, add them, subtract them, and then add the results. Repeat but now multiply the 2 numbers, divide them, and then multiply the results. In each case, how does what you end with compare to what you started with?

LEARNING WITH TECHNOLOGY

4-Function Calculator

Fraction Calculator

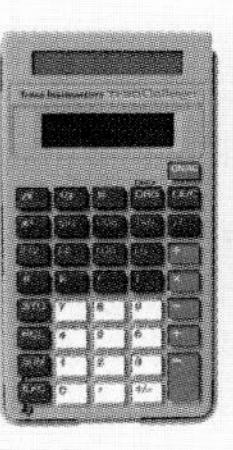

Scientific Calculator

Graphing Calculator

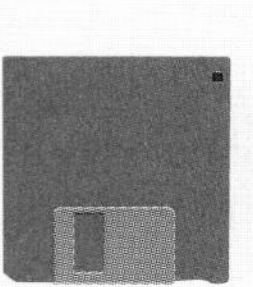

Computer Software

Interactive CD-ROM

www.mathsurf.com

Internet Connections

Learning with Calculators

Calculators as Problem-Solving Tools Calculators save time when students solve problems involving data analysis, areas, number patterns, numerical conjectures, or any tedious computation. Calculators let students spend their time focusing on the problem-solving process.

Calculators as Concept Development Tools While students should not use calculators to do basic facts, mental computation, or simple paper-pencil computation, calculators can help develop other number skills and concepts as shown in the Estimation Target Game below.

Graphing Calculators Graphing calculators can assist learning in statistics and algebra.

ESTIMATION TARGET GAME

One student enters a number and operation and says a target range: enter 8 [×] and say 2000–3000. Another student enters a number and presses [=]. If the answer is within the target range, it's a bull's-eye.

Learning with Computers

Tool Software and Practice Games Computers help students explore and practice math concepts by providing:

- Graphing tools for bar graphs, line graphs, line plots, etc.
- Geometry tools for 2D, 3D work
- Number tools such as a place-value blocks tool and a fraction tool
- Probability tools for simulations
- Spreadsheet tools to explore patterns, relationships, pre-algebra.
- Writing tools for journal work
- Practice games for motivation and instant feedback

Interactive, Multimedia CD-ROM For interactive teaching, math tools, sound, movies, and animation.

Internet Connections For worldwide gathering and sharing of data.

Learning with Video

You can bring real-world math into the classroom with:

- Videotape
- Video on CD-ROMs
- Videodisc, digital videodisc
- Other digital video sources

"Technology can open the door to students learning more math than ever before."

—Cathy Seeley

LEARNING ABOUT TECHNOLOGY

Learning About Calculators

Use key sequences like these to help students learn about their calculators.

- Automatic constant: 4 [+] 3 [=] [=] [=] [7, 10, 13]
- Order of operations: 4 [+] 5 [×] 3 [19]
- Memory: 5 [M+] 3 [+] [MR] [=] [8]
- Integer division: 26 [INT ÷] 3 [=] [8 R 2]

Learning About Computers

Here are some basic computer skills students should learn.

- Starting up; using a floppy disk, CD-ROM, or network
- Finding, opening, and operating a document or program
- Changing, saving, and printing a document; shutdown

Learning About the Internet

Here are some Internet basics.

- Getting on the Internet: you need a computer, a modem to get information, and a browser to display information.
- Getting around the Internet: type a URL to find a "page" (like using an address to find a house); click on hyperlinks (underlined words) to go somewhere else (to "surf"); use a search engine or directory to find information sources.

LEARNING WHEN TO USE TECHNOLOGY

- Teach students that it's not appropriate to use technology as a substitute for thinking or doing basic facts, mental computation, and simple paper-pencil computation. To convince students, have a race between students doing these problems mentally and others using a calculator.

  3 x 5   200 + 500   2 x 800   30 + 10 + 20   100 + 78
- Teach students that it's appropriate to use technology when solving problems and exploring new ideas.
- Stress that technology makes estimation more important, not less, because it's easy to push a wrong button.

TECHNOLOGY FOR TEACHERS

To Plan Use an interactive CD-ROM lesson planner.

To Assess Use test and practice software.

To Present a Lesson Use an overhead display panel or large monitor to show computer screens during presentations.

To Help You Grow Gather and share ideas on the Internet.

TECHNOLOGY TIPS

Managing Calculators

Number the calculators and storage slots for easy distribution and retrieval.

Using Technology Helpers

Ask 3–4 students to volunteer as technology helpers for the class.

Communicating with Others

Find out what technology is available at school and request more that you need. Keep parents informed about how you're using technology and why.

Math/Calculator Discoveries

Students using calculators continue to discover new things about math and about calculators. Have students add their discoveries to a class collection.

Scott Foresman - Addison Wesley Math

The program offers many opportunities to use technology.

Student Book

- Calculators: Scientific calculator assumed, with options for using a fraction calculator and graphing calculator; Calculator Hint and Technology Link in examples.
- Computers: Tool software used in Technology pages; Mathsurf Internet site references; opportunities for using spreadsheets in lessons.

Teacher's Edition

- Technology options keyed into chapters and lessons

Ancillaries

- Calculator and computer activities in Technology Masters
- Interactive, multimedia CD-ROM with lessons and tools
- The New Adventures of Jasper Woodbury for problem solving on videodiscs
- Wide World of Mathematics for Middle School on videotape, videodisc, or multimedia CD-ROM
- For teachers: Teacher's Resource Planner CD-ROM to preview ancillaries and plan lessons, *TestWorks:* Test and Practice Software, Mathsurf Internet site for teachers. Also a Mathsurf Internet site for parents.

Working Together to Make Connections in Middle School

▶ TAKE A MOMENT

What are some of the differences between math in school and math in real life? In real life, math problems don't appear in paragraphs on pages next to other pages that focus primarily on math. One way to get closer to real-life math in school is to do interdisciplinary team teaching. It helps students see knowledge as part of an integrated system. It helps them see the "big picture" and the relevance of math to their lives.

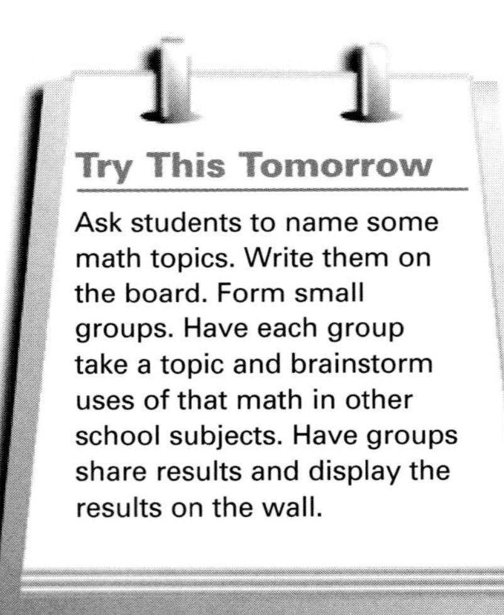

Try This Tomorrow

Ask students to name some math topics. Write them on the board. Form small groups. Have each group take a topic and brainstorm uses of that math in other school subjects. Have groups share results and display the results on the wall.

A RANGE OF WAYS TO DO INTERDISCIPLINARY TEAM TEACHING

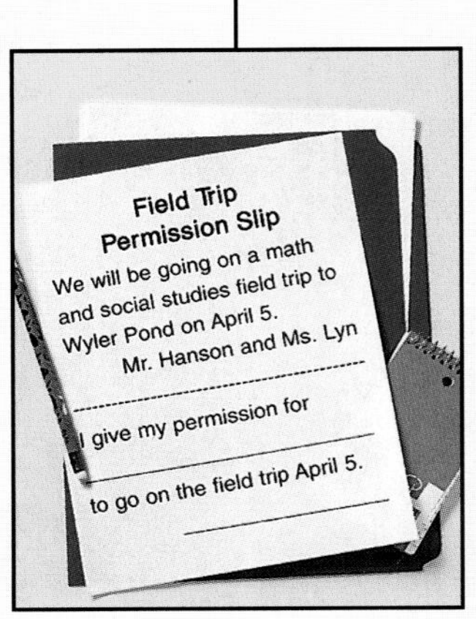

KEEPING IN TOUCH

Two teachers talk during the year and do some activities jointly.

Mr. Hanson teaches math. Ms. Lyn teaches science. At different times during the year, they talk about what they're doing. Once when students were using ratios in sampling in math, the teachers did a field trip to a local pond.

Talking to Colleagues

- Share information. Talk about topics in math that tie into other areas, like measurement in science or symmetry in art.
- Ask what students know about an application you plan to use in math.

CO-PLANNING

Two teachers plan their courses so that some topics will coincide.

At the beginning of the year, Ms. Lopez, the math teacher, and Miss Kennedy, the social studies teacher, sequence topics in each course. Last year they planned for statistics to be done at the same time that elections were studied.

Planning Courses Together

- Share your course outline and time line with colleagues early.
- Help them see that the sequence of topics in math might not be as flexible as in other subjects.

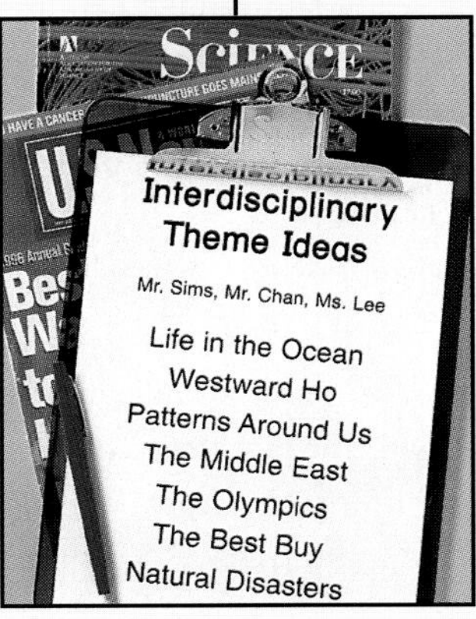

THEMATIC TEACHING

A team of 3 teachers uses themes at specific times during the year.

At Washington Middle School, the math, science, and social studies teachers plan one or more themes they will follow in their courses and when. The team might have a theme run for one week, a few weeks, or longer.

Selecting Themes

- Begin by brainstorming connections between the disciplines. Look for math-rich topics.
- When deciding how long a theme will last, consider students' interest in that topic.

> *"We must choose among the many ways to help students see the connections between math and other disciplines."*
>
> —*Janet Caldwell*

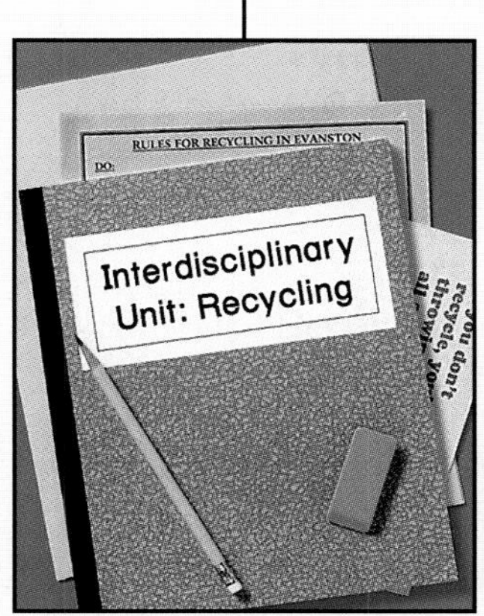

THEMATIC UNITS

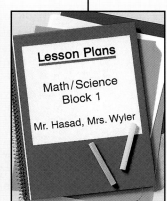

A team of 4 teachers use themes ending with investigations/units.

At Ames School, four teachers (math, science, language arts, and social studies) use a theme each quarter and finish with a 1-week investigation/unit. Last year, one unit was on recycling; another was on proportional reasoning.

Planning Thematic Units

- Take advantage of local opportunities: the need for a new parking lot.
- Have each teacher plan one of the units.
- Rotate classes so each teacher sees all students.
- Do portfolio assessment.

CO-TEACHING

Two teachers co-teach a two-subject course to one large class.

Mr. Hasad teaches math. Mrs. Wyler teaches science. They have a first and second period block for combining two classes of students in a large room. They plan one course that covers both math and science content.

Teaching Together

- Plan the course to maximize opportunities for interdisciplinary work.
- Be flexible so you can take advantage of the freedom to adjust content coverage or sequence along the way.

TEAM TEACHING TIPS

Worthwhile Mathematics
Be sure the math involved in an interdisciplinary theme or unit is worthwhile, not just an occasional use of measurement or graphing.

Maximize Student Involvement
One of the biggest benefits of interdisciplinary units is the excitement they generate when students get really involved.

Communication with Other Math Teachers
Coordinate with other math teachers. It's difficult for a science teacher to plan with you if that teacher's students have three other math teachers.

Covering the Math Content
A math topic can be taught before or during its use in a thematic unit. Plan the year so that you feel units enhance, not interrupt, your instruction.

Scott Foresman - Addison Wesley Math

The program provides support for interdisciplinary connections and for team teaching.

Student Book

- Problems related to other disciplines, such as science, social studies, health, are identified.
- Chapter Projects at the beginning of chapters may involve several disciplines.
- Section themes are often interdisciplinary.

Teacher's Edition

- Lesson-specific Team Teaching suggestions are in Meeting Middle School Classroom Needs.
- Block scheduling for an interdisciplinary course is given at the front of each chapter.
- An Interdisciplinary Bulletin Board is shown for each chapter.
- Units in the Connected Mathematics series are keyed to chapters.

Ancillaries

- For each section, a 2-page Interdisciplinary Team Teaching worksheet is provided. It connects math with science/technology, social studies, language arts, or fine arts and typically includes an open-ended activity encouraging further exploration.
- The Home and School Connections booklet includes a Community Project for each chapter.
- The Wide World of Mathematics videodisc, videotape, or CD-ROM is often interdisciplinary.

Fostering a Community of Learners in the Math Classroom

TAKE A MOMENT

Think back to when your students entered your class. Did they have diverse learning styles, cultural backgrounds, socioeconomic backgrounds, levels of English proficiency, and perhaps physical, emotional, or mental challenges? Which of your students are the hardest to reach in math? In our information society, it is a priority for all students to succeed in math. The best way to achieve this is to build a community of learners in the classroom that support each other on the road to math power.

Try This Tomorrow

To show students ways to overcome language barriers, first have someone give a non-English lecture (just talk) on finding the surface area of a cylinder. Then repeat the explanation using drawings, gestures, symbols, props, and interaction.

ESL STUDENTS

"Show me what you mean."

Overcome Language Barriers When You Communicate

- Use real objects, manipulatives, and pictures, especially ones relating to the students' world.
- Use gestures and highlighting.
- Speak slowly in short, simple sentences and enunciate clearly.
- Provide ample repetition; check comprehension frequently.
- When you model, show what to do; don't just say what to do.
- Use tables and diagrams.
- Use "scaffolding;" rephrase what students say to help them be clear.

Vary How Students Communicate

- Have them demonstrate, write, speak, draw, play math games, use computers, and work with parents.
- Pair students with same-language or English-language speakers.

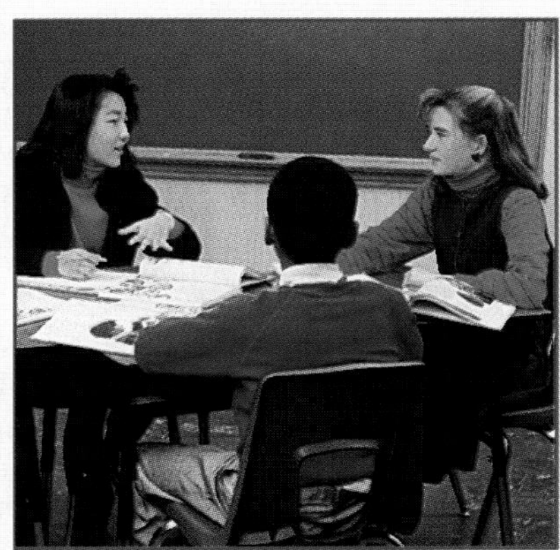

INCLUSION STUDENTS

"Give me some more time."

Identify Student Needs

- Learning disabled (LD) students have normal intelligence but have problems with memory, perception, distractibility, and reasoning.
- Low achievers and the educable mentally handicapped (EMH) have problems with memory, attention span, learning rate, and reasoning.
- Students with attention deficit disorder, ADD, are easily distracted.
- Physical and emotional challenges vary: visual, auditory, speech, orthopedic, hyperactive, etc.

Modify Instruction

- Present lessons in a structured manner with regular checkpoints.
- Collaborate with specialized resource teachers about ways to customize instruction.
- Check activities for too many materials, memory skills, or steps.
- Don't deny students opportunities to learn important content; just modify how it's presented based on students' needs.
- Use graphic organizers, a file of math words, real-world links, group and pair work, a reader.
- Assign less; allow more time.
- Vary assessment methods; use students' writing, speaking, and hands-on work to gain insights into their understanding.

"All students must have access to a curriculum that fosters mathematical thinking."

—Freddie Renfro

DIVERSE LEARNING STYLES

"Let me try it my way."

Use Activities That Support Diverse Learning Styles

Learning Style	Learns Through
Verbal	Reading, writing, talking, listening.
Logical	Exploring, questioning, reasoning.
Visual	Drawing, building, designing, creating
Kinesthetic	Movement, hand-on activities
Musical	Rhythm, melody, tapping, rapping.
Social	Grouping, team participation, and sharing.
Individual	Thinking, reflecting, goal setting.

GIFTED AND TALENTED STUDENTS

"Give me a challenge."

Provide challenging, interesting problems. Have gifted students work others; then everyone benefits.

AT-RISK STUDENTS

"Give me a chance."

Provide extra encouragement and excitement in school with emphasis on problem solving and critical thinking.

GENDER ISSUES

"Treat me the same way."

Some teachers pay more attention to boys, give them more praise, let them talk more, give them more help, and ask them higher-level questions. Be aware of this issue.

CULTURAL DIVERSITY

"Respect my heritage."

Clarify misconceptions, negative beliefs, and stereotypes. Provide relevant, motivating contexts. Encourage all students to share and celebrate their cultures.

A COMMUNITY OF LEARNERS

An Accepting, Supportive Learning Environment
Create an atmosphere that honors students' unique ideas. Encourage peer coaching as a normal part of the classroom culture.

Observing Students
Provide opportunities for interactions, and then observe to assess students' needs.

Promoting Self Confidence
Many students have been told they aren't good at math. Praise small positive steps that will lead to larger ones.

Teaching Strategies for All
Use a variety of teaching and assessment strategies that are age, gender, and culturally appropriate for all learners.

Scott Foresman - Addison Wesley Math

The program is designed to reach all learners.

Overcoming Language Barriers

- Pictures in the Student book that show what to do
- Vocabulary called out; Language Link for help with non-math words; Study Tips as students read the text
- Activities with manipulatives, technology—not just words
- Varied forms of assessment—not just written
- Mathematics Dictionary
- Multilingual Handbook including a multilingual glossary

Accommodating Varied Abilities, Learning Styles, Backgrounds

- Assignment Guide; daily blackline masters for Practice, Reteaching, Enrichment, Guided Problem Solving
- Inclusion tips and Reteaching activities in lesson notes
- Extend Key Ideas pages; For Groups that Finish Early in lesson notes
- Communicate and Journal exercises, Chapter Project, Work Together in Explore, Your Choice (learning styles), multicultural and gender-sensitive contexts
- Learning Modalities and Diversity ideas in lesson notes

A Teacher's Guide to Assessment: What, How, Why, and When

TAKE A MOMENT

Think about the students in your class. Write down the names of any students for whom you'd like more information about what they know and don't know about mathematics. Then write down two ways you might be able to get that information. Perhaps a different form of assessment would help.

Try This Tomorrow

If you haven't tried all the methods of assessment listed at the right, pick one and try it tomorrow. Then use it at least once more in the next week. The suggestions given in the Assessment Sourcebook can help you get started.

WHAT TO ASSESS

Assess Full Math Power

- Concepts
- Facts
- Skills, procedures
- Problem solving: routine problems, nonroutine problems, open-ended problems, decision making
- Mathematical reasoning and critical thinking

Assess Math Habits and Disposition

- Perseverance
- Flexibility
- Confidence, risk-taking
- Motivation
- Participation
- Cooperation
- Reflection on one's own work and learning

Assess content and approaches that are valuable in the real world; don't just assess what is easy to test.

HOW TO ASSESS

Use a Mix of Student Work

- Oral work: explanations, questions
- Written work: skills, drawings, graphs, explanations of student thinking, written reports
- Work with tools: manipulatives, calculators, computers
- Work with others: partners, small groups, and the whole class

Vary Assessment Methods

- Observation, interview
- Journal of student writing
- Performance tasks scored using assessment rubrics
- Free-response or multiple-choice tests
- Warm-ups; quick checks
- Self assessment, peer assessment
- Portfolio of selected student work

Use a variety of student work and assessment methods that reflect how students learn and how you teach.

"What we test tells students what we value. What gets inspected is respected."

—Steve Leinwand

ASSESSMENT TIPS

Ongoing Assessment
Carry a clipboard and checklist. Write on self-stick labels to transfer notes. Be a good listener; be nonjudgmental.

Using Assessment Rubrics
Score papers with a colleague at first.

Portfolios
Have students move papers from their work folder to an assessment portfolio at various times.

Changing How You Assess
Don't change everything all at once. Show students criteria and sample work.

WHY AND WHEN TO ASSESS

Assessment Purposes

- Monitor progress against criteria and give students feedback.
- Adjust instruction as needed.
- Do long-term planning.
- Send progress reports or grades home to parents.
- Compare an individual student or a group of students to other students in the district, state, or nation.

Assessment Times

- Ongoing assessment integrated with daily instruction
- End-of-section quizzes
- End-of-chapter tests
- End-of-quarter or semester tests
- Annual district, state, or national tests

Assess primarily to help students grow and to help you plan. Assess on an ongoing basis during instruction.

Scott Foresman - Addison Wesley Math

Here are some of the many built-in assessment options.

Student Book

- Check Your Understanding, Journal, Test Prep exercises (multiple-choice), Test Prep notes, Project Progress
- Chapter Assessment including Performance Assessment
- Cumulative Review (half in multiple-choice format)

Teacher's Edition

- Ongoing Assessment: Error Intervention, Portfolio, Interview, Observation, Journal, Self-Assessment, Performance Assessment in lessons
- Quick Quiz, Project Assessment, Scoring Rubrics
- Standardized Test Correlation in front of each chapter

Ancillaries

- Assessment Sourcebook: Inventory Test, Quizzes, Chapter Tests (free-response, multiple-choice, mixed formats), Cumulative Tests, record forms, assessment tips, . . .
- TestWorks: Test and Practice Software with ready-made and customized tests, free response or multiple choice
- Interactive CD-ROM with a Journal feature

INSERVICE WORKSHOPS FROM SCOTT FORESMAN-ADDISON WESLEY

At Scott Foresman-Addison Wesley, we offer more than program materials. We also offer our commitment to service with inservice workshops for professional staff development as well as support for implementation of program materials. As part of our ongoing partnership between teacher and publisher, we are at your service. Contact your sales representative to hear how our educational consultants can customize inservice programs to meet your needs.

Northeast	1-800-521-0011
Southeast	1-800-241-3532
Midwest	1-800-535-4391
West	1-800-548-4885
Southwest	1-800-527-2701
In Texas	1-800-441-1438
Web Site	http://www.sf.aw.com

ADDITIONAL RESOURCES

Number Sense

McIntosh, A., B. Reys, R. Reys, and J. Hope. *Number Sense: Simple Effective Number Sense Experiences.* Palo Alto, CA: Dale Seymour Publications, 1996.

Reys, Barbara, et al. *Developing Number Sense in the Middle Grades: Addenda Series, Grades 5–8.* Reston, VA: NCTM, 1991.

Ritchhart, Ron. *Making Numbers Make Sense.* Palo Alto, CA: Dale Seymour Publications, 1993.

Schoen, H. L., and M. J. Zweng, eds. *Estimation and Mental Computation.* Reston, VA: NCTM, 1986.

Sowder, Judith. "Estimation and Number Sense." Grouws, Douglas A. ed. *Handbook of Research on Mathematics Teaching and Learning.* Reston, VA: NCTM, 1992.

Van de Walle, John A. *Elementary and Middle School Mathematics: Teaching Developmentally,* 3rd ed. Reading, MA: Addison Wesley Longman, 1998.

Problem Solving

Charles, Randall, and Frank Lester. *Teaching Problem Solving: What, Why, & How.* Palo Alto, CA: Dale Seymour Publications, 1982.

Charles, Randall, Frank Lester, and Phares O'Daffer. *How to Evaluate Progress in Problem Solving.* Reston, VA: NCTM, 1987.

Charles, Randall, and Edward Silver, eds. *The Teaching and Assessing of Mathematical Problem Solving.* Hillsdale, NJ: Lawrence Erlbaum, 1989.

Dolan, Daniel T., and James Williamson. *Teaching Problem-Solving Strategies.* Palo Alto, CA: Dale Seymour Publications, 1983.

Gibney, T., S. Miering, L. Pikaart, and M. Suydam, eds. *Problem Solving: A Basic Mathematics Goal.* Palo Alto, CA: Dale Seymour Publications, 1980.

Polya, G. *Mathematical Discovery: On Understanding Learning, Teaching Problem Solving.* New York, NY: Wiley, 1962.

Technology

Fey, James T., and Christian R. Hirsch, eds. *Calculators in Mathematics Education.* Reston, VA: NCTM, 1992.

Mathematical Sciences Education Board of the National Research Council. *Reshaping School Mathematics: a Philosophy and Framework for Curriculum.* Washington, DC: National Academy Press, 1990.

Virginia Grant Consortium. *The Educator's Guide to the Internet.* Palo Alto, CA: Dale Seymour Publications, 1997.

Interdisciplinary Team Teaching

Cook, Nancy, and Christine Johnson. *The MESA Series.* Palo Alto, CA: Dale Seymour Publications, 1994–1998.

Lappan, Glenda, James T. Fey, William M. Fitzgerald, Susan N. Friel, and Elizabeth Difanis Phillips. *Connected Mathematics.* Palo Alto, CA: Dale Seymour Publications, 1996.

Diversity

Cech, Maureen. *Global Sense: A Leader's Guide to Games for Change.* Palo Alto, CA: Dale Seymour Publications, 1995.

Perl, Teri. *Math Equals.* Palo Alto, CA: Dale Seymour Publications, 1978.

Reimer, Luetta, and Wilbert Reimer. *Mathematicians Are People, Too.* Palo Alto, CA: Dale Seymour Publications, 1990, 1995.

Skolnick, J, C. Langbort, and L. Day. *How to Encourage Girls in Math and Science.* Palo Alto, CA: Dale Seymour Publications, 1982.

Thornton, Carol A. *Teaching Mathematics to Children with Special Needs.* Palo Alto, CA: Dale Seymour Publications, 1983.

Assessment

Ainsworth, Larry and Jan Christinson. *Student-Generated Rubrics,* Palo Alto, CA: Dale Seymour Publications, 1998.

Barton, James. *Portfolio Assessment* Palo Alto, CA: Dale Seymour Publications, 1996.

Freedman, Robin Lee Harris, *Open-Ended Questioning.* Palo Alto, CA: Dale Seymour Publications, 1993.

Hart, Diane. *Authentic Assessment* Palo Alto, CA: Dale Seymour Publications, 1993.

Stenmark, Jean Kerr, ed. *Mathematics Assessment: Myths, Models, Good Questions, and Practical Suggestions.* Palo Alto, CA: Dale Seymour Publications, 1991.

Other

Burns, Marilyn. *Writing in Math Class.* White Plains, NY: Cuisenaire Company of America, 1995.

Burns, Marilyn. *About Teaching Mathematics.* White Plains, NY: Cuisenaire Company of America, 1992.

Mathematics: for Middle School. Videotapes and discussion guide. White Plains, NY: Cuisenaire Company of America, 1989.

Chapter 1

Page 15

1-2 Exercise Answers

8.

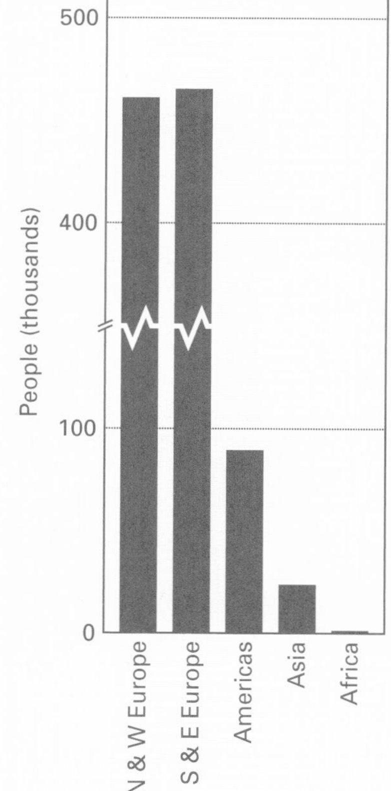

9.

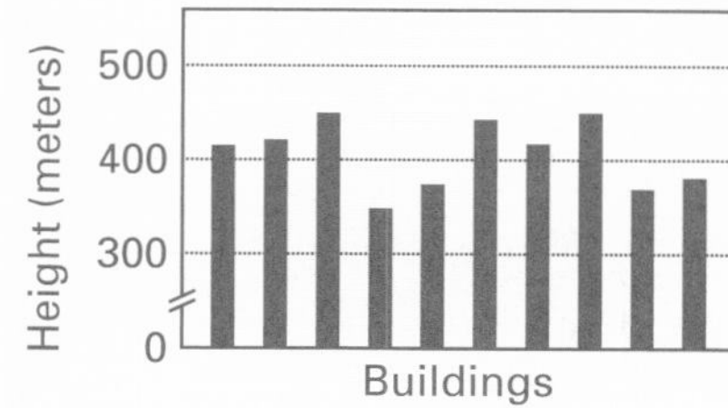

10.

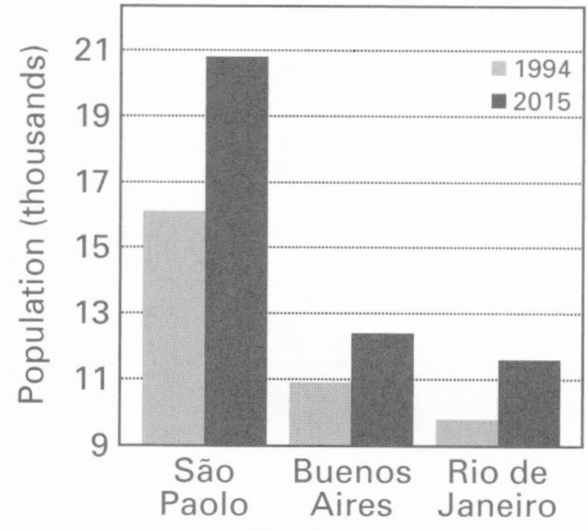

11. a. Bar graph

b.

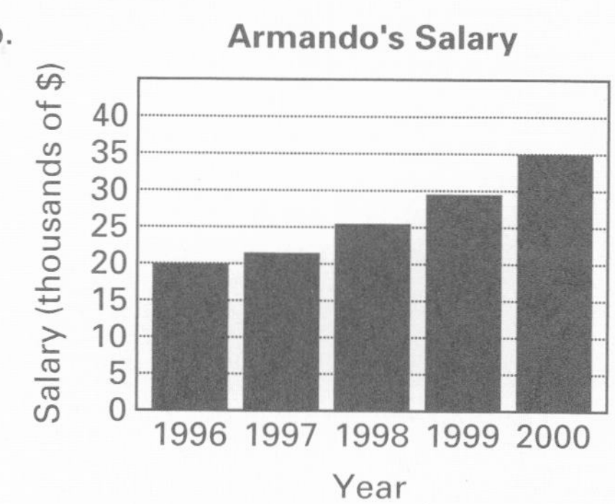

c. It went up by $3000 each year.

d. Possible answers: He got a promotion or changed jobs.

12. Answers may vary but should include reference to a wide range of data to a clustering about a value far removed from 0, or to spreading out very close data values.

Page 17

1-3 Answers for Explore

1.

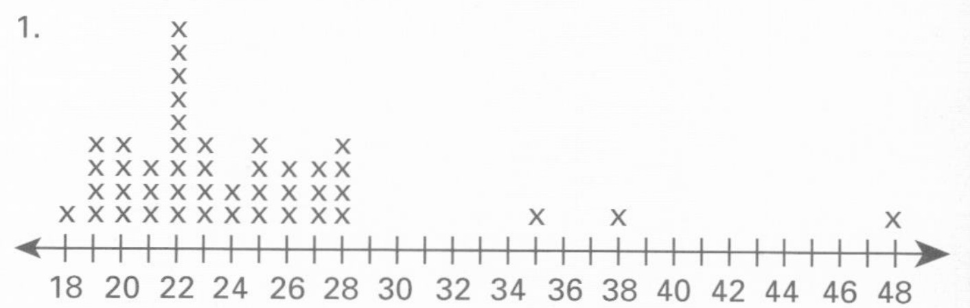

Page 18

1-3 Answers for Try It

1. a.

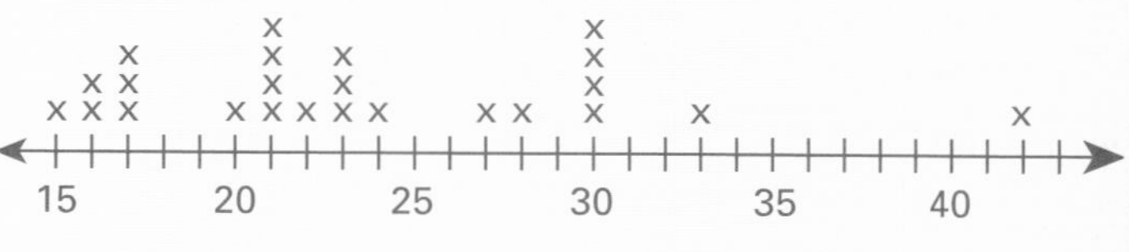

b.

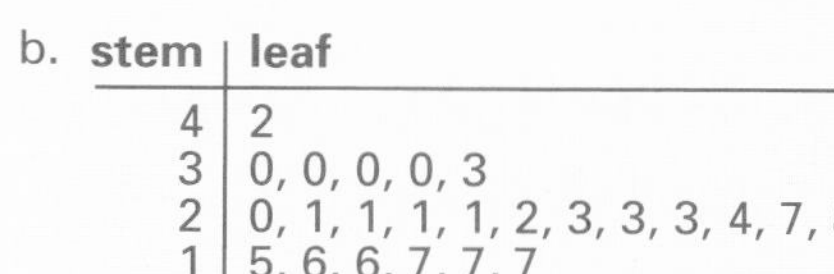

stem	leaf
4	2
3	0, 0, 0, 0, 3
2	0, 1, 1, 1, 1, 2, 3, 3, 3, 4, 7, 8
1	5, 6, 6, 7, 7, 7

c. Possible answers: The outlier 42 is more clearly seen on the line plot; the stem-and-leaf diagram more clearly shows most of the employees' ages are in the 20's.

Page 19

1-3 Exercise Answers

1. a. 29
   b. 36
   c. 29 30 31 32 33 34 35 36
   d. Possible answers: 1, 2, 4 ,5
   e.

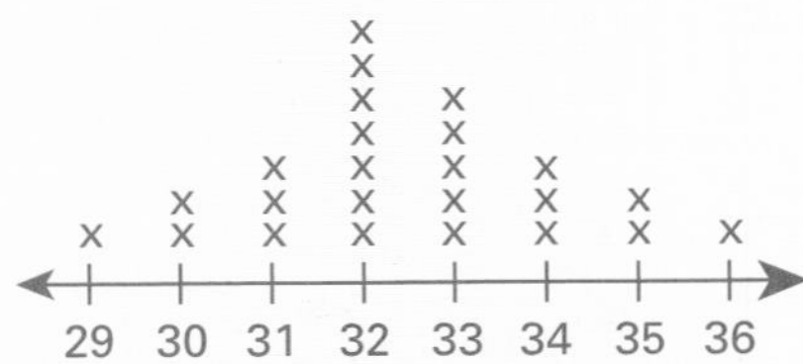

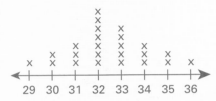

   f. No
2. a.

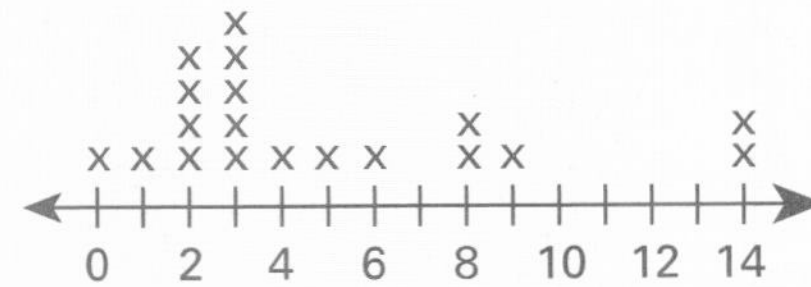

   b. He reached double digits twice and most often scored 2 or 3 home runs a year.
3. 47; 0
4.

   35, 39, and 47 are outliers.
5. D
6. No outliers

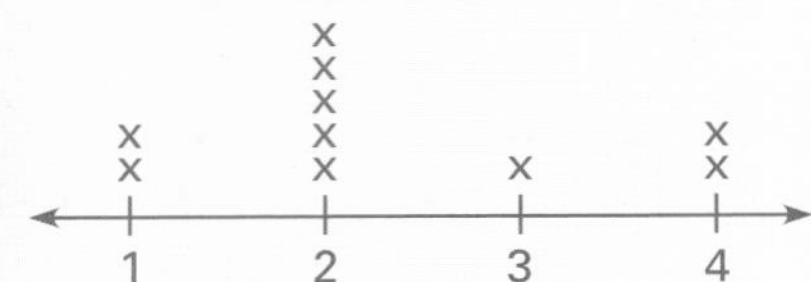

7. Two possible outliers at 17.

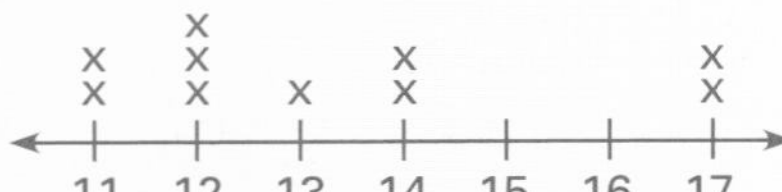

Page 33

1-5 Exercise Answers

1. An increasing trend—more nations compete each time.
2. Horizontal: 2 years; Vertical: 25.
3. **Josie's Bowling Score**

4. Possible answer: 12–17 million
5. Possible answer: Bar graph
6. **People per U.S. Household**

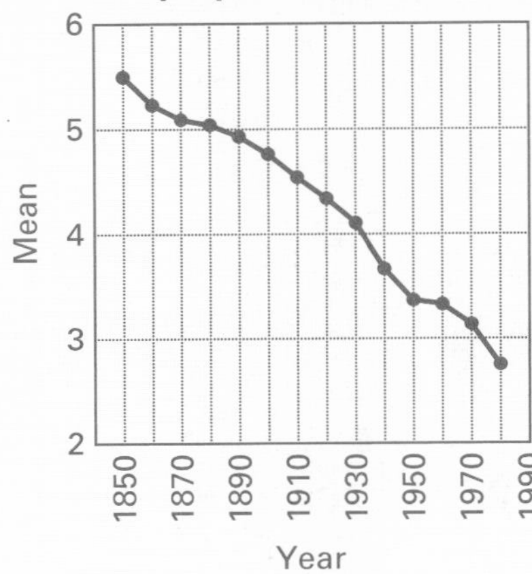

7. Possible answer: Mean number of people per household is decreasing.
8. **Commuters' Transportation**

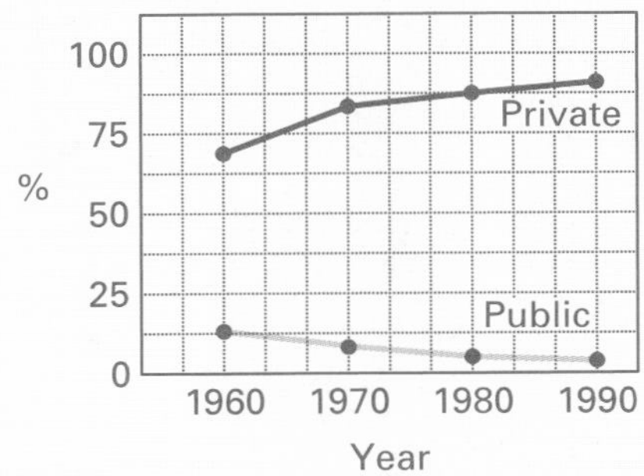

Graph indicates that use of private vehicles in increasing, while use of public transportation is decreasing.

Page 38

1-6 Exercise Answers

4. **Service Aces and Games Played**

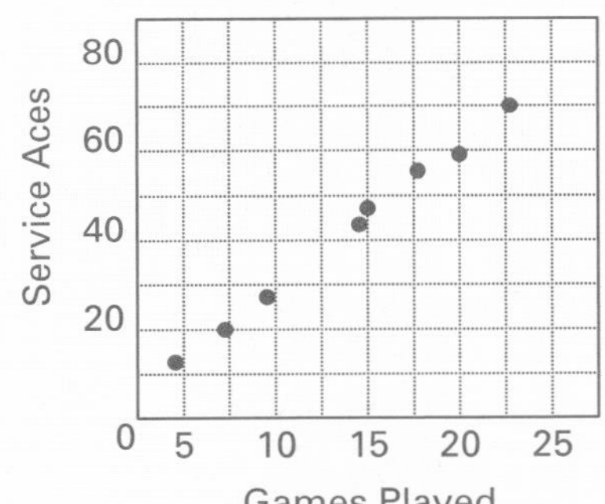

Positive relationship.

5. **Heights of Students and Mothers**

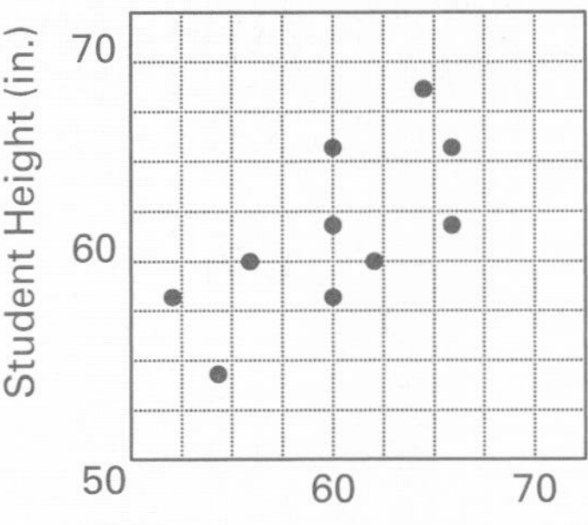

Page 40

1-7 Answers for Explore

1.

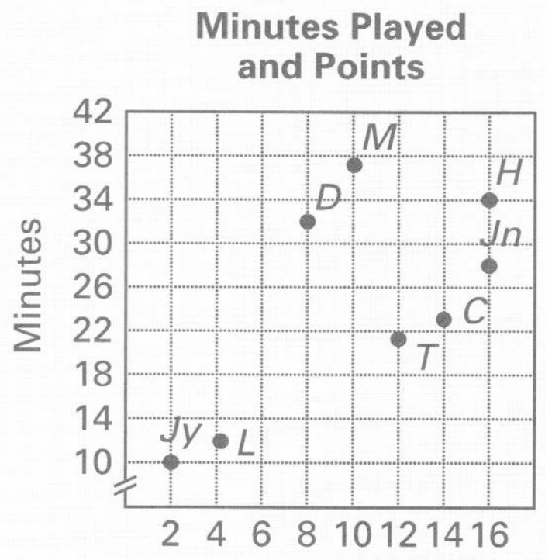

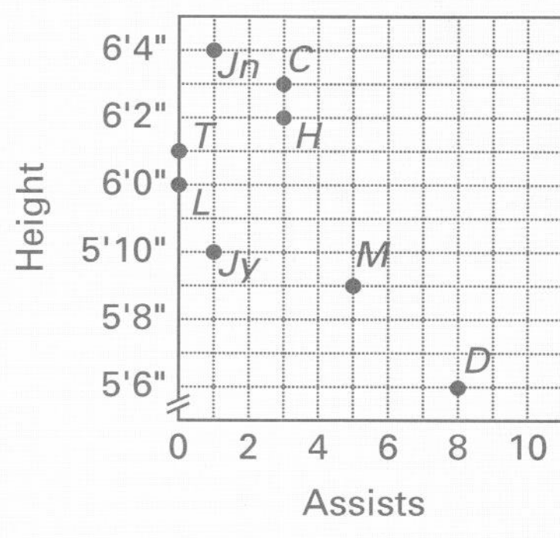

2. Minutes and Points plot seems to demonstrate a positive relationship, while Heights and Assists seems to demonstrate a negative relationship.
3. No; Yes
4. Should be in the range 15–25; Assumed trend.
5. Range: 4ft 10 in.–5ft 6 in.; Assumed trend.
6. Possible answer: Determine a trend line and assume it continues. Likely prediction will come true if it is reasonable and possible.

Page 43

1-7 Exercise Answers

3.

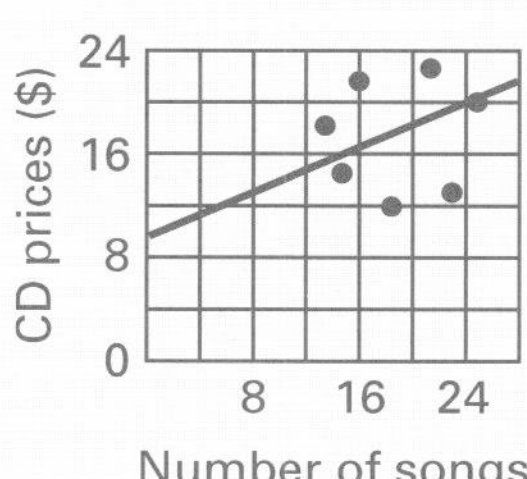

5. a.

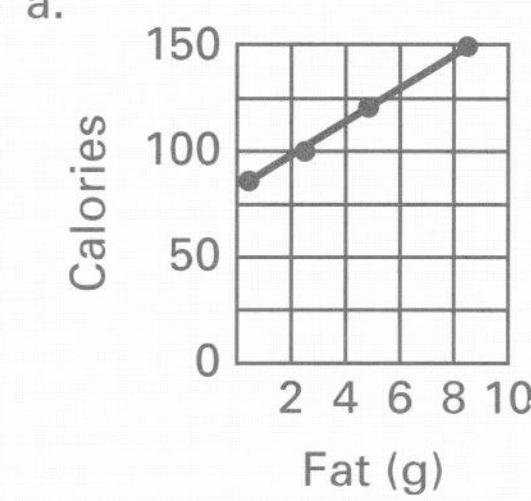

b. Possible answer: About 130.

4. C

Page 44

1-7 Exercise Answers

7. a.

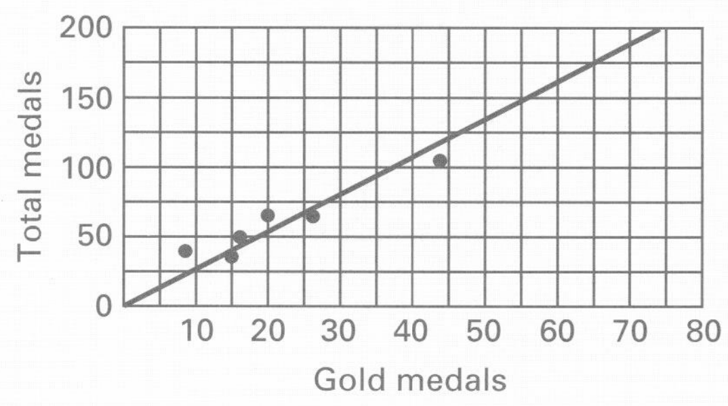

Page 46

Answers for 1B Review

2.

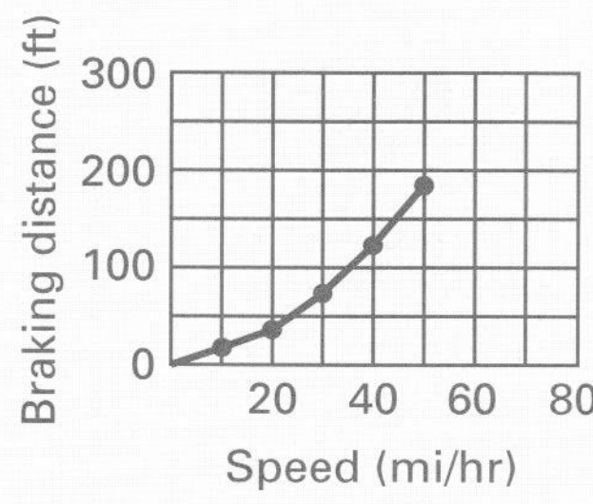

About 225 ft.

3. Your estimate would go up
4. Possible answer: A line graph shows how data changes over time. A scatterplot shows the relationship between two sets of data. Both can be used to make predictions.

5–6.

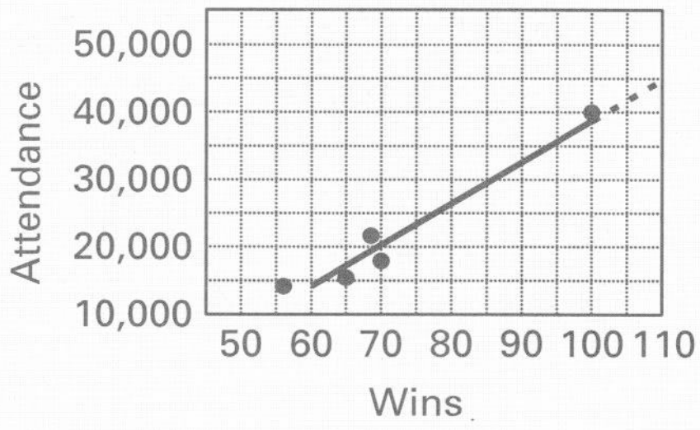

7. Possible answer: About 45,000
8. C

Page 50

Answers for Performance Task

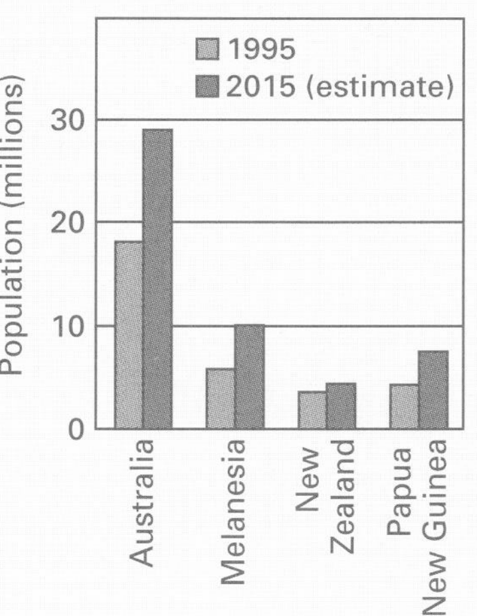

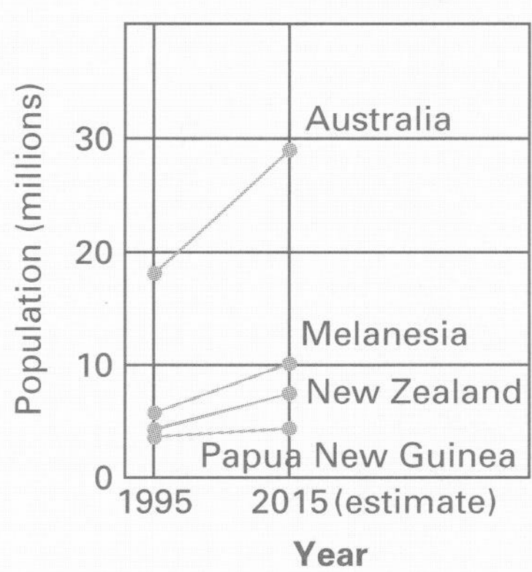

ADDITIONAL ANSWERS

Page 51

Answers for Assessment

- **Capital Capers**

Line plot will show the following information

3 cities with 5 letters (Dover, DE; Boise, ID, Salem, OR.)

10 cities with 6 letters (Mobile, AL, Juneau, AK, Denver, CO; Topeka, KS; Helena, MT; Albany, NY; Pierre, SD; Boston, MA; St. Paul,. MN; Austin, TX)

12 cities with 7 letters (Phoenix, AZ; Atlanta, GA; Lincoln, NE; Concord, NH; Trenton, NJ; Santa Fe, NM; Raleigh, NC; Augusta, ME; Lansing, MI; Jackson, MS; Olympia, WA; Madison, WI)

7 cities with 8 letters (Hartford, CT; Honolulu, HI; Bismarck, ND; Columbus, OH; Columbia, SC; Richmond, VA; Cheyenne, WY.

4 cities with 9 letters (Des Moines, IA; Frankfort, KY; Annapolis, MD; Nashville, TN)

8 cities with 10 letters (Little Rock, AR; Sacramento, CA; Carson City, NV; Harrisburg, PA; Providence, RI; Baton Rouge, LA; Montpelier, VT; Charleston, WV)

2 cities with 11 letters (Tallahassee, FL; Springfield, IL)

3 cities with 12 letters (Indianapolis, IN; Oklahoma City, OK; Salt Lake City, UT)

1 city with 13 letters (Jefferson City, MO)

Possible answers: 13 might be considered an outlier; number of letters seems to cluster around 6, 7, and 8. Explore, Lesson 2-3

- **What Do They Watch?**

Possible answers:

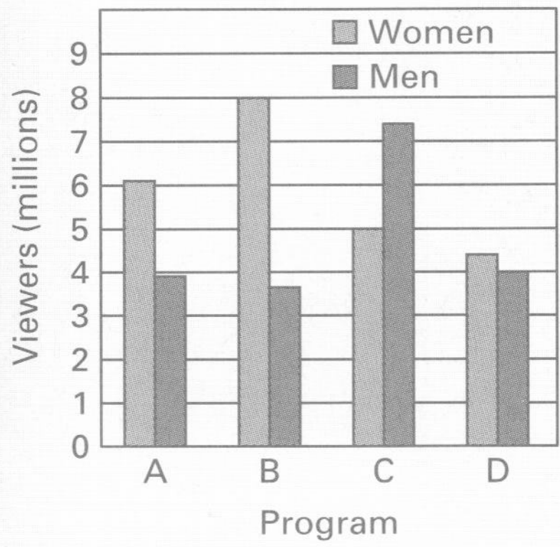

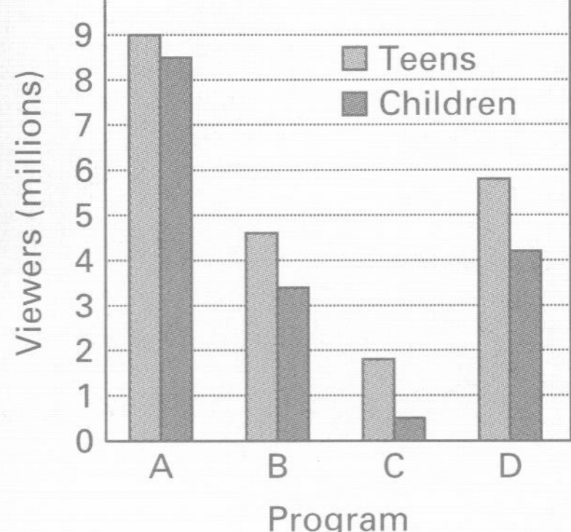

Page 67

2-3 Answers for Explore

4.

	A	B
1	Distance (mi)	Time (hr)
2	633	1
3	1266	2
4	1899	3
5	2532	4
6	3165	5
7	3798	6
8	4431	7
9	5064	8
10	5697	9
11	6330	10
12	6963	11

5.

	A	B	C	D
1	Number of Cars	Weight (lb)	Distance (mi)	Gas (gal)
2	1	250	70	1
3	2	500	140	2
4	3	750	210	3
5	4	1000	280	4

6. The Motorette had only 3 wheels. The Thrust 2 was very fast. The Eshelman got 70 miles to the gallon and weighed only 250 pounds.

Page 70

2-3 Exercise Answers

11.

A	4	8	12	16
C	1	2	3	4

12. a.

s	0	1	2	3	4	5	6	7	8	9	10
D	0	1,480	2,960	4,440	5,920	7,400	8,880	10,360	11,840	13,320	14,800

b. Possible answer: The distances will be smaller; The formula will be $D = 1450s$.

13. 100 times

Chapter 3

Page 107

3-1 Answers for Explore

1. a.

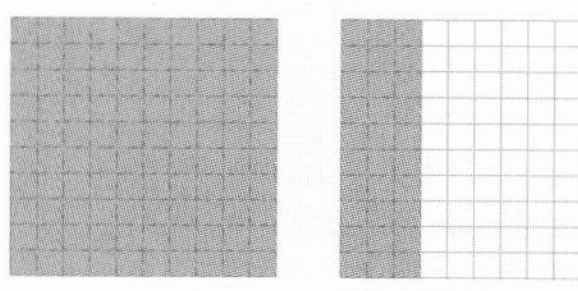

b.

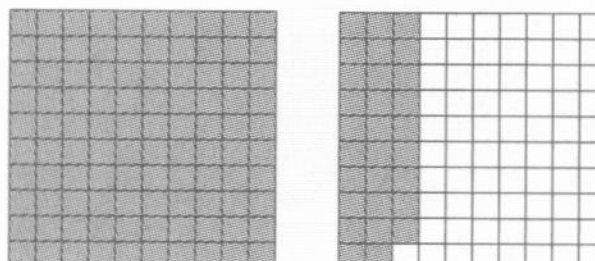

c.

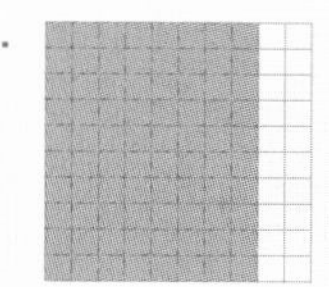

d.

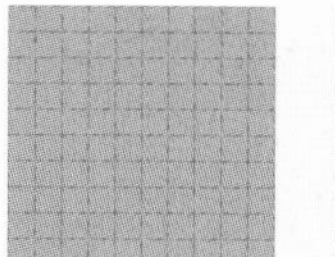

e.

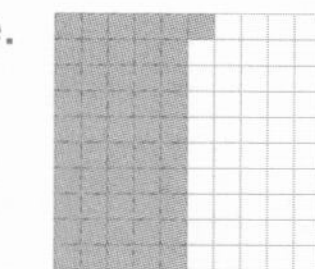

f.

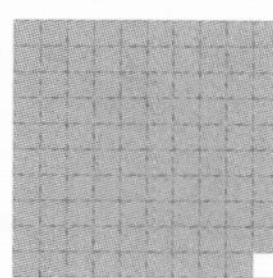

Page 126

3-5 Answers for Explore

1.

Multiply	10	10 x 10	10 x 10 x 10	10 x 10 x 10 x 10	10 x 10 x 10 x 10 x 10
Result	10	100	1,000	10,000	100,000
No. of 0's	1	2	3	4	5

3.

2 x 100	7.2 x 10,000	3.5 x 1,000	4.8 x 1,000,000	36.8 x 1,000,000,000
200	72,000	3,500	4,800,000	36,800,000,000

Page 135

3-6 Answers for Explore

1.

No. of members	30	30	30	30	30	30	30	30	31	31	32	32	32
Members per row	1	2	3	5	6	10	15	30	1	31	1	2	4
No. of rows	30	15	10	6	5	3	2	1	31	1	32	16	8
No. of members	32	32	32	33	33	33	33	34	34	34	34	35	
Members per row	8	16	32	1	3	11	33	1	2	17	34	1	
No. of rows	4	2	1	33	11	3	1	34	17	2	1	35	
No. of members	35	35	35	36	36	36	36	36	36	36	36	36	
Members per row	5	7	35	1	2	3	4	6	9	12	18	36	
No. of rows	7	5	1	36	18	12	9	6	4	3	2	1	

Page 138

3-6 Exercise Answers

44.

stem	leaf
3	2 2 9
4	1 3 7
5	1 3
6	1

45.

stem	leaf
1	5 7
2	3 6 9
3	1 8
4	1 3

46.

stem	leaf
7	1 3 4 4 9
8	3 3 9
9	1

47.

stem	leaf
8	6 7
9	4 5 9
10	3 5
11	7

Page 150

3-9 Answers for Explore

2. $\frac{1}{2}$

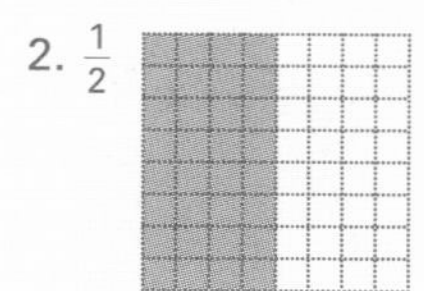

$\frac{1}{4}$

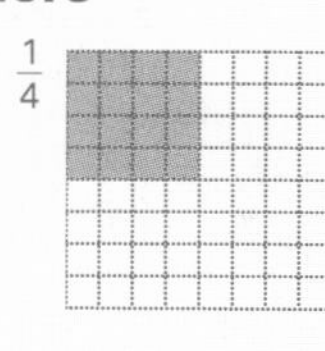

$\frac{3}{8}$

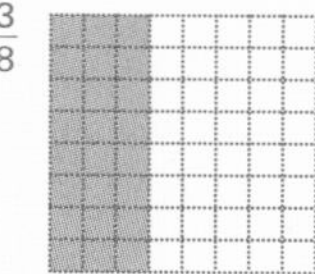

$\frac{5}{16}$

$\frac{7}{32}$

Page 152

3-9 Exercise Answers

25.

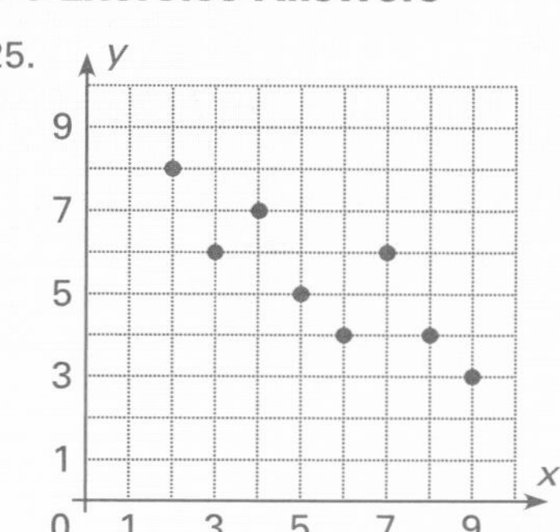

26.

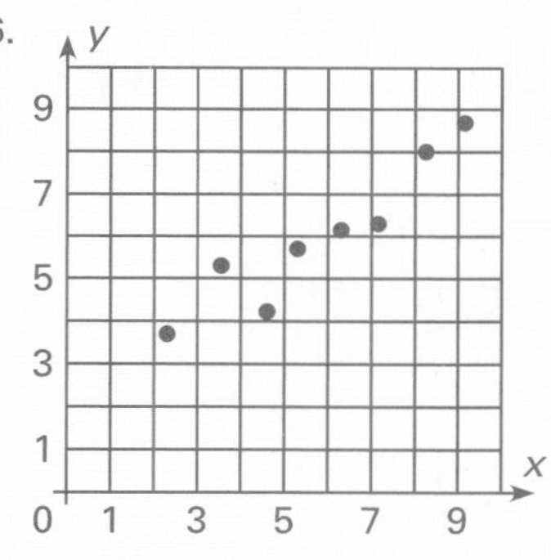

Chapter 4

Page 174

4-2 Answers for Explore

1. a. $\frac{1}{2} + \frac{2}{5} = \frac{9}{10}$

$\frac{1}{2}$ $\frac{2}{5}$ $\frac{9}{10}$

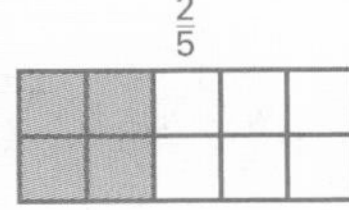

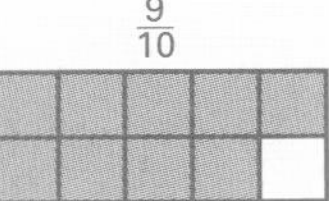

b. $\frac{2}{5} + \frac{1}{3} = \frac{11}{15}$

$\frac{2}{5}$ $\frac{1}{3}$ $\frac{11}{15}$

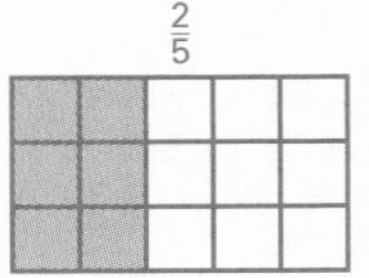

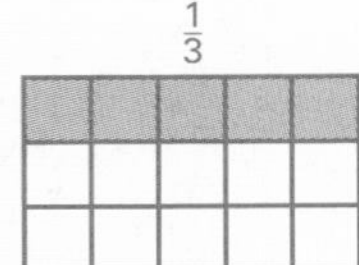

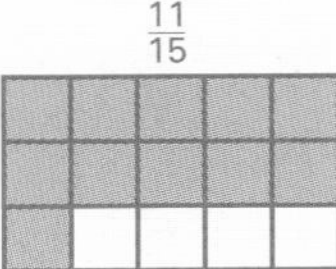

c. $\frac{1}{4} + \frac{3}{5} = \frac{17}{20}$

$\frac{1}{4}$ $\frac{3}{5}$ $\frac{17}{20}$

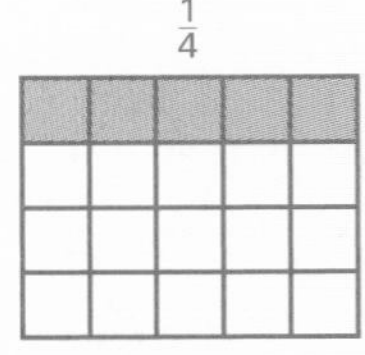

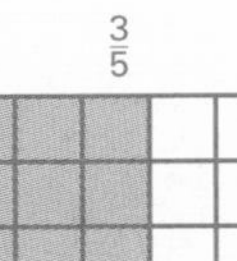

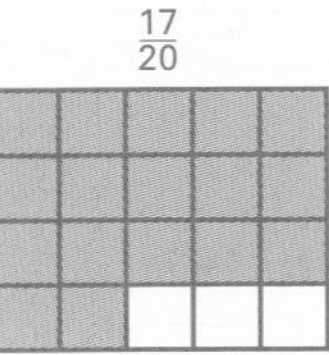

d. $\frac{1}{2} + \frac{1}{3} = \frac{5}{6}$

$\frac{1}{2}$ $\frac{1}{3}$ $\frac{5}{6}$

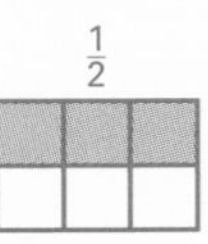

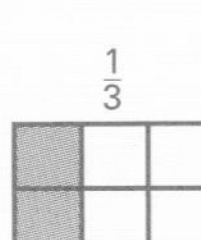

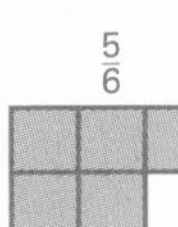

Page 179

4-3 Answers for Explore

1. a. $1\frac{3}{5} + 2\frac{1}{5} = 3\frac{4}{5}$

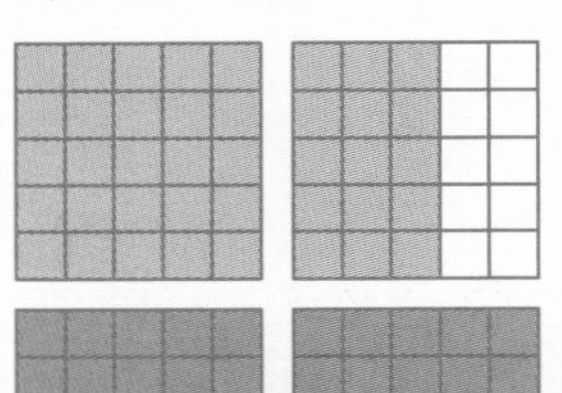

$1\frac{3}{5}$

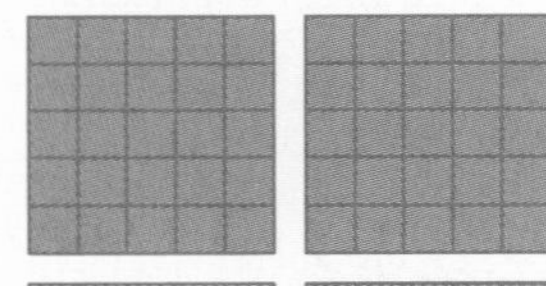

$2\frac{1}{5}$

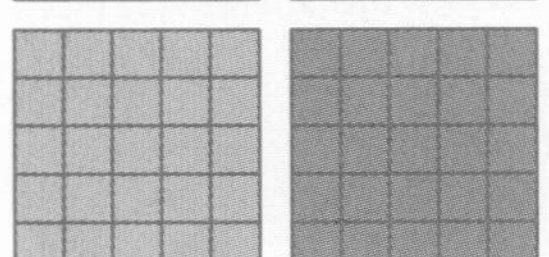

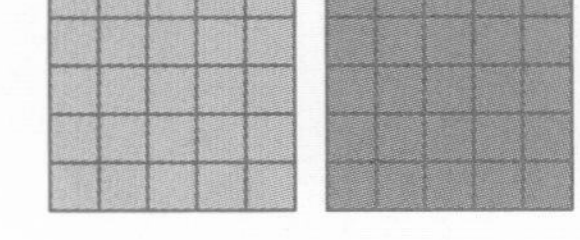

$3\frac{4}{5}$

b. $1\frac{3}{4} + 2\frac{1}{4} = 4$

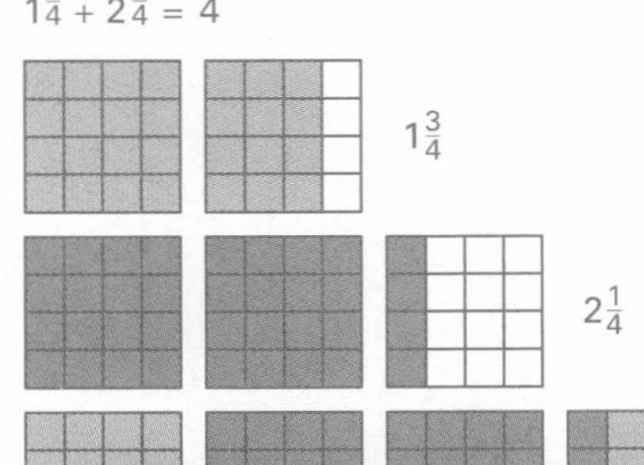

$1\frac{3}{4}$

$2\frac{1}{4}$

4

c. $1\frac{2}{5} + 1\frac{4}{5} = 3\frac{1}{5}$

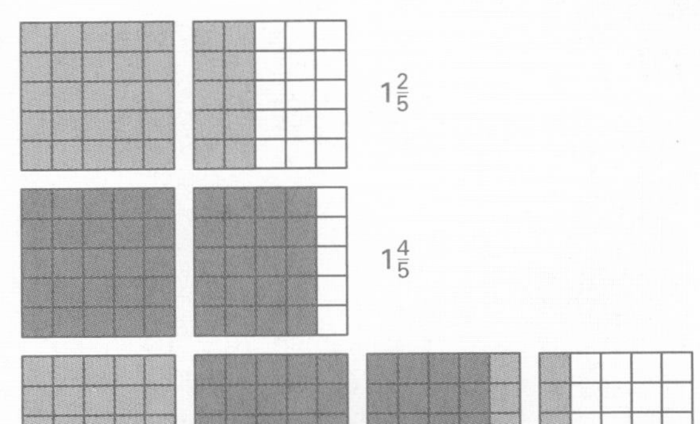

$1\frac{2}{5}$

$1\frac{4}{5}$

$3\frac{1}{5}$

Page 187

4-4 Answers for Explore

1. a.

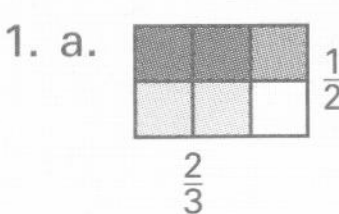

$\frac{1}{2}$ $\frac{2}{3}$

b.

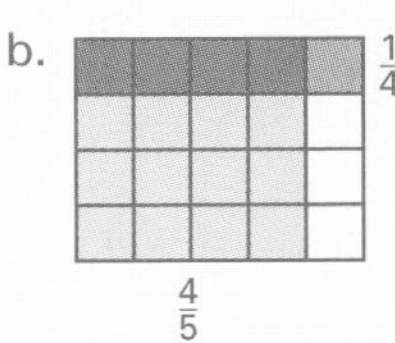

$\frac{1}{4}$ $\frac{4}{5}$

c.

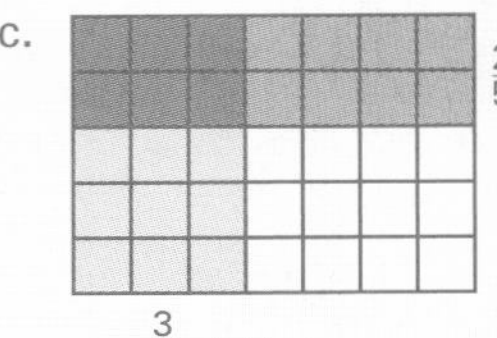

$\frac{2}{5}$ $\frac{3}{7}$

d.

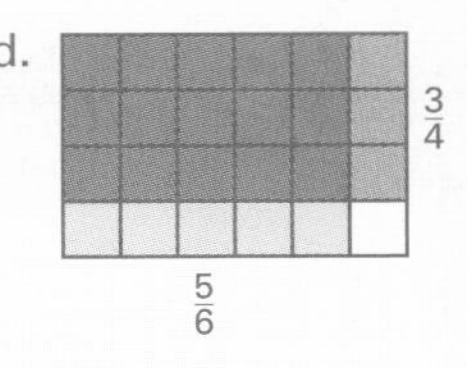

$\frac{3}{4}$ $\frac{5}{6}$

Chapter 5

Page 230

5-4 Exercise Answers

15. a.

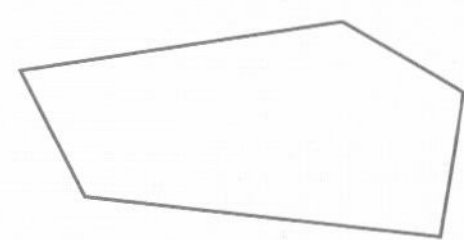

Sides and angles are not congruent.

b.

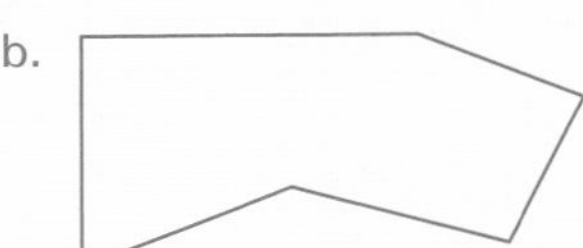

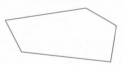

Sides and angles are not congruent.

c.

Sides and angles are not congruent.

Page 258

5-10 Answers for Explore

1. Horizontal side = 10 ft; Vertical side = 14 ft
2. There are 4 possible ways.

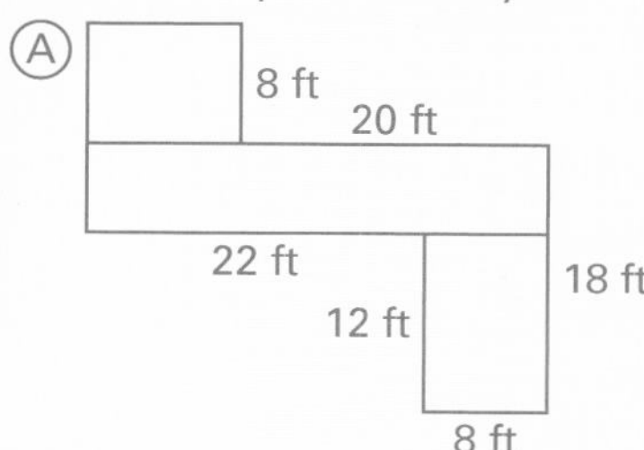

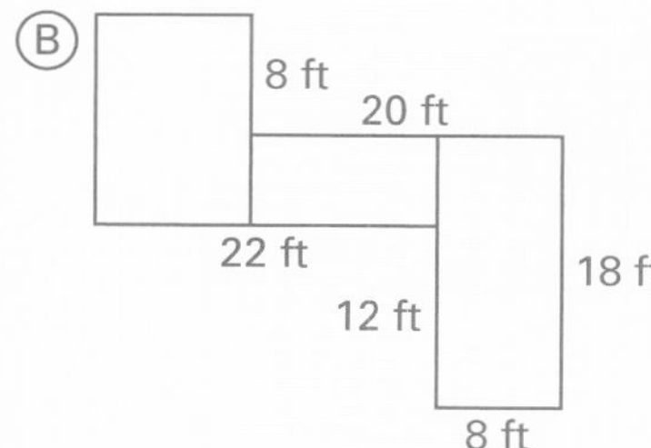

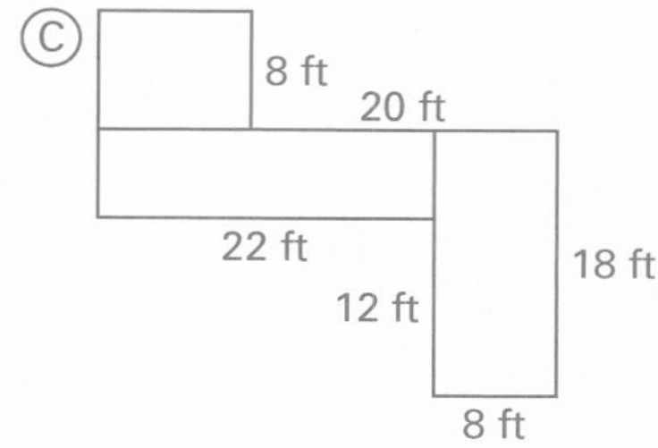

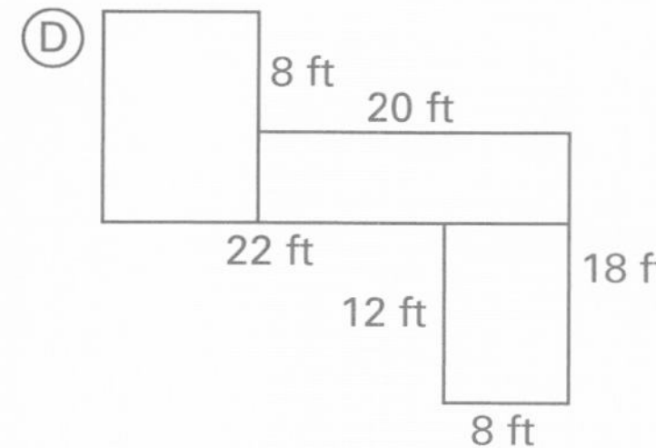

3. Rectangles are A: 80 ft^2, 180 ft^2, 96 ft^2; B: 140 ft^2, 72 ft^2, 144 ft^2; C: 80 ft^2, 132 ft^2, 144 ft^2; D: 140 ft^2, 120 ft^2, 96 ft^2; Total area is 356 ft^2.
4. Yes
5. Find the area of the base of the windmill and subtract it from 356 ft^2.

Chapter 6

Page 295

6-5 Answers for Explore

1. Possible answer:

4 whales; $\frac{2}{9} = \frac{4}{18}$.

2. Possible answer:

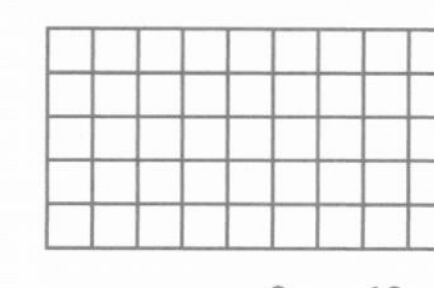

45 sq mi; $\frac{2}{9} = \frac{10}{45}$.

Page 296

6-5 Exercise Answers

3. Possible answers:

5	10	20	50
9	18	36	90

$\frac{5}{9} = \frac{10}{18}, \frac{5}{9} = \frac{20}{36}, \frac{5}{9} = \frac{50}{90}, \frac{10}{18} = \frac{20}{36}$.

4. Possible answers:

9	18	27	36
20	40	60	80

$\frac{9}{20} = \frac{18}{40}, \frac{9}{20} = \frac{27}{60}, \frac{9}{20} = \frac{36}{80}$

5. Possible answers:

7	14	21	28
8	16	24	32

$\frac{7}{8} = \frac{14}{16}, \frac{7}{8} = \frac{21}{24}, \frac{7}{8} = \frac{28}{32}$.

6. Possible answers:

3	6	9	12
11	22	33	44

$\frac{3}{11} = \frac{6}{22}; \frac{3}{11} = \frac{9}{33}; \frac{3}{11} = \frac{12}{44}$.

7. Possible answers:

13	26	39	52
15	30	45	60

$\frac{13}{15} = \frac{26}{30}, \frac{13}{15} = \frac{39}{45}, \frac{13}{15} = \frac{52}{60}$.

8. Possible answers:

20	40	60	80
7	14	21	28

$\frac{20}{7} = \frac{40}{14}, \frac{20}{7} = \frac{60}{21}, \frac{20}{7} = \frac{80}{28}$.

9. Possible answers:

10	20	30	40
14	28	42	56

$\frac{10}{14} = \frac{20}{28}, \frac{10}{14} = \frac{30}{42}, \frac{10}{14} = \frac{40}{56}$.

10. Possible answers:

12	24	36	48
13	26	39	52

$\frac{12}{13} = \frac{24}{26}, \frac{12}{13} = \frac{36}{39}, \frac{12}{13} = \frac{48}{52}$.

11. Possible answers:

2	4	6	8
100	200	300	400

$\frac{2}{100} = \frac{4}{200}; \frac{2}{100} = \frac{6}{300}; \frac{2}{100} = \frac{8}{400}$.

12. Possible answers:

11	22	33	44
5	10	15	20

$\frac{11}{5} = \frac{22}{10}, \frac{11}{5} = \frac{33}{15}, \frac{11}{5} = \frac{44}{20}$.

Answers continue on next page.

Page 296

6-5 Answers

13. Possible answers:

17	34	51	68
19	38	57	76

$\frac{17}{19} = \frac{34}{38}; \frac{17}{19} = \frac{51}{57}; \frac{17}{19} = \frac{68}{76}$.

14. 8 people: $\frac{2}{3}$ c mayonnaise, 3 T vinegar, 6 c sliced cabbage;

12 people: 1 c mayonnaise, $4\frac{1}{2}$ T vinegar, 9 c sliced cabbage;

16 people: $1\frac{1}{3}$ c mayonnaise, 6 T vinegar, 12 c sliced cabbage.

15. Possible answers: $\frac{3 \text{ ft}}{1 \text{ yd}} = \frac{21 \text{ ft}}{7 \text{ yd}}; \frac{1 \text{ yd}}{7 \text{ yd}} = \frac{3 \text{ ft}}{21 \text{ ft}}$.

16. Possible answers: $\frac{4}{3} = \frac{20}{15}; \frac{3}{15} = \frac{4}{20}$.

17. Possible answers: $\frac{7 \text{ teachers}}{2 \text{ teachers}} = \frac{56 \text{ students}}{16 \text{ students}}$; $\frac{2 \text{ teachers}}{16 \text{ students}} = \frac{7 \text{ teachers}}{56 \text{ students}}$.

18. Possible answers: $\frac{60 \text{ calories}}{1 \text{ apple}} = \frac{120 \text{ calories}}{2 \text{ apples}}$; $\frac{60 \text{ calories}}{1 \text{ apple}} = \frac{300 \text{ calories}}{5 \text{ apples}}$.

Page 297

6-5 Exercise Answers

28.

x	2	3	4	5	6
y	0	1	2	3	4

29.

x	2	3	4	5	6
y	8	12	16	20	24

30.

x	2	3	4	5	6
y	19	20	21	22	23

31.

x	2	3	4	5	6
y	19	27	35	43	51

32.

x	2	3	4	5	6
y	3	7	11	15	19

33.

x	2	3	4	5	6
y	16	21	26	31	36

34.

x	2	3	4	5	6
y	15	25	35	45	55

35.

x	2	3	4	5	6
y	2	5	8	11	14

Page 298

6-6 Answers for Explore

Possible answers are given.

1.

Distance (ft)	18	36	72	90	108
Time (sec)	1	2	4	5	6

2.

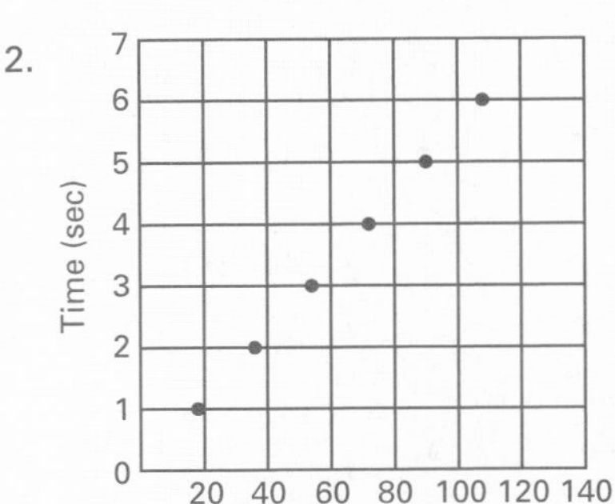

The points fall in a straight line.

3.

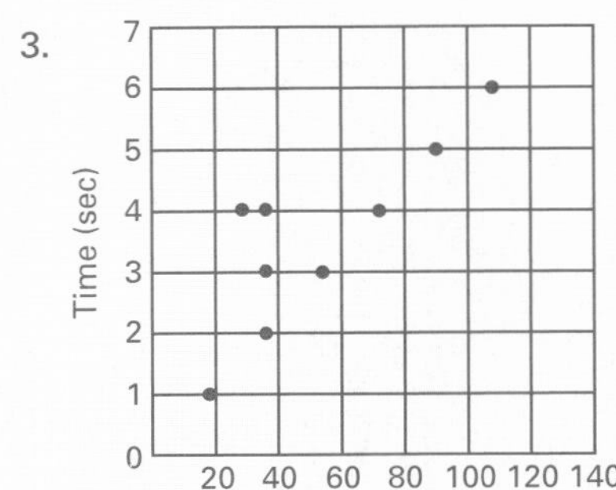

The points for the other whales do not lie on the same line as the points for the killer whale. Points that represent proportional data lie on the same line.

A

B

C

D

E

INDEX

INDEX

INDEX

U

V

W

X

Y

Z